PIGS APLENTY, PIGS GALORE!

DAVID MCPHAIL

Puffin Books

PUFFIN BOOKS
Published by the Penguin Group
Penguin Books USA Inc., 345 Hudson Street, New York, New York 10014, U.S.A.
Penguin Books Ltd, 27 Wrights Lane, London W8 5TZ, England
Penguin Books Australia Ltd, Ringwood, Victoria, Australia
Penguin Books Canada Ltd, 10 Alcorn Avenue, Toronto, Ontario, Canada M4V 3B2
Penguin Books (N.Z.) Ltd, 182-190 Wairau Road, Auckland 10, New Zealand
Penguin Books Ltd, Registered Offices: Harmondsworth, Middlesex, England
Copyright © 1993 by David McPhail
All rights reserved.
Library of Congress number 92-27986
ISBN 978-0-14-055313-0
Published in the United States by Dutton Children's Books,
a division of Penguin Books USA Inc.
Published in Great Britain in Puffin Books 1997
Designer: Riki Levinson
Manufactured in China by RR Donnelley Asia Printing Solutions Ltd.
First Puffin Edition 1996

For Jack,
good friend, true poet

Late one night
As I sat reading,
I thought I heard
The sound of feeding.

Through the kitchen door
I crept,
Barely watching
Where I stepped.

A crash, a bang,
A shout, a yell—
I slipped on something,
Then I fell.

I landed on
A pile of pigs—
Some eating dates,
Some eating figs.

In the cupboards,
On the floor—
Pigs aplenty,
Pigs galore!

Black pigs, white pigs,
Brown and pink,
Making oatmeal
In the sink.

Pigs in tutus,
Pigs in kilts,
Pigs on skateboards,
Pigs on stilts.

Pigs from England,
Pigs from France,
Pigs in just
Their underpants.

The King of Pigs,
The Piggy Queen—
The biggest pigs
I've ever seen.

Pigs arrive
By boat, by plane.
A bus pulls up
And then a train.

A band strikes up.
A piggy sings.
Then, at ten
The doorbell rings.

Someone yells:
"The pizza's here!"
And all the pigs
Begin to cheer.

Flying pizzas
Fill the air.
One goes SPLAT!
Against my chair.

The piggy piggies
Eat their fill.
I get nothing,
Just the bill.

"I've had enough!"
I scream and shout.
"Get out, you pigs!
You pigs, get out!"

"Please let us stay,"
  The piggies cry.
"Don't make us go,
  Don't say good-bye."

"You can stay,"
  I tell them all.
"But sweep the floor
  And scrub the wall."

I give them brooms,
A pail, a mop.
"Now sweep and scrub
Till I say stop."

The piggies work
And when they're done,
Upstairs they stagger
One by one.

They brush their teeth
And comb their tails,
Then wash their snouts
And clean their nails.

The pigs and I
Climb into bed.
I plump the pillows,
Plop my head.

I close my eyes
And try to sleep.
Before too long
I'm dreaming deep—

Of pigs and pigs
And pigs some more—
Of pigs aplenty,
Pigs galore!

THE ELEMENTS

			IIIA	IVA	VA	VIA	VIIA	O
								2 4.00260 **He** Helium
			5 10.81 **B** Boron	6 12.011 **C** Carbon	7 14.0067 **N** Nitrogen	8 15.9994 **O** Oxygen	9 18.9984 **F** Fluorine	10 20.179 **Ne** Neon
IB	IIB		13 26.9815 **Al** Aluminum	14 28.086 **Si** Silicon	15 30.9738 **P** Phosphorus	16 32.06 **S** Sulfur	17 35.453 **Cl** Chlorine	18 39.95 **Ar** Argon
28 58.70 **Ni** Nickel	29 63.546 **Cu** Copper	30 65.38 **Zn** Zinc	31 69.72 **Ga** Gallium	32 72.59 **Ge** Germanium	33 74.9216 **As** Arsenic	34 78.96 **Se** Selenium	35 79.904 **Br** Bromine	36 83.80 **Kr** Krypton
46 106.4 **Pd** Palladium	47 107.868 **Ag** Silver	48 112.41 **Cd** Cadmium	49 114.82 **In** Indium	50 118.69 **Sn** Tin	51 121.75 **Sb** Antimony	52 127.60 **Te** Tellurium	53 126.905 **I** Iodine	54 131.30 **Xe** Xenon
78 195.09 **Pt** Platinum	79 196.967 **Au** Gold	80 200.59 **Hg** Mercury	81 204.37 **Tl** Thallium	82 207.2 **Pb** Lead	83 208.980 **Bi** Bismuth	84 (209) **Po** Polonium	85 (210) **At** Astatine	86 (222) **Rn** Radon

63 151.96 **Eu** Europium	64 157.25 **Gd** Gadolinium	65 158.93 **Tb** Terbium	66 162.50 **Dy** Dysprosium	67 164.930 **Ho** Holmium	68 167.26 **Er** Erbium	69 168.934 **Tm** Thulium	70 173.04 **Yb** Ytterbium	71 174.97 **Lu** Lutetium
95 (243) **Am** Americium	96 (247) **Cm** Curium	97 (247) **Bk** Berkelium	98 (251) **Cf** Californium	99 (254) **Es** Einsteinium	100 (257) **Fm** Fermium	101 (258) **Md** Mendelevium	102 (255) **No** Nobelium	103 (260) **Lr** Lawrencium

Education is an important element in the struggle for human rights. It is the means to help our children and people rediscover their identity and thereby increase self respect. Education is our passport to the future, for tomorrow belongs to the people who prepare for it today.

Annals of New York Academy of Sciences,
volume 184, page 260, 1971

FRANK BRESCIA

Department of Chemistry,
City College of New York, CUNY, New York

STANLEY MEHLMAN

Department of Chemistry, SUNY at Farmingdale,
Farmingdale, New York

FRANK C. PELLEGRINI

Department of Chemistry, SUNY at Farmingdale,
Farmingdale, New York

SEYMOUR STAMBLER

Department of Chemistry, College of Staten Island,
Staten Island, New York

ILLUSTRATED BY GEORGE KELVIN

SAUNDERS GOLDEN SUNBURST SERIES

CHEMISTRY:
A
MODERN
INTRODUCTION

Second Edition

1978

W. B. SAUNDERS COMPANY · PHILADELPHIA · LONDON · TORONTO

W. B. Saunders Company: West Washington Square
Philadelphia, PA 19105

1 St. Anne's Road
Eastbourne, East Sussex BN21 3UN, England

1 Goldthorne Avenue
Toronto, Ontario M8Z 5T9, Canada

Library of Congress Cataloging in Publication Data
Main entry under title:

Chemistry: a modern introduction.

(Saunders golden sunburst series)
Includes bibliographical references and index.
1. Chemistry. I. Brescia, Frank
QD31.2.C4 1978   540   77-23995
ISBN 0-7216-1984-3

Cover painting by George V. Kelvin
Chapter opening photographs by Peter Harris

Listed here is the latest translated edition of this book together with the language of the translation and the publisher.

Spanish (*1st edition*)—Nueva Editorial Interamericana, Mexico City, Mexico

Chemistry: A Modern Introduction   ISBN 0-7216-1984-3

Last digit is the print number: 9 8 7 6 5 4 3 2 1

PREFACE
For Students
and Instructors

This book is written for highly motivated students who wish to pursue careers that require a knowledge of college chemistry but whose previous education did not afford an opportunity for adequate study of chemistry. Our book is not a highly concentrated summary of chemical knowledge accumulated by scholars over centuries of experience, nor is it our purpose to trap the recent knowledge explosion in a small case. Rather, the text is intended to provide an insight into the fundamentals of chemistry for students with varying high school training. The purpose of this book is to teach chemistry as it is practiced today without overwhelming the student.

This work is therefore, in part, intentionally repetitious and written in a language to stimulate students and help maintain their enthusiasm. Many topics are discussed to some extent and then reintroduced later in the belief that this procedure enhances and reinforces learning; entropy, for example, is not treated in one volcanic eruption. We have attempted to eliminate reasoning in a vacuum, by use of brief but meaningful descriptions of substances and by an experimental approach to theoretical discussions, woven with descriptive material. Thus, we hope to achieve some balance between descriptive chemistry and theoretical chemistry without creating the false impression that they stand apart as deadly enemies. We do not regard as a tragedy the failure of the student to learn the color or the absorption spectrum of, let us say, ethyl alcohol (a colorless, intoxicating liquid). It is more important that students learn the significance of substance properties and develop a sense of direction that will take them to the library or the laboratory. Necessary mathematical tools and language are presented, not in the Appendix, but together with the chemistry when the need arises. Color, drawings, diagrams, photographs, arrows, and different type faces are also used to reinforce learning as well as to isolate critical material and maintain interest.

All specialized fields of chemistry are equally important, but equal coverage is unnecessary and impossible. Choices must therefore be made. We have not, for example, discussed all the representative elements but have selected only a few. Chemistry has its language, but we have resisted the temptation to pack in a complex vocabulary fit for experts only. Fully aware of our obligation to provide sufficient and adequate footing for a second year course, a minimum number of terms and concepts have been translated into language we hope the student will understand. Mechanics (classical and quantum) as applied to chemical problems is developed verbally without "quantum jumps." The concept of equivalent weight has been omitted as unnecessary and irrelevant in the closing decades of the 20th Century. Its elimination presents no educational problems to us as teachers and no practical handicap to us as chemists. Further, we believe that memorization of fundamental constants and formulas such as $PV = nRT$ should be minimized to permit maximum understanding of them and to recognize the important message in them. On the other hand, by devoting a chapter to the principles of instrumental analysis we recognize that analytical instrumentation has advanced so rapidly that it is now the workhorse of clinical, industrial, and research laboratories.

We have attempted to limit the number of special category "labels" for topics. For example, instead of the so-called common ion effect standing alone as a separate and sometimes difficult topic to learn, it has been included as another example of Le Chatelier's principle. The "conversion factor" method of solving problems is consistently used. By reducing many apparently different phenomena to one, we have lessened the urge to memorize and thus increased learning.

Although we have not attempted to popularize our presentation, current problems of national concern are discussed. An historical view of science and particularly chemistry is presented. In many little ways, the idea that science is an old vehicle in which theories (models) and critical experiments painfully evolve through human activity is emphasized. Further, historical notes may serve as the "pause that refreshes."

Labeling sections as optional has been dropped in this edition to allow instructors greater freedom in selection of topics and chapter order. Problems, as a guide to the degree of understanding by students, are made part of the text. These text problems also set the *minimum objective goals of each chapter*. The student is therefore urged to work out each text problem before proceeding further. Additionally, there is a selection of problems at the end of each chapter, and answers are given to allow students to check their progress. Footnotes should not be bypassed. They provide historical background material, additional information, and warning signs that allow us to qualify our generalizations.

Topics of interest to students in health, medical, and biochemical courses, scattered throughout the text as illustrative material and in problems, are indexed under the heading of Biochemistry. Many such items are also individually indexed. We have not included a bibliography. Rather, "library questions" and footnote references are used to relate subject matter to topics of current interest. These recommend relevant articles published in journals such as *Science, Scientific American, Chemistry, Journal of Chemical Education,* and *Chem Tech* (*Chemical Technology*).

Some changes made in writing this edition include the following:
The presentation of molecular orbital theory is delayed until the chapters dependent upon an understanding of this theory are presented.
The topics of concentration and solution are moved forward to improve correlation with laboratory work.
The treatment of thermodynamics is increased, *verbally but not mathematically,* to emphasize more clearly the significance of observable quantities in determining the natural tendency of a chemical reaction to occur.
Since atomic weights are no longer derived from molecular weights of gases, Chapter 4 has been rewritten so that the determination of atomic weights of elements follows the development of the atomic theory. The terms gram atomic weight and gram molecular weight are discarded in favor of the mole definition, applicable with equal validity to atoms and molecules.

The section on oxidation numbers is moved from chemical bonding to the subject of oxidation-reduction so that the student may spot less obvious oxidation-reduction reactions, such as the fermentation of table sugar to ethyl alcohol and carbon dioxide. The concept of crystalline and amorphous states of matter is added to the chapter on Liquids and Solids.

More descriptive chemistry is woven into the text, and the use of heats of formation as an alternative scheme for obtaining heats of reaction is added to Chapter 9.

The International System of Units is employed, but the use of cm, ml, liter, atmosphere, torr, and calorie has not been completely abandoned.

The variety of examples is maintained while the variety and number of realistic and interesting problems are tremendously expanded so that the student may "learn by doing chemistry," and making supplementary problem books unnecessary. The new additional problem section contains mainly challenging problems. Appropriate units and significant figures are used in all examples and problem answers.

Essential key terms are summarized in the vocabulary question at the end of each chapter, and the glossary serves as a useful supplement to the text.

The Appendix is enlarged to include tables of thermodynamic data, flame tests, solution constants, and units of radioactivity.

The index is further enlarged to permit its use as a general chemistry reference source. Finally, sample examination questions are added to the Instructor's Guide to increase its usefulness.

A Student Guide, written by Professors David Brooks and Thomas Tipton of the University of Nebraska exclusively for use with this textbook, is organized to guide the student through the course with supplementary text, examples, problems, and testing material. Experience has shown that it facilitates learning by helping students use study hours more efficiently. "Modern Descriptive Chemistry" by Professor Emeritus Eugene Rochow of Harvard University (W. B. Saunders Company, 1977) is recommended for more detailed information on the properties and chemistry of the elements.

PROLOGUE
For the
Instructor

This text is student-oriented and, judging from student and instructor reactions to the First Edition, it is very successful. Its success is mainly due to an instinctive application of the Jean Piaget theory of learning. However, "concrete operational" and "formal operational" (J. Dudley Herron, *J. Chem. Ed.,* **52** 146 (1975) and D. W. Beistel, *ibid.,* 151) came to our attention after years of lecturing experience proved that only failure can characterize attempts to explain phenomena that a student does not understand. Therefore, our fundamental approach is always from the descriptive and observable to the theoretical, to insure that at least the student understands what we are attempting to explain. Further, we shun the rather common approach of beginning with atomic structure. Experience teaches us that the gas model and its applications to changes of state are more easily grasped by the student than the explanation of the laws of chemical change. The sequence—Introduction, Gases, Liquids and Solids, Dalton's atomic theory—therefore remains unchanged in this edition as the vehicle to ease the student into the course.

We do not claim to have discovered the road map to the promised land on which only **A**pples grow, firm and tasty without lowering **FDA** standards. We do claim that the text offers the student a better chance of learning sufficient chemistry to move on into second year courses, and ample opportunities for intellectual development.

ACKNOWLEDGMENTS

We sincerely thank the students who used our Preliminary Edition for their patience and valuable suggestions. We are also grateful to Dr. Lawrence F. Koons and his staff (Tuskegee Institute), Dr. Earl K. Jones and his staff (Prairie View A & M College), Dr. Louis J. Kotnik and his staff (Cuyahoga Community College), Dr. Emil Wildman (College of Staten Island), and the Chemistry Department at SUNY at Farmingdale for their helpful comments and skillful use of the Preliminary Edition. Further, we sincerely thank Dr. Eugene G. Rochow (Professor Emeritus, Harvard University), Dr. Norman J. Juster (Pasadena College), Dr. Jon M. Bellama (University of Maryland), Dr. Gilbert Gordon (University of Iowa), and Dr. Stanley M. Cherim (Community College of Delaware County), who through their critical reading contributed to the correction of the Preliminary Edition. Critical discussions with Dr. John Arents and Dr. Neil McKelvie (City College, CUNY) are gratefully acknowledged. Our generous thanks are extended to the instructors who used the First Edition for their helpful criticisms and encouraging response; in particular, we acknowledge the suggestions from Professors John Clevenger (Lord Fairfax Community College), Crayton Crawford (Mississippi State University), Ned Daugherty (Colorado State University), Jeff Davis, Jr. (University of South Florida), C. M. Delaney (Wells College), John Ganchoff (Elmhurst College), Arnulf Hagen (University of Oklahoma), David Johnston (David Lipscomb College), W. H. Jordan, Jr. (College of the Albemarle), Lawrence F. Koons (Tuskegee), Warren McAllister and Edgar Heckel (East Carolina University), and David Williamson (California Polytechnic State University). We are thankful to Professors Henry Heikkinen (University of Maryland) and Joseph Wiebush (U.S. Naval Academy) for their painstaking reviews of the manuscript. We are also especially indebted to Dr. David Brooks for checking answers to all problems. It was a pleasure to work with George Kelvin, who provided the artwork for the text. Nevertheless, the responsibility for any errors in the text remains with the authors.

Acknowledgment to institutions and individuals who sent us photographs is included with the illustrations. Finally, we are indeed grateful to John Vondeling, Editor, to Lorraine Battista, Book Designer, and to the staff of W. B. Saunders Company for their helpful and gracious support in converting our manuscript into a colorful and artistic book.

FRANK BRESCIA
STANLEY MEHLMAN
FRANK PELLEGRINI
SEYMOUR STAMBLER

CONTENTS

11

IONIC SOLUTIONS, OXIDATION AND REDUCTION 354

12

CHEMICAL EQUILIBRIUM 372

13

ACIDS AND BASES 406

CHEMISTRY:
A MODERN INTRODUCTION

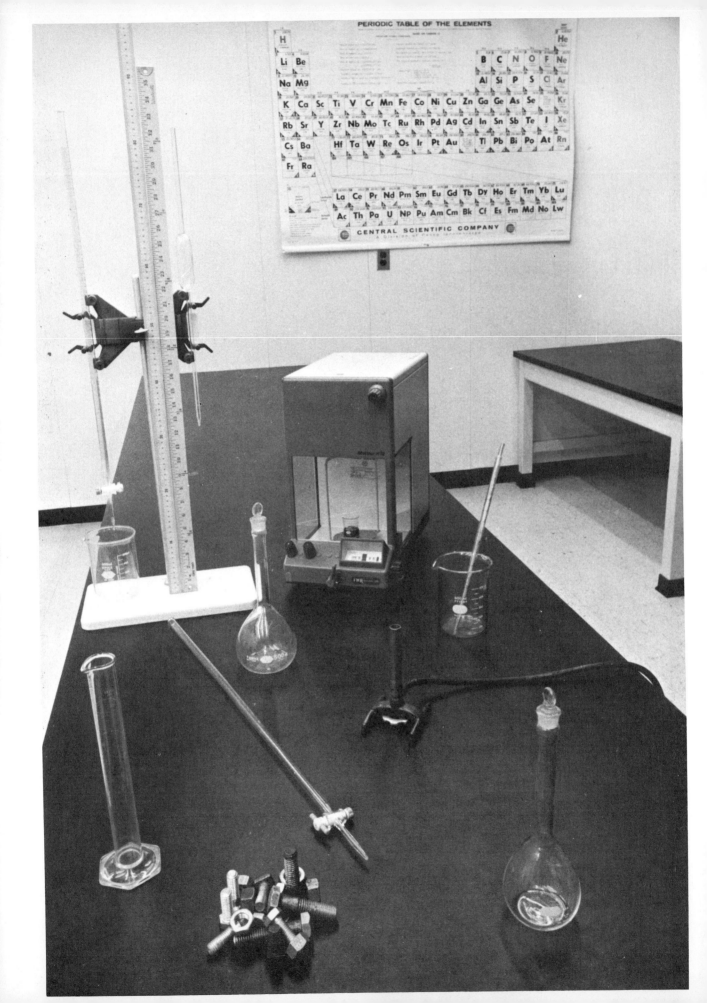

INTRODUCTION 1

The progress of western civilization has always been measured by the scope of technological advances which provide better food, housing, and clothing and which improve communication and transportation. We have come to accept and expect from chemistry an ever-increasing variety of those things that we believe represent a "better life." Drugs to combat disease, plastics and synthetic fabrics to extend our natural resources, synthetic pain-killers with little addictive power, new petroleum products, fertilizers, and pesticides are a few examples. In recent years, however, we have come to realize that progress through chemistry has generated problems that threaten the quality of life. Science stands accused. In particular, the chemist is caught between the economics of his productivity and the social implications of his work. Avoidance of widespread hunger in the world required new substances to increase agricultural output—fertilizers and pesticides. But these have resulted in salt and DDT contamination of lakes, rivers, and oceans. This has interfered with the life cycle of fish, birds, and other animals. Yet, substances like DDT have prevented the deaths of millions of people, both by controlling insects that transmit disease and by destroying insects that devour crops.

Chemistry, from klem, Egyptian word for black, or from chemia, Greek for chemical work, or from al kimia, Arabic for chemical work, or from jiu-yi, Chinese for gold juice.

The demand for energy of all types has resulted in significant pollution of our air and water and depletion of vast quantities of coal, oil, and natural gas. Yet, who can deny the necessity of many of the machines and devices that consume that energy and drastically decrease the labor of man? More and more we look to the scientist to provide alternatives that minimize environmental pollution. Acceptance of alternatives without proper studies, however, may present more harmful effects. The need for a more scientifically educated population capable of understanding and evaluating the impact of these alternatives is greater now than in the past. The chemist, as scientist and citizen, is expected to lay the foundation for a responsible technology that will provide better things for better living for more people without adverse effects on our environment. Science, like most knowledge, is cumulative; it learns from its mistakes.

Problems are being studied and progress is evident: nuclear power plants and synthetic fuels are being developed to produce "clean energy"; new types of fertilizers and pesticides are being studied that do not pollute water and food; new manufacturing techniques are being developed that recycle waste products and remove toxic materials from smokestacks. The development of biodegradable plastic containers—containers that are decomposed to harmless substances by bacteria—will be a distinct advantage in minimizing accumulation of solid waste.

Pollution and energy problems may be solved, but only if changes are made with an awareness of scientific fact. We must understand that a scientific fact is not subject to arbitration, as is a wage dispute or the spelling of "labeled" ("labelled"). Nature will not permit us to repeal the law that states that the lower the temperature at which gasoline (a fuel) is burned, the lower is the power generated. And even though science does not fully understand the nature of the law of gravity, it is not a good idea to step

3

off the roof of a 10-story building. Society must do its homework. We recognize that training in chemistry is needed for solutions to environmental problems; it is also needed to make wise decisions about appropriations and legislation. But do we recognize the economic impact of fighting pollution? If the fundamental cause of pollution is, as many experts suggest, our drive for affluence, it may be impossible to find only a technological solution to pollution. A radical change in life style, in addition to technological advances, may be necessary to really clean up our Earth.

1.1   METHODS OF SCIENCE

Progress in any branch of knowledge usually, but not necessarily, begins with observation. Facts (data) are accumulated and organized for more effective study. In the sciences, facts are obtained and verified by *controlled experiments,* experiments in which all known factors—for example, the temperature, pressure, nature and quantity of *all* materials used, and the presence or absence of light—are so controlled that the information is reproducible. The same result is obtained, regardless of the number of times the experiment is repeated. A scientist does not say that water boils at 100 degrees Celsius (page 22). Long ago he discovered that the purity of water affects its boiling temperature and that even pure water boils at a lower temperature on the top of a mountain. He does say that pure water, at sea level, boils at 100 degrees Celsius. Chemistry is an *experimental science;* the chemist therefore spends a good deal of his time in the laboratory collecting the necessary facts.

Chemistry, however, is more than just an experimental subject. The study of science includes attempts to *understand* nature, to *explain,* for example, the observation that pure water boils below 100 degrees Celsius on mountain tops but above 100 degrees Celsius at the bottom of a mine shaft.

After data are accumulated, it may be possible to propose a *generalization,* a statement which summarizes the known data. If the generalization is consistently validated by experiment, the generalization is called a *law of nature,* a scientific law. Such laws describe the behavior of nature. They do not explain natural phenomena, they merely state what will happen under a given set of experimental conditions. The law of gravity, for example, summarizes a familiar natural phenomenon: in the absence of a wind, all objects, regardless of size and shape, released from the top of a building fall downward and strike the earth, each object taking almost the same time to reach the earth. We say the force of gravity of the earth attracts all objects downward. But this does *not* explain the presence of a gravitational field around the earth or the origin of the force of gravity. It does not tell us what constitutes gravity. It does, however, *predict*—it tells us exactly what will happen if a marble, a 1 pound object, or a 1 ton truck is dropped from a tall cliff in the absence of a wind.

The first step in offering a scientific explanation is to construct a **theoretical model,** a series of *assumptions,* an *imaginary picture* of the way nature behaves. The model has no physical existence; it is not physical reality but only represents physical reality. Its existence is only in the human mind.

A model or theory has two important functions. First, it correlates—it ties together a variety of observations. It interprets and gives meaning to these observations, and in this sense the theoretical scientist is like a poet. Second, and more important, it suggests experiments that otherwise would not be performed. It also attempts to predict the results of these experiments. Such experimentation generally has the effect of widening the scope of the theory (model). But such experimentation frequently produces results that contradict the theory (model). The scientist is then compelled usually to modify the theory (model) or, rarely, to create a new theory.

Chemistry is an intimate and related mixture of experiment and theory. Man differs from a head of cabbage in that he can think—Man wonders; a head of cabbage does not. It is impossible to say which comes first in the development of science—observation or ideas. We can say, though, that experimentation is the life blood of science and that theoretical models serve as the pump. Philosophers no longer accept the "Blank-Mind Experimenter" theory—the view that a scientist can operate without a preconceived idea he is trying to verify.

We do not wish to create the impression that the invention of a beautifully attractive model generates an excitement that propels the scientist into his laboratory to test the theory to determine whether it should be rejected or accepted. Delay between the creation of a model, the testing of it, and acceptance or modification of it is common in the growth of scientific theories. For example, after presenting his doctoral thesis (1879), Max Planck [page 208] wrote

"None of my professors at the University had any understanding of its contents. I found no interest, let alone approval, even among the very physicists who were closely connected with the topic. Helmholtz probably did not even read my paper at all. Kirchoff [page 192] expressly disapproved—I did not succeed in reaching Clausius [page 64]. He did not answer my letters and I did not find him at home when I tried to see him in person."

Journal of Chemical Education, Volume 52, 1975, page 647.

Planck concluded that the presentation of a new scientific truth does not generally convince its opponents; rather, they gradually die off and new generations become familiar with the new idea from the start of their education.

Scientists settle scientific arguments through experimentation. Philosophers argued for thousands of years whether or not two heavy objects of different weights dropped simultaneously from a high place would hit the earth at the same time. The argument was finally settled when Jean Grotius and Simon Stevin (about 1555) used two lead balls, "one ball ten times the other in weight and let them go together from a height of 30 feet; you will clearly perceive that the lighter will fall, not ten times more slowly, but equally with the other." Galileo (1604), experimenting with rolling balls on an inclined board, came to the same conclusion. Experimentation thus ended centuries of discussion and guessing. Another example concerns the great interest that has been shown in the study of the causes of earthquakes. Earthquakes are accompanied by a wobbling motion, a motion that slightly displaces the position of the North Pole. Some geologists believe that the wobble causes earthquakes, others believe that the earthquakes cause the wobble, while still others believe that a third factor, not yet discovered, causes both the wobble and the earthquake. This argument will not be settled in lecture halls, but only by further observation and measurements.

Influence of air resistance and wind is not important in these experiments.

Scientists are generally objective about science, but when the focus is on human problems, poverty, degrading effects of welfare, or social injustice, the scientist is as human as the man next door and generally possesses the same prejudices and emotions. Neither science nor technology or social studies has invented the pipeline for the transfer of wisdom and leadership in science to wisdom and leadership in human affairs.

CHEMISTRY AND MATTER_____1.2

Chemistry is the study of substances, the "stuff," the **matter** of which life, the Earth, and the Universe are composed. We shall examine matter many times in many different ways. Chemists study the preparation, properties, structure, and interactions of matter. Generally speaking, matter can exist in three **states:** gas, liquid, or solid.

Derived from mater, *the Latin word for mother.*

Stated formally by Isaac Newton (1687) as a further development of the works of the first modern physicist, Galileo Galilei, and the first modern astronomer, Johannes Kepler (1619).

Matter can be touched. The amount of matter is measured by its **mass** and determines its weight. The greater the mass, the greater the weight. Matter also has the property of *inertia*. Inertia is matter's resistance to being moved when at rest or to being stopped when in motion. If an object is in a fixed position, it will remain in that position until it is pushed or pulled; that is, until a *force* acts on the object. If an object is moving, it will continue to move in the same direction and at the same velocity unless some force, such as car brakes, acts upon it.

The term phase is frequently used when referring to a uniform piece of matter. Pure water or a solution of sugar and water is a typical liquid phase; the air we breathe is a typical gas phase; pure iron, steel, and brass are typical solid phases. Different phases are separated by definite visible boundaries (surfaces) (further discussed on page 28).

Although in everyday usage the words mass and weight are used interchangeably, they do not really measure the same property of matter. The **weight** of an object is the force that it exerts; this force—for example, against a bathroom scale—is due to the pull exerted by the Earth's gravity. An astronaut may weigh 210 pounds on the ground in Houston, Texas, but he weighs only 35 pounds on the moon because its force of gravity is much less than that of the Earth. In outer space he is weightless. He can float freely because he is too far from planets and stars to feel their pull (gravity). But he is the *same astronaut* with the *same mass*.

The significance of volume and mass can best be discussed in terms of the measurement of matter.

1.3 SCIENTIFIC MEASUREMENT: THE INTERNATIONAL SYSTEM OF UNITS, SI

About 186,000 miles per second.

Nature is beautiful, but she plays the numbers game. She is "quantitative," concerned with quantities that can be measured. She has fixed several quantities, called *natural* (*physical,* or *fundamental*) constants, such as the velocity of light in empty space, 2.9979250×10^{10} centimeters per second, and she has combined other natural constants into numbers that still baffle philosophers and theoretical scientists.* A list of fundamental constants is given in App. I.

A physical quantity is always a number, a numerical value, followed (multiplied) by a unit, such as 10 feet. Any system of measurement therefore depends on the definition of arbitrary standard units. The ancient standard for *length,* the foot, was 36 barley corns (a grain of barley) laid end to end. This was a definite improvement on an earlier definition, the width of 4 palms or 16 fingers, which proved to be too variable. The inch was defined as the distance from the first knuckle to the tip of the thumb, the yard as the distance from the nose to the tip of the middle finger on an outstretched arm, and an acre as the amount of land plowed by a yoke of oxen in a day. Evidently, one man's yard was not the same as another's. These varying measurements created problems in transmitting information; in manufacturing items of precisely fitted parts; and in the requirement, with increasing trade, that "weights and measures" be the same in different places. These problems led to the establishment of standards that could be *reproduced exactly*. The same measure could then be

---

*For example, consider the history of π (pi), 3.14159265358979323846 . . . . , which has been traced back to the time of ancient Egypt and Babylon. Actually computed to 500,000 places (1966), pi is the ratio of the circumference of a circle (the length of the line around the circle) to the diameter of the circle (the length of the line passing from one side to the other through the center).

obtained every time and everywhere. The fact that we have agreed to accept the same units allows us to make reproducible measurements.

The *SI units,* officially called the **International System of Units** (SI for Système International d'Unités), are used in all scientific work throughout the world and in the general commerce of almost all countries.* SI units are based on the decimal system and are therefore much easier to learn and use than the English system.

The SI list of symbols, abbreviations, and prefixes is given in App. II.

Unit of Length   The SI standard of length is the **meter.** It is defined as the length equal to 1,650,763.73 times the length of a wave of orange-red light (page 188) given off by the element krypton. It is *not* necessary at this point to understand what a wavelength is, but it is important to appreciate that its length is very accurately reproducible and is available as long as the element krypton, freely obtainable from air, exists. (See Fig. 1.1.)

Examine the meter stick shown in Fig. 1.2, and note that the meter is divided into 100 equal parts. Each part is 1 **centimeter,** so that 1 meter, m, = 100 centimeters, cm. In conformity with scientific usage, symbols for all units will be used in this text, and the student should learn the symbol when each unit is introduced. Each centimeter is

A ruler marked off in SI units.
From centum, the Latin word for 100.

---

*While the British and others have given up their drams, pecks, and bushels, the United States has legislated voluntary conversion to SI units. Major automobile manufacturers are now producing cars tooled in SI units; road signs are showing distances in both English and SI units; soft drinks and alcoholic beverages are being sold in SI units of volume.

**The metric system originated (1790) from the work of the French National Assembly. The meter was defined as one ten-millionth, $\frac{1}{10,000,000}$, of the distance from the North Pole to the equator, a distance that was not likely to change. It was redefined in 1875, by the Treaty of the Meter, as the distance between two engraved lines on a bar of platinum-iridium alloy (this material is extremely stable) kept at zero degrees Celsius (page 22). The bar was stored in a vault near Paris and was available for comparison with the standard of length of any nation. In the United States, standards are maintained by the National Bureau of Standards. In 1960 the General Conference of Weights and Measures adopted the International System of Units (SI). This system depends on seven fundamental units for length, mass, time, temperature, electric current, luminosity (the intensity or brightness of light), and amount of substance. All other units are derived from these standard units.

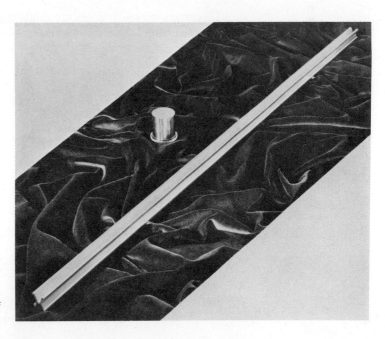

FIGURE 1.1 A duplicate of the meter bar, now replaced as the SI standard of length by a wavelength emitted by the element krypton; and a duplicate of the SI kilogram standard of mass. *Courtesy of U.S. National Bureau of Standards, Washington, D.C.*

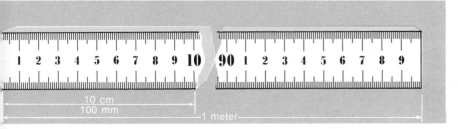

FIGURE 1.2 The SI unit of length. The two ends of a meter stick are reproduced, showing the relationship between the centimeter and the millimeter. Manufacturer compares markings with a standard meter.

From mille, the Latin word for 1000.

divided into 10 equal parts. Each part is 1 **millimeter,** so that 1 cm = 10 millimeters, mm, and 1 m = 1000 mm.

Example 1

How many centimeters in 2.00 meters?

Answer

$$? \text{ cm} = 2.00 \text{ m}$$

Since there are 100 cm in 1 m, there are 200 cm in 2.00 m:

$$\text{cm} = 2.00 \cancel{\text{m}} \times \frac{100 \text{ cm}}{1 \cancel{\text{m}}} = 200 \text{ cm}$$

In solving this problem, we used the relation 100 cm = 1 m, which can be written as $\frac{100 \text{ cm}}{1 \text{ m}}$ or $\frac{1 \text{ m}}{100 \text{ cm}}$.

This fraction, which gives the relationship between centimeters and meters, is called a **conversion factor;** it converts one unit, m, into another, cm. Both fractions say the same thing: 1 meter equals 100 cm or 100 cm equal 1 meter, and are read 100 cm *per* meter, $\frac{100 \text{ cm}}{1 \text{ m}}$; or 1 meter *per* 100 cm, $\frac{1 \text{ m}}{100 \text{ cm}}$. A quantity can be multiplied or divided by a conversion factor without changing the value of the quantity. It is like saying, "I have 10 pennies," instead of saying, "I have 1 dime"; the conversion factor is 10 pennies *per* dime, $\frac{10 \text{ penny}}{1 \text{ dime}}$, or 1 dime *per* 10 pennies, $\frac{1 \text{ dime}}{10 \text{ penny}}$.

The particular factor used in a given problem depends on how the problem is stated. In our example, the factor used is $\frac{100 \text{ cm}}{1 \text{ m}}$, since an answer in centimeters is requested for a given quantity in meters. We therefore multiplied the given quantity, 2.00 m, by the conversion factor 100 cm/m:

$$2.00 \cancel{\text{m}} \times \frac{100 \text{ cm}}{1 \cancel{\text{m}}} = 200 \text{ cm}$$

This is a typical equation. The left and right side of the equal sign (=) do not look the same. Nevertheless, the right side is the same quantity as the left side. We conclude, then that $2.00\,m = 200\,cm$; that is, $200\,cm$ is the same length as $2.00\,m$. It is extremely important to note that the meter unit in the denominator (the number below the line in the conversion factor) *cancels* the meter unit in the given quantity, leaving the centimeter unit in the numerator (the number above the line in the conversion factor) as the unit for our answer. Since the problem called for an answer in centimeters, our interpretation and method of solving the problem are correct:

$$\cancel{m} \times \frac{cm}{\cancel{m}} = cm$$

If we had used the factor incorrectly, $\dfrac{1\,m}{100\,cm}$, the answer would have to be written as

$$2.00\,m \times \frac{1\,m}{100\,cm} = 0.0200\,\frac{m^2}{cm}$$

and our answer would have had the incorrect units, $\dfrac{m \times m}{cm} = \dfrac{m^2}{cm}$.* The incorrect units immediately tell us that our method for solving the problem is incorrect.

Example 2

How many millimeters in 2.0 meters?

Answer

$$?\,mm = 2.0\,m$$

Since there are 1000 millimeters in 1 meter, $\dfrac{1000\,mm}{1\,m}$,

$$mm = 2.0\,\cancel{m} \times \frac{1000\,mm}{1\,\cancel{m}} = 2000\,mm$$

This relationship is another typical equation; it expresses an equality of two quantities.

You may not be aware of the fact that we use this method of solving problems in our daily lives. Very frequently we convert a quantity expressed in one unit to a quantity expressed in another unit. In general,

Called dimensional analysis, or the conversion factor method.

a given quantity and unit × conversion factor ⟶ desired quantity and unit

The conversion factor relates the desired quantity to the given quantity, and is determined by the units of these two quantities. For example, in converting dollars to

---

*Any number, a, multiplied by itself can be represented as $a \times a = a^2$. The 2 in a^2 is known as an **exponent**. Thus a^3 ("a cubed") $= a \times a \times a$; 2^2 ("two squared") $= 2 \times 2 = 4$; 2^3 ("two cubed") $= 2 \times 2 \times 2 = 8$; 10^2 ("ten squared") $= 10 \times 10 = 100$. This topic is further considered in Section 1.4.

cents, $\dfrac{100 \text{ cents}}{1 \text{ dollar}}$, or cents to dollars; gallons to quarts, 4 qt/gal; and dollars to merchandise, we use the conversion factor method:

How many dollars in 25 cents?

$$? \text{ dollar} = 25 \text{ cents}$$

$$\text{dollar} = 25 \text{ cents} \times \frac{1 \text{ dollar}}{100 \text{ cents}} = 0.25 \text{ dollar}$$

given quantity × conversion factor = desired quantity

How many quarts in 1.5 gallons?

$$? \text{ qt} = 1.5 \text{ gal}$$

$$\text{qt} = 1.5 \text{ gal} \times \frac{4.0 \text{ qt}}{1 \text{ gal}} = 6.0 \text{ qt}$$

given quantity × conversion factor = desired quantity

How many dollars are needed to buy 10.5 gal of gasoline? The conversion factor (the price) is 60.0 cents per gal:

$$\text{cents} = 10.5 \text{ gal} \times \frac{60.0 \text{ cents}}{1 \text{ gal}} = 630 \text{ cents}$$

$$\text{dollars} = 630 \text{ cents} \times \frac{1 \text{ dollar}}{100 \text{ cents}} = 6.30 \text{ dollars}$$

The major advantages of dimensional analysis are that it forces us to *analyze* a problem, regardless of how complicated the problem may sound, to determine the correct conversion factors to use, and to *check* our method by comparing the unit obtained for the answer with the desired unit.

Example 3

(a) How many mm in 2.00 m? (b) How many miles, mi, are covered in 2.0 hours, h, by a car whose speed is 30 mi per h? (c) How long, in h, will it take for the same car to travel 75 mi?

Answer

(a) Units of mm are required for the answer. We know the conversion factor that relates mm and cm, $\dfrac{10 \text{ mm}}{1 \text{ cm}}$, and the conversion factor that relates cm and m, $\dfrac{100 \text{ cm}}{1 \text{ m}}$. Thus,

$$\text{mm} = 2.00 \text{ m} \times \frac{100 \text{ cm}}{1 \text{ m}} \times \frac{10 \text{ mm}}{1 \text{ cm}} = 2000 \text{ mm}$$

If either factor had been incorrectly used, $\frac{1 \text{ m}}{100 \text{ cm}}$ or $\frac{1 \text{ cm}}{10 \text{ mm}}$, the error would have been noticed, since the units obtained for the answer would not have been mm. (b) We are given the time in hours and want to know the distance in miles; hence, the conversion factor must be the relation between mi and h, 30 mi/h:

$$\text{mi} = 2.0 \,\cancel{h} \times \frac{30 \text{ mi}}{1 \,\cancel{h}} = 60 \text{ mi}$$

(c) Here, we are given 75 mi and want to know the time in hours; hence, the conversion factor must be the relation between h and mi, 1 h/30 mi:

$$\text{h} = 75 \,\cancel{\text{mi}} \times \frac{1 \text{ h}}{30 \,\cancel{\text{mi}}} = 2.5 \text{ h}$$

Example 4

How many meters in 250 centimeters?

Answer

$$? \text{ m} = 250 \text{ cm}$$

To convert centimeters to meters, we use 1 m/100 cm as the conversion factor:

$$\text{m} = 250 \,\cancel{\text{cm}} \times \frac{1 \text{ m}}{100 \,\cancel{\text{cm}}} = 2.50 \text{ m}$$

PROBLEM 1 (a) **How many millimeters, mm, are there in 2.5 meters, m? (b) How many m in 600 mm? (c) How long, in h, does it take a car traveling at 50 mi per h to travel 160 mi?**

Conversions of one unit to a larger or smaller unit in the SI system are fairly easy, as units are expressed by the same *prefixes,* such as **centi** or **milli**. A **kilo** expresses a larger unit; there are 1000 meters in 1 *kilometer,* km, or 1 km = 1000 m, $\frac{1000 \text{ m}}{1 \text{ km}}$ or $\frac{1 \text{ km}}{1000 \text{ m}}$. The SI units of length in common use are given in Table 1.1. The relationship between inches, in, and centimeters, cm, 2.54 cm (exactly) = 1 in, is shown in Fig. 1.3.

**TABLE 1.1
SI UNITS OF LENGTH**

megameter, M	1 M = 1 million m
kilometer, km	1 km = 1000 m
meter, m	base unit
centimeter, cm	100 cm = 1 m
millimeter, mm	1000 mm = 1 m
*micrometer,** μm	1 million μm = 1 m

*Also known as a *micron,* μm. See App. II for a list of SI symbols, prefixes, and abbreviations.

11

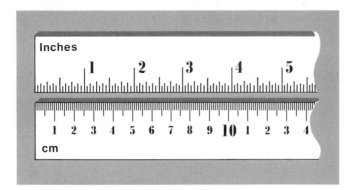

FIGURE 1.3 The relationship between centimeters and inches: 2.54 cm (exactly) are in 1 in, 2.54 cm/in.

Example 5

(a) How many centimeters in 1.50 feet? Recall that there are 12 inches in 1 foot.
(b) Find the speed of the car in Example 3 in kilometers per hour. 1 mile = 1.6 kilometers.

Answer

(a) $\qquad$? cm = 1.50 ft.

The desired unit in the answer is cm; thus,

$$\text{cm} = 1.50 \, \cancel{ft} \times \frac{12 \, \cancel{in}}{1 \, \cancel{ft}} \times \frac{2.54 \, \text{cm}}{1 \, \cancel{in}} = 45.7 \, \text{cm}$$

(b) $\qquad$ $? \dfrac{\text{km}}{\text{h}} = \dfrac{30 \, \text{mi}}{\text{h}}$

$$\frac{30 \, \cancel{mi}}{1 \, \text{h}} \times \frac{1.6 \, \text{km}}{1 \, \cancel{mi}} = 48 \, \frac{\text{km}}{\text{h}}$$

PROBLEM 2 **The length of a popular foreign car is 455 cm. Calculate the length of the car in (a) meters, (b) inches, and (c) feet.**

Unit of Volume   The volume of a box, such as the one shown in Fig. 1.4, is the product obtained by multiplying the length, l, by the width, w, by the height, h, of the box, all of which are length measurements; volume, $V = l \times w \times h$. If the box shown measures 10 cm × 10 cm × 10 cm, the volume is 1000 cm^3; cm^3 is a volume unit.

The term cm^3 is read as cubic centimeter.

One cm^3 is the volume of a box 1 cm on each edge; that is, the length, width, and height are each 1 cm. The volume of the larger box shown in Fig. 1.4 can be thought of as being made up of 1000 little boxes, each little box having a volume of 1 cm^3.

Volumes are often expressed in **liters;** 1 liter, ℓ, is equal to 1000 cm^3. A **milliliter,** ml, is equal to 1 cm^3, so that 1 liter is also equal to 1000 ml, $\dfrac{1000 \, \text{ml}}{1 \, \ell}$ or $\dfrac{1 \, \ell}{1000 \, \text{ml}}$. One liter is slightly larger than 1 quart, $\dfrac{1.06 \, \text{qt}}{1 \, \ell}$.

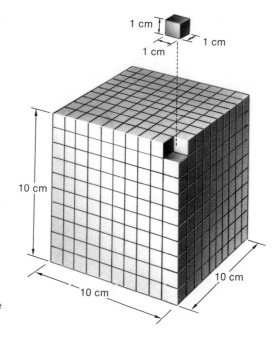

FIGURE 1.4 The volume of the small box is 1 cm³. The volume of the large box is 1000 cm³.

We measure volumes with apparatus that are *calibrated* against a known volume, just as a meter stick is calibrated against a known length. The graduated cylinder and the buret, shown in Fig. 1.5, are designed to deliver various known volumes, from zero to the capacity of the apparatus. The pipet (Fig. 1.5) is designed to deliver a definite volume, while the volumetric flask is calibrated to contain a definite volume.

Example 6

What is the volume of a box, 20 cm × 10 cm × 7.0 cm, (a) in cm³, (b) in ml, and (c) in *ℓ*?

1.4   *1400 cm³*

Answer

(a) The volume, *V*, of the box in cm³ is

$$V = 20 \text{ cm} \times 10 \text{ cm} \times 7.0 \text{ cm} = 1400 \text{ cm}^3$$

(b) Since 1 ml = 1 cm³, the volume in ml is the same as in cm³:

$$V = 1400 \text{ cm}^3 \times \frac{1 \text{ ml}}{1 \text{ cm}^3} = 1400 \text{ ml}$$

(c) To convert milliliters to liters, we use the conversion factor 1 *ℓ*/1000 ml:

$$V = 1400 \text{ ml} \times \frac{1 \ell}{1000 \text{ ml}} = 1.4 \ \ell$$

13

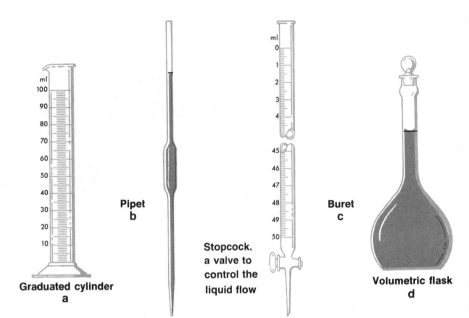

Graduated cylinder
a

Pipet
b

Stopcock,
a valve to
control the
liquid flow

Buret
c

Volumetric flask
d

FIGURE 1.5 Laboratory apparatus used to measure volumes of liquids.

Example 7

How many gallons, gal, can be contained in a box exactly 1 m on each edge?
There are 1000 ℓ in a cubic meter, m^3, and 3.785 ℓ in 1 gal.

$1\ell = 1.06\ qt$ $1\ell = 1000\ cm^3$

Answer

First, find the volume of the box from the given length, width, and height:

$$V,\ \text{volume} = 1\ m \times 1\ m \times 1\ m = 1\ m^3$$

Then, use the conversion factor, 1000 ℓ/m^3, to convert to liters, and use the
given conversion factor, 3.785 ℓ/gal, to convert liters to gallons:

$$1\ \cancel{m^3} \times \frac{1000\ \cancel{\ell}}{\cancel{m^3}} \times \frac{1\ gal}{3.785\ \cancel{\ell}} = 264.2\ gal$$

The cubic meter is the SI volume unit obtained from the SI length unit, the
meter.

PROBLEM 3   **Oil is imported into the United States by the barrel, each barrel containing
42 gallons, gal, of crude oil. What is the volume of a barrel of oil in (a) quarts, (b) liters?**

Unit of Mass   The **kilogram,** kg, which equals exactly 1000 grams, g, is the
base SI unit of mass. One kilogram is the mass of an arbitrary chunk of metal, a
platinum-iridium block stored at the International Bureau of Weights and Measures
in France. See Fig. 1.1. The SI units of mass in common use are give in Table 1.2.
There are 453.6 g in 1 pound, lb, $\dfrac{453.6\ g}{1\ lb}$ or $\dfrac{1\ lb}{453.6\ g}$, and 16 ounces, oz, in 1 lb, $\dfrac{16\ oz}{1\ lb}$

or $\dfrac{1\ lb}{16\ oz}$.

TABLE 1.2
SI UNITS OF MASS

kilogram, kg	base unit
gram, g	1000 g = 1 kg
milligram, mg	1000 mg = 1 g
microgram, μg	1 million μg = 1 g

Example 8

If the large cube in Fig. 1.4 is made of gold, its mass would be 19,300 g. What is its mass in (a) kilograms, kg, (b) milligrams, mg, and (c) pounds, lb?

Answer

(a) Using the conversion factor that relates kilograms to grams, $\dfrac{1\ kg}{1000\ g}$, convert g to kg as shown:

$$19{,}300\ g \times \frac{1\ kg}{1000\ g} = 19.3\ kg$$

In a similar fashion,

$$\text{(b)}\ 19{,}300\ g \times \frac{1000\ mg}{1\ g} = 19{,}300{,}000\ mg$$

$$\text{(c)}\ 19{,}300\ g \times \frac{1\ lb}{453.6\ g} = 42.5\ lb$$

Example 9

What is the total mass in grams of three samples whose masses are 0.1000 kg, 105.0 g, and 300 mg?

Answer

Quantities of matter cannot be added or subtracted unless they have the same units. We cannot add or subtract 2 dollars and 2 dimes without first converting dollars to dimes or dimes to dollars. Therefore, all given units must be converted to the same unit, grams in this case, before addition:

$$0.1000\ kg \times \frac{1000\ g}{1\ kg} = 100.0\ g$$

$$300\ mg \times \frac{1\ g}{1000\ mg} = \quad 0.3\ g$$

$$\underline{\qquad\qquad\qquad\qquad\ \ 105.0\ g}$$

$$\text{Total mass} = 205.3\ g$$

PROBLEM 4 **Express the mass of 32.0 g of oxygen gas in (a) milligrams, (b) kilograms, and (c) pounds.**

PROBLEM 5 The weight of a letter is 85.2 g. If the postage is 13 cents per ounce, how much postage is required for the letter?

PROBLEM 6 (a) The "Stoop," the Dutch unit for measuring beer, is equal to 10.56 pints. How many gallons of beer are there in a 20 Stoop container? (b) In Indonesia, opium is measured by the "Thail"; 1 Thail = 1.24 oz. What is the weight in (i) pounds and (ii) in grams of a 50 Thail bag of opium?

A summary of SI units is given in App. III.

1.4 PRECISION OF MEASUREMENTS AND SIGNIFICANT FIGURES

A measurement that indicates a number of objects, such as 10 pencils or 321 students, is an exact quantity. Either there are exactly 10 pencils or there are not; there is no uncertainty about the measurement. However, the only measurement that can be made exactly is the *counting of discrete (separated) objects like pencils and books.* Measurements of quantities that continuously vary, such as length, mass, volume, and temperature, must be made with some kind of measuring device. They are therefore always subject to some uncertainty, some *error.* Measurements of such quantities can be made with different degrees of precision. **Precision** refers to the agreement between repeated measurements of the same quantity. Precision indicates the ability to reproduce an experimental result. The following experiment illustrates how we determine the precision, or the degree of uncertainty, in measurements: we weigh a given stainless steel bar on an insensitive scale or balance. We find that the mass of the bar is 21 g; we reweigh the *same* bar on the *same* balance and find the mass is 22 g; a third weighing gives us 20 g as the mass of the bar, while a fourth weighing gives us 21 g. The mass of the bar is said to be between 20 and 22 g, written as 21 ± 1 g, read as twenty-one grams plus or minus one gram. This shows that the precision of this measurement is ± 1 g. We now weigh the bar on a more sensitive balance and find the mass to be 21.37 g. Repeated weighings give 21.37, 21.36, and 21.38 g. We now report the mass of the bar as 21.37 ± 0.01 g, indicating that the precision in this measurement is ± 0.01 g. Using an even more sensitive balance, the mass of the bar is reported as 21.369213 ± 0.000001 g. However, in common usage, the ± 1, ± 0.01, and ± 0.000001 are frequently eliminated from such measurements, and they are simply reported as 21 g, 21.37 g, and 21.369213 g, but with the *understanding* that there is an *uncertainty*, some error in the last digit of the reported value. All digits of a number in a reported value are known as **significant figures.** Thus, the reported values, 21 g, 21.37 g, and 21.369213 g, contain two, four, and eight significant figures, respectively. The number of significant figures in 37.20 g is four. The zero in 37.20 g is significant because it implies a precision of ± 0.01 g; that is, the mass is between 37.21 and 37.19 g. A less obvious case involves a reported value such as 0.04261 kg. Are the zeros to the left and right of the decimal point significant? They are not; they are used only to locate the decimal point. If this mass is expressed in grams (1 kg = 1000 g), the zeros disappear, $0.04261 \text{ kg} \times \dfrac{1000 \text{ g}}{1 \text{ kg}} = 42.61$ g, yielding a number that clearly has four significant figures.

We cannot change the precision of measurements by changing the units in which they are reported. The safest rule to follow in determining the number of significant figures is to start the count with the *first digit at the left end* of the number that is *not a zero.*

Bilanx, *Latin for balance, derived from* bis *and* lanx, *Latin for two dishes or two pans. Modern balances have only one pan and a set of removable weights.*

Example 10

How many significant figures in each of the following quantities? (a) 0.00736 g, (b) 421 ml, (c) 0.421 ℓ, (d) 0.4210 ℓ, (e) 421.0 ml, (f) 26 mm.

Answer

(a) Three significant figures; we start to count with the digit 7 at the left. The zeros serve only to locate the decimal point. The number could be reported as 7.36 mg. (b) Three significant figures. (c) Three significant figures; this is the same quantity as in (b). (d) and (e) Four significant figures. (f) Two significant figures.

PROBLEM 7 How many significant figures in (a) **12.13 g**, (b) **0.002 ℓ**, (c) **200.0 ml**, (d) **356 cm**?

When we add or subtract numbers, the answer cannot be more precise than the individual measurements. Hence, the sum or difference cannot go beyond the first decimal position for which nothing is recorded, as illustrated in the following example.

Example 11

(a) Add the following masses: 20.11 g, 8026.000 g, and 1.1764 g. (b) Subtract 1.251 ml from 203.7653 ml.

Answer

(a)   20.11 g   *first decimal position beyond which nothing is recorded; there-*
  8026.000 g   *fore, the digits 64 in the answer are discarded.*
     1.1764 g
  8047.2864 g   *discard*

However, in "rounding off" numbers, the last significant figure, the digit 8 in this case, is increased by 1 if the next digit, 6 in this case, is exactly 5 or more. Hence, the sum in our example is reported as 8047.29 g. The sum of 2.1 and 2.149 is 4.2, not 4.3.

(b) 203.7653 ml
    1.251 ml   *first decimal position beyond which nothing is recorded; there-*
  202.5143 ml   *fore, the last digit 3 in the answer is discarded.*
        discard

In "rounding off" numbers, the last significant figure, the digit 4 in this case, is unchanged if the next digit, 3 in this case, is less than 5. Hence, the subtraction is reported as 202.514 ml.

PROBLEM 8 Perform the indicated addition and subtraction, rounding off the answer to the proper number of significant figures. (a) **33.31 g + 8002.0 g + 1.703 g**, (b) **542 cm − 2.13 cm**.

Similarly, when we multiply and divide, those operations cannot add any precision to the numbers. Hence, the number of significant figures in the answer should be the same as the number of significant figures in the quantity that has the smallest number of significant figures.

Example 12

12.0 ml of chloroform (colorless, toxic liquid with pungent odor) has a mass of 17.981 g. What is the mass of 1.00 ml of chloroform?

Answer

If 12.0 ml of chloroform has a mass of 17.981 g, then the mass of 1 ml, g/ml, is

$$\frac{17.981 \text{ g}}{12.0 \text{ ml}} = 1.498 \frac{\text{g}}{\text{ml}} = 1.50 \frac{\text{g}}{\text{ml}}$$

The smallest number of significant figures in the quantities involved in this calculation is three, corresponding to the 12.0 ml. Hence, the number of significant figures in the answer cannot be more than three. Thus, the mass per milliliter of chloroform is reported as $1.50 \frac{\text{g}}{\text{ml}}$.

Used in the 19th century as a general anesthetic and long used in cough remedies and liniments, chloroform produces cancer in mice.

PROBLEM 9 **Calculate the mass per milliliter, g/ml, of benzene (flammable, colorless, toxic liquid), 15.0 ml of which has a mass of 13.185 g.**

Precision and Accuracy   Scientists make a distinction between the terms precision and accuracy. Precision measures the agreement between the results of repeated experiments. But precise experiments are not necessarily accurate, because it is possible to repeat the same error as many times as a measurement is repeated. **Accuracy** measures the agreement between a reported value and the known accepted value. For example, the mass of a steel bar is reported as 21.369213 g (page 16), but its certified (accepted) mass is 21.369221 g. The error in the weighing is then said to be the difference between the two values, -0.000008 g. The minus sign indicates that the measured value is less than the accepted value.

Writing Small and Large Numbers   Nature frequently deals with numbers that are fantastically large or small, far beyond our usual concept of size. For example, the number of oxygen particles (molecules) in 32.0 g of oxygen is 602,209,000,000,000,000,000,000, and the mass of one oxygen particle (molecule) is 0.000000000000000000000053 g, numbers impractical to express in words. Consequently, a practical scheme for writing such numbers has been invented. The scheme may seem complicated, but with a little practice it works out easily.

The number 100 is equal to 10^2, that is, 10×10. The exponent is 2, and 10^2 is read as "ten squared" or "ten raised to the second power"; the exponent indicates how many times the number is used in multiplying itself. Thus $3^2 = 3 \times 3 = 9$, $2^3 = 2 \times 2 \times 2 = 8$, $10^1 = 10$, $10^3 = 10 \times 10 \times 10 = 1000$, $10^6 = 10 \times 10 \times 10 \times 10 \times 10 \times 10 = 1,000,000$. Since $1000 = 1.0 \times 10^3$, the exponent 3 actually *indicates the number of places the decimal point has been shifted to the left*. Thus,

$10,000 = 1.0 \times 10^4$, and $100,000 = 1.0 \times 10^5$. Hence, any number can be represented as a number multiplied by 10 raised to the proper power. For example, 3.6×10^3 equals $3.6 \times 1000 = 3600$. Here 3600 has only two significant figures because it is derived from 3.6, a number that clearly has two significant figures. We cannot change the precision of a measurement by changing units or rewriting numbers. Yet, if no information is available, we may be tempted to say that 3600 has four significant figures. This confusion in a measured quantity is eliminated when the exponential notation is used. Thus, 3600 g, actually measured to four significant figures, is written as 3.600×10^3 g in preference to 3600 g. But 3600 g, measured to only two significant figures, is written as 3.6×10^3 g, and not incorrectly as 3600 g.

Example 13

Write the following as exponential numbers: (a) 4127 g, (b) 4160 (four significant figures) g.

Answer

(a) 4127 g can be written as 4.127 g $\times$ 1000 or 4.127×10^3 g. Shifting the decimal point three places to the left raises 10 to the third power. (b) This number can also be written as 4.160×10^3 g. Both numbers have four significant figures because 4127 g and 4160 g imply a precision of ± 1 g. It would therefore be incorrect to write 4160 g as 4.16×10^3 g.

As another example, the number 602,209,000,000,000,000,000,000, which has only six significant figures, is written as 6.02209×10^{23} by shifting the decimal point 23 places to the left.

We now apply the method to small numbers. One-tenth, 0.10, may also be written as $\frac{1.0}{10}$. Equally correct, $\frac{1.0}{10}$ may be written as 1.0×10^{-1}; in summary,

$$0.10 = \frac{1.0}{10} = 1.0 \times 10^{-1}$$

Similarly, for one-hundredth

$$0.010 = \frac{1.0}{100} = 1.0 \times 10^{-2}$$

and one-thousandth

$$0.0010 = \frac{1.0}{1000} = 1.0 \times 10^{-3}$$

Notice that in each case *the exponent is the number of places the decimal point has been shifted to the right;* the minus sign indicates that the decimal point has been moved to the right. Without exception, the exponent of 10 is *increased by the number of places the decimal point has been shifted to the left* and *decreased by the number of places the decimal has been shifted to the right*. Equally well, we can say that as a quantity is *increased* in value by moving the decimal point, the exponent is *decreased;* conversely, as the quantity is *decreased,* the exponent is *increased*. For example, the mass of one particle (molecule) of oxygen (page 18) is written as 5.3×10^{-23} g by shifting the decimal point 23 places to the right. Other examples follow:

4 places to the right   1 place to right   1 place to right

$$0.000017 = 0.17 \times 10^{-4} = 1.7 \times 10^{-5} = 17 \times 10^{-6}$$

2 places to the left   3 places to the right   2 places to the right   4 places to the left

$$116.777 = 1.16777 \times 10^{2} = 1167.77 \times 10^{-1} = 116777 \times 10^{-3} = 11.6777 \times 10^{1}$$

1 place to the right   2 places to the left

Notice that the number of significant figures is *not* changed by changing the form in which the given value is written: there are two significant figures for the first example and six for the second.

PROBLEM 10   **Write each of the following as an exponential number (pay attention to the number of significant figures): (a) 0.000010 g, (b) 178,300 ft (only four significant figures), (c) 0.072 cm, (d) 2,010,000 lb (only five significant figures), (e) 0.000040 mg, (f) 0.13 ft.**

A major advantage of the use of exponential numbers is the ease with which small and large numbers may be added, subtracted, multiplied, and divided. For example, to find the mass of 4120 oxygen particles (molecules) involves multiplication by the mass of one particle (molecule), $0.0000000000000000000000053 \dfrac{g}{\text{molecule}} \times$ 4120 molecules, a rather impractical situation. Using exponential numbers, the multiplication can be done with less chance of human error. In multiplication, exponents are added; in division, exponents are subtracted. For example, $200 \times 200 = 40,000$ is the same as

$$(2.0 \times 10^{2}) \times (2.0 \times 10^{2}) = 2.0 \times 2.0 \times 10^{2} \times 10^{2} = 4.0 \times 10^{(2+2)}$$
$$= 4.0 \times 10^{4} = 40,000$$

The mass of 4120 oxygen molecules is calculated as shown:

$$4.120 \times 10^{3} \text{ molecules} \times 5.3 \times 10^{-23} \frac{g}{\text{molecule}}$$

$$= 5.3 \times 4.120 \times (10^{3-23}) \, g = 22 \times 10^{-20} \, g$$

$$= 2.2 \times 10^{-19} \, g$$

In division, $\dfrac{80,000}{200} = 400$ is the same as

$$\frac{8.00 \times 10^{4}}{2.00 \times 10^{2}} = \frac{8.00}{2.00} \times \frac{10^{4}}{10^{2}} = \frac{8.00}{2.00} \times 10^{(4-2)} = 4.00 \times 10^{2} = 400$$

Other examples follow:

$$(5.0 \times 10^{12}) \times (4.0 \times 10^{2}) \times (2.0 \times 10^{-10}) = 5.0 \times 4.0 \times 2.0 \times 10^{(12+2-10)}$$
$$= 40 \times 10^{4} = 4.0 \times 10^{5}$$

$$\frac{(32.0 \times 10^{3}) \times (3.00 \times 10^{6})}{4.00 \times 10^{16}} = \frac{32.0 \times 3.00 \times 10^{(3+6-16)}}{4.00}$$
$$= 24.0 \times 10^{-7} = 2.40 \times 10^{-6}$$

$$\frac{(32.0 \times 10^{-3}) \times (3.00 \times 10^{-6})}{4.00 \times 10^{-16}} = \frac{32.0 \times 3.00 \times 10^{(-3-6+16)}}{4.00}$$
$$= 24.0 \times 10^{7} = 2.40 \times 10^{8}$$

In addition and subtraction, all numbers must first be converted to the *same* power of 10. For example, in the addition or subtraction of 6.02×10^{23} and 1.14×10^{24}, first change 6.02×10^{23} to 0.602×10^{24} and then add or subtract:

$$
\begin{array}{r}
1.14 \times 10^{24} \\
+0.60 \times 10^{24} \\
\hline
1.74 \times 10^{24}
\end{array}
\qquad
\begin{array}{r}
1.14 \times 10^{24} \\
-0.60 \times 10^{24} \\
\hline
0.54 \times 10^{24}
\end{array}
$$

Equally correctly, we may first change 1.14×10^{24} to 11.4×10^{23} and then add or subtract:

$$
\begin{array}{r}
11.4 \times 10^{23} \\
+ \ 6.0 \times 10^{23} \\
\hline
17.4 \times 10^{23} = 1.74 \times 10^{24}
\end{array}
\qquad
\begin{array}{r}
11.4 \times 10^{23} \\
- \ 6.0 \times 10^{23} \\
\hline
5.4 \times 10^{23} = 0.54 \times 10^{24}
\end{array}
$$

PROBLEM 11

(a) $(1.6 \times 10^{21}) \times (3.0 \times 10^{3}) \times (2.0 \times 10^{-19}) = ?$

(b) $\dfrac{(8.0 \times 10^{23}) \times (6.00 \times 10^{3})}{4.0 \times 10^{21}} = ?$

(c) $7.0 \times 10^{20} + 2.0 \times 10^{19} = ?$

(d) $7.0 \times 10^{20} - 2.0 \times 10^{19} = ?$

Lastly, the exponent -1 is commonly used to indicate a unit such as "per second" or "per inch"; $\dfrac{1}{\text{second}}$ and $\dfrac{1}{\text{inch}}$ are usually written as s^{-1} and in^{-1}. For example, 60 miles per hour, $\dfrac{60 \text{ mi}}{1 \text{ h}}$, may also be written as 60 mi h^{-1}.

Per, Latin "for each"; 12 inches for each foot, 12 in per ft, 12 in ft^{-1}, $12 \frac{in}{ft}$, $\frac{12 in}{1 ft}$.

TEMPERATURE AND ENERGY_____ 1.5

Most of us are familiar with the consequences of touching a *hot* stove or jumping into a *cold* pool, and with the idea of temperature as a measure of the "hotness" or "coldness" of an object. The stove is hotter than your finger, and when the two are brought in contact with each other, *heat* flows from the stove to your finger. The burn received is the result of the damage done to body tissue by the heat. The flow of heat from your body to cold water gives you the feeling of being chilled.

Heat and temperature do not measure the same quantity (page 25). Nevertheless, they are mutually defined. If two objects are in contact, heat *always* flows from an object of higher temperature to an object of *lower* temperature until the temperatures are equal. A hot object in contact with a cold object *never* gets hotter. However, to measure and study temperature effects, some measurable change that occurs with temperature must be used. Our sensations of hot, warm, cool, and cold are not scientifically useful. But, with few exceptions, substances expand in volume when heated and contract when cooled. The expansion of air with changes in temperature was used by Galileo Galilei (1603) as a crude **thermometer.*** Advances made by

Frostbite results from freezing of body tissue due to loss of body heat from localized areas.

---

*From *therme* and *metron,* the Greek words meaning heat measure. The word thermometer first appeared in print in 1624. Sanctorius (1611), Galileo's friend, first adapted Galileo's air thermometer, in which the expansion of air pushed down on a column of colored liquid, to measure the body's change in temperature.

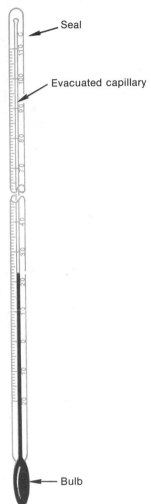

<- Seal

<- Evacuated capillary

<- Bulb

FIGURE 1.6 A typical mercury-in-glass thermometer. The length of the mercury liquid column is used to measure temperature.

Ferdinand II (1654), Guillaume Amontons, Isaac Newton (1701), and others, led Gabriel Fahrenheit (1714) to construct a thermometer which contained mercury (silver-colored liquid metal) in a glass tube.

The mercury thermometer, still in use today, is constructed from a glass capillary tube, a very narrow tube, that has an expanded part, a bulb, at one end. The bulb and part of the tube are filled with mercury, the tube is evacuated (air is removed), and the upper end is sealed. A typical thermometer is shown in Fig. 1.6. The mercury in the tube rises when the bulb of the thermometer is placed in contact with a hot object, because the mercury in the bulb expands. Since the tube has such a narrow diameter, a small change in the volume of the mercury in the bulb leads to a large change in the height of the mercury column. Mercury has the property of expanding in a regular way with rise in temperature over a wide range. Thus, experimentally, the length of the mercury column is used to measure temperature. The temperature scale used in scientific work is the Celsius scale (formerly called the Centigrade scale*) established by Anders Celsius (1742).

Fig. 1.7 shows the steps in the calibration of a Celsius thermometer. The thermometer is placed in an ice-water-air mixture and the mercury level is marked zero degrees, 0 degrees Celsius, 0 °C. The thermometer is then placed above boiling water (at standard pressure, page 47), and the mercury level is marked 100 degrees Celsius, 100 °C. The distance between the 0 °C and 100 °C marks is divided into 100 equal parts, each of which corresponds to a degree Celsius, °C. If the thermometer is placed in contact with an object and the mercury column comes to rest at 82 °C, 82 divisions above the 0 °C mark, the temperature of the object is said to be 82 °C.

Fahrenheit used several temperature scales in the development of his thermometer but finally settled on the scale that assigns 32 degrees to the temperature at which water freezes and 212 degrees to the temperature at which water boils. The distance between the 32 °F and 212 °F marks is divided into 180 equal parts, each corresponding to a degree Fahrenheit, °F.

The temperature of an object can be expressed as degrees Celsius or degrees Fahrenheit, since the height of the mercury column in a thermometer is independent of the scale marked on the glass tube. Thus, 0 °C is the same temperature as 32 °F, and 100 °C is the same temperature as 212 °F. For every temperature on one scale there is an equivalent temperature on the other scale.

The relationship between the two temperatures is clearly shown by a **graph.** A graph is a diagram which gives us a pictorial view of how two different measurements are related to each other or how one quantity changes with changes in another quantity. For example, graphs that relate population with years, or temperature with time of day, are common in newspapers and magazines. The relationship between the Celsius and Fahrenheit temperatures is represented by a linear or *straight-line* graph (Fig. 1.8). The linear graph is the simplest and generally the most valuable type of graph. One arm (*y*-axis) of the graph is labeled °F, and the other arm (*x*-axis) is labeled °C. The point labeled *a* corresponds to 32 ° on the Fahrenheit scale and to 0 ° on the Celsius scale. Point *b* corresponds to 212 °F and 100 °C. Every point on the line between positions *a* and *b*, read as line *ab*, represents the relationship of the Fahrenheit temperature to the Celsius temperature. Thus, to find what Fahrenheit temperature corresponds to 40 °C, read up the vertical line from 40 °C until the line *ab* is reached, and then read across to the left to find the °F, namely 104 °F. This procedure is illustrated in Fig. 1.8 by the dashed line.

---

*Centigrade is derived from the Latin words meaning hundred steps. Celsius actually proposed 0° as the boiling point and 100° as the freezing point of water. Pierre Martel (1742) made a thermometer with 0° as the freezing point.

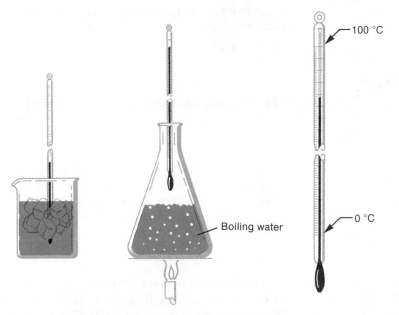

Thermometer is placed in a mixture of ice, water, and air, and the mercury level is marked 0 °C.

a

Thermometer is placed above boiling water (at standard pressure), and the mercury level is marked 100 °C.

b

Boiling water

100 °C

0 °C

The distance between 0 °C and 100 °C is divided into 100 parts, each of which corresponds to a degree Celsius. Finally, the marks are permanently etched in the glass thermometer

c

FIGURE 1.7 The calibration of a mercury thermometer.

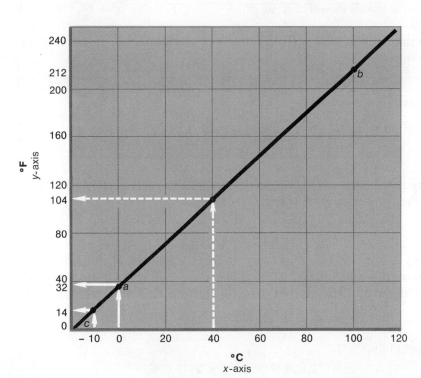

FIGURE 1.8 Relationship between °F and °C; 40 °C is the same temperature as 104 °F.

PROBLEM 12   Using the graph in Fig. 1.8, find the Celsius temperature that corresponds to 200 °F.

Example 14

From the graph in Fig. 1.8, find the Fahrenheit temperature that corresponds to −10 °C.

Answer

Although we *measured* only the information represented by the line *ab*, we can extend (*extrapolate*) the line past points *a* and *b on the assumption* that the relationship between the temperatures is still linear in these temperature regions. The line *ac* represents such an extrapolation. Thus, −10 °C corresponds to 14 °F.

The difference between the boiling point (b.p.) and the freezing point of water on the Fahrenheit scale, 180 divisions (212 − 32), covers the same distance as the difference on the Celsius scale, 100 divisions (100 − 0). The 180 divisions on the Fahrenheit scale therefore equal 100 divisions on the Celsius scale, or 9 Fahrenheit degrees equal 5 Celsius degrees:

$$\frac{°F_{b.p.} − 32 \; °F}{°C_{b.p.} − 0 \; °C} = \frac{180 \; °F}{100 \; °C} = \frac{9 \; °F}{5 \; °C}$$

Generalizing,

$$\frac{\text{Fahrenheit degrees} − 32 \; \text{deg F}}{\text{Celsius degrees} − 0 \; \text{deg C}} = \frac{°F − 32 \; °F}{°C} = \frac{9 \; °F}{5 \; °C} \tag{1}$$

This relationship may be used to change degrees F and degrees C, as shown in the following example.

Example 15

(a) Convert 50 °F to °C. (b) Convert 25 °C to °F.

Answer

(a) The given temperature, 50 °F, is substituted into the general relationship (1) between the two temperature scales:

$$\frac{50 \; °F − 32 \; °F}{°C} = \frac{9 \; °F}{5 \; °C}$$

We now solve this equation for °C, the temperature reading in Celsius degrees corresponding to 50 Fahrenheit degrees. Subtracting 32 °F from 50 °F gives

$$\frac{18 \; °F}{°C} = \frac{9 \; °F}{5 \; °C}$$

Then, cross multiplying,

$$°C \times 9 \; °F = 18 \; °F \times 5 \; °C$$

To solve for °C, divide both sides by 9 °F:

$$°C = \frac{18\ °\cancel{F} \times 5\ °C}{9\ °\cancel{F}} = 10\ °C$$

(b) Here, the known temperature is 25 °C, so the general relationship (1) becomes

$$\frac{°F - 32\ °F}{25\ °C} = \frac{9\ °F}{5\ °C}$$

from which, on cross multiplying,

$$°F - 32\ °F = \frac{9\ °F \times 25\ °C}{5\ °C}$$

Transferring $-32\ °F$ to the other side of the equal sign changes the minus sign to a plus sign:

$$°F = \frac{9\ °F \times 25\ °\cancel{C}}{5\ °\cancel{C}} + 32\ °F$$

Solving for °F,

$$°F = 45\ °F + 32\ °F = 77\ °F$$

PROBLEM 13   (a) Convert 185 °C to °F. (b) Convert normal body temperature, 98.6 °F, to °C.

Temperature measures the intensity of heat and determines the direction of heat flow. Temperature, however, does not measure the *quantity* of heat. A burning match is at a higher temperature than a large bucket of hot water, and if the match is brought into contact with the water, heat flows from the match to the water. Yet, the bucket of hot water contains a greater quantity of heat than the hot flame of the match. One puff and out goes the match, but it takes more than a few puffs to cool the water.

Experimentally, when the *same* quantity of *heat* is added to the *same mass* of different substances, the temperature is *not* increased by the same number of degrees. For example, it takes twice as much heat to raise the temperature of a given quantity of water 1 °C as it takes to raise the temperature of the *same quantity* of ethyl alcohol (colorless, intoxicating liquid) 1 °C. To put it another way, 10 g of ethyl alcohol at 50 °C contains less heat than 10 g of water at 50 °C, yet both substances are at the same temperature.

From observations by Joseph Black (1760), Benjamin Thompson, Count Rumford (1798), and especially James Joule (1840), it has been concluded that heat is not a kind of matter.* Heat can be converted into work, as in a steam engine, an automobile, or a jet engine. However, the reverse is also true; work of various kinds can be converted into heat (for example, friction). Joule found that the same amount of any kind of work always produced the same quantity of heat. Moreover, energy is defined as the *capacity to do work,* the ability to move against a force. Since a definite quantity of heat can be converted into a definite quantity of work, heat is accepted as a form of energy. The SI unit of energy is the **joule,** J, named in honor of James Joule.

The **calorie,** cal, is defined as equal to 4.184 joules (exactly), $\frac{4.184\ J}{1\ cal}$ or $\frac{1\ cal}{4.184\ J}$. This number of joules changes the temperature of 1 g of water 1 Celsius degree. There are 1000 cal in 1 kilocalorie, kcal, $\frac{1000\ cal}{1\ kcal}$ or $\frac{1\ kcal}{1000\ cal}$.

Joule is pronounced "jewel."

* Originally called "caloric," heat was assumed to be a substance that flowed from one object to another. The nature of heat is further discussed in Chap. 9.

More accurately, it raises the temperature of 1 g of water from 14.5 °C to 15.5 °C.

PROBLEM 14   **How many calories and kilocalories are there in 253 joules?**

The term energy, derived from energos, the Greek word for work, was first used by Thomas Young (1805).

Energy, a concept invented long ago to explain the behavior of matter, appears in different forms, such as light (Chap. 6), electricity (Chap. 4), and objects in motion. When matter can possibly do work because of its *position*—for example, a suspended weight, a rock high up on a mountain top, water trapped behind a dam, a tightly wound watch spring—it is said to possess *potential energy*. These objects are capable of doing work; they can do work when allowed to fall, flow, or unwind. The rock and the weight can crush a car, the water can drive an electric generator, and the spring can drive the gears of a watch.

The term was introduced by William Thompson (Lord Kelvin) in 1856, from kinema, the Greek word for motion.

When these objects are in motion, the potential energy possessed by them is said to change to **kinetic energy.** All objects in motion possess kinetic energy. The kinetic energy depends on the mass and the velocity (speed) of the object. A train moving at 30 mi/h possesses more kinetic energy than a baseball moving at 30 mi/h; a car moving at 60 mi/h possesses more kinetic energy than the same car moving at 20 mi/h.*

The concept of energy is used throughout this book. We shall see that many changes which matter undergoes are related to the absorption and emission of energy. All life processes, for example, can be discussed in these terms, a subject referred to as bioenergetics.

1.6 PROPERTIES OF MATTER; SUBSTANCES

We can sense the difference between the white solid (sugar) we put into tea or coffee and the white solid (salt) we sprinkle on food by their different tastes. Your experiences tell you to fuel a fire not with an iron bar but with wood. Nor would you put water into the gas tank of a car and expect it to run properly. You would not be surprised if a light bulb connected to a battery with a piece of cotton failed to glow.

We make decisions every day based on the characteristics of the substances around us, and we use one or another on the basis of its particular characteristics. For example, a clear colorless liquid in a glass on the kitchen table is probably water. Yet, children have been fatally injured by drinking lye solution, a clear colorless liquid mixture of lye and water (lye is a white solid, *sodium hydroxide,* also known as *caustic soda*). It appears, then, that just one or two characteristics of the substance, such as color or odor, do not necessarily identify it. Actually, there is a set of unique characteristics, called **properties,** that distinguishes one substance from another. In fact, chemists define a **substance** as matter that possesses a unique identity; that is, it is the only one of its kind, and it has a set of properties possessed by no other piece of matter.

Lye is used in oven cleaner sprays and Drano.

See center of text for Color Plates.

Some properties that serve to identify a substance include *taste, odor, color* (Color Plate I), the *temperature* at which a substance *melts* (melting point) or *boils* (boiling point), *density, solubility,* and *composition.* While many substances may be sweet or salty, a substance has a definite melting point and a definite boiling point different from those of just about all other substances. These properties are therefore very specific and are used to help identify substances. Water boils at 100 °C; the lye solution boils at a higher temperature.

The composition, or the make-up, of a substance is even more specific.

---

*The dependence of kinetic energy on mass and velocity is expressed by $E_k = \frac{1}{2}mv^2$, where m is the mass and v the velocity (speed) of the object, discussed further in Chapters 2 and 4.

Water—made from two gases, hydrogen, a colorless explosive gas, and oxygen—has a composition different from that of all other substances (Chap. 4).

Density is also commonly used to help identify substances. Lead (grey-black poisonous solid used to manufacture pipes, fishing sinkers, battery plates, and solder) is a "heavy" metal. Of course, this means that lead is heavy compared to the same volume of most other substances. One ml of lead weighs 11.3 g. The same volume of aluminum weighs 2.7 g, while the same volume of water weighs 1.0 g. The mass of 1 ml of any substance is called the **density** of the substance. It measures how much matter is packed into a given space: density = mass/volume. Thus, more correctly, we should say that lead is *denser* than aluminum and water. The units of density are g/cm^3, g/ml, or g/ℓ. The densities of lead, aluminum, and water are 11.3 g/ml, 2.7 g/ml, and 1.0 g/ml, respectively. It should be observed that the density of a substance is independent of its quantity. Thus, 2.0 ml of water weigh 2.0 g

Since the volume of a substance changes with temperature, densities are given at definite temperatures. Recall that 1 ml = 1 cm³.

$$\left(\text{density} = \frac{2.0\,g}{2.0\,ml} = 1.0\,\frac{g}{ml}\right) \text{ and 10 ml weigh 10 g } \left(\text{density} = \frac{10\,g}{10\,ml} = 1.0\,\frac{g}{ml}\right).$$

Example 16

A block of lead measures $10.00\,cm \times 5.000\,cm \times 2.000\,cm$ at 16.0 °C and weighs 1.134×10^3 g. What is the density of lead at 16.0 °C?

Answer

The volume of a square solid is length, $l \times$ width, $w \times$ height, h. The volume* of the lead block is then given by

$$10.00\,cm \times 5.000\,cm \times 2.000\,cm = 100.0\,cm^3$$

The density, mass/volume, is therefore

$$\frac{1.134 \times 10^3\,g}{100.0\,cm^3} = \frac{1134\,g}{100.0\,cm^3} = 11.34\,g/cm^3 = 11.34\,g/ml$$

Example 17

What is the mass of 10.0 ml of benzene at 20 °C, density 0.88 g/ml?

Answer

Since 1 ml of benzene has a mass of 0.88 g, 10.0 ml of benzene has a mass of 8.8 g. Or, to convert the given 10 ml of benzene to grams of benzene, we use the density, 0.88 g/ml, as the conversion factor:

$$10.0\,\cancel{ml} \times \frac{0.88\,g}{1\,\cancel{ml}} = 8.8\,g$$

---

*The volume of a cube, a solid with six sides and equal edges, is l^3, where l is the length of one edge. The volume of a sphere is $(4/3)\pi r^3$, where r is the radius of the sphere and $\pi = 3.14$ (page 6). The volume of a cylinder is $\pi r^2 l$, where l is the length and r is the radius of the cylinder.

Example 18

The density of carbon tetrachloride (nonflammable, toxic liquid, formerly used for cleaning electric motors) is 1.60 g/ml. Find the volume in ml that 50.0 g of carbon tetrachloride occupies.

Answer

We are asked to convert 50.0 g of carbon tetrachloride to its volume in ml. We therefore need a conversion factor containing the units ml/g, namely, $\dfrac{1 \text{ ml}}{1.60 \text{ g}}$:

$$50.0 \text{ g} \times \frac{1 \text{ ml}}{1.60 \text{ g}} = 31.3 \text{ ml}$$

PROBLEM 15   **Find the volume, in ml, occupied by 68.0 g of mercury, density 13.6 g/ml.**

When two or more substances of unequal density are mixed, the substance of lowest density will rise to the top. If gasoline, density 0.67 g/ml, and water, density 1.0 g/ml, are mixed at room temperature, the gasoline floats on top of the water. Gasoline and water form a typical **heterogeneous** mixture consisting of two distinct **phases,** two separated portions of matter, each with characteristic properties. The phases are separated by definite and distinct boundaries. However, when ethyl alcohol and water are mixed, only one phase appears; a boundary does not form between the alcohol and the water. The alcohol dissolves in water, forming a typical **homogeneous** mixture. Any part of the alcohol-water mixture has the same properties as any other portion. A mixture of six ice-cubes, some copper wire, and some water consists of two states of matter, solid and liquid, but three phases, the ice, the copper, and the water. Color Plate II A and B illustrate the difference between phases and

See center of book for Color Plates.

states of matter. Density can be fun, as illustrated in Color Plate II C by a bartender's supreme creation, the *pousse-café*. The six layers (six phases, but one liquid state) are formed by pouring successively less dense liqueurs on top of one another.

PROBLEM 16   **A chocolate chip cookie is a heterogeneous mixture consisting of dough, chocolate chips, and walnuts, all of which are solids with characteristic properties. The chocolate chip cookie consists of how many (a) phases, and (b) states of matter?**

Chemists sometimes talk about chemical changes and physical changes. **Physical changes** do not involve a change in the composition or the identity of a substance. For example, cutting, breaking, freezing, melting, boiling, and deforming a substance such as lead are considered physical changes. A **chemical change** or **chemical reaction,** however, changes the composition and characteristic properties of a substance.

For example, sodium, a silver-colored metal, is soft enough to be cut with a knife and easily conducts electricity. It is also a very *reactive* substance; it tends to change very quickly to other substances. It is therefore stored under liquid kerosene to prevent contact with air and moisture, with which it very rapidly reacts, evolving much heat. Sodium, however, does not react with kerosene.

For these reasons, chemically reactive substances are never touched with the fingers.

Chlorine is a deadly greenish-yellow gas. But sodium and chlorine react rapidly and violently to produce the white harmless solid called sodium chloride (table salt), a substance whose properties and composition are completely different from those of either sodium or chlorine. The reaction of sodium with chlorine is a typical chemical reaction.*

PURITY AND IDENTIFICATION OF SUBSTANCES _____ 1.7

Water is a colorless, odorless, tasteless, transparent liquid with a boiling point of 100.0 °C. However, the properties of samples of water taken from the Hudson River and from Lake Erie are measurably different. Depending on the location of sampling, the water may be brown, black, green, or yellow with an odor of rotting garbage or dead fish, difficult to see through, and with a density greater than that of pure water. These differences are due, of course, to the presence of impurities in the water. The river or lake water is a mixture of substances, some dissolved in it and others suspended in it. The components of mixtures can be separated by a number of processes.

Purification (Separation) Processes The suspended (undissolved) substances in a sample of polluted water can be removed by **filtration,** as shown in Fig. 1.9. The mixture (a) is poured through filter paper (b); the suspended solid is stopped, while the water and the substances dissolved in it pass through the filter (c).

Water can be separated from many dissolved substances by **distillation.** This process is based on the differences in the boiling points of the components of a mixture. A typical distillation apparatus is illustrated in Fig. 1.10. When a salt-water mixture is heated, the water (b.p. 100 °C) is converted to vapor, which enters the water-cooled condenser where it is cooled and condensed back into liquid water. The salt (b.p. 1413 °C) remains in the flask.** The thermometer measures the boiling point of the liquid being distilled and so helps to identify the liquid.

---

* Some changes are not so obviously classified as physical or chemical. Our recommendation is not to waste time over the classification. If the change is of interest, study it to understand its meaning and significance.

** Distillation may be used for the purification of sea-water, but the fuel cost makes it uneconomical for most situations. Solar distillation, in which the sun provides the heat, is a possible alternative, particularly in desert areas.

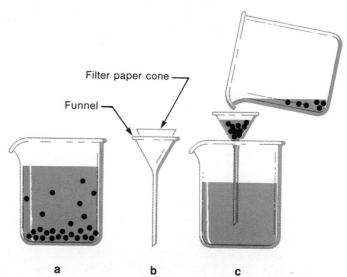

FIGURE 1.9 Filtration, a process in which suspended material (a) is strained out by passing the mixture through paper (c) (or sand or charcoal).

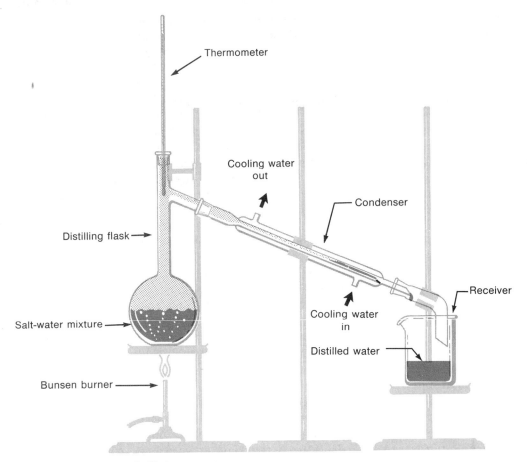

FIGURE 1.10 A typical distillation apparatus.

The distilled water so obtained is considered a **pure substance.** The term "pure," however, is relative; when a chemist says, "This is a pure substance," he means that with presently available techniques, he cannot detect or separate other components. Purity, then, changes with the standards used to judge it. Because of better instrumentation, what is considered pure today may be considered impure tomorrow.

From the practical point of view, allowable impurities vary considerably. The U.S. Food and Drug Administration (FDA) has the responsibility to establish impurity limits in consumer goods such as prepared foods, cosmetics, paints, and drugs, while scientific organizations such as the American Chemical Society establish impurity limits for substances used in scientific and industrial research and development.

The sensitivity—the extraordinary ability—of techniques and instruments to detect impurities is indicated by some of the limits set by these agencies in terms of "parts per million," ppm, or "parts per billion," ppb. These expressions mean grams of impurity in one-million or one-billion grams of matter. For example, the FDA recommends 0.5 ppm by mass as the maximum allowable amount of mercury in fish; this means that no more than 0.5 g of mercury in one million grams of fish is acceptable for consumption. Analysis of lunar samples required the use of chemicals with impurity contents of less than 1 ppb (1 g in one billion grams). The amount of sample generally used is less than 1 g, so that the amount of impurity being detected is less than one-millionth of a gram, 1×10^{-6} g, or one-billionth of a gram, 1×10^{-9} g.

One of the instruments used actually separates, identifies, and determines the amount of each component of a mixture. The basis of the separation is called **chromatography**, originally developed by Mikhail Tswett (1906), a botanist interested in the nature of the plant pigments that produce the beautifully colored leaves in the fall season. The technique depends on the observation that certain powdered-solid substances adsorb various other substances and hold them. But some substances are held more tightly than others. In the usual procedure, the mixture (yellow and red dye) to be separated is dissolved in a liquid (alcohol) and poured through the powdered solid (Color Plate III). The components of the mixture are adsorbed by the solid. Additional liquid (alcohol) is poured through the column and the components of the mixture are carried along as the liquid flows down the column. But the components are not held with equal strength. The component most strongly held moves very slowly, while the component least strongly held moves more rapidly down the column. The result is that the various components become separated into different

Chromatography is derived from chroma and graphein, the Greek words for color and write, used here to mean the separation of a mixture of colors.

See center of book for Color Plates.

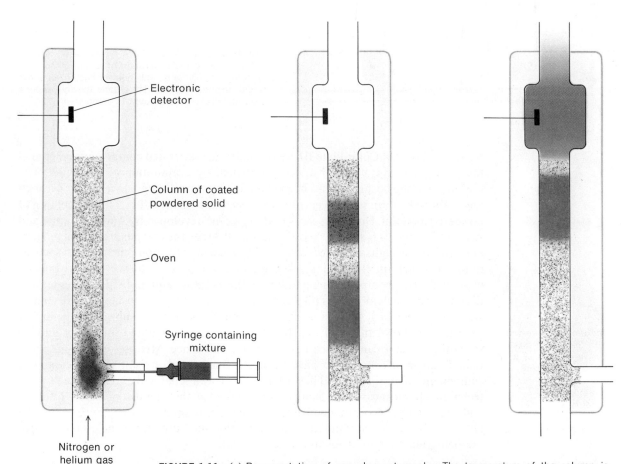

FIGURE 1.11 (a) Representation of gas chromatography. The temperature of the column is controlled so as to keep all components vaporized. The components of the mixture separate owing to differences in adsorption on the column packing. The detector electrically senses (detects) and then draws, on a roll of paper, a peak for each component detected.

Figure continued on following page.

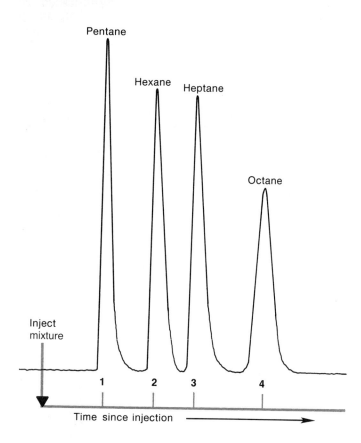

Pentane

Hexane   Heptane

Octane

Inject
mixture

1   2   3   4

Time since injection ⟶

FIGURE 1.11 *continued* (*b*) A typical result is illustrated, showing the separation of a four-component mixture of highly flammable liquids. Each peak corresponds to one substance. The greater the area under a peak, the greater the amount of component.

bands, as shown in Color Plate III.* Eventually, the separated components emerge at the bottom and the pure substance is obtained by evaporation of the liquid. The usefulness of this technique has been extended by substituting paper (*paper chromatography*) and a thin, solid layer (*thin-layer chromatography*—TLC) for the column of powdered material. However, *gas chromatography,* developed by Anthony James and Archer Martin (1941–1950), is most widely used. Here, the components of the mixture are carried through a packed column by a chemically non-reactive gas such as nitrogen or helium (Fig. 1.11a). The mixture is injected into the gas stream and vaporized. The components separate in the column and individually enter the detector. The detector senses (detects) the presence of these substances and sends a signal to a pen which draws a peak. The greater the amount of substance, the higher the peak, as shown in Fig. 1.11b. In addition, the time required for a substance to reach the detector can be used to identify the substance. Mixtures containing more than *75 different components* have been identified from one sample injection. The components of marijuana and hashish have also been separated and identified by this technique. In most cases, the sample injected is a few thousandths of a gram (10^{-3} g), and the amount of component detected may be as small as a *trillionth* of a gram (10^{-12} g). Gas chromatographic instruments that measure only 7 inches on an edge are being manufactured for use in space probes.

The time is compared with the time it takes known substances to reach the detector under exactly the same operating conditions.

A picogram = 10^{-12} g, App. II.

---

*The Painted Desert of Arizona is a striking example of the separation of a crude oil mixture into black, red, green, and yellow substances by passage through *bentonite,* a clay, the main component of fuller's earth.

Using separation and detection techniques, chemists have isolated and identified about six million substances. Practically all of these, however, can be broken down (decomposed) into two or more simpler substances. A very few substances, about 107, cannot be decomposed. They are called the **elements,** the substances from which all other substances, called **compounds,** are made. Compounds contain at least two elements. For example, heating red, solid mercury(II) oxide produces liquid mercury and oxygen, a colorless gas. Oxygen and mercury are typical elements. A few of these elements, not found naturally, have been prepared in the laboratory (Chap. 17). Table 1.3 summarizes a suitable classification of matter.

They cannot be decomposed by absorbing about 10^5 to 10^6 cal/g, but they can be decomposed (Chap. 17). The absorption of 10^6 cal can raise the temperature of 10 kg of water 100 °C.

TABLE 1.3
THE CLASSIFICATION OF MATTER, SUFFICIENT FOR OUR PURPOSE.

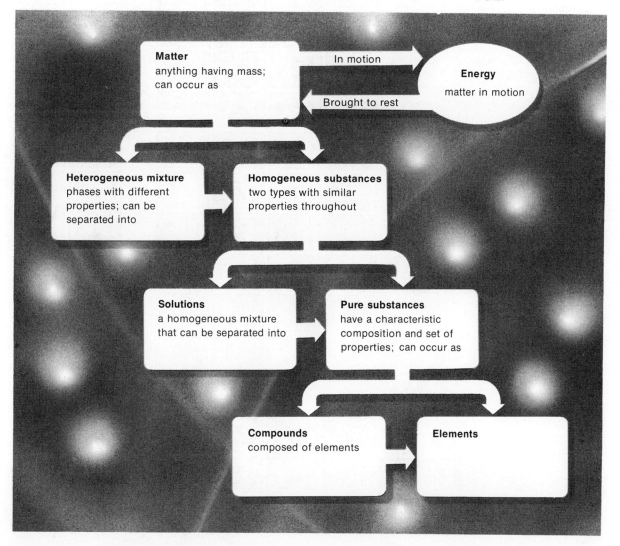

TABLE 1.4
THE SYMBOL, STATE (ROOM CONDITIONS), AND COLOR OF THE ELEMENTS.
UNLESS OTHERWISE INDICATED, THE METALS RANGE IN COLOR FROM
DULL GREY TO BRIGHT SILVER.? INDICATES ELEMENTS NOT YET
OFFICIALLY RECOGNIZED.

Gas

Liquid

Solid

Lithium	Beryllium													Boron	Carbon	Nitrogen	Oxygen	Fluorine	Helium
Li metal	**Be** metal																		**H** colorless

Hydrogen **H** colorless

| Helium **He** colorless |

Neon **Ne** colorless

Fluorine **F** pale yellow

Argon **Ar** colorless

Chlorine **Cl** green yellow

Krypton **Kr** colorless

Bromine **Br** red

Xenon **Xe** colorless

Iodine **I** purple

Radon **Rn** colorless

Astatine **At** metal

Oxygen **O** colorless

Sulfur **S** yellow

Selenium **Se** gray

Tellurium **Te** gray

Polonium **Po** metal

Nitrogen **N** colorless

Phosphorus **P** white or violet

Arsenic **As** gray or yellow

Antimony **Sb** metal

Bismuth **Bi** metal

Carbon **C** diamond graphite

Silicon **Si** blue-silver

Germanium **Ge** metal

Tin **Sn** gray or metallic

Lead **Pb** metal

Boron **B** colorless or brown

Aluminum **Al** metal

Gallium **Ga** metal

Indium **In** metal

Thallium **Tl** metal

Zinc **Zn** metal

Cadmium **Cd** metal

Mercury **Hg** metal

Copper **Cu** reddish metal

Silver **Ag** metal

Gold **Au** yellow metal

Nickel **Ni** metal

Palladium **Pd** metal

Platinum **Pt** metal

Cobalt **Co** metal

Rhodium **Rh** metal

Iridium **Ir** metal

Iron **Fe** metal

Ruthenium **Ru** metal

Osmium **Os** metal

Manganese **Mn** metal

Technetium **Tc*** metal

Rhenium **Re** metal

*** ? ? ? ?***

Chromium **Cr** metal

Molybdenum **Mo** metal

Wolfram **W** metal

Vanadium **V** metal

Niobium **Nb** metal

Tantalum **Ta** metal

Titanium **Ti** metal

Zirconium **Zr** metal

Hafnium **Hf** metal

Ce ➤ Lu

Th ➤ Lr

Scandium **Sc** metal

Yttrium **Y** metal

Lanthanum **La** metal

Actinium **Ac** metal

Beryllium **Be** metal

Magnesium **Mg** metal

Calcium **Ca** metal

Strontium **Sr** metal

Barium **Ba** metal

Radium **Ra** metal

Sodium **Na** metal

Potassium **K** metal

Rubidium **Rb** metal

Cesium **Cs** metal

Francium **Fr** metal

Cerium **Ce** metal

Praseodymium **Pr** metal

Neodymium **Nd** metal

Promethium **Pm*** metal

Samarium **Sm** metal

Europium **Eu** metal

Gadolinium **Gd** metal

Terbium **Tb** metal

Dysprosium **Dy** metal

Holmium **Ho** metal

Erbium **Er** metal

Thulium **Tm** metal

Ytterbium **Yb** metal

Lutetium **Lu** metal

Thorium **Th** metal

Protactinium **Pa** metal

Uranium **U** metal

Neptunium **Np*** metal

Plutonium **Pu*** metal

Americium **Am*** metal

Curium **Cm*** metal

Berkelium **Bk*** metal

Californium **Cf*** metal

Einsteinium **Es*** metal

Fermium **Fm*** metal

Mendelevium **Md*** metal

Nobelium **No*** metal

Lawrencium **Lr*** metal

*Artificially prepared (Chap. 17).

THE ELEMENTS _____ 1.9

The search for new elements has always been a fascinating study. Most, if not all, of the elements have existed since the beginning of time, but it is only recently that we have come to recognize their uniqueness. Some elements such as gold, silver, and copper were known in ancient times. Most of the elements, however, are naturally found in various combinations. Historically, the problem in recognizing the elements as the basic stuff from which all other matter is made resulted from the view of Greek philosophers (5th century B.C.) that all matter is composed of four basic "elements"; earth, air, water, and fire. Aristotle (4th century B.C.) suggested a fifth element, "ether," to explain the presence of stars in the sky. This idea was accepted for over 20 centuries until scientists in the 17th century began to perform experiments to test their ideas.* Antoine Lavoisier developed (1780) the concept of quantitative measurements and recognized the elements as the fundamental substances from which all compounds are made. In 1789 he compiled a list containing 23 elements. The interest generated by the atomic theory (Chap. 4) of John Dalton (1808) resulted in many searches for new elements. By 1870, 65 elements were known, and by 1925, 88 elements had been discovered. At present, about 107 elements are known.

They are found uncombined in nature.

From the Greek word aether, meaning to glow, a characteristic of heavenly bodies. This term is not to be confused with the anesthetic, ethyl ether.

For convenience, Dalton devised a set of symbols for the elements; for example, $\odot$ represented hydrogen and $\oplus$ represented sulfur, but these symbols proved confusing and impractical. Finally, Jöns Berzelius (1813) originated the present system of letter symbols. Many of the symbols are derived from the first letters of the Latin or Greek names for the elements. Thus, the symbol for silver is Ag, from the Latin name argentum; copper, Cu, from cuprum; mercury, Hg, from hydrargyrum (liquid silver), and helium, He, from the Greek name helios. The elements and their symbols are given in Table 1.4. The table also indicates the state (gas, liquid, or solid) in which the element exists at room conditions.

Commenting on this, Dalton wrote, "Berzelius' symbols are horrifying. A young student might as soon learn Hebrew as make himself acquainted with them." The first letter is always capitalized but the second letter is not.

EPILOG from Alfred Stock, 1932 (page 151)

"In Ostwald's** pyramid of the sciences, sociology stands as the apex. It may be counted as one of the natural sciences, but its subject is the most complicated and incomputable of all natural products. The highest problem for the scientific mind to solve will be: How to free mankind from political, economic and social limitations and how to give it a purer and broader minded understanding of humanity and sympathetic mutual cooperation."

PROBLEMS

You are advised to read problems carefully and write:
  (a) What information is given, with *units*, where appropriate;

  (b) What answer is sought, with *units*, where appropriate;
  (c) What additional information—conversion fac-

---

*Some historians believe that Aristotle's support of the four-element theory delayed the advent of modern science for more than a 1000 years. Further, because the abundance of slave labor made it less imperative to think in physical terms, Greek science and technology never developed. The Chinese philosophy of matter, originated in the time of Tsou Yen (4th century B.C.), was based on five "elements": earth, wood, metal, fire, and water. Robert Boyle, in his book *The Sceptical Chymist* (1661), argued against the four-element theory and proposed that "elements are certain primitive and simple or perfectly unmingled bodies, not being made of other bodies. . . ."

**Wilhelm Ostwald (1853–1932) is generally recognized as the father of physical (theoretical) chemistry.

tors, data, relationships, generalizations—do I need to answer the question? Is this information given as part of the problem? Is it in the text? Is it something I was asked to memorize?

Then, (a) ask yourself whether this problem can be answered in one step? two steps? three steps?

(b) Write down an answer.

(c) Check your answer for correctness through dimensional analysis; if units are not involved, does your answer sound reasonable in view of generalizations and relationships discussed?

(d) Rewrite your answer if necessary.

Don't give up! Millions did it before you—why not you? The best sea-captains still remember their seasick days! Good luck!

17 Vocabulary Illustrate or define the following: (a) matter, (b) law of nature, (c) theory, (d) gram, (e) liter, (f) conversion factor, (g) accuracy, (h) precision, (i) significant figures, (j) exponential number.

18 Vocabulary Illustrate or define the following: (a) density, (b) temperature, (c) kinetic energy, (d) potential energy, (e) calorie, (f) phase, (g) state, (h) distillation, (i) chromatography, (j) substance, (k) element, (l) compound.

19 Units Conversion to SI units will require changes in some time-honored sayings. (a) Convert the English measurements in the following to their SI equivalents:
(i) "I wouldn't touch that with a 10 foot pole."
(ii) "An ounce of prevention is worth a pound of cure."
(iii) "Give them an inch and they'll take a yard."
(b) Someone said "312 mm equals my foot." Using your foot as a standard, is this approximately correct or very incorrect?

20 Units 200 cm skis are popular with downhill skiers. What is the length of the skis (a) in inches, (b) in feet?

21 Many photographers use "35 mm" film. Express 35 mm (a) in cm, (b) in inches.

22 (a) Arrange the following in order of increasing mass: $2.0\,g$, $1.1 \times 10^4\,mg$ and $1.2 \times 10^{-3}\,kg$. (b) What is the sum of the masses in part (a)?

23 Energy 265 kcal are used to increase the temperature of a mass of water. How many (a) calories and (b) joules are absorbed by the water?

24 Significant figures (a) How many significant figures occur in each of the following quantities? (i) $0.00200\,\ell$, (ii) 4.010 m, (iii) 3.00103 g, (iv) 27.2 km. (b) Give an example of an exact quantity.

25 Calculate y to the proper number of significant figures:

(a) $y = \dfrac{1.0 \times 2.65 \times 6.0}{10.00}$

(b) $y = \dfrac{360{,}000 \times 2{,}320{,}000 \times 0.020}{31{,}000 \times 0.00030 \times 201}$

(c) $y = \dfrac{2.2 \times 10^{-3} \times 2.161 \times 12{,}323}{3.1 \times 10^{-4} \times 62.1 \times 10^6}$

26 Classification Classify each of the following as an element, compound, or mixture: (a) cola soft drink, (b) chlorine water bleach, (c) sugar, (d) water, (e) iron powder, (f) wine, (g) chocolate chip ice cream, (h) an apple.

27 Properties Indicate which of the following processes involve a chemical change: (a) evaporation of water, (b) melting iron, (c) burning wood, (d) grinding salt, (e) exploding dynamite, (f) propane gas burning to carbon dioxide and water, (g) food digestion.

28 Purification What difference in property allows a separation of the following mixtures? (a) sand and water, (b) salt and water, (c) sugar and stainless steel, (d) sand and salt.

29 Exponential numbers Express the following masses as exponential numbers. (a) 0.0003001 g, (b) 135000 g (4 significant figures), (c) 41000000 g (5 significant figures), (d) 0.0003 g, (e) 0.000072 g, (f) 43.1 g, (g) 37.132 g, (h) 0.301 g.

30 Temperature conversion Calculate the Celsius temperature corresponding to each of the following: (a) 10 °F, (b) −25 °F, (c) 60 °F, (d) 330 °F.

31 Calculate the Fahrenheit temperature for each of the following: (a) −40 °C, (b) 930 °C, (c) 190 °C, (d) −8.6 °C.

32 Gasoline in Europe costs about 50 cents per liter. Estimate the cost in dollars of 10.0 gal of gasoline. 1 gal = 3.79 ℓ.

33 A standard bushel in the U.S. has a capacity of 2150.42 in³. What is the capacity of a bushel (a) in gal, (b) in ℓ? 1 gal = 3.79 ℓ, 1 in³ = 16.387 cm³.

34 Density The density of benzene (page 18) is 0.880 g/ml. What volume, in ml, is occupied by 196 g of benzene?

35 The speed of light in a vacuum is 186,000 mi/s. (a) Calculate its speed in cm/s. (b) How many miles does light travel in one day?

36 As defined in the Bible, Noah's ark was 300 cubits long, 50 cubits wide, and 30 cubits high. If a cubit is the distance from the point of the elbow to the tip of the outstretched middle finger (about 18 in), find the volume of the ark (a) in ft³ (b) in yd³.

37 Density Find the mass of 60.0 ml of a substance whose density is 3.00 g/ml.

38 (a) How many tablespoons (i) in 1.0 qt? (ii) in 1.0 gal? (b) How many ml in 1 teaspoon? 1 tablespoon = 0.50 oz, 1 oz = 29.6 ml, 3 teaspoon = 1 tablespoon.

39 How many grams of sugar, selling at 19 cents per pound, can be purchased for $2.40? 453.6 g = 1 lb.

40 The fathom, a nautical unit for measuring ocean depth, is equal to 6.0 ft. The bathyscaph Trieste has descended to a world record depth of 6.0×10^3 fathoms. Find this depth (a) in feet, (b) in meters, (c) in miles.

41 (a) A micrometer, μm, is 10^{-6} m. The diameter (page 6 ftn.) of a red blood cell is 8 μm. What is this diameter (i) in mm, (ii) in inches? (b) Very small distances are measured in nanometers, 10^9 nm = 1 m. The diameter of a gold atom is 0.268 nm. What is this diameter (i) in mm, (ii) in inches?

42 A fishtank holds 10.0 gal of water. (a) What is the volume in liters? (b) What is the mass of the water (i) in grams, (ii) in pounds? 1 gal = 3.79 ℓ; $d = 1.00$ g/ml.

43 Automobile engines are measured in the U.S. by cubic inches of displacement (the combined volume of the cylinders swept by the pistons) and in Europe by liters of displacement. How many liters is 326 in^3? 2.54 cm = 1 in.

44 The mass of a diamond is measured in carat units, from the Greek word *keration,* for a horn-shaped bean used as a weight; 1 carat = 0.2 g exactly. The world's largest cut diamond, the Cullinan (South Africa), has a mass of 530.2 carats. Calculate its mass (a) in grams, (b) in ounces.

45 Density What mass of lead, density 11.3 g/ml, occupies the same volume as 100 g of magnesium, density 1.74 g/ml?

46 Density A gold bar measures 2.00 in by 2.00 in by 6.00 in and has a mass of 267.5 oz. Calculate the density of gold in g/ml. 2.54 cm = 1 in.

47 A company manufactures a set consisting of 100 nails, each 0.100 oz; two braces, each 10.1 oz; and four screws, each 0.200 oz. Calculate the weight of a set in grams.

48 A water sample from a municipal swimming pool contains 4×10^{10} bacteria per quart. Calculate the number of bacteria in the pool, capacity 2.0×10^6 gal of water.

49 In 1873, excitement was generated by the proposal to lay an oil pipe-line from Titusville, Pa. to Philadelphia (260 mi), with a capacity of 2.3×10^4 barrels per day at a cost of 0.32 cents per gallon for transport. (a) Express the mileage in km. (b) Calculate the 1873 cost, in dollars, of transporting 5.6×10^6 barrels of oil. 42 gal = 1 barrel.

50 An empty graduated cylinder weighs 60.13 g. When 8.20 ml of a liquid are added, the mass of the liquid and the cylinder is 72.32 g. Calculate the density of the liquid.

51 A metal block has a density of 5.00 g/ml, and measures 50.0 cm by 10.2 mm by 0.222 m. Find the volume and the mass of the block.

52 A person with 6.0 quarts of blood has 1.2×10^3 mg cholesterol per liter of blood. Find the mass, in grams, of cholesterol in the blood.

53 Measurement Using a balance, a student determines the mass of a sample of metal three different times and records the results as 165.22 g, 165.23 g and 165.21 g. However, the 100 g mark was incorrectly labeled. It should have been labeled "200 g." Discuss the precision and the accuracy of the experiment.

54 Air-borne lead is an environmental problem. Breathing air containing 3.0 micrograms, μg $(3.0 \times 10^{-6}$ g) of lead per cubic meter (m^3) results in the absorption of about 25 μg of lead per day. About 20 μg of lead per day is absorbed from a normal diet. If 95 % of the absorbed lead is excreted, what quantity of lead, in grams, will be retained in the body over a 10 year period? 365 days = 1 year.

55 Density A student takes two pieces of modeling clay, each weighing 10 g, and molds one piece into a round ball and the other piece into a thin cylinder. (a) Do the two pieces still weigh 10 g each? (b) If each piece is dropped into a separate graduated cylinder containing 50.0 ml of water, should one piece displace more water than the other? If so, which one? If not, why not?

56 Mass and weight The weight of an object is determined on a spring scale, shown on the following page. If the same object is weighed on the same scale on the surface of the moon, should the scale indicate the same weight? Explain. If this experiment is repeated with a two-pan balance, should the balance indicate the same weight on the moon? Explain.

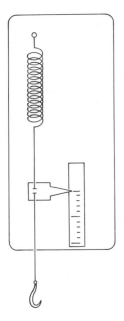

A spring scale (see Problem 56).

57 Graph Measurements of the lead content of snow layers in northern Greenland show an increasing amount of lead deposited yearly. Plot the following lead contents in micrograms of lead per kilogram snow (y-axis), versus year of deposit (x-axis):

μg lead/kg snow	year
0.003	1600
0.005	1650
0.008	1700
0.01	1750
0.035	1800
0.05	1850
0.07	1900
0.08	1940
0.25	1950

Draw a conclusion from this observation.

ADDITIONAL PROBLEMS

60 Metals can be refined so that they contain one impurity atom per 10^{11} atoms (1 part per 100 billion by atoms). Find the number of impurity atoms in 10^{25} atoms of a metal so prepared.

61 Using SI units, a person would buy food by the kilogram. (a) Is the interest in the mass of the food or in the force it exerts? (b) As used in the supermarket, do the terms "mass" and "weight" have the same meaning? (c) When you weigh an object on a two-pan balance (even if only one pan is seen), are you matching "weights" or "masses"?

62 A scale with a sensitivity of 1 lb in 25,000 lb is used to measure small changes in body weight caused by perspiration losses. Express this sensitivity in terms of grams. 454 g = 1 lb.

58 Knowledge Discuss the following statements: (a) "The principle of science is the following: the test of all knowledge is experiment." (Richard Feynman, 1913) (b) "Imagination is more important than knowledge." (Albert Einstein) (c) "In science, a wrong theory can be valuable and better than no theory at all." (Sir Lawrence Bragg) (d) "Chance favors the prepared mind." (Louis Pasteur)

59 Library Read one of the following: (a) "Can Only Scientists Make Government Science Policy?" Emmanuel Mesthene, *Science,* volume 145, 17 July 1965, page 237. (b) "Applied Research for the Public Good," Harold Gershinowitz, *Science,* volume 176, 28 April 1972, page 380. (c) *The Nature of Physical Reality,* Henry Margenau, McGraw-Hill Book Co., New York, 1950, pages 12–13 ("Metaphysics of Natural Science"), and pages 16–18 ("Sciences vs. Humanities"). (d) "Chance and Chemical Discoveries," G. D. Bishop, *Chemistry,* April 1976, page 14. (e) "The American University Today," Philip Handler, *American Scientist,* volume 64, 1976, page 254. (f) "How to Get the Most Out of Your Textbooks," "How to Prepare Successfully for Examinations," "How to Improve Your Reading Skills." Booklets available free from AAP Student Service, *Association of American Publishers,* One Park Avenue, New York, N.Y. 10016. (g) "SI Units," G. Socrates, *Journal of Chemical Education,* volume 46, 1969, page 710. (h) *The Philosophy of Human Knowing,* Joseph Hassett and co-authors, The Newman Press, Westminster, Maryland, 1953, Chapter 1, pages 3–12 ("I Wonder Why"). (i) "The International System of Units (SI)," *National Bureau of Standards Special Publication 330,* 1974 Edition, U.S. Government Printing Office, Washington, DC, 20402.

63 The expanding universe has a radius of 1.0×10^{28} cm. The circumference of the earth (the distance around the Equator) is 4.01×10^4 km. Given a string 10^{28} cm long, how many times can it be wrapped around the earth?

64 Urine has a density of 1.03 g/ml. What is the weight of dissolved solid in a liter of urine? A liter of urine contains 1.00×10^3 g of water.

65 The density of an alcohol-water mixture is 0.910 g/ml and contains 50.0 % of each substance by mass. Find the mass of alcohol in 1.00 ℓ of the mixture.

66 Suggested methods of providing fresh water include towing Antarctic icebergs to warmer climates. It has been calculated that if an iceberg measuring 2.7×10^3 m $\times 2.7 \times 10^3$ m $\times 2.5 \times 10^2$ m is towed at a speed of half a knot from Antarctica to Australia, 30 per cent of the ice would arrive unmelted. Calculate the mass of water remaining on arrival at Australia (a) in g (b) in lb.

67 The energy cost of walking at 3.5 miles per hour for a 70 kg person is 5.2 kcal per minute. (a) How many minutes can this person walk at 3.5 miles per hour on the energy supplied by a large apple, 101 kcal? (b) How many miles are covered by this quantity of energy?

68 If 1.0 ml of water is spread out as a film 1 nm thick, find the area of the rectangle, length $\times$ width, (a) in cm² and (b) in ft² that it covers. 10^9 nm = 1 m.

69 Isaac Newton (1701) devised a temperature scale based on the freezing point of ice, labeled 0, and the temperature of the armpit (98.5 °F) of a healthy Englishman, labeled 12. What is the boiling point of water on Newton's scale?

70 The oceans of the earth measure about 3.2×10^8 mi³. If there are 6.0×10^{-6} mg of gold per kg of sea water, calculate the mass of gold in the oceans (a) in kg, (b) in pounds. Density of sea water is 1.025 g/ml.

71 The universe contains more than 10^{46} metric tons of matter. How many times greater is this mass compared to the SI unit of mass? See Appendix III.

72 In 1938, 1.41 lb of coal was needed to produce 1 kilowatt of electricity. Today, 0.80 lb is needed to produce the same amount of electricity. But coal consumption has increased from 13×10^6 tons to 2.1×10^8 tons, while boiler operating temperatures have increased from 750 °F to 649 °C. Find the percentage increase in (a) efficiency in production of electricity, (b) coal consumption, (c) operating temperature.

73 At the same temperature, the density of water is 1.0 g/ml, the density of hydrogen is 9.0×10^{-5} g/ml, and the density of tin is 5.8 g/ml. You are given 10.0 g of each. Which substance would have (a) the largest volume, (b) the smallest volume?

74 Pick the best answer in each set: (a) The mass of a hand flashlight is 100 g, 100 mg, 0.10 g. (b) The mass of liquid in a glass of water is 100 g, 10 kg, 10 nanograms. (c) The mass of meat in a hamburger is 1 kg, 125 g, 0.25 mg. (c) The volume of gasoline in the tank of a car is 80 ml, 80 ℓ, 80 m³. (e) The length of an automobile is 7 km, 7 m, 7 cm.

ANSWERS

1 (a) 2500 mm
  (b) 0.6 m
  (c) 3.2 hr
2 (a) 4.55 m
  (b) 179 in
  (c) 14.9 ft
3 (a) 168 qt
  (b) 159 ℓ
4 (a) 32000 mg
  (b) 0.032 kg
  (c) 0.071 lb
5 39 cents
6 (a) 26.4 gal
  (b) (i) 3.9 lb (ii) 1758 g
7 (a) four
  (b) one
  (c) four
  (d) three
8 (a) 8037.0 g
  (b) 540 cm
9 0.879 g/ml
10 (a) 1.0×10^{-5} g
  (b) 1.783×10^5 ft
  (c) 7.2×10^{-2} cm
  (d) 2.0100×10^6 lb
  (e) 4.0×10^{-5} mg
  (f) 1.3×10^{-1} ft
11 (a) 9.6×10^5

  (b) 1.2×10^6
  (c) 7.2×10^{20}
  (d) 6.8×10^{20}
12 93 °C
13 (a) 365 °F
  (b) 37.0 °C
14 60.5 cal, 6.05×10^{-2} kcal
15 5.00 ml
16 (a) three phases
  (b) one state
19 (a) (i) 3.0 m (ii) 28.35 g, 453.6 g (iii) 2.54 cm, 91.4 cm
  (b) 12.3 in, approximately correct
20 (a) 78.7 in
  (b) 6.56 ft
21 (a) 3.5 cm
  (b) 1.4 in
22 (a) 1.2×10^{-3} kg < 2.0 g $< 1.1 \times 10^4$ mg
  (b) 14 g
23 (a) 2.65×10^5 cal
  (b) 1.11×10^6 J
24 (a) three
  (b) four
  (c) six
  (d) three
25 (a) 1.6
  (b) 8.9×10^6
  (c) 3.0×10^3
26 element: iron; compound: sugar, water

27 (c), (e), (f), (g)

29 (a) 3.001×10^{-4} g (e) 7.2×10^{-5} g
(b) 1.350×10^5 g (f) 4.31×10^1 g
(c) 4.1000×10^7 g (g) 3.7132×10^1 g
(d) 3×10^{-4} g (h) 3.01×10^{-1} g

30 (a) -12 °C
(b) -32 °C
(c) 16 °C
(d) 166 °C

31 (a) -40 °F
(b) 1.71×10^3 °F
(c) 374 °F
(d) 16.5 °F

32 18.95 (19.0) dollars

33 (a) 9.30 gal
(b) 35.2 ℓ

34 223 ml

35 (a) 2.99×10^{10} cm/s
(b) 1.61×10^{10} mi/day

36 (a) 1.5×10^6 ft^3
(b) 5.6×10^4 yd^3

37 1.80×10^2 g

38 (a) (i) 64 tbs/qt, (ii) 256 tbs/gal
(b) 4.9 ml

39 5.7×10^3 g

40 (a) 3.6×10^4 ft
(b) 1.1×10^4 m
(c) 6.8 mi

41 (a) (i) 8×10^{-3} mm, (ii) 3×10^{-4} in
(b) (i) 2.68×10^{-7} mm, (ii) 1.06×10^{-8} in

42 (a) 37.9 ℓ
(b) (i) 3.79×10^4 g, (ii) 83.5 lb

43 5.34 ℓ

44 (a) 1.060×10^2
(b) 3.739 oz

45 649 g

46 19.3 g/ml

47 8.80×10^2 g

48 3×10^{17} bacteria

49 (a) 418 km
(b) 7.5×10^5 dollars

50 1.49 g/ml

51 1.13×10^3 cm^3, 5.66×10^3 g

52 6.8 g

54 8.2×10^{-3} g

56 scale, no; balance, yes

60 10^{14} impurity atoms

61 (a) mass of food, (b) yes, (c) masses

62 1 g in 25000 g

63 2×10^{18} times

64 30 g

65 455 g

66 (a) 5.5×10^{14} g
(b) 1.2×10^{12} lb

67 (a) 19 min
(b) 1.1 mi

68 (a) 10^7 cm^2, (b) 10^4 ft^2

69 32.5 °N

70 (a) 8.2×10^9 kg
(b) 1.8×10^{10} lb

71 10^{49}

72 (a) 176 %
(b) 1.5×10^2 %
(c) 60 %

73 (a) hydrogen, (b) tin

74 (a), (b) 100 g; (c) 125 g, (d) 80 ℓ, (e) 7 m

GLOSSARY

accuracy A measure of the agreement between a reported result and a standard or accepted value.

adsorption The adhesion ("sticking") of a thin layer of a substance to the surface of another substance.

calorie A unit of energy; the quantity of energy required to raise the temperature of 1 g of water 1 °C (more accurately, from 14.5 °C to 15.5 °C). 1 cal = 4.184 joules (exactly).

chemical change A change in the composition and properties of a substance.

chromatography The process of separating a substance from a mixture by adsorption on a stationary material. The method depends on differences in the adsorption of substances (see **adsorption**).

compound A substance of uniform composition, composed of two or more elements (see **element**).

density The mass of matter in a given volume; density = mass/volume.

distillation The process of separating a substance from a mixture by boiling and then condensing the substance. The method depends on differences in the boiling points of substances.

element A substance that cannot be separated into other substances by ordinary chemical means.

gaseous state A gas takes the shape of its container and fills any container. It has no shape or definite volume; these properties are determined by the container. See **liquid state** and **solid state.**

gram A unit of mass; equals 0.001 kilogram (exactly), or 10^3 g/kg.

graph A diagram which gives a pictorial view of how two different quantities are related to each other.

heterogeneous mixture A mixture composed of different phases (see **phase**).

homogeneous mixture Matter that has a uniform composition throughout.

joule SI unit of energy; 4.184 J (exactly) = 1 cal. See **calorie.**

kilogram SI unit of mass

kinetic energy The energy of motion, the energy possessed by a moving object because of its motion.

liquid state A liquid (under the influence of gravity) takes the shape of its container but has a definite volume; it does not expand to fill the container. See **gaseous state** and **solid state.**

liter A unit of volume; equals 10^3 ml (exactly) or 0.001 meter^3 (exactly).

mass A measure of the quantity of matter in an object. The SI unit of mass is the kilogram. See **matter.**

matter Anything that has mass and has the property of inertia.

meter SI unit of length.

phase A homogeneous portion of matter separated by a definite surface from other parts of a heterogeneous mixture.

physical change A change in the state of matter but not in the composition of a substance. See **states of matter.**

potential energy The energy possessed by a body because of its position.

precision A measure of the agreement among a number of measurements of the same quantity.

properties A set of characteristics that distinguishes one substance from all other substances.

significant figures The number of digits in a measurement that are definitely known plus one doubtful digit with a given limit of error, such as 26.34 ± 0.01 g with four significant figures.

solid state A solid has a fixed volume and shape, independent of the volume and shape of the container. See **gaseous state** and **liquid state.**

states of matter Matter may exist in three states, gas, liquid, or solid. The state of a substance depends on its temperature and pressure. See **gaseous state, liquid state,** and **solid state.**

substance Matter whose composition is uniform throughout and which has a definite uniform set of properties. Compounds and elements are substances.

temperature A measure of the hotness or coolness of an object on an accepted scale, which determines the direction of heat flow; heat always flows from objects at a higher temperature to objects at a lower temperature. (Do not confuse temperature with the quantity of heat contained in an object.)

theory A generally accepted set of assumptions based on related observations and controlled experiments that explains the known facts and makes predictions that can be experimentally verified.

weight The force an object exerts due to gravitational attraction. The force depends on the mass of the object; the greater the mass, the greater the force.

GASES   2

In this chapter we shall study the properties of gases and develop a theory about the nature of gases. Gases are the simplest of the states of matter. The relationships among the physical properties of gases are also comparatively simple to use. Further, since gases generally can be converted into liquids and solids—for example, steam to liquid water to ice—and then back again to the gaseous state without altering the chemical composition of the gas, a theory about the nature and properties of gases should provide an insight into the nature of liquids and solids.

PROPERTIES OF GASES   2.1

Since you are surrounded by air, a mixture of gases,* some observations about the properties of gases may be made by personal examination:

1. Gases are transparent; you can see through all gases, including colored gases.

2. Gases can be compressed; you can push air into a tire with an airpump. The pump takes a large volume of air and compresses (reduces) it to the volume of the tire. On the other hand, liquids and solids are relatively incompressible. Pumps push liquids or solid dust particles, but the volume of the liquid or the solid is *not* decreased. A pump merely moves liquids or solids from one place to another.

3. Gases expand without any apparent limit. They fill any container into which they are put; in other words, *the volume of a gas is the volume of the container that confines it*. The same mass of air will fill any container; the larger the volume of the container, the larger the volume of the air, but the mass of the air remains the same.

For example, bromine (red), chlorine (yellow-green), fluorine (green-yellow), and nitrogen dioxide (red-brown). These gases are extremely poisonous and corrosive.

---

*Clean, dry air (a purely theoretical concept, considering today's pollution problems) is a mixture containing, by volume, the following gases:

Nitrogen, N_2	78.09 %	
Oxygen, O_2	20.94 %	
Argon	0.93 %	
Carbon dioxide, CO_2 (variable)	0.03 %	
Other noble gases (page 234)	0.0024 %	$(2.4 \times 10^{-3} \%)$
Methane (variable)	0.00015 %	$(1.5 \times 10^{-4} \%)$
Hydrogen	0.00005 %	$(5 \times 10^{-5} \%)$
Nitrogen oxides (variable)	0.000025 %	$(2.5 \times 10^{-5} \%)$
Carbon monoxide (variable)	0.00001 %	$(1 \times 10^{-5} \%)$
Ozone (variable)	0.000002 %	$(2 \times 10^{-6} \%)$
Ammonia (variable)	0.000001 %	$(1 \times 10^{-6} \%)$
Sulfur dioxide (variable)	0.00000002 %	$(2 \times 10^{-8} \%)$

From "Cleaning our Environment, The Chemical Basis for Action," A Report of the American Chemical Society, Washington, D.C., page 24, 1969. The origin of symbols such as N_2, O_2 and CO_2 is explained in Chap. 4. Methane (*marsh gas*), the main component of natural gas, is colorless and explosive.

PROBLEM 1   **10.0 g of carbon dioxide, CO_2 (colorless, odorless, asphyxiating gas; solid CO_2 is "Dry Ice"), is placed (a) in a 20 ℓ container, and (b) in a 500 ℓ container. What are the mass and volumes of CO_2 in each container?**

4. Gases mix with one another; they **diffuse** (mix) rapidly in all directions and *without* external influence. For example, sulfur dioxide, SO_2, emitted from a smokestack, rapidly mixes with the surrounding air even on a windless day. The odor of vaporized perfume is clearly detectable across a room.

5. Gases exert pressure; they *push* against the inside of any container. In an experimental automobile crash, plastic bags stored under the dashboard are automatically and instantaneously filled with air. The pressure of the air expands the bag against the passengers, holding them in their seats and preventing forward movement into the dashboard and windshield.

PROBLEM 2   **Tires and basketballs are stiff because they contain compressed air. What happens if these containers are too weak to withstand the pressure?**

6. Gases expand rapidly on heating; the force of an explosion results from the sudden expansion of gases caused by the heat evolved by the exploding material. For example, *TNT* (a pale yellow crystalline solid) explodes, producing carbon monoxide, CO, nitrogen, N_2, other gases, and heat.

These are some of the general properties our theory of gases must explain.

2.2 PRESSURE OF A GAS

In the middle of the 17th century, Evangelista Torricelli performed a number of experiments with glass tubes and liquid mercury, Hg. He filled a glass tube about 3 feet in length, closed at one end, with mercury. Keeping his finger on the open end of the tube, he inverted the tube into a small cup half-filled with mercury, so that the open end of the tube was under the surface of the mercury. He then removed his finger. Instead of the mercury running out of the tube, as you might expect, most of it remained in the tube. This experiment is illustrated in Fig. 2.1. Torricelli noted that the height, *h,* of the mercury in the tube, measured from the surface of the mercury in the cup, averaged about 76 cm (76 cm = 30 in) in many experiments.

Why doesn't the mercury completely run out of the tube? Also, what is in the space above the mercury in the tube? Since precautions were taken to exclude air, this space must be a vacuum; this is called a Torricellian vacuum.

The mercury in the tube has a definite mass and therefore exerts a downward pressure. If you remove the tube from the cup, your finger must exert a pressure against the mercury to keep it from spilling. Apparently, something is *pushing down on the mercury in the cup* to keep the mercury in the tube; the downward pressure exerted by the mercury in the tube is balanced by some outside pressure. After years of debate and uncertainty, Torricelli concluded that the downward pressure of the mercury in the tube is balanced by the pressure exerted by our atmosphere on the mercury in the cup. This is illustrated in Fig. 2.2. The atmosphere is the layer of air surrounding the earth to a height of about 600 miles. The atmosphere, like any substance, has a definite weight and therefore exerts a pressure. The density of the atmosphere decreases with increasing altitude (the height above the earth's surface).

We can define **pressure** as force per unit area: the push or the *force* exerted by an object (*a given weight*) on a *given area of surface*. Pressure, *P,* is commonly expressed

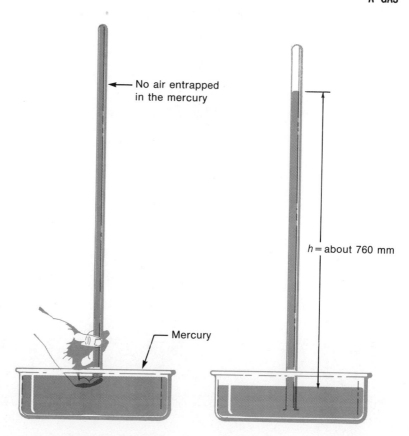

← No air entrapped
in the mercury

$h=$ about 760 mm

Mercury

FIGURE 2.1 The Torricelli experiment. Precautions are taken to prevent air from entering the tube. Torricelli was not aware of the danger of mercury poisoning.

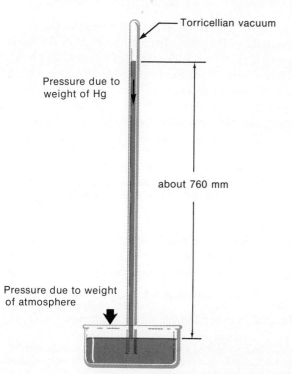

Torricellian vacuum

Pressure due to
weight of Hg

about 760 mm

Pressure due to weight
of atmosphere

FIGURE 2.2 Illustrating that the pressure of mercury is balanced by the pressure of the atmosphere.

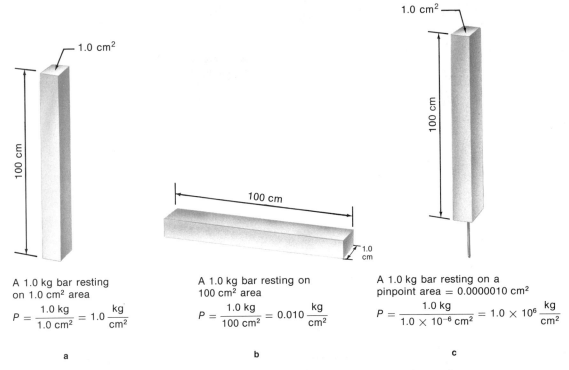

FIGURE 2.3 A comparison of the force per unit area obtainable from the same weight covering different areas.

as $\dfrac{\text{weight}}{\text{area}}$ and therefore has the dimensions of kg/cm², g/cm², or lb/in². This is illustrated with the kilogram bar in Fig. 2.3. In position (a), the weight of the bar is resting on 1.0 cm²; the pressure is therefore 1.0 kg/cm². In (b), the weight of the bar is resting on 100 cm² area; the pressure is therefore 1.0 kg/100 cm², or 0.010 kg/cm². Increasing the area by a factor of 100 reduces the pressure exerted by the same weight by a factor of $\frac{1}{100}$. In (c), the bar is placed on a pinpoint, area 0.0000010 cm²; the pressure exerted is therefore 1.0 kg/(1.0 × 10⁻⁶ cm²), or 1.0 × 10⁶ kg/cm². This illustrates the principle of obtaining the high pressures required to manufacture diamonds from ordinary carbon (graphite):* a heavy weight is placed on a pinpoint area.

PROBLEM 3   An 8.00 × 10³ kg weight is placed on a steel rod with an area of 10.0 cm² and then on another steel rod with an area of 25.0 cm². What is the pressure, in kg/cm², exerted in each case?

In the Torricelli tube, the force exerted by the weight of the column of mercury per unit area is balanced by the force exerted by the weight of air per unit area. The weight of the mercury in the tube sitting on each square centimeter (height × area × density = $\text{cm} \times 1\ \text{cm}^2 \times \dfrac{\text{g}}{\text{cm}^3}$ = g) is equal to the weight of air sitting on each square centimeter. The difference between the height of the mercury column,

Or,
height × density
= g/cm²

—————————

*Graphite is subjected to pressures of about 5.7 × 10⁴ kg/cm² at temperatures of about 2000 °C. Antoine Lavoisier (1799) showed that diamond is nothing more than carbon; burned in oxygen, equal masses of diamond and charcoal yield equal volumes of carbon dioxide.

about 76 cm, and the height of the column of air, about 600 miles, is due to the difference in their densities.

What would happen to the height of the mercury in the tube if the pressure on the mercury in the cup is decreased? The height of the mercury column would decrease. A lower mercury column corresponds to a smaller weight and, therefore, a smaller pressure.

PROBLEM 4   **If the pressure on the mercury in the cup is increased, will the height of the mercury column increase, decrease, or remain the same? Explain.**

The instrument Torricelli constructed is still in use today and is known as a **barometer.** Since the weather appears to vary with atmospheric pressure,* the barometer serves as a valuable source of information in weather forecasting.

The pressure exerted by a mercury column exactly 760 mm high (at 0 °C at sea level)** is called one **standard atmosphere.** Further, exactly $\frac{1}{760}$ of a standard atmosphere is known as a **torr,** named in honor of Torricelli. Thus, exactly one standard atmosphere = exactly 760 mm Hg (mercury) = exactly 76 cm Hg = exactly 760 torr. In daily use, one standard atmosphere is simplified to one atmosphere, abbreviated atm.

The SI unit of pressure is the **pascal,** Pa, named after Blaise Pascal, who recognized (1654) pressure as a force per unit area and whose principle is the basis of hydraulic brakes; 1 atm = 1.01325×10^5 Pa or roughly 100 kPa (see App. III).

PROBLEM 5   **(a) How many atmospheres, atm, are there in (i) 380 torr, (ii) 76.0 torr? (b) How many torr are there in (i) 0.500 atm, (ii) 400 mm Hg, (iii) 1.25 atm? (c) How many pascals are there in 0.500 atm? (d) How many atm are there in 1.01 Pa?**

Example 1

The liquid in a barometer is water, density 1.00 g/cm³, instead of mercury, density 13.6 g/cm³. What is the height, in cm, of the water column when subjected to a pressure of 76.0 cm Hg?

Answer

Any two liquids exert the same pressure only when the weights per unit area of each liquid are equal. Since the density of mercury is 13.6 times greater than the density of water, the height of the water column must be 13.6 times higher than the mercury column to obtain equal weights per unit area. Thus,

$$\text{cm H}_2\text{O} = 76.0 \text{ cm Hg} \times \frac{13.6 \frac{g}{cm^3 \text{ Hg}}}{1.00 \frac{g}{cm^3 \text{ H}_2\text{O}}} = 1034 \text{ cm H}_2\text{O}$$

---

*Atmospheric pressure, the pressure exerted by the atmosphere, is not constant, because the density of air is variable, depending on whether the air is hot or cold, wet or dry. Wet air has a lower pressure because the water vapor has a lower density than the air it dilutes.

**The temperature is specified because the weight of mercury and, therefore, its pressure, depend on its density. Density, in turn, is dependent on temperature; density usually decreases with increasing temperature. Sea level is specified because the force exerted by any object—solid, liquid, or gas—is determined by the force of gravity (page 4). This attractive force is not the same everywhere on the earth; gravity also decreases with increasing height. In outer space, far removed from the force of gravity of the earth or other large masses, an astronaut is nearly weightless—the mass of his body exerts almost no force.

The weights per unit area of the two columns are now equal, as shown:

Water barometer: $1034 \text{ cm H}_2\text{O} \times 1.00 \dfrac{\text{g H}_2\text{O}}{\text{cm}^3 \text{ H}_2\text{O}} = 1034 \dfrac{\text{g H}_2\text{O}}{\text{cm}^2}$

Mercury barometer: $76.0 \text{ cm Hg} \times 13.6 \dfrac{\text{g Hg}}{\text{cm}^3 \text{ Hg}} = 1034 \dfrac{\text{g Hg}}{\text{cm}^2}$

We can now convert the height of the water column, 1034 cm H_2O, to feet:

$$\text{ft} = 1034 \text{ cm H}_2\text{O} \times \dfrac{1 \text{ in}}{2.54 \text{ cm}} \times \dfrac{1 \text{ ft}}{12.0 \text{ in}} = 33.9 \text{ ft H}_2\text{O}$$

Example 2

Calculate the pressure of 1.00 atm (a) in lb/in² and (b) in SI units of kg/m². The density of mercury is 13.60 g/cm³.

Answer

(a) A mercury column 76.00 cm high equals 1.00 atm. The density of mercury is 13.60 g/cm³. Therefore, the weight of mercury per cm² is 1033.6 g:

$$76.00 \text{ cm} \times 13.60 \dfrac{\text{g}}{\text{cm}^3} = 1033.6 \dfrac{\text{g}}{\text{cm}^2}$$

But there are 453.6 g in 1 lb. Therefore,

$$1033.6 \dfrac{\text{g}}{\text{cm}^2} \times \dfrac{1 \text{ lb}}{453.6 \text{ g}} = 2.279 \dfrac{\text{lb}}{\text{cm}^2}$$

The pressure is now stated as 2.279 lb/cm². Because there are 2.540 cm in 1 inch, the number of cm² in 1 in² is given by

$$2.540 \dfrac{\text{cm}}{\text{in}} \times 2.540 \dfrac{\text{cm}}{\text{in}} = 6.452 \dfrac{\text{cm}^2}{\text{in}^2}$$

Therefore, 1.00 atm, in lb/in², is found as shown:

$$2.279 \dfrac{\text{lb}}{\text{cm}^2} \times 6.452 \dfrac{\text{cm}^2}{\text{in}^2} = 14.70 \dfrac{\text{lb}}{\text{in}^2}$$

The value 14.7 lb/in² is the average pressure exerted at sea level by the Earth's atmosphere.

(b) From (a), 1 atm = 1033.6 g/cm². There are 10^3 g in 1 kg, so:

$$1033.6 \dfrac{\text{g}}{\text{cm}^2} \times \dfrac{1 \text{ kg}}{10^3 \text{ g}} = 1.0336 \dfrac{\text{kg}}{\text{cm}^2}$$

There are 10^2 cm in 1 m; therefore, the number of cm² in 1 m² is given by:

$$10^2 \dfrac{\text{cm}}{\text{m}} \times 10^2 \dfrac{\text{cm}}{\text{m}} = 10^4 \dfrac{\text{cm}^2}{\text{m}^2}$$

Then, 1 atm in kg/m² is given by:

$$1.0336 \frac{kg}{cm^2} \times \frac{10^4 \, cm^2}{1 \, m^2} = 1.0336 \times 10^4 \frac{kg}{m^2}$$

PROBLEM 6   (a) If each square inch of your body is subjected to a weight of 14.7 lb, why are you not aware of this pressure? (b) At sea level, a tin can is completely evacuated (all matter is removed from it); the can collapses. Astronauts repeat the same experiment in outer space; the can does not collapse. Explain.

PROBLEM 7   The pressure at the bottom of the Marianas Trench (11.0 km or 6.86 mi deep) in the Pacific Ocean is about 1000 times greater than average atmospheric pressure at the surface. What is this pressure (a) in atm, (b) in torr, (c) in kilopascals, kPa? 1 atm = 1.01×10^5 Pa.

A device somewhat similar to a barometer, called a **manometer,** is used in laboratories to measure gas pressures. A glass U-tube is partially filled with mercury, and the two ends of the tube are open to the pressures being compared. If the mercury levels in the two arms of the manometer are the same, the pressures of the gas samples are the same. But if the height of the mercury in one arm of the manometer is *greater* than the height in the other arm, the *pressures* of the gas samples must be different. The difference between the two levels represents the difference between the two gas pressures.

PRESSURE-VOLUME RELATIONSHIP FOR A GAS: BOYLE'S LAW _____ 2.3

In 1660, Robert Boyle published a book entitled *New Experiments Physico-Mechanicall, Touching The Spring of the Air and its Effects* (made, for the most part, in a *New Pneumatical Engine*), in which he described experiments on the nature of a vacuum, on the weight and pressure of air, and on many other matters relating to the Torricellian experiment. In a defense against criticism* of his views, he published in 1662 the results of a series of experiments in which he measured "the spring of air," the pressure of a gas.

Boyle poured a quantity of mercury into a J-shaped tube, illustrated in Fig. 2.4, trapping a volume of air in the closed end. Adding different amounts of mercury into the open arm compressed (decreased the volume of) the air trapped in the closed end. After each addition, he measured the air volume and *h,* the difference in height between the two mercury levels. The height difference added to the atmospheric pressure in mm Hg is the pressure of the entrapped air. The original pressure-volume data Boyle obtained in these experiments are reproduced in Table 2.1. The first

---

*Franciscus Linus suggested that the column of mercury in a barometer is kept in suspension by a "funiculus" or an "invisible thread" attached to the top of the tube. This criticism led Boyle to study the volume-pressure relationship of gases, and Torricelli to study the relationship between change in altitude and change in height of the mercury column in a barometer. As Torricelli climbed the hills of Florence, Italy, he observed that the height of the mercury column continuously decreased. Since this would require an infinite number of "invisible threads" of different lengths, Linus' view was rejected. It would be a mistake on our part, however, to ridicule Linus for his ideas. Paul Dirac (1948), in his discussion of electric charges (page 116) and magnetic poles (page 201), supposes "each pole to be at the end of an unobservable string." Dirac's work is acknowledged as one of the greatest intellectual achievements of this century. And a modern theory of light talks about massless strings whose ends move at the velocity of light.

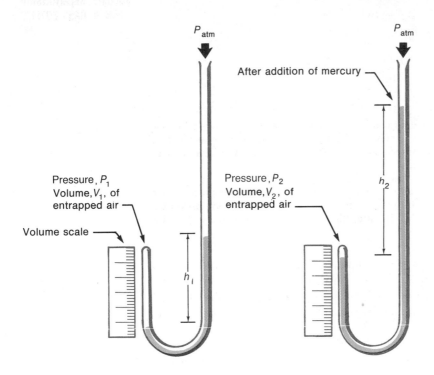

P_{atm}

P_{atm}

After addition of mercury

h_2

Pressure, P_1
Volume, V_1, of
entrapped air

Pressure, P_2
Volume, V_2, of
entrapped air

Volume scale

h_1

FIGURE 2.4 Boyle's experiment. A sample of air is entrapped in a tube, such that the pressure on the air can be changed and the volume of the air measured. P_{atm} is the atmospheric pressure, measured with a barometer. $P_1 = h_1 + P_{atm}$, $P_2 = h_2 + P_{atm}$.

column gives the measured volume, V. The second column gives the air pressure, P. The temperature of the gas most likely did not vary much during the experiments. Boyle noted that as the pressure, P, increased, the volume, V, decreased. He discovered that the decrease in volume is inversely proportional to the increase in pressure; that is, the volume decreases as the pressure increases so that the product of

TABLE 2.1
BOYLE'S DATA ON THE CHANGE IN THE VOLUME OF ENTRAPPED AIR WITH PRESSURE

V Volume,* cm^3	P Pressure, inches of mercury	$P \times V$ Product of Pressure and Volume
48	$29^2/_{16}$	1398
46	$30^9/_{16}$	1406
44	$31^{15}/_{16}$	1405
42	$33^8/_{16}$	1407
40	$35^5/_{16}$	1412
38	37	1406
36	$39^5/_{16}$	1415
34	$41^{10}/_{16}$	1415
32	$44^3/_{16}$	1414
30	$47^1/_{16}$	1412
28	$50^5/_{16}$	1416
26	$54^5/_{16}$	1412
24	$58^{13}/_{16}$	1411
23	$61^5/_{16}$	1410
22	$64^1/_{16}$	1409
21	$67^1/_{16}$	1408
20	$70^{11}/_{16}$	1414

*Boyle used an arbitrary volume scale, but that need not concern us.

pressure × volume remains practically constant. These measurements can be represented by

Pressure × Volume = a constant (*temperature* and *mass constant*)

or

$$PV = k_1 \text{ (temperature and mass constant)}$$

from which

$$P = \frac{k_1}{V} \text{ or } V = \frac{k_1}{P}$$

The value of the constant, k_1, depends on the mass of the gas sample and its temperature.

Boyle's data can also be represented by a graph. In Fig. 2.5, the pressure, P, of the entrapped air is plotted against its volume, V. Note that as the pressure of the gas increases, the volume decreases so as to keep the product, $P \times V$, constant. If the pressure is doubled, the volume is halved. The curve of P vs. V is a hyperbola, typical of inverse relationships such as $P \times V = k_1$. This plot represents a way of stating **Boyle's law:** *at constant temperature, the volume of a fixed mass of gas is inversely proportional to the pressure:*

$$V \propto \frac{1}{P} \text{ (temperature and mass constant)}$$

where $\propto$ is a symbol which means proportional or directly related to. Equally

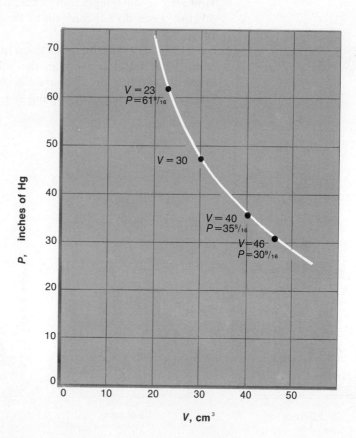

FIGURE 2.5 A graph of Boyle's data from Table 2.1.
The curve obtained is a hyperbola.

correctly, we can say that the pressure is inversely proportional to the volume of a fixed mass of gas at constant temperature

$$P \propto \frac{1}{V} \text{ (temperature and mass constant)}$$

or that the product of the volume and the pressure of a fixed mass is constant at constant temperature

$$V \times P = k_1 \text{ (temperature and mass constant)}$$

k_1 is fixed for a fixed mass of gas at a fixed temperature. Then, for two different pressures

so that

$$P_1V_1 = k_1 \text{ and } P_2V_2 = k_1$$

$$P_1V_1 = P_2V_2 \tag{1}$$

The symbols V_1 and P_1 give the initial volume and pressure; V_2 and P_2 give the volume and pressure when the initial pressure or volume is changed. This is another way of writing Boyle's law.

No gas conforms exactly to this inverse pressure-volume relationship over wide ranges of pressure and temperature. Boyle's original data, shown in Table 2.1, are typical for most gases near room temperature and pressure. As the temperature is increased and the pressure decreased, gases conform more exactly to Boyle's law. However, at low temperatures (below about 0 °C) and high pressures (above about 50 atm), gases do *not* conform to Boyle's law. These deviations are discussed later (page 72).

Boyle's law is further illustrated in Fig. 2.6. If a gas is confined in a cylinder with a movable, frictionless piston, the volume of gas decreases as the pressure is increased. Doubling the pressure (the weight on the piston) reduces the volume to one-half its initial value; tripling the pressure reduces the volume to one-third its initial value.

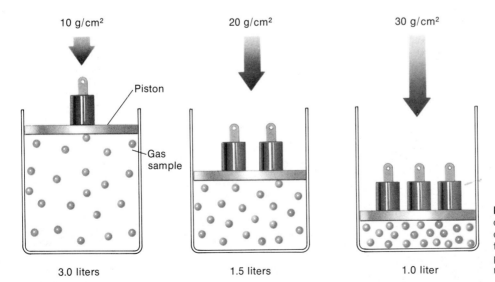

10 g/cm²   20 g/cm²   30 g/cm²

Piston

Gas sample

3.0 liters   1.5 liters   1.0 liter

FIGURE 2.6 Illustrating the change in volume of a gas with changes in pressure (temperature constant). Raise or lower piston as shown. (Entire apparatus is enclosed in vacuum.)

Example 3

A sample of oxygen gas occupies 5.0 ℓ at 380 torr. What is the volume of the oxygen at 1.00 atm, 760 torr, if the temperature remains constant?

Answer

Boyle's law tells us that doubling the pressure decreases the volume by one-half; the volume of the oxygen is, therefore, 2.5 ℓ at 1.00 atm. Or, since the pressure increases from 380 torr to 760 torr, the volume must decrease proportionately:

$$\text{new volume} = 5.0 \text{ } \ell \times \frac{380 \text{ torr}}{760 \text{ torr}} = 2.5 \text{ } \ell$$

Note that the fraction of the two pressures, 380/760, is less than one; the fraction is less than one since the gas volume must *decrease* as the pressure increases.

This calculation can also be made by using Equation (1) above:

$$\text{new volume} \rightsquigarrow V_2 = V_1 \times \frac{P_1}{P_2} \quad \begin{matrix} \text{initial pressure} \\ \text{new pressure} \end{matrix}$$
$$\text{initial volume}$$

Then,

$$V_2 = 5.0 \text{ } \ell \times \frac{380 \text{ torr}}{760 \text{ torr}} = 2.5 \text{ } \ell$$

This is the same as the first calculation. Either method is acceptable.

Example 4

The pressure on 10.0 ℓ of a gas at 740 torr at 0 °C is reduced to 700 torr at 0 °C. What is the new volume of the gas?

Answer

Since the pressure on the gas is decreased, its volume must increase:

$$\text{new volume} = 10.0 \text{ } \ell \times \frac{740 \text{ torr}}{700 \text{ torr}} = 10.6 \text{ } \ell$$

In this case, the fraction of the two pressures, 740/700, is greater than one since the gas volume must increase as the pressure decreases. Or, using Equation (1),

$$V_2 = V_1 \times \frac{P_1}{P_2} = 10.0 \text{ } \ell \times \frac{740 \text{ torr}}{700 \text{ torr}} = 10.6 \text{ } \ell$$

Example 5

A sample of gas occupies 546 ml at 1.00 atm. What is the gas volume if the pressure is increased to 1.50 atm (temperature constant)?

Answer

Since the pressure is increased, the volume must decrease; that is, the fraction of the two pressures must be less than one:

$$\text{new volume} = 546 \text{ ml} \times \frac{1.00 \text{ atm}}{1.50 \text{ atm}} = 364 \text{ ml}$$

or

$$V_2 = V_1 \times \frac{P_1}{P_2} = 546 \text{ ml} \times \frac{1.00 \text{ atm}}{1.50 \text{ atm}} = 364 \text{ ml}$$

PROBLEM 8   **A gas sample occupies 2.95 ℓ at a pressure of 2.25 atm. What is the gas volume at 2.50 atm (temperature constant)?**

2.4 _____ **VOLUME-TEMPERATURE RELATIONSHIP FOR A GAS: CHARLES' LAW**

Although Boyle (1662) recognized that heat produced changes in the volume of air, it was not until 1787 that Jacques Charles measured the effects of temperature on the volume of a fixed mass of a gas. His observations can be illustrated with the apparatus shown in Fig. 2.7. Liquid mercury is placed in a glass tube sealed at one end, forming a mercury frictionless piston that traps a mass of air in the closed end of the tube. As the temperature of the gas is increased by heating the water in which the tube is immersed, the volume of the gas increases. Notice that the mercury plug plus the atmosphere maintains a constant pressure on the trapped air during the course of the experiment. A plot of the volume of the gas as a function of the temperature yields a straight line, shown in Fig. 2.8. The broken part of the line represents an *extrapolation* (extension) of the experimental line to a temperature at which the gas volume would be expected to become zero.

For a number of gases, Charles found that for every degree Celsius rise in temperature, the volume of a gas increases by $\frac{1}{273}$ of its volume at 0 °C when the pressure is held constant. Thus, if a gas at 0 °C is warmed to 1 °C at constant pressure, its volume is increased by $\frac{1}{273}$ of its original value:

$$\text{new volume at 1 °C} = \text{original volume at 0 °C} + \frac{1}{273} \times \text{original volume}$$

If the temperature is increased to 100 °C, the volume is increased by $\frac{100}{273}$:

$$\text{new volume at 100 °C} = \text{original volume at 0 °C} + \frac{100}{273} \times \text{original volume}$$

He also observed that when the gas is cooled, its volume is *decreased* by $\frac{1}{273}$ of its initial volume at 0 °C for every degree Celsius cooled:

$$\text{new volume at } -1 \text{ °C} = \text{original volume at 0 °C} - \frac{1}{273} \times \text{original volume}$$

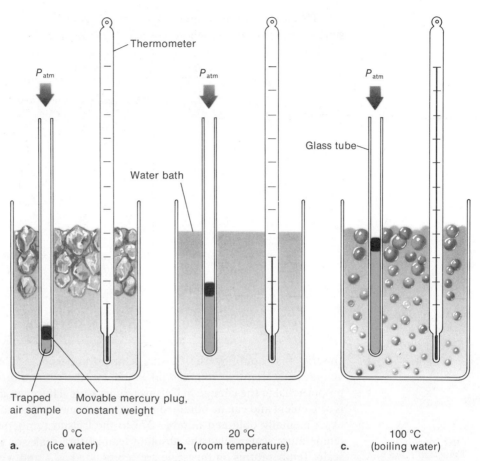

a. 0 °C (ice water) **b.** 20 °C (room temperature) **c.** 100 °C (boiling water)

FIGURE 2.7 Illustrating that the volume of a gas increases as the temperature is increased at constant pressure. A mercury plug of constant weight plus atmospheric pressure (P_{atm}) maintains a constant pressure on the trapped air.

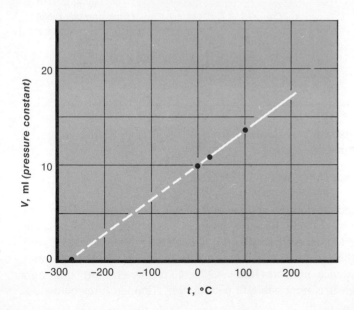

FIGURE 2.8 A plot (graph) of volume vs. temperature shows that gases expand when heated at constant pressure.

This temperature-volume relationship becomes more apparent if we arbitrarily start with a gas sample whose volume is 273 ml at 0 °C:

t, °C	V, ml
273	$273 \text{ ml} + \dfrac{273}{273} \times 273 \text{ ml} = 546 \text{ ml}$
100	$273 \text{ ml} + \dfrac{100}{273} \times 273 \text{ ml} = 373 \text{ ml}$
2	$273 \text{ ml} + \dfrac{2}{273} \times 273 \text{ ml} = 275 \text{ ml}$
1	$273 \text{ ml} + \dfrac{1}{273} \times 273 \text{ ml} = 274 \text{ ml}$
0	273 ml ⟵ Start here
−1	$273 \text{ ml} - \dfrac{1}{273} \times 273 \text{ ml} = 272 \text{ ml}$
−100	$273 \text{ ml} - \dfrac{100}{273} \times 273 \text{ ml} = 173 \text{ ml}$
−273	$273 \text{ ml} - \dfrac{273}{273} \times 273 \text{ ml} = 0$

Observe that doubling the Celsius temperature from 1 °C to 2 °C increases the volume only slightly, from 274 ml to 275 ml; the change in volume is *not* directly proportional to the change in Celsius temperature. However, a direct proportionality is convenient and can be obtained by defining a new temperature scale. By adding the experimentally obtained number 273 to the Celsius temperature, we define a new temperature scale called the **absolute temperature scale,** or the **kelvin temperature scale.** Temperatures on this scale are represented as T and written in units of K, for example, $T = 273$ K. The absolute temperature scale now gives us a *direct proportionality with volume,* shown below:

After William Thompson (Lord Kelvin), who proposed the absolute temperature scale in 1848. See App. II.

t, °C (from previous table)	t, °C + 273 = T, K	V, ml (from previous table)
273	273 + 273 = 546	546
100	100 + 273 = 373	373
0	0 + 273 = 273	273
−100	−100 + 273 = 173	173
−273	−273 + 273 = 0	0

When the absolute temperature is doubled from 273 K to 546 K, the volume is doubled (pressure constant).

PROBLEM 9   **Convert (a) 50 °C and (b) −73 °C to K.**

This relationship predicts that the volume of a gas will be zero at absolute zero, 0 K. This prediction is not realistic, because the mass of gas does not measurably change regardless of the temperature to which it is cooled. In reality, gases liquefy and then solidify (with the exception of helium) before reaching −273 °C at 1 atm. Nevertheless, much evidence indicates that −273 °C is the absolute minimum temperature below which it is impossible to cool matter. Temperatures below 0 K

From careful experiments, absolute zero is −273.15 °C.

would correspond to negative volumes, a meaningless quantity. Later (page 66), we shall interpret absolute zero more satisfyingly on a theoretical basis.

In summary, *at constant pressure, the volume of a fixed mass of gas varies directly with the absolute temperature*. Known as the **law of Charles,** it can be represented by

$$V = k_2 T \text{ (pressure and mass constant)}$$

Confirmed by Joseph Gay-Lussac (1802), it is also known as the law of Charles and Gay-Lussac.

k_2 is fixed for a fixed mass of gas at a fixed pressure. Then, for two different absolute temperatures,

$$\frac{V_1}{T_1} = k_2 \text{ and } \frac{V_2}{T_2} = k_2$$

so that

$$\frac{V_1}{T_1} = \frac{V_2}{T_2} \tag{2}$$

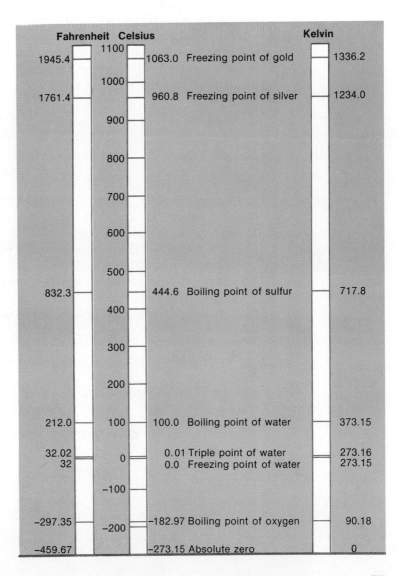

FIGURE 2.9 The relationships between the kelvin, Celsius, and Fahrenheit temperature scales.

The symbols V_1 and T_1 give the initial volume and absolute temperature; V_2 and T_2 give the volume and absolute temperature when the initial temperature or volume is changed. This is another way of writing Charles' law.

Charles' law can also be stated as: *at constant volume, the pressure of a fixed mass of gas varies directly with absolute temperature:*

$$P = k_3 T \text{ (volume and mass constant)}$$

or

$$\frac{P_1}{T_1} = k_3 \text{ and } \frac{P_2}{T_2} = k_3$$

so that

$$\frac{P_1}{T_1} = \frac{P_2}{T_2} \tag{3}$$

This relationship predicts that the pressure of a gas should be zero at absolute zero. The value of k_3 depends on the mass of the gas sample and the fixed volume.

It is convenient to define standard reference conditions for work with gases. By convention, 0 °C (273 K) and 760 torr (1 atm) represent **standard temperature** and **standard pressure** (STP), respectively. The relationship between the three temperature scales we have considered is shown in Fig. 2.9.

Example 6

A 5.00 ℓ sample of gas is cooled from 50.0 °C to −20.0 °C at constant pressure. What is the volume of the gas at the lower temperature?

Answer

Remembering that volume varies directly with the *absolute temperature,* it is first necessary to convert the given Celsius temperatures, °C, to the kelvin temperature scale. The gas is cooled from 323 K (50 °C + 273) to 253 K (−20 °C + 273). The temperature is decreased; the volume is then decreased by that fraction of the two absolute temperatures that decreases the initial volume; namely, a fraction less than one:

$$\text{new volume} = 5.00 \ \ell \times \frac{253 \ K}{323 \ K} = 3.92 \ \ell$$

or, using Equation (2),

$$\text{new volume} \longrightarrow V_2 = V_1 \times \frac{T_2}{T_1} \quad \begin{array}{l} \text{new temperature} \\ \text{initial temperature} \end{array}$$

$$\text{initial volume}$$

Then,

$$V_2 = 5.00 \ \ell \times \frac{253 \ K}{323 \ K} = 3.92 \ \ell$$

the same as above. Either method is acceptable.

Example 7

A gas occupies 10.0 l at STP (0 °C and 1 atm). Calculate its volume at 100 °C and 760 torr.

Answer

Keeping the pressure constant (1 atm = 760 torr), but changing the temperature from 273 K (0 °C + 273) to 373 K (100 °C + 273) increases the volume of the gas; thus, the initial volume is multiplied by that fraction of the two absolute temperatures that increases the volume:

$$\text{new volume} = 10.0 \; l \times \frac{373 \; K}{273 \; K} = 13.7 \; l$$

or

$$V_2 = V_1 \times \frac{T_2}{T_1} = 10.0 \; l \times \frac{373 \; K}{273 \; K} = 13.7 \; l$$

PROBLEM 10   A sample of gas occupies 5.00 liters at 30.0 °C and 0.500 atm. At constant pressure, calculate its volume at 60.0 °C.

PROBLEM 11   A 1.55 liter steel cylinder is filled with a gas to a pressure of 3.00 atm at 50.0 °C. What is the pressure if the cylinder temperature is raised to 200 °C?

COMBINED GAS LAW EXPRESSION _____ 2.5

Boyle's law and Charles' law can be combined to give an expression that relates the temperature, pressure, and volume of a *fixed mass* of a gas. The volume of the gas is inversely related (inversely proportional) to its pressure and directly related (directly proportional) to its absolute temperature, or

$$V \propto \frac{T}{P} \quad \text{or} \quad \frac{VP}{T} = k_4 \; (\text{mass constant})$$

k_4 is fixed for a fixed mass of gas. Then, for two different absolute temperatures and pressures,

$$\frac{V_1 P_1}{T_1} = k_4 \quad \text{and} \quad \frac{V_2 P_2}{T_2} = k_4$$

so that

$$\frac{V_1 P_1}{T_1} = \frac{V_2 P_2}{T_2} \tag{4}$$

and

$$V_2 = V_1 \times \frac{T_2}{T_1} \times \frac{P_1}{P_2} \tag{5}$$

The symbols V_1, T_1, and P_1 give the initial volume, absolute temperature, and pressure; V_2 gives the new volume when the initial temperature and pressure are changed. This is a method of combining Boyle's and Charles' laws.

Example 8

The volume of a gas is 342 ml at 25.0 °C and 730 torr. Find the volume of the gas at STP.

Answer

Each of the changes in conditions may be considered separately: the decrease in temperature from 298 K (25 °C + 273) to 273 K (0 °C + 273) decreases the volume; the pressure increase from 730 torr to 760 torr also decreases the volume. The original volume is, therefore, multiplied by the temperature and pressure fractions which will cause the volume to decrease:

$$342 \text{ ml} \times \frac{273 \text{ K}}{298 \text{ K}} \times \frac{730 \text{ torr}}{760 \text{ torr}} = 301 \text{ ml}$$

Or, using Equation (5) above,

$$V_2 = 342 \text{ ml} \times \frac{273 \text{ K}}{298 \text{ K}} \times \frac{730 \text{ torr}}{760 \text{ torr}} = 301 \text{ ml}$$

Example 9

A sample of gas occupies 1.00 ℓ at STP. Find the volume at 100 °C and 10.0 atm.

Answer

The increase in temperature from 273 K to 373 K increases the volume, but the pressure increase from 1.00 atm to 10.0 atm decreases the volume; the original volume is therefore multiplied by the temperature and pressure fractions corresponding to these volume changes:

$$1.00 \text{ ℓ} \times \frac{373 \text{ K}}{273 \text{ K}} \times \frac{1.00 \text{ atm}}{10.0 \text{ atm}} = 0.137 \text{ ℓ}$$

Example 10

The volume of a gas is 420 ml at 25.0 °C and 740 torr. Find the volume of the gas at 75.0 °C and 1.20 atm.

Answer

The increase in temperature from 298 K to 348 K increases the volume. The increase in pressure, from 740 torr to 912 torr$\left(1.20 \text{ atm} = 1.20 \text{ atm} \times \dfrac{760 \text{ torr}}{\text{atm}} = \right.$

Numerator is the number above the line, denominator is the number below the line in a fraction.

912 torr; this conversion must be made so that the numerator and denominator of the pressure fraction have the same units, or, 740 torr could have been converted to atm: $740 \text{ torr} = 740 \text{ torr} \times \dfrac{1 \text{ atm}}{760 \text{ torr}} = 0.974 \text{ atm}\Big)$, decreases the volume. The original volume is therefore multiplied by the temperature and pressure fractions corresponding to these volume changes:

$$420 \text{ ml} \times \frac{348\ \cancel{K}}{298\ \cancel{K}} \times \frac{740\ \cancel{\text{torr}}}{912\ \cancel{\text{torr}}} = 398 \text{ ml}$$

PROBLEM 12 **A sample of gas occupies 50.0 ml at 20.0 °C and 650 torr. Find the volume of the gas at STP.**

It should now be emphasized that the volume of a gas as a measure of the quantity (the mass) of a gas is meaningless. The volume of a gas is merely the space it occupies—the volume of the container made available to it—under certain conditions of temperature and pressure.

DALTON'S LAW OF PARTIAL PRESSURES _____ 2.6

We have considered the pressure exerted by one gas in a container. What is the situation regarding the pressure exerted by a mixture of gases? What contribution does each gas make to the total measured pressure of the mixture? Refer to Fig. 2.10. Two 1 l containers, each confining a gas at the same pressure, 1.00 atm, are separated by a stopcock (Fig. 2.10 a). Opening the stopcock allows the two gases to mix (diffuse) with each other (Fig. 2.10 b). However, no change in the measured *pressure* is observed, even though the *volume* of each gas has doubled.

We assume that the gases do not react chemically with each other.

How can we explain this observation? When a gas expands to twice its initial volume, its pressure is decreased to one-half the initial pressure (1.00 atm $\times$ $\frac{1.00\ \cancel{l}}{2.00\ \cancel{l}} = 0.500$ atm).

Thus, as shown in Fig. 2.10, the volume of each gas is doubled from 1.0 to 2.0 liters so that the pressure of each gas decreases from 1.00 to 0.50 atm. The sum of the pressures is therefore 1.00 atm:

$$P_{\text{Total}} = p_{\text{A}} + p_{\text{B}} = 0.50 \text{ atm} + 0.50 \text{ atm} = 1.00 \text{ atm}$$

This relationship, known as **Dalton's law of partial pressures,** is generally represented by

$$P_{\text{Total}} = p_1 + p_2 + p_3 + \cdots$$

where p_1, p_2, and p_3 represent the **partial pressure** of each gas in the mixture.

Example 11

A mixture of gases in a 3.00 l flask consists of nitrogen at a pressure of 100 torr and oxygen at 300 torr. (a) What is the volume of each gas? (b) What is the total pressure of the mixture?

Answer

(a) The volume of a gas is the volume of the container that confines it. Therefore, the volume of each gas is the same, 3.00 l. (b) The total pressure is the sum of the partial pressures of the gases in a mixture. The partial pressure of

---

61

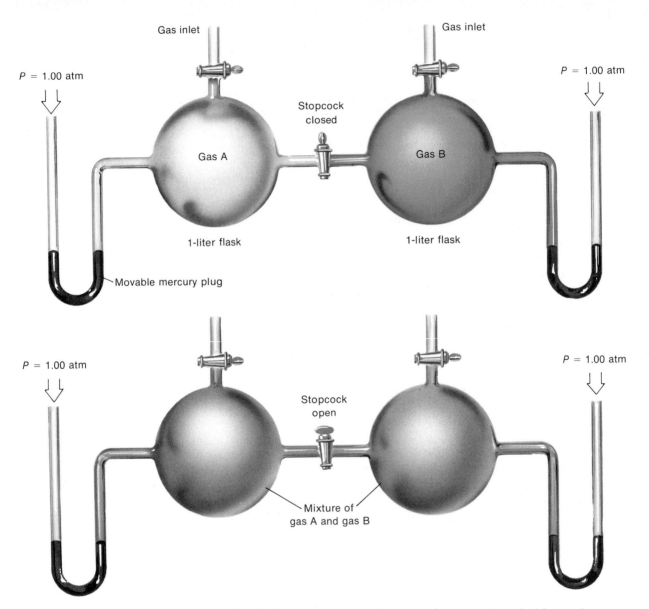

P = 1.00 atm

Gas inlet

Gas inlet

P = 1.00 atm

Stopcock
closed

Gas A

Gas B

1-liter flask

1-liter flask

Movable mercury plug

P = 1.00 atm

P = 1.00 atm

Stopcock
open

Mixture of
gas A and gas B

FIGURE 2.10 Apparatus to demonstrate the effect of mixing gases on the measured pressure at constant temperature.

nitrogen is 100 torr and that of oxygen is 300 torr. Therefore, the total pressure is 400 torr:

$$P_{\text{Total}} = 100 \text{ torr} + 300 \text{ torr} = 400 \text{ torr}$$

PROBLEM 13   A mixture of gases in a 20.0 ℓ flask at 30 °C consists of oxygen at 650 torr and water vapor at 31.8 torr. What is the total pressure of the mixture? What is the volume of oxygen and water vapor in the flask?

The partial pressures of gases are especially important in measurements of gases in contact with liquids. Evaporation of the liquid adds a gas (vapor) to the container and therefore causes a partial pressure to be exerted. This subject is further discussed in Chap. 3.

DIFFUSION OF GASES: GRAHAM'S LAW _____ 2.7

When two gases are allowed to mix, they diffuse into each other and eventually form a homogeneous (same throughout) mixture. In 1831, Thomas Graham observed *"that gases diffuse into the atmosphere and into each other, with different degrees of ease and rapidity. This was observed by allowing each gas to diffuse from a bottle into the air through a narrow tube . . . the result was that the same volumes of different gases escape at rates which are exceedingly different but which have a relation to the densities of the gases."* For example, Graham found that 1.0 ml of hydrogen diffuses (escapes) much faster than 1.0 ml (same conditions) of oxygen. Also, oxygen is denser than hydrogen. He stated (1846) that the rates, r_1 and r_2, at which gases diffuse are inversely proportional to the square roots of their densities, d_1 and d_2:*

Thomas Graham, Elements of Chemistry, H. Bailliére, London, 1850.

$$\frac{r_1}{r_2} = \frac{\sqrt{d_2}}{\sqrt{d_1}} = \sqrt{\frac{d_2}{d_1}}$$

This relationship is known as **Graham's law.** It means that the smaller the density of a gas, the faster it diffuses.

The square is the product obtained when a number is multiplied by itself (page 9): 4 is the square of 2, (2^2); 16 is the square of 4, (4^2); 100 is the square of 10, (10^2). The *square root* of a given number is the number that when multiplied by itself produces the given number. Thus, the square root of 4, represented by $\sqrt{4}$, is 2, because $2 \times 2 = 4$; $\sqrt{4} = 2$. The square root of 16, $\sqrt{16}$, is 4, because $4 \times 4 = 16$; $\sqrt{16} = 4$. The square root of 8, $\sqrt{8}$, is approximately 2.83.

$\sqrt{4}$ may also be written as $4^{1/2}$.

Example 12

Naturally occurring uranium metal is essentially a mixture of two types of uranium of slightly different masses (page 122). However, for many purposes (Chap. 17), it is desirable to separate the two types. The uranium is converted into gaseous uranium hexafluorides, UF_6, with slightly different densities; at STP, the density of type I is 15.71 g/ℓ and the density of type II is 15.58 g/ℓ. How much faster will type II UF_6 diffuse?

Answer

The gas with the smaller density diffuses faster, according to the relationship $\frac{r_1}{r_2} = \sqrt{\frac{d_2}{d_1}}$. Thus,

The actual separation (Oak Ridge, Tennessee) is accomplished by allowing the two gases to effuse through about 4000 barriers, each barrier having thousands of extremely small holes.

---

*Densities are measured at the same temperature and pressure; at STP, the density of hydrogen is 0.089 g/ℓ and oxygen, 1.4 g/ℓ. This relationship is actually valid only for gases *effusing* into a vacuum. Effusion refers to the escape of gases through a small opening. It is, however, approximately true for diffusion processes as well, if we ignore the effects of the gas into which the test gas is diffusing.

$$\frac{r_1}{r_2} = \sqrt{\frac{15.71 \text{ g/}\ell}{15.58 \text{ g/}\ell}} = \sqrt{1.008} = 1.004$$

Type II therefore diffuses 1.004 times faster than type I.

PROBLEM 14   At 0 °C and 760 torr, the density of oxygen gas is 1.43 g/ℓ and that of helium gas is 0.178 g/ℓ. Which gas diffuses faster, and how much faster?

2.8 ———————— KINETIC MOLECULAR THEORY OF GASES

The observations about the properties of gases that we have discussed are explained by a theory developed over many years, largely by Daniel Bernoulli (1738), John Waterston (1845), Ludwig Boltzmann (1868), James Maxwell (1860), and Rudolf Clausius (1857), and known as the **kinetic molecular theory of gases.** The theory makes the following *assumptions:*

1. Gases are made up of extremely small (invisible), separate particles called **molecules.** The molecules are considered as hard spheres, extremely difficult to compress. They possess mass but have practically no volume. Under room conditions of temperature and pressure, the molecules are so far apart that the space in which the gas is confined—the container—contains very little matter. The volume of the molecules is very small compared to the volume of the container. The model shown in Fig. 2.11 offers an explanation of the low densities of gases at ordinary conditions and the ease with which gases are compressed: it is the *empty space,* rather than the matter represented by molecules, that is actually compressed. It follows that liquids and solids (which have much greater densities than gases) are more difficult to compress because the molecules are now crowded together with very little space between them. We easily see through gases because their molecules are too small to reflect light effectively.

The Royal Society of London rejected Waterston's paper as "nonsense, unfit for the Society".

Latin molecula, from moles, Latin for mass.

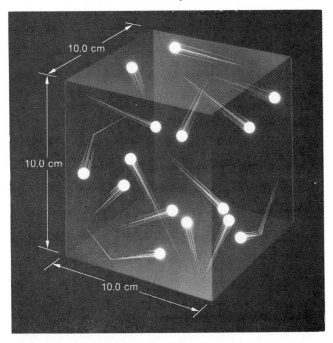

FIGURE 2.11 The kinetic theory model of a gas: A schematic representation of molecules in the space of 1.00 liter. The volume of the gas is 1.00 liter. But the volume of the molecules is very much smaller. Therefore, most of the space in the container is empty.

Example 13

The same carbon dioxide molecule, CO_2, is present in gaseous carbon dioxide and in solid carbon dioxide. Is the CO_2 molecule in the gaseous state more easily compressed than it is in the solid state?

Answer

No, gaseous carbon dioxide is easier to compress than solid carbon dioxide because of the greater amount of empty space in the gaseous state. The molecules themselves arc not compressed.

2. Gas molecules are always in aimless motion. They travel in straight lines interrupted only by collisions with other molecules or with the walls of the container. The molecules, therefore, like moving bullets, possess kinetic energy; all objects moving from one place to another have kinetic energy.

3. No attractive or repulsive forces exist between molecules, or between the molecules and the walls of the container. In *all* collisions, no energy is lost as friction (heat). The energy lost by one molecule in a collision with another molecule is gained by the other molecule. However, the molecules bounce off the walls of the container without loss of energy. This explains the ability of gases to fill the confining container and the failure of gases to come to rest at the bottom of the container.*

Straight-line or linear motion is also known as translational motion; kinetic energy is therefore also known as translational energy.

PROBLEM 15 **(a) A sensitive thermometer is placed at the spot hit by a bouncing rubber ball. Will the thermometer register a temperature change? If so, will the temperature rise or fall? (b) A sensitive thermometer is placed on a container wall being bombarded by gas molecules. Will the thermometer register a temperature change? If so, will the temperature rise or fall?**

The space between the molecules accounts for the diffusion of one gas into another; this is illustrated in Fig. 2.12. The force exerted on the walls of the container by the collisions of the molecules gives rise to the pressure of the gas (Fig. 2.12).

4. Not all the molecules in a gas have the same speed. Consequently, not all molecules have the same kinetic energy. However, we *assume* that the *average kinetic energy* of all gas molecules is the same at the *same temperature*. The fundamental assumption here is that the average kinetic energy of gas molecules is *directly* proportional to the absolute temperature, *T*. The kinetic energy of any object depends on its mass, *m*, and its velocity, *v*. The kinetic energy for gas molecules is given by the formula

$$\text{average kinetic energy, } E_k = \tfrac{1}{2}\, mv^2, \text{ and } E_k \propto T$$

Energy first defined as $\tfrac{1}{2} mv^2$ by Thomas Young (1807).

in which m = the mass of a molecule and v = the average velocity of the molecules. Consider a body with a mass of 2 g and a velocity of 1 cm/s; its kinetic energy is

$$E_k = \tfrac{1}{2} \times 2\,\text{g} \times \left(1\,\frac{\text{cm}}{\text{s}}\right)^2 = 1\,\text{g}\,\frac{\text{cm}^2}{\text{s}^2}$$

---

*Consider a bouncing rubber ball. In a short time the rubber ball slows down and eventually comes to rest on the ground. The kinetic energy possessed by the rubber ball is lost as friction (heat) each time the ball hits the ground. Eventually, unlike gaseous molecules, all of the kinetic energy is converted to heat and the ball comes to rest.

a

Gas inlet Gas inlet

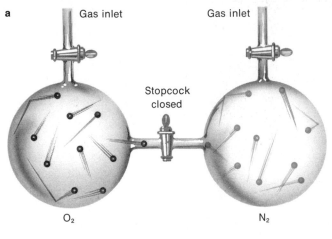

Stopcock
closed

O₂   N₂

b

Pressure of the gas results from
collisions of molecules with the
walls of the container

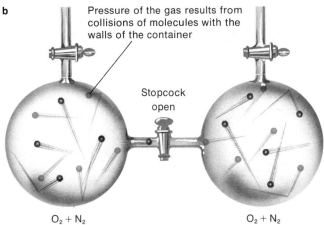

Stopcock
open

O₂ + N₂   O₂ + N₂

FIGURE 2.12 Representation of diffusion of gases.
The space between the molecules allows for ease of
admission of one gas into another. Collision of molecules with the walls of the container explains the pressure of the gas.

From ergon, *the Greek
word for work.*

This unit of energy is called the **erg,** and $1 \text{ erg} = 1 \text{ g} \frac{\text{cm}^2}{\text{s}^2}$. There are 10^7 ergs in

1 joule, $\frac{10^7 \text{ erg}}{1 \text{ J}}$, and 4.184×10^7 ergs in 1 calorie, $4.184 \times 10^7 \frac{\text{erg}}{\text{cal}}$.

The greater the temperature, the greater the average kinetic energy of the molecules. This assumption gives a comparatively simple answer to that difficult question, "What do we mean by temperature?" Kinetic theory answers: "When we measure the temperature of a gas, we measure the average kinetic energy of the gas molecules. Heat is molecular motion." This picture also offers an interpretation of absolute zero. At absolute zero, the kinetic energy of gas molecules is zero. The molecules come to rest at the bottom of the container, and the pressure is consequently zero. Or, equally well, we can say that at absolute zero, the kinetic energy is zero, the molecular motion is zero, or "the heat in the gas is zero." It is therefore impossible to cool the gas below absolute zero, since there is now *no heat left to remove from the gas.*

This assumption also tells us that at the same temperature, molecules with *different masses* have *different velocities* but the *same average kinetic energy.*

The kinetic theory also gives us an explanation of all the gas laws. We have defined pressure (page 44) as the force on a given area of surface. In a gas, the pressure is caused by molecules striking the walls of the container. Each molecule thus exerts a force; the pressure therefore depends on the area being hit and on the number of molecules in the container. The larger the number of molecules in a given volume (that is, the greater the density of the molecules), the larger the number of collisions per second against the walls, and the higher the pressure, P:

$$P \propto \frac{\text{number of molecules, } N}{\text{ml, } V} \times \text{kinetic energy, } E_k, \text{ of molecules}$$

or

$$P \propto \frac{N}{V} E_k$$

but the E_k of molecules is proportional to absolute temperature, T. Hence,

$$P \propto \frac{N}{V} T \tag{6}$$

The molecular motion is completely random. This aimless movement of molecules makes the number of molecules moving in one direction, on the average, the same as the number of molecules moving in any other direction. The observed pressure, then, is the same on each wall of the container. Doubling the number of molecules in a given volume of gas doubles the number of collisions per second, and thereby doubles the pressure. But reducing a given volume of gas by one-half, without changing the number of molecules (mass fixed), also doubles the number of molecules per unit volume. Thus, reducing the volume by one-half doubles the pressure, as described by Boyle's law (page 51). Or, reducing the distance between any two walls of the container by one-half allows a given molecule moving between these walls to make two collisions in the time it formerly took to make one collision. Thus, reducing the volume by one-half results in twice the number of collisions per second, thereby doubling the pressure.

Charles' law also follows from our generalization (6). If we fix N, the number of molecules (fixed mass), and the volume, V, of the container, then $P \propto \frac{N}{V} T$ becomes $P \propto T$. Thus, if we double the absolute temperature, the average E_k of the molecules doubles. This, in turn, doubles the pressure. When we double the absolute temperature, but wish to keep the pressure constant, we must decrease the number of molecules per unit volume by one-half. This can be accomplished by expanding the container to twice the original volume. This is in agreement with Charles' law (page 57).

The assumption that at the same temperature, molecules of all gases possess the same average kinetic energy leads to another interesting conclusion: the lighter the mass of a molecule, the faster it travels, in spite of the vast number of collisions tending to change the direction of motion. The rate of diffusion of a gas depends on how fast the molecules move. Therefore, kinetic theory predicts a relationship between the rate of diffusion and the mass of the molecules. This follows from our definition of kinetic energy and our assumption that the kinetic energy of molecules is proportional to absolute temperature. Then, at the same temperature, the kinetic energies of the molecules of two different gases are the same:

$$E_{k_1} = E_{k_2} \text{ (same temperature)}$$
$$\frac{m_1 v_1^2}{2} = \frac{m_2 v_2^2}{2}$$

After canceling the $\frac{1}{2}$ factor on each side, the equation is rearranged to

$$\frac{v_1{}^2}{v_2{}^2} = \frac{m_2}{m_1}, \text{ the same as } m_1 v_1{}^2 = m_2 v_2{}^2$$

Taking the square root of both sides of this expression gives

$$\frac{v_1}{v_2} = \sqrt{\frac{m_2}{m_1}}$$

It is reasonable to assume that the rate of diffusion of a gas is directly proportional to the velocity of its molecules; thus, the rates of diffusion of molecules are inversely proportional to the square root of their masses:

$$\frac{r_1}{r_2} = \sqrt{\frac{m_2}{m_1}}$$

Surprisingly, we come up with a method for measuring the relative masses of molecules! It can tell us how much heavier is the mass of a molecule of one gas compared to the mass of a molecule of another gas.

Example 14

A volume of oxygen gas at STP requires 400 seconds to pass through a pinhole into a vacuum. The same volume of hydrogen at STP requires 100 seconds. Which molecule is heavier, and how much heavier is it?

Answer

The time of diffusion is inversely proportional to the rate of diffusion. The faster the rate, the shorter the time:

$$\frac{r_1}{r_2} = \frac{t_2}{t_1}$$

We may then say that the times of diffusion of gases are directly proportional to the relative masses of their molecules:

$$\frac{t_2}{t_1} = \sqrt{\frac{m_2}{m_1}}$$

The more massive the molecule, the slower is its velocity, the longer is the time required to cover a given distance, and the longer is the diffusion time. From the given data,

$$\frac{400 \,s}{100 \,s} = \sqrt{\frac{m\,O_2}{m\,H_2}}$$

$$4.0 = \sqrt{\frac{m\,O_2}{m\,H_2}}$$

Squaring both sides of the expression removes the square root sign:

Recall page 63. More accurately, this is effusion—the escape of molecules through small openings.

$$16 = \frac{m\,O_2}{m\,H_2}$$

In words, the mass of an oxygen molecule is 16 times greater than that of a hydrogen molecule. We can also say that the masses of these molecules are in the **ratio** of 16 to 1, the same as $^{16}/_1$ or $^{32}/_2$ or $^{64}/_4$. Thus, ratio means relative quantities.

If we knew the actual mass of an oxygen or hydrogen molecule, we could then calculate the mass of the other. But there is no method known by which a single molecule may be weighed. Therefore, we satisfy ourselves with these *relative weights*. We can say that the mass of an oxygen molecule is 16 times the mass of a hydrogen molecule. These relative weights are known as **molecular weights,** a subject further discussed in Chapter 4.

Since the densities of molecules, the masses of gases per unit volume, are related to the masses of molecules, we can write

$$\frac{r_1}{r_2} = \sqrt{\frac{m_2}{m_1}} \quad \text{as} \quad \frac{r_1}{r_2} = \sqrt{\frac{d_2}{d_1}}$$

in agreement with Graham's law.

The Sea-Lab project provides an interesting application of the diffusion of gases. Recently, scientists and engineers have been developing equipment and procedures to enable people to survive at the bottom of the ocean. Because nitrogen gas may have a very harmful effect* on the aquanauts, the atmosphere in the Sea-Lab chamber is artificially composed of oxygen and helium. Although the temperature in the chamber was maintained at room temperature (70 °F), the aquanauts complained of chills and unpleasant coldness. How can this unexpected effect be explained? Relative to nitrogen, helium moves through the atmosphere about 2.6 times faster. Helium molecules therefore collide with the skin 2.6 times more frequently than nitrogen molecules. The faster moving helium molecules transport heat away from the body more efficiently than nitrogen; hence the cooling effect.

The pressure of a gas is directly proportional to the number of molecules and to the absolute temperature, and inversely proportional to the volume of the container, independent of their relative masses (page 59). *Two different gases containing the same number of molecules in the same volume at the same temperature therefore exert the same pressure.*

Example 15

100 molecules of oxygen contained in a 1 ℓ flask at 25 °C exert a pressure, *P*. What pressure is exerted by 100 molecules of hydrogen contained in a 1 ℓ flask at 25 °C? The mass of an oxygen molecule is 16 times the mass of a hydrogen molecule.

---

*Nitrogen gas may cause the *bends,* a painful condition associated with the formation of gas bubbles in the blood when a diver is returned from a region of high pressure to atmospheric pressure. Nitrogen at high pressures produces a narcotic effect which sometimes causes skin divers and scuba divers to exhibit unwise behavior that may be fatal. Oxygen at high pressures causes acute poisoning, resulting from lung damage and central nervous system reactions.

Answer

Since equal numbers of molecules in the same volume at the same temperature will exert the same pressure, independent of their relative masses, the 100 molecules of hydrogen in a 1 ℓ flask at 25 °C exert the same pressure, P.

Dalton's law follows directly. Mixing two gases that have the same temperature and, therefore, the same average kinetic energy does not change the average velocity of the molecules in the mixture. Each gas collides with the container walls with the same average frequency as it would if confined alone in the container. Each gas, therefore, exerts the same pressure as it would if confined alone in the container. Hence, in a mixture of gases, the sum of the pressures of each gas equals the total pressure.

2.9 _____ MOLECULAR SPEEDS

At a given temperature, the average kinetic energy of gas molecules is fixed. Molecules in a gas sample will therefore have an average speed. This means that there is a distribution of speeds—some slower, some faster. Even if all of the molecules in a container had the same speed initially, collisions among the molecules would soon cause some to speed up and others to slow down. A particular molecule may have different speeds at different times, although the temperature of the gas remains unchanged. However, there are so many molecules that there will be a practically constant number with a particular speed. The relative number of molecules having any particular speed can be plotted as shown in Fig. 2.13.

The area under the curve represents the total number of molecules in our gas sample at a particular temperature. As we increase the temperature, the speeds of the molecules, on the average, increase, and more of the molecules travel at the higher speeds. Fig. 2.14 shows the distribution of speeds of molecules of a gas at two different temperatures.

PROBLEM 16   A burst of 10^{20} silver (gas) molecules at constant temperature is aimed at a very quickly moving target. (a) Are all the silver molecules traveling at the same speed? (b) Would you expect all of the silver molecules to arrive at the same time or at different times? (c) Should all of the silver molecules be deposited on the same spot on the target or spread out along the target?

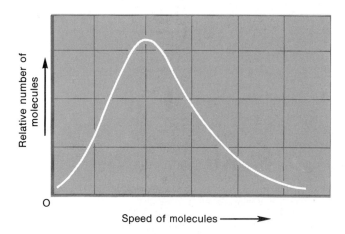

Relative number of molecules

Speed of molecules ⟶

FIGURE 2.13 Distribution of molecular speeds, obtained from the kind of experiment described in Problem 16.

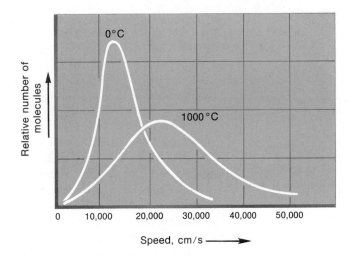

FIGURE 2.14 Distribution of speeds of nitrogen molecules at two different temperatures.

AVOGADRO'S LAW_____2.10

The kinetic theory leads to another significant conclusion. As we have already stated (page 67), the pressure of a gas, P, is proportional to the number of molecules, N, regardless of their masses, and to the absolute temperature, T, and inversely proportional to the volume of the gas, V. For two different gases,

Jean Perrin's experiment (1909) confirming the kinetic theory of Brownian movement (page 343) proved the existence of moving molecules and saved the theory from decline.

$$P_1 \propto \frac{N_1 T_1}{V_1} \quad \text{and} \quad P_2 \propto \frac{N_2 T_2}{V_2}$$

Thus, two different gases at the same pressure, at the same temperature, and in the same volume must have equal numbers of molecules. This is **Avogadro's law,** postulated in 1811: equal volumes of gases at the same temperature and pressure contain the same number of molecules. But the masses of these molecules need not be the same. Therefore, as we shall study in Chapter 4, Avogadro's law provides another method of determining the relative masses of molecules.

Example 16

Of the gases, oxygen, O_2, nitrogen, N_2, and hydrogen, H_2, the molecule of O_2 is the heaviest and the molecule of H_2 is the lightest. A container at a fixed temperature holds 4×10^{12} molecules of O_2, 8×10^{12} molecules of N_2, and 8×10^{12} molecules of H_2. How are the pressures of these gases related?

Answer

The volume and temperature of each gas are the same; then each gas pressure depends only on the number of molecules, independent of their masses. Since the number of molecules of N_2 and H_2 is the same (8×10^{12} molecules), their pressures are equal. But half the number of O_2 molecules (4×10^{12} molecules) exerts half the pressure of either N_2 or H_2: $P_{N_2} = P_{H_2}$, and $P_{O_2} = \frac{1}{2} P_{H_2}$.

PROBLEM 17 **A container at fixed temperature holds four gases whose pressures, in atm, are $P_1 = 4.00$, $P_2 = 4.00$, $P_3 = 2.00$, $P_4 = 1.00$. (a) Pick the gases that have the same number**

of molecules in the container. **(b)** Pick the gas(es) that **(i)** has (have) the largest, and **(ii)** has (have) the smallest number of molecules in the container. **(c)** What is the total pressure of the mixture?

2.11 ————————— REAL GASES

A gas which exactly follows the gas laws we have studied and summarized in the expression $PV \propto NT$ is known as an **ideal gas.** Under average room conditions, most real gases behave nearly like an ideal gas. However, at high pressures and low temperatures, most gases become more individualistic and deviate from ideal behavior. Typical data are presented in Fig. 2.15. The product PV is plotted against P, temperature constant. For 1.00 liter of an ideal gas at 1.00 atm at 0 °C, $PV = 1.00$ liter atm. The PV product for an ideal gas remains constant over all ranges of pressures, as shown by the dark horizontal line.

Kinetic theory assumes that no forces of attraction exist between molecules; it also assumes that molecules are practically without volume. However, the behavior of real gases (Fig. 2.15) may be explained if we assume that the molecules have definite volumes and that intermolecular attractive forces do exist (page 257). In other words, real molecules occupy space and attract each other. As the volume of a gas is decreased (pressure is increased) the molecules are crowded closer and closer together. The molecules then attract each other so that *sticky collisions* occur; the molecules do not instantly separate on contact. Rather, they stick together long enough so that, effectively, the number of molecules is decreased, as illustrated in Fig. 2.16. But decreasing the number of molecules makes the pressure of the real gas less

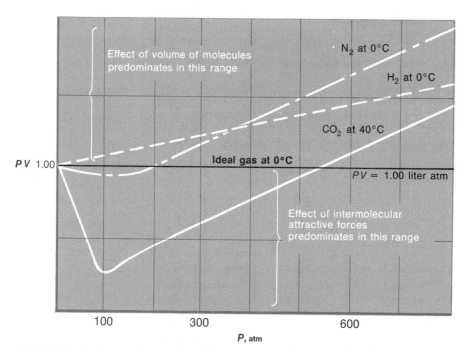

FIGURE 2.15 Deviations from ideal gas behavior given for three gases. The product PV is plotted against P (T is constant).

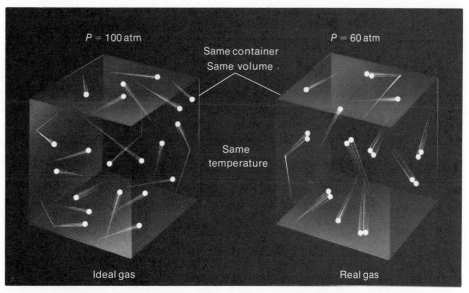

Molecules separate instantly upon collision, because no intermolecular forces exist. There are 20 ideal molecules in the container.

Molecules stick together long enough before separating, so that at any instant the number of real molecules effectively present in the container is 12.

FIGURE 2.16 A representation of the effect of intermolecular attractive forces on the behavior of real gases. The idea of attractive forces between molecules was first introduced by Johannes van der Waals (1873).

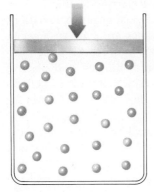

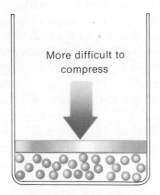

Largely empty space under low pressures

Volume of gas = volume of container

The container volume is much larger than the volume of the molecules; the gas is therefore easily compressed—the volume of empty space is decreased.

Comparatively little empty space under high pressures

Volume of gas = volume of container

A large fraction of the container is now occupied by the molecules. The gas is more difficult to compress. While it is easy to decrease the volume of empty space, it is extremely difficult to decrease the volume of a real molecule.

FIGURE 2.17 Representation of the effect of the volume of real molecules on the compressibility of gases.

73

than the pressure of the ideal gas. Hence, the PV product of a real gas decreases with increasing pressure. This is illustrated in Fig. 2.15 for CO_2 and N_2.

As the volume of the gas is further decreased, the molecules are packed closer together, and more and more of the volume of the container is occupied by the molecules; less and less of the volume of the container is empty space. The volume occupied by the molecules then becomes larger, as compared to the volume of the container (Fig. 2.17). To reduce further the volume of the gas, it is necessary to compress the molecules. It is easy to decrease the volume by pushing the molecules closer together as long as there is ample empty space between them. But it is very difficult to decrease the volume by compressing the molecules themselves when they are in contact with each other. Therefore, increasing the pressure of a real gas produces a decrease in volume *less* than that for the ideal gas. The situation becomes comparable to attempts to decrease the volume of a liquid or a solid. The PV product thus increases. This is illustrated in Fig. 2.15 and 2.17, and in the following table:

The electrical clouds of which molecules are composed (Chapters 6 and 18) repel each other.

	IDEAL GAS			REAL GAS	
P, atm	V, liter	P × V	P, atm	V, liter	P × V
1.00	1.00	1.00	1.00	1.00	1.00
50.0	0.0200	1.00	50.0	0.010	0.50
200	0.00500	1.00	200	0.00600	1.20

These two opposing effects—one tends to decrease PV, and the other tends to increase PV—operate in real gases over all ranges of pressure and temperature. However, in certain ranges one effect may predominate. Referring to Fig. 2.15, in nitrogen the intermolecular attractive forces are strong and yield negative deviations to about 200 atm (PV *real* less than PV *ideal*). These forces are even stronger in carbon dioxide, producing negative deviations to about 550 atm. Above these pressures, the effect of the volume occupied by molecules predominates, and positive deviations (PV *real* greater than PV *ideal*) are obtained. Notice that these two effects may balance each other, so that the product PV becomes ideal at about 200 atm for N_2 and 550 atm for CO_2.

In hydrogen, intermolecular attractive forces are so weak that the effect of the volume of the molecules predominates at all pressures, yielding a positive deviation (Fig. 2.15).

At low pressures, the volume of a given mass of gas becomes large, and the volume occupied by the molecules becomes comparatively small. The molecules are now very far apart, and their attraction, and tendency to stick together, decreases. At higher temperatures, the molecules have greater kinetic energies and their tendency to stick together decreases. Thus, the higher the temperature and the lower the pressure, the more closely a real gas behaves like an ideal gas.

PROBLEM 18   *PV* data are given on p. 75 for methane at 0 °C. Write in the last column the **predominant effect on** *PV:* **volume of molecule, intermolecular attractive force, or neither (ideal).**

P, atm	V, liter	P V, liter atm	Predominant Effect
0.100	224	22.4	ideal
1.00	22.4	22.4	
50	0.374	18.7	
100	0.169	16.9	
200	0.0885	17.7	
300	0.0683	20.5	
400	0.0608	24.3	
600	0.0420	25.2	

Many equations relating *P, V,* and *T* for a fixed mass of gas have been devised to describe the behavior of real gases at high pressures. These equations, relating the deviation of real gases from ideal behavior, contain many constants that are evaluated by experimentation. The first of these equations was given by Johannes van der Waals (1873) and in his honor, intermolecular attractive forces are also known as **van der Waals forces** (Chapter 8).

CRITICAL TEMPERATURE AND PRESSURE_____2.12

From our discussion of real gases, we may conclude that gases can be converted into liquids or solids by increasing the pressure, crowding molecules together, and lowering the temperature. Then the attractive forces so strongly hold the molecules together that liquids and solids form. But what happens if we decide to increase the

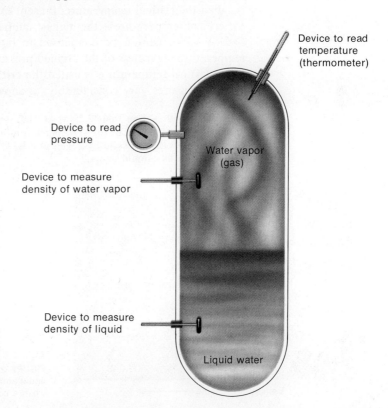

Device to read
temperature
(thermometer)

Device to read
pressure

Water vapor
(gas)

Device to measure
density of water vapor

Device to measure
density of liquid

Liquid water

FIGURE 2.18 Representation of apparatus to study the density of a liquid and its vapor as the temperature is increased. Since the container is sealed, the pressure in the container increases as the temperature increases. This experiment should not be attempted by the student, because the pressures that develop are usually high enough to cause even strong containers to explode.

temperature of a confined liquid? Let us load a strong container with liquid water at 25 °C, so that it contains only water and water vapor. Also, we shall provide instruments to measure the pressure of the vapor, the temperature, the density of the liquid, and the density of the water vapor (Fig. 2.18). While attractive forces hold molecules together in the liquid state, the kinetic energy—the tendency to move apart—favors the separation of molecules:

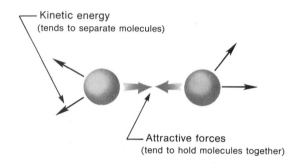

As the temperature is increased, the kinetic energy of the molecules increases. Molecular motion becomes more violent, molecules separate, the liquid expands, and its density decreases. But as the temperature increases, more and more of the molecules escape into the vapor, and the density of the vapor increases. Eventually, a temperature is reached at which the densities of the liquid and the vapor become identical (Fig. 2.19). At this temperature, other properties of the liquid and the vapor also become identical and the visible boundary between liquid and vapor disappears. The temperature at which the properties of liquid and vapor become identical is called the **critical temperature.** Present experimental knowledge also tells us that the critical temperature is the highest temperature at which the vapor can be liquefied. A vapor cannot be condensed to liquid at temperatures above the critical temperature regardless of the applied pressure. The pressure in the sealed container at the critical temperature is called the **critical pressure.** Critical temperatures and critical pressures vary considerably, as shown in Table 2.2.

PROBLEM 19 See Table 2.2. (a) At what temperature are the properties of liquid helium and helium vapor identical? (b) At *room temperature,* hydrogen is compressed so that its density is greater than that of solid hydrogen at 1 K. What is the physical state of hydrogen under these conditions—liquid or gas?

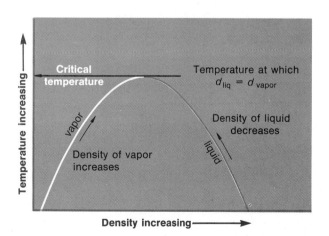

FIGURE 2.19 Illustrating the decrease in density of a liquid and the increase in density of the vapor that occur when a confined liquid is heated.

TABLE 2.2
CRITICAL TEMPERATURE AND PRESSURE
FOR VARIOUS SUBSTANCES

| Substance | CRITICAL TEMPERATURE | | Critical Pressure, atm |
	°C	K	
Helium, He	−269	4	2.26
Hydrogen, H_2	−240	33	12.8
Nitrogen, N_2	−147	126	33.5
Oxygen, O_2	−119	154	47.8
Carbon dioxide, CO_2	31	304	73.0
Water, H_2O	374	647	217.7

Note also in Table 2.2 that oxygen cannot be liquefied until its temperature is lowered to −119°C and, even then, not until a pressure of 47.8 atm is applied.

The critical temperature of a substance can be related to intermolecular attractive forces. The greater the attractive forces, the higher the kinetic energy needed to separate the molecules and keep them in the gaseous state; the higher the kinetic energy required, the higher the critical temperature. Table 2.2 shows that intermolecular attractive forces are strongest in water and weakest in helium.

PROBLEM 20   **Intermolecular attractive forces are stronger in ammonia than in oxygen. Which should have the higher critical temperature?**

PROBLEMS

21 **Vocabulary** Illustrate and/or define (a) diffusion, (b) pressure, (c) barometer, (d) manometer, (e) Boyle's law, (f) Charles' law, (g) Dalton's law, (h) partial pressure, (i) absolute zero, (j) Avogadro's law, (k) ideal gas, (l) critical temperature, (m) critical pressure, (n) van der Waals forces.

22 **Pressure** How many (a) lbs/in², (b) kg/m², (c) kPa of nitrogen are required to balance 1.00 atm?

23 **Pressure** Early references describing water wells state that suction pumps bring water to the surface from a maximum depth of only 34 feet. Explain.

24 **Boyle's law** A gas occupies 2.25 ℓ at a pressure of 3.00 atm. At constant temperature, what is the pressure in torr of the gas if it is allowed to expand into a 3.00 ℓ container?

25 **Boyle's law** A sample of gas occupies 24.1 ml at 763 torr. Calculate the volume at 700 torr, temperature constant.

26 **K** Convert the following temperatures to the kelvin temperature scale: (a) 0 °C, (b) −250.10 °C, (c) 200 °C, (d) 4.00 × 10² °C, (e) −80 °C.

27 **°C** Convert the following temperatures to °C: (a) 173 K, (b) 50.0 K, (c) 593 K.

28 **Charles' law** A sample of hydrogen gas occupies 4.2 ℓ at 30 °C and 1.0 atm. Calculate its volume at −30 °C and 1.0 atm.

29 **Charles' law** The volume of a gas is 273 ml at STP. Calculate the volume of the gas at 80.0 °C, pressure constant.

30 **Gas volume** A 4.0 ℓ heavy steel cylinder is filled with nitrogen at 20 °C and 2.0 atm. What is the volume of nitrogen in the same cylinder at 100 °C and 4.0 atm?

31 **Gas laws** The density of oxygen gas is 1.429 g/ℓ at STP. Calculate the density at 300 °C, pressure constant.

32 **Charles' law** A gas sample occupies 4.00 ℓ at 30.0 °C and 1.00 atm. If it is allowed to expand into a 10.00 ℓ

container at constant pressure, what should be the temperature of the gas?

33 Relate the increase in the average speed of gas molecules as the temperature increases at constant volume to an increase in pressure.

34 **Gas laws** A gas sample occupies 150 ml at 20.0 °C and 700 torr. Calculate the volume of the gas at STP.

35 **Gas laws** If 300 ft^3 of gas is contained in a weather balloon at ground level, 1.00 atm and 60.0 °F, what will be the volume of the gas at 3.0 km (about 10,000 ft), 0.690 atm and 23.3 °F? Assume that the pressure and temperature of the gas in the balloon are the same as the pressure and temperature outside the balloon at all altitudes.

36 0.280 g of a gas occupies 230 ml at 550 torr and 25.0 °C. Calculate the density of the gas, in g/ml, at STP.

37 A tire is filled with air to an absolute pressure of 22 lb/in^2 at 56 °F. After sustained use, the air temperature in the tire reaches 200 °F. Assuming the volume of the tire is constant, find the absolute pressure in the tire at 200 °F (a) in lb/in^2 and (b) in kPa. 1 atm = 14.7 lb/in^2 = 101 kPa.

38 The density of a gas is 1.46 g/ℓ at STP. Find the density of the gas at 50.0 °C and 730 torr.

39 A gas occupies 6.56 ℓ at -10.5 °C and 1.21×10^5 Pa. Find its volume at 27.0 °C and 5.55×10^5 Pa.

40 **Graham's law** A balloon with a gas-tight seal nevertheless gradually deflates. Explain.

41 **Kinetic theory** Explain (a) "Hot air rises," though air is of constant pressure. (b) Should a mass of hot air near the ground rise into a higher colder layer? (c) Should a mass of cold air near the ground rise into a higher warmer layer*? Explain.

42 **Kinetic theory** Use the kinetic theory to explain each of the following observations: (a) A weather balloon is only half-filled before it is released to record high altitude radiation. (b) A warning is printed on aerosol spray cans not to dispose of the can in an incinerator.

43 **Molecular speeds** From the following list, pick the gas molecule with (a) the highest and (b) the lowest average speed at 25 °C. (c) What statement can you make about their kinetic energies? (Relative masses are given in parentheses.) SO_2(64), O_2(32), H_2(2.0), Ar (40), He (4).

*Known as a temperature inversion, this condition is an important factor in smog formation (Chap. 6).

44 **Real gases** At 200 atm and 0 °C, $PV = 17.7$ liter atm for methane and 5.6 liter atm for ammonia. (a) In which gas is the molecular attractive force stronger? (b) Which gas should have the higher critical temperature?

45 A 5.0 ℓ empty steel tank at a fixed temperature is loaded with 2.0×10^{24} molecules of oxygen. The pressure is 1.2 atm. 4.0×10^{24} molecules of nitrogen are now added to the tank. (a) What is the volume of nitrogen in the tank? (b) What is the pressure of nitrogen in the tank? (c) What is the total pressure of gases in the tank?

46 The molecules of gas A are three times heavier than the molecules of gas B. 200 molecules of each gas are added to separate containers of equal volume at the same temperature. Will the pressures of the two gases be identical? If they are not, which gas will exert the higher pressure?

47 (a) There are two containers containing different gases: one at 0.0 °C and 1.0 atm, and the second at 273 °C and 0.10 atm. Is the average kinetic energy of the molecules of these gases the same? If not, for which gas is the average kinetic energy higher? (b) The molecules of two gases, A and B, are at the same temperature; the mass of molecule A is three times the mass of molecule B. (i) Is the average kinetic energy of the molecules of A the same as, smaller than, or larger than the average kinetic energy of the molecules of B? (ii) Is the average speed of the molecules of A the same as, smaller than, or larger than the average speed of the molecules of B? If the speeds differ, which molecules move faster?

48 A container at 250 °C holds 4.00×10^{23} molecules at 800 torr. The container is illuminated with a light beam that causes molecules to combine, reducing the number to 1.00×10^{23} molecules. What is the final pressure in the container?

49 (a) A 100.0 ml container holds 2.50×10^{20} molecules of H_2 at 1.00 atm at a fixed temperature. The volume of one H_2 molecule is 1.12×10^{-23} ml. What fraction of the volume of the gas is occupied by the molecules of the gas? (b) At 1.00×10^3 atm, the volume of the gas (temperature constant) is 0.0030 ml; what fraction of the volume is now occupied by the volume of the molecules?

50 **Partial pressures** A mixture of helium and oxygen is stored at constant temperature in a container of fixed volume, 4.0 ℓ, at 1.5 atm. All the oxygen is then removed. The pressure is now 500 torr. What are now (a) the volume and (b) the pressure of the helium?

51 **Avogadro's law** A 100.0 ml container holds 3.1×10^{12} molecules of oxygen at fixed temperature and

pressure. How many molecules (a) of SO_2, 2 times as massive as O_2, and (b) of nitrogen, 0.88 times as massive as O_2, are in a 100.0 ml container at the same temperature and pressure?

52 At STP, an unknown gas diffuses 1.50 times faster than nitrogen. (a) What is the density of the unknown gas if the density of nitrogen is 1.25 g/ℓ? (b) If a nitrogen molecule has a mass of 28 mass units, what is the mass of the unknown molecule?

53 Dalton's law A 500 ml flask containing neon at 200 torr is connected to a second 500 ml flask containing helium at 800 torr. The gases are allowed to diffuse into each other, temperature constant. Calculate (a) the partial pressure of each gas, and (b) the total pressure in the final mixture.

54 If 1.00 liter of hydrogen, H_2, density 0.090 g/ℓ, diffuses in 1.00 minute, calculate the time required for 1.00 liter of nitrogen, N_2, density 1.25 g/ℓ, to diffuse at the same conditions.

55 Library Read one of the following:

(a) "Near Zero," D. K. C. MacDonald, Chapter 1, Science Study Series, Doubleday Anchor Books, Garden City, New York, 1961.
(b) "Robert Boyle," Marie Hall, *Scientific American,* page 96, August 1967.
(c) "Whatever Happened to Air Bags?", *Consumer Reports,* April 1976, page 190, April 1977, page 188.
(d) "Auto Safety; Controversial Air Bag Issue," *Science,* Volume 193, 24 Sept. 1976, page 1219.

ADDITIONAL PROBLEMS

56 (a) An experiment requires the addition of 2.00 ℓ of ammonia, NH_3, at STP. How many experiments can be run if the source of NH_3 is a 100 liter tank at 25 °C and 5.00 atm? (b) Ammonia stops flowing from the tank when its pressure is reduced to 1.00 atm. What volume of NH_3 remains in the tank when it is shipped back to the manufacturer for refilling?

57 (a) 1.00 ml of solid titanium dioxide, TiO_2 (white solid, melting point 1830 °C), subjected to 1.6×10^3 atm, temperature constant, is reduced only to 0.94 ml. Explain. (b) On the other hand, solid neon is compressed by $\frac{1}{5}$ of its original volume by the application of 5×10^3 atm. Which solid, neon or TiO_2, has a larger fraction of empty space between molecules? Explain.

58 A very thin 200 ml glass bulb containing a gas at 900 torr is placed in a 1.00 liter flask, which is then loaded with a gas at 60 torr. The thin bulb is then broken. What is the pressure in the flask (temperature constant)?

59 Gas was also termed "wild" (*spiritus sylvestria*) since it could not "be constrained by vessels nor reduced into a visible body." Is this (17th century) statement correct? If not, correct it.

60 The critical temperature of ammonia is 406 K and its

critical pressure is 112 atm. At what temperature are the densities of liquid and gaseous ammonia identical? What phase is present at 410 K and 112 atm—liquid, gas, or both?

61 4.0×10^{24} molecules of CO_2 and 2.0×10^{24} molecules of N_2 are added to the same container, giving a total pressure of 18 atm. Find the partial pressure of each gas.

62 For a given mass of an ideal gas, use a graph to show the relationship between: (a) P and V when T is constant; (b) PV and P when T is constant; (c) PV and V when T is constant; (d) P and T when V is constant; (e) V and T when P is constant.

63 One theory suggests that, in the formation of our solar system, the contraction of gaseous hydrogen atoms continued until the temperature increased to 2.0×10^7 °C and the pressure increased to 7.0×10^9 atm, sufficient to start a thermonuclear reaction (Chap. 17). Starting with 1.0 ml of gaseous hydrogen atoms at STP, having a mass of 4.5×10^{-5} g, calculate the density of gaseous hydrogen atoms (a) at STP; (b) at 2×10^7 °C and 7×10^9 atm. Assume that the sample behaves as an ideal gas. (c) What is the percentage increase in density? (d) Which answer, (a) or (b), most likely agrees with experimental results? (e) Is the other answer too small or too large?

ANSWERS

1 (a) 10.0 g, 20 ℓ
  (b) 10.0 g, 500 ℓ
3 (a) 8.00×10^2 kg/cm²
  (b) 3.20×10^2 kg/cm²

5 (a) (i) 0.500 atm, (ii) 0.100 atm
  (b) (i) 380 torr, (ii) 400 torr, (iii) 950 torr
  (c) 5.07×10^4 Pa
  (d) 9.97×10^{-6} atm

7 (a) 1000 atm
  (b) 7.60×10^5 torr
  (c) 1.01×10^5 kPa
8 2.66 ℓ
9 (a) 323 K
  (b) 200 K
10 5.50 ℓ
11 4.39 atm
12 39.8 ml
13 682 torr, 20.0 ℓ
14 2.83 times faster
17 (c) 11.00 atm
19 (a) 4 K; (b) gas
22 (a) 14.7 lb/in^2
  (b) 1.04×10^4 kg/m^2
  (c) 101 kPa
24 2.25 atm
25 26.3 ml
26 (a) 273 K
  (b) 22.9 K
  (c) 473 K
  (d) 6.73×10^2 K
  (e) 193 K
27 (a) -100 °C
  (b) -223 °C
  (c) 320 °C
28 3.4 ℓ
29 353 ml
30 4.0 ℓ
31 0.681 g/ℓ
32 485 °C
34 129 ml

35 412 ft^3
36 1.84×10^{-3} g/ml
37 (a) 28 lb/in^2, (b) 1.9×10^2 kPa
38 1.19 g/ℓ
39 1.63 ℓ
43 (a) H_2, (b) SO_2
44 (a), (b) NH_3
45 (a) 5.0 ℓ
  (b) 2.4 atm
  (c) 3.6 atm
46 identical
48 200 torr
49 (a) 2.80×10^{-5}
  (b) 0.93
50 (a) 4.0 ℓ
  (b) 500 torr
51 (a), (b) 3.1×10^{12} molecules
52 (a) 0.556 g/ℓ, (b) 16 mass units
53 (a) 100 torr, 400 torr
  (b) 500 torr
54 3.7 min
56 (a) 183 experiments
  (b) 100 ℓ
58 228 torr
60 406 K, gas
61 12 atm CO_2, 6.0 atm N_2
63 (a) 4.5×10^{-2} g/ℓ
  (b) 4.5×10^3 g/ℓ (5×10^3 g/ℓ)
  (c) 1×10^7 %
  (d) (a)
  (e) too large

GLOSSARY

absolute temperature scale See **kelvin temperature scale.**
absolute zero $T = 0$ K, the lowest possible temperature that a substance may have, -273.15 °C; the kinetic theory of gases tells us that it is the temperature at which the kinetic energy of a molecule is zero.
Avogadro's law Equal volumes of gases at the same temperature and same pressure contain equal numbers of molecules, regardless of the mass of the molecules.
barometer A device for measuring atmospheric pressure; the pressure is generally measured as the height of a liquid column—usually mercury—sustained by the pressure.
Boyle's law When the pressure or the volume of a fixed mass of a gas is changed at constant temperature, the product of the pressure and the volume remains constant.
Charles' law The volume of a fixed mass of a gas at constant pressure is directly proportional to the absolute temperature (or the pressure of the gas is directly proportional to the absolute temperature at constant volume).

critical pressure The pressure in a sealed container at the critical temperature. See **critical temperature.**
critical temperature The temperature above which a gas cannot exist as a liquid regardless of the applied pressure.
Dalton's law of partial pressures The total pressure of a mixture of gases is the sum of the partial pressures of the individual gases in the mixture. See **partial pressure.**
diffusion The spreading of a substance throughout the space available to it. See **effusion.** Diffusion and effusion rates are nearly the same for a given substance.
effusion The escape of a gas through a small hole. See **diffusion.**
erg A unit of energy; 10^7 ergs (exactly) = 1 joule.
Graham's law The rate of diffusion of a gas is inversely proportional to the square root of its density.
ideal gas A fictitious gas that follows exactly the gas laws summarized as $PV \propto NT$ over all ranges of temperature and pressure.
intermolecular attractive forces See **van der Waals forces.**

kelvin temperature scale The SI unit of temperature; based on the properties of gases, its zero point is $-273.15\ ^\circ C$ so that $K = {}^\circ C + 273.15$. Also known as the absolute temperature scale.

kinetic energy The energy of motion, given by $\frac{1}{2}\,mv^2$.

kinetic molecular theory The theoretical model (set of assumptions) that explains the behavior of gases, summarized in the expression $PV \propto NT$.

manometer A device for measuring gas pressures.

partial pressure The pressure that a gas in a mixture of gases would exert if it alone occupied the same container as the mixture at the same temperature. See **Dalton's law of partial pressures.**

pascal SI unit of pressure.

pressure The force per unit area; pressure = force/area over which the force is distributed; for a liquid, pressure = density of liquid $\times$ depth of liquid.

standard atmosphere 1 atm; it equals 760 torr (exactly) or 1.01×10^5 pascals.

standard conditions 1 atm and 0 °C.

temperature According to the kinetic theory of gases, it is a measure of the average kinetic energy of a molecule; the average kinetic energy of gas molecules is directly proportional to the absolute temperature.

torr A unit of pressure, 1 torr = 1 mm Hg.

van der Waals equation An equation applicable to real gases; it contains experimentally determined constants that correct the ideal gas equation for the volume occupied by molecules and for the attractive forces between them.

van der Waals forces The forces of attraction existing between molecules. Also known as intermolecular attractive forces.

LIQUIDS AND SOLIDS   3

LIQUIDS, SOLIDS, AND KINETIC THEORY _____ 3.1

In Chapter 2, we observed that gases can be converted into liquids or solids by lowering the temperature and/or increasing the pressure. Cooling a gas decreases the average kinetic energy and, therefore, the speed of the molecules. At lower speeds, the molecules have a greater chance to respond to the attractive forces that exist between them. If the temperature is low enough, the molecules are brought sufficiently close to form a liquid. Increasing the pressure on a gas also forces the molecules together. In the liquid state, the molecules are not moving as independently of each other or as freely as they are in the gaseous state. The motion of the molecules is greatly restricted by the attractive forces between them. The molecules in the liquid, therefore, behave in a more orderly fashion than those in the gaseous state.

Liquids have definite volumes but not definite shapes. Like gases, they assume the shape of their container. Liquids, under ordinary conditions, have greater density than gases. For example, 1.0 g of water vapor occupies about 4.3×10^4 ml at room conditions, but as a liquid it occupies only 1.0 ml. That is, liquid water is about 4.3×10^4 times more dense than water vapor. The volume of a given mass of gas decreases greatly when it changes to a liquid because the molecules are brought very much closer together. Since the molecules are now very crowded and molecules themselves are difficult to compress (page 64), liquids are only slightly compressible. But they are sufficiently compressible to be useful in hydraulic brake systems.

A vapor is a gaseous substance that can be condensed to a liquid or a solid at a given temperature by increasing its pressure.

One drop of food (water soluble) coloring dye added to a beaker of water slowly diffuses throughout the water. Since molecular motion is more restricted in a liquid, diffusion is much slower in liquids than in gases.

Example 1

(a) How could you increase the rate of diffusion of a food coloring dye in water?
(b) Explain the increase in terms of kinetic theory.

Answer

The rate of diffusion in liquids can be increased by stirring or heating the liquid. Stirring moves the molecules of the dye through the liquid, increasing the rate of mixing. Heating increases the motion (speed) of the molecules, increasing the rate of mixing.

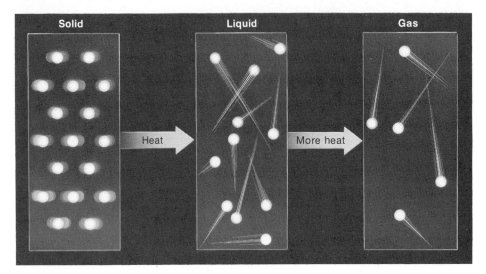

The molecules are in fixed positions about which they vibrate.

The molecules are no longer in a highly ordered arrangement and move more freely than in the solid.

The molecules are almost completely randomly arranged and relatively independent of each other.

FIGURE 3.1 Representation of the general arrangement of molecules in the solid, liquid, and gaseous states. Increasing the temperature causes the molecules to move faster and causes an increase in distance between the molecules. The density of a substance, therefore, usually decreases as it changes from solid to liquid to gas. The liquid is an intermediate state between the highly ordered arrangement of the solid and the almost completely random arrangement of the molecules in the gas.

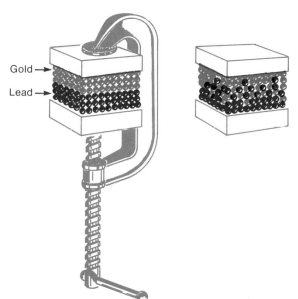

Gold →

Lead →

FIGURE 3.2 Illustrating the diffusion of solids. A block of gold is placed on top of a block of lead and pressure is applied. After an extended period of time, it is found that some of the gold particles have diffused into the lead, and that some of the lead has diffused into the gold.

Cooling a liquid eventually causes solidification. A solid has a definite shape and volume. Molecular motion in a solid, then, is even more restricted than in a liquid; the molecules are more orderly than they are in the liquid state. The density of most solids is only slightly greater* than that of the corresponding liquid, indicating that molecules in a solid are only slightly more crowded than they are in the corresponding liquid. However, solids are extremely difficult to compress (noncompressible), indicating that the molecules are practically touching one another; they vibrate slightly over more or less fixed sites.

Alternatively, consider the heating of a solid. As the kinetic energy of the molecules increases by heating, they vibrate faster and faster. Eventually, they acquire enough energy to break up their fixed arrangement in solids and assume the more random arrangement of molecules in liquids. The molecules are arranged in a more disorderly fashion than in the corresponding solid. Further heating causes molecules to acquire more and more kinetic energy, and eventually, some of the molecules leave the liquid surface and enter the gas phase. The molecules are now most disorderly. In fact, the word gas is derived from the Greek word *chaos,* meaning great confusion. The general arrangement of molecules in the three states of matter is represented in Fig. 3.1.

Johannes von Helmont invented (1624) the word "gas."

Diffusion of solids occurs, as illustrated in Fig. 3.2. However, owing to the very limited motion of the molecules, diffusion of solids is generally very slow. Diffusion of solids finds a number of commercial applications in the manufacture of glass, ceramics, and screens for television tubes.**

ARRANGEMENT OF MOLECULES IN SOLIDS _____ 3.2

When molecules are fixed—"frozen"—in definite positions, the solid is called a **crystal.** In a crystal, the particles are packed together in a regular, orderly way. In one of these arrangements, the particles occupy the corners and the centers of cubes. Since a particle occupies the center of a cube, the arrangement is called a **body-centered cubic** packing. Typical is the crystal structure of hexamethylenetetramine, $N_4(CH_2)_6$, used as a urinary antiseptic (*Urotropin*) and in the manufacture of the explosive cyclonite. This arrangement is illustrated in Fig. 3.3. Another very common arrangement is called **face-centered cubic** packing. It is so called because the particles are located at the eight corners and in the center of each of the six sides of a cube (Fig. 3.4). Carbon dioxide, CO_2, nitrogen, N_2, and neon, Ne, are typical of the substances that crystallize in this arrangement. The extension of these packing arrangements in three dimensions generates a visible crystal, illustrated in Fig. 3.5 for carbon dioxide.

Sublimes at 263 °C.

Crystalline solids are characterized by sharp melting (freezing) points (page 97). The temperature of the liquid remains fixed until it is completely crystallized. The molecules are small enough and move rapidly enough to find suitable sites in the solid. On the other hand, liquids composed of large, complicated molecules, too slow-moving to orient themselves into a definite and orderly arrangement, do not form crystals. They do not possess definite freezing (melting) points. Rather, they solidify over a temperature range and are therefore regarded as stable supercooled

---

* Some important exceptions exist. Water pipes may burst if the water in them freezes, indicating that the density of the solid is smaller than that of liquid water; the volume therefore increases as the water freezes, and ice floats on water (page 264).

** The General Electric Company has developed a technique for diffusing particles of one solid into the surface of another for the purpose of obtaining surface properties quite different from those of the bulk of the material. The process, called metalliding, involves a high-temperature electrolysis (Chap. 15).

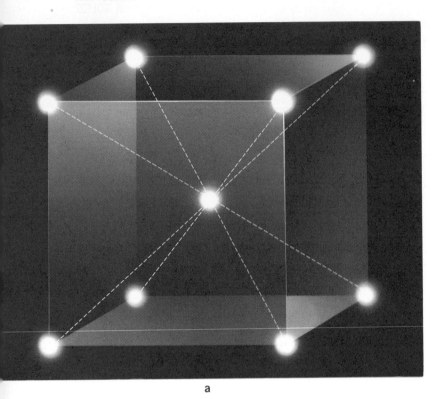

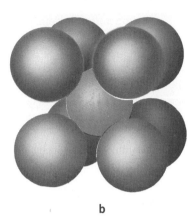

a

b

FIGURE 3.3 In the body-centered cubic arrangement, a particle (molecule, atom, or ion) is located at each of the eight corners of the cube and one particle is in the center of the cube. (a) The spheres represent the molecules of hexamethylenetetramine, $N_4(CH_2)_6$. Actually, the particles are closely packed, as shown in (b).

FIGURE 3.4 In the face-centered cubic arrangement, a particle (molecule, atom, or ion) is located at each of the eight corners of the cube and one particle is at the center of each of the six sides of the cube. (a) The spheres represent the molecules of nitrogen, N_2, or carbon dioxide, CO_2. (b) The closely packed model.

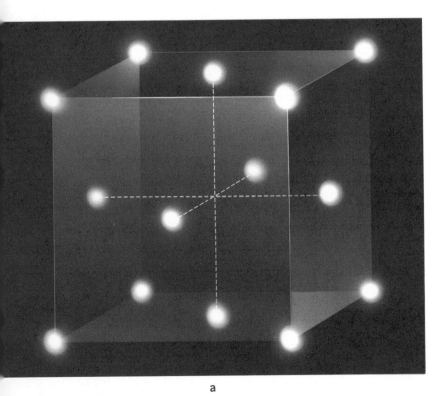

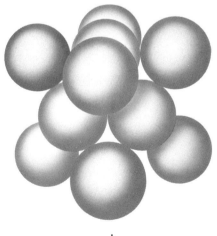

a

b

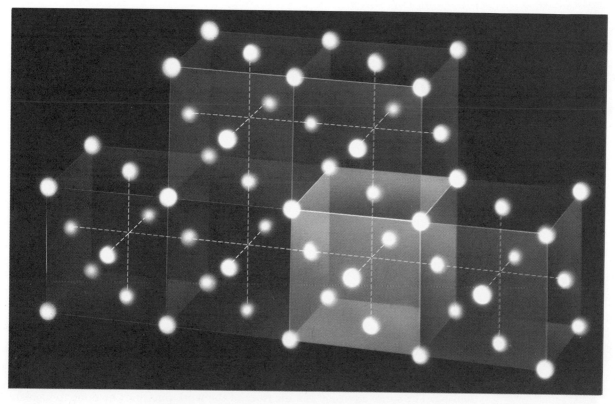

FIGURE 3.5 The repetition of the face-centered cubic arrangement of carbon dioxide (heavy lines) leading to the formation of a visible crystal.

liquids (page 101). Such solids are called **amorphous.** Tars, charcoals, gums, and glasses (Chap. 23) are typical amorphous solids. But no real solids contain molecules that are perfectly arranged as illustrated in our figures, nor are amorphous solids completely devoid of orderly arrangements. However, the high degree of order existing throughout a crystalline solid is lacking in amorphous solids.

From amorphe, the Greek word for "without shape."

PROPERTIES OF LIQUIDS_____3.3

It is not difficult to visualize a gas as composed of molecules widely spaced, moving through empty space, and colliding with each other and with the walls of the container. It is not difficult to visualize a solid as a regular three-dimensional structure of particles held together by attractive forces. On the other hand, it is difficult to visualize a liquid. It is generally agreed that the liquid is intermediate in structure between gas and solid. But the problem of exact liquid structure is very much unresolved. The particles are generally somewhat further apart than in a solid, and they do not possess the order of a solid. They are more disordered than the solid but not as disordered as the gas. We can, nevertheless, discuss several physical properties of liquids in terms of kinetic theory.

The nature of forces between particles in liquids and solids is discussed in Chapters 8 and 20.

Surface Tension   If two insoluble liquids with unequal densities are mixed, the substance with the smaller density will float on top. Yet, if carefully done, a sewing needle (density about 8 g/ml) can be floated on the surface of water (density

Molecule on surface is attracted only
by molecules below and beside it;
there are practically no molecules
above it.

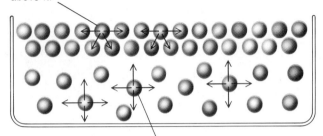

Molecules in body of liquid attracted
equally on all sides by surrounding
molecules.

FIGURE 3.6 Representation of molecules in a liquid, showing the forces of attraction that exist between the molecules. The molecules at the surface, unlike the molecules in the body of the liquid, are attracted unevenly and tend to be pulled inward.

1 g/ml). The water surface behaves as if there were an invisible "skin" or membrane stretched over it, through which the needle must penetrate to sink. Consider a collection of molecules in a liquid, shown in Fig. 3.6. A molecule in the body of the liquid is attracted equally in all directions by molecules surrounding it. A molecule on the surface, however, is attracted only by molecules below and beside it. Therefore, the surface molecules feel an unbalanced attraction and are pulled inward. This inward pull causes the molecules at the surface to jam closer together; the surface area tends to become smaller, giving rise to the membrane effect, called **surface tension.** The surface tension is a measure of the work that must be done to increase the surface area of a liquid.

Solids also have a surface tension, much higher than liquids and very difficult to measure accurately.

Example 2

Liquid drops tend to assume spherical shapes—that is, shapes like a globe or ball. Explain.

Answer

Surface tension causes a liquid drop to contract to the smallest possible surface area. The smallest surface area for a given volume of liquid is a sphere.

A 1 cm³ cube has a larger surface area than a 1 cm³ sphere.

Astronauts have observed that when liquids are spilled in a spaceship at zero gravity, the drops are perfect spheres.

Surface tension is also responsible for the curved surface of liquids in narrow tubes, shown in Fig. 3.7. The molecules in the water surface are more strongly attracted to the glass than to other water molecules, pulling the surface upward (Fig. 3.7a). On the other hand, a mercury surface curves in the opposite direction (Fig. 3.7b). The forces of attraction between mercury molecules are stronger than the attraction of the glass for the mercury molecules, and the liquid is depressed (tends to take a spherical shape).*

---

*Respiratory Distress Syndrome (RDS) is a leading cause of death among small or premature babies. Molecules in the lining of immature lungs have an abnormally high surface tension. These molecules strongly attract each other, causing the collapse of the air cells in the lungs. It becomes difficult for the baby to breathe, and death results from exhaustion and oxygen starvation.

Specific Heat As a liquid is heated, its temperature rises and the average kinetic energy and speed of its molecules increase. The amount of heat that must be supplied to increase the temperature of a liquid depends on the amount of liquid, the change in temperature, and the kind of molecules involved. This difference among molecules is reflected in the different amounts of heat required to increase the temperatures of equal masses of two liquids by the same number of degrees. For example, 1.00 cal (page 25) is required to increase the temperature of 1.00 g of water 1.00 °C, but only 0.54 cal is necessary to increase the temperature of 1.00 g of ethyl alcohol 1.00 °C. The number of calories required to raise the temperature of 1.00 g of a substance 1.00 °C is called its **specific heat.** Therefore, the units of specific heat are cal/(g °C). The specific heats of some common liquids are given in Table 3.1.

TABLE 3.1
**SPECIFIC HEATS OF SOME
COMMON LIQUIDS AT 0 °C***

| | SPECIFIC HEAT | |
SUBSTANCE	$\dfrac{cal}{g \ ^\circ C}$	$\dfrac{J}{g \ ^\circ C}$
Water	1.00	4.18
Mercury	0.033	0.14
Carbon tetrachloride	0.198	0.828
Chloroform	0.232	0.971
Ethyl alcohol	0.535	2.24

*Specific heats are not constants; they depend on the state and temperature of a particular substance. For example, the specific heat of ice is about 0.5 cal/(g °C), and the specific heat of liquid water is 1.00129 cal/(g °C) at 10 °C and 0.99854 cal/(g °C) at 50 °C.

The specific heat also represents the number of calories that are *released* or liberated when 1.00 g of a substance *cools* 1.00 °C. As the temperature decreases, the average kinetic energies of molecules decrease, and heat is liberated to the surroundings.

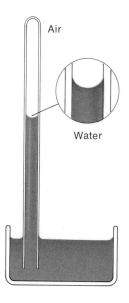

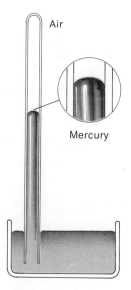

FIGURE 3.7 Illustrating the combined effects of surface tension and the attraction of glass on water and mercury in a narrow tube. The curved surface is called a **meniscus,** from *meniskos,* the Greek word for crescent moon.

Example 3

How many calories are necessary to heat 10.0 g of water from 0 °C to 30.0 °C?

Answer

1.00 cal is required to increase the temperature of each gram of water 1 °C; therefore,

$$\text{specific heat, } \frac{cal}{g \ ^\circ\!\!\!/C} \times \text{mass, } \not{g} \times \text{temperature change, } ^\circ\!\!\!/C = cal$$

$$1.00 \frac{cal}{\not{g} \ ^\circ\!\!\!/C} \times 10.0 \not{g} \times 30.0 \ ^\circ\!\!\!/C = 300 \text{ cal}$$

Example 4

How many calories are liberated when 10.0 g of water is cooled from 80.0 °C to 50.0 °C?

Answer

1.00 g of water liberates 1.00 cal for each degree it cools. Therefore, the number of calories liberated by 10.0 g is given by

$$1.00 \frac{cal}{\cancel{g}\,°\cancel{C}} \times 10.0 \cancel{g} \times 30.0 \,°\cancel{C} = 300 \text{ cal}$$

PROBLEM 1   How many calories are required to increase the temperature of (a) 50 g of water from 20 °C to 45 °C; (b) 30 g of ethyl alcohol (see Table 3.1, page 89) from 27 °C to 47 °C?

PROBLEM 2   How many calories are liberated when 35 g of ethyl alcohol cool from 65 °C to 35 °C?

Evaporation   The molecules in a liquid are in continual motion, the speed depending on the temperature. As with gases, there is a distribution of speeds at any temperature; some molecules move more rapidly than others. Molecules which have a greater than average speed can overcome intermolecular forces, leave the liquid surface, and so form a **vapor.** If the molecule returns to the liquid, there is no net change. If, however, collisions with air molecules or a breeze prevent the molecule's return, there is a decrease in the mass of the liquid. The escape of molecules from the surface of a liquid into the gas phase is called **evaporation** (Fig. 3.8) and, in an open container, this process continues until all of the liquid has evaporated. Since the molecules with the highest average kinetic energy leave the liquid, there is a decrease in the average kinetic energy of the remaining molecules. This corresponds to a lower temperature; hence, evaporation produces a cooling effect, and the temperature of the remaining liquid decreases. Thus, to keep the temperature of an evaporating liquid constant, heat must be added.

Also known as vaporization.

Example 5

How can the rate of evaporation of a liquid be increased?

Answer

Increasing the number of molecules that leave the liquid surface and are carried away increases the rate of evaporation. Heating a liquid increases the number of

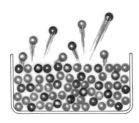
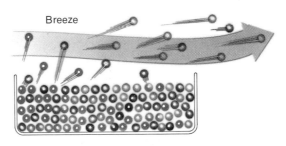

Breeze

a

b   Larger surface area

FIGURE 3.8 Evaporation of a liquid. The molecules with the highest average kinetic energy escape from the surface of a liquid (a), and some are carried away. Heating, increasing the surface area (b), and providing a breeze increase the rate of evaporation.

molecules having sufficient kinetic energy to escape from the liquid. A breeze across the container increases the rate of evaporation by preventing the return of molecules to the liquid. Increasing the surface area of the liquid (putting the liquid into a wider container) also makes it possible for more molecules to leave the surface (Fig. 3.8b).

PROBLEM 3   **Will a liquid evaporate faster into a vacuum or into air at the same temperature? Explain.**

PROBLEM 4   **How is the rate of evaporation affected if a container is insulated from its surroundings; that is, if no heat can flow into the container?**

The body cools because of evaporation of moisture from the skin. The greater the breeze, the faster the rate of evaporation and the colder one feels. The "Wind-Chill Index," reported by the Weather Bureau, is an attempt to relate body-heat losses at a given temperature to wind speed; in other words, the extent to which the wind adds to the chilling effect of lower temperatures. For example, the cooling effect of a 10 mile per hour (mph) wind at 20 °F (−6.7 °C) is the same as 2 °F (−17 °C) with zero   *16 km/h* wind speed; the cooling effect of a 50 mph (80 km/h) wind at 30 °F (−1.1 °C, *moderately cold*) is the same as −7 °F (−22 °C, *very cold*) with zero wind.

Vapor Pressure   If a liquid is placed in a closed container at a given temperature, only a small quantity evaporates. It is impossible for molecules which have escaped into the gas phase to leave the container. However, as more and more of the liquid evaporates, the number of molecules in the gas phase increases and the chance that they strike the surface and return to the liquid phase also increases. The change from gas phase (vapor) to liquid phase is called **condensation.** Eventually, the rate of   *Also known as* condensation becomes the same as the rate of evaporation. The number of molecules   *liquefaction.* escaping per second from the liquid and the number returning per second to the liquid are the same.

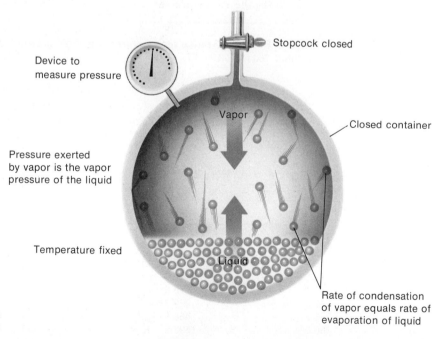

FIGURE 3.9   Illustrating   the meaning of vapor pressure of a liquid.

The condition in which the rates of two *opposing* changes are the same is very important in chemistry and is known as **dynamic equilibrium** or, simply, **equilibrium.** Equilibrium is characterized by *two opposing changes going on at the same time and at the same rate,* so that the net effect is *no change.* In this particular case, at equilibrium, evaporation and condensation are occurring at the same rate, so that the mass of liquid and the number of molecules in the vapor in the closed container remain constant. For every molecule that leaves the liquid, another returns to the liquid. The *pressure* exerted by the vapor that is in *equilibrium* with the liquid, at a given temperature, is called the **vapor pressure of the liquid** at that temperature, shown in Fig. 3.9. This equilibrium may be represented as

$$\text{liquid} \underset{\text{condensation}}{\overset{\text{evaporation}}{\rightleftharpoons}} \text{vapor} \; (\textit{vapor pressure of the liquid})$$

(*temperature constant*)

The double arrow means that both actions take place at the same time.

The vapor pressure is a characteristic property of a given liquid; it also depends on the temperature. On increasing the temperature, a greater number of molecules acquire sufficient energy to enter the vapor and the vapor pressure increases. Table 3.2 and Fig. 3.10 illustrate typical vapor pressure–temperature data for several liquids. Fig. 3.10 allows us to find the vapor pressure over a range of temperatures.

Example 6

From Fig. 3.10, approximate the vapor pressure (a) of ethyl alcohol at 25 °C, and (b) of carbon tetrachloride at 70 °C.

Answer

From Fig. 3.10, (a) the vapor pressure of ethyl alcohol at 25 °C is about 60 torr, and (b) the vapor pressure of carbon tetrachloride at 70 °C is about 635 torr.

PROBLEM 5   **At what temperature is the vapor pressure (a) of water 760 torr; (b) of ethyl alcohol 760 torr? Use Fig. 3.10.**

Evaporation requires that molecules overcome the attractive forces that hold them in the liquid state. Thus, at a given temperature, liquids with strong attractive forces have fewer molecules in the vapor phase and, therefore, a smaller vapor pressure than liquids with weak attractive forces.

TABLE 3.2
VAPOR PRESSURES OF WATER, ETHYL ALCOHOL, AND BENZENE

t, °C	WATER, torr	ETHYL ALCOHOL, torr	BENZENE, torr
−10	2.1	5.6	15
0	4.6	12.2	27
10	9.2	23.6	45
20	17.5	43.9	74
30	31.8	78.8	118
50	92.5	222.2	271
75	289.1	666.1	643
100	760.0	1693.3	1360

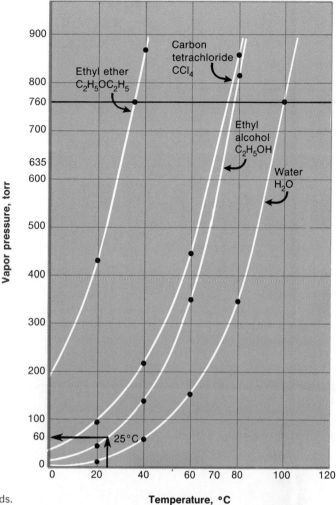

FIGURE 3.10 Vapor pressures of some common liquids.

Example 7

From the data in Fig. 3.10, determine which of the four liquids has the strongest intermolecular attractive force.

Answer

At any particular temperature, for example, 20 °C, water has the *lowest vapor pressure* (water, 17.5 torr; ethyl alcohol, 43.9 torr; carbon tetrachloride, 91 torr; ethyl ether, 422 torr) and, therefore, the *strongest intermolecular attractive force*.

Pressure of a Gas Confined by a Liquid For convenience, many gases are collected in the laboratory by displacement of water. A container filled with water is immersed in a pan also filled with water, so that no air enters the container. As the gas is transferred to the container, it pushes water out of the container, as shown in Fig. 3.11a. If the container is calibrated for volume, the gas volume can be measured, as illustrated in Fig. 3.11b. The volume of the gas is 37.2 ml at 29.0 °C and p_{gas}. But p_{gas}

The gas collected, of course, must be insoluble in the liquid being displaced.

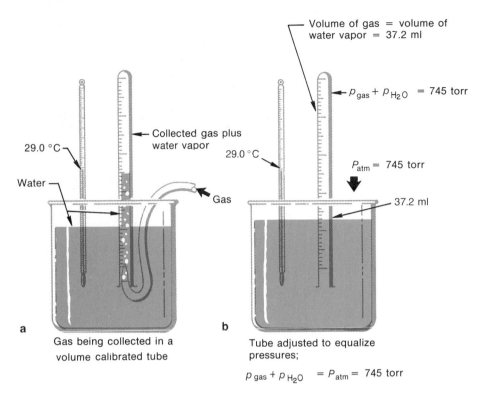

FIGURE 3.11 (a) Collecting a gas by displacement of water. (b) Measuring the volume of the collected gas.
   The volume-calibrated tube is moved up or down so that the water levels in the tube and outside the tube are equal. In this position, the sum of the pressures of the gas and water vapor in the tube equals the barometric pressure (P_{atm}).

is unknown. However, since $p_{gas} + p_{H_2O} = p_{atm} = 745$ torr, we need to know only the vapor pressure of water at 29 °C to determine p_{gas}. The vapor pressures of water at various temperatures are obtained from vapor pressure tables. The vapor pressure of water at 29 °C is 30 torr. Then, the pressure of the gas is the measured atmospheric pressure less the vapor pressure of water:

$$p_{gas} = p_{atm} - p_{H_2O} = 745 \text{ torr} - 30 \text{ torr} = 715 \text{ torr}$$

We can now record that 37.2 ml of gas at 29.0 °C and 715 torr were collected.
   Frequently, however, the volume of a collected gas at standard conditions (STP) is desired:

Example 8

A chemical reaction produces hydrogen gas collected by displacement of water as was shown in Fig. 3.11b. After adjusting the tube so that the pressures are equalized, the gas volume is 37.2 ml. The temperature is 29.0 °C and the barometric pressure is 745 torr. p_{H_2O} at 29.0 °C = 30 torr. (a) What is the volume of the hydrogen at STP? (b) What is the volume of the water vapor at STP? Assume that the gas and the water vapor behave as ideal gases.

Answer

(a) The temperature of the hydrogen is 302 K (29.0 °C + 273) and its pressure
is 715 torr:

$$p_{H_2} = 745 \text{ torr} - 30 \text{ torr} = 715 \text{ torr}$$

Thus, 37.2 ml of hydrogen is collected at 302 K and 715 torr. Its volume at STP
is then given by (page 59)

$$37.2 \text{ ml} \times \frac{715 \text{ torr}}{760 \text{ torr}} \times \frac{273 \text{ K}}{302 \text{ K}} = 31.6 \text{ ml}$$

It is convenient to refer to the 31.6 ml as the volume of "dry" hydrogen. (b) The
water vapor is in the same container with hydrogen; therefore, their volumes are
equal (page 43) and 37.2 ml of water vapor is also collected at 302 K and
30 torr. Its volume at STP is then given by

$$37.2 \text{ ml} \times \frac{30 \text{ torr}}{760 \text{ torr}} \times \frac{273 \text{ K}}{302 \text{ K}} = 1.33 \text{ ml}$$

PROBLEM 6   **30.0 ml of oxygen is collected by water displacement at 22.0 °C. The
barometer reading, P_{atm}, is 765.0 torr. What is the volume of "dry" oxygen at STP? p_{H_2O} at
22.0 °C = 19.8 torr.**

   Boiling Point   Upon being heated, most liquids eventually boil. **Boiling** is
characterized by the *formation of bubbles* of vapor in the body of the liquid. These
masses of vapor break through the surface and escape, so that rapid vaporization
accompanies boiling. The temperature of the liquid, however, remains constant. At
this temperature, the vapor pressure of the liquid is equal to the atmospheric pressure
pushing down on the liquid. The temperature at which the vapor pressure of a liquid
is equal to atmospheric pressure is called the **boiling point** of the liquid. However, the
temperature at which a liquid boils may be changed merely by changing the pressure
in contact with the liquid. For example, the vapor pressure of water at 80 °C is
355 torr. In other words, if atmospheric pressure is reduced to 355 torr, then water
boils at 80 °C. The **normal boiling point** of a liquid is, therefore, defined as that
temperature at which the vapor pressure of a liquid is one standard atmosphere,
760 torr.

   (normal boiling point) liquid $\rightleftharpoons$ vapor *(vapor pressure = 760 torr)*

Thus, the normal boiling point of water is 100 °C, the temperature at which its vapor
pressure is 760 torr. Normal boiling points are usually called simply boiling points.

Example 9

From Fig. 3.10, page 93, estimate the normal boiling points (a) of ethyl
alcohol, and (b) of ethyl ether.

Answer

(a) The temperature at which the vapor pressure of ethyl alcohol is 760 torr is
79 °C. The normal boiling point of ethyl alcohol is, therefore, 79 °C. (b) The
normal boiling point of ethyl ether is 35 °C, the temperature at which its vapor
pressure is 760 torr.

PROBLEM 7   (a) Using Fig. 3.10, estimate the normal boiling point of carbon tetrachloride. (b) At what temperature would water boil if the atmospheric pressure is reduced to
150 torr?

Heat of Vaporization   Since molecules escaping from a liquid are those with
the highest kinetic energy, heat must be added to maintain constant temperature
(page 90). The **heat of vaporization** of a liquid is therefore the number of calories per
gram of liquid necessary to maintain constant temperature while evaporation or
boiling occurs.* The heat of vaporization for several liquids at their (normal) boiling
points is given in Table 3.3. The heat of vaporization of a liquid decreases as the

TABLE 3.3
HEAT OF VAPORIZATION OF SOME COMMON
LIQUIDS AT THEIR (NORMAL) BOILING POINTS

| SUBSTANCE | HEAT OF VAPORIZATION | | (NORMAL) BOILING POINT °C |
	$\dfrac{cal}{g}$	$\dfrac{J}{g}$	
Chloroform	59	247	61
Carbon tetrachloride	46	192	77
Ethyl alcohol	204	854	79
Benzene	94	393	80
Water	540	2259	100
Mercury	71	297	357

temperature increases. The higher the temperature, the greater is the average energy
of the molecules and the smaller is the energy required to overcome the intermolecular attractive forces. In general, the stronger the intermolecular attractive forces, the
higher the heat of vaporization.

*The high heats of
vaporization of water
and ethyl alcohol
result from an
unusually strong type
of intermolecular
attractive force (page
266).*

Example 10

Calculate the number of calories required to convert 100 g of water to vapor at
its (normal) boiling point.

Answer

From Table 3.3, 540 calories are required to convert 1 g of liquid water to water
vapor at 100 °C. Therefore, for 100 g, the number of calories is given by

$$100 \, g \times \frac{540 \text{ cal}}{g} = 54,000 \text{ cal} = 5.40 \times 10^4 \text{ cal}$$

Example 11

How many calories are required to convert 10.0 g of water at 20.0 °C to vapor at
its boiling point, 100 °C?

---

*It is also equal to the heat evolved, the number of calories per gram that must be removed, to
maintain constant temperature during condensation. Steam, condensing on your hand, produces severe
burns due to the heat liberated on condensation. Steam at 100 °C is therefore more damaging than water
at the same temperature.

Answer

The temperature of the water must first be raised 80.0 degrees (100.0 °C − 20.0 °C), to 100.0 °C. To do this, 10.0 g of water requires 800 cal (page 89):

$$\frac{1.00 \text{ cal}}{g \cdot °C} \times 10.0 \text{ g} \times 80.0 \text{ °C} = 800 \text{ cal}$$

At 100 °C, the 10.0 g sample of water requires 5400 cal for vaporization to steam:

$$10.0 \text{ g} \times 540 \frac{\text{cal}}{g} = 5400 \text{ cal}$$

Therefore, the total number of calories required is 6200 cal:

$$800 \text{ cal} + 5400 \text{ cal} = 6200 \text{ cal}$$

PROBLEM 8 Using Tables 3.1 (page 89) and 3.3, determine how many calories are required to convert 10.0 g of chloroform at 20.0 °C to vapor at its boiling point, 61.0 °C.

PROPERTIES OF SOLIDS _____3.4

Freezing Point As a liquid is cooled (heat is removed), a temperature is eventually reached at which the liquid *freezes;* it becomes a solid. This temperature, which remains constant until all of the liquid is converted into solid, is known as the **freezing point** of the liquid. This is the temperature at which the liquid and solid are in equilibrium at standard pressure, 760 torr:

$$\text{(freezing point) liquid} \underset{\substack{\text{melting} \\ \text{fusion}}}{\overset{\substack{\text{freezing} \\ \text{crystallization}}}{\rightleftharpoons}} \text{solid } (P_{\text{atm}} = 760 \text{ torr})$$

As the liquid cools, the average kinetic energy decreases. Eventually, the kinetic energy becomes sufficiently low that attractive forces hold the molecules in relatively fixed positions; the liquid solidifies. Alternatively, warming a solid eventually causes the solid to *melt;* it becomes a liquid. But the **melting point** is exactly the same as the freezing point. The difference in terms is based only on the direction of approach. The

TABLE 3.4
HEAT OF FUSION OF VARIOUS SUBSTANCES AT THEIR MELTING POINTS

SUBSTANCE	MELTING POINT °C	HEAT OF FUSION	
		$\frac{cal}{g}$	$\frac{J}{g}$
Ethyl alcohol	−114	24.9	104
Mercury	−39	2.8	11.7
Carbon tetrachloride	−24	4.2	17.6
Water (ice)	0	79.7	333
Silver	961	26.0	109

**TABLE 3.5
SPECIFIC HEAT OF
SOME SOLIDS**

	SPECIFIC HEAT	
SUBSTANCE	$\dfrac{cal}{g\ °C}$	$\dfrac{J}{g\ °C}$
Ice (−2 °C)	0.50	2.1
Iron (25 °C)	0.11	0.46
Copper (25 °C)	0.092	0.38
Silver (25 °C)	0.056	0.23

amount of heat necessary to convert 1 g of solid into liquid at the melting point is called the **heat of fusion.** The amount of heat liberated (removed) when 1 g of a liquid freezes is exactly equal to the heat of fusion. The heats of fusion of several solids are given in Table 3.4; the specific heats of several solids are given in Table 3.5.

Example 12

(a) How many calories are required to convert 15.0 g of ice at 0 °C to liquid water at 0 °C? (b) Find the number of joules required to melt 25.0 g of solid mercury at its melting point.

Answer

(a) From Table 3.4, 1 g of ice requires 79.7 cal; therefore, 15.0 g of ice requires

$$15.0\ g \times 79.7\ \frac{cal}{g} = 1196\ cal$$

(b) From Table 3.4, 1 g of solid mercury requires 11.7 J; therefore, 25.0 g requires

$$25.0\ g \times 11.7\ \frac{J}{g} = 293\ J$$

Example 13

What is the total number of calories required to convert 30.0 g of ice at 0 °C to water at 20.0 °C?

Answer

The ice at 0 °C is first converted into water at 0 °C.

$$30.0\ g \times 79.7\ \frac{cal}{g} = 2391\ cal$$

Then, the 30.0 g of water must be heated 20 degrees from 0 °C to 20.0 °C:

$$1.00\ \frac{cal}{g\ °C} \times 30.0\ g \times 20.0\ °C = 600\ cal$$

The total number of calories is therefore 2391 cal + 600 cal = 2991 cal.

PROBLEM 9   How many calories are necessary to convert 100.0 g of ice at 0 °C to water at 25.0 C?

Vapor Pressure of Solids   Although molecules are more confined in solids, many solids have measurable vapor pressures and evaporate directly into vapor. A solid in a closed container eventually establishes equilibrium with its vapor:

$$\text{solid} \; \underset{\substack{\text{deposition}}}{\overset{\substack{\text{sublimation}}}{\rightleftharpoons}} \; \text{vapor} \; (\textit{vapor pressure of solid})$$
$$\textit{(temperature constant)}$$

"Dry Ice," solid carbon dioxide, for example, evaporates (sublimes). Snow evaporates (sublimes) at temperatures much below the melting point. Solid naphthalene also sublimes. The odor of vapor from solid naphthalene, used as a moth repellent, is easily detected.

The vapor pressures of solids are related to the forces of attraction that exist between the particles. Thus, the force of attraction between particles in Dry Ice and in naphthalene are relatively weak compared to those in solids such as sand, sugar, and sodium chloride (table salt) that do not have measurable vapor pressures at room temperature.

SOLID-LIQUID-VAPOR RELATIONSHIPS_____3.5

The relationship among different phases of the same substance may be summarized in a graph showing how the melting point and the boiling point change with pressure. The same graph may also show how the vapor pressures of the liquid and solid change with temperature. For example, we have already shown (Fig. 3.10, page 93) how the vapor pressure of liquid water increases with temperature. This graph also shows how the boiling point of water changes with pressure. It may therefore be called the boiling point line of water. The vapor pressure-temperature curve of liquid water may be combined into one diagram with the melting point-pressure curve of ice and with the vapor pressure-temperature curve of ice. Such a diagram, called a **phase diagram,** is determined experimentally and is specific for a given substance. Such diagrams conveniently show the conditions under which a substance can exist as solid(s), liquid(s), or vapor. Fig. 3.12 shows the phase diagram for water.

The diagram summarizes the equilibria of its three phases:

solid (*ice*) $\rightleftharpoons$ liquid (*water*) (*melting point of ice*),

                                     line AD in Fig. 3.12

liquid (*water*) $\rightleftharpoons$ vapor (*water vapor*) (*vapor pressure of water*),

                                     line AB in Fig. 3.12

solid (*ice*) $\rightleftharpoons$ vapor (*water vapor*) (*vapor pressure of ice*),

                                     line AC in Fig. 3.12

Line AB is the vapor pressure curve of liquid water. As in Fig. 3.10 (page 93), each point gives the vapor pressure of liquid water at the indicated temperature. For example, at 100 °C, the vapor pressure of liquid water is 760 torr; at 0.01 °C the vapor pressure is 4.59 torr. Point B represents the critical temperature, 374 °C, and critical pressure, 218 atm (page 76).

Line AC is the vapor pressure-temperature curve of ice. Each point on this curve

99

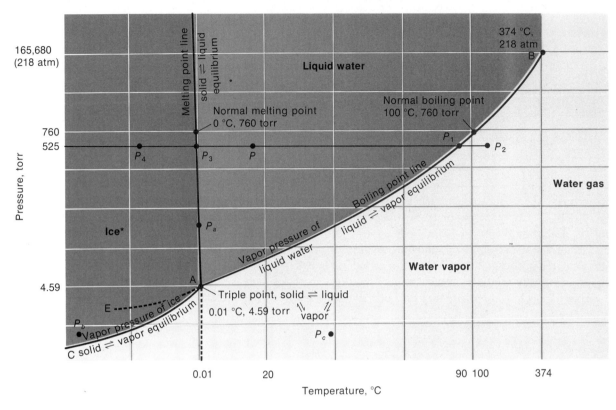

165,680
(218 atm)

760
525

4.59

*At pressures above about 2000 atm, several different ice phases exist.

FIGURE 3.12 Phase diagram for water. Diagram (*not to scale*) of the equilibrium of three phases of water.

represents the vapor pressure of ice at the indicated temperature. For example, the vapor pressure of ice is 4.59 torr at 0.01 °C.

Line AD is the melting (freezing) point-pressure curve of water. For example, the melting point is 0.01 °C at 4.59 torr and decreases only slightly with increasing pressure to 0 °C at 760 torr. The three curves join together at point A, 0.01 °C and 4.59 torr, called the triple point. It is called the triple point because at these conditions, three phases coexist at equilibrium: ice, liquid water, and water vapor.

The triple point of water is used as a reference point to define the kelvin temperature scale; it is defined as 273.160 K.

Any three phases coexisting at equilibrium, such as three solid phases, or two solid phases plus one liquid phase, is represented by a triple point.

The diagram tells us what phase or phases exist at a given set of pressure-temperature conditions. Conditions in an *area* on the diagram correspond to one phase, on a *line* two phases, and at a *point* three phases. For example, at 525 torr and 20 °C, point P in Fig. 3.12, water exists only as liquid. Keeping the pressure at 525 torr while increasing the temperature, at 90 °C, point P_1, the liquid boils and equilibrium is established between liquid and vapor. If heating is continued, eventually all the liquid becomes vapor. Conversely, holding the pressure at 525 torr and decreasing the temperature from point P_2 causes condensation at P_1 and freezing at P_3. At P_4, only ice exists.

The line AD shows that the melting point of ice, unlike most solids, decreases as the pressure is increased. Thus, ice below 0 °C melts if subjected to pressures above 1 atm. This makes it easier to skate on ice at temperatures below 0 °C. At the pressure exerted by the skater, a thin film of liquid water may form, serving as a lubricant. But more important, the heat generated by the friction between the skate and ice raises the surface temperature above the melting point.

PROBLEM 10   See Fig. 3.12. What phase(s) exist(s) at temperature-pressure conditions P_a, P_b, P_c, and A?

PROBLEM 11   The critical temperature of water is 374 °C. What is the vapor pressure (the critical pressure) of water at this temperature? See Fig. 3.12.

THE SUPER STATES_____3.6

The freezing point of water is 0 °C. Under certain conditions, however, water can be cooled well below 0 °C without freezing. A liquid at a temperature below its freezing point is said to be **supercooled.** This condition is described by a dashed line in a phase diagram; typical is the line AE for water in Fig. 3.12 (page 100). The supercooled liquid is highly unstable with respect to solid ice. The supercooled water can be crystallized to ice by introducing a piece of ice, a crystal of silver iodide-silver bromide (AgI-AgBr)*, or a bit of dust, or by scratching the inside wall of the container. It is interesting that although liquids can be supercooled, solids have not been superheated; the temperature of a solid cannot be increased above its melting point without liquefaction. However, a liquid, free of air or dust, can be heated well above its boiling point without bubbling. Such a **superheated** liquid is very unstable with respect to its vapor phase and may explosively change to vapor. Typical is the behavior of a *Freon*, trichlorofluoromethane, CCl_3F, a commonly used refrigerant (Fig. 3.13). Its boiling point is 24 °C, but in water at 70 °C it shows no signs of

Supercooling in water has been observed to temperatures of −40 °C.

Scratching causes the release of a microbubble (a bubble too small to be seen without the aid of a microscope), about which crystallization can occur.

Exception: Under special conditions (microscopic quantities of liquid water and vapor trapped in certain minerals) ice crystals persist at temperatures as high as 6 °C.

_____
* The arrangement of silver, iodine, and bromine in solid AgI-AgBr closely resembles the arrangement of hydrogen and oxygen in ice; AgI-AgBr is, therefore, used in "seeding" clouds composed of drops of supercooled liquid water ("making rain").

FIGURE 3.13 A liquid *Freon*, CCl_3F, with a boiling point of 24 °C, is poured into water at 70 °C. It does not vaporize or boil; it is superheated. Courtesy Robert Reid, M.I.T., *American Scientist*, March/April 1976, page 148, and Argonne National Laboratory.

vaporization or boiling. Raising the temperature of the liquid Freon above 70 °C eventually causes it to change to vapor with explosive force.

Conversely, a dust-free vapor can be cooled below its condensation point without forming a liquid. Such a supercooled vapor is called a **supersaturated** vapor. Superheated liquids and supersaturated vapors have important applications in nuclear chemistry (Chap. 17).

3.7 _____ LAW AND ORDER

Law and order is a pressing issue for man. Nature, however, prefers disorder in matter. This brief statement actually ranks among the most fundamental natural laws because of its unfailing ability to predict a physical or chemical change. And there is nothing like a verified prediction to keep a scientist happy.

Let us examine this natural tendency of matter to become more disorganized—more disordered—with phase changes. Carbon dioxide (CO_2) gas at room conditions *never* changes to solid CO_2. On the other hand, solid CO_2 evaporates—it changes to gaseous CO_2—regardless of the temperature: solid CO_2 evaporates even at low temperatures. There is thus a natural drive for the solid $\longrightarrow$ gas change. But the solid is more orderly than the gas (page 85):

$$\text{solid (}order\text{)} \longrightarrow \text{gas (}disorder\text{)}$$

Similarly, it is not necessary to warm a liquid for it to evaporate: liquid water, including supercooled liquid water, evaporates over the entire temperature range in which it exists.

It is not natural for iron to organize itself into the beautiful suspension bridges that grace our rivers and bays. But much effort is expended in converting iron ore, Fe_2O_3, into steel beams systematically placed during the construction of bridges. However, if unprotected, the bridge in time will naturally crumble to iron oxide:

$$\text{bridge (}orderly\text{)} \underset{\text{much effort}}{\overset{\text{naturally}}{\rightleftharpoons}} \text{iron oxide powder (}disorderly\text{)}$$

Man builds stone monuments but nature crumbles them. All natural changes, it appears, cause an increase in disorderliness.

A more personal example would be the disorderly appearance of a room if, over a period of time, no effort is made to replace books, papers, pencils, and other personal items to their proper locations:

$$\text{personal items (}orderly\text{)} \underset{\text{effort}}{\overset{\text{no effort}}{\rightleftharpoons}} \text{personal items (}disorderly\text{)}$$

The amount of disorder (randomness) in a substance is measured by its **entropy.*** We may then say that all natural changes cause an increase in entropy (disorderliness). A definite relationship exists between temperature and entropy changes. As the temperature of a substance increases, molecular motion (page 000) increases, and

---

*Upon the first introduction to entropy, the word does not generate a known or familiar mental image. The concept of entropy was invented by Rudolf Clausius (1865). The word is derived from *entropia*, the Greek word for turning towards, but scientifically used as a measure of the natural drive to change towards greater disorder. The order-disorder interpretation of entropy was introduced by Ludwig Boltzman (1866).

hence its molecular arrangements become more disordered; the entropy of the substance, therefore, increases. A perfect solid at absolute zero has zero entropy. As its temperature is increased, its entropy also increases. Increases in entropy, therefore, favor the changes solid ⟶ liquid ⟶ gas. In fact, practically all matter present in the universe is in the gaseous state, the liquid and solid states of planets appearing as exceptions.

The association of entropy with a measurement is treated later, Chap. 15.

PROBLEM 12   **From the choices given, pick the copper, Cu, phase (a) with the highest and the lowest disorder and (b) with the highest and lowest entropy: (i) liquid Cu, (ii) gaseous Cu, (iii) Cu crystal in which some Cu particles are out of place, (iv) a perfect Cu crystal.**

The reader may observe that nature uses plants to convert carbon dioxide and water into sugars (page 195), a process in which the entropy decreases; the products are more orderly than carbon dioxide and water. However, while nature decreases the entropy in this change, it increases *to a greater extent* the entropy elsewhere—namely, the sun (page 188), which furnishes the necessary effort by consuming itself. Supercooled water (page 101) is not stable with respect to ice; it has a natural tendency to change to ice. The freezing of the water decreases the entropy; the ice is more orderly than the liquid. But this decrease is *more than counterbalanced* by the increase in entropy of the surrounding substances resulting from the heat evolved while the supercooled liquid freezes.

Example 14

The only case known in which the entropy of a solid substance is greater than its liquid at the melting point involves a peculiar form of the element helium, known as "helium-3." At temperatures below 0.3 K the *entropy of solid* helium-3 is *greater* than the entropy of liquid helium-3. Predict the change that occurs when liquid helium-3 is warmed in the temperature range from 0.1 K to 0.3 K.

Answer

In this special case, the entropy of the solid is greater than that of the liquid; hence, the solid must be more disordered than the liquid. But a basic law of nature demands that matter must change to the state of greater disorder. Therefore, we predict that, on warming, liquid helium-3 should solidify. This prediction has been verified.

PROBLEMS

13 Vocabulary Define or illustrate (a) surface tension, (b) attractive forces, (c) meniscus, (d) specific heat, (e) evaporation, (f) equilibrium, (g) vapor pressure (i) of liquid (ii) of solid, (h) boiling point, (i) heat of vaporization, (j) freezing point, (k) heat of fusion, (l) crystallization, (m) sublimation, (n) phase diagram, (o) supercooling, (p) superheating, (q) entropy, (r) face-centered cubic arrangement, (s) body-centered cubic arrangement, (t) crystal, (u) amorphous.

14 Specific heat (a) How many calories are removed to cool 50.0 g of ethyl alcohol from 25.0 °C to −3.0 °C? See Table 3.1, page 89. (b) Find the number of joules needed to warm 15.0 g of chloroform from 20.0 °C to 35.0 °C.

15 Specific heat How many grams of silver can be heated from 15 °C to 25 °C by the number of calories evolved when 100 g of iron cool from 70 °C to 60 °C? See Table 3.5, page 98.

16 Liquids spilled in a spacecraft at zero gravity form perfectly spherical drops. Explain.

17 Evaporation (a) What factors affect the rate of evaporation of a liquid? (b) "Rubbing alcohols" are used to reduce high fevers. Explain. (c) Water in gasoline sometimes freezes in the carburetor (a device that sprays gasoline into the engine cylinders), preventing the car from starting, even on days when the temperature is above 32 °F. Explain.

18 Gas laws Oxygen gas is collected over water at 26.0 °C in the apparatus illustrated in Fig. 3.11b. Barometric pressure is 767 torr. If the tube is adjusted so that the water levels are equalized, (a) what is the partial pressure of oxygen? p_{H_2O} at 26.0 °C = 25 torr. (b) If the volume reading is 38.0 ml, what is the volume of the oxygen at STP?

19 70.0 ml of nitrogen is collected by water displacement when the barometer reads 770 torr and the temperature is 20.0 °C. Calculate the volume of "dry" nitrogen at STP. See Table 3.2, page 92.

20 50.0 g of ice is added to 100 g of water at 80.0 °C. Calculate the final temperature of the water. See Table 3.4, page 97.

21 Attractive forces Comparing the heats of vaporization for ethyl alcohol, water, and chloroform in Table 3.3, page 96, indicate which of these substances should have the weakest intermolecular attractive forces. Explain your answer.

22 Boiling point (a) It takes a longer time to hard-boil an egg in Denver (elevation: 1609 m or 5280 ft above sea level) than in New York City (elevation: 15 m or 50 ft). Explain. (Recall that atmospheric pressure decreases with altitude.) (b) Food cooks faster in a pressure cooker (the pressure is about 1.1 atm). Explain.

23 Heat of vaporization A paper cup filled with water is heated with a bunsen burner. The cup does not catch fire until practically all of the water is evaporated.* Explain.

24 Heat of fusion Because temperatures below −2 °C will damage grape vines, grape growers spray a mist of water on their vines when severe frost conditions occur. In what way does this provide frost protection?

25 How many calories of heat are needed to melt 20.0 g of solid ethyl alcohol at −114 °C, warm the liquid to

79 °C, and vaporize it at 79 °C? See Table 3.3, page 96, and Table 3.4, page 97.

26 Vapor pressure A liquid is enclosed in a 1.0 ℓ flask at 25 °C. Its measured vapor pressure is 20.0 torr. Another sample of the same liquid is enclosed in a 2.0 ℓ flask at 25 °C. Liquid is present in both flasks. What is the vapor pressure of the liquid in the 2.0 ℓ flask?

27 Find the number of calories and joules required to change 25 g of ice at −2.0 °C to vapor at 100 °C. See the tables in the text.

28 Triple point A highly accurate value of the vapor pressure of water at the triple point has been determined (1976) by the U.S. National Bureau of Standards, reported as 611.657 pascals. Express this value in atm and in torr. See App. III.

29 Phase diagram (a) Under what pressure conditions can liquid water exist at temperatures above 100 °C? (b) Refer to Fig. 3.12, page 100. Indicate the changes that occur when (i) ice at −5 °C and 4.5 torr is heated to 200 °C at constant pressure, (ii) vapor at 120 °C and 450 torr is cooled to −10 °C at constant pressure, and (iii) vapor at 0.01 °C and 1.00 torr is compressed to 650 torr at constant temperature.

30 The phase diagram for carbon dioxide is given below. What phase(s) exist(s) at P_1, P_2, P_3, P_4, P_5, and P_6?

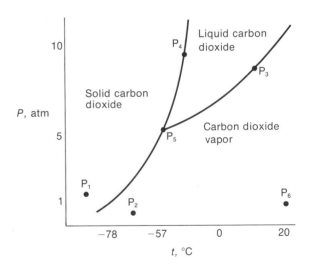

31 Humidity The vapor pressure of water defines the partial pressure of water vapor that can be present in air in equilibrium with liquid water at a given temperature. For example, at 20 °C, 17.5 torr, the vapor pressure of water, is the partial pressure of water vapor in air in equilibrium with liquid water. When

---

Caution: Do not perform this experiment; it is particularly dangerous with plastic, plastic-coated, or wax-coated cups.

the partial pressure of water vapor in air actually equals the vapor pressure of water, the air is said to be *saturated* with water vapor and its **humidity*** is said to be 100 percent. The percent humidity is thus defined as

$$\frac{\text{partial pressure of water in air at temperature } t}{\text{vapor pressure of water at temperature } t} \times 100$$

If the temperature is 50 °C and the partial pressure of water in air is 22.5 torr, what is the humidity?

32 Entropy Pick the water phase with the highest and lowest (a) disorder, and (b) entropy: (i) water vapor, (ii) water gas, (iii) liquid water, (iv) ice frozen with trapped air, (v) ice frozen from high purity water.

33 Discuss in entropy terms (a) the most probable appearance of a library after a week of use in the absence of the librarian; (b) the chances of throwing a mixture of pepper and salt to the floor and having them separate into two neat piles; (c) the statement,

---

* More accurately, this defines the relative humidity, commonly abbreviated to humidity.

"Life postpones the effect of entropy; it builds highly complex biological molecules from simpler substances"; (d) the statement, "Pollution generally increases environmental entropy (disorder) and is thus a natural process."

34 Seeding Like seeding clouds to make rain (page 101), diamond can grow in an environment of carbon atoms. The growth rate of diamond seed exposed at 1050 °C to methane at 0.001 atm ($CH_4 \rightarrow C + 2H_2$) is 0.05 micrometer per hour. Find the growth in mm after 10 hours. See App. II.

35 Library Read one of the following:

(a) "Man-Made Diamonds," F. Bundy and co-workers, *Nature*, volume 176, pages 51–54, 9 July 1955.
(b) "Haste Makes Waste—Pollution and Entropy," Henry A. Bent, *Chemistry*, pages 6–15, October, 1971.
(c) "The Structure of Liquids," J. D. Bernal, *Scientific American*, pages 124–134, August, 1960.
(d) "The Flow of Energy in the Biosphere," David Gates, *Scientific American*, pages 89–100, September, 1971.

36 A substance (carbon) has a triple point at about 3300 °C. What statement can you make about the vapor pressure of graphite (solid) and liquid carbon at this temperature?

37 The working parts of a refrigerator are illustrated:

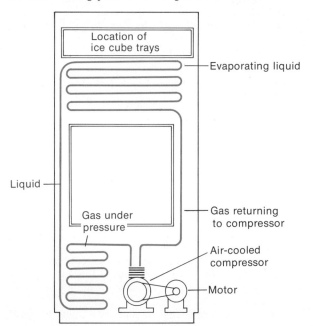

Location of ice cube trays

Evaporating liquid

Liquid

Gas under pressure

Gas returning to compressor

Air-cooled compressor

Motor

The coils form a closed system containing a *Freon*, CCl_2F_2, boiling point −28 °C. In operation, an air-cooled compressor pumps the *Freon* through the system. A portion of the liquid vaporizes, but the gas is then compressed to a liquid. Explain how these phase changes maintain the refrigerator temperature.

38 Most substances undergo a sharp change between the solid crystal phase and the liquid phase. Some molecules, usually long and narrow ones like $CH_3OC_6H_4NONC_6H_4OCH_3$, however, do not pass directly from the solid to the liquid phase. Instead, they pass into a phase ("liquid crystals") between that of the solid crystal and the liquid. Arrange these three phases in order of increasing entropy. Explain your arrangement.

39 Pick the change involving a larger increase in entropy: ice $\longrightarrow$ liquid water or liquid water $\longrightarrow$ vapor. Explain.

40 The phase diagram for sulfur is given on the following page. Write the different phases in equilibrium at the triple point(s).

41 Explain the statement: "Irregularity is the general rule even for crystals."

Diagram for
Problem 40.

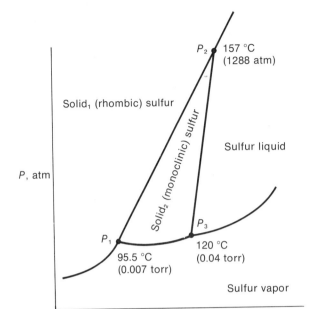

P, atm

P_2 ● 157 °C
(1288 atm)

Solid₁ (rhombic) sulfur

Solid₂ (monoclinic) sulfur

Sulfur liquid

P_1
95.5 °C
(0.007 torr)

P_3
120 °C
(0.04 torr)

Sulfur vapor

T, °C

ANSWERS

1 (a) 1.3×10^3 cal
   (b) 3.2×10^2 cal
2 5.7×10^2 cal
5 (a) 100 °C
   (b) about 78 °C
6 27.2 ml
7 (a) about 76 °C
   (b) about 60 °C
8 685 cal
9 10470 (1.05×10^4) cal
11 218 atm
14 (a) 749 cal
   (b) 218 J
15 196 g
18 (a) 742 torr
   (b) 33.9 ml
19 64.5 ml

20 26.8 °C
25 6643 (6.64×10^2) cal
26 20.0 torr
27 1.8×10^4 cal, 7.5×10^4 J
28 6.03659×10^{-3} atm, 4.58781 torr
30 P_1(solid), P_2, P_6(vapor), P_3(liquid-vapor),
   P_4(S-L), P_5(S-L-V)
31 24.3 %
34 5×10^{-5} mm
36 same
38 solid crystal ⟶ liquid crystal
   ⟶ liquid
39 liquid ⟶ vapor
40 rhombic, monoclinic,
   vapor; rhombic, monoclinic,
   liquid; monoclinic, liquid,
   vapor

GLOSSARY

amorphous solid A stable supercooled liquid whose
molecular arrangement lacks a regular orderly pattern.
body-centered cubic packing An arrangement in which
particles occupy the corners and the centers of cubes.
boiling The formation of vapor bubbles within a
liquid.
boiling point The temperature at which the vapor
pressure of a liquid equals the external pressure.

crystal A solid in which the particles are arranged in
an orderly pattern throughout the solid.
crystallization The change of state from liquid to solid.
entropy A measure of the disorder in a substance;
highly ordered substances have low entropies.
equilibrium The condition obtained when opposing
changes proceed at equal rates, resulting in no net
change.
evaporation The change of state from liquid to vapor,

resulting from the random motion of molecules that permits some of them to escape from the liquid surface.

face-centered cubic packing An arrangement in which particles occupy the corners and the center of each side of a cube.

freezing point The temperature at which the solid and liquid states of a substance are in equilibrium.

heat of condensation The quantity of heat released when one gram of vapor is condensed to liquid at a given temperature. It is equal to the heat of vaporization (see **heat of vaporization**).

heat of crystallization The quantity of heat released when one gram of solid freezes at the freezing point. It is equal to the heat of fusion (see **heat of fusion**).

heat of fusion The number of joules (or calories) required to convert one gram of solid at its melting point into liquid.

heat of vaporization The number of joules (or calories) required to convert one gram of liquid into vapor at a given temperature.

melting point The same as freezing point (see **freezing point**).

meniscus The curved upper surface of a liquid column.

normal boiling point The temperature at which the vapor pressure of a liquid equals one standard atmosphere, commonly called the boiling point of the liquid.

normal freezing point The temperature at which the liquid and solid states of a substance are in equilib-

rium at one standard atmosphere pressure, commonly called the freezing point of the liquid.

phase diagram A graph of pressure against temperature, showing the condition at which a substance exists as a gas, liquid, or solid and the conditions at which the different phases of the substance are in equilibrium.

specific heat The number of joules (or calories) required to raise the temperature of one gram of a substance one degree Celsius.

sublimation The change of state from solid to gas.

supercooled liquid A liquid cooled below its freezing point without freezing.

superheated liquid A liquid heated above its boiling point without boiling.

supersaturated vapor A vapor cooled below its condensation point without forming a liquid.

surface tension The tendency of a liquid surface to contract in area owing to unbalanced intermolecular attractive (inward) forces at the surface.

triple point The temperature at which three different phases of a substance coexist in equilibrium.

vapor The gaseous state of a substance below its critical temperature.

vaporization The same as evaporation (see **evaporation**).

vapor pressure of liquid or solid The pressure exerted by a vapor in equilibrium with its liquid or solid. See **equilibrium**.

volatility The tendency of a liquid to evaporate.

ATOMS AND MOLECULES 4

In our newspapers, we almost daily read something about "The Age of the Atom," "Citizens Fight Atom Test," "Atomic Power," or "Peaceful Uses of the Atom," so that today everyone hears something about atoms and believes that atoms exist. Most likely atoms do exist; nevertheless, their existence is an assumption of a theory of the structure of matter. Leucippus and Democritus (about the 5th century B.C.) assumed matter to be composed of separated indivisible particles that they called atoms.* Further, Democritus believed that atoms were the ultimate particles of matter, and that they differed only in size, shape, and movement. Nevertheless, the atomic theory was not generally accepted until chemical changes were studied and explained. These studies, made during the 18th and 19th centuries, are summarized in the laws describing chemical changes: the law of conservation of matter, the law of constant composition, the law of multiple proportions, and the law of combining volumes. The atomic theory, then, is an imaginary model of the nature of matter, invented by man to understand experimental facts, some of which follow.

THE LAW OF CONSERVATION OF MATTER_____4.1

Measurements show that, within the experimental error, the mass (weight) of substances in a sealed container does not change during a chemical change. For instance, hydrogen, H_2, and oxygen, O_2, are enclosed in a tube. No matter can now enter or escape from the tube. The tube and contents are weighed on a balance. Passage of an electric spark within the tube causes the hydrogen and oxygen gases to disappear, and liquid water, H_2O, and heat are produced. After cooling to the original temperature, the tube and contents are reweighed. The observed masses, before and after the chemical change, are identical *within the precision of the measurement*. Such observations are summarized in the **law of conservation of matter:** *the mass of a chemically reacting system remains constant.*** This law is supported by measurements with the most precise balances available. If matter is created or destroyed (page 301), the change in mass is less than can be detected with the best available balance.

Another example of matter conservation is the use of a photoflash bulb, a sealed

---

*From *atomos,* the Greek word for unchangeable, indivisible, incapable of being cut. Leucippus and Democritus, Athenian philosophers, were influenced by the earlier philosophies of Thales of Miletus (Asia Minor, 6th Century B.C.), and Parmenides of Elea (Southern Italy, about 450 B.C.).

**Based on the work of Mikhail Lomonosov (1756), Antoine Lavoisier (1774), and others. Although balances were known to the ancient Egyptians, accurate weighing became routine only in the 18th century.

A white solid with a
very high melting
point, 2800 °C, used
in the manufacture of
heat insulators,
furnace linings, and
milk of magnesia.

system containing magnesium metal, Mg, and oxygen gas, O_2. When the bulb is fired, the magnesium and oxygen are consumed, but magnesium oxide, MgO, and heat are produced. At room temperature, the weights of the bulb before and after the chemical reaction are the same, within the error of the balance measurement. Similarly, when a definite quantity of lighter fluid (butane gas, C_4H_{10}) is burned in a definite quantity of air, the mass of exhausted gases equals the sum of the masses of the butane and the air.

PROBLEM 1   **(a) Is matter destroyed when TNT explodes? (b) Is matter created when a flower develops from a seed?**

PROBLEM 2   **Joseph Black (1775) started with 5.4 g of magnesium carbonate, $MgCO_3$ (white solid, insoluble in water); heated it to form magnesium oxide, MgO; treated the MgO with sulfuric acid (highly corrosive, capable of producing severe burns), forming magnesium sulfate, $MgSO_4$ (colorless solid, very soluble in water); and then reformed the $MgCO_3$ from the $MgSO_4$. How many grams of $MgCO_3$ did he recover? Explain your answer.**

4.2 THE LAW OF CONSTANT COMPOSITION

When elements form a given compound, they always combine in the same mass ratio. This means that each compound has a constant composition; no matter how obtained or prepared, it always contains the same proportion by mass of its constituent elements. In forming a compound, a given quantity of one element always combines with a fixed quantity of another element. For example, 2.43 g of magnesium, Mg, always combines with 1.60 g of oxygen, O_2, to form magnesium oxide, MgO. We can then calculate the mass percentage (%) of magnesium and of oxygen in magnesium oxide:

From percentum, Latin
"for each hundred."
Percentage by
definition is $\dfrac{part}{whole} \times$
100 % whole = part %

$$\text{mass percentage of magnesium} = \frac{2.43 \text{ g Mg}}{(2.43 + 1.60) \text{ g compd}} \times 100 \text{ % compd} = 60.3 \text{ % Mg}$$

$$\text{mass percentage of oxygen} = \frac{1.60 \text{ g O}}{(2.43 + 1.60) \text{ g compd}} \times 100 \text{ % compd} = 39.7 \text{ % O}$$

Magnesium oxide always contains magnesium and oxygen combined in the proportion of 60.3 % magnesium and 39.7 % oxygen by mass. This is the same as saying that 60.3 g of magnesium combines with 39.7 g of oxygen in forming 100.0 g of magnesium oxide.

Quartz is another example; independent of its source or method of formation, quartz, silicon dioxide, SiO_2, always contains 46.7 % silicon and 53.3 % oxygen by mass. Table (cane) sugar, $C_{12}H_{22}O_{11}$, whether from Cuba, Australia, or any other place, always contains 42.1 % carbon, 6.5 % hydrogen, and 51.4 % oxygen by mass. This knowledge is summarized in the **law of constant composition:** *the mass composition of a given compound is constant;* it always contains the same elements in the same mass percentages.

Also known as the law
of definite proportions;
stated by Joseph
Proust (1799) and
others.

Example 1

Silicon dioxide, SiO_2, is the main component of glass, of beach sand, and of glass fiber, no thicker than human hair, which is used to guide light around loops, curves, and corners. 10.0 g of silicon dust, Si, is exploded in oxygen, O_2, forming silicon dioxide. How many grams of SiO_2 are formed? SiO_2 contains 46.7 % Si by mass.

Answer

We wish to find the mass of SiO_2 formed from 10.0 g Si. Practically, we wish to "convert" 10.0 g of Si to grams of SiO_2. As in Example 1 (page 8), we need an expression, a "conversion factor," which gives the relationship between the number of grams of Si and the number of grams of SiO_2. We are told that SiO_2 contains 46.7 % Si by mass. This means that 46.7 g of Si combines with 53.3 g of O_2 to form 100 g of SiO_2. The "conversion factor" is therefore $\dfrac{100 \text{ g SiO}_2}{46.7 \text{ g Si}}$.

Then, for 10.0 g of Si, the mass of SiO_2 formed is

$$10.0 \text{ g Si} \times \frac{100 \text{ g SiO}_2}{46.7 \text{ g Si}} = 21.4 \text{ g SiO}_2$$

PROBLEM 3   **The mass composition of water is 88.9 % oxygen and 11.1 % hydrogen. Calculate the quantity of water formed from 25.0 g of hydrogen.**

THE ATOMIC THEORY: THE PARTICLE NATURE OF MATTER _____ 4.3

The mass relationships of substances participating in chemical reactions are clearly explained in terms of the atomic theory. In his poem, "De Rerum Natura," the Roman Lucretius summarized (57 B.C.) Greek ideas on the structure of matter. Carried over to the Arabs and the Hindus, the theory was not further developed. The poem was then practically forgotten, but was rediscovered by Poggio Braccioloni (1414) in a German monastery. The publication of the poem greatly revived interest in the atomic theory and exerted a powerful influence on the scientists of the following centuries. Nevertheless, John Dalton (1803) is generally recognized as the inventor of the theory, although his ideas evolved from the ideas of other scientists, particularly William Higgins (1789).

"Concerning the Nature of Things."

The shadow of doubt, however, hung over the atomic theory throughout the 19th Century. Hermann Kolbe (1877), a famous and respected experimental chemist (page 679), used such words as "a freshly rouged prostitute," "stupid," "hallucinations," "table-tapping," and "supernatural explanations" in his attack on the use of theory in chemistry. The atomic theory has survived such bitter attacks and remains unchallenged since about 1905.

The atomic theory of matter has been verified in many different ways. The prediction of the law of multiple proportions, (page 113), constitutes one of the strongest arguments in its favor. However, the novel and central point of Dalton's activities was the attempt to determine the relative masses of atoms (how the mass of one atom compares with the mass of another atom). This goal focused attention on the theory, and started a series of studies that ultimately made chemistry a systematized body of knowledge.

The assumptions of Dalton's atomic theory are as follows:
The elements are composed of indivisible particles called atoms.

*All the atoms of a given element possess identical properties; for example, the same mass, so that all the atoms of hydrogen are assumed to possess the same mass.**

---

*Present knowledge recognizes that the atoms of a given element do not always possess the same masses. Silver, for example, occurs as atoms of different masses (page 122), but, as found in nature, these silver atoms are always mixed in the same way so that the average mass of the silver atoms is always the same.

The atoms of different elements differ in properties; for example, atoms of different elements have different masses. The masses of the atoms of all other elements are assumed to differ from the mass of a hydrogen atom.

These atoms are the units of chemical changes; chemical changes merely involve the combination or the rearrangement of atoms; atoms are not destroyed, created, or changed.

When atoms combine, they combine in fixed ratios of whole numbers, such as 1 atom to 1 atom, or 2 atoms to 3 atoms, *forming particles known as molecules.*

The term *molecule,* meaning a particle composed of similar or not similar atoms, such as O_2 and H_2O, was introduced by Amedeo Avogadro in 1811.

The theory holds that matter, in spite of its appearance, is discontinuous rather than continuous. The materials surrounding us—water, wood, metals, rocks, food—certainly appear to be continuous. But this appearance is deceiving because our eyes cannot detect the fundamental units of which, we believe, all matter is composed. In fact, the human eye cannot even see bacteria without the aid of a microscope.

We express this view by saying that *"matter is quantized"*—it consists of *separated individual particles* and nothing exists between the particles. In this sense, we can say that coins are quantized; a cashier separates pennies, nickels, dimes, quarters, and half-dollars into separate stacks. All dimes are identical, but they differ from other coins.

The theory offers an acceptable explanation of the laws of chemical change:

The conservation of matter: Since atoms merely combine or rearrange during a chemical change, the number of atoms of each element in the *products* of the reaction is the same as the original number in the *reactants,* the starting materials. Since it is further assumed that the mass of an atom does not change, the mass of a chemically

From the Latin word quantum, *meaning how much, how many, but used in the sense of being discrete, discontinuous rather than continuous; one individual particle.*

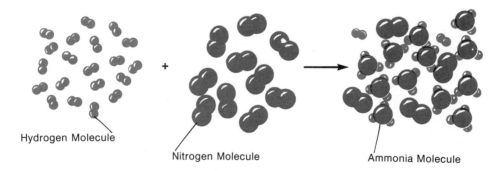

Hydrogen Molecule

Nitrogen Molecule

Ammonia Molecule

20 H_2 molecules (40 H atoms) and 10 N_2 molecules (20 N atoms) produce ⟶

12 NH_3 molecules (12 N atoms + 36 H atoms)

4 N_2 molecules (8 N atoms) *uncombined*

2 H_2 molecules (4 H atoms) *uncombined*

FIGURE 4.1 Conservation of matter in terms of the atomic theory. Some nitrogen and hydrogen molecules combine to form ammonia, NH_3,* molecules. The atoms present at the start of the reaction are present at the end of the reaction, and each atom retains its original mass. This situation is comparable to a given collection of 5 dimes and 7 nickels which is arranged in 5 stacks, each stack containing 1 dime and 1 nickel, leaving 2 nickels unstacked. The mass of the arranged collection is the same as the original collection. (The student need not be concerned here with relative positions of atoms.)

*A colorless, toxic gas, with an extremely pungent odor, ammonia is used as a commercial fertilizer (page 374), as a refrigerant in refrigerating plants, and in the manufacture of household ammonia, a solution of ammonia in water.

reacting system remains constant. We illustrate with carbon monoxide, CO, a colorless, odorless, explosive, extremely poisonous gas produced when fuels burn incompletely. The combustion of a fuel in a closed area can be fatal. A concentration of 0.1 % CO by volume produces unconsciousness in one hour and death in four hours. CO is one of the major pollutants emitted by internal combustion engines (automobiles, trucks, planes), improperly adjusted fuel-burning appliances, and tobacco or grass smokers (pages 205 and 310).

Treat 100 carbon atoms, C, and 60 oxygen atoms, O, at 1000 °C so that 20 C atoms combine with 20 atoms of O, forming carbon monoxide, CO. We now have 20 C atoms combined in the oxide, 80 C atoms uncombined, 20 O atoms combined, and 40 O atoms uncombined. This adds up to the original number of atoms, 100 C and 60 O. Since the mass of an atom is assumed to remain constant, the mass of the reacting system remains constant during the chemical change. See Fig. 4.1.

Very frequently, the change of reactants to products is incomplete (Chap. 12).

The law of constant composition: A given compound consists of only one kind of molecule. A given molecule always contains the same whole number of atoms of each element. Each kind of atom has a fixed mass. It follows, therefore, that the mass ratio of the elements in a given compound must be constant. For example, 20 C atoms combine with 20 O atoms, forming 20 CO molecules. Each CO molecule contains 1 C atom and 1 O atom. But each molecule contains the same number of C and O atoms, and the masses of these atoms are also constant. Therefore, the mass ratio of carbon to oxygen must be constant in any given quantity of carbon monoxide. This is illustrated in Fig. 4.2, which includes water, H_2O, as another example.

THE LAW OF MULTIPLE PROPORTIONS_____4.4

The atomic theory restricts combinations of elements to ratios of whole numbers of atoms; fractional numbers are excluded. Further, the number ratio is fixed for any given combination. The theory, however, *does not restrict* the number of possible combinations between atoms. Thus, hydrogen and oxygen atoms may combine

In 1 H to 1 O ratio, HO, to form one compound.

In 2 H to 1 O ratio, HOH, to form a second compound.

In 1 H to 2 O ratio, OHO, to form a third compound.

However, the theory *does not predict* that these combinations must occur; in fact, the theory is *not even capable* of predicting whether or not hydrogen and oxygen will combine. But it does predict that if hydrogen and oxygen do form more than one compound, a relationship must exist among the masses of hydrogen and oxygen in these compounds. Let us make the mass of one element, hydrogen, identical by using the same number of hydrogen atoms in each of these combinations:

1 molecule contains
2 hydrogen atoms
and 2 oxygen atoms

1 molecule contains
2 hydrogen atoms
and 1 oxygen atom

1 molecule contains
2 hydrogen atoms
and 4 oxygen atoms

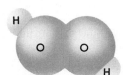

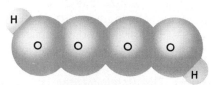

Compound (a)
Hydrogen Peroxide
(Pale blue liquid, corrosive
and explosive)

Compound (b)
Water

Compound (c)
Hydrogen Superoxide
(Exists below about 100 K)

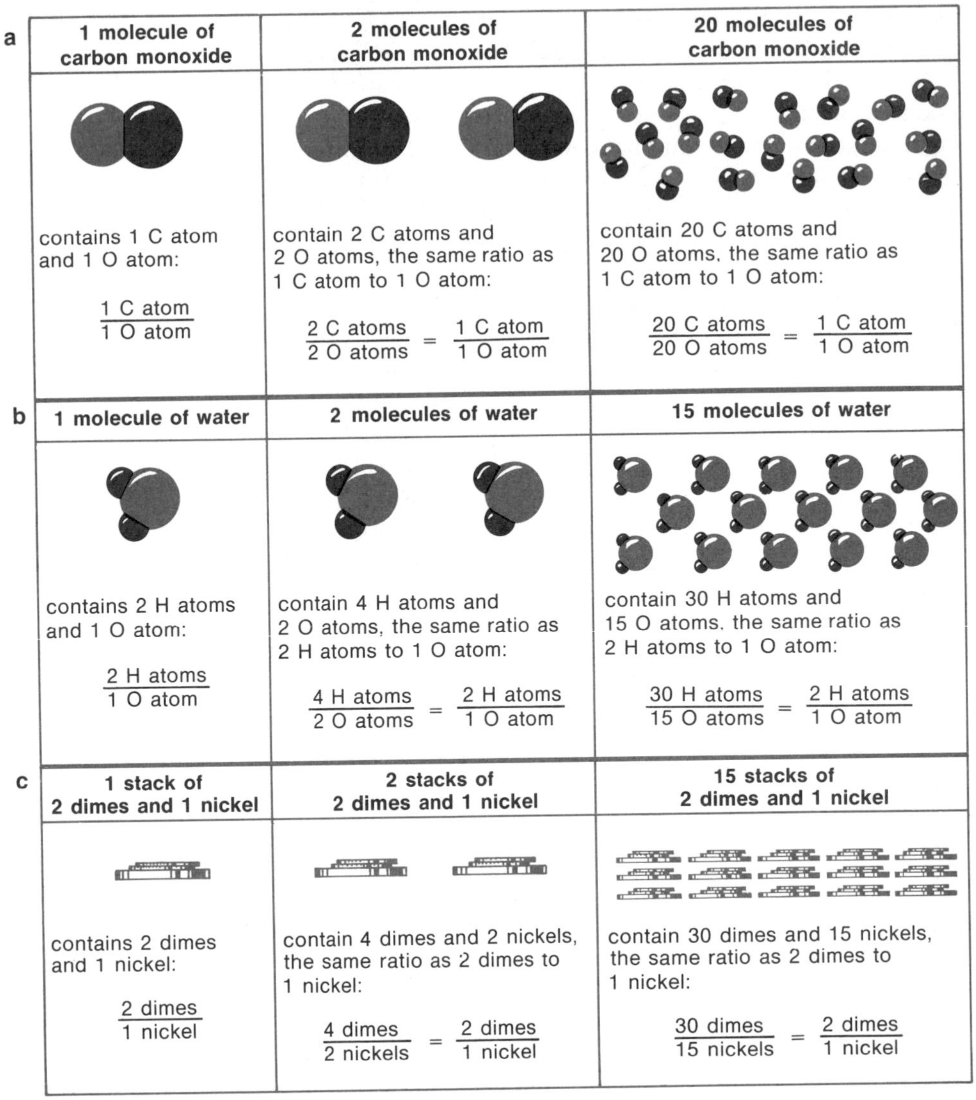

a	**1 molecule of carbon monoxide**	**2 molecules of carbon monoxide**	**20 molecules of carbon monoxide**
	contains 1 C atom and 1 O atom: $$\frac{1\ \text{C atom}}{1\ \text{O atom}}$$	contain 2 C atoms and 2 O atoms, the same ratio as 1 C atom to 1 O atom: $$\frac{2\ \text{C atoms}}{2\ \text{O atoms}} = \frac{1\ \text{C atom}}{1\ \text{O atom}}$$	contain 20 C atoms and 20 O atoms, the same ratio as 1 C atom to 1 O atom: $$\frac{20\ \text{C atoms}}{20\ \text{O atoms}} = \frac{1\ \text{C atom}}{1\ \text{O atom}}$$

b	**1 molecule of water**	**2 molecules of water**	**15 molecules of water**
	contains 2 H atoms and 1 O atom: $$\frac{2\ \text{H atoms}}{1\ \text{O atom}}$$	contain 4 H atoms and 2 O atoms, the same ratio as 2 H atoms to 1 O atom: $$\frac{4\ \text{H atoms}}{2\ \text{O atoms}} = \frac{2\ \text{H atoms}}{1\ \text{O atom}}$$	contain 30 H atoms and 15 O atoms, the same ratio as 2 H atoms to 1 O atom: $$\frac{30\ \text{H atoms}}{15\ \text{O atoms}} = \frac{2\ \text{H atoms}}{1\ \text{O atom}}$$

c	**1 stack of 2 dimes and 1 nickel**	**2 stacks of 2 dimes and 1 nickel**	**15 stacks of 2 dimes and 1 nickel**
	contains 2 dimes and 1 nickel: $$\frac{2\ \text{dimes}}{1\ \text{nickel}}$$	contain 4 dimes and 2 nickels, the same ratio as 2 dimes to 1 nickel: $$\frac{4\ \text{dimes}}{2\ \text{nickels}} = \frac{2\ \text{dimes}}{1\ \text{nickel}}$$	contain 30 dimes and 15 nickels, the same ratio as 2 dimes to 1 nickel: $$\frac{30\ \text{dimes}}{15\ \text{nickels}} = \frac{2\ \text{dimes}}{1\ \text{nickel}}$$

FIGURE 4.2 Law of constant composition in terms of the atomic theory. (a) Every carbon monoxide molecule has 1 carbon atom, with a fixed mass, and 1 oxygen atom, with a fixed mass. The mass ratio of carbon to oxygen in any number of carbon monoxide molecules, then, is the same as in any one carbon monoxide molecule.

(b) Every water molecule, regardless of the number in the sample, has 2 hydrogen atoms, each with a fixed mass, and 1 oxygen atom with a fixed mass. The mass ratio of hydrogen to oxygen in any given number of water molecules must then be the same as in any one water molecule. This situation is analogous to (c) a collection of stacks of dimes and nickels, each stack containing 2 dimes and 1 nickel. The mass ratio of dimes to nickels in any given number of stacks is the same as in any one stack.

Hydrogen peroxide antiseptic solution is about 3 % peroxide in water. Superoxol (dangerous) is 30 % peroxide.

It is evident now that the numbers of oxygen atoms in the three compounds are related as whole numbers, 2 to 1 to 4. Since each oxygen atom has the same mass, the masses of the oxygen atoms in each case are also related as whole numbers, 2 to 1 to 4. Stated otherwise, *when two elements form more than one compound, the masses of one element, combined with a fixed mass of the other element, are in ratios of whole numbers.* This statement, the **law of multiple proportions,** is further illustrated by nitrogen oxide, NO (page 385), in which *1 nitrogen atom* combines with *1 oxygen atom,* and by nitrogen dioxide, NO_2 (page 385), in which *1 nitrogen atom* combines with *2 oxygen atoms:*

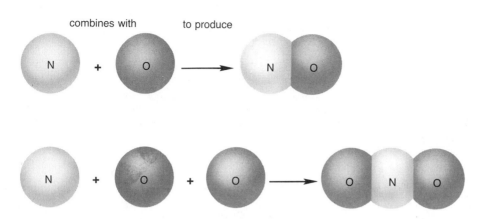

The masses of the oxygen for a given mass of nitrogen in these two compounds are in the ratio of 1 to 2. This situation is comparable to a comparison of the masses of the dimes in separate stacks, one stack containing 2 dimes and 1 nickel and the other stack having 1 dime and 1 nickel.

PROBLEM 4 Show that the metal borides, UB_2, UB_4 and UB_{12}, characterized by high melting points and extreme hardnesses, illustrate the law of multiple proportions.

The verification of the prediction of the law of multiple proportions generates much confidence in our assumption that matter is quantized, that is, composed of individual particles. Science, however, is not always a series of successful developments. It is only presented that way in teaching science.

PROBLEM 5 Assume relative masses of 35 and 19 for the atoms of elements Cl and F. Show how these atoms should combine to satisfy (a) the law of constant composition, (b) the law of conservation of matter, and (c) the law of multiple proportions.

Next, we should concern ourselves with the determination of the relative masses of atoms and molecules, the mass of one atom or molecule compared to the mass of another atom or molecule. How do we determine that an atom of oxygen, O, is 16 times heavier than an atom of hydrogen, H, and that a molecule of water, H_2O, is 18 times heavier than an atom of hydrogen? The mass of a single atom or molecule is extremely small; so small that we cannot weigh a single atom or molecule by any method. We can, however, determine *relative* weights by taking advantage of the properties of electrically charged atoms and molecules. Therefore, our attention must now be given to the electrical nature of matter.

THE ATOMIC THEORY OF ELECTRICITY: _____ 4.5
THE ELECTRICAL NATURE OF MATTER

The success of the atomic theory in explaining the laws of chemical change, the verification of its prediction of the law of multiple proportions, and the verification of the Avogadro hypothesis (page 137) generate much confidence in our hypothesis that matter is quantized. Nevertheless, Dalton's concept of an atom without structure—a simple indestructible sphere—does *not* provide an explanation for the observation that the atom of hydrogen combines with only 1 atom of fluorine (pale yellow, extremely poisonous, reactive gas) to form a molecule of hydrogen fluoride, HF (colorless, extremely corrosive, poisonous gas)

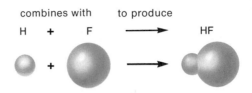

while the atom of nitrogen combines with 3 atoms of fluorine to form nitrogen trifluoride (colorless, unreactive gas):

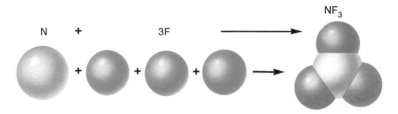

Table 4.1 illustrates a small sample of the variety of chlorides (compounds composed of two elements, one of which is chlorine). We are therefore obligated to probe further into the nature of the atom. In this section we shall consider several of the experiments involving electricity that led to the conclusion that the atom is electrical in nature. This means that we now believe that atoms are composed of electrically charged particles. We shall see in Chap. 8 that this theory will give us an acceptable explanation of chemical combinations.

Some Characteristics of Electricity   The effects of gravity are familiar to us. Objects naturally fall to the ground. Gravity is the name given to the force that attracts all objects—solids, liquids, gases—toward the (center of the) earth. But an object on the ground is not repelled by the earth; an object does not rise from the ground. This attractive force exists between all bodies. While gravitational forces are only attractive, electric forces can be repulsive as well as attractive. About 30 centuries ago, it was discovered that an amber (a natural plastic of plant origin) rod rubbed with silk becomes "electrified"; it acquires an "electric charge." The rod attracts and holds small pieces of paper. Rubbing—making many contacts be-

TABLE 4.1
SOME TYPICAL CHLORIDES*

LiCl^W	BeCl$_2$^{C}	BCl$_3$^{C}	CCl$_4$^{C}	NCl$_3$^{Y}	Cl$_2$O^{YR}	ClF^C
1382	487	12	77	71	4, expl	-101
NaCl^C	MgCl$_2$^{W}	AlCl$_3$^{W}	SiCl$_4$^{C}	PCl$_3$^{C}	SCl$_2$^{R}	BrCl^{RY}
1441	1418	180	57	74	59	5
	CaCl$_2$^{C}		GeCl$_4$^{C}	AsCl$_3$^{C}		
	$>$1600		84	122		
			SnCl$_4$^{C}	SbCl$_3$^{C}		ICl^R
			114	219		97
CsCl^C			PbCl$_4$^{Y}	BiCl$_3$^{W}		
1303			expl	441		

* Key:
The number given with the chloride compound is the boiling point in °C.
The superscript indicates color of the chloride: R = red
$>$ means greater than (App. II).   Y = yellow
expl means explosive.   W = white
                                           C = colorless

4.5 / THE ATOMIC
THEORY OF
ELECTRICITY:
THE ELECTRICAL
NATURE OF
MATTER

tween—two objects is the oldest known method of producing electricity and accounts for the "shock" experienced after walking on a rug and touching a doorknob (an electric conductor). We now know that almost any substance may be electrified simply by rubbing it with any other substance.

A glass or rubber rod, rubbed with silk or cat's fur, behaves like an electrified amber rod. A fundamental difference is noted, however. The glass rod rubbed with silk is suspended by a thread, and the rubber rod rubbed with cat's fur is brought near it (Fig. 4.3 a), and the rods *attract* each other; the electric charge on the rubber strongly attracts the charge on the glass. Now, a second glass rod, rubbed with silk, is substituted for the rubber rod (Fig. 4.3 b). The suspended glass rod is strongly *repelled*. Only two kinds of electric charge are known. The electricity on the glass rod, rubbed with silk, is called *positive* (+) and that on the rubber rod, rubbed with cat's fur, is called *negative* (−). Then, the silk is said to carry a negative charge (−), while the cat's fur carries a positive charge (+). It is thus not possible to "charge," or electrify, one object without a second object acquiring the opposite charge. All electrically neutral objects have the same quantity of negative and positive electricity.

These names were introduced by Benjamin Franklin (1750), who believed that "electrical matter consists of particles."

These experiments also show that similar charges repel each other, and unlike charges attract each other. The possible interactions among charged (| or −) or electrically neutral (uncharged) objects, designated by a zero, are

Discovered by Charles Du Fay in 1733.

Charge of Matter		Electric Interaction
−	+	Attraction
−	−⎫	
+	+⎭	Repulsion
−	0⎫	
+	0⎬	None
0	0⎭	

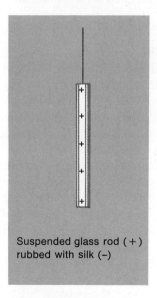
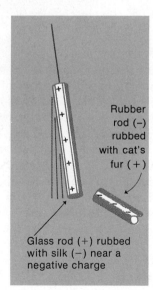
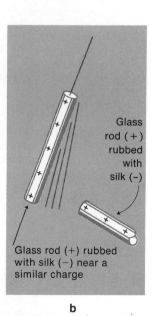

Suspended glass rod (+) rubbed with silk (−)

Glass rod (+) rubbed with silk (−) near a negative charge

Rubber rod (−) rubbed with cat's fur (+)

Glass rod (+) rubbed with silk (−) near a similar charge

Glass rod (+) rubbed with silk (−)

a

b

FIGURE 4.3 Demonstration of the two kinds of electricity: (a) unlike charges, attraction; (b) similar charges, repulsion.

By tradition, positive charge refers to the charge on the glass rod rubbed with silk, while negative charge refers to the charge on the rubber rod rubbed with cat's fur. The silk becomes negatively charged, and the cat's fur becomes positively charged.

Known as Coulomb's law, discovered by Charles Coulomb in 1785 after his invention of the torsion balance (measures the force necessary to twist a charged rod suspended on a wire).

In Xerox (dry-copying) machines, positively charged black areas of the image of the page to be copied attract negatively charged black dust.

The fundamental law of electricity is similar to the law of gravity: the electric force (attractive or repulsive), F, between two charged objects, Q_1 and Q_2, is proportional to the product of the charges on the objects divided by the square of the distance, d, between them:

$$F \propto \frac{Q_1 Q_2}{d^2}$$

The greater the charges, the larger the force; the longer the distance, the smaller the force.

The coulometer is analogous to a water-meter.

An electric current may be considered as a flow of electricity through a wire (conductor). The practical unit of charge—meaning the quantity of electricity—is the coulomb (C), measured with a coulometer.

Theory of Electricity

Michael Faraday (1833) studied the chemical changes that occur when electricity is passed through liquids, such as molten sodium chloride or sodium chloride dissolved in water (Chap. 15). To explain these chemical changes, George Johnstone Stoney in 1874 concluded that electricity, like matter, is quantized; it is atomic in nature and consists of particles. "Nature," Stoney said, "presents us with a *single definite quantity of electricity* which is independent of the particular bodies (substances) acted on." He called the "atom of electricity" the **electron,** a particle that carries a definite charge of electricity. He calculated that the charge of the electron is 10^{-20} coulomb, later corrected to 1.6×10^{-19} coulomb. By direct experimentation (page 142), Robert Milliken (1911) proved that the electron always carries the definite and unchanging charge of 1.6×10^{-19} coulomb. This means that electricity is a stream of individual particles, called electrons, each carrying 1.6×10^{-19} coulomb of electricity.

Elektron, Greek for amber; recall that amber is electrified when rubbed with wool or silk.

Electric Discharge Tubes

The passage of an electric current through a gas, called an electric discharge, was studied by Faraday, William Crookes, and many other investigators. The results of these studies are best explained in terms of the electron particle suggested by Stoney.

A sealed glass tube with two electrodes attached to a source of electricity constitutes a discharge tube (Fig. 4.4 a). The electrodes are the metal rods through which current enters $(-)$ and leaves $(+)$ the tube. When the gas pressure in the tube is reduced to about 10 torr, electric current flows, and the gas fluoresces (emits light like a fluorescent lamp). When the pressure is reduced, emission of light by the gas stops. The current, however, still flows between the electrodes, and if the positive (anode) end of the tube is coated with a luminescent material, it glows brilliantly like a television picture tube. The TV picture tube is, in fact, a discharge tube. It thus appears that a radiation is emitted from the cathode (the negative electrode). This radiation, because of its origin, is named the **"cathode ray,"** or more correctly, an **electron beam.**

These electrons behave like molecules in motion; a powerful (dangerous) beam of electrons can push a toy sailboat. Thus, the electrons, like molecules, possess mass. But unlike molecules, they are deflected (repelled and attracted) in electric fields in a manner predicted for negatively charged particles (Fig. 4.4 b). These properties are independent of the nature of the gas in the tube. These experiments, especially those performed by Joseph J. Thomson (1897) established the particle character of the

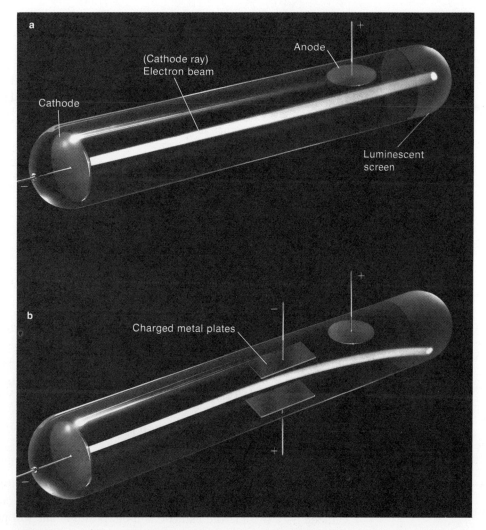

FIGURE 4.4 (a) A discharge tube showing the production of an electron beam (cathode ray). (b) Experiment showing that the electron beam possesses a negative charge; note position of the beam in an electric field. The beam is repelled by the negative plate and attracted to the positive plate. The gas pressure in the tube is about 10^{-3} torr.

electron. From such experiments, the mass of the electron is calculated as 9.11×10^{-28} g and the charge of the electron as 1.60×10^{-19} coulomb. This is in agreement with the previously determined electronic charge based on Faraday's discoveries. We thus conclude that 1.6×10^{-19} coulomb is the natural and fundamental charge of electricity and that any given quantity of electricity must be a multiple of 1.6×10^{-19} coulomb; that is, 1.6×10^{-19} coulomb times a whole number. The electron is therefore used as a unit of electric charge, designated as -1. The search for an electrical charge less than 1.6×10^{-19} coulomb has not been successful (page 203).

The mass and charge of the electron are independent of the nature of the gas in the discharge tube and of the materials of which the tube is composed. Also, electrons from other sources, such as a hot cathode in a radio or television tube, possess the same charge and mass. This, with the observation that the mass of the electron is about 2×10^3 times smaller than the lightest atom known, implies that *the electron is a universal constituent of matter.*

Wilhelm Röntgen, while performing experiments on electron beams, discovered

Thomson wrote: "However we twist and deflect the cathode rays the negative electricity follows the same path as the cathode ray."

However, these experiments do not prove that the electron is without structure.

in 1895 a radiation that penetrates metal plates, which are not penetrated by light and electrons. This radiation, named the **X-ray,** is produced when high-speed electrons strike a dense object. X-rays are of the same nature as light, radio "waves," radar, and ultraviolet radiation (page 191). They affect a photographic plate, and they can be reflected, but they are not deflected in an electric field. In addition, they *ionize* gases. The conversion of neutral particles to charged particles, called **ions,** is **ionization.** The removal of electrons from a neutral particle leaves the particle positively charged. A neutral particle becomes negatively charged when it acquires electrons:

$$\text{Na (atom)} \xrightarrow{\text{ionization}} \text{Na}^+ \text{(ion)} + \text{e}^- \text{(electron)}$$
$$0 \xrightarrow{} +1 \qquad -1 \quad = 0$$

$$\text{Ca (atom)} \xrightarrow{\text{ionization}} \text{Ca}^{2+} \text{(ion)} + 2\text{e}^- \text{(electron)}$$
$$0 \xrightarrow{} +2 \qquad -2 \quad = 0$$

$$\text{F (atom)} + \text{e}^- \text{(electron)} \xrightarrow{\text{ionization}} \text{F}^- \text{(ion)}$$
$$0 \qquad -1 \xrightarrow{} -1$$

$$\text{H}^+ \text{(ion)} + 2\text{e}^- \text{(electron)} \longrightarrow \text{H}^- \text{(ion)}$$
$$+1 \qquad -2 \longrightarrow -1$$

Charges are thus not created or destroyed. After *any* change, no matter what kind of language is used to describe the change—electrification, friction, frictional contact, ionization, chemical change, physical change, nuclear reactions, atomic reactions, ionic combination, oxidation, reduction, and so on—the sum of the resulting charges must equal the sum of the charges (0, +, −) before the change occurs.

PROBLEM 6   **(a) A molecule of hydrogen chloride, HCl, is ionized to H and Cl⁻. What is the charge on H? (b) Two electrons are added to an oxygen atom. What is the charge on the resulting ion?**

The Positive Ions   An electron beam ionizes neutral particles—atoms or molecules—into electrons and positive ions:

$$\text{H (atom)} \longrightarrow \text{H}^+ \text{(ion)} + \text{e}^- \text{(electron)}$$

$$\text{CO}_2 \text{(molecule)} \longrightarrow \text{CO}_2^+ \text{(ion)} + \text{e}^- \text{(electron)}$$

Electrons (−) are attracted to the anode (+); the positive ions are attracted to the cathode (−). If a pierced cathode is used, positive ions will pass through the holes

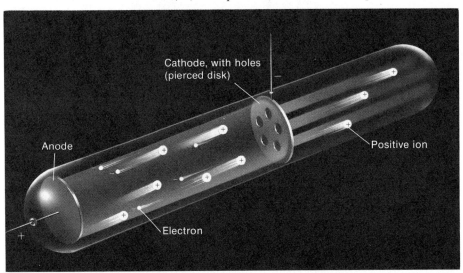

FIGURE 4.5 Discharge tube for producing positive ions.

(Fig. 4.5). Eugen Goldstein performed such an experiment in 1866 and detected these positive ions. Unlike electrons, the nature of the positive ion is *characteristic* of the gas being ionized. The mass of the positive ion depends on the mass of the atom or the molecule being ionized. Since positive ions are produced by the removal of one or two electrons from neutral particles, the mass of the ion is almost equal to that of the neutral particle. Under controlled conditions, only one electron may be removed. Mass determination of positive ions is the basis of the most widely used methods of determining atomic and molecular weights.

ATOMIC WEIGHTS OF ELEMENTS: _____ 4.6
MASS SPECTROMETER

The quantity that a chemist calls the atomic weight of an element is not the mass of one atom. It is the mass of one atom relative to the mass of another atom.

We shall now study how the atomic weights of the elements, as found in nature, are determined. The instrument developed by Joseph Thomson (about 1910), Francis Aston, Arthur Dempster, Kenneth Bainbridge, Alfred Nier, and many others to measure the mass of positive ions is known as a **mass spectrometer.** Several types are in use; only one will be described.

Atoms or molecules are bombarded with an electron beam to produce ions carrying a charge of $1+$ such as H^+, H_2^+, He^+, O^+, C^+, or H_2O^+. As shown in Fig. 4.6, the positive ions are then accelerated ("pushed") by an electric field to the *same kinetic energy* into a long straight tube. At the end of the tube an ion detector detects the arrival of the ions. The lighter the ion, the shorter the time required to reach the ion detector.

Although it appears possible to measure the mass of a charged atom from its

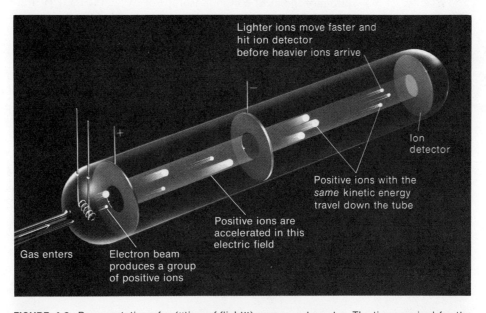

Lighter ions move faster and hit ion detector before heavier ions arrive

Ion detector

Positive ions with the *same* kinetic energy travel down the tube

Positive ions are accelerated in this electric field

Gas enters

Electron beam produces a group of positive ions

FIGURE 4.6 Representation of a ("time-of-flight") mass spectrometer. The time required for the positive ions to reach the ion detector is measured. The heavier ion takes a longer time to travel down the tube. The ion detector is a metal plate connected to a galvanometer, an instrument for measuring an electric current. The apparatus is vacuum sealed; gas pressure is about 10^{-6} torr.

motion (kinetic energy), it is more practical to measure *relative masses*. The ions of different masses have the same kinetic energy; thus

$$E_{k_1} = E_{k_2}$$
$$\tfrac{1}{2}\,m_1v_1{}^2 = \tfrac{1}{2}\,m_2v_2{}^2 \quad \text{or} \quad m_1v_1{}^2 = m_2v_2{}^2 \qquad (1)$$

This is the same as the equation known as Graham's law (p. 67). The lighter the ion, the faster it moves. But the time required for an ion to travel the distance of the tube is inversely proportional to its velocity—the faster the ion, the shorter the flight time, *t*, the time required to reach the detector (Example 14, page 68). Thus, Equation (1) also tells us that the *relative masses* of the ions are related to their flight times. The *heavier* the ion, the slower it will travel, and the longer the time required to cover the distance of the tube. The same principle applies to other objects. If an equal force (muscular effort) is applied for the same length of time to a golf ball and to a bowling ball, the lighter golf ball will move faster and cover a given distance in less time.

PROBLEM 7   **A dense hardball is 5 times more massive than a softball. Both balls are thrown at a target so that they have the same kinetic energy. Which ball will strike the target first?**

We shall now study how this mass spectrometer is used to determine atomic weights. When atoms of the element helium are accelerated in the mass spectrometer, *two different flight times* are observed. We must therefore conclude that there are two kinds of helium atoms, differing in mass. Actually, one atom of helium is found to be 1.3271 times more massive than the other atom. Atoms of the same element having different masses are called **isotopes.*** Like pennies, some isotopes are slightly heavier than others. Oxygen possesses three isotopes.

While the atom of the most common isotope of helium is 1.3271 times more massive than the other atoms of helium, the mass spectrometer also tells us that an atom of the most common isotope of oxygen is 1.33291 times more massive than the atom of the most common isotope of carbon:

$$\frac{\text{mass of 1 atom of oxygen}}{\text{mass of 1 atom of carbon}} = 1.33291$$

On the other hand, the atom of the most common isotope of carbon is 2.9981 times more massive than the atom of the most common isotope of helium:

$$\frac{\text{mass of 1 atom of carbon}}{\text{mass of 1 atom of helium}} = 2.9981$$

Since we cannot weigh a single atom, a standard number is needed to compare conveniently the masses in grams of the atoms. We are at liberty to choose any number, a dozen (12), a gross (144), 10^{20}, or 2.06×10^{24}. Each is equally correct:

$$\frac{(144\ \cancel{\text{atoms}}) \times (\text{mass of 1 atom of oxygen})}{(144\ \cancel{\text{atoms}}) \times (\text{mass of 1 atom of carbon})} = 1.33291$$

or

$$\frac{(10^{20}\ \cancel{\text{atoms}}) \times (\text{mass of 1 atom of oxygen})}{(10^{20}\ \cancel{\text{atoms}}) \times (\text{mass of 1 atom of carbon})} = 1.33291$$

---

*Named, from the Greek word *isotopos,* meaning "same place," by Frederick Soddy (1914), to indicate that these atoms occupy the same position in the periodic system of elements (Chap. 7). The existence of isotopes was noted in 1913 by Kasimir Fajans.

A standard number is chosen to avoid confusion. This *standard number,* and the *amount of substance* in this number, is called the **mole.*** By common consent, the mole is defined as *the amount of substance which contains as many particles as there are carbon atoms in exactly 12 g of the most common isotope of carbon.*** This isotope of carbon is therefore given the name "carbon-12" and the symbol ^{12}C. We can then say that 1 mole of ^{12}C has mass of 12 g, written as 12 g/mole. This mass also represents the atomic weight of the ^{12}C isotope.

0.012 kg

From experiment (page 137), the value of the standard number is $(6.02209 \pm 0.00001) \times 10^{23}$ particles, or 6.02×10^{23} particles/mole. This means that 6.02209×10^{23} atoms of carbon-12 have a mass of exactly 12 g:

$$\text{mass of 1 } ^{12}C \text{ atom, } \frac{\text{g}}{\cancel{\text{atom}}} \times 6.02209 \times 10^{23} \frac{\cancel{\text{atoms}}}{\text{mole}} = 12 \frac{\text{g}}{\text{mole}} \text{ (exactly)}$$

This standard number is less troublesome than a dozen or a gross.

PROBLEM 8   **One penny has a mass of 3.15 g. Calculate the mass of (a) 1 dozen, (b) 1 mole of pennies.**

PROBLEM 9   **The mass of an atom of carbon-12 isotope is 1.993×10^{-23} g. Calculate the mass of ^{12}C atoms in 1 dozen, 1 gross, and 1 mole.**

The mole represents 6.02×10^{23} particles and therefore must contain the mass of these 6.02×10^{23} particles. In the same sense, a dozen dimes contains the mass of 12 dimes.

We call this standard number the Avogadro number, N_A. Then, a mole of atoms contains N_A atoms, a mole of molecules contains N_A molecules, and a mole of electrons contains N_A electrons. Therefore, the quantity of substance in a mole may be expressed as 6.02×10^{23} particles per mole. From experiment, we also know that one mole of any (ideal) gas, regardless of its mass, occupies 22.4136 liters (STP). The quantity of substance in a mole may therefore also be expressed as 22.4 ℓ (STP) per mole of gas.

Named in honor of Amedeo Avogadro (page 112).

One mole of oxygen atoms obtained from air contains 6.0221×10^{23} O atoms and has a mass of 15.9994 g; one mole of fluorine atoms contains 6.0221×10^{23} F atoms and has a mass of 18.9984 g. Then these masses, 15.9994 and 18.9984, are the atomic weights of these elements; they represent the *relative weights* of one atom of each of these elements. The mass of 1 mole of atoms (6.02×10^{23} atoms) of an element represents the **atomic weight** of that element. For example,

$$\text{mass of 1 atom of F} \times 6.02209 \times 10^{23} \frac{\text{atoms}}{\text{mole}} = ?$$

$$\text{mass of 1 atom of } ^{12}C \times 6.02209 \times 10^{23} \frac{\text{atoms}}{\text{mole}} = 12 \frac{\text{g}}{\text{mole}}$$

Divide one equation by the other:

$$\frac{\text{mass F atom} \times \cancel{6.02209 \times 10^{23}}}{\text{mass of } ^{12}C \text{ atom} \times \cancel{6.02209 \times 10^{23}}} = \frac{?}{12 \frac{\text{g}}{\text{mole}}}$$

---

* Introduced by Wilhelm Ostwald (1896), from *moles,* Latin for "mass" or "bulk," used in the sense of describing a collection of a fixed number of similar objects, such as a gross of eggs or a gross of dimes.

** By a majority vote of chemists taken in 1905 through the International Union of Pure and Applied Chemistry, the value 32.0000 g of molecular oxygen, O_2, was chosen to avoid a number smaller than 1 for the atomic weight of hydrogen, the lightest element known. In 1961, this was changed to ^{12}C = exactly 12. This produced only small changes in atomic weights; for example, the atomic weight of fluorine changed from 19.0045 to 18.9984.

This does away with the Avogadro number and leaves us with

$$\frac{\text{mass F atom}}{\text{mass } ^{12}\text{C atom}} \times 12 \,\frac{\text{g}}{\text{mole}} = ?$$

But the ratio mass F atom/mass ^{12}C atom is just the kind of information the mass spectrometer gives us; the atom of F is 1.58320 times more massive than the ^{12}C atom:

$$\frac{\text{mass F atom}}{\text{mass } ^{12}\text{C atom}} = 1.58320$$

So

$$1.58320 \times 12 \,\frac{\text{g}}{\text{mole}} = 18.9984 \,\frac{\text{g}}{\text{mole}}$$

Thus, 1 mole of F atoms has a mass of 18.9984 g, or its atomic weight is 18.9984.* So, when chemists say, "The atomic weight of lead, Pb, is 207.2," they mean that 1 mole of Pb atoms (6.02×10^{23} atoms) has a mass of 207.2 g. We also say that the atomic weight of Pb is 207.2 g/mole Pb atoms. The dimensional units of an atomic weight are grams per mole of atoms.

IUPAC terminology prefers to say, "the molar mass of Pb is 207.2 g/mole."

PROBLEM 10   Fill in the dashes for gaseous helium (see inside back cover): _____ g/mole He atoms; _____ liters (STP)/mole; _____ He atoms/mole.

PROBLEM 11   The mass of 100 nickels is 500 g. The mass of 100 dimes is 240 g. What is the mass of (a) 1 nickel, (b) 1 dime? Show that 240 and 500 may be used to represent the relative weights of 1 nickel and 1 dime.

PROBLEM 12 6.02×10^{23} atoms of the element nickel, Ni, have a mass of 58.7 g. The same number of tin, Sn, atoms has a mass of 119 g. Write the atomic weights of Ni and Sn. Write the relative weight of 1 atom of Sn to 1 atom of Ni.

Compared to ^{12}C, the atomic weight of the most common isotope of oxygen (see page 122) is $(1.33291 \times 12) = 15.9949$. This isotope is called "oxygen-16," written as ^{16}O. The atomic weights of the other isotopes of oxygen are 16.9991 and 17.9992, called oxygen-17 and oxygen-18 and written as ^{17}O and ^{18}O. In these symbols, the superscript, the nearest whole number to the atomic weight of the isotope, is called the **mass number.**

   To convert the atomic weights of the isotopes of an element to an average atomic weight of the element, as found in nature, the relative number of atoms of each isotope present must be known. This situation is comparable to the calculation of the average weight of a collection of golf balls, 90.0 % of which have individual weights of 70.0 g and 10.0 % of which have individual weights of 71.1 g. The average weight of the golf balls is then

$$70.0 \,\frac{\text{g}}{\text{ball}} \times 90.0\,\% + 71.1 \,\frac{\text{g}}{\text{ball}} \times 10.0\,\% = 70.0 \,\frac{\text{g}}{\text{ball}} \times 0.900 + 71.1 \,\frac{\text{g}}{\text{ball}} \times 0.100$$

$$= 63.0 \,\frac{\text{g}}{\text{ball}} + 7.11 \,\frac{\text{g}}{\text{ball}} = 70.1 \,\frac{\text{g}}{\text{ball}}$$

---

*Notice the cleverness of this scheme. The value of the Avogadro number is known from experiment, but it cancels out of the calculation. The mass of 1 mole of atoms can therefore be determined from mass spectrometer measurements without knowing the Avogadro number.

PROBLEM 13 In a collection of dimes and pennies, 60.0 % have individual masses of 2.40 g and 40.0 % have individual masses of 3.15 g. (a) Calculate the average weight of the coins. (b) The collection contains a total of 100 dimes and pennies; use your answer for the average weight to calculate the weight of the collection. (c) The collection contains 60 dimes and 40 pennies. From the data already given, 1 dime weighs 2.40 g and 1 penny weighs 3.15 g. Calculate the weight of the collection. Your answer to (c) should agree with your answer to (b).

In mass spectrometers, the ion detector also measures the relative number of atoms, the *relative abundance,* of each isotope. A graph, such as that in Fig. 4.7, showing the relative abundance of atoms as a function of mass number is known as a **mass spectrum.***

Example 2

Atmospheric oxygen consists of 99.756 % ^{16}O (atomic weight 15.9949), 0.039 % ^{17}O (16.9991), and 0.205 % ^{18}O (17.9992). Calculate the atomic weight of oxygen found in air.

Answer

To obtain the atomic weight of an element, calculate the average relative weight from the relative weight and the relative abundance of each isotope. Thus, the atomic weight of atmospheric oxygen is

15.9949 g/mole $\times$ 0.99756 + 16.9991 g/mole $\times$ 0.00039

$$+ \ 17.9992 \text{ g/mole} \times 0.00205 = 15.9994 \text{ g/mole}$$

---

*From the Latin word *spectrum,* meaning an appearance, an image, but now used to mean a beam, such as a beam of particles, a sound beam, or a light beam, separated into its individual components arranged in some order. We can also say that the opinions of a student body represent "a spectrum of political views."

FIGURE 4.7 The mass spectrum of antimony, Sb. This plot shows the relative number of atoms (peaks), the relative abundance of the two naturally-occurring isotopes, ^{121}Sb and ^{123}Sb, of antimony (silvery metal used in the manufacture of alloys; also exists as a yellow powder). The relative abundance is measured by the relative electric currents produced at the ion detector (Fig. 4.6, page 121) by the ions of the isotopes.

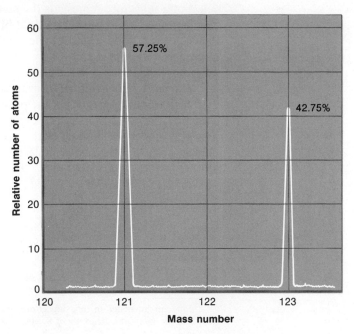

PROBLEM 14   Natural boron consists of 19.8 % ^{10}B, atomic weight 10.01 g/mole, and 80.2 % ^{11}B, atomic weight 11.01 g/mole. Find the atomic weight of natural boron. Check your answer against the Table of Atomic Weights (inside back cover).

Natural hydrogen consists of three isotopes. Of all the positive ions whose masses have been determined, the *lightest ion found*, mass number 1, atomic weight 1.00728, is obtained from protium, the lightest isotope of hydrogen, atomic weight 1.007825.

From protos, the Greek word for first.

This ion, named the **proton,** H$^+$, has a charge equal to that of an electron but opposite in sign, $+1$. The ion obtained from deuterium, an isotope of hydrogen of mass number 2, is known as the **deuteron,** D$^+$. The removal of 2 electrons from a helium atom produces an **alpha particle,** ^{4}He^{2+}.

The International Commission on Atomic Weights was established in 1900 by the International Union of Pure and Applied Chemistry and given the duty of issuing periodically a table of atomic weights after the consideration of all papers dealing with the subject. The values chosen by the Commission (inside back cover) become the **accepted atomic weights.**

Mass spectrometers also offer an extremely sensitive technique for the analysis of insecticides and complex biochemicals. Quantities as small as 10^{-12} g may be identified by the mass spectrum produced. For example, this technique combined with gas chromatography (page 31) shows that the organic matter discovered in meteorites is not of biological origin.* Mass spectrometers are also useful in manufacturing products as in the industrial separation of ^{235}U from ^{238}U for use in nuclear reactors (Chap. 17).

4.7 _____ **MOLECULAR WEIGHTS OF GASES; IDEAL GAS EQUATION**

Molecular weight is analogous to atomic weight. The molecular weight of a substance is not the mass of one molecule. It is the mass of one molecule relative to the mass of another molecule. The mass of 1 mole of molecules (6.02 $\times$ 10^{23} molecules) of a substance represents the **molecular weight** of that substance. Thus, when chemists say, "The molecular weight of water is 18," they mean that 1 mole of H$_2$O molecules (6.02 $\times$ 10^{23} H$_2$O molecules) has a mass of 18 g. We also say that the

IUPAC prefers to say, "the molar mass of H$_2$O is 18 g/mole."

molecular weight of H$_2$O is 18 g/mole. The dimensional units of a molecular weight are grams per mole of molecules.

The molecular weight of a gas may be calculated from the ideal gas laws (Chap. 2). Recall from Chapter 2 that the pressure, P, of a gas depends on the volume of its container, the number of molecules, N, in the gas, and the absolute temperature of the gas. This makes the product of the pressure and volume, PV, directly related (proportional) to the number of molecules, N, and the absolute temperature, T (page 67):

$$PV \propto NT$$

Now, the number of molecules depends on the number of moles; this is another way of saying that the number of molecules is proportional to the number of moles. If we double the number of moles, we double the number of molecules. Therefore, PV

_____

*Students interested in this subject are referred to "Interstellar Molecules and Cosmochemistry," *Annals of the New York Academy of Sciences,* volume 194, 3 May 1972.

must also be proportional to the number of moles, *n*. We can now say that *PV* depends on the number of moles and the absolute temperature:

$$PV \propto nT$$

This proportionality can now be written as an equality (equation) by introducing a proportionality constant, *R*:

$$PV = RnT$$

commonly written as

$$PV = nRT \qquad (2)$$

This operation is exactly identical to the derivation of the relationship between dimes and dollars:

$$\text{number of dimes, } d \propto D, \text{ number of dollars}$$

Inserting the proportionality constant, *k*,

$$d = kD$$

To determine the value of *k* and *its units,* information about dimes, *d*, and dollars, *D*, must be known. Since there are 10 dimes in 1 dollar,

$$10 \text{ dimes} = k \times 1 \text{ dollar}$$

from which

$$k = 10 \frac{\text{dimes}}{\text{dollar}}$$

giving us the general relationship

$$d \text{ (number of dimes)} = 10 \frac{\text{dimes}}{\text{dollar}} \times D \text{ (number of dollars)} \qquad (3)$$

Equation (3) may be used to convert any number of dollars to dimes or dimes to dollars. It cannot be used to convert dollars to pennies or to Mexican pesos. Similarly, to obtain the value and units of *R*, we use experimental data for *P*, *V*, *n*, and *T*. For *n* = 1 (exactly 1 mole of gas) at standard conditions, *P* = 1.0000 atm, *T* = 273.15 K, and *V* = 22.4136 *l*. Then, from Equation (2)

$$R = \frac{PV}{nT} = \frac{1.0000 \text{ atm} \times 22.4136 \; l}{1.0000 \text{ mole} \times 273.15 \text{ K}} = 0.082056 \frac{l \text{ atm}}{\text{mole K}}$$

Corrected for deviations from ideal gas behavior.

giving us

$$PV = 0.0821 \frac{l \text{ atm}}{\text{mole K}} nT$$

This general relationship is known as the **ideal gas law.** It is found, within experimental precision, that the proportionality constant *R* is the same for all gases. However, the value of *R* is used *only* when *P* is expressed in atm, *V* in liters, and *n* in moles, and *T* is the absolute temperature.

PROBLEM 15 Evaluate the proportionality constant, *R*, in the equation *PV = nRT* in units of pascal meter^3/(mole K), when *P* = 1.01×10^5 pascals, Pa, *V* = $22.4 \times 10^{-3} \text{ m}^3$, *T* = 273 K, and *n* = 1.00 mole.

1 atm = 1.01325×10^5 Pa

The ideal gas law may be used to calculate the molecular weights of gases.

Example 3

The density of nicotine (vapor), an addictive drug found in tobacco, is 1.68 g/ℓ at 327 °C and 388 torr. Calculate the molecular weight of nicotine.

Answer

First calculate n, the number of moles of nicotine in 1.00 ℓ at 327 °C and 388 torr. From Equation (2), page 127:

$$n = \frac{PV}{RT}$$

However, the units of R as calculated above are liter atm/(mole K), so we convert the given quantities to these units:

$$V = 1.00 \; \ell, \; P = 388 \; \text{torr} \times \frac{1 \; \text{atm}}{760 \; \text{torr}} = 0.511 \; \text{atm},$$

$$T = 327 \; °C + 273 = 600 \; K,$$

and then

$$n = \frac{0.511 \; \text{atm} \times 1.00 \; \ell}{0.0821 \; \frac{\ell \; \text{atm}}{\text{mole} \; K} \times 600 \; K} = 0.0104 \; \text{mole}$$

This number of moles, 0.0104 mole, *is the same for all gases in the same volume,* 1.00 liter, *at the same temperature,* 600 K, *and pressure,* 388 torr—merely a statement of Avogadro's law (page 71). But the density, the mass of the 1 liter, differs for different gases. For nicotine, the mass of the 1 liter and, therefore, the mass of 0.0104 mole is 1.68 g. Then the molecular weight of nicotine, the mass of 1 mole, is

$$\frac{1.68 \; g}{0.0104 \; \text{mole}} = 162 \; \frac{g}{\text{mole}}$$

Example 4

Hydrocarbons are compounds composed only of hydrogen and carbon. 0.483 g of the hydrocarbon pentane (colorless, flammable liquid) occupies 204 ml as a vapor at 100 °C and 765.0 torr. Calculate the molecular weight of pentane.

Answer

Calculate n:

$$n = \frac{PV}{RT}$$

$$V = 204 \; \text{ml} \times \frac{1 \; \ell}{10^3 \; \text{ml}} = 0.204 \; \ell$$

$$P = 765.0 \; \text{torr} \times \frac{1 \; \text{atm}}{760 \; \text{torr}} = 1.007 \; \text{atm}$$

$$T = 100 \; °C + 273 = 373 \; K$$

$$n = \frac{1.007 \; \text{atm} \times 0.204 \; \ell}{0.0821 \; \frac{\ell \; \text{atm}}{\text{mole} \; K} \times 373 \; K} = 0.00671 \; \text{mole}$$

Then the molecular weight of pentane, the mass of 1 mole, is

$$\frac{0.483 \; g}{0.00671 \; \text{mole}} = 72.0 \; \frac{g}{\text{mole}}$$

28.2 ml
6.02 × 10²³
molecules
44.0 g

22.4 liters (STP)
6.02 x 10²³ molecules
44.0 g

22.4 liters (STP)
6.02 × 10²³ molecules
2.02 g

22.4 liters (STP)
6.02 × 10²³ molecules
222 g

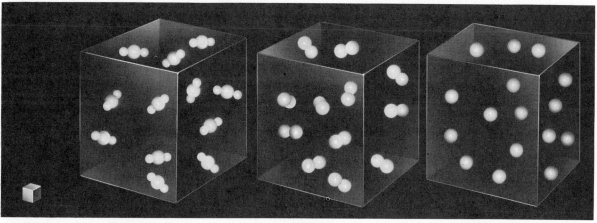

1 mole of
solid CO₂

1 mole CO₂
A triatomic* gas
Triatomic molecules

1 mole H₂
A diatomic* gas
Diatomic molecules

1 mole Rn**
A monatomic* gas
Monatomic molecules

*From *tri, di,* and *monos,* the Greek words for
three, two, and one.

**Rn, radon, a radioactive gas, consists of
individual atoms.

FIGURE 4.8 The molar volume of all *gases* is the same, 22.4 ℓ (STP), and contains the Avogadro number of molecules. On the other hand, the molecular volumes of liquids and solids vary considerably; for example, the volume occupied by one mole of solid CO_2, "Dry Ice" (−79 °C), is only 28.2 ml.

PROBLEM 16 **Trichloroethylene, used for degreasing metals and formerly used for coffee decaffeination, in high doses causes liver cancer. It has a mass of 2.75 g in a volume of 1.80 ℓ at 291 torr and 127 °C. Find its molecular weight.**

The volume occupied by 1 mole of a substance is known as the **molar volume.** The molar volume is the same for all (ideal) gases at the same temperature and the same pressure. At STP, the molar volume of gases is 22.4 ℓ/mole. See Fig. 4.8.

CONVERSIONS: SAME QUANTITY, DIFFERENT UNITS _____ 4.8

The same quantity of bread may be expressed in pounds, ounces, kilograms, grams, or number of slices. Depending on the situation, scientists may express the same quantity of a substance in units of mass, volume, amount of substance (mole), or number of particles. This requires the use of the proper conversion factor: 6.02×10^{23} particles/mole, 22.4 ℓ (STP)/mole, or g/mole. We play safe by always specifying the nature of the particle: use 1.0 g/mole H, not 1.0 g/mole hydrogen; use 2.0 g/mole H_2, not 2.0 g/mole hydrogen. Also acceptable is the language, "the molecular weight of H_2O is 18 g/mole," "the molecular weight of H_2 is 2.0 g/mole," "the atomic weight of H is 1.0 g/mole," "1 mole of H_2O has a mass of 18 g," "1 mole of H_2 has a mass of 2.0 g," "1 mole of H has a mass of 1.0 g," or "2 mole of H_2 has a mass of 4 g."

129

Example 5

Diethyl lysergamide (LSD) is a drug that produces a schizophrenic state, suppresses the essential brain chemical serotonin (page 727), inhibits formation of essential liver enzymes, and produces chromosome damage under certain conditions. It is one of the most potent and most dangerous of the "psyche-delics."* The molecular weight of LSD is 311.3 g/mole. Calculate the number of moles, ml (STP) as a gas, and molecules of LSD in 12.1 mg of LSD.

Answer

One mole has a mass of 311.3 g, and there are 10^3 mg in one gram; hence the number of moles is given by

$$12.1 \text{ mg} \times \frac{1 \text{ g}}{10^3 \text{ mg}} \times \frac{1 \text{ mole}}{311.3 \text{ g}} = 0.0389 \times 10^{-3} \text{ mole} = 3.89 \times 10^{-5} \text{ mole}$$

Since there are 22.4 l (STP) in 1 mole of gas,

$$3.89 \times 10^{-5} \text{ mole} \times \frac{22.4 \, l \text{ (STP)}}{1 \text{ mole}} \times \frac{10^3 \text{ ml}}{1 \, l} = 0.871 \text{ ml (STP)}$$

and since there are 6.02×10^{23} molecules in 1 mole,

$$3.89 \times 10^{-5} \text{ mole} \times 6.02 \times 10^{23} \frac{\text{molecules}}{\text{mole}} = 23.4 \times 10^{18} \text{ molecules}$$
$$= 2.34 \times 10^{19} \text{ molecules}$$

Example 6

The atomic weight of gold, Au, is 197 g/mole Au. How many grams are there in 0.0120 mole, and how many moles in 1.33×10^{20} Au atoms?

Answer

$$0.0120 \text{ mole Au} \times \frac{197 \text{ g}}{1 \text{ mole Au}} = 2.36 \text{ g}$$
$$1.33 \times 10^{20} \text{ atoms} \times \frac{1 \text{ mole}}{6.02 \times 10^{23} \text{ atoms}} = 0.221 \times 10^{-3} \text{ mole}$$
$$= 2.21 \times 10^{-4} \text{ mole}$$

Example 7

A quantity of butane, C_4H_{10}, occupies a volume of 6.22 l (STP). Find the number of moles of butane.

Answer

$$6.22 \, l \text{ (STP)} \times \frac{1 \text{ mole}}{22.4 \, l \text{ (STP)}} = 0.278 \text{ mole}$$

---

*The hallucinogenic effects of LSD were first described in 1943 by Albert Hofmann after he accidentally ingested some of the compound.

PROBLEM 17   The atomic weight of silver is 108 g/mole Ag. How many silver atoms are there (a) in 45.0 g of silver, (b) in 1 gross and 1 mole of silver atoms?

PROBLEM 18   The molecular weight of DDT, a potent but banned insecticide, is 354 g/mole. Calculate the number of (a) moles and (b) molecules of DDT in 118 g of DDT.

PROBLEM 19   The mass of formaldehyde* vapor in 1.40 ℓ at 1.50 atm and 47 °C is 2.40 g. (a) Calculate the molecular weight of formaldehyde. (b) Calculate the mass, number of molecules, and volume (STP) of 1.10 moles of formaldehyde. (c) Calculate the number of moles of formaldehyde in 120 g and in 67.2 ℓ (STP) of formaldehyde vapor.

MOLECULAR FORMULAS_____4.9

By convention, a chemical symbol such as C represents not only the element C but also a definite quantity of carbon, 1 mole of C atoms or 12.0 g. A molecular formula such as C_6H_6, benzene, tells you that there are six carbon atoms and six hydrogen atoms in one molecule of benzene. It also tells you that there are 6 moles of carbon atoms and 6 moles of hydrogen atoms in 1 mole of benzene. Thus, the molecular formula gives the *actual composition* in number of atoms per molecule or in number of moles of atoms per mole of molecules. Molecules are composed of atoms. The molecular weight must then be the sum of the atomic weights of all the atoms in the molecule. Thus, the molecular formula C_6H_6 also represents a definite quantity of the substance, 1 mole or 78 g $[(6 \times 12.0) + (6 \times 1.0)]$. A molecular formula summarizes the mass composition as the number of moles of each element per mole of compound. Hence, to calculate such a formula, the molecular weight, the mass composition of the substance, and the atomic weights of the constituent elements must be known. For example, the molecular weight of pentane (Example 4, page 128) is 72.0 g/mole and its mass composition is 16.7 % hydrogen and 83.3 % carbon. We can now calculate the mass of each element in 1 mole of pentane. Recall (page 110) that a percentage gives the number of parts in 100 parts.

$$72.0 \, \frac{\text{g compd}}{\text{mole compd}} \times \frac{16.7 \text{ g hydrogen}}{100 \text{ g compd}} = 12.0 \, \frac{\text{g hydrogen}}{\text{mole compd}}$$

$$72.0 \, \frac{\text{g compd}}{\text{mole compd}} \times \frac{83.3 \text{ g carbon}}{100 \text{ g compd}} = 60.0 \, \frac{\text{g carbon}}{\text{mole compd}}$$

But the atomic weight of hydrogen is 1.0 g/mole H, and that of carbon is 12.0 g/mole C. Therefore, the number of moles of atoms of each element per mole of compound is given by

$$12.0 \, \frac{\text{g hydrogen}}{\text{mole compd}} \times \frac{\text{mole H}}{1.0 \text{ g hydrogen}} = 12.0 \, \frac{\text{mole H}}{\text{mole compd}} = 12 \, \frac{\text{atoms of hydrogen}}{\text{molecule}}$$

$$60.0 \, \frac{\text{g carbon}}{\text{mole compd}} \times \frac{\text{mole C}}{12.0 \text{ g carbon}} = 5.00 \, \frac{\text{mole C}}{\text{mole compd}} = 5 \, \frac{\text{atoms of carbon}}{\text{molecule}}$$

The molecular formula of pentane is therefore C_5H_{12}.

---

*Generally sold as *formalin,* an aqueous solution of formaldehyde (colorless, very irritating odor), it is used as a disinfectant, as a preservative of biological samples, and in the manufacture of plastics, embalming fluids, and wash-wear textiles.

Example 8

Sucrose, cane sugar, 342.3 g/mole, contains 42.1 % carbon, 6.48 % hydrogen, and 51.4 % oxygen by mass. Find the molecular formula of sucrose. See inside back cover for the table of atomic weights.

Answer

A molecular formula represents the number of moles of the elements per mole of compound. So, first calculate the mass of each element in 1 mole of compound:

$$342.3 \frac{g\ compd}{mole\ compd} \times \frac{42.1\ g\ carbon}{100\ g\ compd} = 144 \frac{g\ carbon}{mole\ compd}$$

$$342.3 \frac{g\ compd}{mole\ compd} \times \frac{6.48\ g\ hydrogen}{100\ g\ compd} = 22.2 \frac{g\ hydrogen}{mole\ compd}$$

$$342.3 \frac{g\ compd}{mole\ compd} \times \frac{51.4\ g\ oxygen}{100\ g\ compd} = 176 \frac{g\ oxygen}{mole\ compd}$$

Then, convert these masses to the corresponding numbers of moles of elements:

$$144 \frac{g\ carbon}{mole\ compd} \times \frac{mole\ C}{12.0\ g\ carbon} = 12.0 \frac{mole\ C}{mole\ compd} = 12 \frac{atoms\ of\ carbon}{molecule}$$

$$22.2 \frac{g\ hydrogen}{mole\ compd} \times \frac{mole\ H}{1.01\ g\ hydrogen} = 22.0 \frac{mole\ H}{mole\ compd} = 22 \frac{atoms\ of\ hydrogen}{molecule}$$

$$176 \frac{g\ oxygen}{mole\ compd} \times \frac{mole\ O}{16.0\ g\ oxygen} = 11.0 \frac{mole\ O}{mole\ compd} = 11 \frac{atoms\ of\ oxygen}{molecule}$$

The molecular formula is therefore $C_{12}H_{22}O_{11}$.

Accuracy of molecular weights obtained from the ideal gas equation is limited by accuracy of Boyle's, Charles', and Avogadro's laws.

A more accurate molecular weight of a substance may be calculated from its molecular formula. For sucrose, the accurate molecular weight is 342.299 g/mole ($12 \times 12.011 + 22 \times 1.0079 + 11 \times 15.9994 = 342.299$).

PROBLEM 20 The recent discoveries of compounds of carbon, nitrogen, oxygen, and hydrogen in outer space from "spectral fingerprints" (page 191) are significant in discussions on theories of the origin of life. One such compound, dimethyl ether, a colorless gas with a molecular weight of 46.1 g/mole, has the mass composition 52.1 % carbon, 13.2 % hydrogen, and 34.7 % oxygen. Calculate the molecular formula of dimethyl ether and its accurate molecular weight.

4.10 _____ EMPIRICAL FORMULAS

It is evident that if the molecular weight of a substance is unknown, then its molecular formula cannot be calculated. For such substances, however, it is possible to calculate the **empirical (*simplest*)** *formula—the smallest whole-number ratio in which the atoms combine.* For example, the empirical formula corresponding to benzene, C_6H_6, is CH. This is the empirical formula because C_1H_1 is the smallest whole-number ratio that can be written for the atoms in one molecule of this compound.

Chemists do not like to write formulas like $C_{0.5}H_{0.5}$. However, notice that *the empirical formula is related to the molecular formula by a whole number,* 6 in this case. The empirical formula for saccharin, discovered in 1879 and used as a non-caloric sweetening agent in nearly all countries of the world, is $C_7H_5NSO_3$. This is the empirical formula because $C_7H_5NSO_3$ is the smallest whole-number ratio that can be written for the atoms in one molecule of saccharin. However, since the molecular weight of saccharin is 183 g/mole, $C_7H_5NSO_3$ is also its molecular formula. The empirical formula is thus related to the molecular formula by a whole number, 1 in this case.

In large doses, saccharin produces liver cancer in mice.

The mass composition expresses the relative masses of the elements in a particular compound. If we divide each relative mass by the atomic weight of the corresponding element, the relative number of moles of each constituent element is obtained.

Example 9

The compound tetrahydrocannabinol, $C_{12}H_{30}O_2$, responsible for the hallucinogenic ("high") effect of marijuana,* is metabolized to a compound containing 76.36 % carbon, 9.18 % hydrogen, and 14.55 % oxygen. What is the simplest (empirical) formula of this metabolite (product of metabolism)?

Answer

Dividing the relative mass of each element by its atomic weight gives the relative number of moles of the elements; for

$$\textbf{carbon:}\quad 76.36 \text{ g carbon} \times \frac{1 \text{ mole C}}{12.0 \text{ g carbon}} = 6.36 \text{ moles C}$$

$$\textbf{hydrogen:}\quad 9.18 \text{ g hydrogen} \times \frac{1 \text{ mole H}}{1.01 \text{ g hydrogen}} = 9.09 \text{ moles H}$$

$$\textbf{oxygen:}\quad 14.55 \text{ g oxygen} \times \frac{1 \text{ mole O}}{16.0 \text{ g oxygen}} = 0.909 \text{ mole O}$$

The relative numbers of moles of the elements are thus

$$6.36 \text{ C to } 9.09 \text{ H to } 0.909 \text{ O}$$

or $C_{6.36}H_{9.09}O_{0.909}$. To find the relative whole-number ratios, divide by the smallest number, 0.909:

$$\frac{6.36}{0.909} \text{ C to } \frac{9.09}{0.909} \text{ H to } \frac{0.909}{0.909} \text{ O}$$

---

*The major difference between tetrahydrocannabinol (THC) (marijuana) and alcohol is in the greater depressing effect of alcohol on muscular coordination, whereas THC greatly alters sensory stimuli to the brain (alters mental functions). From a review of the death statistics in 17 nations, it can be concluded that cigarette smoking is the strongest factor limiting the life expectancy of adults. Readers interested in these subjects are referred to "Marijuana: The Grass May No Longer Be Greener," *Science,* volume 185, 1974, pages 683, 775, and volume 190, 1975, pages 865, 912; "Effects of Marijuana," *Nature,* volume 241, 1973, page 137; *Science,* volume 192, 14 May 1976, page 647; "Chronic Cannabis Use," *Annals of New York Academy of Sciences,* volume 282, 30 December 1976; and "Alcohol and Health," First Special Report to the U.S. Congress, National Institute on Alcohol Abuse and Alcoholism, December 1971.

yielding

7 C to 10 H to 1 O

or $C_7H_{10}O$. For each O atom, there are 7 C atoms and 10 H atoms; the simplest (empirical) formula is, therefore, $C_7H_{10}O$.

PROBLEM 21 **Mercury(II) chloride, a colorless, poisonous solid, consists by mass of 73.9 % mercury and 26.1 % chlorine. What is its empirical formula?**

The sum of the atomic weights of all the atoms indicated by either an empirical formula or a molecular formula is called a formula weight; the molecular weight is, of course, related to the formula weight by a whole number. By general usage, the dimensional units of a formula weight, like a molecular weight, are grams per mole.

Example 10

(a) What is the formula weight of hydroxytetrahydrocannabinol, $C_7H_{10}O$?
(b) The molecular weight of this compound is 330 g/mole. Find its molecular formula.

Answer

(a) The formula weight $= 7 \times$ atomic weight of carbon $+ 10 \times$ atomic weight of hydrogen $+ 1 \times$ atomic weight of oxygen $= 7 \times 12.0 + 10 \times 1.0 + 1 \times 16.0 = 110$. The formula weight is 100 g/mole of $C_7H_{10}O$. (b) Since the molecular weight is related to the formula weight by a whole number, the molecular formula must be three times $\left(\dfrac{330}{110} = 3\right)$ the simplest (empirical) formula; namely, $C_{21}H_{30}O_3$.

A colorless liquid, main ingredient of vinegar, pure liquid acetic acid (f.p. 16.6 °C) is called "glacial acetic acid" from the days when it froze in cold laboratories.

PROBLEM 22 **Acetic acid and formaldehyde have the same empirical formula, CH_2O. (a) What is the formula weight? (b) The molecular weight of acetic acid is 60 g/mole and that of formaldehyde is 30 g/mole. Find the molecular formula of each of these compounds. (c) Calculate the accurate molecular weight of acetic acid to 5 significant figures.**

Formulas derived from molecular weights of substances in the gaseous state are valid only for the gaseous state. We are not justified in assuming that the ultimate particles of liquids and solids must be identical with the molecules of the corresponding gaseous state. For example, the molecular weight of sodium chloride vapor is about 59, determined at 1970 °C and atmospheric pressure. Since the sum of the atomic weights of Na and Cl is 59, we conclude that the vapor consists essentially of NaCl molecules; NaCl is thus the molecular formula for sodium chloride in the vapor state at about 2000 °C. But solid *sodium chloride* is a typical *ionic compound*. The solid is not composed of NaCl or $(NaCl)_2$ or $(NaCl)_x$ molecules; nor is it composed of sodium atoms and chlorine atoms. Rather, it is composed of positively charged sodium ions (Na^+) and negatively charged chloride ions (Cl^-). It is, therefore, impossible to write a molecular formula for an ionic solid. However, an empirical formula—for example, NaCl for sodium chloride—is acceptable. By general usage, the dimensional units of a formula weight of an ionic substance, like a molecular weight, are grams per mole.

While others were studying mass relationships, Joseph Louis Gay-Lussac measured the volumes of gases involved in chemical changes. He concluded (1808) that *when gases react, the volumes consumed and produced, measured at the same temperature and pressure, are in ratios of small whole numbers.* For example, at the same temperature and pressure:

20.0 ml hydrogen gas combines with 10.0 ml oxygen gas to produce 20.0 ml water vapor (20.0 ml to 10.0 ml to 20.0 ml, the same as 2 volumes to 1 volume to 2 volumes).

10.6 ml hydrogen gas combines with 10.6 ml chlorine gas to produce 21.2 ml hydrogen chloride (colorless, corrosive, poisonous) gas (10.6 ml to 10.6 ml to 21.2 ml, the same as 1 volume to 1 volume to 2 volumes).

12 ml hydrogen gas combines with 4.0 ml nitrogen gas to produce 8.0 ml ammonia gas (12 ml to 4.0 ml to 8.0 ml, the same as 3 volumes to 1 volume to 2 volumes).

6.3 ml water vapor combines with solid carbon to produce 6.3 ml hydrogen and 6.3 ml carbon monoxide gas (ratios, 1 to 1 to 1).

Dalton's atomic theory explained only mass relationships; it could not explain these observed volume relationships. However, in 1811 Amedeo Avogadro, whose theoretical work was ignored for half a century, showed how these volume relationships may be explained. He assumed that
Molecules of elements are composed of similar atoms.
Molecules of compounds are not composed of similar atoms.
Equal volumes of all gases differing in mass but at the same conditions of temperature and pressure contain the same number of molecules. Dalton rejected Gay-Lussac's results and Avogadro's hypothesis, now known as Avogadro's law (page 71).
Let N be the number of molecules in a given volume of gas. Then, according to the Avogadro hypothesis (assumption), the experimental observation

1 volume of hydrogen	combines with +	1 volume of chlorine	to produce →	2 volumes of hydrogen chloride

means that

N molecules of hydrogen	combines with +	N molecules of chlorine	to produce →	2 N molecules of hydrogen chloride

Now, dividing by N yields

1 molecule of hydrogen	combines with +	1 molecule of chlorine	to produce →	2 molecules of hydrogen chloride

A molecule of hydrogen chloride must contain at least 1 atom of hydrogen and 1 atom of chlorine. The symbol HCl may then be used to represent a hydrogen chloride molecule. But there are 2 hydrogen chloride molecules for every 1 hydrogen molecule and 1 chlorine molecule. Hence, to satisfy the law of conservation of matter, 1 hydrogen molecule must contain at least 2 hydrogen atoms and 1 chlorine molecule must contain at least 2 chlorine atoms:

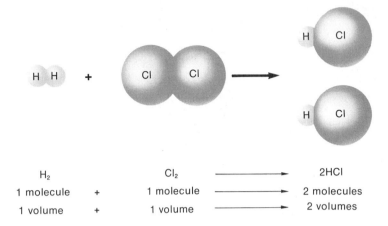

H_2

1 molecule +

1 volume +

Cl_2 $\longrightarrow$ 2HCl

1 molecule $\longrightarrow$ 2 molecules

1 volume $\longrightarrow$ 2 volumes

This explanation, however, does not prove that hydrogen and chlorine molecules in the gaseous state are composed of 2 atoms (diatomic). Nor does it prove that hydrogen chloride molecules are composed of 1 atom of each of these elements. Thus, if we assume H_4, Cl_4, and H_2Cl_2 to be the molecules, we can write

$$H_4 + Cl_4 \longrightarrow 2H_2Cl_2$$

1 molecule + 1 molecule $\longrightarrow$ 2 molecules

1 volume + 1 volume $\longrightarrow$ 2 volumes

This also explains the volume relations experimentally observed, 1 to 1 to 2. We have, however, proved that the gaseous molecules of hydrogen and chlorine contain an even number of atoms (e.g., H_2 or H_4, Cl_2 or Cl_4), and *not* an odd number (*e.g.*, H or H_3, Cl or Cl_3).

If hydrogen and chlorine gases consisted of individual atoms (monatomic molecules), then

$$H + Cl \longrightarrow HCl$$

1 atom + 1 atom $\longrightarrow$ 1 molecule

or

1 molecule + 1 molecule $\longrightarrow$ 1 molecule

1 volume + 1 volume $\longrightarrow$ 1 volume

This disagrees with the experimentally observed combination of 1 volume to 1 volume to 2 volumes. Experimentally determined molecular and atomic weights prove that H_2, Cl_2, and HCl are the correct molecular formulas.

Example 11

At a given temperature and pressure, 10 ml of arsenic gas, As_2, combines with 30 ml of chlorine, Cl_2, to produce arsenic trichloride: $As_2 + 3Cl_2 \longrightarrow 2AsCl_3$. How many ml of gaseous arsenic trichloride, $AsCl_3$,* are produced?

---

*When heated, arsenic, a toxic element, burns, producing a very poisonous oxide. Arsenic trichloride, an oily liquid at room temperature, is rapidly decomposed by water, with the formation of a cloud of hydrochloric acid and hydrated arsenic(III) oxide, $As_2O_3(H_2O)_x$.

Answer

From the Avogadro assumption, the given expression, $As_2 + 3Cl_2 \longrightarrow 2AsCl_3$, means that 1 molecule of As_2 combines with 3 molecules of Cl_2 to produce 2 molecules of arsenic trichloride. Further, the same number of different molecules at the same temperature and pressure occupy the same volume. The expression therefore also tells us that 1 volume of As_2 combines with 3 volumes of Cl_2 to produce 2 volumes of $AsCl_3$. Therefore, 10 ml of As_2 combines with 30 ml of Cl_2 to produce 20 ml of $AsCl_3$. In summary,

$$As_2 + 3Cl_2 \longrightarrow 2AsCl_3$$

means

$$1 \text{ molecule} + 3 \text{ molecules} \longrightarrow 2 \text{ molecules}$$

$$1 \text{ volume} + 3 \text{ volumes} \longrightarrow 2 \text{ volumes}$$

Hence,

$$10 \text{ ml} + 30 \text{ ml} \longrightarrow 20 \text{ ml}$$

PROBLEM 23   **At constant temperature and pressure, 20.0 ml carbon monoxide, CO, combines with oxygen, O_2, producing carbon dioxide: $2CO + O_2 \longrightarrow 2CO_2$. How many ml of oxygen are consumed?**

PROBLEM 24   **At constant temperature and pressure, 10 ml fluorine gas combines with 10 ml bromine gas, producing 20 ml bromine fluoride (red-brown, corrosive, poisonous gas). Use these data to show that each fluorine and bromine molecule most likely consists of two atoms rather than one.**

The law of combining volumes is *not* applicable to solids or liquids:

$$2H_2(gas) + O_2(gas) \longrightarrow 2H_2O(liquid)$$

$$40 \text{ liters of hydrogen} + 20 \text{ liters of oxygen} \longrightarrow 0.032 \text{ liter of water}$$

Also, the number of molecules does not necessarily remain constant during a chemical change. The number of molecules produced may be larger or smaller than the initial number. For example, 2 hydrogen molecules combine with 1 oxygen molecule but only 2 molecules of water are produced. Thus, atoms, but *not* molecules, are conserved in chemical changes. The atoms in molecules rearrange to produce different kinds and, frequently, different numbers of molecules.

COUNTING MOLECULES, DETERMINING THE AVOGADRO NUMBER _____ 4.12

The diameter of an atom is about 10^{-8} cm. If an atom were extended to the size of a grain of sugar, then the diameter of the sugar crystal would extend to about 8.8 km. Molecules, however, vary in size, roughly from 2×10^{-8} cm to 3000×10^{-8} cm. Although it is possible to obtain images of single atoms and molecules (Fig. 4.9), no one has yet invented an instrument to count neutral atoms and molecules. It is, however, possible to count charged particles with a Geiger counter.*

Radium, Ra, a radioactive element (Chap. 17), emits alpha particles, He^{2+},

---

*Invented by Hans Geiger and Ernest Rutherford in 1908. The charged particle, upon entering a gas-filled tube, ionizes the gas. The ions are then attracted to electrically charged plates, giving rise to a "pulse," a momentary flow of electric current. This current is amplified and used to operate a counter.

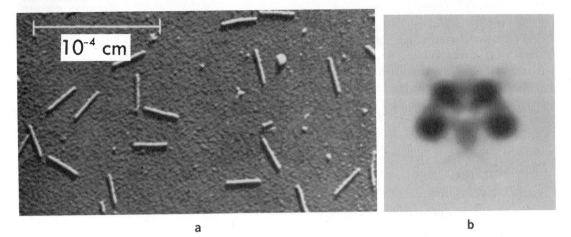

FIGURE 4.9 (a) Electron microscope image of large individual molecules, the molecules of tobacco mosaic virus, 2800 × 10⁻⁸ cm long by 152 × 10⁻⁸ cm in diameter, reproduced from photographs taken by Wendell Stanley and co-workers (1947). (*From* Gerald Oster, C. Knight, and W. Stanley, *Archives of Biochemistry,* volume 15, 1947, p. 279.) (b) The latest techniques in electron microscopy clearly reveal the images of the four mercury atoms and the one sulfur (smaller) atom in a molecule. (The other atoms in the molecule—carbon, oxygen, and hydrogen atoms—are too small to be revealed.) Photo courtesy of F. P. Ottensmeyer. The electron microscope was invented by Hans Busch in 1926.

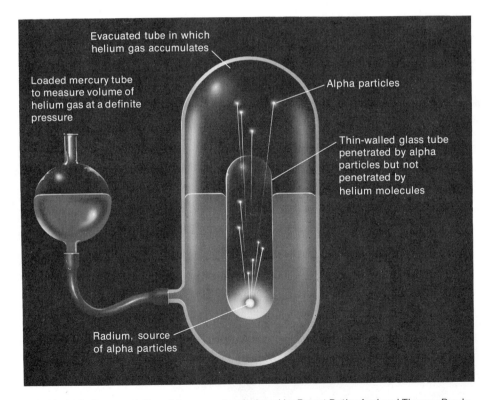

FIGURE 4.10 Representation of the apparatus designed by Ernest Rutherford and Thomas Royds, used to measure the volume of helium gas obtained from radium in the first direct determination (1910) of the Avogadro number.

which can be counted. One gram of Ra emits 11.6×10^{17} alpha particles in one year. Each alpha particle picks up 2 electrons and becomes a neutral molecule of helium gas, $He^{2+} + 2e^- \longrightarrow He$. The volume of the 11.6×10^{17} molecules is 0.0430 ml (STP) (Fig. 4.10). But there are 22.4×10^3 ml (STP) in 1 mole of any gas. Then, the number of molecules in 1 mole, the Avogadro number, is given by

$$\frac{22.4 \times 10^3 \text{ ml (STP)}}{1 \text{ mole}} \times \frac{11.6 \times 10^{17} \text{ molecules}}{0.0430 \text{ ml (STP)}} = 6.04 \times 10^{23} \frac{\text{molecules}}{\text{mole}}$$

The Avogadro number has been determined by several other methods, and the currently accepted value is $(6.02209 \pm 0.00001) \times 10^{23}$ particles/mole.

_____ EPILOG From J. L. Comstock, M.D., *Elements of Chemistry*, 1853

"Nothing, perhaps, even the sublimest works of nature, are more calculated to elicit the wonder and astonishment of a reflecting mind, than the fact that substances combine with each other in exact and definite quantities, and that these quantities or proportions, are the same in relation to the same substance throughout the world, and have been so ever since the creation. This discovery may be considered as a new proof, directed expressly to the present age, that the most minute works of what we call nature, do indeed bear the most indubitable marks of divine agency and design.

"But while the discovery itself is an evidence of the profound philosophy of the present age, the development of its principles, by the constant accession of new ideas, is calculated rather to humble the pride of human knowledge, by as constant a conviction, that after all our acquirements, we know comparatively nothing of the laws and operations of nature. The very fact, that the laws of proportions, now comparatively just known to man, have existed ever since the creation of mat-

ter, and have been in perpetual exercise all over the universe, without a suspicion of their existence, is of itself a sufficient proof of the almost entire ignorance of man even of the phenomena of nature, and a still stronger proof of his ignorance of her laws. And if facts, in themselves so simple, yet so wonderful, and when once known, so obvious, have escaped the observation of man for thousands of years, is it not probable that phenomena are constantly going on before our eyes, which, could we understand them, would astonish us still more, and at the same time afford a still stronger conviction of our ignorance, and want of penetration?

"These considerations, while they are calculated to humble the pride of human intellect, by showing how little we know of the laws which govern even the ordinary operations of nature, ought, by the conviction of ignorance, to prove an incentive to constant observation on natural phenomena, that, if possible, we might arrive at the knowledge of their true causes."

_____ PROBLEMS

(See inside back cover for atomic weights.)

25 Vocabulary Define or illustrate (a) law of conservation of matter; (b) law of constant composition; (c) the atomic theory of (i) matter, (ii) electricity; (d) quantization of (i) matter, (ii) electricity; (e) law of multiple proportions; (f) law of combining volumes; (g) monatomic molecules; (h) molar volume of gases; (i) Coulomb's law; (j) ionization; (k) isotopes, using ^{12}C, $^{12}C^+$, ^{13}C, ^{14}C, ^{15}N; (l) empirical formula, using acetylene, C_2H_2, butene, C_4H_8, and ethylene, C_2H_4.

26 Vocabulary Define or illustrate (a) the Avogadro law; (b) the Avogadro number; (c) triatomic molecule; (d) molecular weight; (e) atomic weight; (f) mole; (g) electron; (h) mass spectrum; (i) alpha particle; (j) proton; (k) mass number.

27 Conservation A beam of 200 molecules of Cl_2 collides with 50 atoms of C, forming 20 molecules of carbon tetrachloride, CCl_4. How many Cl_2 molecules and C atoms remain uncombined?

28 Constant composition (a) Carbon dioxide is composed of 27.3 % carbon and 72.7 % oxygen by mass. Find the quantity of carbon dioxide formed from 46.4 g of carbon. (b) Verify that carbon dioxide, CO_2, contains 27.3 % C.

29 Atomic theory A mixture contains 12 atoms of nitrogen and 8 atoms of oxygen. Show how these atoms may combine to satisfy (a) the law of constant composition, and (b) the law of conservation of matter.

30 In his discussion of forces between atoms, William Higgins would have used essentially the following diagram to represent the mass composition of phosphorus-oxygen compounds and to illustrate the combination of atoms:

Show that for a given mass of phosphorus, the masses of oxygen are in ratios of whole numbers.

31 The formulas of three oxides of carbon are C_3O_2 (tricarbon dioxide), CO, and CO_2. For each oxide, calculate the mass of carbon that combines with 8.0 g of oxygen. Are these carbon masses in a ratio of whole numbers? Are the results in agreement with the law of multiple proportions?

32 Atomic weight 500 dimes weigh 1200 g and 500 nickels weigh 2550 g, while 50 dimes weigh 120 g and 50 nickels weigh 255 g. (a) Find the weight of 1 dime and 1 nickel. (b) Show that for equal numbers of dimes and nickels, their relative weights are the same.

33 Natural rhenium consists of 37.40 % ^{185}Re, 184.95 g/mole, and 62.60 % ^{187}Re, 186.96 g/mole. Calculate the atomic weight of rhenium, an exceedingly rare metal.

34 Natural neon consists of three isotopes: ^{20}Ne, 90.5 %, 19.99 g/mole; ^{21}Ne, 0.27 %, 20.99 g/mole; and ^{22}Ne, 9.2 %, 21.99 g/mole. Find the atomic weight of neon.

35 Molecular weight Peroxyacetyl nitrate (PAN) produced in photochemical smogs (page 196) has a density of 1.85 g/liter at 380 torr and 125 °C. Find its molecular weight.

36 (a) Ethylene, a gaseous hydrocarbon, used mainly in the manufacture of plastics and whose production is expected to reach 1.5×10^{13} g/year, has a mass of 3.22 g in 750 ml at 25.0 °C and 2.85×10^3 torr. Find its molecular weight. (b) How many moles of ethylene are there in 1.5×10^{13} g?

37 (a) Hexachlorobenzene (b.p. 326 °C) is a popular antibacterial agent used in soaps, sprays, and skin cleansers. The density of its vapor at STP is 12.7 g/ℓ. Calculate its molecular weight. (b) The mass composition of hexachlorobenzene is 25.3 % C and 74.8 % Cl. Calculate its empirical formula. Write its molecular formula.

38 Mole You are responsible for purchasing steering wheels (weight: 5 kg/wheel), steering posts (20 kg/post), and threaded pipe (2 kg/pipe) to fit the wheel and post together for a specific car model, "*EZKRUSH*." An order arrives to furnish 10^5 cars. Would you order the same weight or the same number of these parts? In what way is this situation similar to the use of a mole?

39 During the operation of a storage battery (Chap. 15), 0.0108 mole of white solid lead sulfate, $PbSO_4$, is formed. Calculate the number of grams formed.

40 Find the number of moles of atoms and the number of atoms in 125 g of each of the following elements: (a) bromine, (b) sulfur, (c) chromium.

41 Express the following iodine quantities in units of moles of atoms: (a) 38.0 g, (b) 38.0 moles I_2, (c) 38.0×10^{23} atoms, (d) 38.0×10^{23} molecules I_2.

42 Express the following iodine quantities in units of moles of I_2 molecules: (a) 38.0 g, (b) 38.0 moles I, (c) 38.0×10^{23} atoms, (d) 38×10^{23} molecules I_2.

43 Pick the substance(s) whose number of particles differ(s) from the others: (a) 2.0 moles of protons, (b) 2.0 moles of electrons, (c) 2.0 moles Ag, (d) 1.0 mole N_2, (e) 2.0 moles Na^+.

44 The annual production of ammonia, NH_3, is 2.0×10^7 metric tons. How many grams, moles, and molecules of NH_3 are produced annually? 1 metric ton = 10^6 g.

45 (a) How many moles and molecules of CO are in 75.6 g carbon monoxide, CO? (b) Find the mass of 125 atoms (i) of neon, Ne, and (ii) of tin, Sn.

46 Mole, pollution Emission standards for the State of California restrict automobile pollutants to 0.9 g hydrocarbons/mile, 9.0 g CO/mile, and 2.0 g NO_x/mile. If the average molecular weight of the hydrocarbons is 58 g/mole and the average molecular weight of the oxides of nitrogen (NO_x) is 35 g/mole, express the standards in terms of moles of molecules and number of molecules.

47 Different quantities of several gases (with different molecular weights) each occupy the same volume at the same temperature and pressure. Is the number of moles of molecules the same for each gas? Explain.

48 In the upper atmosphere, 4.0×10^6 hydroxyl, OH, molecules (*not* hydroxyl ions, OH⁻) are detected in 1.0 ml. Find the number of moles of hydroxyl molecules in 1.0 ℓ.

49 (a) The combustion of a gasoline sample produces 3.45×10^3 ℓ of CO_2 at 105 °C and 775 torr. How many moles of CO_2 are produced? (b) An electric current neutralizes gold ions, Au^{3+}, plating 1.05×10^{20} Au atoms onto a piece of metal. (i) How many moles and grams of Au are plated? (ii) How many electrons are needed to neutralize 1 Au^{3+} ion and 1 mole of Au^{3+} ions to Au atoms?

50 A test rocket engine is loaded with 2.54 moles of hydrazine, N_2H_4, and 14.6 moles of dinitrogen tetroxide, N_2O_4. Calculate the mass in grams and the number of molecules of each substance loaded.

51 (a) A water trimer (combination of three H_2O molecules), H_6O_3, can be formed in various ways. Calculate the number of moles of H_6O_3 and the number of moles of H_2O in 66.5 g of the trimer. (b) The mass of a 5.68 kg child is 80 % water. Calculate (i) the number of moles and (ii) the number of molecules of H_2O in the child.

52 On a weight basis, 2.75×10^{-2} mg of saccharin, $C_6H_4COSO_2NH$ (artificial sweetener), has about the same sweetness as 8.25 mg of sucrose (cane sugar), $C_{12}H_{22}O_{11}$. Express these quantities as the number of moles of each substance.

53 Manganese is among the trace metals essential for good health. A food, analyzed by spectroscopic methods (Chaps. 6 and 24) contains 175 μg Mn/g food. Find the number of Mn atoms in a 100 g portion of the food. 1 μg = 10^{-6} g.

54 **Molecular formula** The mass composition of the insecticide hexachlorocyclohexane, known as *Lindane* or "666," is 24.7 % C, 2.06 % H, and 73.2 % Cl. At 0.0131 atm and 575 K, 12.5 ℓ of the insecticide has a mass of 1.01 g. Calculate the molecular formula of the insecticide. Use atomic weights: C = 12.0, H = 1.0, Cl = 35.5.

55 The neurotransmitter serotonin, an alkaloid* in the brain that transmits signals across the brain and to muscle cells, is a white solid with a molecular weight of 174 g/mole, containing by mass 69.0 % carbon,

---
Alkaloids are a class of nitrogen-containing compounds of natural (vegetable) origin that possess strong physiological activity, and include nicotine (page 128), reserpine (tranquilizer used in the treatment of high blood pressure), morphine, indigo (dark blue dye), quinine (used as an antimalarial), and caffeine (a stimulant found in tea, coffee, and many soft drinks). Narcotics like cocaine and tranquilizers like reserpine react with substances that control nerve transmission. The drug reserpine is obtainable from a plant root that the people of India have used for centuries to calm severe agitation.

5.80 % hydrogen, 16.1 % nitrogen, and 9.20 % oxygen. Calculate the molecular formula of serotonin.

56 Dimethyl sulfoxide (DMSO) is an experimental drug that has not yet found its proper place in medical treatment. It has a mass composition of 30.7 % C, 7.76 % H, 41.1 % S, and 20.5 % O. Its vapor has a density of 3.01 g/ℓ at 1.50 atm and 200 °C. Find its molecular formula.

57 Exposure to about 10^{-6} g of TCDD (tetrachloro-dibenzo-dioxin) causes chloracne, a severe skin disease. By mass, TCDD is composed of 44.3 % C, 2.47 % H, 9.82 % O, and 43.5 % Cl. (a) Calculate its empirical formula. (b) Its molecular weight is 326 g/mole. Write its molecular formula.

58 A gaseous oxide of nitrogen consists, by mass, of 30.4 % nitrogen and 69.6 % oxygen. (a) Find its empirical formula. (b) At about 50 °C, the gas is a mixture of two types of molecules with molecular weights of 46.0 g/mole and 92.0 g/mole. Write the molecular formulas of these two molecules.

59 Standard marijuana cigarettes produce more carcinogenic chemicals than standard tobacco cigarettes. Many of these compounds are related to pyrene, an aromatic hydrocarbon (page 695). At 350 °C and 600 torr, 1.17 g of pyrene has a volume of 375 ml. (a) Calculate the molecular weight of pyrene. Check your answer against its molecular formula, $C_{16}H_{10}$. (b) Write its empirical formula.

60 **Empirical formula** "Saltpeter," with a mass composition of 38.7 % K, 13.9 % N, and 47.5 % O, is an ingredient of black gunpowder. Calculate its empirical formula.

61 Ammonia gas and hydrogen chloride gas combine to form a white smoke whose mass composition is 26.2 % nitrogen, 7.5 % hydrogen, and 66.4 % chlorine. Find its empirical formula.

62 Long-term use of amphetamine sulfate (by mass, 46.3 % C, 6.48 % H, 6.00 % N, 13.8 % S, 27.5 % O) in treating hyperactive children is not advisable. Calculate its empirical formula.

63 0.50 mole of a blue crystalline substance contains 0.50 mole of Cu atoms, 3.01×10^{23} S atoms, 5.0 g of hydrogen, and 2.71×10^{24} oxygen atoms. Write the empirical formula for this substance.

64 The smell of onions is due to propyl mercaptan, a colorless volatile liquid with the mass composition 47.3 % C, 10.6 % H, and 42.0 % S. Find its empirical formula.

65 **Formula** (a) Find the number of moles of H atoms and calculate the mass percentage of hydrogen (to three significant figures) in one mole of each of the following compounds: (i) ammonia, NH_3; (ii) DDT, $C_{14}H_9Cl_5$; (iii) $CuSH_{10}O_9$, blue solid. (b) (i) 16 g of $CuSO_4$, a greenish-white solid, reacts with 200 g of water, while (ii) 30 g of water is added to 200 g of $CuSO_4$. Find the maximum quantity of $CuSO_4(H_2O)_5$ that can be formed and the quantity of each compound remaining unreacted in (i) and (ii).

66 **Avogadro's law** (a) If, at a given temperature, T, and pressure, P, 32 ml of H_2 gas reacts with C_2 gas forming methane gas, $C_2 + 4H_2 \longrightarrow 2CH_4$, what volume of C_2 reacts and what volume of methane is formed? (b) Phosphine, PH_3, a very toxic gas, burns readily in air and explodes in pure oxygen. For the gaseous reaction $4PH_3 + 8O_2 \longrightarrow P_4O_{10} + 6H_2O$, what volumes of PH_3 and O_2 are consumed and what volume of H_2O is produced when 10 ml of P_4O_{10} forms?

67 Under certain conditions, nitrogen and oxygen react in the volume ratios, 1 volume oxygen + 1 volume nitrogen $\longrightarrow$ 2 volumes oxide of nitrogen. Assume that nitrogen is a diatomic molecule, N_2. Show that the oxygen molecule is most likely diatomic, O_2, and not monatomic, O.

68 The atomic weight of lead, Pb, density 11.3 g/ml, is 207 g/mole Pb. Calculate the volume of one mole of lead. Estimate the volume of one lead atom.

69 **Library** Read one of the following:

(a) "Theodore William Richards and the Atomic Weight Problem," Aaron Ihde, *Science,* volume 164, 1969, pages 647–651.
(b) "Chemistry and Atomic Structure," J. D. Main-Smith, D. Van Nostrand Co., New York, 1924, Chapter 1.
(c) "Avogadro's Number: Early Values by Loschmidt and Others," Robert Hawthorne, *Journal of Chemical Education,* volume 47, 1970, pages 751–755.
(d) "Signs of the Times," H. Kolbe (1877), reprinted in *Tetrahedron,* volume 30, 1974, page 2004, and in "Advanced Organic Chemistry," G. W. Wheland, John Wiley and Sons, New York, 2nd Edition, 1949, page 132.
(e) "The Atomicity of Electric Charge," Chapter 4 in "The Discovery of the Electron," David Anderson, D. Van Nostrand Co., New York, 1964.

ADDITIONAL PROBLEMS

70 The Roman poet Lucretius concluded, "yet things that are the tiniest will be composed of infinite parts just the same." Explain in your own words.

71 The atomic weight of the electron,* determined in a primitive mass spectrometer invented by J. J. Thomson, is about $1/2000$ of that of hydrogen. (a) Estimate the atomic weight of the electron and calculate the mass of an electron. (b) Thomson also determined the ratio of the charge of the electron to the mass of the electron, $e/m = 1.8 \times 10^8$ coulomb/g. Calculate the charge of one electron and of 1 mole of electrons.

72 (a) How many isotopes of lithium are here represented: ^6Li, $^6Li^+$, ^7Li, $^7Li^+$. (b) The atomic weight of oxygen obtained from air is a constant (15.9994 g/mole O), and the atomic weight of oxygen obtained from water is also a constant (15.9993 g/mole O). The difference in atomic weight is real and reproducible. All other properties are identical. Explain the difference.

73 Natural chlorine, 35.453 g/mole, has two isotopes, ^{35}Cl, 34.97 g/mole (abundance 75.77 %) and ^{37}Cl (abundance 24.23 %). Calculate the atomic weight of ^{37}Cl.

74 (a) A surface of magnetite (page 200) with an area of 1.00 m^2 is covered by 3.22 mg of trypsin. Trypsin, involved in protein digestion, is an enzyme (page 728) produced by the pancreas. The trypsin is spread over the surface as a monolayer, meaning that the surface is completely covered by one layer of trypsin molecules. The molecules may be assumed to behave like rigid spheres with a diameter of 4.0×10^{-7} cm. (i) How many trypsin molecules cover the surface? (Area of circle = πr^2.) (ii) Calculate the molecular weight of trypsin and check your answer against 2.38×10^4 g/mole, determined by another method. (b) 1.0 ml of blood contains 5.0×10^9 red cells. Each red cell contains 3.0×10^8 hemoglobin molecules. The mass of each molecule is 1.07×10^{-19} g. Find (i) the molecular weight of hemoglobin, (ii) the mass of hemoglobin in 1.0 ml of blood, (iii) the volume of blood in an average-sized person containing 1 kg of hemoglobin.

75 A sample of morphine,* by mass 71.6 % C, 6.72 % H,

---

*Heroin, diacetyl morphine, $C_{21}H_{23}NO_5$, was first synthesized from morphine in 1874; since it was originally thought not to produce addiction, it was proposed as a cure for morphine addiction. Because the use of narcotic drugs reflects an illness or a mental condition rather than the cause of the illness or condition, it is not likely that chemical wizardry will provide a cure for drug addiction, but it may play an important role in treatment.

---

*Thomson used the term "corpuscle" in place of electron.

4.91 % N, and 16.9 % O, occupies 5.01 ℓ at 190 °C and 380 torr and weighs 18.8 g. Calculate its molecular formula.

76 0.500 mole of a compound used in the production of *Nylon,* composed of carbon, hydrogen, and nitrogen, burns yielding 3.00 moles of CO_2, 4 moles of H_2O, and 1 mole of NO. Write the empirical and molecular formulas of the original compound.

77 Hexamethylphosphoramide, mass composition 40.2 % C, 10.1 % H, 23.5 % N, 17.3 % P, and 8.94 % O, is a very good solvent but is a potential carcinogen; 400 parts per billion parts of air by pressure can produce cancer in rats. 0.585 g of the compound occupies 200 ml at 100 °C and 380 torr. (a) Calculate the molecular weight and the molecular and empirical formulas of the compound. (b) Calculate the number of moles and molecules and the mass of the compound in 1 ml of air at 23 °C and 770 torr when its quantity is 400 ppb by pressure.

78 A magnetic, harmless compound, mass composition 72.36 % Fe and 27.64 % O, was used in the development of an instrument for detecting harmful asbestos* particles (page 203) in the lungs. Find the empirical formula of the compound. (Use four significant figures for atomic weights and retain four significant figures.

79 The mass composition of a perbromate compound is 21.4 % K, 43.7 % Br, and 35.0 % O. (a) Calculate its empirical formula. (b) The mass spectrum of the compound shows two ions at mass numbers 182 and 186. (Similar to those of atoms, the mass number of a molecule is the nearest whole number to its molec-

---

*From *asbestos,* Greek for inextinguishable, from its use as lamp wick material.

ular weight). Write the molecular formula of the compound.

80 (a) Food spoilage is retarded by refrigeration. It is also retarded by storage under low air pressure, 10 torr at 23 °C. Bacterial growth is retarded by the decreased oxygen supply. (i) Calculate the number of air molecules present per ml under these conditions. (ii) Air contains 20 % oxygen "by volume" (20 % of the air molecules are oxygen, O_2, molecules). Find the number of O_2 molecules per ml. (b) Fatal cases of CO poisoning can occur at 0.10 torr CO pressure at 25 °C. Express this quantity as (i) the number of molecules of CO per ml and (ii) the mass of CO in mg per liter.

81 (a) (i) How many molecules are in *any* gas having the same volume, 5.25 ℓ, at STP? (ii) How many molecules are in *any* gas having the same volume, 44.8 ℓ, at 0.164 atm and 600 K? (b) Coal gas, a useful fuel obtained in the manufacture of coke (page 692), consists of 60 % H_2, 36 % CH_4, and 4 % N_2 by mass. Find the number of moles and molecules of each gas in 1 kg of coal gas.

82 (a) Vitamin C, ascorbic acid, has a molecular weight of 175 g/mole and the mass composition 41.2 % carbon, 54.8 % oxygen, and 4.04 % hydrogen. In the body, it forms (among other products) oxalic acid, with molecular weight 90.0 g/mole and mass composition 26.7 % carbon, 71.1 % oxygen, and 2.24 % hydrogen. Find the empirical and molecular formulas of each compound. (b) (i) The mass composition of *Benadryl,* diphenhydramine, a white powder used in the prevention of allergic reactions and "motion sickness" (page 459), is 80.0 % C, 8.31 % H, 6.27 % O, and 5.49 % N. Calculate its empirical formula. (ii) 0.278 g of *Benadryl* occupies a volume of 15.0 ℓ at 2.00 torr and 167 °C. Find its molecular weight and molecular formula.

ANSWERS

1 no
2 5.4 g
3 225 g
6 (a) H^+; (b) O^{2-}
7 softball
8 (a) 37.8 g/doz
   (b) 1.90×10^{24} g/mole
9 2.392×10^{-22} g,
   2.870×10^{-21} g, 12.00 g
10 4.00, 22.4, 6.02×10^{23}
11 (a) 5.00 g/nickel, (b) 2.40 g/dime;
   500/240 = 5.00/2.40
12 58.7 and 119, or 58.7 g/mole
   Ni atoms and 119 g/mole Sn atoms;
   119 to 58.7 or 2.03 to 1 (but
   division not necessary)

13 (a) 2.70 g; (b) 270 g; (c) 270 g
15 8.29 Pa m³/(mole K)
16 131 g/mole
17 (a) 2.51×10^{23} atoms;
   (b) 144 atoms/gross, 6.02×10^{23} atoms/mole
18 (a) 0.333 mole; (b) 2.01×10^{23} molecules
19 (a) 30.0 g/mole; (b) 33.0 g,
   6.62×10^{23} molecules, 24.6 ℓ
   (STP); (c) 4.00 mole, 3.00 mole
20 C_2H_6O, 46.069 g/mole
21 $HgCl_2$
22 (a) 30 g/mole; (b) $C_2H_4O_2$, CH_2O;
   (c) 60.052 g/mole
23 10.0 ml
27 160 Cl_2 molecules, 30 C atoms
28 170 g

31 9 g C, 6 g C, 3 g C; 3:2:1; yes
32 (a) 2.40 g/dime, 5.10 g/nickel
33 186.21 g/mole
34 20.17 g/mole
35 121 g/mole
36 (a) 28.0 g/mole; (b) 5.4×10^{11} mole
37 (a) 285 g/mole; (b) CCl, C_6Cl_6
39 3.27 g
40 (a) 1.56 mole, 9.39×10^{23} atoms;
     (b) 3.89 mole, 2.34×10^{24} atoms;
     (c) 2.40 mole, 1.44×10^{24} atoms
41 (a) 0.299 mole; (b) 76.0 mole;
     (c) 6.31 mole; (d) 12.6 mole
42 (a) 0.150 mole; (b) 19.0 mole;
     (c) 3.16 mole; (d) 6.31 mole
43 (d)
44 2.0×10^{13} g, 1.2×10^{12} mole,
     7.2×10^{35} molecules
45 (a) 2.70 mole, 1.63×10^{24}
     molecules; (b) (i) 4.19×10^{-21} g,
     (ii) 2.47×10^{-20} g
46 0.016, 0.32, 0.057 mole;
     1×10^{22}, 1.9×10^{23},
     3.4×10^{22} molecules
47 yes
48 6.6×10^{-15} mole
49 (a) 1.13×10^{2} mole; (b) (i)
     1.74×10^{-4} mole, 0.0343 g;
     (ii) 3 electrons, $1.81 \times$
     10^{24} electrons
50 81.3 g, 1.53×10^{24} molecules
     N_2H_4; 1.34×10^{2} g, 8.79×10^{24}
     molecules N_2O_4
51 (a) 1.23, 3.69 mole; (b) 252 mole, $1.52 \times$
     10^{26} molecules
52 1.50×10^{-7}, 2.41×10^{-5} mole
53 1.92×10^{20} atoms
54 $C_6H_6Cl_6$
55 $C_{10}H_{10}N_2O$
56 C_2H_6SO
57 (a) $C_6H_4OCl_2$; (b) $C_{12}H_8O_2Cl_4$

58 (a) NO_2; (b) NO_2, N_2O_4
59 (b) C_8H_5
60 KNO_3
61 NH_4Cl
62 $C_9H_{15}NSO_4$
63 $CuSH_{10}O_9$
64 C_3H_8S
65 (a) (i) 3 mole, 17.8 %; (ii) 9 mole,
     2.56 %; (iii) 10 mole, 4.04 %;
     (b) (i) 25 g $CuSO_4(H_2O)_5$, 191 g H_2O;
     (ii) 83 g $CuSO_4(H_2O)_5$, 147 g $CuSO_4$
66 (a) 8.0 ml C_2, 16 ml CH_4; (b) 40 ml
     PH_3, 80 ml O_2, 60 ml H_2O
68 18.3 ml/mole, 3.04×10^{-23} ml/atom
71 (a) 5.0×10^{-4} g/mole, 8.3×10^{-28} g;
     (b) 1.5×10^{-10} C, 9.0×10^{4} C
72 (a) two
73 36.96 g/mole
74 (a) (i) 7.96×10^{16} molecules,
     (ii) 2.4×10^{4} g/mole; (b) (i)
     6.44×10^{4} g/mole, (ii) 0.16 g/ml,
     (iii) 6 ℓ
75 $C_{17}H_{19}NO_3$
76 C_3H_8N, $C_6H_{16}N_2$
77 (a) 179 g/mole, $C_6H_{18}N_3PO$; (b) 1.67 $\times$
     10^{-11} mole, 1.01×10^{13} molecules,
     2.99×10^{-9} g
78 Fe_3O_4
79 (a) (b) $KBrO_4$
80 (a) (i) 3.2×10^{17} molecules,
     (ii) 6.4×10^{16} molecules;
     (b) (i) 3.2×10^{15} molecules/ml,
     (ii) 0.15 mg/ℓ
81 (a) (i) 1.41×10^{23} molecules,
     (ii) 8.90×10^{22} molecules;
     (b) 3.0×10^{2} mole, 1.8×10^{26}
     molecules H_2; 2.3×10^{1} mole,
     1.4×10^{25} molecules CH_4; 1.4 mole,
     9×10^{23} molecules N_2
82 (a) $C_6O_6H_7$, $C_6O_6H_7$; $C_2O_4H_2$, CO_2H;
     (b) (i) $C_{17}H_{21}ON$; (ii) 255 g/mole,
     $C_{17}H_{21}ON$

GLOSSARY

alpha particles Helium ions, He^{2+}.

atom The unit particle of elements; it is the smallest particle of an element that combines with other elements. Molecules are composed of atoms.

atomic weight The relative average mass of an atom of an element, compared to the mass of a ^{12}C atom. See **Avogadro's number** and **mole.**

Avogadro's law Equal volumes of different gases, at the same temperature and the same pressure, contain equal numbers of molecules.

Avogadro's number The number of particles in exactly 12 g of ^{12}C or in one mole, 6.02×10^{23} particles/mole (e.g., 6.02×10^{23} atoms in one mole of atoms, or 6.02×10^{23} molecules in one mole of molecules). See **mole.**

cathode ray An electron beam, a stream of high-speed electrons.

compound A substance composed of two or more elements chemically united in constant composition by mass. A compound consists of ions or molecules composed of unlike atoms.

Coulomb's law The force between two charges varies directly as the product of the charges and inversely as the square of the distance between the charges.

electric current In solid conductors like a copper wire, a stream of electrons through the circuit.

electron The "atom of electricity," which always carries a definite negative charge, 1.6×10^{-19} coulomb, and is the unit of electric charge, designated as -1.

empirical formula The simplest formula that can be assigned to a substance; it represents the relative number of atoms of each element in a compound. P_2O_5 is an empirical formula; P_4O_{10} is a molecular formula.

formula weight The sum of the atomic weights of the atoms in an empirical formula; dimensional units are g/mole.

ionization The conversion of neutral particles to charged particles (ions).

ions Charged atoms or molecules, such as Na^+, F^-, and CO_2^+.

isotopes Atoms of the same element having different mass numbers; ^{16}O, $^{17}O^+$, ^{18}O are typical isotopes.

law of combining volumes At the same temperature and same pressure, the volumes of gases consumed and produced are in ratios of small whole numbers.

law of conservation of matter The mass of the products of a chemical reaction is the same as the mass of the reactants.

law of constant composition A given compound always has the same composition by mass.

law of multiple proportions In a series of two or more compounds containing the same elements, the masses of one element that combine with a fixed mass of another element are in ratios of small whole numbers.

mass number The nearest whole number to the atomic weight of an atom.

mass spectrum A graph showing the relative abundances of the isotopes of an element.

molar volume The volume occupied by one mole of substance, the same *only* for gases at the same conditions of temperature and pressure, 22.4 liters (STP)/mole of gas.

mole The amount of substance containing the same number of particles as there are carbon-12 atoms in exactly 0.012 kg of ^{12}C; dimensional units are 6.02×10^{23} particles/mole, g/mole, or 22.4 liters (STP)/mole of gas. See **Avogadro's number.**

molecular formula Represents one mole of a substance and gives the actual number of atoms of each element in one molecule of the substance.

molecular weight The sum of the atomic weights of the atoms in a molecular formula, or the relative average mass of a molecule of a substance compared to the mass of a ^{12}C atom.

molecule The unit particle of substances made up of one or more kinds of atoms. A monatomic molecule consists of one atom, a diatomic molecule consists of two atoms, and a triatomic molecule consists of three atoms.

products Substances produced in a chemical reaction.

proton The ion, $^1H^+$, obtained from the lightest isotope of hydrogen. It carries a charge, $+1$, equal to that of the electron but opposite in sign.

quantization Refers to quantities that are restricted to certain values, meaning, for example, that the mass of a given substance is made up of individual atoms or molecules and that any charge of electricity is made up of a number of electrons.

reactants Substances originally mixed in a chemical reaction.

MULTIPLICATION TABLE

1	2	3	4	5	6	7	8	9	10	11
2	4	6	8	10	12	14	16	18	20	22
3	6	9	12	15	18	21	24	27	30	3.
4	8	12	16	20	24	28	32	36	40	4.
5	10	15	20	25	30	35	40	45	50	5.
6	12	18	24	30	36	42	48	54	60	66
7	14	21	28	35	42	49	56	63	70	7.
8	16	24	32	40	48	56	64	72	80	88
9	18	27	36	45	54	63	72	81	90	9.
10	20	30	40	50	60	70	80	90	100	11
11	22	33	44	55	66	77	88	99	110	12
12	24	36	48	60	72	84	96	108	120	13

NOMENCLATURE– CHEMICAL ARITHMETIC   5

INTRODUCTION————————5.1

The general acceptance of the Avogadro hypothesis led to the determination of molecular and atomic weights and the derivation of chemical formulas. This ended, by 1870, an era of chemical confusion during which, for example, over a dozen formulas were used to represent acetic acid, CH_3COOH, a colorless liquid, the essential ingredient of vinegar.

There was also no consistency in naming compounds. This situation developed because chemists had used numerous systems for naming elements and compounds over the years. Compounds were named after such diverse things as persons, places, or even some aspect of a property of a compound that most impressed the investigator.

As long ago as 1780, scientists became dissatisfied with the state of chemical nomenclature. Antoine Lavoisier and Claude Berthollet, among others, attempted to devise a system that would provide information about the elements of a compound. To accomplish this, Lavoisier devised a system of nomenclature based on Latin and Greek words and a systematic use of word endings that is still in use today.

In more modern times, attempts have again been made to devise a general system of nomenclature for both inorganic and organic (carbon-containing) compounds. The International Union of Pure and Applied Chemistry (IUPAC) has established rules of nomenclature for both of these classes of compounds. Many of the rules of inorganic chemical nomenclature incorporate the suggestions of Alfred Stock (page 151).

"Nomenclature of Inorganic Chemistry, IUPAC," 2nd Edition (Red Book), Crane, Russak and Co., New York, N.Y., 1971.

MEANING OF ELEMENT SYMBOLS————————5.2

The symbols for the elements represent much more than an abbreviation of the name (page 131). They provide a convenient way to represent the state of an element in a specific situation. For example, Cl is the symbol for chlorine. When present as a monatomic molecule (page 136) in the gaseous state, chlorine is represented as $Cl(g)$, but as $Cl_2(g)$ when present as a diatomic molecule (page 136), and as $Cl^-(g)$ when it exists as a negatively charged gaseous ion (page 120).

The symbol represents a definite quantity of the element. This means that the symbol represents a definite number of atoms and a definite mass. The symbol Cl may represent 1 atom and the mass of 1 atom. Cl may also represent 1 mole of atoms, an Avogadro number of atoms, and the mass of 1 mole of atoms. Thus, Cl represents 1 mole of atoms, or 6.02×10^{23} atoms, or 35.453 grams of chlorine.

Notations such as $\frac{1}{2}$ Cl_2 are frequently used. This does *not* represent $\frac{1}{2}$ molecule of chlorine. Rather, it represents $\frac{1}{2}$ mole of molecules, or $\frac{1}{2}$ of an Avogadro number of molecules, or $\frac{1}{2}$ of the mass of 1 mole of molecules.

5.3 _____ FORMULAS

The formula for sulfuric acid is H_2SO_4. This indicates that a molecule of sulfuric acid consists of 2 atoms of hydrogen, 1 atom of sulfur, and 4 atoms of oxygen. The formula also shows that 1 mole of sulfuric acid consists of 2 moles of hydrogen atoms, 1 mole of sulfur atoms, and 4 moles of oxygen atoms. The molecular weight of sulfuric acid is thus 98.08 g/mole $(2 \times 1.008 + 1 \times 32.06 + 4 \times 16.00)$. If 2 moles of sulfuric acid are needed in a reaction, it is written as $2H_2SO_4$. The 2 here is called the **coefficient**; it multiplies the number of molecules by 2. Thus, the mass of 2 H_2SO_4 is 2×98.08 g or 196.16 g. If $\frac{1}{2}$ mole of sulfuric acid is involved in a reaction, the coefficient is $\frac{1}{2}$, and the mass of $\frac{1}{2}$ mole is $\frac{1}{2} \times 98.08$ g or 49.04 g.

PROBLEM 1 **How many (a) moles of hydrogen atoms and (b) grams of hydrogen are in (i) H_2O, (ii) $2H_2O$, (iii) $\frac{1}{2} H_2O$, (iv) H_2O_2, (v) $\frac{1}{2} H_2O_2$?**

PROBLEM 2 **How many moles of LiOH are in 62.1 g of LiOH?**

5.4 _____ CHEMICAL COMBINATIONS

Elements combine with other elements in definite proportions by mass (page 110). The element symbols are used to represent the union of two or more elements, as illustrated: H_2O, HCl, $NaCl$, NaF, AlF_3, Na_2O, and MgO. These formulas show that the *combining capacity* of the elements—that is, the number of atoms of one element that unites with one atom of another element—is not necessarily the same. The combining capacities of hydrogen and chlorine are the same; 1 atom of hydrogen combines with 1 atom of chlorine. But the combining power of oxygen is twice that of hydrogen; 1 atom of oxygen combines with 2 atoms of hydrogen to form H_2O. The combining capacity of an element is commonly called its **valence.** Thus, hydrogen and chlorine have the same valence, and the valence of oxygen is *twice* that of hydrogen. The formulas NaF and AlF_3 show that while the valences of sodium and fluorine are the same, the valence of aluminum is *three* times that of fluorine. By common consent, a valence of 1 is assigned to the hydrogen atom. The valence of an element is, therefore, *the number of atoms of hydrogen that combine with one atom of the element.* The valence of chlorine is thus 1, while the valence of oxygen is 2. The formula NaCl shows that sodium and chlorine have the same combining capacity and, therefore, the same valence. The valence of sodium is thus 1. From the formulas NaF and AlF_3, we conclude that the valence of fluorine is 1, while that of aluminum is 3. The formula MgO shows that magnesium and oxygen have the same combining capacity and, therefore, the same valence. The valence of magnesium is 2, the same as oxygen.

Very frequently, certain combinations of atoms remain combined and behave as a chemical unit during chemical reactions. Such combinations of atoms are known as

From valentia, the Latin word for capacity.

The choice is arbitrary. It was chosen to avoid valence values less than 1.

All peroxides where oxygen appears to have a valence of 1 as in H_2O_2 are exceptions.

TABLE 5.1
COMMON VALENCES OF SOME ELEMENTS
AND GROUPS

VALENCE OF 1	NAME	ION	ILLUSTRATIVE COMPOUNDS	
Metals and positive ions	ammonium	NH_4^+	NH_4Cl	$(NH_4)_2SO_4$
	copper(I)	Cu^+	$CuCl$	Cu_2O
	mercury(I)	$(Hg_2)^{2+}$	Hg_2Cl_2	$Hg_2(NO_3)_2$
	potassium	K^+	KBr	K_2SO_4
	silver	Ag^+	$AgNO_3$	AgI
	sodium	Na^+	$NaCl$	Na_2O
Nonmetals and negative ions	acetate	CH_3COO^-	$NaCH_3COO$	CH_3COOH
	chloride	Cl^-	$NaCl$	HCl
	chlorate	ClO_3^-	$KClO_3$	$HClO_3$
	cyanide	CN^-	KCN	HCN
	fluoride	F^-	KF	HF
	hydrogen carbonate*	HCO_3^-	$NaHCO_3$	$Ca(HCO_3)_2$
	hydroxide	OH^-	$NaOH$	$Al(OH)_3$
	nitrate	NO_3^-	KNO_3	HNO_3
	nitrite	NO_2^-	$NaNO_2$	HNO_2

VALENCE OF 2	NAME	ION	ILLUSTRATIVE COMPOUNDS	
Metals and positive ions	barium	Ba^{2+}	$BaCO_3$	BaF_2
	calcium	Ca^{2+}	CaO	$CaCl_2$
	copper(II)	Cu^{2+}	CuF_2	$CuCO_3$
	iron(II)	Fe^{2+}	$FeSO_4$	$FeBr_2$
	lead(II)	Pb^{2+}	PbF_2	$Pb(CH_3COO)_2$
	magnesium	Mg^{2+}	MgF_2	MgS
	mercury(II)	Hg^{2+}	$HgBr_2$	HgO
	tin(II)	Sn^{2+}	$SnBr_2$	SnO
	zinc	Zn^{2+}	$ZnCl_2$	ZnS
Nonmetals and negative ions	carbonate	CO_3^{2-}	$CaCO_3$	H_2CO_3
	chromate	CrO_4^{2-}	K_2CrO_4	$MgCrO_4$
	oxygen (in oxides)	O^{2-}	Na_2O	H_2O
	oxygen (in peroxides)	O_2^{2-}	Na_2O_2	H_2O_2
	sulfate	SO_4^{2-}	Na_2SO_4	H_2SO_4
	sulfide	S^{2-}	K_2S	CdS
	sulfite	SO_3^{2-}	K_2SO_3	$CaSO_3$

VALENCE OF 3	NAME	ION	ILLUSTRATIVE COMPOUNDS	
Metals and positive ions	aluminum	Al^{3+}	Al_2O_3	AlH_3
	bismuth(III)	Bi^{3+}	BiF_3	$BiCl_3$
	chromium(III)	Cr^{3+}	$Cr_2(SO_4)_3$	$CrCl_3$
	iron(III)	Fe^{3+}	Fe_2O_3	$FeBr_3$
Nonmetals and negative ions	arsenate	AsO_4^{3-}	K_3AsO_3	H_3AsO_4
	phosphate	PO_4^{3-}	Na_3PO_4	H_3PO_4

*Common name, bicarbonate.

groups. Typical groups are *sulfate* (SO_4), *phosphate* (PO_4), and *nitrate* (NO_3). Combination with hydrogen to form HNO_3, H_2SO_4, and H_3PO_4 indicates that the valence of the nitrate group is 1, the sulfate group 2, and the phosphate group 3.

PROBLEM 3   What is the valence of (a) iron in iron tribromide, $FeBr_3$, (b) calcium in calcium sulfide, CaS, (c) tin in tin sulfate, $Sn(SO_4)_2$, (d) the carbonate (CO_3) group in sodium carbonate, Na_2CO_3?

Chemists *do not* assign a valence to the individual atoms combined in a group, such as the sulfur in the sulfate group. It is nevertheless useful to assign a number, known as the oxidation number (page 364), to these atoms.

Some elements have more than one valence. For example, the valence of tin is 2 in tin difluoride, SnF_2, an ingredient of many toothpastes, and 4 in tin tetrachloride, $SnCl_4$, a fuming liquid occasionally used for sky-writing. The *common* valences of some elements and groups are given in Table 5.1, with typical illustrative compounds.

The empirical (simplest) formula of many compounds can be written directly from the assigned valences. Elements and groups combine so as to satisfy their valences (combining capacities). When the valences are equal—for example, magnesium and sulfur (Table 5.1)—the simplest formula for the compound magnesium sulfide is a 1 to 1 ratio; namely, MgS. If the valences are not equal, then the ratio is written to equalize the combining capacities of each element; for example, silver, Ag, valence 1, and phosphate, PO_4, valence 3, mean that the combining capacity of phosphate is three times that of silver. Thus, taking 3 silver atoms to 1 phosphate group will equalize the combining capacities. The simplest formula for silver phosphate is thus Ag_3PO_4. For the combination of aluminum, Al, valence 3, with sulfate, SO_4, valence 2, the combining capacities are equalized by taking 2 atoms of aluminum (2×3 = combining capacity of 6) and 3 sulfate groups (3×2 = combining capacity of 6); the simplest formula for aluminum sulfate is then $Al_2(SO_4)_3$. The subscript outside the parentheses applies to *all atoms within the parentheses*. That is, all elements within the parentheses are multiplied by the subscript. Thus, 1 mole of $Al_2(SO_4)_3$ contains 2 moles of Al atoms, 3 moles of S atoms, and 12 moles of O atoms.

PROBLEM 4   (a) Write the simplest formula for (i) potassium bromide, (ii) calcium phosphate, (iii) bismuth(III) nitrate, (iv) ammonium sulfate. (b) How many moles of magnesium, phosphorus, and oxygen atoms are in 1 mole of $Mg_3(PO_4)_2$?

An empirical formula written from the valence table does not prove that the compound must exist. We may correctly write Hg_2O as the simplest formula for an oxide of mercury. But this compound is non-existent; attempts to prepare it yield mercury, Hg, and mercury oxide, HgO. On the other hand, many compounds exist (for example, acetylene, C_2H_2) whose formulas cannot be written from a valence table.

5.5 _____NAMING COMPOUNDS

Over a million known compounds have been named by the presently accepted rules. However, many very common compounds, such as H_2O (water), and NH_3 (ammonia), are still identified by their traditional names, water and ammonia.

From the Latin word binarius, meaning two at a time.

Naming Binary Compounds   Compounds consisting of two elements are **binary compounds.** These compounds are named by the **Stock** or **IUPAC method:** the metal name with its valence in Roman numerals I, II, III, and IV is named first. This is followed by the name of the second element, for which the ending has been changed to *ide*. For example:

Roman numerals I, II, III, IV correspond to the numbers 1, 2, 3, 4.

Alfred Stock is famous for his work (1910–1936) on the chemistry of the boron and silicon hydrogen compounds (hydrides) and his high vacuum apparatus, crucial in the further development of chemistry.

Compound	Stock or IUPAC Name	Traditional Name
$CuCl$	copper(I) chloride	cuprous chloride
$FeCl_2$	iron(II) chloride	ferrous chloride
$FeCl_3$	iron(III) chloride	ferric chloride
$NaCl$	sodium(I) chloride	sodium chloride
$AlCl_3$	aluminum(III) chloride	aluminum chloride
MnO_2	manganese(IV) oxide	manganese dioxide
MgH_2	magnesium(II) hydride	magnesium hydride

Most chemists prefer the traditional names for $NaCl$, $AlCl_3$, MnO_2, and MgH_2, but not for $CuCl$, $FeCl_2$, and $FeCl_3$. Compounds of elements having more than one common combining capacity, such as $CuCl$, $CuCl_2$, $FeCl_2$, $FeCl_3$, $SnCl_2$, and $SnCl_4$, are named by the IUPAC method.

In the older system, when an element has more than one valence, the ending *ous* is used for the lower valence state, and the ending *ic* is used for the higher valence state.

**TABLE 5.2
PREFIXES USED TO INDICATE
THE NUMBER OF ATOMS
IN ONE MOLECULE**

mono	one	penta	five
di	two	hexa	six
tri	three	hepta	seven
tetra	four	octa	eight

IUPAC usage also designates the number of atoms of each element with a prefix, *mono* for one and *di* for two. See Table 5.2 for other prefixes. The names of some other binary compounds are given:

Compound	Stock or IUPAC Name	Acceptable Name
N_2O	nitrogen(I) oxide	dinitrogen oxide
NO_2	nitrogen(IV) oxide	nitrogen dioxide
N_2O_5	nitrogen(V) oxide	dinitrogen pentoxide
$FeCl_3$	iron(III) chloride	iron trichloride
$SnCl_4$	tin(IV) chloride	tin tetrachloride
Li_3N	lithium(I) nitride	trilithium nitride

PROBLEM 5 Name the following compounds: (a) $SbCl_3$, (b) $CuCl_2$, (c) $SnCl_4$, (d) IBr_3.

Binary Acids Binary acids are compounds of hydrogen and another element; HCl and H_2S are typical. Dissolved in water, the solutions are acidic. Acids have a sour taste and change the color of the natural dye called litmus from blue to red.* The name of the acid is obtained by adding *hydro* before and *ic* after the abbreviated name of the element that is combined with hydrogen, as shown:

From the Greek word hydor for water. From icus, used in Latin to form adjectives.

---

*Acids are extensively treated in Chap. 13. Binary acids, with few exceptions, are largely restricted to the elements fluorine, chlorine, bromine, iodine, sulfur, selenium, and tellurium, because water solutions of the hydrogen compounds of the other elements, for all practical purposes, are not acidic.

Acid		Name			Ion
HF	hydro	fluor	ic acid		F^- fluoride
HCl		chlor			Cl^- chloride
HBr		brom			Br^- bromide
HI		iod			I^- iodide
H_2S		sulfur			S^{2-} sulfide
H_2Se	↓	selen	↓ ↓		Se^{2-} selenide

But not recommended; may reach toxic levels in the body.

From idus, used in Latin to form adjectives.

Binary acids react under certain conditions to form *salts,* such as sodium bromide, NaBr, a central nervous system depressant used as a sedative, and calcium sulfide, CaS, used to remove hair from skin. As shown above, the negative ion obtainable from the acid is named by adding *ide* to the abbreviated name of that element.

PROBLEM 6   **Name and write the formulas for the potassium salts derived from the following acids: (a) HF, (b) HI, (c) H₂S.**

From the Latin word terni, for three each.

Ternary Compounds   Compounds containing three elements are **ternary compounds.** Most important for us are the **hydroxides** and the **oxyacids.** The simplest formula and name of the hydroxides may be written directly from the valence table (Table 5.1, page 149), as illustrated:

Hydroxide	Stock or IUPAC Name	Acceptable Name
NaOH	sodium(I) hydroxide	sodium hydroxide
$Ca(OH)_2$	calcium(II) hydroxide	calcium hydroxide
$Al(OH)_3$	aluminum(III) hydroxide	aluminum hydroxide
$Fe(OH)_3$	iron(III) hydroxide	iron(III) hydroxide

Hydroxides are extensively treated in Chap. 13.

PROBLEM 7   **Give the acceptable name for each of the following hydroxides: (a) LiOH, (b) Fe(OH)₂, (c) Zn(OH)₂, (d) Cu(OH)₂, (e) Cr(OH)₃.**

The oxyacids (Chap. 13) consist of hydrogen, oxygen, and a third element. Sulfuric acid, H_2SO_4, and chloric acid, $HClO_3$, are typical. They are named by adding *ic* to the abbreviated name of the group, sulfate (SO_4) and chlorate (ClO_3), that is combined with hydrogen. However, if two different oxyacids are formed from the three elements, the *ic* is replaced by *ous* for the acid with less oxygen, as shown:

From osus, used in Latin to form adjectives meaning have much of; used here to indicate that the sulfur to oxygen ratio is larger in sulfurous acid.

$$H_2SO_4 \text{ sulfur}ic\ acid \qquad H_2SO_3 \text{ sulfur}ous\ acid$$

If three oxyacids form, the one with the *least* number of oxygen atoms takes the *ous* ending with the addition of *hypo* before the abbreviated group name, as illustrated with the oxyacids of phosphorus:

$$\begin{array}{ll} H_3PO_4 & \text{phosphor}ic\ acid \\ H_3PO_3 & \text{phosphor}ous\ acid \\ H_3PO_2 & hypo\text{phosphor}ous\ acid \end{array}$$

Of Greek origin, hypo is used to indicate the lowest place in a series of compounds.

If four oxyacids form, the one with the *largest* number of oxygen atoms takes the *ic* ending with the addition of *per* before the abbreviated group name, as illustrated with the oxyacids of chlorine:

HClO$_4$ *perchloric acid*
HClO$_3$ chlor*ic acid*
HClO$_2$ chlor*ous acid*
HClO   *hypo*chlor*ous acid*

*Of Latin origin, per is
used to indicate the
highest place in a
series of compounds.*

Oxyacids react under certain conditions to form **oxysalts,** such as potassium
chlorate, KClO$_3$, and sodium hypochlorite, NaClO. Oxysalts are named by changing
the ending of the corresponding acids, *ic* or *ous,* to *ate* or *ite.*

*Oxyacid nomenclature
is further treated in
Chap. 19.*

Most oxyacids and oxysalts have strong oxidizing properties (Chap. 11). They are
relatively unstable and easily decompose. Chlorates and perchlorates, mixed with
other substances, generally form very sensitive explosives.

CHEMICAL EQUATIONS _____ 5.6

Since formulas represent substances, the chemist uses them to write chemical
equations which are a form of chemical shorthand. These equations show the substances that react and those that result from a chemical change. Equally important,
the equation also gives the *relative quantities* of each reacting substance, the *reactants,*
and of each substance formed, the *products.*

The reaction between hydrogen and oxygen to form water may be written as

$$H_2 + O_2 \xrightarrow{\text{yields}} H_2O \qquad \text{(not complete)}$$
$$\underset{\textit{reactants}}{} \qquad \underset{\textit{product}}{}$$

As is shown, in a chemical equation the reactants and products are separated by
an arrow which signifies "yields" or "produces."

The equation as written is not correct because it violates the law of conservation
of matter (page 109). We have 2 atoms of oxygen reacting to form a product with only
1 atom of oxygen. Atoms are neither destroyed nor created in chemical changes; they
are only rearranged. Therefore, we must "balance" the equation; that is, we must
have the same number of atoms of each element in the products as we have in the
reactants. Consequently, we must change the coefficients (page 148), the numbers
before each formula, to conserve atoms. In order to balance the oxygen atoms, we
start by placing 2 before H$_2$O as shown:

$$\overset{\text{balanced}}{H_2 + O_2 \longrightarrow 2H_2O} \qquad \text{(not balanced)}$$
$$\underset{\textit{not balanced}}{}$$

This balances the oxygen atoms, but it does not balance the hydrogen atoms. The
equation is now balanced by placing 2 before H$_2$, as shown:

$$\overset{\text{balanced}}{2H_2 + O_2 \longrightarrow 2H_2O} \qquad \text{(balanced)}$$
$$\underset{\text{balanced}}{}$$

The equation now states that for *every* 2 molecules (moles) of hydrogen that
react, 1 molecule (mole) of oxygen reacts to form 2 molecules (moles) of water. Thus,

if 4 moles of H_2 react, then 2 moles of O_2 must also react, forming 4 moles of water. If 0.2 mole of H_2 reacts, then 0.1 mole of O_2 must react, forming 0.2 mole of water. If 1 mole of H_2 reacts, then $\frac{1}{2}$ mole of O_2 must react, forming 1 mole of water.

Equally correct, the equation may be written as

$$\text{H}_2 + \tfrac{1}{2}\text{O}_2 \longrightarrow \text{H}_2\text{O} \qquad (balanced)$$

The expression $\frac{1}{2} O_2$ corresponds to 1 atom ($\frac{1}{2} \times 2$ atoms = 1 atom) and so balances the 1 atom of oxygen in H_2O. However, the equation is read as 1 mole of hydrogen reacts with $\frac{1}{2}$ mole of oxygen, forming 1 mole of water. It is *not* read as 1 molecule of hydrogen reacts with $\frac{1}{2}$ molecule of oxygen, forming 1 molecule of water.

PROBLEM 8   **If 5.0 moles of O_2 react to form water, (a) how many moles of H_2 must react, and (b) how many moles of water are formed?**

Notice that the subscripts are not changed; only coefficients are changed in balancing equations. For example, we can just as easily change O_2 to O and write

$$\text{H}_2 + \text{O} \longrightarrow \text{H}_2\text{O} \qquad (balanced, \text{ but } incorrect)$$

as the balanced equation. But it is incorrect because it violates our laboratory observation; we started with molecular oxygen (dioxygen), O_2, not with atomic oxygen (monoxygen), O.

Similarly, the equation

$$\text{H}_2 + \text{O}_2 \longrightarrow \text{H}_2\text{O}_2 \qquad (balanced, \text{ but } incorrect)$$

is incorrect; the product obtained is water, H_2O, *not* hydrogen peroxide, H_2O_2. We cannot, therefore, change the experimentally determined formulas of reactants and products.

Methane is also known as marsh gas.

The combustion of natural gas, mainly methane, CH_4, may be represented by the equation

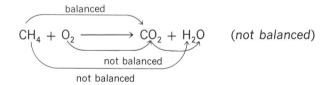

$$\text{CH}_4 + \text{O}_2 \longrightarrow \text{CO}_2 + \text{H}_2\text{O} \qquad (not \text{ } balanced)$$

Inspection shows that although the carbon atoms are balanced, the hydrogen and oxygen atoms are not. Recall that only the coefficients may be changed. So, placing 2 before H_2O balances the hydrogen atoms, but not the oxygen atoms:

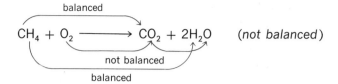

Note that there are two substances among the products that contain oxygen atoms. The total number of oxygen atoms in the products must equal the number in the reactant. Thus, we place a 2 before O_2, producing a balanced equation:

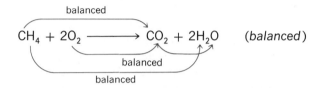

As a final example, let us balance the equation for the combustion of sugar (glucose). Known as respiration in animals, it is the process whereby an animal takes in oxygen and gives off carbon dioxide (page 195):

$$C_6H_{12}O_6 + O_2 \longrightarrow CO_2 + H_2O \quad \textit{(not balanced)}$$

Counting each element separately, we may start with carbon. There are 6 carbon atoms in the reactants and only one in the products. Thus, the CO_2 molecule is multiplied by 6; its coefficient is changed to 6:

Since this is a trial and error method, there are several acceptable variations. A systematic method is considered in Chap. 11.

$$C_6H_{12}O_6 + O_2 \xrightarrow{\text{balanced}} 6CO_2 + H_2O \quad \textit{(not balanced)}$$

Next, note that there are 12 hydrogen atoms in the reactants. If the H_2O molecule is multiplied by 6 this balances the hydrogen atoms:

$$C_6H_{12}O_6 + O_2 \longrightarrow 6CO_2 + 6H_2O \quad \textit{(not balanced)}$$

Now, there are 18 oxygen atoms in the products, but only 8 in the reactants. The coefficient of $C_6H_{12}O_6$, however, cannot be changed without upsetting the carbon and hydrogen balance already achieved. The only remaining step is to multiply the oxygen molecule by 6. This balances the equation:

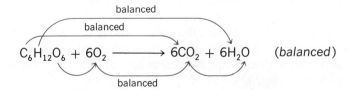

155

PROBLEM 9   Balance the following equations:

(a) $CH_4 + O_2 \longrightarrow CO_2 + H_2O$
(b) $H_2 + Br_2 \longrightarrow HBr$
(c) $HBr + Cl_2 \longrightarrow HCl + Br_2$
(d) $H_2S + O_2 \longrightarrow SO_2 + H_2O$

The usefulness of a chemical equation may be increased by showing the physical state of substances. This is done by writing abbreviations in parentheses immediately following the chemical formulas. Gases are shown as (*g*), while liquids are shown by (*l*). Solids are classified either as crystalline (*c*) or amorphous (*amorph*). A substance in solution is indicated as (*sol*); if a relatively large amount of water is present, the abbreviation is (*aq*).

The usefulness of the balanced equation is that it represents a quantitative relationship. It concerns itself with definite measurable quantities. The balanced equation shows the *relative* quantities of each reactant and product involved in a given reaction. That is, the coefficients (page 148) in chemical equations *give the mole ratios,* not the absolute quantities needed for a given reaction. The coefficients are like the ratios we call "prices." The price of a dozen eggs gives the ratio, 99 cents/12 eggs; it does not tell you that you must buy 1 dozen or that you must spend 99 cents.

The quantities may be expressed in terms of number of molecules, atoms, and moles, or in mass (usually in grams), or in volume (at specified temperatures and pressures). For example,

$$2H_2(g) + O_2(g) \longrightarrow 2H_2O(l)$$

means

2 molecules of hydrogen + 1 molecule of oxygen $\longrightarrow$ 2 molecules of water

Or,

2 moles of H_2 + 1 mole of $O_2 \longrightarrow$ 2 moles of H_2O

Since 1 mole contains 6.02×10^{23} molecules, we can write

$2 \times 6.02 \times 10^{23}$ molecules of $H_2 + 6.02 \times 10^{23}$ molecules of $O_2 \longrightarrow$
$2 \times 6.02 \times 10^{23}$ molecules of water

One mole of a gas occupies 22.4 liters at standard conditions (STP) (page 129); then, equally correct, we can write

2×22.4 liters (STP) H_2 + 22.4 liters (STP) $O_2 \longrightarrow 2 \times 22.4$ liters (STP) H_2O vapor

or

2 liters (STP) H_2 + 1 liter (STP) $O_2 \longrightarrow$ 2 liters (STP) H_2O vapor

or, using molecular weights, the number of grams per mole,

2×2.0 g H_2 + 32 g $O_2 \longrightarrow 2 \times 18.0$ g H_2O

The balanced equation summarizes the overall reaction as obtained from experimentation, but it gives no information about *how* the reaction occurs (Chap. 16). Equally important, it gives no information about *how fast* the products are formed (Chap. 16), or whether all of the reactants used in an experiment are converted into products. Frequently, substances appear to be stubborn and refuse to convert to products (Chap. 12).

A water solution is frequently called an aqueous solution, from the Latin aqua, for water. aq is an abbreviation for aqueous.

We shall first learn how to calculate the maximum amount of product formed when all reactants are converted to products and all reactants are adequately supplied. Unfortunately, these ideal conditions do not always occur, so we shall also learn how to calculate the amount of product formed when the supply of one of the reactants is limited or one of the reactants is impure.

WEIGHTS AND MEASURES FROM CHEMICAL EQUATIONS — 5.7

As previously stated, the balanced equation shows the *relative* quantities of substances reacting and forming. Thus, we can calculate the quantity of water formed when a given quantity of hydrogen or oxygen reacts. Let us say 10 g of oxygen reacts with hydrogen and we wish to calculate the quantity of water formed:

$$2H_2(g) + O_2(g) \longrightarrow 2H_2O(l)$$

Such calculations arc of interest to space engineers who design hydrogen-filled rockets and battery (fuel) cells.

This equation shows that for each mole of oxygen consumed, 2 moles of water are formed; or, 32 g (2×16) of oxygen yield 36 g (2×18) of water. Since we do not have 32 g of oxygen, we will not produce 36 g of water, but we can work out a relationship to determine how much water is formed. As in Example 1, page 8, and Example 1, page 110, we do this by first setting up an expression, the "conversion factor," that gives us the relationship between the number of grams of water and the number of grams of oxygen, namely

$$\frac{2 \times 18 \text{ g H}_2\text{O}}{32 \text{ g O}_2}$$

Calculations based on the quantitative relationship of a balanced equation are referred to as stoichiometry, *from the Greek words* stoicheion, element, *and* metrein, to measure.

It is not necessary to work out the value of this fraction, which, for convenience, we have called a "conversion factor." Then, to determine how many grams of water we obtain from 10 g of oxygen, we multiply the 10 g by the conversion factor:

$$10 \text{ g O}_2 \times \frac{2 \times 18 \text{ g H}_2\text{O}}{32 \text{ g O}_2} = \text{g H}_2\text{O}$$

Observe that each quantity is *associated with a unit*. Before working out the arithmetic, make certain that *the calculated unit is the one the problem requires*. In this problem, we are interested in obtaining the quantity of water in grams, so the units correctly check out, thus:

$$10 \text{ g O}_2 \times \frac{2 \times 18 \text{ g H}_2\text{O}}{32 \text{ g O}_2} = 11 \text{ g H}_2\text{O}$$

If we had used the incorrect conversion factor, such as

$$10 \text{ g O}_2 \times \frac{32 \text{ g O}_2}{2 \times 18 \text{ g H}_2\text{O}} = \frac{8.9 \text{ g}^2 \text{ O}_2}{\text{g H}_2\text{O}}$$

or

$$10 \text{ g O}_2 \times \frac{2 \times 22.4 \text{ } l \text{ (STP) H}_2\text{O}}{32 \text{ g O}_2} = 14 \text{ } l \text{ (STP) H}_2\text{O}$$

the error would be detected since neither $\dfrac{g^2\,O_2}{g\,H_2O}$ nor ℓ (STP) H_2O agrees with the desired answer, $g\,H_2O$.

The choice of units is extremely important. The units used for the conversion factor are determined solely by the statement of the problem. Here, we used $\dfrac{2 \times 18\,g\,H_2O}{32\,g\,O_2}$ because we were given the quantity of oxygen in grams and we wanted the quantity of water in grams. On the other hand, if we were given 10 ℓ (STP) of O_2, the conversion factor would be

$$\frac{2 \times 18\,g\,H_2O}{22.4\,\ell\,(STP)\,O_2}$$

and the quantity of water obtained would be

$$10\,\ell\,(STP)\,O_2 \times \frac{2 \times 18\,g\,H_2O}{22.4\,\ell\,(STP)\,O_2} = 16\,g\,H_2O$$

Let us summarize this method of solving problems. Carefully read the problem and list *the quantity given with its unit* and *the quantity sought with its unit*. No matter how a problem is worded, it must contain a given quantity and it seeks an answer. However, *overlooking the units could be disastrous*. Then, examine the given balanced equation and write the required conversion factor, the *relationship* between the substance given and the substance sought. Pay attention to the coefficients in the equation and write the conversion factor with the desired units. Next, multiply the given quantity by the conversion factor:

given quantity, unit $\times$ conversion factor = quantity sought, unit

Now, cancel units; the units should cancel out, leaving the unit you need for your answer. If cancellation leaves a wrong unit, your conversion factor is wrong. Finally, if the units check, work out the arithmetic.

Example 1

Manganese may be prepared by the Goldschmidt thermite process, in which aluminum is used to prepare other metals (page 635). How many grams of manganese are produced when 50 g of Al_2O_3 forms as shown?

$$4Al(c) + 3MnO_2(c) \longrightarrow 2Al_2O_3(c) + 3Mn(c)$$

Answer

Quantity given: 50 g Al_2O_3
Quantity sought: ? g Mn

In this reaction, 3 moles of Mn forms for every 2 moles of Al_2O_3 produced. But we are given the quantity of Al_2O_3 in grams and seek a quantity of Mn in grams. We therefore use atomic and molecular weights to express the quantity of Mn and Al_2O_3. From the table of atomic weights (inside back cover), the atomic weight of Mn is 55 g/mole and the molecular weight of Al_2O_3 is

---

$2 \times 27 + 3 \times 16 = 102$ g/mole. Then, 3 moles Mn has a mass of 3×55 g and 2 moles Al_2O_3 has a mass of 2×102 g, so the conversion factor is

$$\frac{3.0 \times 55 \text{ g Mn}}{2.0 \times 102 \text{ g } Al_2O_3}$$

Therefore, the number of grams of Mn obtained when 50 g of Al_2O_3 forms is

$$50 \text{ g } \cancel{Al_2O_3} \times \frac{3 \times 55 \text{ g Mn}}{2 \times 102 \text{ g } \cancel{Al_2O_3}} = 40 \text{ g Mn}$$

PROBLEM 10 **(a) How many g of aluminum must react to yield 36 g of aluminum oxide in the reaction given in Example 1? (b) How many g of MnO_2 must react to form 43 g of Mn? The student is advised to reread the summary on page 158.**

Example 2

What volume of CO_2, in liters at STP, forms when 18.0 g of sugar, $C_6H_{12}O_6$, reacts as shown?

$$C_6H_{12}O_6(c) + 6O_2(g) \longrightarrow 6CO_2(g) + 6H_2O(l)$$

Answer

Quantity given: 18.0 g $C_6H_{12}O_6$
Quantity sought: ? liters (STP) CO_2
The equation shows that the consumption of 1 mole of $C_6H_{12}O_6$ yields 6 moles of CO_2. Since the problem is concerned with grams of $C_6H_{12}O_6$ and liters (STP) of CO_2, the 1 mole of $C_6H_{12}O_6$ is expressed as its molecular weight, 180 g/mole, and the 6 moles of CO_2 is expressed as 6×22.4 l (STP). Hence, 1 mole $C_6H_{12}O_6$ has a mass of 180 g and 6 moles CO_2 has a volume of 6×22.4 l (STP) and the conversion factor is

$$\frac{6 \times 22.4 \text{ l (STP) } CO_2}{180 \text{ g } C_6H_{12}O_6}$$

Then, the number of liters (STP) CO_2 obtained from 18.0 g $C_6H_{12}O_6$ is

$$18.0 \text{ g } \cancel{C_6H_{12}O_6} \times \frac{6 \times 22.4 \text{ l (STP) } CO_2}{180 \text{ g } \cancel{C_6H_{12}O_6}} = 13.4 \text{ l (STP) } CO_2$$

PROBLEM 11 **What volume of O_2, in liters at STP, is consumed when 82 g sugar, $C_6H_{12}O_6$, reacts?**

Example 3

How many liters of oxygen at room conditions (rc) are needed to burn 4.0 liters of methane measured at the *same conditions:*

$$CH_4(g) + 2O_2(g) \longrightarrow CO_2(g) + 2H_2O(l)$$

Answer

Quantity given: 4.0 ℓ CH_4, room condition (*rc*)
Quantity sought: ? liters O_2 same conditions (*rc*)

The equation shows that the consumption of 1 mole of CH_4 requires 2 moles of O_2. But the problem is concerned with the volume of these gases at the same conditions. However, 1 mole of any gas at the same conditions of temperature and pressure occupies the same volume (Avogadro's law). Hence 1.0 liter of CH_4(*rc*) requires 2 liters of O_2(*rc*). The conversion factor is therefore

$$\frac{2 \ \ell \ O_2(rc)}{1 \ \ell \ CH_4(rc)}$$

Then, the number of liters of O_2 needed to react with 4.0 liters of CH_4 is

$$4.0 \ \ell \ CH_4(rc) \times \frac{2.0 \ \ell \ O_2(rc)}{1.0 \ \ell \ CH_4(rc)} = 8.0 \ \ell \ O_2(rc)$$

PROBLEM 12   **What volume of oxygen at 22 °C and 740 torr is needed to burn 8.0 ℓ of propane gas, C_3H_8, at 22 °C and 740 torr?**

$$C_3H_8(g) + 5O_2(g) \longrightarrow 3CO_2(g) + 4H_2O(l)$$

5.8 _____ MOLES AND LITERS

Solutions are discussed in Chap. 10.

Moles are also used to express the amount of substance present in solution, a homogeneous mixture of two or more substances. Sugar dissolved in water forms a typical solution. As the properties of solutions vary with composition, it is necessary to specify the amount of substance in a definite quantity of solution. The concentration of the dissolved substance is expressed in moles per liter of solution, the number of moles of a substance dissolved per liter of solution, abbreviated to molarity, M. The units of molarity are then moles/liter:

$$\text{molarity} = \frac{\text{moles of dissolved substance}}{\text{liters of solution}} = \frac{\text{moles}}{\text{liter}}$$

One mole of sodium hydroxide, NaOH, has a mass of 40.0 g. Thus, 40.0 g of NaOH dissolved in 1.00 ℓ of solution is a 1.00 molar solution, written as 1.00 M; 4.00 g of NaOH in 1.00 ℓ of solution is a 0.100 M solution; 80.0 g of NaOH in 1.00 ℓ of solution is a 2.00 M solution; and 20.0 g of NaOH in 1.00 ℓ of solution is a 0.500 M solution.

The molarity of a solution offers another way of delivering an amount of a substance in moles.

Example 4

How many moles of sulfuric acid, H_2SO_4, are in 0.250 ℓ of 0.125 M H_2SO_4?

Answer

Quantity given: 0.250 ℓ of 0.125 M H_2SO_4
Quantity sought: ? moles of H_2SO_4

The given quantity, 0.125 M H_2SO_4, tells us that we have 0.125 mole of H_2SO_4 in 1 liter of solution. The conversion factor is therefore $\dfrac{0.125 \text{ mole } H_2SO_4}{1\ \ell}$. Then, the amount of H_2SO_4 in moles is given by

$$0.250\ \ell \times \frac{0.125 \text{ mole } H_2SO_4}{1\ \ell} = 0.0313 \text{ mole } H_2SO_4$$

Example 5

What volume, in liters, of 0.150 M NaOH solution is needed to obtain 0.0300 mole of NaOH?

Answer

Quantity given: 0.0300 mole NaOH

Quantity sought: ? ℓ of 0.150 M NaOH

0.150 M NaOH tells us that we have 0.150 mole of NaOH in 1 liter of solution. The conversion factor is therefore $\dfrac{1\ \ell}{0.150 \text{ mole}}$. Then, the volume is given by

$$0.0300 \text{ mole NaOH} \times \frac{1\ \ell}{0.150 \text{ mole NaOH}} = 0.200\ \ell$$

Example 6

Find the mass in grams of magnesium, Mg, consumed when 125 ml of 0.220 M HCl reacts as shown:

$$Mg(c) + 2HCl(aq) \longrightarrow MgCl_2(aq) + H_2(g)$$

Answer

First recognize that the given quantity is actually the number of moles of HCl that react, as in Example 4:

$$250 \text{ ml} \times \frac{1\ \ell}{10^3 \text{ ml}} = 0.250\ \ell$$

$$0.250\ \ell \times \frac{0.220 \text{ mole HCl}}{1\ \ell} = 0.0550 \text{ mole HCl}$$

Then:

Quantity given: 0.0550 mole HCl

Quantity sought: ? grams of Mg

In this reaction, 1 mole of Mg is consumed for every 2 moles of HCl. The mass of 1 mole of Mg is 24.3 g. The conversion factor is therefore $\dfrac{24.3 \text{ g Mg}}{2 \text{ moles HCl}}$, and

$$0.0550 \text{ mole HCl} \times \frac{24.3 \text{ g Mg}}{2 \text{ moles HCl}} = 0.668 \text{ g Mg}$$

PROBLEM 13 Find the mass in grams of zinc, Zn, atomic weight 65.4 g/mole Zn, consumed when 200 ml of 0.110 M HCl reacts as shown:

$$Zn(c) + 2HCl(aq) \longrightarrow ZnCl_2(aq) + H_2(g)$$

5.9 _____ IMPURE MATERIALS AND INCOMPLETE REACTIONS

For several reasons, chemists very frequently use an excess of one reactant. For example, the use of impure materials, a common procedure in many chemical processes, makes it necessary for the chemist to use an amount of one reactant in excess of the proper mole ratio given by the balanced equation. This is done to assure completeness of the reaction. Also, when a reaction is incomplete (Chap. 12), the chemist frequently uses an excess of one reactant; this has the advantage of obtaining the maximum amount of product from the reactants. We illustrate with the following examples.

Example 7

Carborundum, silicon carbide, SiC, a substitute for industrial diamonds and used as an abrasive in industrial grinding wheels (page 259), is manufactured from sand and coke:

$$SiO_2(c) + 3C \ (coke) \longrightarrow SiC(c) + 2CO(g)$$

Calculate the number of grams of coke, 90.0 % pure carbon, required to make 12.5 g of SiC.

Answer

First, as in Example 1 (page 158), calculate the quantity of pure coke needed to make 12.5 g of SiC:

Quantity given: 12.5 g SiC
Quantity sought: ? g C

The equation tells us that 3 moles of C form 1 mole of SiC. We are given grams of SiC and also want the quantity of C in grams. From the table of atomic weights (inside back cover), 1 mole of SiC has a mass of 40.1 g and 3 moles of C has a mass of 3×12.0 g. The conversion factor is thus $\dfrac{3 \times 12.0 \text{ g C}}{40.1 \text{ g SiC}}$ and the number of grams of C required is

$$12.5 \text{ g SiC} \times \frac{3 \times 12.0 \text{ g C}}{40.1 \text{ g SiC}} = 11.2 \text{ g C}$$

Now, we account for the impurity of materials; 90.0 % pure carbon means that there are 90.0 g of pure carbon in 100.0 g of impure carbon, or $\dfrac{90.0 \text{ g pure C}}{100 \text{ g impure C}}$.

Then, using the conversion factor method,

Quantity given: 11.2 g pure C
Quantity sought: ? g impure C
Conversion factor: $\dfrac{100 \text{ g impure C}}{90.0 \text{ g pure C}}$

$$11.2 \text{ g pure C} \times \frac{100 \text{ g impure C}}{90.0 \text{ g pure C}} = 12.4 \text{ g impure C}$$

PROBLEM 14 Pure hydrogen peroxide, H_2O_2, solution, used as an antiseptic, may be prepared from sulfuric acid, H_2SO_4, and barium peroxide, BaO_2 (page 421):

$$BaO_2(c) + H_2SO_4(aq) \longrightarrow BaSO_4(c) + H_2O_2(g)$$

Find the number of grams of barium peroxide, 95.0 % pure, required to prepare 31.5 g of H_2O_2.

Example 8

White, water-soluble, solid tin(II) fluoride, SnF_2, a toothpaste additive used to reduce tooth decay (page 150), may be prepared in the laboratory from tin and hydrogen fluoride (extremely poisonous, corrosive gas used to etch glass):

$$Sn(c) + 2HF(aq) \longrightarrow SnF_2(aq) + H_2(g)$$

95.0 g of Sn and 66.0 g of HF are mixed so that one of these reactants is completely consumed. Find the mass in grams of SnF_2 formed and determine which reactant is present in excess.

Answer

As in previous problems, let us first calculate the quantity of SnF_2 that can be produced from 95.0 g of Sn, as well as the quantity that can be produced from 66.0 g of HF. 1 mole of Sn has a mass of 119 g; 1 mole of SnF_2 has a mass of 157 g; and 2 moles of HF has a mass of 2×20.0 g. Then,

$$95.0 \text{ g Sn} \times \frac{157 \text{ g SnF}_2}{119 \text{ g Sn}} = 125 \text{ g SnF}_2$$

$$66.0 \text{ g HF} \times \frac{157 \text{ g SnF}_2}{2 \times 20.0 \text{ g HF}} = 259 \text{ g SnF}_2$$

We now observe that 125 g of SnF_2 obtained from 95.0 g of Sn is less than the 259 g of SnF_2 from 66.0 g of HF. *It is impossible* to obtain 259 g of SnF_2 from only 95.0 g of Sn. Therefore, 125 g SnF_2 is formed and HF is present in excess.

PROBLEM 15 Tin(II) fluoride, SnF_2, converts calcium hydroxide, $Ca(OH)_2$, a component of dental enamel, to the harder and more acid-resistant calcium fluoride, CaF_2 (page 396 ftn):

$$SnF_2(aq) + Ca(OH)_2(c) \longrightarrow CaF_2(c) + Sn(OH)_2(c)$$

When 10.0 g of $Ca(OH)_2$ and 9.55 g of SnF_2 are mixed, only one of the reactants is completely consumed. Find the amount of CaF_2 formed and determine which reactant is present in excess.

Example 9

In the manufacture of fertilizer ammonia, NH_3, by the reaction

$$N_2(g) + 3H_2(g) \longrightarrow 2 NH_3(g)$$

26.4 g of hydrogen is added for every 112 g of nitrogen. At the conditions used in chemical plants, only 55.0 % of the nitrogen reacts. Starting with 112 g N_2 and 26.4 g H_2, find the mass in grams of ammonia formed.

Answer

First, find how much of the nitrogen reacts. We are given 112 g N_2, but *only* 55.0 % of it reacts. This means that for every 100 g N_2 used, only 55.0 g N_2 reacts. The conversion factor is therefore $\dfrac{55.0 \text{ g } N_2 \text{ reacts}}{100 \text{ g } N_2 \text{ used}}$. Then

Quantity given: 112 g N_2 used
Quantity sought: ? g N_2 that reacts
Therefore, the number of grams of N_2 that reacts is

$$112 \text{ g } N_2 \text{ used} \times \frac{55.0 \text{ g } N_2 \text{ reacts}}{100 \text{ g } N_2 \text{ used}} = 61.6 \text{ g } N_2 \text{ reacts}$$

Now, as in previous examples, calculate the mass of ammonia formed from 61.6 g N_2:

Quantity given: 61.6 g N_2
Quantity sought: ? g NH_3
Conversion factor: $\dfrac{2 \times 17.0 \text{ g } NH_3}{28.0 \text{ g } N_2}$

The number of grams of NH_3 formed is

$$61.6 \text{ g } N_2 \times \frac{2 \times 17.0 \text{ g } NH_3}{28.0 \text{ g } N_2} = 74.8 \text{ g } NH_3$$

PROBLEM 16 **Small amounts of pure nitrogen may be prepared (page 605) from sodium nitrite, $NaNO_2$, and ammonium chloride, NH_4Cl:**

$$NaNO_2(aq) + NH_4Cl(aq) \longrightarrow NaCl(aq) + 2H_2O + N_2(g)$$

33.0 g $NaNO_2$ and 40.0 g NH_4Cl are mixed, but only 80.0 % of the $NaNO_2$ reacts. Find the mass of nitrogen formed.

PROBLEMS

17 Vocabulary Define the following: (a) valence, (b) binary compound, (c) ternary compound, (d) binary acid, (e) oxyacid, (f) molarity.

18 Symbols Name the following substances and ions: (a) Br_2, (b) F_2, (c) N_2, (d) NH_4ClO_3, (e) H_2O, (f) NH_3, (g) SO_4^{2-}, (h) CN^-, (i) OH^-, (j) CO_3^{2-}, (k) PO_4^{3-}, (l) NO_3^-, (m) CrO_4^{2-}.

19 Valence State the valence of the element combined with oxygen in each of the following compounds: (a) SO_2, (b) P_2O_5, (c) CuO, (d) Cu_2O, (e) Fe_2O_3, (f) PbO, (g) Pb_2O_3, (h) Mn_2O_3, (i) MnO_2, (j) Mn_2O_7.

20 Nomenclature Name the following compounds: (a) Ag_3PO_4, (b) $AgNO_3$, (c) K_2SO_4, (d) BaS, (e) $PbSO_4$, (f) $CuCN$, (g) $Fe(NO_3)_2$, (h) $Fe_2(SO_4)_3$, (i) $FeSO_4$, (j) Hg_2Cl_2, (k) $SnBr_4$, (l) Hg_2Br_2, (m) Bi_2O_5, (n) $Al(OH)_3$, (o) PCl_3, (p) $Ba(NO_3)_2$, (q) $BaSO_4$, (r) $Ba(OH)_2$, (s) $KHCO_3$, (t) $KClO$, (u) $Ca(CN)_2$.

21 Nomenclature Name the following oxyacids of iodine: HOI, HIO_2, HIO_3, HIO_4.*

22 Formula (a) Write the simplest formula for each of

_____

*Actual composition is $HIO_4(H_2O)_2$.

the following compounds: (i) sodium acetate, (ii) ammonium chlorate, (iii) aluminum phosphate, (iv) mercury(II) sulfate, (v) arsenic(III) sulfide, (vi) zinc sulfate, (vii) tin(IV) sulfate, (viii) potassium fluoride, (ix) ammonium hydroxide, (x) ammonium carbonate, (xi) magnesium hydroxide, (xii) sodium carbonate. (b) The formula for radium chloride is $RaCl_2$. Write the formula for: (i) radium acetate, (ii) radium bromide, (iii) radium cyanide, (iv) radium phosphate, (v) radium sulfate, (vi) radium sulfite.

23 Chemical equations Balance the following:

(a) $H_2(g) + Cl_2(g) \longrightarrow HCl(g)$
(b) $C(amorph) + O_2(g) \longrightarrow CO(g)$
(c) $P_2O_5(c) + H_2O(l) \longrightarrow H_3PO_4(l)$
(d) $Sb(c) + O_2(g) \longrightarrow Sb_4O_{10}(c)$
(e) $Li(c) + N_2(g) \longrightarrow Li_3N(c)$
(f) $Al(c) + Fe_2O_3(c) \longrightarrow Al_2O_3(c) + Fe(c)$
(g) $Ag^+(aq) + SO_4{}^{2-}(aq) \longrightarrow Ag_2SO_4(c)$
(h) $Ag^+(aq) + Cl^-(aq) \longrightarrow AgCl_2{}^-(aq)$
(i) $AgNO_3(c) + MgCl_2(c) \longrightarrow$ $AgCl(c) + Mg(NO_3)_2(c)$
(j) $PtCl_4(c) + Cl^-(aq) \longrightarrow PtCl_6{}^{2-}(aq)$

24 Balance the following:

(a) $Al(c) + Cl_2(g) \longrightarrow AlCl_3(c)$
(b) $Al_2(SO_4)_3(aq) + Pb(NO_3)_2(aq) \longrightarrow$ $PbSO_4(c) + Al(NO_3)_3(aq)$
(c) $Na(c) + H_2O \longrightarrow NaOH(aq) + H_2(g)$
(d) $Sn(c) + HCl(aq) \longrightarrow SnCl_2(aq) + H_2(g)$
(e) $Sn(c) + H_3PO_4(aq) \longrightarrow Sn_3(PO_4)_2(c) + H_2(g)$
(f) $Fe_2O_3(c) + CO(g) \longrightarrow Fe(c) + CO_2(g)$
(g) $Al(c) + O_2(g) \longrightarrow Al_2O_3(c)$
(h) $Li_3N(c) + H_2O \longrightarrow NH_3(g) + LiOH(aq)$
(i) $Sr(c) + N_2(g) \longrightarrow Sr_3N_2(c)$
(j) $MgO(c) + PCl_5(g) \longrightarrow MgCl_2(c) + P_4O_{10}(c)$
(k) $Al(c) + AgNO_3(aq) \longrightarrow$ $Al(NO_3)_3(aq) + Ag(c)$
(l) $NaBr(c) + F_2(g) \longrightarrow NaF(c) + Br_2(g)$
(m) $H_2S(g) + NaOH(aq) \longrightarrow Na_2S(aq) + H_2O$
(n) $Mg(NO_3)_2(aq) + Na_2S(aq) \longrightarrow$ $MgS(c) + NaNO_3(aq)$
(o) $Zn(OH)_2(c) + HNO_3(aq) \longrightarrow$ $Zn(NO_3)_2(aq) + H_2O$
(p) $Ca(OH)_2(c) + H_3PO_4(l) \longrightarrow$ $Ca_3(PO_4)_2(c) + H_2O$

25 Write the formula for each of the following compounds and balance the equation:

(a) calcium carbonate(c) + hydrochloric acid(aq) $\longrightarrow$ calcium chloride(aq) + water(l) + carbon dioxide(g)
(b) calcium(c) + water(l) $\longrightarrow$ calcium hydroxide(aq) + hydrogen(g)
(c) potassium carbonate(aq) + sulfuric acid(aq) $\longrightarrow$ potassium sulfate(aq) + carbon dioxide(g) + water(l).
(d) iron(c) + chlorine(g) $\longrightarrow$ iron(III) chloride(c)

(e) zinc(c) + silver nitrate(aq) $\longrightarrow$ zinc nitrate(aq) + silver(c)
(f) sodium sulfite(aq) + sulfuric acid(aq) $\longrightarrow$ sodium sulfate(aq) + sulfur dioxide(g) + water(l).
(g) copper oxide(c) + hydrogen(g) $\longrightarrow$ copper(c) + water(l)
(h) sodium sulfite(aq) + hydrochloric acid(aq) $\longrightarrow$ sodium chloride(aq) + sulfur dioxide(g) + water(l).
(i) mercuric oxide(c) $\longrightarrow$ mercury(l) + oxygen(g)
(j) calcium chloride(aq) + sodium sulfate(aq) $\longrightarrow$ calcium sulfate(c) + sodium chloride(aq)

26 Binary compounds may react with water to form hydrides. Write the balanced equation for each reaction:

(a) $\underset{\text{calcium acetylide}}{CaC_2(c)} + H_2O(l) \longrightarrow$ $Ca(OH)_2(c) + \underset{\text{acetylene}}{C_2H_2(g)}$

(b) $\underset{\text{dimagnesium silicide}}{Mg_2Si(c)} + H_2O(l) \longrightarrow$ $Mg(OH)_2(c) + \underset{\text{silane}}{SiH_4(g)}$

(c) $\underset{\text{trimagnesium dinitride}}{Mg_3N_2(c)} + H_2O(l) \longrightarrow$ $Mg(OH)_2(c) + \underset{\text{ammonia}}{NH_3(g)}$

(d) $\underset{\text{tricalcium diphosphide}}{Ca_3P_2(c)} + H_2O(l) \longrightarrow$ $Ca(OH)_2(c) + \underset{\text{phosphine}}{PH_3(g)}$

(e) $\underset{\text{magnesium sulfide}}{MgS(c)} + H_2O(l) \longrightarrow$ $Mg(OH)_2(c) + \underset{\text{hydrogen sulfide}}{H_2S(g)}$

(f) $\underset{\text{tetra-aluminum tricarbide}}{Al_4C_3(c)} + H_2O(l) \longrightarrow$ $Al(OH)_3(c) + \underset{\text{methane}}{CH_4(g)}$

27 Write balanced equations for the following reactions:

(a) $\underset{\text{magnesium boride}}{Mg_3B_2(c)} + H_2O(l) \longrightarrow$ $Mg(OH)_2(c) + \underset{\text{diborane}}{B_2H_6(g)}$

(b) $C_2H_6(g) + O_2(g) \longrightarrow CO_2(g) + H_2O(l)$
(c) $\underset{\text{potassium hexafluorosilicate(IV)*}}{K_2SiF_6(c)} + K(c) \longrightarrow$ $KF(c) + Si(c)$

(d) $\underset{\text{potassium hexacyanoferrate(II)**}}{K_4Fe(CN)_6(c)} \longrightarrow KCN(c) +$ $Fe(c) + 2C(amorph) + N_2(g)$

(e) $Na_2HPO_4(c) \longrightarrow Na_4P_2O_7(c) + H_2O(l)$

---

*The nomenclature of complex inorganic compounds is discussed in Chap. 21.
**Traditional name is potassium ferrocyanide.

(f) $Al_2O_3(c) + C(amorph) + Cl_2(g) \longrightarrow$
   $Al_2Cl_6(c) + CO(g)$
(g) $H_2(g) + Fe_2O_3(c) \longrightarrow Fe(c) + H_2O(g)$
(h) $Sb_2S_3(c) + Fe(c) \longrightarrow FeS(c) + Sb(c)$
(i) $PbS(c) + O_2(g) \longrightarrow PbO(c) + SO_2(g)$

28 Calculate the number of moles in (a) 42 g $CaCO_3$, (b) 14 g $NaNO_2$, (c) 6.0 g $Ca_3(PO_4)_2$, (d) 34 g $NaOH$, (e) 8.0 g H_2SO_4, (f) 24 g H_3PO_4.

29 **Moles and atoms** (a) How many atoms of hydrogen are in 2.5 moles of ammonium hydrogen carbonate, NH_4HCO_3? (b) How many moles of N atoms are in 3.0 moles of ammonium nitrate?

30 **Chemical arithmetic** In photography (page 196), the developed film still contains some silver bromide, which is removed by washing with sodium thiosulfate ("hypo") (page 667) to prevent spoilage of the picture. The reaction may be represented as

$2Na_2S_2O_3(aq) + AgBr(c) \longrightarrow$
   $Na_3Ag(S_2O_3)_2(aq) + NaBr(aq)$

Find the number of grams of $Na_2S_2O_3$ consumed to remove 1.4 g of $AgBr$.

31 Nitrogen in the air may be "fixed" by the following reaction:

$Na_2CO_3(c) + 4C(amorph) + N_2(g) \longrightarrow$
   $2NaCN(c) + 3CO(g)$

Find the number of (a) grams of $NaCN$ and (b) liters of CO (STP) formed when 44.0 g of N_2 reacts.

32 Ammonia has been suggested as a clean fuel; it burns without the emission of carbon monoxide:

$2NH_3(g) + 1\frac{1}{2} O_2(g) \longrightarrow N_2(g) + 3H_2O(g)$

Calculate (a) the mass of nitrogen in grams formed and (b) the volume of ammonia in liters (STP) consumed when 36.0 g of O_2 reacts.

33 Nitrosyl chloride, an intensely irritating substance, is made from nitrosyl sulfuric acid and hydrogen chloride:

$HNOSO_4(c) + HCl(g) \longrightarrow$
   $NOCl(g) + H_2SO_4(g)$

Find the number of (a) grams of $HNOSO_4$ reacting and (b) liters of NOCl (STP) formed when 26.1 g of HCl reacts.

34 Carbon suboxide, C_3O_2, undergoes a reaction with propylene, C_3H_6:

$C_3O_2(g) + C_3H_6(g) \longrightarrow C_4H_6(g) + 2CO(g)$

Calculate how many liters of CO (STP) form (a)

from 24.6 g of C_3O_2, and (b) from 38.0 l (STP) of C_3H_6.

35 Calcium cyanamide, $CaCN_2$, used as a defoliant for cotton plants before harvesting and as a fertilizer, is made from nitrogen and calcium acetylide in an electric furnace:

$CaC_2(c) + N_2(g) \longrightarrow CaCN_2(c) + C(amorph)$

Find how many (a) grams of calcium cyanamide form, and (b) liters of N_2 (STP) react when 74.0 g of CaC_2 reacts.

36 SO_2, used in the manufacture of sulfuric acid, may be prepared from sulfide ores:

$4FeS_2(c) + 11O_2(g) \longrightarrow 2Fe_2O_3(c) + 8SO_2(g)$

Find the number of (a) liters of SO_2 (STP) produced, and (b) liters of O_2 (STP) consumed when 2.5 tons of FeS_2 (iron(II) disulfide) reacts. 1 ton = 2000 lb, and 1 lb = 454 g.

37 In 1775, when the French were at war with Spain, the French Academy of Sciences offered a prize of 100,000 francs for a process to manufacture "alkali" from nonvegetable sources. In 1790, Nicholas Leblanc developed a process in which the desired product, Na_2SO_4,* was produced from sodium chloride and sulfuric acid:

$2NaCl(c) + H_2SO_4(aq) \longrightarrow Na_2SO_4(c) + 2HCl(g)$

(a) Calculate the number of grams of NaCl required to prepare 32.7 g of Na_2SO_4. (b) At the same time, how many liters of HCl (STP) form?

38 Oil paintings in which the *white lead*** has been blackened by reaction with hydrogen sulfide in the air, forming black lead sulfide, may be cleaned with hydrogen peroxide:

$PbS(c) + 4H_2O_2(aq) \longrightarrow PbSO_4(c) + 4H_2O(l)$
black   white

Find how many grams of H_2O_2 must react to clean 0.17 g of PbS.

39 Consider the following reaction:

$BH_3(g) + PF_3(g) \longrightarrow H_3BPF_3(g)$

Find how many (a) liters (STP) of PF_3 react, and (b) liters of H_3BPF_3 (STP) form when 14.5 l (STP) of BH_3 reacts. (c) Are the number of grams of PF_3

---

*Leblanc never received his prize and committed suicide after his patent rights and factory were seized during the French Revolution.

**The approximate composition of *white lead* is $Pb(OH)_2(PbCO_3)_2$.

reacting and the number of grams of H_3BPF_3 forming equal?

40 Ammonia and hydrogen chloride react as follows:

$$NH_3(g) + HCl(g) \longrightarrow NH_4Cl(g)$$

At 800 °C, 4.00 moles $NH_3(g)$ and 2.00 moles $HCl(g)$ are mixed, but *only* 0.50 mole NH_3 reacts. Find the number of moles (a) of $HCl(g)$ that react; (b) of $NH_4Cl(g)$ that form.

41 Zinc ions washed out of mining sites may become toxic to fresh water fish. They are produced by weathering of ZnS (*zinc blende*):

$$ZnS(c) + 2O_2(g) \longrightarrow Zn^{2+}(aq) + SO_4^{2-}(aq)$$

How much oxygen, in moles of O_2 and in grams, reacts with 150.4 g ZnS?

42 Calculate the number of grams of ammonia produced by the action of the enzyme urease on 5.32 g of urea (page 608):

$$\underset{\text{urea}}{H_2NCONH_2(aq)} + H_2O \longrightarrow 2NH_3(aq) + CO_2(aq)$$

43 Ozone, formed by electrical sparking in air and a hazardous air pollutant (Chap. 6), is analyzed by the following reaction:

$$O_3(g) + 2I^-(aq) + 2H^+(aq) \longrightarrow I_2(c) + H_2O + O_2(g)$$

Calculate the number of grams of I_2 obtained when 50 mg of O_3 is detected.

44 A possible reaction for the removal of two common air pollutants, CO and NO (page 520), is:

$$NO + CO \longrightarrow \tfrac{1}{2} N_2 + CO_2$$

How much CO in liters (STP) is needed to change 4.8 g of NO to N_2?

45 Many observations point to the presence of H_2SO_4 in the thick clouds surrounding the planet Venus. In the presence of H_2O vapor, H_2SO_4 is broken down according to the following equation:

$$H_2SO_4(g) + H_2O(g) \longrightarrow H_3O^+(aq) + HSO_4^-(aq)$$

Find the number of grams of HSO_4^- formed when 43.4 g of H_2SO_4 reacts.

46 The automobile storage battery generates electrical energy from a chemical reaction. Find the weight in grams of H_2SO_4 that reacts with 16.4 g of lead(IV) oxide, PbO_2, according to the following reaction:

$$PbO_2(c) + Pb(c) + 2H_2SO_4(aq) \longrightarrow 2PbSO_4(c) + 2H_2O$$

47 Toxic mercury vapor can be detected by using a test paper impregnated with palladium(II) chloride ($PdCl_2$). What is the maximum quantity of mercury detectable by 2.0 mg of $PdCl_2$?

$$Hg(g) + PdCl_2(c) \longrightarrow HgCl_2(c) + Pd(c)$$

48 Minerals containing *pyrite*, FeS_2, exposed during mining are responsible for harmful acid mine drainage, the seepage of sulfuric acid into streams around coal mines:

$$2FeS_2(c) + 2H_2O + 7O_2(g) \longrightarrow 2FeSO_4(c) + 2H_2SO_4(aq)$$

How much H_2SO_4 in grams is produced when 84.3 g of FeS_2 reacts?

49 In a star like the sun, 5.64×10^6 tons of H atoms are transformed per second into helium (page 549):

$$4H(g) \longrightarrow He(g)$$

Find the mass in tons of He formed in (a) 24 hours; (b) 1.0 year. 365 days = 1 year.

50 Small quantities of uranium present in waste solutions from nuclear reactors can be recovered by precipitation with H_2O_2:

$$UO_2^{2+}(aq) + H_2O_2(l) + 2NH_4^+(aq) + 2F^-(aq) \longrightarrow 2H^+(aq) + UO_4(NH_3)_2(HF)_2(c)$$

How many grams of $UO_4(NH_3)_2(HF)_2$ form when 842 mg of H_2O_2 reacts?

51 If diamond is pure carbon, what volume in ml (STP) of CO_2 should be produced by completely burning a 0.010 carat diamond? 1 carat = 0.2 g exactly.

$$C(diamond) + O_2(g) \longrightarrow CO_2(g)$$

52 The chemical reaction used to cook wood chips in the manufacture of paper pulp by the *Kraft* process is:

$$Na_2S(aq) + Na_2CO_3(aq) + Ca(OH)_2(c) \longrightarrow Na_2S(aq) + 2NaOH(aq) + CaCO_3(c)$$

How much $CaCO_3$ is formed when 54.3 g of $Ca(OH)_2$ is consumed? The Na_2S, although not consumed, is needed to fix the conditions for the reaction to go as written.

53 **Library** Read one of the following: (a) "The Evolution of Valence Theory and Bond Symbolism," Henry MacKlein, *Journal of Chemical Education,* volume 31, 1954, page 618; (b) "Notes on Nomenclature," *Journal of Chemical Education,* volume 48, 1971, page 730; (c) "Alfred E. Stock and the Insidious *Quecksilbervergiftung,*" E. K. Mellon, *Journal of Chemical Education,* volume 54, April 1977, page 211.

ADDITIONAL PROBLEMS

54 Tetraphosphorus trisulfide, P_4S_3, used in matches (page 614), is manufactured from phosphorus and sulfur above 100 °C:

$$P_4(l) + 3S(l) \longrightarrow P_4S_3(c)$$

When 62.0 g of P_4 and 48.2 g of S are mixed, 80 % of the S reacts. Find the mass in grams (a) of P_4S_3 formed and (b) of P_4 consumed.

55 A *Freon,* dichlorodifluoromethane, CCl_2F_2, one of the compounds now being accused of depleting the ozone layer in the upper atmosphere (Chap. 16), is made by the reaction of carbon tetrachloride, CCl_4, with HF:

$$CCl_4(l) + 2HF(g) \longrightarrow CCl_2F_2(g) + 2HCl(g)$$

(a) How many grams of *Freon* are produced when 64.3 g of CCl_4 reacts? (b) About 5.0×10^5 tons of CCl_2F_2 are manufactured each year for use as aerosol propellant (in "spray cans") and as a refrigerator coolant (page 105). How much HF must react to make this amount of *Freon?*

56 How many grams of CS_2 (93 % pure) must be burned to form 6.3 g of SO_2?

$$CS_2(g) + 3O_2(g) \longrightarrow CO_2(g) + 2SO_2(g)$$

57 Laughing gas, N_2O, dinitrogen oxide, one of the first anesthetics used by the dental profession, is made by the controlled decomposition of aqueous ammonium nitrate:

$$NH_4NO_3(aq) \longrightarrow N_2O(g) + 2H_2O$$

How many grams of NH_4NO_3 must react to prepare 350 ml of N_2O collected at STP over a liquid whose vapor pressure is 12.4 torr?

58 Treatment of calcium phosphate, $Ca_3(PO_4)_2$, the main constituent of *phosphate rock* (page 614), with sulfuric acid converts it to a more soluble form known as *superphosphate* fertilizer:

$$Ca_3(PO_4)_2(c) + 2H_2SO_4(aq) \longrightarrow \\ Ca(H_2PO_4)_2(c) + 2CaSO_4(c)$$

What weight in grams of H_2SO_4, 95 % pure, must react to produce 150.8 g of $Ca(H_2PO_4)_2$?

59 Attempts to reduce automobile-caused air pollution by the use of catalytic mufflers involve a number of reactions. One is the reaction of SO_3 with the aluminum container, forming $Al_2(SO_4)_3$, which is then changed to SO_2 by CO:

$$2Al \longrightarrow Al_2(SO_4)_3 + 3CO \longrightarrow \\ Al_2O_3 + 3CO_2 + 3SO_2$$

Calculate (a) the mass in grams and (b) the volume in liters (STP) of SO_2 produced when 12.2 mg of Al reacts.

60 The reactions of ozone with ammonia, NH_3, in photochemical smog are:

(1) $2NH_3(aq) + 4O_3(g) \longrightarrow$
$\quad 4O_2(g) + H_2O(l) + NH_4NO_3(c)$
(2) $NH_4NO_3(c) \longrightarrow N_2O(g) + 2H_2O(l)$
(3) $2NH_3(g) + 3O_3(g) \longrightarrow$
$\quad 3O_2(g) + H_2O(l) + NH_4NO_2(c)$
(4) $NH_4NO_2(c) \longrightarrow N_2(g) + 2H_2O(l)$

Given that 3.00×10^{-5} g of O_3 reacts. (a) If 99.0 % of the O_3 reacts as shown in Reaction (1) and the remainder as in Reaction (3), find the mass in g of (i) NH_4NO_3 and (ii) NH_4NO_2 formed. (b) If 2.00 % of the NH_4NO_3 formed reacts as shown in Reaction (2) and 2.10 % of the NH_4NO_2 formed reacts as shown in Reaction (4), find the mass in g of (i) N_2O, (ii) N_2, (iii) NH_4NO_3, and (iv) NH_4NO_2 at the end of these reactions.

61 Oxygen masks used in emergency breathing situations contain canisters of potassium superoxide, KO_2. When the exhaled breath, CO_2, passes through the KO_2, it is converted to O_2 (page 602). What volume in ml (STP) of O_2 is formed from 45.4 g of KO_2, 25.0 % of which reacts?

$$4KO_2(c) + 2CO_2(g) \longrightarrow 2K_2CO_3(c) + 3O_2(g)$$

62 A solution containing 3.21 g of silver nitrate, $AgNO_3$, reacts with a solution containing 2.46 g of sodium chloride, NaCl, forming a white suspension of silver chloride and leaving an excess of one reactant:

$$AgNO_3(aq) + NaCl(aq) \longrightarrow \\ AgCl(c) + NaNO_3(aq)$$

Calculate the mass in grams of AgCl formed and name the reactant in excess.

63 In the manufacture of carbon tetrachloride by the reaction

$$S_2Cl_2(l) + C(coke) \longrightarrow CCl_4(l) + 4S(c)$$

a batch of 2.15 tons of S_2Cl_2 and 0.200 ton of coke are mixed; 82.0 % of the S_2Cl_2 reacts. How many tons of CCl_4 are obtained?

64 Methyl alcohol* is made commercially by the addition of H_2 to CO at 200 atm and 400 °C:

$$2H_2(g) + CO(g) \longrightarrow CH_3OH(g)$$

2.22×10^6 l of H_2 and 1.02×10^6 l of CO, initially at STP, are loaded into the reaction chamber. If 90.0 % of the CO reacts, (a) what volume of H_2 in liters (STP) reacts, and (b) what volume in liters (STP) of CH_3OH forms? (c) Assume that CH_3OH behaves as an ideal gas, and calculate its volume at 200 atm and 400 °C.

65 A process has been developed for producing carborundum, SiC (Example 4), from rice hulls which contain nearly the required mole ratio of silicon and carbon. Assume that the process is 75.0 % efficient; what quantity (in grams) of Si must a batch of hulls contain in order to produce 10.0 g of SiC?

66 A mixture of CO and H_2 passed over a Rh-SiO_2 catalyst (Chap. 16) produces a mixture containing the following percentages by mass of four important industrial compounds: acetic acid, CH_3COOH, 65 %; acetaldehyde, CH_3CHO, 15 %; ethyl alcohol, C_2H_5OH, 10 %; and methyl alcohol, CH_3OH, 10 %. In one experiment, 60 kg of products per hour was obtained over a period of 10 hours. Find the minimum number of moles and grams of H_2 that must be consumed in this experiment.

---

*Methyl alcohol (methanol), formerly obtained by the destructive distillation of wood, is also known as wood alcohol. It is sometimes confused with ethyl alcohol but it is much more toxic; death from ingestion of less than 30 ml has been reported. Small quantities produce headache, visual impairment, or complete blindness; both methyl alcohol and its oxidation products attack the optic nerve.

67 More than 7×10^9 plastic bottles, average mass 125 g, containing about 80 % ethylene, C_2H_4, are produced annually. Find the minimum amount of C_2H_4 required to meet this demand.

68 How many moles of H_2 must be consumed to meet an annual demand of 2.0×10^{10} lb of ethylene, C_2H_4 (see Problem 67)?

69 A solution containing 3.31 g of $Pb(NO_3)_2$ is mixed with a solution containing 1.95 g of HCl, consuming one reactant completely. (a) How many grams of lead(II) chloride, $PbCl_2$, are formed? (b) Which reactant is in excess?

$$Pb(NO_3)_2(aq) + 2HCl(aq) \longrightarrow$$
$$PbCl_2(c) + 2HNO_3(aq)$$

70 How many moles of phosphoric acid are in (a) 0.500 l and (b) 250 ml of 0.200 M H_3PO_4?

71 What volume of 0.200 M H_3PO_4 (phosphoric acid) should be taken to obtain 0.125 mole of H_3PO_4?

72 Find the number of grams of calcium, Ca, consumed when 300 ml of 0.500 M HI reacts as shown:

$$Ca(c) + 2HI(aq) \longrightarrow CaI_2(aq) + H_2(g)$$

73 Calculate the volume of H_2 in liters (STP) produced when 250 ml of 0.100 M HCl reacts with magnesium:

$$Mg(c) + 2HCl(aq) \longrightarrow MgCl_2(aq) + H_2(g)$$

74 Find the mass in grams of white silver chloride formed when 750 ml of 0.160 M sodium chloride reacts as shown:

$$NaCl(aq) + AgNO_3(aq) \longrightarrow$$
$$AgCl(c) + NaNO_3(aq)$$

75 How many grams of aluminum, Al, atomic weight 27.0 g/mole Al, react when 100.0 ml of 0.100 M H_2SO_4 reacts?

$$2Al(c) + 3H_2SO_4(aq) \longrightarrow Al_2(SO_4)_3(aq) + 3H_2(g)$$

ANSWERS

1 (i) (a) 2 mole, (b) 2.0 g
  (ii) (a) 4, (b) 4.0 g
  (iii) (a) 1, (b) 1.0 g
  (iv) (a) 2, (b) 2.0 g
  (v) (a) 1, (b) 1.0 g
2 2.60 moles
3 3, 2, 4, 2
4 (a) (i) KBr

  (ii) $Ca_3(PO_4)_2$
  (iii) $Bi(NO_3)_3$
  (iv) $(NH_4)_2SO_4$
  (b) Mg–3, P–2, O–8 moles
5 (a) antimony trichloride or antimony(III) chloride, (b) cupric chloride or copper(II) chloride, (c) stannic chloride or tin(IV) chloride, (d) iodine tribromide or iodine(III) bromide.

6 (a) potassium fluoride, (b) potassium iodide, (c) potassium sulfide.

7 (a) lithium hydroxide, (b) iron(II) hydroxide, (c) zinc hydroxide, (d) copper(II) hydroxide, (e) chromium(III) hydroxide

8 (a) 10 moles H_2
(b) 10 moles H_2O

10 (a) 19 g Al, (b) 68 g MnO_2

11 61 ℓ (STP) O_2

12 40 ℓ O_2 (22 °C, 740 torr)

13 0.719 g Zn

14 165 g impure BaO_2

15 4.75 g CaF_2 formed, $Ca(OH)_2$ present in excess

16 10.7 g N_2 formed

18 (a) bromine, (b) fluorine, (c) nitrogen, (d) ammonium chlorate, (e) water, (f) ammonia, (g) sulfate, (h) cyanide, (i) hydroxide, (j) carbonate, (k) phosphate, (l) nitrate, (m) chromate

19 (a) 4, (b) 5, (c) 2, (d) 1, (e) 3, (f) 2, (g) 3, (h) 3, (i) 4, (j) 7

20 (a) silver phosphate, (b) silver nitrate, (c) potassium sulfate, (d) barium sulfide, (e) lead(II) sulfate, (f) copper(I) cyanide, (g) iron(II) nitrate, (h) iron(III) sulfate, (i) iron(II) sulfate, (j) mercury(I) chloride, (k) tin(IV) bromide, (l) mercury(I) bromide, (m) bismuth(V) oxide, (n) aluminum hydroxide, (o) phosphorus(III) chloride, (p) barium nitrate, (q) barium sulfate, (r) barium hydroxide, (s) potassium hydrogen carbonate, (t) potassium hypochlorite, (u) calcium cyanide.

21 hypoiodous acid, iodous acid, iodic acid, periodic acid.

22 (a) (i) $NaCH_3COO$, (ii) NH_4ClO_3, (iii) $AlPO_4$, (iv) $HgSO_4$, (v) As_2S_3, (vi) $ZnSO_4$, (vii) $Sn(SO_4)_2$, (viii) KF, (ix) NH_4OH, (x) $(NH_4)_2CO_3$, (xi) $Mg(OH)_2$, (xii) Na_2CO_3; (b) (i) $Ra(CH_3COO)_2$, (ii) $RaBr_2$, (iii) $Ra(CN)_2$, (iv) $Ra_3(PO_4)_2$, (v) $RaSO_4$, (vi) $RaSO_3$

28 (a) 0.42 mole $CaCO_3$
(b) 0.20 mole $NaNO_2$
(c) 0.019 mole $Ca_3(PO_4)_2$
(d) 0.85 mole $NaOH$
(e) 0.082 mole H_2SO_4
(f) 0.24 mole H_3PO_4

29 (a) 7.5×10^{24} atoms
(b) 6 moles of atoms

30 2.4 g $Na_2S_2O_3$

31 (a) 154 g $NaCN$
(b) 106 ℓ CO (STP)

32 (a) 21.0 g N_2
(b) 33.6 ℓ NH_3 (STP)

33 (a) 90.8 g $HNOSO_4$
(b) 16.0 ℓ $NOCl$ (STP)

34 (a) 16.2 ℓ CO (STP)
(b) 76.0 ℓ CO (STP)

35 (a) 92.5 g $CaCN_2$
(b) 25.9 ℓ N_2 (STP)

36 (a) 8.5×10^5 ℓ SO_2 (STP)
(b) 1.2×10^6 ℓ O_2 (STP)

37 (a) 26.9 g $NaCl$
(b) 10.3 ℓ HCl (STP)

38 0.097 g H_2O_2

39 (a) 14.5 ℓ BH_3 (STP)
(b) 14.5 ℓ H_3BF_3 (STP)
(c) No—masses of molecules differ.

40 (a) 0.50 mole HCl
(b) 0.50 mole NH_4Cl

41 98.78 g O_2
3.087 moles O_2

42 3.01 g NH_3

43 0.27 g I_2

44 3.6 ℓ CO (STP)

45 43.0 g HSO_4

46 13.5 g H_2SO_4

47 2.3×10^{-3} g Hg

48 68.9 g H_2SO_4

49 (a) 4.84×10^{11} tons He/day
(b) 1.77×10^{14} tons He/year

50 9.31 g $UO_4(NH_3)_2(HF)_2$

51 3.7 ml (STP) CO_2

52 73.3 g $CaCO_3$

54 (a) 88.2 g P_4S_3
(b) 49.7 g P_4

55 (a) 50.5 g CCl_2F_2
(b) 1.7×10^5 tons HF

56 4.0 g impure CS_2

57 1.23 g NH_4NO_3

58 133 g impure H_2SO_4

59 (a) 43.4 mg SO_2
(b) 15.2 ml SO_2 (STP)

60 (a) (i) 1.24×10^{-5} g NH_4NO_3
(ii) 1.3×10^{-7} g NH_4NO_2
(b) (i) 1.36×10^{-7} g N_2O
(ii) 1.2×10^{-9} g N_2
(iii) 1.22 g NH_4NO_3
(iv) 1.3×10^{-7} g NH_4NO_2

61 2.68×10^3 ml O_2 (STP)

62 2.71 g $AgCl$, $NaCl$ in excess

63 2.01 tons CCl_4

64 (a) 1.84×10^6 ℓ H_2 (STP)
(b) 9.18×10^5 ℓ CH_3OH (STP)
(c) 1.13×10^4 ℓ CH_3OH

65 9.3 g Si

66 5.0×10^4 g H_2, 2.5×10^4 moles H_2

67 7×10^{11} g C_2H_4

68 6.5×10^{11} mole H_2

69 2.78 g $PbCl_2$, HCl in excess

70 (a) 0.100 M H_3PO_4, (b) 0.0500 mole H_3PO_4

71 0.625 ℓ

72 3.01 g Ca

73 0.280 ℓ (STP)

74 17.2 g $AgCl$

75 0.180 g Al

binary acid A compound consisting of hydrogen and another element, such as HCl and H_2S.

binary compound A compound consisting of two elements, such as NaCl and $FeCl_3$.

chemical equation A shorthand statement using chemical formulas to represent a chemical change, showing the relative quantities of reactants and products.

coefficients The numbers in a chemical equation that give the mole ratios of reactants and products, such as 2 and 3 in $2H_3PO_4 + 3Ca(OH)_2$.

combining capacity The ability of elements to combine with other elements to form compounds. See **valence.**

group A combination of atoms that stays combined and behaves as a unit during chemical reactions, such as NO_3^- and SO_4^{2-}.

oxyacid An acid consisting of hydrogen, oxygen, and a third element, such as $HClO_4$ and H_3PO_4.

ternary compound A compound consisting of three elements, such as the hydroxides, $Mg(OH)_2$ and $Fe(OH)_3$, and the oxyacids.

valence The number of hydrogen atoms combining with one atom of an element.

Photo by Madison Devlin

ELECTRICITY AND ATOMIC STRUCTURE

6

In a previous chapter (page 115) we discussed several experiments involving the use of electricity that led to the conclusion that the atom is electrical in nature. Dalton's concept of a structureless neutral atom cannot explain this conclusion. Also, his concept of the atom provides no scheme to explain the observation that 1 atom of hydrogen combines with 1 atom of fluorine, while 1 atom of nitrogen combines with 3 atoms of fluorine (page 116). Further, the decomposition (Chap. 17) of radioactive atoms into smaller particles contradicts the assumption that atoms cannot be altered. In this chapter, we examine a more complete theory of the structure of atoms—the nuclear theory of the atom. This theory reaffirms the atom as the unit of chemical change and provides a scheme to distinguish between the structures of the atoms of different elements.

THE RUTHERFORD NUCLEAR THEORY OF THE ATOM_____6.1

The existence of nuclei, central cores within atoms, was suggested by Ernest Rutherford in 1911 to explain his experimental results (discussed below) on the deflection of alpha particles, He^{2+}. Niels Bohr in 1913 also assumed the presence of a nucleus in his successful explanation of the color patterns displayed by hydrogen atoms (page 191). However, these ideas evolved over a period of years, with significant contributions of other scientists.

A theory to account for the conclusion that matter is electrical in nature and that electrons are parts of atoms was proposed by Joseph J. Thomson in 1904. He assumed that an atom is composed of a sphere of positive electricity enclosing a sufficient number of electrons to neutralize the positive charge. He further assumed that the positive electric charge is *uniformly distributed* within the sphere. By analogy, his postulated atom is like a uniform ball of raisin-bread, in which the bread represents the positive electricity and the raisins represent the negatively charged electrons. The mass of an electron is very small compared to the mass of an atom. It then follows that nearly *all the mass of an atom is associated with the positive charge*. A **Thomson model of an atom,** containing 3 electrons in a uniform sphere of positive electricity carrying a charge of $3+$, is illustrated in Fig. 6.1.

Sphere of constant density of positive charge
(The charge per ml is practically the same
throughout the sphere.)

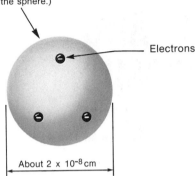

Electrons

About 2 x 10⁻⁸ cm

FIGURE 6.1 The Thomson model of the atom: a sphere of positive electricity uniformly distributed over the volume of the known size of the atom, in which are enclosed a number of electrons so that the atom is electrically neutral.

The Flight of the Arrow   Let us pause for a moment to examine what happens to an arrow in flight. This examination will help us understand the experiments performed to test the validity of the Thomson atom. If a man in outer space shoots a heavy arrow straight ahead, the direction in which the arrow travels will remain unchanged. It will neither rise nor drop; it will not sway to the left or to the right (Fig. 6.2). On the other hand, the same man, shooting a similar arrow straight ahead on Earth, will observe that the arrow gradually sinks to the ground. In the absence of a wind, the arrow only curves downward; it does not sway to the left or right. However, in the presence of a cross wind, the arrow not only drops but also sways to one side or the other, depending on the wind direction.

In 1687, Isaac Newton (page 6) published some definitions and assumptions that explain the motion of objects, their direction, and their changes in direction. More important, these "laws" make it possible to predict the motion of objects, *provided that the forces acting on the object are known*. In common terms, whenever you push or pull an object, you are exerting a force. To change the path of an object in motion, an *unbalanced force* must act on it. On Earth, the forces acting on the arrow are gravity and the wind (movement of the molecules of which air is composed). The arrow curves downward because the force of gravity pulls the arrow toward the Earth. The force of the cross wind causes the arrow to sway. In outer space, the arrow is so far removed from the Earth and other heavenly bodies that the gravitational force of attraction is practically zero. Also, a wind in outer space is practically impossible because the density of matter, 1 molecule per liter, is almost zero. However, on Earth, if the arrow is subjected to an *upward* wind whose force *exactly balances the downward force* of gravity, the arrow will behave as in outer space.

Air resistance, which decreases the speed of the arrow, is not important in this discussion.

PROBLEM 1   **(a) A pitcher throws a knuckleball straight at the catcher's glove. However, after the ball has traveled some distance, the flow of air passing over the ball is not distributed uniformly over the ball. In the distance between the pitcher and the catcher, the ball shifts about a foot to the side. Explain. (b) The forces in an earthquake cannot be evaluated. Can a physicist, with all the computers in the world at his command, predict the location, after an earthquake, of a highway that was built on a fault?**

These principles are applicable to the operation of all forces, independent of the name used to describe the force—gravitational, electrical, magnetic, frictional, or wind.

Man in outer space shoots an arrow

Arrow remains unchanged on course because no forces act on arrow

Man shoots an arrow at ground level

Arrow curves downward because of the force of gravity exerted by the earth

Man shoots an arrow at ground level

Arrow does not drop to ground as long as the force of gravity is exactly *balanced* by an upward draft of wind

a

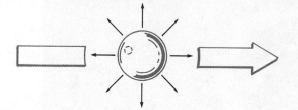

A moving gas molecule equally attracted in all directions by other molecules will continue to move in a straight line.

b

FIGURE 6.2 (a) The flight of an arrow under various conditions, illustrating one of Newton's laws of motion. An object moves in a straight line with constant speed unless acted on by an *unbalanced* force.

(b) A moving object attracted with equal force in all directions (all forces are balanced) will continue to move in a straight line. A stationary object attracted with equal force in all directions will remain stationary.

About 186,000 mi/s.

The Flight of the Alpha Particle   Let us now make a prediction on the basis of the Thomson atom. If an alpha particle, He^{2+}, traveling at almost the speed of light (3.00×10^{10} cm/s), hits a Thomson atom, the He^{2+} particle should continue to move in a straight line along its original path. It should not be deflected, moving neither up nor down nor sideways from its original path. To alter the path of the He^{2+}, an unbalanced force must act on it. Deflection would result from the electrical repulsion between the positive He^{2+} particle and the sphere of positive electricity. But the positive electricity, by assumption, *uniformly* occupies the volume of the atom. Therefore, it is *not* sufficiently concentrated in any region of the atom to repel the fast-moving He^{2+} particle. A He^{2+} particle entering such an atom, Thomson reasoned, would then be surrounded equally by positive electricity. The He^{2+} particle within the positive sphere is repelled equally on all sides and is thus subjected to a balanced force (Fig. 6.3). An atom, Thomson concluded, will produce no appreciable deflection of a He^{2+} particle. Therefore, if a beam of He^{2+} particles is aimed at a thin metal foil, practically all the particles should pass through the foil undeflected. The atoms making up the metal foil should not change the direction in which the He^{2+} particles are moving. Thomson's theory on the effect of the foil on the He^{2+} particle is similar to the action of a truck moving at 60 miles per hour against a sheet of newspaper; the newspaper will not stop or deflect the truck.

An experiment in which He^{2+} particles were directed against a foil was performed in 1909 by Ernest Rutherford with Hans Geiger and Ernest Marsden. As predicted (Fig. 6.4), nearly all of the He^{2+} particles passed straight through the foil. But much to their amazement, a small but significant number of the particles were *deflected through large angles*. In fact, some particles were almost completely stopped and turned back. In Rutherford's own words, "It was almost as incredible as if you fired a 15 inch shell at a piece of tissue paper and it came back and hit you."* The Thomson model offers no explanation for these deflections.

To explain these results, Rutherford in 1911 assumed that the atom must be almost completely empty space. This would account for the passage of most of the particles in a straight line through the foil. But how is the electric charge distributed

---

*These experiments were not originally planned by Rutherford as a test of the Thomson model of the atom. They were planned more or less as particle-detection experiments.

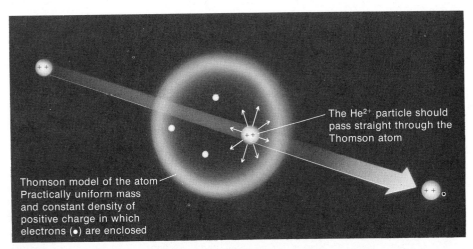

FIGURE 6.3 In the postulated Thomson atom, the He^{2+} particle, indicated as a small sphere carrying a 2+ charge, is subjected to a balanced force and undergoes practically no deflection.

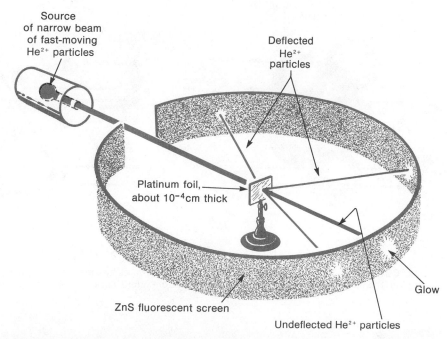

FIGURE 6.4 The principle of the alpha (He^{2+}) particle deflection experiments. Positively charged helium atoms are directed at a metal foil. The effect of the foil on the particles is observed by detecting devices placed at various angles relative to the original path. The angle is a measure of the deflection. A Geiger counter (page 137) may be used to detect alpha particles. Geiger originally employed a zinc sulfide (fluorescent) screen to count alpha particles; each alpha particle that hits the screen produces a light flash.

in the atom to create the enormous repulsive force necessary to change the direction of a fast, massive, positively charged particle? To answer this question, he concluded that the positive electricity of the atom is *not* spread throughout the volume of the atom. Rather, he assumed that the positive electricity of the atom, and, therefore, nearly all the mass of the atom, must be *concentrated* in a very small volume. This very small portion of the atom is called the **nucleus of the atom.** When a He^{2+} particle approaches a nucleus, it will be repelled. The closer its approach to the nucleus, the

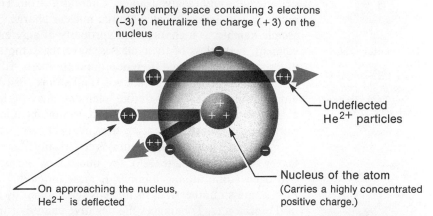

FIGURE 6.5 (Not to scale.) On approaching the nucleus of a postulated Rutherford atom, the He^{2+} particle, subjected to a strong unbalanced force, is deflected through large angles. If the nucleus were represented with a diameter of 1 foot, the atom would then occupy a sphere with a diameter of roughly 19 miles.

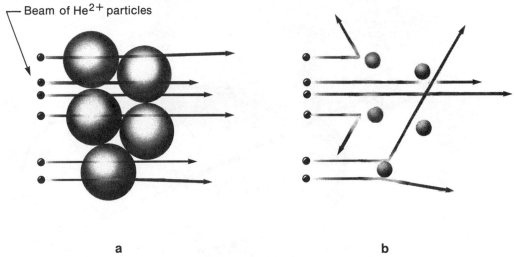

Beam of He^{2+} particles

a

b

FIGURE 6.6 Representation of the deflection of alpha, He^{2+}, particles by a metal foil, as predicted (a) by the Thomson model of an atom, and (b) by the Rutherford nuclear model of an atom.

greater its deflection (Figs. 6.5 and 6.6). Since the atom is electrically neutral, electrons, sufficient in number to equal the positive charge of the nucleus, are located around the nucleus. For example, 3 electrons (charge of -3) occupy the space outside a nucleus carrying a charge of $+3$. The diameter of an atom, roughly 1×10^{-8} cm to 3×10^{-8} cm, is determined by the electrons surrounding the nucleus. The diameter of a nucleus is roughly 10^{-13} cm. The density (g/ml) of an atom is thus extremely high in its nucleus but extremely low in the space occupied by the electrons.

Composition of the Nucleus Nuclei of different atoms have different *nuclear charges;* that is, the number of unit positive charges on a *nucleus* differs for different atoms. The nuclear charge on an atom of gold, for example, differs from the charge on an atom of platinum. The greater the nuclear charge, the stronger is the repulsive force experienced by an He^{2+} particle, and the larger is the number of He^{2+} particles deflected through a given angle. Therefore, from He^{2+} particle deflection experiments, it is possible to calculate the nuclear charge. The nuclear charge, called the **atomic number,** is a characteristic property of an element. All the atoms of a given element, regardless of their masses, have the same atomic number. The atoms of different elements have different atomic numbers. All atoms of hydrogen, regardless of mass, have an atomic number of 1; all atoms of silver, regardless of mass, have an atomic number of 47. Therefore, elements may be identified by determining their atomic numbers. An alpha-particle deflection technique was used by an unmanned Surveyor spacecraft to analyze the chemical composition of the moon's surface.

This number is also the number of the space the element occupies in the periodic table (Chap. 7), developed about 1870.

The hydrogen atom (protium) is electrically neutral. The removal of one electron leaves the proton (page 126), the nucleus of the lightest of all natural atoms. A hydrogen atom, atomic number 1, mass number 1 (page 124), thus consists of a proton, mass number 1, as its nucleus surrounded by 1 electron. The positive charge of the proton ($+1$) balances the negative charge of the electron (-1). All atoms of hydrogen (protium) contain 1 proton and 1 electron. It is then assumed that protons are common constituents of atomic nuclei. The number of protons gives the nucleus its characteristic positive charge. For example, the nucleus of any atom of neon,

a | Particles making up atoms

Particle	Charge	Mass, grams	Atomic weight
electron	1 negative charge (−1), 1.60 x 10⁻¹⁹ C	9.110×10^{-28}	0.000549
proton	1 positive charge (+1), 1.60 x 10⁻¹⁹ C	1.6726×10^{-24}	1.0073
neutron	no charge	1.6750×10^{-24}	1.0087

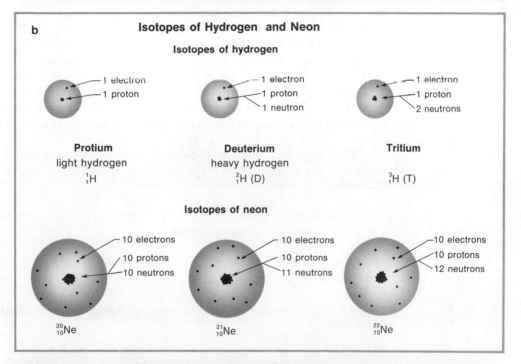

b | Isotopes of Hydrogen and Neon

Isotopes of hydrogen

Protium
light hydrogen
$_1^1H$

Deuterium
heavy hydrogen
$_1^2H$ (D)

Tritium
$_1^3H$ (T)

Isotopes of neon

$_{10}^{20}Ne$ $_{10}^{21}Ne$ $_{10}^{22}Ne$

c | Table of some Elements

Name	Atomic number	Number of protons in nucleus	Number of electrons outside nucleus
Helium, He	2	2	2
Carbon, C	6	6	6
Oxygen, O	8	8	8
Chlorine, Cl	17	17	17
Iron, Fe	26	26	26
Gold, Au	79	79	79
Fermium, Fm	100	100	100

FIGURE 6.7 (a) A comparison of the particles of which, according to theory, all atoms are composed.
(b) A summary of the composition of the neutral atoms of hydrogen and neon.
(c) A list of some other elements according to atomic number.

atomic number 10, regardless of its mass, contains 10 protons. All atoms of neon also contain 10 electrons because atoms are electrically neutral.

These protons account for only about half the mass of a neon atom. The remainder of the mass, according to accepted theory, is made up by the presence of neutrons in the nucleus. The existence of the **neutron,** an electrically neutral particle with mass number 1 and atomic weight 1.00867, was predicted by Rutherford but was not discovered until 1932 by James Chadwick (page 543). The number of neutrons in a nucleus, plus the number of protons in the nucleus, make up the mass number of the atom:

mass number = number of neutrons + number of protons (atomic number)

The number of neutrons in a nucleus is then given by the difference between the mass number and the atomic number. Thus, the three isotopes of neon, atomic weights 19.99, 20.99, and 21.99, have the same atomic number, 10, but different mass numbers, 20, 21, and 22. All the nuclei of neon have 10 protons, but the nuclei of the isotope of mass number 20 have 10 neutrons (20 − 10), those of mass number 21 have 11 neutrons (21 − 10), and those of mass number 22 have 12 neutrons (22 − 10) (Fig. 6.7). Symbolically, the nuclei are represented as $^{20}_{10}Ne$, $^{21}_{10}Ne$, $^{22}_{10}Ne$. Recall (page 124) that the mass number is written as a superscript at the upper left of the symbol of the element. The atomic number is written as a subscript at the lower left.

When it is unnecessary to distinguish between protons and neutrons, both are referred to as **nucleons.** The mass number thus represents the number of nucleons in the nucleus:

mass number = number of neutrons + number of protons (atomic number)
= number of nucleons

The number of electrons outside a nucleus in a neutral atom is equal to the atomic number (Fig. 6.7).

PROBLEM 2   **Describe the main features of the Dalton, Thomson, and Rutherford models of the atom.**

PROBLEM 3   **(a) A high-speed arrow, fired from a mechanical device, strikes a piece of paper and a concrete wall at an angle. Will the paper deflect the arrow? Will the wall deflect the arrow? (b) An alpha particle, about 7400 times more massive than an electron, traveling at the speed used in alpha particle deflection experiments, about 1.2×10^6 km/h, hits an electron in an atom. Which is more likely to be deflected, the alpha particle or the electron? (c) The same kind of alpha particle approaches a nucleus of $_{78}Pt$. Which will be deflected, the particle or the nucleus? Explain.**

PROBLEM 4   **Is the mass of an atom distributed throughout the volume of the atom? If not, where is most of the mass located?**

PROBLEM 5   **State the nuclear composition of each isotope of sulfur, atomic number 16, with the following atomic weights: 31.9721, 32.9715, 33.9679, and 35.9671 g/mole.**

6.2 —————————— ATOMIC ORBITALS

The electrons surrounding the nucleus balance the nuclear charge. Much evidence indicates that the arrangement of these electrons determines the properties of the elements. These electrons, however, are not stationary. If they were stationary, the attractive force would pull them into the positively charged nucleus and the atom would collapse. Rather, we believe that the electrons are engaged in some kind of random motion.

The Flight of the Electron   We are familiar with the flight of a bee in springtime, flittering up, down, and sideways but remaining more or less within the area of a cluster of flowers. The bee is attracted to the flowers by the nectar, the sweet-smelling liquid found in flowers.

Similarly, modern theory (page 209) tells us that electrons flitter about the nucleus in an extremely erratic fashion; the negative electron "likes" to be near the attractive nucleus but, unlike the bee, is too "nervous" to stop at any one place. In fact, the movements of electrons are presently unpredictable, so that we cannot say anything definite about their locations in the space about the nucleus. However, the theory permits us to say that the *movement of the electrons is largely confined to regions of space of definite shapes*. These definite space-shapes described by the movement of electrons in atoms are known as **atomic orbitals.** Atomic orbitals have characteristic shapes and sizes. The shapes of atomic orbitals may be roughly represented by "electron cloud" diagrams, shown in Fig. 6.8. These electron cloud

19th Century physics taught that an electron traveling in a circular path should throw out all its energy as light and fall into the nucleus.

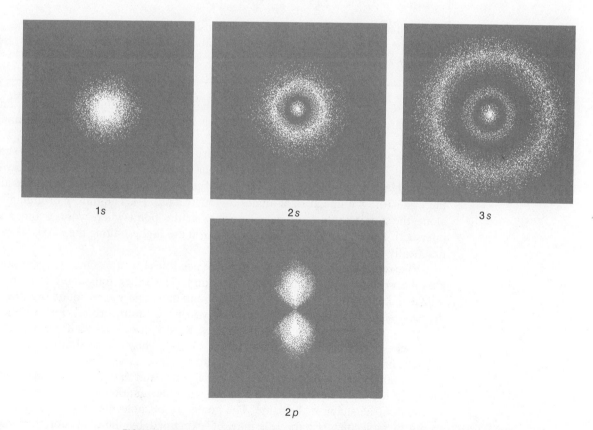

1s   2s   3s

2p

FIGURE 6.8 Electron cloud diagrams representing the shapes of atomic orbitals of hydrogen. These should be visualized as three-dimensional clouds surrounding the *nucleus* of the hydrogen atom. The density of the cloud is related to the chances of finding the electron in the cloud. *Caution:* These are photographs *not* of electrons but of models based on a mathematical theory of the atom (page 208). (Modified from H. E. White, *Physical Reviews,* volume 37, 1931, page 1416.)

diagrams show us the chances, the probability, of finding an electron in the region of the nucleus. The chances of finding an electron in a unit of volume in space at a distance from the nucleus are related to the density of the cloud; the denser the cloud, the greater the chances. For example, in the electron cloud diagram labeled $1s$ in Fig. 6.8, the chances of finding the electron are highest at the nucleus, decrease rapidly, and become practically zero at about 2.5×10^{-8} cm from the nucleus. The atomic orbital labeled $2p$ is shaped like a "dumbbell."

Atomic orbitals are commonly designated by the letters s, p, d, f, g, and continuing with letters of the alphabet as needed. An electron in an s atomic orbital is referred to as an "s electron," an electron in a p atomic orbital is referred to as a "p electron," and so on.

Before modern theories of the atom were developed, these letters, further explained on page 209, were used to classify colored lines emitted by elements (page 191).

Example 1

The cloud density for a $1s$ electron is nearly zero at about 2.5×10^{-8} cm from the nucleus (proton). Look at the $1s$ electron cloud for the hydrogen atom shown in Fig. 6.8. Describe the chances of finding the electron on a given part of the surface of a sphere as its distance from the nucleus increases.

Answer

The chances are very high on a sphere close to the nucleus, but they decrease as the size of the sphere is increased. At about 2.5×10^{-8} cm, the chances are nearly zero, and beyond that they are even closer to zero.

These atomic orbitals have different shapes. Representations of the $s, p,$ and d orbitals are given in Fig. 6.9. The s orbitals have only one representation, namely spherical.

Three representations of the p atomic orbital are possible (Fig. 6.9). Their shapes are identical but they differ in their positions in space. One, p_x, lies along the x axis (draw a horizontal line, _____, on a piece of paper). A second p orbital, p_y, lies along the y axis (draw a line at right angles to your x axis, $+$). The third p orbital, p_z, lies along the z axis (hold your pencil upright at the point where your x and y axes intersect). The chances of finding a p_x electron are highest along the x axis; they are practically zero along the y and z axes.

Five representations of the d orbital are possible (Fig. 6.9). One, designated d_1, is a p-like orbital in a doughnut-shaped cloud. The other four d orbitals are like four-leaf clovers. Picture one "clover," d_2, along the x and y axes; rotate the clover 45 degrees, without tilting up or down, and you have the d_3 orbital. Picture another clover, d_4, upright between the y and z axes. Rotate this clover 90 degrees so that it now faces you; you are looking at the d_5 orbital. These representations are independent of the nuclear charge (atomic number) of an atom. There is only *one* such representation for s electrons, *three* for p electrons, and *five* for d electrons. For our purposes, we may assume that the same letter designation for an atomic orbital means that the shape is the same. The geometry of molecules, the arrangement of atoms in molecules (Chap. 18), may be explained by the shape of the orbitals involved in chemical combinations.

PROBLEM 6 Describe the shape of the region of space to which a p electron is practically confined.

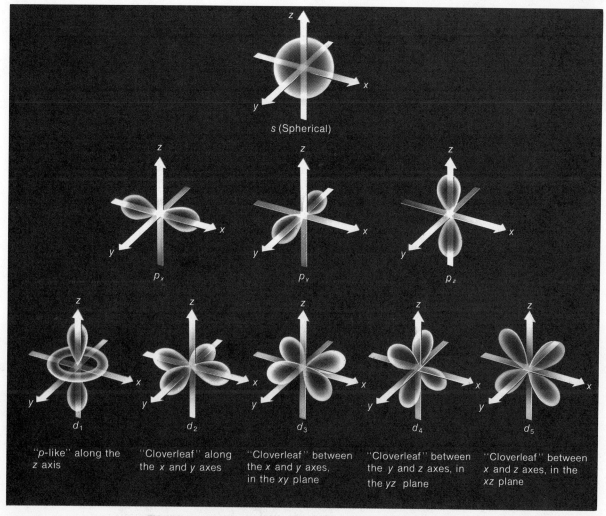

s (Spherical)

p_x p_y p_z

d_1 d_2 d_3 d_4 d_5

"p-like" along the
z axis

"Cloverleaf" along
the x and y axes

"Cloverleaf" between
the x and y axes,
in the xy plane

"Cloverleaf" between
the y and z axes, in
the yz plane

"Cloverleaf" between
x and z axes, in the
xz plane

FIGURE 6.9 Representation of the s, the three p, and the five d orbitals. The nucleus is at the point where the three axes cross each other.

ENERGY OF AN ATOMIC ORBITAL; NATURAL NUMBERS _____ 6.3

While the energy of a bee changes as it speeds up or slows down, flies to a higher flower or drops to the ground, the energy of an electron does *not* change as it journeys through the region of an atomic orbital. The energy of an electron changes *only* when it changes from one atomic orbital (one electron distribution) to a second atomic orbital (a second electron distribution). The energy of the atomic orbital is the energy of the electron in it. Equally correct, we can say that the energy of the electron determines the energy of the atomic orbital. But the electron is part of an atom. Therefore, the energy of an atom is determined by the energy of its electrons. Equally well, we can say that the energy of a hydrogen atom is x ergs, the energy of the electron in the hydrogen atom is x ergs, or the energy of the atomic orbital in the hydrogen atom is x ergs. For simplicity, we shall continue our discussion with the hydrogen atom, the simplest atom.

Based on the discovery by Johann Balmer (1885) and Johannes Rydberg (1890), it has been shown that the energy of the hydrogen atom is given by a relation *involving whole numbers:*

*Although this is not
the equation originally
used, it is acceptable
for teaching purposes.
Reminder, the erg,
page 66, is a unit of
energy.*

$$E, \text{ energy of a hydrogen atom} = \frac{21.79 \times 10^{-12} \text{ erg}}{n^2} \qquad (1)$$

This is also the energy of the electron or of the atomic orbital holding the electron in the hydrogen atom. Here, n is a *whole number* without units; n may be 1 or any other whole number greater than 1. *Do not* memorize Equation (1); it is more important to recognize its significance; namely:

(a) *The energy of the hydrogen atom is quantized.* This should not surprise us, since nature prefers quantized matter (page 112), quantized electricity (page 118), quantized light (page 191), and quantized magnets (page 203). Nature allows only certain energies for the hydrogen atom, determined by a whole number; n cannot be a number such as 1.1, 1.5, 99.2, or any other fraction. Thus, the energy of the hydrogen atom is restricted only to certain definite quantities fixed by Equation (1). Dimensionless numbers like n that are restricted only to certain definite values are therefore called **quantum numbers.** They are natural numbers determined by experiment, n is known as the **principal quantum number.**

(b) *These energy values give the quantity of work that must be done* against the attractive force of the proton to remove the electron from an atomic orbital to a distance so far from the proton that the attractive force becomes practically zero. In short, the energy required to ionize the hydrogen atom is given by

$$\text{H (proton-electron)} + E, \text{ energy} \longrightarrow \text{H}^+ \text{ (proton)} + e^-$$

where e^- is a free electron, no longer bound to the proton. When $n = 1$, E, from Equation (1), is 21.79×10^{-12} erg/atom; this is the work required to remove the electron to infinity. When $n =$ infinity, symbolized (App. II) by ∞, $E = 0$; this means that the electron is at infinity, the hydrogen atom has already been ionized and,

**TABLE 6.1
SOME QUANTIZED ENERGY STATES
OF THE HYDROGEN ATOM (QUANTIZED ENERGIES
OF SOME ATOMIC ORBITALS)**

PRINCIPAL QUANTUM NUMBER OF THE ELECTRON, n	ENERGY, IN ERGS PER ATOM; WORK REQUIRED TO IONIZE THE HYDROGEN ATOM	DESIGNATION OF THE ATOMIC ORBITAL
1	$\dfrac{21.79 \times 10^{-12}}{1} = 21.79 \times 10^{-12}$	1s
2	$\dfrac{21.79 \times 10^{-12}}{4} = 5.448 \times 10^{-12}$	2s
3	$\dfrac{21.79 \times 10^{-12}}{9} = 2.421 \times 10^{-12}$	3s
4	$\dfrac{21.79 \times 10^{-12}}{16} = 1.362 \times 10^{-12}$	4s
5	$\dfrac{21.79 \times 10^{-12}}{25} = 0.8716 \times 10^{-12}$	5s
6	$\dfrac{21.79 \times 10^{-12}}{36} = 0.6053 \times 10^{-12}$	6s
∞	$\dfrac{21.79 \times 10^{-12}}{\infty} = 0$	

therefore, no further work is required. We may also say that when the hydrogen atom absorbs 21.79×10^{-12} erg, the electron can no longer be held by the positive charge of the proton and so escapes.

(c) We also refer to the energy values allowed by Equation (1) as the **"energy states"** of the electron or of the hydrogen atom. Thus, an atomic orbital not only describes the region of space about the nucleus to which the electron is confined, but it also corresponds to an energy state. These energy states are then restricted to the values given by Equation (1), illustrated in Table 6.1. The first energy state, when the principal quantum number of the electron, n, equals 1, is known as the **"ground state"** of the hydrogen atom. In general, an atom is in its ground state when its electrons are in their lowest energy states (Section 6.7). All other energy states are known as

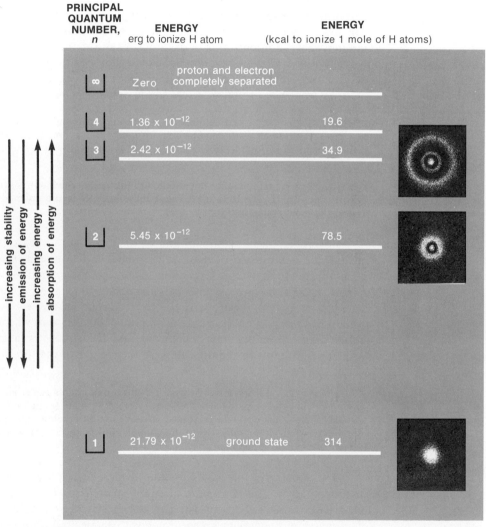

FIGURE 6.10 (Not to scale.) Energy state diagram* of the hydrogen atom (energies of atomic orbitals). The energy is expressed as the work required to remove the electron from the hydrogen atom against the attractive force of the nucleus. Zero energy means no further work is required to remove the electron; the removal has been completed.

* Also known as an **energy level diagram,** introduced in 1920 by W. Grotrian. The energy can also be expressed as the heat evolved when the hydrogen atom forms from an electron and a proton, or as the *negative* of the work required to ionize the H atom. These values then take a minus sign.

185

"excited states." A convenient method of representing the ground and excited states of the hydrogen atom is illustrated in Fig. 6.10. It shows the energy states as lines. Such a diagram is known as an **energy state diagram.**

An orbital is commonly designated by a symbol that gives its n value and its shape. For example, $2s$ refers to a spherical orbital for which $n = 2$; $3p$ refers to a "dumbbell" shaped orbital (Fig. 6.9, page 183) for which $n = 3$. Also shown in Fig. 6.10 are the electron cloud diagrams of the s atomic orbitals corresponding to the first three energy states. Notice that the size (volume) of the atomic orbital is related to the principal quantum number, n.

Stability of the Hydrogen Atom   The energy of the electron in an atomic orbital depends on the force with which it is attracted by the proton. The electron in a $3s$ orbital ($n = 3$) is not attracted as strongly as the electron in a $1s$ orbital ($n = 1$). The lower energy states, the atomic orbitals with smaller n values, require a *larger* input of energy for ionization of the atom. They are, therefore, *more stable,* indicated by the arrow in Fig. 6.10. (A blind person walking on the roof of a building is said to be unstable with respect to the ground level.) Energy is always required to raise an electron from one orbital to a less stable orbital above it in the diagram.

PROBLEM 7   **(a) Use Equation (1) to calculate the energy of a hydrogen atom when $n = 3$. (b) How much work must be done to ionize this hydrogen atom? (c) How much less work is required to ionize the H atom ($n = 3$) compared to the H atom ($n = 1$)?**

PROBLEM 8   **Of the following atomic orbitals, state which one is (a) most stable, and (b) least stable: $3s$, $11s$, $7s$, $105s$. (c) Arrange these orbitals in the order of decreasing stability (place the most stable first).**

Absorption and Emission of Energy   Force has to be exerted to lift a weight against the pull exerted by the Earth's gravity. Let us assume that 200 ergs of work (energy) are required to raise a weight 10 cm from the ground. As work is done on the weight in the lifting process, energy is absorbed and *the energy of the weight increases.* At the top (10 cm), it will be richer by 200 ergs. But the *work required* to lift the weight *decreases* as it approaches the top and becomes zero when it reaches the top. When the weight drops, energy is emitted; it will lose 200 ergs as heat on striking the ground. But the work required to raise the weight to the top is again 200 ergs.

PROBLEM 9   **Lifting a weight from the ground to a table-top requires 175 ergs. (a) How much work must be done to move the weight from the ground to the top? (b) By how many ergs has the energy of the weight increased or decreased in reaching the top? (c) The weight is allowed to fall from the table-top to the ground. How many ergs of heat are emitted when the weight strikes the ground?**

The same principle holds for the absorption and emission of energy by the hydrogen atom. The *absorption* of energy corresponds to an electron change—an electron transition—between any two energy states, from a *lower* to a *higher* state. The *emission* of energy again corresponds to an electron transition between any two energy states, but from a *higher* to a *lower* state. In absorption, the energy of the electron is increased, and in emission, the energy of the electron is decreased. The gain or loss equals the difference between the two energy states. But these energy states of the hydrogen atom are quantized (page 184). Therefore, *the hydrogen atom can absorb or emit only quantities of energy equal to the difference between two energy states.*

Example 2

A hydrogen atom in the ground state (in the 1s orbital) is "hit" by a particle, exciting the electron to the 4s orbital. This electron then "drops" (undergoes a transition) to the 2s orbital. What is the energy absorbed and then emitted by the hydrogen atom? Refer to Table 6.1 (page 184) or Fig. 6.10 (page 185).

Answer

The energy absorbed or emitted by a hydrogen atom must be the difference between the energy states of the electron. In the transition from $n = 1$ to $n = 4$, energy is absorbed. In the transition from $n = 4$ to $n = 2$, energy is emitted. Hence, from Table 6.1 or Fig. 6.10

$$\text{Energy absorbed} = 21.79 \times 10^{-12}\,\frac{\text{erg}}{\text{atom}} - 1.36 \times 10^{-12}\,\frac{\text{erg}}{\text{atom}}$$

$$= 20.43 \times 10^{-12}\,\frac{\text{erg}}{\text{atom}}$$

$$\text{Energy emitted} = 5.45 \times 10^{-12}\,\frac{\text{erg}}{\text{atom}} - 1.36 \times 10^{-12}\,\frac{\text{erg}}{\text{atom}}$$

$$= 4.09 \times 10^{-12}\,\frac{\text{erg}}{\text{atom}}$$

PROBLEM 10   A hydrogen atom is excited from the energy state $n = 2$ to the energy state $n = 5$, and then "drops" to the ground state $n = 1$. What is the energy (a) absorbed and then (b) emitted by the hydrogen atom? Use Table 6.1.

In summary, electron transitions always occur between one energy state and another when energy is absorbed or emitted.

The energy change is always the difference between the two energy states.

This difference is always the quantity of energy absorbed or emitted.

Number of Atomic Orbitals   As n increases, the number of atomic orbitals available to an electron increases regularly. For many purposes, orbitals may be conveniently represented by a dash, —. The number of atomic orbitals for a given value of n follows:

Principal Quantum Number, n	s	p	d	f	Total Number of Orbitals
1	—	none	none	none	one $s = 1$
2	—	———	none	none	one s, three $p = 4$
3	—	———	——————	none	one s, three p, five $d = 9$
4	—	———	——————	————————	one s, three p, five d, seven $f = 16$

Note the regular increase in the number of orbitals available to an electron as n increases: one s, one + *two* = three p, three + *two* = five d, five + *two* = seven f, and so forth.

PROBLEM 11   (a) How many of each of the following atomic orbitals are available to an electron for which $n = 5$: s? p? d? f? g? (b) What is the total number of available orbitals?

6.4 _____ THE NATURE OF LIGHT

The discussion of the structure of atoms and the colors displayed by excited elements and compounds—such as in "neon" signs, mercury lamps, and the firefly—is very much dependent on an understanding of the nature of light. Therefore, we are compelled to pause here for a review on the nature of light.

Experimental   Light is associated with our sense of sight. It is the form of energy that acts on the retina of the eye. Light is emitted by a flame, an electric light bulb (a hot tungsten wire), the sun, a firefly, a laser (page 214), and a fluorescent lamp (gas in a discharge tube, page 118). A light beam transmits energy. The light energy poured upon us by the sun not only maintains reasonable temperature, but also accounts for the photosynthesis of food (page 195) that makes life on Earth possible. The quantity of light energy required for vision is very small; staring at the sun can permanently damage vision (the retina). A laser beam can carry a "wallop" sufficient to kill a horse or bore a hole in steel.

All except black objects reflect light, making our environment visible. In the absence of light ("darkness"), the human eye cannot detect objects.* In the presence of light but complete absence of objects, the human eye detects nothing; it "sees" complete darkness. An astronaut in space rides in a sea of darkness because he is not passing through clouds or smog. A "light beam" ("light ray") is not visible; the eye detects dust, smoke, or water particles that reflect the light into the retina.**

When light passes through a slit, a straight narrow opening, it produces more than one bright line. It spreads out, producing a series of dark and bright lines. This process of spreading light is called *diffraction,* illustrated in Fig. 6.11. The importance of this property of light is its use to obtain the so-called wavelength of light. The distance between the tops of two consecutive waves, as in a plucked guitar string, is called the **wavelength,** illustrated in Fig. 6.12. The common symbol for wavelength is the Greek letter λ (*lambda*), the equivalent of our letter l; the unit of wavelength is cm. We must stress that no one has seen or detected, with or without the aid of instruments, a "light wave." Experiments *do not measure wavelengths of light* from a wave shape. Although the word "wave" suggests a visible shape like that of a water wave or a vibrating string, no material form or shape need be imagined for a "light wave."

Nevertheless, we characterize light by its wavelength. The separation of the colored lines, produced by passing a colored beam through a slit (Fig. 6.11b), differs for each color. For example, the separations of the lines produced by red light are greater than the corresponding separations for blue light. The experimenter, therefore, calculates a larger wavelength for the red light. Table 6.2 gives the approximate wavelength of the colors of the rainbow.

---

*However, complete exclusion of light, as in a totally dark room, does not end visual perception. Rather, colored images may be generated *within* the eye and brain, without the need of outside light. Many chemical agents—for example, those responsible for alcoholic (delirium tremens) and psychedelic intoxication—may induce such images. They may also be electrically induced. Students interested in this subject are referred to *Scientific American,* February, 1970, page 83.

**Light flashes seen by the Apollo astronauts were the result of collisions of *cosmic rays* (atomic particles traveling with almost the speed of light and, therefore, very penetrating and dangerous) with atoms in the retina.

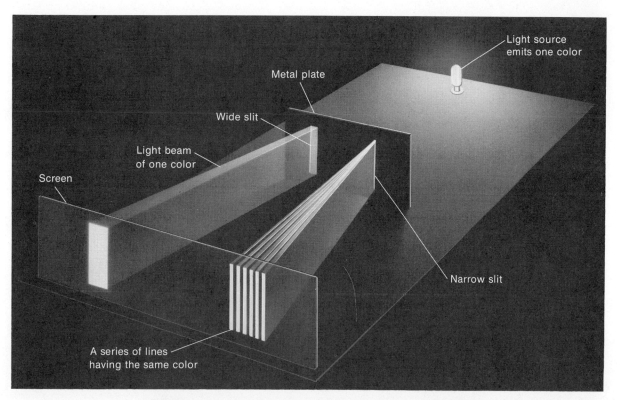

FIGURE 6.11 (a) A wide opening produces one bright area. (b) Representation of the diffraction (spreading) produced by a single (extremely narrow) slit. The original beam, upon passing through the slit, is separated into a series of bright colored lines separated by darkness (black areas).

The speed of light, c, is the same (in a vacuum) for all wavelengths, 2.998×10^{10} cm/s, first measured by Ole Roemer in 1675. Light is also characterized by its **frequency,** f. The frequency is commonly visualized as the number of waves passing a given point in one second; the unit of frequency is therefore $1/s$ or s^{-1}. The frequency

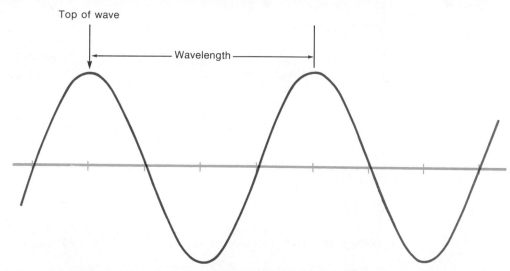

FIGURE 6.12 Illustrating the wavelength of the wave set up in a vibrating string. The distance between any two consecutive crests, the tops of the waves, is called the wavelength.

189

TABLE 6.2
APPROXIMATE WAVELENGTH
AND COLOR OF LIGHT

COLOR	WAVELENGTH, λ, cm
not visible ("black light")	below 4.00×10^{-5}
violet	$4.00 - 4.24 \times 10^{-5}$
blue	$4.24 - 4.91 \times 10^{-5}$
green	$4.91 - 5.75 \times 10^{-5}$
yellow	$5.75 - 5.85 \times 10^{-5}$
orange	$5.85 - 6.47 \times 10^{-5}$
red	$6.47 - 7.00 \times 10^{-5}$
not visible ("black light")	above 7.00×10^{-5}

$1 s^{-1} = 1$ hertz, Hz, named after Heinrich Hertz, who used a sparking device in 1887 to generate radio waves.

of light is related to its wavelength by the equation

speed of light = wavelength of light $\times$ frequency of light

$$c = \lambda \text{ cm} \times f \frac{1}{s} = \frac{cm}{s}$$

Since the speed of light is a constant, the higher the frequency, the shorter is the wavelength of the light.

Example 3

The wavelength of a violet line is 4.102×10^{-5} cm and the wavelength of a red line is 6.563×10^{-5} cm. Find the frequency of each line.

Answer

The frequency and wavelength of light are related by

speed, c = wavelength, λ $\times$ frequency, f

Solving for f:

$$\text{(violet)} \quad f = \frac{c}{\lambda} = \frac{2.998 \times 10^{10} \frac{cm}{s}}{4.102 \times 10^{-5} \text{ cm}} = 7.309 \times 10^{14} \text{ s}^{-1}$$

$$\text{(red)} \quad f = \frac{c}{\lambda} = \frac{2.998 \times 10^{10} \frac{cm}{s}}{6.563 \times 10^{-5} \text{ cm}} = 4.568 \times 10^{14} \text{ s}^{-1}$$

Notice that the shorter wavelength (4.102×10^{-5} cm) has the higher frequency (7.309×10^{14} s^{-1}).

PROBLEM 12   **The frequency of an orange line emitted by helium is 5.103×10^{14} s^{-1} (5.103×10^{14} hertz). Calculate its wavelength ($c = 2.998 \times 10^{10}$ cm/s).**

Theoretical   The development of theoretical models of light is a long and complicated story, involving the pioneering studies of Christian Huygens (wave theory, 1690), Isaac Newton (corpuscular theory, 1704), James Maxwell (electro-magnetic theory, which related light to moving electric charges, 1864), Max Planck (quantum theory, 1900), and Paul Dirac (corrected quantum theory for relativity effects, 1928). We shall content ourselves with the simplest theoretical model: Like matter, electricity, and orbital energies, *light energy is quantized*. It consists of "atoms of light." The "atom of light" was named the **photon** in 1926 by Gilbert Lewis, who wrote, "I therefore take the liberty of proposing for this hypothetical new atom, which is not light but plays an essential part in every process of radiation, the name *photon*." In fact, Antoine Lavoisier listed light as an element in his table of elements (1789). Like a hail of bullets, a laser beam can support the weight of a glass bead (Color Plate IV).

The energy, E, carried by a photon is determined by the frequency, f:

$$\text{energy of a photon} = \text{a constant} \times \text{frequency}$$

$$E = h \times f$$

h is a constant, 6.626×10^{-27} erg second per particle, known as Planck's constant. Any quantity of light can consist only of a whole number of photons. The total number of photons determines the energy of a light source in the same sense that the total number of copper atoms in a piece of copper determines its mass. Each frequency corresponds to photons possessing a definite energy. For example, the violet line with a frequency of 7.309×10^{14} s^{-1} (Example 3) corresponds to an energy of 4.843×10^{-12} erg/photon, calculated as follows:

$$\text{energy, } E = \text{constant, } h \times \text{frequency, } f$$

$$E = 6.626 \times 10^{-27} \frac{\text{erg} \cdot s}{\text{photon}} \times 7.309 \times 10^{14} \frac{1}{s}$$

$$= 4.843 \times 10^{-12} \frac{\text{erg}}{\text{photon}}$$

PROBLEM 13 **The quantum of light is (pick the correct expression): a constant wavelength; a constant frequency; a photon; a nucleus; Planck's constant.**

PROBLEM 14 **What is the energy of the photon corresponding to the helium yellow line with a frequency of 5.103×10^{14} s^{-1}?**

The higher the frequency, the greater the energy of the photon. The range of frequencies is illustrated in Color Plate V(A). It includes X-rays and radio waves, as well as visible light. Nearly all of these frequencies are in a range that humans cannot see. The reality of these frequencies, however, is detected by instruments developed by humans. All of these radiations travel at the same speed as visible light. An X-ray photon is more dangerous than a radio wave photon because its frequency, and therefore its energy, is very much higher. The symbol hf is commonly used to represent a photon.

SPECTRA OF ELEMENTS: IMPORTANT "FINGERPRINTS" _____ 6.5

Experimental   When light enters a glass prism, it is separated into its various colors, and the wavelength composition of the initial light is seen (or photographed). The resulting display of colors is called a spectrum. See Color Plate VI.

When light *emitted* from a source is separated into its colors, the spectrum obtained is called an **emission spectrum**.

But, mathematically, the most complex and the only theory capable of explaining all known experimental observations of light; it is based on the work of Planck and Dirac.

See center of text for Color Plates.

See footnote on page 125. See center of text for Color Plates.

At high temperatures solids, liquids, and dense gases emit "white" light. The spectrum obtained from "white" light consists of a *continuous band of colors* as observed in a rainbow, called a **continuous spectrum.** The visible region in Color Plate V(A) illustrates the continuous spectrum obtained from a hot tungsten wire, as in a light bulb. One color gradually merges into another; there are no sharp divisions.

A gas in an electric discharge tube, as in a neon sign, glows brightly. The spectrum obtained from this light is *not* a rainbow. Rather, as illustrated for selenium in Color Plate VI and for hydrogen in Color Plate V(B), several colored lines separated by black spaces appear. This type of spectrum is called a **line spectrum.** *Each colored line represents a definite wavelength (frequency), and therefore a definite energy.*

PROBLEM 15   **The spectrum produced by a tungsten wire at 1000 °C is obtained, and the spectrum produced by gaseous tungsten under low pressure in a discharge tube is also obtained. Pick the continuous spectrum. Describe the general features of each spectrum.**

It is very important to note that regardless of its source, *the line spectrum of an element is characteristic of that element.* Sodium, for example, always yields the same yellow line spectrum, which differs from the spectrum of any other element. It is, thus, the atoms of the element that emit the line spectrum. The study of the spectra of elements is, therefore, an important source of information in the determination of the structure of atoms. In fact, scientists who studied spectra strongly opposed the 19th century trends against the atomic theory of matter.

The examination of the spectra of compounds is also a very practical method of identifying substances. In fact, a study of the lines in the spectrum of the sun led to the discovery (1868) of helium before it was detected (1895) on Earth. Of the "fingerprints" (properties) most commonly used to identify substances, the various spectra rank very high; see Table 6.3. A variety of instruments that record spectra find applications in industrial, medical, pollution control, and police laboratories.

From helios, *the Greek word for sun.*

From the earliest days of spectrum analysis, founded by Robert Bunsen and Gustav Kirchhoff* (1859), continuous improvements now make it possible to identify as little as 10^{-14} mole of metal ions in 10^{-9} liter of solution, or 5×10^{-12} mole of

---

*Based on the previous work of David Brewster (1822), William Talbot (1825), and William Swan (1857), Bunsen and Kirchhoff invented the *spectroscope,* an instrument used to analyze light by separating its various components. With this instrument, they verified the principle that each metal (element) has a characteristic *spectrum.* This branch of chemistry is known as *spectroscopy,* and the scientists—chemists, physicists, biochemists—engaged in this study are known as *spectroscopists.*

TABLE 6.3
PROPERTIES MOST OFTEN USED BY
CHEMISTS IN THE UNITED STATES
TO IDENTIFY SUBSTANCES＊

PROPERTY	RELATIVE NUMBER OF TIMES USED
Spectra	4596
Boiling point	2990
Melting point	2767
Solubilities (Chap. 10)	2495
Thermodynamic properties: heats of reactions (Chap. 9), *etc.*	1786
Density	910

＊Adapted from a 1965 survey of the members of the American Chemical Society, A. Lee Smith, *American Laboratory,* October 1970, page 27.

polluting mercury atoms in 1 g of water, or to detect art forgeries by identification of the components of the paint, or to detect molecules (page 132) in the space between stars where the average density is about 10^{-30} g/ml. These molecules are providing information about the evolution of stars and life.

Theoretical The energy emitted as radiation by a number of identical atoms can be emitted only as a whole number of photons. The continuous spectrum corresponds to photons possessing a continuous range of frequencies. In a line spectrum, each line corresponds to photons of a definite frequency and, therefore, a definite energy. For example, the 4.102×10^{-5} cm (violet) line in the spectrum of hydrogen corresponds to 4.843×10^{-12} erg/photon (page 191, and Color Plate V(B)). Since each element possesses a characteristic line spectrum, *the atoms must emit only photons of definite, characteristic energies.* All atoms emit photons, but only the atoms of hydrogen, ^{1}H, emit photons having the energies given in Color Plate V(B). In fact, the identification of *only one line* suffices to identify hydrogen from any source in the universe.

Elements (and compounds) also *absorb* energy. Atoms absorb only photons of characteristic energies. For example, only the atoms of hydrogen absorb photons having the energies shown in Color Plate V(B).

We shall now restrict our explanation of the absorption and emission of energy to the hydrogen atom, the simplest atom. The *absorption of photons* (radiation) corresponds to a transition between any two of the possible energy states (orbitals) of hydrogen, from a *lower* to a *higher* state (orbital). The *emission of photons* (radiation) corresponds to a transition between any two of the possible energy states (orbitals), but from a *higher* to a *lower* state (orbital). Thus, in absorption the energy of the electron is increased, and in emission the energy of the electron is decreased, but only in accord with the *differences between any two energy states*. The *energy lost appears as a photon.* The greater the difference between the two energy states, the greater is the energy of the photon. Since the energy of the electron is quantized (Table 6.1, page 184, and Fig. 6.10, page 185), *the hydrogen atom can emit or absorb only photons whose energy is equal to the difference between the two energy states:*

E (energy of photon absorbed or emitted) = difference between two energy states

Therefore, the energy state diagram of the hydrogen atom (Fig. 6.10) can be used to predict the energy of the photons that should be emitted or absorbed by the hydrogen atom. A line in the emission spectrum thus appears when the electron "drops" from one energy state to a lower state.

Example 4

A hydrogen atom is excited from the ground state ($n = 1$) to the state $n = 6$. The electron then "drops" to the state $n = 2$. What is (a) the energy of the photon absorbed by the hydrogen atom, (b) the energy of the photon emitted? Refer to Table 6.1 (page 184).

Answer

This example is similar to Example 2 (page 187). The energy absorbed or emitted by the hydrogen atom can only be the difference between two energy states. Hence,

(a) Energy of photon absorbed $= 21.79 \times 10^{-12} \dfrac{\text{erg}}{\text{atom}} - 0.61 \times 10^{-12} \dfrac{\text{erg}}{\text{atom}}$

$= 21.18 \times 10^{-12} \dfrac{\text{erg}}{\text{atom}} = 21.18 \times 10^{-12} \dfrac{\text{erg}}{\text{photon}}$

(b) Energy of photon emitted $= 5.4475 \times 10^{-12} \dfrac{\text{erg}}{\text{atom}} - 0.6053 \times 10^{-12} \dfrac{\text{erg}}{\text{atom}}$

$= 4.842 \times 10^{-12} \dfrac{\text{erg}}{\text{atom}} = 4.842 \times 10^{-12} \dfrac{\text{erg}}{\text{photon}}$

This predicted energy for the emitted photon is in perfect agreement with one of the lines in the spectrum of hydrogen in Color Plate V(B). Predicted wavelengths for the line spectrum of hydrogen are given in Color Plate V(C). This figure is another way of expressing the information shown in Figure 6.10 (page 185).

PROBLEM 16   Refer to Table 6.1. Calculate the energy of the photon emitted for the transition $n = 5$ to $n = 2$. Check your answer against Color Plate V(B), (C).

It is significant to note that the lines in the ultraviolet region of the hydrogen spectrum, as well as many other lines in the invisible region, were discovered after theory predicted their existence.

In summary, the electron of the hydrogen atom is represented or described by an atomic orbital whose quantum number, n, determines its energy. This energy is the work required to separate the electron completely from the atom. These energy values are also known as the energy states of the hydrogen atom. Electron transitions always occur between one energy state and another when a photon (radiation) is absorbed or emitted. The energy change is always the difference between the two energy states. The difference is always the energy of the photon absorbed or emitted.

Example 5

What is the maximum number of lines obtainable from four different energy states?

Answer

Energy states may be conveniently represented by an energy state diagram labeled as follows:

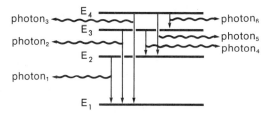

Emission of a photon with a characteristic energy (frequency) may occur between any two energy states, the energy being determined by the difference between the two states. As shown with arrows, a maximum of six differences are possible. The maximum number of lines obtainable is, therefore, six.

The absorption and emission of photons by chlorophyll (below) is illustrated in Color Plate VII.

PROBLEM 17 (a) Five energy states are given for nitrogen oxide, NO: 6.08×10^{-12} erg, 4.22×10^{-12} erg, 3.11×10^{-12} erg, 1.99×10^{-12} erg, and 1.43×10^{-12} erg. How many lines in the spectrum of NO come from these energy states? (b) What is the maximum number of lines obtainable from two different energy states?

When atoms are excited by the absorption of heat from an electric arc or a flame, they return to the ground state, emitting photons with characteristic frequencies. This technique is known as atomic emission spectroscopy; such a spectroscope, when hooked up to a computer, may accurately analyze, for example, a bar of 99.999 % pure aluminum for seven to ten metal impurities in less than 3 minutes. The atomic emission spectrum is also the basis of the "flame test" used in general chemistry laboratories for the identification of some metals like sodium and calcium (App. V).

PHOTOCHEMISTRY _____ 6.6

The relationship between the principal quantum number and energy states for atoms more complex than hydrogen and for molecules is more complicated. Nevertheless, each line in the spectrum of these substances can still be represented as a difference between two energy states determined by quantum numbers. Like hydrogen, these energy differences are characteristic of elements and compounds, no matter how complicated the atom or the molecule. Independent of the name used to classify the nature of experiments or natural occurrences—dayglow of Mars, identification of molecules in the space between stars, vision, photosynthesis, photochemistry, radiation chemistry, photography, luminescence, chemiluminescence, fluorescence, phosphorescence, northern lights, excited oxygen molecules, sunburn, lightning, UV spectra, IR spectra, NMR spectra, ESR spectra—all such interactions between radiation and matter (Chap. 24) involve the absorption and emission of energies corresponding to differences between two energy states, fixed by quantum numbers.

Photosynthesis The conversion of carbon dioxide by plants into a large variety of substances is made possible by photosynthesis, the most fundamental reaction of life. It is the original source of energy for all animals and plants: photosynthesis makes life on Earth possible.* In green plants, a green compound, chlorophyll, absorbs photons (in the visible region), converting the carbon dioxide in the air and water to sugar, $C_6H_{12}O_6$, and oxygen:

From the Greek, chlorus, green, and phyllon, leaf.

$$6\ CO_2(g) + 6\ H_2O(l) + hf(\text{photons}) \longrightarrow C_6H_{12}O_6(sol) + 6\ O_2(g)$$

Several sugars (Chap. 22) of this composition are formed, and are then partly converted into table sugar (sucrose, $C_{12}H_{22}O_{11}$) and starch, cellulose, protein and fat. Photons break water into hydrogen atoms and oxygen, the hydrogen finally appearing in several compounds after reacting with carbon dioxide.** Photosynthesis thus fixes solar energy in the form of organic compounds—the world of plants.

---

*On the biological scale, the first organism capable of photosynthesis appeared about four billion years ago, billions of years before the appearance of green algae, green and purple bacteria, green plants, and mammals.

**Intensive studies, among them the work of Joseph Priestley (1772), Jan Ingenhousz (1779), Nicholas De Saussure (1804), Henri Dutrochet (1837), Vernon Blackman (1905), Richard Willstätter (1918–1933), Samuel Rubin (1939), and Melvin Calvin (1947–1962), have given us an almost complete knowledge of the pathway from CO_2 and H_2O to the final products. Methods, for example, are known by which leaves producing mostly sucrose may be made to switch to protein production, a possible valuable aid in reducing the world's protein-food deficiencies.

Photography   A photographic film consists essentially of fine grains of a silver compound, usually silver bromide, AgBr, uniformly suspended in gelatin upon paper or cellulose acetate (Chap. 23). Exposure of the film to photons produces an excited state of silver bromide, in which state it is chemically changed by developer solution to silver (Chap. 21) much more rapidly than is the unexposed silver bromide in the ground state.

Firefly   The emission of light from a firefly, first recorded about the 16th Century B.C., is typical of the "chemiluminescence" in living matter (bacteria, fish, insects). In general, the reaction of a compound with oxygen produces a compound in an excited state:

Referred to as "cold light," because the emission of photons in the visible region, unlike a photoflash, is not accompanied by the emission of heat (photons in the IR range).

$$\text{Compound A} + O_2 \longrightarrow \text{Compound B (excited state)}$$

When the compound in the excited state returns to the ground state, a photon is emitted. In the firefly, the excited state product, a negatively charged ion,

$$C_{10}N_2S_2O_2H_5^-\text{(excited state)} \longrightarrow C_{10}N_2S_2O_2H_5^-\text{(ground state)} + hf(photon)$$

is produced from luciferin, $C_{10}N_2S_2O_3H_6$. This is the basis of *Coolite*, a plastic tube which when bent breaks a glass vial, mixing substances that emit light for about three hours.

Air Pollution: Photochemical Smog   Photochemical smog results from the action of sunlight on auto and industrial emissions, producing more harmful and more irritating pollutants. The action of photons on nitrogen oxides and hydrocarbons, producing compounds found in smog, was demonstrated in 1952 by Arie Haagen-Smit. Excited molecular oxygen is produced by direct absorption of photons from sunlight, $O_2 + hf \longrightarrow O_2$ *(excited state)*. Evidence is strong that excited O_2 molecules react with pollutants like NO and hydrocarbons (page 128) to produce powerful irritants such as NO_2 (Chap. 12), ozone (trioxygen, * O_3), peroxide type compounds, formaldehyde (page 131), and acrolein (CH_2CHCHO), a powerful eye irritant. Typical of the peroxides is peroxyacetyl nitrate ("PAN"), CH_3COONO_3, a strong eye irritant that can also damage crops. Smog has killed 8 % of the Ponderosa pines in the San Bernardino National Forest in California.

The word "smog," derived from "smoke" and "fog," was coined and first used in England in 1905.

The normal level of ozone is about zero to 0.02 ml per million ml (ppm) of air. Levels of about 12 ppm kill rodents in several hours. Levels of 0.25 ppm are not uncommon in heavy traffic, and the alert level in smog areas is about 0.50 ppm.

The chemical reactions that lead to the formation of a photochemical smog have not yet been deciphered. Because of the complex chemistry involved and the lack of detailed knowledge, many assumptions are necessarily made in accounting for such smogs. Only a simplified overall scheme is therefore given here:

$$\text{NO (from internal combustion engines, page 385)} + O_2 \text{ (excited state)} \longrightarrow NO_2 + O$$
$$NO_2 + hf \longrightarrow NO + O$$
$$O_2 \text{ (excited state)} + O \longrightarrow O_3$$

This action of photons on NO_2 is the most important reaction because it determines the quantity of O_3 and O. In the *absence of hydrocarbons,* the O_3 would react with NO

---

*From the Greek word *ozein,* to smell. It has a pungent odor, particularly noticeable near electrical machines. The gas is blue, the liquid is dark blue, and the solid is dark purple. It is highly explosive.

to reform NO_2 and O_2 (O_3 + NO $\longrightarrow$ NO_2 + O_2). In the *presence of hydrocarbons* from auto and industrial emissions, the following complex reactions occur:

O_2 (*excited state*), O, or O_3 + hydrocarbons $\longrightarrow$ organic peroxides, formaldehyde, acrolein

The formation of photochemical smogs depends upon the quantity of water vapor present. The greater the quantity of water vapor, the denser the smog. Weather conditions producing stagnant air masses are also required. However, our knowledge about the causes of air pollution is still limited. The role of automobile emissions in producing photochemical smog is still incompletely understood. Some evidence shows that hydrocarbons released from trees and plants might be as important as those released from automobiles.

No winds or upward motion of air.

DISTRIBUTION OF ELECTRONS IN ATOMS: ELECTRONIC STRUCTURES _____ 6.7

Number of Electrons in One Atomic Orbital   One negative electron in an atomic orbital feels comfortable because it finds the positive nucleus rather attractive. But will this electron tolerate the presence of a second electron? The two electrons, having the same electric charge, feel mutually repulsive, but they are sufficiently tolerant so that an atomic orbital can house two electrons. But a third electron is so repulsive that it will not be housed. This conclusion, *applicable to all orbitals,* is summarized in the law known as the **Pauli exclusion principle:** *no more than two electrons can occupy any orbital.*

Wolfgang Pauli discovered this fundamental law in 1925 from a study of atomic spectra and the periodic table (Chap. 7).

Atoms with More than One Electron   All atoms, except hydrogen atoms, have more than one electron. In these atoms the atomic orbitals (energy states) with the same principal quantum number, *n,* such as 3*s,* 3*p,* 3*d,* do not have exactly the same energy. An atom in its ground state is stable when the attraction between its positive nucleus and the electrons balances the repulsion between its electrons. Each electron is attracted to the nucleus and each electron is repelled by every other electron. These many interactions make the energy a function of the atomic number. But, fortunately, the orbital composition of all atoms can be described in terms of the hydrogen orbitals. The order of the energy and stability of the atomic orbitals for neutral atoms are given in Fig. 6.13. The most stable orbital is the 1*s* orbital, placed at the bottom of the diagram. Recall that energy is always required to raise an electron from one orbital to a less stable orbital above it; the least stable orbital is therefore located at the top of the diagram.

Also true for the atomic orbitals of the hydrogen atom, but we have intentionally avoided this unnecessary complication in our discussion of the hydrogen spectrum.

PROBLEM 18   **Refer to Fig. 6.13. Arrange the following atomic orbitals in the order of increasing energy: 3*s,* 4*s,* 5*s,* 2*p,* 3*p,* 4*p,* 3*d.***

An atomic orbital can house a maximum of two electrons. Then, recalling page 187:

An *s* orbital can house a maximum of two electrons.
The three *p* orbitals can house a maximum of six electrons.
The five *d* orbitals can house a maximum of 10 electrons.
The seven *f* orbitals can house a maximum of 14 electrons.
We can now distribute the electrons in the (ground state of) atoms. The basis of the distribution follows:

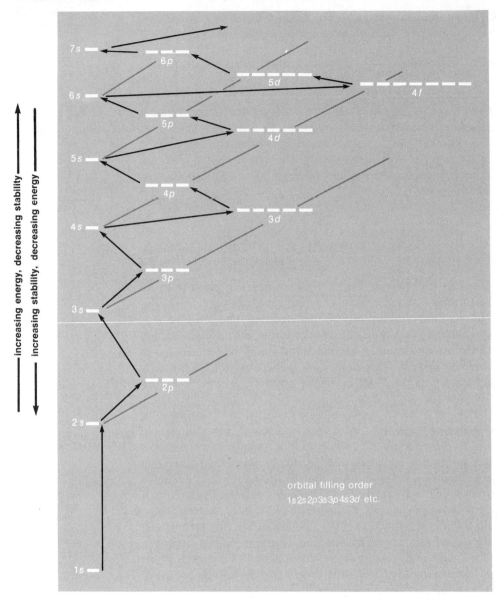

FIGURE 6.13 (Not to scale.) The order of the energy and stability of atomic orbitals in neutral atoms in the gaseous state. This order is *not* applicable to positive ions. The colored lines show the spread of the orbitals with the same values of *n*. Notice that this spread makes the 3*d* orbital more unstable than the 4*s* orbital. Thus the order of orbital filling is 1s 2s 2p 3s 3p 4s 3d, etc.

The number of electrons in an atom must equal the atomic number.

Each added electron enters the orbitals in the *order of decreasing stability* (increasing energy); see Fig. 6.13. That is, electrons are placed first in the 1*s* orbital, then in the 2*s*, the 2*p*, and so forth. For example,

$_1$H, *hydrogen,* with one electron; the one electron occupies the 1*s* orbital.

$_2$He, *helium,* with two electrons; both electrons can go into the 1*s* orbital. The symbols 1s^1 and 1s^2, referred to as the **electronic structure of the atom,** are used to summarize these arrangements. $1s^1$ means that there is one electron in the $1s$ orbital; $1s^2$ represents two electrons in the $1s$ orbital.

$_3$Li, *lithium,* with three electrons; since the $1s$ orbital cannot house more than two electrons, we put two electrons in the $1s$ orbital and the third electron in the next available orbital, the $2s$ orbital. The electronic structure of the lithium atom is thus $1s^2\, 2s^1$.

$_4$Be, *beryllium,* with four electrons; the $2s$ orbital can house two electrons; therefore, we put the fourth electron in it, giving the structure $1s^2\, 2s^2$ for the beryllium atom.

$_5$B, *boron,* with five electrons; the $1s$ and $2s$ orbitals accept four electrons; the next available orbital, $2p$, accepts the fifth electron. The structure of the boron atom is thus $1s^2\, 2s^2\, 2p^1$.

$_6$C, *carbon,* with six electrons; since the three $2p$ orbitals can house six electrons, the sixth electron is put in a $2p$ orbital. The structure of the carbon atom is $1s^2\, 2s^2\, 2p^2$. By following the same procedure, the structures for nitrogen, oxygen, and neon are obtained:

$_7$N, *nitrogen,* $1s^2\, 2s^2\, 2p^3$ $\quad$ $_8$O, *oxygen,* $1s^2\, 2s^2\, 2p^4$ $\quad$ $_{10}$Ne, *neon,* $1s^2\, 2s^2\, 2p^6$

PROBLEM 19 $\quad$ **Write the electronic structure for the atom of fluorine, $_9$F.**

$_{11}$Na, *sodium,* with 11 electrons; since the three p orbitals cannot house more than six electrons, the eleventh electron is put in the next available orbital, $3s$, giving the structure $1s^2\, 2s^2\, 2p^6\, 3s^1$ for the sodium atom. Continuing, the structure for $_{12}$Mg, *magnesium,* is $1s^2\, 2s^2\, 2p^6\, 3s^2$, and the structure for $_{13}$Al, *aluminum,* is $1s^2\, 2s^2\, 2p^6\, 3s^2\, 3p^1$. Since the three $3p$ orbitals can house six electrons, the following structures are obtained for the atoms of $_{14}$Si, *silicon,* and $_{18}$Ar, *argon:*

$_{14}$Si, $1s^2\, 2s^2\, 2p^6\, 3s^2\, 3p^2$ $\quad$ $_{18}$Ar, $1s^2\, 2s^2\, 2p^6\, 3s^2\, 3p^6$

PROBLEM 20 $\quad$ **Write the electronic structure for the atom of $_{17}$Cl, chlorine.**

For $_{19}$K, *potassium,* and $_{20}$Ca, *calcium,* the next available orbital, $4s$, is used, giving the following structures:

$_{19}$K, $1s^2\, 2s^2\, 2p^6\, 3s^2\, 3p^6\, 4s^1$ $\quad$ $_{20}$Ca, $1s^2\, 2s^2\, 2p^6\, 3s^2\, 3p^6\, 4s^2$

The next available orbital is a $3d$. The five $3d$ orbitals can house 10 electrons. The structures for the atoms of $_{21}$Sc, *scandium,* $_{25}$Mn, *manganese,* and $_{30}$Zn, *zinc,* are as follows:

$_{21}$Sc, $1s^2\, 2s^2\, 2p^6\, 3s^2\, 3p^6\, 4s^2\, 3d^1$ $\quad$ $_{25}$Mn, $1s^2\, 2s^2\, 2p^6\, 3s^2\, 3p^6\, 4s^2\, 3d^5$

$_{30}$Zn, $1s^2\, 2s^2\, 2p^6\, 3s^2\, 3p^6\, 4s^2\, 3d^{10}$

PROBLEM 21 $\quad$ **Write the electronic structure for the atom of $_{27}$Co, cobalt.**

The electronic structures of the atoms of the remaining elements may be obtained by similar reasoning with the aid of Fig. 6.13.

Although the energy of the orbitals is a function of the atomic number, the order given in Fig. 6.13 closely follows the order of stability obtained from the experimental properties of the elements. However, several of the predicted electronic structures do

1 Å

a

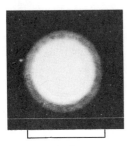

1 Å

b

FIGURE 6.14 Direct (holographic) images of the electron clouds in (a) atomic neon and (b) atomic argon obtained (1975) by Lawrence Bartell, University of Michigan. 1 Å = 10^{-8} cm. (Magnification: 2×10^8 diameters.)

not agree with the experimentally assigned structures (App. IV). Therefore, it is not wise to memorize the order of atomic orbital filling beyond $4s^2$, namely, $1s^2\,2s^2\,2p^6\,3s^2\,3p^6\,4s^2$. For example, the predicted electronic structure for the atom of $_{24}$Cr, chromium, is $1s^2\,2s^2\,2p^6\,3s^2\,3p^6\,4s^2\,3d^4$, but the experimental structure is $1s^2\,2s^2 2p^6\,3s^2\,3p^6\,4s^1\,3d^5$. Another typical example is the predicted structure for $_{29}$Cu, copper, $1s^2\,2s^2\,2p^6\,3s^2\,3p^6\,4s^2\,3d^9$; however, the experimental structure of this atom is $1s^2\,2s^2\,2p^6\,3s^2\,3p^6\,4s^1\,3d^{10}$. It appears that nature prefers half-filled (d^5) or filled (d^{10}) sets of orbitals. Unusually high stability is generally associated with these conditions.

It is frequently advantageous to represent an orbital with a dash and to represent each of the two electrons in the orbital with an arrow, one pointing down ($\downarrow$) and the other pointing up ($\uparrow$). Thus, the electronic structures of $_3$Li, lithium, and $_{30}$Zn, zinc, may be written as follows:

$_3$Li $\underline{\downarrow\uparrow}$ $\underline{\downarrow}$ $_{30}$Zn $\underline{\downarrow\uparrow}$ $\underline{\downarrow\uparrow}$ $\underline{\downarrow\uparrow}\,\underline{\downarrow\uparrow}\,\underline{\downarrow\uparrow}$ $\underline{\downarrow\uparrow}$ $\underline{\downarrow\uparrow}\,\underline{\downarrow\uparrow}\,\underline{\downarrow\uparrow}$ $\underline{\downarrow\uparrow}\,\underline{\downarrow\uparrow}\,\underline{\downarrow\uparrow}\,\underline{\downarrow\uparrow}\,\underline{\downarrow\uparrow}$ $\underline{\downarrow\uparrow}$

$\quad\quad$ 1s $\;$ 2s $\quad\quad\quad$ 1s $\;$ 2s $\quad\;$ 2p $\quad\;$ 3s $\quad\;$ 3p $\quad\quad\;$ 3d $\quad\quad\;$ 4s

One electron in an orbital, as in $_3$Li, is referred to as **unpaired.** Two electrons in an orbital are referred to as **paired.**

Shells and Subshells$\quad$ The atomic orbitals possessing the same principal quantum number, n, are said to belong to a **shell.** The shell is called K when $n = 1$, L when $n = 2$, M when $n = 3$, and so on. The set of orbitals possessing the same n and the same letter ($s, p, \ldots$) designation is called a **subshell.** Thus, the K shell consists of one $1s$ orbital. The L shell contains two subshells: the $2s$ and the three $2p$ orbitals. The M shell contains three subshells: the $3s$, the three $3p$, and the five $3d$ orbitals. The faint lines in Fig. 6.13 indicate the subshells. The first direct view of electron clouds in atoms is shown in Fig. 6.14. The sharp separation of shells that scientists find convenient to imagine does not appear. Fully occupied shells are represented by shell letters, $K, L, \ldots$. Shells and subshells are also known as levels and sublevels.

PROBLEM 22$\quad$ **What is the maximum number of electrons that can be put into each of the following subshells: $2s$, $4s$, $2p$, $4p$, $3d$, $6d$?**

6.8————————**DOES AN ELECTRON IN AN ATOM
OR MOLECULE SPIN?**

Experimental: Magnetic Properties of Matter$\quad$ The needle of a compass at a given location on the ground will always point in a definite direction, no matter how the compass is rotated. The needle is called a natural *magnet;* it consists of *magnetite,* magnetic oxide of iron, Fe_3O_4, known since ancient times as a "lodestone."* The Earth is also regarded as a large spherical magnet giving rise to a magnetic field that surrounds the Earth. The needle, we say, is *drawn, attracted,* into this magnetic field. Since the needle has two ends, the end pointing toward the geographic north is

---

*From the Greek *magnetis lithos,* named after a district in Thessaly in Asia Minor. Fe_3O_4 is now recognized as a mixed Fe(II)-Fe(III) oxide (page 671). The origin of the magnetic compass (originally polished lodestone floating on a piece of wood) has been traced back about 20 centuries to Chinese scholars and about 21 centuries to the Olmec (Mexico) Civilization. The Chinese were the first to employ the magnetic compass at sea. Modern compasses use a needle of magnetic steel. The strongest magnets made are alloys of cobalt, Co, and the rare earth metals such as samarium, Sm. Alnico (Al, Ni, and Co) is a magnetic alloy used in loudspeakers.

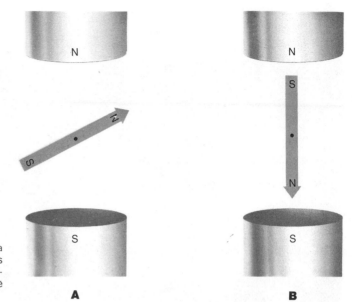

FIGURE 6.15 (a) A small magnetic needle placed in a large magnetic field. (b) The repulsion of similar poles and attraction of opposite poles cause the small needle to line up as shown, the N pole of the small needle facing the S pole of the large magnet.

A   **B**

arbitrarily called the "magnetic north pole," or simply north pole, designated *N*. The other end is called the "south pole," designated *S*.*

Similar poles, *N-N* or *S-S*, of two magnets repel each other; opposite poles, *N-S*, attract each other (Fig. 6.15). Some magnets are stronger than others: one magnet may lift a car, another may be incapable of lifting a grain of iron.

The direction of the magnetic field of the Earth and of a bar magnet is compared with the direction of the gravitational field of the Earth in Fig. 6.16. The movement of the compass needle, a bar magnet, results from the interaction of its magnetic field with the magnetic field of the Earth.

Can the south pole be separated from the north pole, in the same way an electron, a negative charge, can be kept away from a positive charge? By experiment, the answer is no. If you break a magnet in half, you will find two magnets in your hands; each half will have its own *N* and *S* poles. Cut a bar magnet into five parts; each part behaves as a magnet with a *N* and *S* pole.

Natural or synthetic magnets attract pieces of iron, steel, nickel, and other metals. These metals are attracted into the magnetic field; they are typical **paramagnetic** substances. Liquid and gaseous oxygen, gaseous atomic sodium, and atomic hydrogen are also paramagnetic; they are attracted into a magnetic field, illustrated in Fig. 6.17.

Hans Oersted (1820) discovered that an electric current (electrons) flowing through a wire generates a magnetic field around the wire. This discovery led to the development of the electromagnet, a coil of wire carrying an electric current. The magnetic field outside the coil has the same properties as those of any other magnet. It loops around from one end to the other. The use of an electromagnet to clean up tanker oil spills is based on the addition of a suspension of magnetic iron oxide to the oil slick. Your pulsating heart also produces electric currents that generate a magnetic field that loops around your body. Although extremely weak, its detection is the basis of the magnetocardiograph method of checking the heart. Electric currents within the

---

*So named in 1600 by William Gilbert, who concluded that the Earth is a magnet and introduced such terms as "electric force," "electric attraction," "magnetic pole," and "magnetic field."

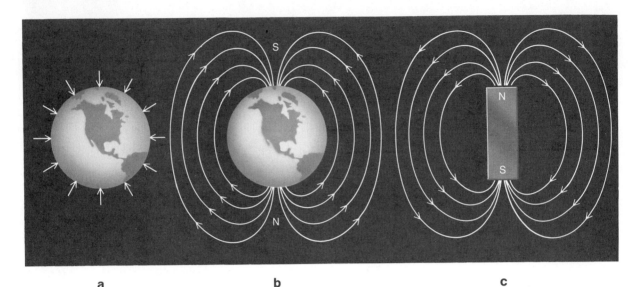

a   b   c

FIGURE 6.16 Comparison of the direction of (a) gravitational and (b) magnetic fields. Objects fall to the ground; the Earth, we say, is surrounded by a gravitational field. The gravitational field is directed toward the center of the Earth. The magnetic field comes out of one end, arbitrarily called the "North Pole," N, and loops toward and enters the "South Pole," S. The *geographic North Pole*, named before the introduction of the term magnetic pole, is the *magnetic south pole*.

(c) The properties of the magnetic field set up by a bar magnet are the same as the field set up by the earth, but of course the magnetic strengths differ.

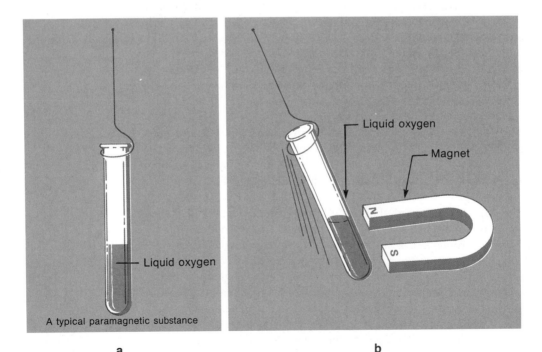

a   b

FIGURE 6.17 Representation of the action of a magnet on a paramagnetic substance. It is attracted into the magnetic field. (a) In the absence of a magnet, and (b) in the presence of a magnet.

human brain produce a detectable magnetic field outside the head. Striking electrical events are recorded, for example, when the brain of an epileptic is examined. Contaminating magnetic particles like asbestos (page 724) and metal particles from arc welding are detectable in the lungs and stomach by applying an external magnetic field to the body. Magnetic separation of enzymes (page 728) from other material has been achieved by fixing them on magnetite.

Theoretical   The key to our present understanding of the magnetic properties of matter is the kind of reasoning Democritus (page 109) used to reach his atomic theory of matter. Break a piece of chalk in half; each half will have the properties of the original piece. If this process is continued until the pieces become too small to manipulate, each broken part still will have the properties of the original piece. This property of matter led Democritus to the conclusion that matter is composed of tiny particles, the atoms.

Similarly, with magnets (page 201): break a magnet in half. Each half will be a magnet. Continue this process until the pieces become too small to manipulate. Each broken part will be a separate magnet. This suggests that a magnet is *quantized,* composed of tiny individual magnets of atomic or molecular sizes.

Our present knowledge of the structure of atoms, molecules (Chap. 18), and even nuclei* is well advanced. But, at present, we have no knowledge about the structure of an electron. An instrument capable of walloping an electron with sufficient force to decompose it into smaller particles** has not yet been invented.

However, an old but still useful theory describes the electron in the hydrogen atom as a tiny ball in orbital motion about the proton and, at the same time, spinning like a top. It is further *assumed* that the electron can spin in *only two* possible ways, say west to east, or east to west. (It cannot, for example, spin in any position like a rolling ball.) No knowledgeable scientist really believes that an electron is anything like a revolving, spinning ball (shown in Fig. 6.18), but many *assume* such a picture because it gives us a reasonable and acceptable explanation for the magnetic properties of matter. Thus, a single, spinning electron in orbital motion about the nucleus *should behave like an electric current (a stream of electrons)* flowing in a loop of wire and, therefore, *should act as though it were a tiny bar magnet* with a characteristic N and S pole strength. This is a reasonable inference, since it is known that electrons in motion generate a magnetic field (page 201), and account for the magnetic field generated by an electric current in a wire. The electron, then, is believed to be "the atom of magnetism," the basic unit of magnetism, the permanent "micromagnet." The electron, we believe, generates the magnetic fields (Figs. 6.18 and 6.19) observed in experiments. The properties of magnets are then related to the number of *unpaired electrons* in the atoms of which the magnet is composed, such as in the gaseous atomic hydrogen, sodium, or silver. The unpaired electrons, the "micromagnets," attracted

into a magnetic field, account for paramagnetism. Thus, the lithium atom, $_3\mathrm{Li}\dfrac{\downarrow}{2s}$,

and the oxygen molecule, with two unpaired electrons (Color Plate VIIIA) are para-

The Niels Bohr theory of the atom (1913), and the "electron-spin" hypothesis (1925) of George Uhlenbeck and Samuel Goudsmit.

See center of text for Color Plates.

---

*Like atoms, nuclei are pictured as quantized nuclear orbitals, each with a characteristic energy and each of which can take only two protons or two neutrons. This theoretical view of the nucleus is known as the "nuclear shell model."

**A theory of particles, invented by Murray Gell-Mann (1964), assumes the existence of particles, named *quarks, not yet definitely observed in nature:* one has a charge of $\frac{1}{3} e^-$ and another has a charge of $\frac{2}{3} e^+$. The theory holds that a proton is composed of one particle, with a charge of $\frac{1}{3} e^-$, and two particles, each with a charge of $\frac{2}{3} e^+$; the net charge is then $\frac{1}{3} e^- + 2 \times \frac{2}{3} e^+ = \frac{1}{3} e^- + \frac{4}{3} e^+ = \frac{3}{3} e^+ = 1 e^+$, the experimentally determined charge carried by a proton. William Fairbank and coworkers at Stanford University have reported (1977) evidence of fractional charges.

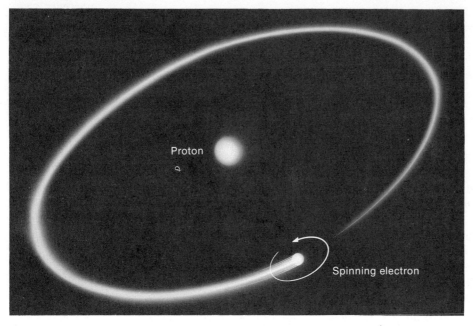

FIGURE 6.18 The spinning electron in orbital motion about the proton is pictured like an electric current flowing in a loop of wire.

magnetic. But neither the hydrogen molecule nor the helium atom, with no unpaired electrons, is paramagnetic; they are not attracted into a magnetic field.

The observation that paired electrons are not paramagnetic is explained by the restriction placed upon the spin of an electron. Only two kinds of spin about its axis are permitted, as pictured in Fig. 6.20. When two electrons occupy the same orbital, they spin in opposite directions. Thus, the paramagnetism of electron ↑ is canceled by the paramagnetism of the second electron, ↓. Recent applications of magnetometers are given in Color Plate IX.

See center of text for Color Plates

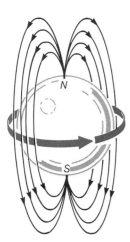

FIGURE 6.19 In atoms and molecules, the electron in motion generates a magnetic field whose properties are identical to the field set up by a bar magnet or by the Earth. (The magnetic strengths are, of course, different, but they are related to the number of unpaired electrons.)

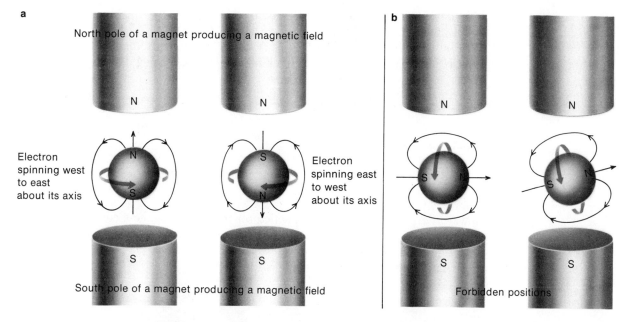

FIGURE 6.20 (a) The two assumed spins of the electron, "the micromagnet," relative to a magnetic field: one spinning west to east, with the north pole of the electron facing the north pole of the external magnet; the second spinning in the opposite direction, with the north pole of the electron facing the south pole of the external magnet. Any other position, such as those illustrated in (b), is forbidden. Therefore, we can say that the spin of an electron is quantized.

PROBLEM 23   An atom of titanium, Ti, contains 22 electrons, two of which are unpaired. A neon, Ne, atom contains 10 electrons, all paired. A molecule of oxygen contains 16 electrons, two unpaired. A molecule of hemoglobin, molecular weight 64,500 g/mole, the protein (Chap. 23) that carries oxygen in the blood from the lungs to the body cells* and brings back carbon dioxide to the lungs, has four unpaired electrons. A helium ion, He^+, has one electron; Ne^+ has nine electrons; an F atom has nine electrons; and a Na^{2+} ion has nine electrons. Pick the substance(s), atom, molecule, or ion, that is (are) not paramagnetic.

Electron Pairing   Electronic structures are frequently written (App. IV) in the shell order $K, L, M, \ldots$, although electron filling does not follow that order. Illustrative is a silver atom containing one unpaired electron in its $5s$ orbital:

$$_{47}Ag, \; 1s^2\, 2s^2\, 2p^6\, 3s^2\, 3p^6\, 3d^{10}\, 4s^2\, 4p^6 \;\; \underline{\downarrow\uparrow} \;\; \underline{\downarrow\uparrow} \;\; \underline{\downarrow\uparrow} \;\; \underline{\downarrow\uparrow} \;\; \underline{\downarrow\uparrow} \qquad \underline{\downarrow}$$
$$\qquad\qquad\qquad\qquad\qquad\qquad\qquad\qquad\qquad 4d^{10} \qquad\qquad 5s$$

Representing the filled shells ($n = 1, 2,$ and 3) by the symbols $K, L,$ and M, this is written

$$_{47}Ag, \; KLM\, 4s^2\, 4p^6 \;\; \underline{\downarrow\uparrow} \;\; \underline{\downarrow\uparrow} \;\; \underline{\downarrow\uparrow} \;\; \underline{\downarrow\uparrow} \;\; \underline{\downarrow\uparrow} \qquad \underline{\downarrow}$$
$$\qquad\qquad\qquad\qquad\qquad 4d^{10} \qquad\qquad 5s$$

The filled orbitals make no contribution to paramagnetic properties. Also, in silver, there is no question of the order of occupancy of the five $4d$ orbitals, since 10 electrons

---

*Carbon monoxide acts as a poison (pages 113 and 665) by forming a compound with hemoglobin, displacing the oxygen so that the necessary oxygen does not reach body cells.

are available. Regardless of the order used to place the 10 electrons, the five d orbitals will be filled. However, in the manganese atom, $_{25}$Mn, $1s^2\,2s^2\,2p^6\,3s^2\,3p^6\,3d^5\,4s^2$, five electrons are available for the five d orbitals. The order of occupancy is now very important: We may, for example, pair four electrons, leaving one unpaired,

$$_{25}\text{Mn, } KL\ 3s^2\ 3p^6\ \underline{\downarrow\uparrow}\ \underline{\downarrow\uparrow}\ \underline{\downarrow}\ \underline{\ \ }\ \underline{\ \ }\quad \underline{\downarrow\uparrow}\quad (incorrect)$$
$$\phantom{_{25}\text{Mn, } KL\ 3s^2\ 3p^6\ \underline{\downarrow\uparrow}\ \underline{\downarrow\uparrow}}\ 3d\ \phantom{\underline{\ \ }\ \underline{\ \ }}\quad 4s$$

or pair none of the 5 electrons,

$$_{25}\text{Mn, } KL\ 3s^2\ 3p^6\ \underline{\downarrow}\ \underline{\downarrow}\ \underline{\downarrow}\ \underline{\downarrow}\ \underline{\downarrow}\quad \underline{\downarrow\uparrow}\quad (correct)$$
$$\phantom{_{25}\text{Mn, } KL\ 3s^2\ 3p^6\ \underline{\downarrow}\ \underline{\downarrow}}\ 3d\ \phantom{\underline{\downarrow}\ \underline{\downarrow}}\quad 4s$$

However, experimentally, the magnetic properties of manganese correspond to five unpaired electrons. Thus, nature prefers that *electrons stay unpaired in a given set of p, d, or f orbitals until each such orbital has at least one electron in it*. For example, the occupancy of the three p orbitals is as follows:

Known as the Hund
rule, named in honor
of Freidrich Hund for
his work with atomic
and molecular spectra.

$$_5\text{B, } 1s^2\ 2s^2\ \underline{\downarrow}\ \underline{\ \ }\ \underline{\ \ }\qquad\qquad _6\text{C, } 1s^2\ 2s^2\ \underline{\downarrow}\ \underline{\downarrow}\ \underline{\ \ }$$
$$\phantom{_5\text{B, } 1s^2\ 2s^2\ \underline{\downarrow}}\ 2p\ \phantom{\underline{\ \ }\ \underline{\ \ }}\qquad\qquad \phantom{_6\text{C, } 1s^2\ 2s^2\ \underline{\downarrow}}\ 2p$$

$$_7\text{N, } 1s^2\ 2s^2\ \underline{\downarrow}\ \underline{\downarrow}\ \underline{\downarrow}$$
$$\phantom{_7\text{N, } 1s^2\ 2s^2\ \underline{\downarrow}}\ 2p$$

Each of the three p orbitals contains one electron; electron pairing then occurs. One electron in an orbital accepts another electron only if it has the opposite spin, as shown:

$$_8\text{O, } 1s^2\ 2s^2\ \underline{\downarrow\uparrow}\ \underline{\downarrow}\ \underline{\downarrow}\qquad\qquad _9\text{F, } 1s^2\ 2s^2\ \underline{\downarrow\uparrow}\ \underline{\downarrow\uparrow}\ \underline{\downarrow}$$
$$\phantom{_8\text{O, } 1s^2\ 2s^2\ \underline{\downarrow\uparrow}\ \underline{\downarrow}}\ 2p\ \phantom{\underline{\downarrow}}\qquad\qquad \phantom{_9\text{F, } 1s^2\ 2s^2\ \underline{\downarrow\uparrow}\ \underline{\downarrow\uparrow}}\ 2p$$

$$_{10}\text{Ne, } 1s^2\ 2s^2\ \underline{\downarrow\uparrow}\ \underline{\downarrow\uparrow}\ \underline{\downarrow\uparrow}$$
$$\phantom{_{10}\text{Ne, } 1s^2\ 2s^2\ \underline{\downarrow\uparrow}}\ 2p$$

PROBLEM 24   Write the electronic structure of the atom of nickel, $_{28}$Ni, showing the order of occupancy of the five d orbitals. How many electrons are unpaired?

The paramagnetic properties of the isolated atoms in each case are related to the number of unpaired electrons.*

The tendency of electrons to remain unpaired in orbitals of equal energy in an

---

*Actually, paramagnetic properties arise from two sources: the spin and the orbital motion of the electron. In a few cases, these effects cancel each other, so that it is possible for an atom with unpaired electrons not to be paramagnetic.

Here, the student may inquire about the contribution of the nucleus—for example, the proton in the hydrogen atom—to the magnetic properties of the atom. Why not assume that protons and neutrons, like electrons, spin? Indeed, we do. Analogous to the electron (Figs. 6.18 and 6.19), unpaired spinning protons and neutrons in nuclear orbital motion give rise to a magnetic field. But, because these particles are much heavier and therefore move much more slowly, the field strength is so small that its contribution may be neglected. Nevertheless, these extremely weak fields generated by nuclei, detectable with modern instruments, are *characteristic for each nucleus*. But a nucleus immediately identifies an atom of an element. This technique, known as "nuclear magnetic resonance," "NMR," constitutes another valuable "fingerprint" for identifying elements (Chap. 24).

isolated atom is reasonable. The electrons in atoms repel each other. In isolated carbon atoms, for example, electrical repulsion is greater when the two *p* electrons are in the same orbital than when they spread out in separate orbitals.

RULES AND REGULATIONS _____ 6.9

Automobile (ground) traffic is controlled by complex interacting forces, physical in nature but largely of social origin, illustrated in Fig. 6.21. In spite of the apparent complexity, it is possible to evaluate the forces involved and, therefore, to predict accurately the arrival of a car in one location upon departure from another, provided *no* unpredictable events occur (such as unexpected storms or collision with another car or a pedestrian). "Mechanics" is a branch of science which considers the action of forces upon bodies. It attempts to describe these forces in terms of laws of motion, that is, equations that relate change in position with time (Fig. 6.2, page 175). Thus, ground traffic mechanics involves a highly complex mixture of physical and social laws. On the other hand, air traffic mechanics involves the same physical forces, but social forces are fewer, and consequently, more accurate predictions regarding flight arrivals may be made, in the absence, of course, of hijackers. Highly accurate automatic control and automatic navigation are available for aircraft.

In 1920, Robert Goddard* developed a rocket capable of pushing an object

_____

*An article, "On the Possibility of Navigating Interplanetary Space," written by Goddard in 1907 when he was an undergraduate, concluded that "atomic disintegration" (Chap. 17) would eventually provide the energy necessary for space travel. The article was rejected by the editor of *Popular Astronomy* because "the impossibility of ever doing it is so certain." His 1925 project for sending a rocket to the moon was criticized for being "theoretically incorrect."

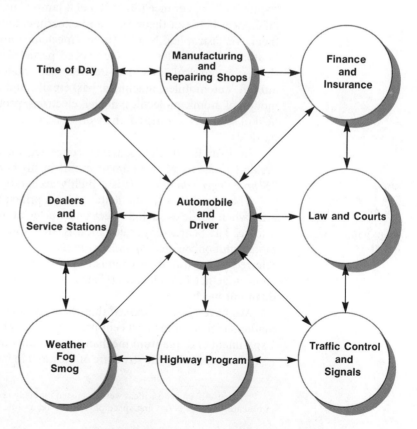

FIGURE 6.21 Some interactions of physical and social forces affecting the flow of ground traffic. (Modified from *Scientific American*, February 1970, page 16.)

beyond the influence of the Earth's gravitational field. This development opened the gateway to outer space and the moon. Space mechanics also involves the same physical forces operative in ground and air traffic mechanics, but social forces are minimized. Hence, the course and arrival time of a spacecraft are very accurately controlled and predicted by the laws of motion and the law of gravity, provided the vehicle is not hit by a missile under the control of another operator. These laws, generally known, as "classical mechanics" or "Newtonian mechanics," assign a definite velocity (energy) and, at the same time, a definite position to each body. Astronomers, recently joined by space scientists,* have been doing this for centuries in correctly predicting the motion of planets, such as the time and place of the next complete eclipse of the sun by the moon. In fact, classical mechanics was so successful during the 19th Century that Max Planck, the father of quantum theory (page 191), was advised by his university counselors (University of Munich) to study music instead of physics "since in the field of physics there was nothing new to be discovered." Many famous scientists, such as James Maxwell (pages 64 and 191), predicted that "the search for the next decimal place in the physical constants," for example, the velocity of light, would be the central issue of research throughout the 20th Century. This success also gave rise to the philosophy of determinism in science—once the position and velocity of an object are known, then its position and velocity at any future time can be precisely predicted.

Minimized, but not yet completely eliminated; failure of physical laws was not the cause of the unfortunate deaths of six astronauts trapped in space vehicles.

A decisive change, however, was brought about by the results of several experiments involving a study of the energy (color) distribution of light emitted by several sources under different temperature conditions. All attempts to explain the quantization of energy and the intensity of the color lines in terms of classical mechanics failed. It could not, for example, explain the "red hot" appearance (800 °C) and "white hot" appearance (3000 °C) of a lamp filament. So bad were the failures—the differences between theoretical and experimental results—that scientists referred to them as catastrophes. Nor is classical mechanics applicable to the motion of electrons in atoms or molecules or to high-speed particles approaching the speed of light. In short, the physical laws that describe the motion of planets, rockets, spacecraft, aircraft, automobiles, machines, basketballs, and dust particles do not apply to the motion of atoms, molecules, nuclei, electrons, protons, and neutrons. An entire new field of science was opened, the world of molecular, atomic, nuclear, and elementary particles.

In 1926 Erwin Schroedinger conceived an equation regarded as one of the greatest products of the human mind; in his honor the equation is known as the "*Schroedinger equation*." It is a highly acceptable assumption.

The equation is fundamental; it is, in principle, applicable to the problems that arise when particles such as electrons, nuclei, atoms, and molecules are subjected to a force. The Schroedinger equation is, therefore, the basis of "*particle mechanics*," more commonly called "*quantum mechanics*." Its application to chemical problems is referred to as "quantum chemistry." For example, the nature of the force holding atoms together in molecules (Chaps. 8 and 18) can be understood only in terms of quantum mechanics.

Also known as the "wave equation," because the equation was discovered by analogy to the properties of waves.

We have always *assumed* that the equations of motion developed by the great mathematicians of the past centuries apply to *all* bodies, regardless of size and speed. Experiment and quantum mechanics contradict this assumption. Quantum mechanics does not describe the structure of the atom in terms that are familiar to us from the

---

*Hannes Alfvén, whose ideas were dismissed for many years and who was forced to publish his works in obscure journals, is the first space physicist to be awarded (1970) a Nobel Prize.

behavior of visible bodies. Nevertheless, when the Schroedinger equation is applied, it is assumed that the force (page 118) between charged particles—an electron and a proton—is described by the same law used for visible bodies. Therefore, quantum mechanics is a part of the evolution of our knowledge. It evolved from classical mechanics and therefore retains many of its characteristics. Schroedinger could not have done his work without the previous work of Niels Bohr (1913), Max Planck (1900), and Louis de Broglie (1924). Pioneers responsible for the development of quantum mechanics into the most unifying theory known include Werner Heisenberg, Max Born, Paul Dirac, Douglas Hartree, Vladimir Fock, James Slater, and Robert Mulliken. The Schroedinger equation will be with us until a scientist provides another set of rules that will give better predictions and suggest experiments inconceivable under present rules.

The Message in the Schroedinger Equation   Our explanations in this chapter have been given in the *language* of quantum mechanics. We now attempt a verbal description of the Schroedinger equation. The equation relates two important quantities; namely, the energy, E, of an electron in an atom is related to the distribution of the electron in space. Applied to the hydrogen atom, E refers to an energy state of the electron (or of the hydrogen atom). The distribution refers to an atomic orbital, or the shape of the region of space about the proton which the electron occupies. It also determines the densities of electron clouds (Figs. 6.8 and 6.14, pages 181 and 200). The results obtained are summarized as follows:

(a) The energy states are quantized and characterized by four quantum numbers having the symbols n, l, m_l, and m_s. The values of these four quantum numbers determine the energy of the electron, but in the absence of an external magnetic field, the energy is practically determined by only n. For this reason, n is known as the principle quantum number.

(b) The distribution of the electron in space in a given energy state, called an atomic orbital (Fig. 6.8, page 181), is determined by three quantum numbers, n, l, and m_l.

n determines the size of the orbital; the $2s$ or the $3p$ orbital is larger than, respectively, the $1s$ or the $2p$ orbital. The diameter of an H atom in the ground state $n = 1$ is about 10^{-8} cm. But when $n = 105$, the excited H atom approaches the size of bacteria, 10^{-5} cm.

l determines the shape of the orbital (Fig. 6.9, page 183). The symbols used to designate an orbital, s, p, d, and so on, correspond to definite values of l: 0, 1, 2, and so on.

m_l determines the orientation of the orbital in space—the direction one orbital takes relative to another. The different orientations of the p orbitals, for example, correspond to different values of m_l.

Unlike the classical mechanical description of a dust particle, quantum mechanics *does not* assign, at any instant, both a definite energy and a definite position to the electron in the hydrogen atom. Rather, the chances of finding an electron in the space about the nucleus are related to the density of the electron cloud (page 181). This means that while we know the exact position and velocity (energy) of a spacecraft on its journey through outer space, we do not know the exact location of the electron on its journey through the atomic orbital, illustrated in Fig. 6.22. But we *do* know its exact energy.

(c) The quantum number m_s can have *only* *two* possible values ($+\frac{1}{2}$, $-\frac{1}{2}$), leading to significant consequences:

It determines the maximum number of electrons that may occupy a given atomic

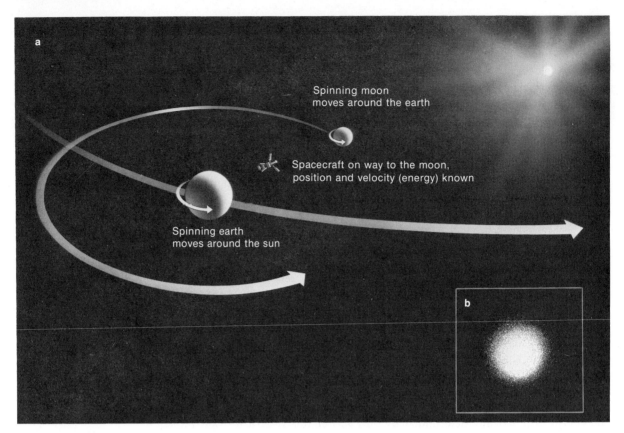

FIGURE 6.22 Computers in space centers in the U.S.A. and the U.S.S.R. can tell us the exact location of a spacecraft (a) at any instant, but they cannot give us the exact location of the electron in the hydrogen atom at any time (b). At best, they can tell us where the electron might be found most of the time.

Several scientists, such as Albert Einstein (1935) and David Bohm (1951), believe that this difference results from an incomplete treatment. All significant forces acting on the spacecraft are known. For the hydrogen atom, the only force acting on the electron is *assumed* to be electrical. But perhaps other forces, "quantum forces," too weak to detect, also operate to kick the electron. The search for such "hidden forces" (John Clauser, 1969) has not yet yielded results.

orbital. An orbital is defined by the three quantum numbers n, l, and m_l. But no two electrons in an atom can have the same four quantum numbers. Since the fourth quantum number, m_s, can have only two values, an atomic orbital can accommodate a maximum of two electrons. For example, a p orbital defined by $n = 3$, $l = 1$, and $m_l = 1$ can only take two electrons, corresponding to two sets of quantum numbers: 3, 1, 1, $+\frac{1}{2}$, and 3, 1, 1, $-\frac{1}{2}$.

The two "spin" positions, pictured in Fig. 6.20 (page 205), correspond to the two values of m_s.

Other Applications The application of the Schroedinger equation to a hydrogen molecule moving between the walls of a container also yields interesting results. Quantum mechanics predicts that the kinetic energy of a molecule is quantized. This prediction contradicts the assumption of the kinetic theory of gases that the kinetic energy of molecules continuously increases as the temperature is increased, namely, $\frac{1}{2} mv^2 \propto T$ (page 65). This *apparent* contradiction is explained as follows: For most practical purposes, the energy differences between quantum energy states are so small (relative to the average energy) that the molecule *appears* to change its kinetic energy continuously. The situation can be compared to a stairway where the height between the steps is so small that the stairway looks like a ramp. Near absolute zero temperature, however, the differences between energy states become significant, and the quantum mechanical treatment is necessary. Further, according to kinetic theory, at absolute zero the kinetic energy of a hydrogen molecule should be zero. But such a situation is prohibited by the Schroedinger equation: It predicts that a hydrogen molecule in linear motion can never be entirely stopped. These conclusions are necessary to explain many experimental observations in the region of absolute zero.

However, when applied to a large body—for example, a weight attached to a string and set in motion—the equation predicts that the weight will behave exactly as we see it behave. The quantum mechanical predictions regarding the weight are in exact agreement with the classical mechanical predictions. We should add that quantum mechanics, which visualizes a beam of light as a stream of photons, also includes all the successes of earlier theories of light. As Dirac wrote, "Quantum mechanics works so well that nobody can afford to disagree with it." Quantum mechanics stands presently as the most embracing and successful description of nature.

Conclusion   The common feature of classical and quantum mechanics is the trademark of science. Sooner or later, the time arrives when talk ceases and action takes over. *Experimentation decides the validity of a scientific theory.* At any given time, any theoretical model is an incomplete description of nature. But it is essential, as a growing scientist, to listen to scientific "talk" because experimental (empirical) knowledge is also *never* complete. Three speculative hypotheses now receiving experimental attention may be mentioned.

No one has yet observed an object "fall up" under the influence of gravity, but Philip Morrison and Thomas Gold (1957) predict that a particle, exactly identical with an electron except that the sign of its charge is positive (*positron*), will *fall up* under the influence of gravity.

While it is possible for a particle to have either a positive or a negative charge, no one has yet prepared a magnet with *only one* pole, either a north or a south pole (page 201); but Dirac (1931) and Julian Schwinger (1969) predict the existence of a particle that will carry an electric charge and *only one* pole. The predicted properties of this particle, named the *dyon,** include fractional electronic charges (page 203, ftn.).

Einstein theoretically concluded (1905) that "velocities greater than that of light in a vacuum, c, have no possibility of existence." Nevertheless, Gerald Feinberg has predicted (1967) the existence of tachyons, particles with velocities greater than c, and the experimental search for them has begun.

From tachys, *the Greek word for swift.*

The give and take between experiment and theory is a continuing process. Intellectual disaster follows the neglect and ignorance of either theory or experiment.

"Nothing is too wonderful to be true, if it be consistent with the laws of nature, and in such things as these, experiment is the best test of such consistency."

Michael Faraday

---

* So-called because the predicted particle carries two (dy) charges, an electric charge and a magnetic charge (one pole).

6.10_____WHAT'S AN ATOM? from *Alchemist*—Edgar N. Johnson, Springfield College, Springfield, Massachusetts. In *Journal of Chemical Education*, July, 1970, page 500

I used to know—I passed all sorts of tests—
    electron location to Eigen functions.
Now I'm sure, atoms don't exist.
Oh yes, I know you can identify one by its fingerprint
    like color absorbance. But bringing another to interact
        yields a new fingerprint. Atoms—like people—
        change in the presence of others.
Oh yes, you can pile up lots of atoms (6.02×10^{23}) and
    call it an element with atomic mass of zuh. Look at
    a well worn doorknob and see all the joyous patterns.
Copper atoms can appear black, yellow, and many shades of red,
    Just like people—the individual has no property but
        among different peers the properties vary like copper
        atoms in color, brilliance and brittleness—
        like people among peers.
I've never seen an atom, nor do I expect to. By itself there
    is nothing. But in a polar solvent it loses something
        to the solvent, becomes charged and then can be counted
        and manipulated. People in a crisis lose something,
        become polarized and then can be counted
        and manipulated.
Singular atoms like singular persons exist only in the
    interaction with others. What does an atom contribute
    to the crystal, molecule, or solution? What does a
    student contribute to his peers, school or society?
Atoms—like you and I—do not exist but interact!

PROBLEMS

25 **Vocabulary** Define or explain (a) atomic number, (b) atomic orbital, (c) principal quantum number, (d) ground and excited states, (e) emission spectrum, (f) continuous spectrum, (g) line spectrum, (h) photon, (i) paramagnetic substance.

26 **Nuclear composition** (a) Write the nuclear composition of the isotopes (i) of tin, $^{112}_{50}Sn$, $^{115}_{50}Sn$, $^{118}_{50}Sn$, $^{124}_{50}Sn$; (ii) of zinc, $^{64}_{30}Zn$, $^{66}_{30}Zn$, $^{72}_{30}Zn$. (b) Find the number of neutrons in the nucleus of each given atom: ^{40}Cl, ^{29}Mg, ^{100}Cd, ^{30}Na. (c) Pick the isotopes out of the following group: ^{210}Tl, ^{210}Pb, ^{210}Po, ^{218}At, ^{218}Po, $^{210}Po^+$, ^{214}Po, ^{206}Hg. Write the nuclear composition of these isotopes. (See inside back cover for atomic numbers.)

27 (a) Find the nuclear composition of the isotopes of $_{78}Pt$, atomic weights 189.96, 193.96, 195.96, and 197.97 g/mole. (b) Write the atomic number, mass number, and symbol of the atom whose nucleus

contains 79 protons and 118 neutrons (see inside front cover).

28 **Atomic structure** (a) Which force, gravitational or electrical, confines electrons to the space about the nuclei of atoms? (b) Explain the following statement in your own words: "The density of one portion of an atom is unbelievably high compared to the remaining portion." (c) Originally, Thomson believed that atoms were composed of electrons so that the mass of the electrons equaled the mass of the atom. What mass did he assign to the positive electricity?

29 $c = \lambda f$ If 110 cars pass a given railroad signal post per minute (frequency) and if each car length is 13.7 m ("wavelength"), what is the speed of the train in m/min and in km/h?

30 $c = \lambda f$, $E = hf$ (a) Interstellar gas contains a variety of molecules; one such molecule (CO) is detected at

a wavelength of 1.393×10^{-5} cm. Calculate the frequency and energy of the photon. (b) Another such molecule is ethyl alcohol, C_2H_5OH, detected at one of its characteristic frequencies, 90.1 gigahertz (90.1×10^9 s^{-1}) with a radiotelescope (at Kitt Peak, Arizona) aimed at the Milky Way. Calculate the wavelength and energy of the photon emitted by C_2H_5OH. $c = 2.998 \times 10^{10}$ cm/s, $h = 6.626 \times 10^{-27}$ erg s/photon.

31 (a) The retina of the toad responds to 5.02×10^{-5} cm (green) light. Calculate the frequency and the energy of the photon. Find the energy falling on the retina when 10^3 photons are flashed into the toad's eye. (b) The FM station WQXR in New York operates on a frequency of 96.3×10^6 s^{-1} (96.3 megahertz). Calculate the wavelength and photon energy. See Problem 30 for c and h values.

32 λ, f, hf (a) The formation of PAN (page 196) may be represented as $(CH_3)_2CO + O_2 + NO_2 + hf \longrightarrow CH_3COONO_3 + CH_3$. Assume that two photons are required for each PAN molecule formed. Calculate the number of moles and number of photons consumed in producing 10.0 ng (1 nanogram = 10^{-9} g) of PAN. The energy of the photons absorbed is 5.52×10^{-12} erg/photon. Find the photon frequency. (b) Warm objects radiate photons in the infrared range. *Thermography,* the study of temperature differences, uses a special camera that converts the invisible radiation into visible light. Following the discovery (1956) that the skin temperature over a cancer tumor is at least 1 °C higher than that of healthy skin, thermographs detecting abnormal temperatures in body tissues to a depth of 10 cm have been used to detect cancers too small for detection by other methods. The wavelength used is 4.97×10^{-3} cm. Find the frequency and the photon energy.

33 An intense blue line appears in the spectrum of mercury at 4.3583×10^{-5} cm. Predict the energy that must be absorbed by a mercury atom to cause the appearance of this line.* $c = 2.9979 \times 10^{10}$ cm/s, $h = 6.6262 \times 10^{-27}$ erg s/particle.

34 Ionization (a) In theoretical terms, the ionization energy of a hydrogen atom, the energy required to ionize the H atom (H $\longrightarrow$ proton + electron), is the energy required to move the electron from the energy state $n = 1$ to the state $n = \infty$. Calculate the ionization energy in ergs/atom, ergs/mole H atoms, kcal/mole H atoms (4.184×10^{10} ergs = 1 kcal), and joules/mole H atoms (10^7 ergs = 1 joule, J). (b) Calculate the work, in ergs/atom and in ergs/

mole H atoms, required to remove the electron in the H atom from energy state $n = 6$ to $n = \infty$. $N_A = 6.022 \times 10^{23}$ particles/mole.

35 How much work, in erg/ion, is required to remove an electron from the azide ion,* N_3^-, to infinity (ionize it) when the ion is in an energy state of 6.42×10^{-12} erg/ion?

36 Energy states Use Equation (1), page 184. Hydrogen atoms with the principal quantum number of 105, the size of bacteria, have been prepared. Calculate (a) the energy, in erg/atom, of these atoms and (b) the work in erg/atom and erg/mole H required to ionize them.

37 Energy states (a) Hydrogen atoms are hit with particles having a maximum energy of 19.57×10^{-12} erg/particle. What is the highest energy state to which the H atom is excited? Show the maximum number of lines emitted by these H atoms. (b) The energy states of a dye may be represented in terms of frequency as shown:

E_5 ——————— 0.06×10^{14} s^{-1}

E_4 ——————— 1.60×10^{14}

E_3 ——————— 3.21×10^{14}

E_2 ——————— 7.50×10^{14}

E_1 ——————— 9.06×10^{14}

The molecules of the dye are hit with particles having a maximum energy of 5.00×10^{-12} erg/particle. What is the highest state to which the molecule is excited? Show the maximum number of lines that can be emitted by these molecules.

38 Line spectra Refer to Table 6.1, page 184. (a) Find the energy of the photon emitted when the electron in a hydrogen atom "drops" from the energy state $n = 6$ to $n = 3$. (b) What is the largest photon energy that an H atom can emit?

39 Line spectra (a) Hydrogen atoms in the energy state $n = 250$ have been observed in outer space. Such an atom "drops" to the ground state in a series of steps: $n = 250 \longrightarrow n = 100 \longrightarrow n = 10 \longrightarrow n = 7 \longrightarrow n = 1$. How many photons are emitted by this H atom? (b) Find the photon energy for the transition $n = 250 \longrightarrow n = 1$. Use 21.79383×10^{-12} erg/n^2. (c) Refer to Color Plate V(C). Is it

---

*This prediction was verified in 1913 by the experiment of James Franck and Gustav Hertz, in which electrons of precisely known energy were passed through mercury vapor at low pressure.

*All azides decompose when heated; some, like sodium azide, NaN_3, decompose slowly but others, the azides of heavy metals such as $Pb(N_3)_2$ and $Hg(N_3)_2$, explode when heated or when struck sharply. They are therefore used in detonation caps. HN_3, hydrazoic acid, is "fearfully and dangerously explosive." Azides are best admired from a safe distance.

possible for an H atom to emit a line corresponding to the transition from $n = 4.3$ to $n = 2.1$?

40 Excited azide ions (Problem 35) emit three lines on returning to the ground state. What must be the minimum number of excited states in the ion?

41 An instrument aboard the Skylab detected a line, at a wavelength of 9.498×10^{-6} cm, emitted from a distant planet. Hydrogen was immediately suspected of being the emitter source. Check this possibility against the data in Color Plate V(C) and verify the recorded wavelength by calculating the wavelength of the line for the transition $n = 5 \longrightarrow n = 1$. See Problem 30 for equations and constants.

42 Spectrum The energy states in solid light emitters like naphthalene, $C_{10}H_8$, are shown in the diagram below, in which the arrows indicate the transitions that occur. Naphthalene is colorless, but it is used as a "bluing agent" in white shirts to make them appear "whiter than white." Find the frequency and wavelength of the blue light that it emits.* See Problem 30 for equations and constants. Also see Table 6.2, page 190.

43 Sketch the general shapes of an *s* and a *p* orbital.

44 Pick the atom with a spherical (*s*) electron cloud: Be, B, C, O, F.

45 Describe the electron cloud diagram for a 2*p* electron.

---

*The $E_3 \longrightarrow E_1$ transition gives rise to *fluorescence,* while the $E_2 \longrightarrow E_1$ gives rise to *phosphorescence* (derived from the Greek words meaning light-bearer). Fluorescent and phosphorescent (phosphor) materials absorb comparatively high frequency photons ("black light"; *e.g.*, UV) and radiate photons in the visible range. Since phosphorescence occurs from a more stable state, emission continues for some time, seconds to hours, after the "black light" is turned off, while fluorescence, from the more unstable state, stops after about 10^{-6} s.

46 (a) Identify these representations as *s, p,* or *d* orbitals:

 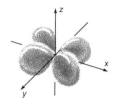

(b) An excited firefly is confined in a small glass globe; the room is darkened and the firefly is photographed with a time-exposure camera. Will the photograph obtained be most like an *s, p,* or *d* orbital? (c) Describe the 2*s* orbital shown in Fig. 6.8 (page 181) in terms of the chances of finding an electron on a given portion of the surface of a sphere as its distance from the nucleus increases.

47 Laser (*Light Amplification by Stimulated Emission of Radiation*) The laser makes a beam of photons from excited atoms. Now used in medicine, surgery, welding, communications, underwater spotlights, photography, and many areas of chemistry, it was developed by Charles Townes (1955) through experimentation and application of quantum mechanical theory. Various substances—for example, carbon dioxide, CO_2, ammonia, NH_3, and ruby crystals—have an excited state that can be highly populated before returning to the ground state. 10^{23} electrons are excited 3.0×10^{-12} erg/electron above the ground state. When "triggered," *all* of the electrons return to the ground state at precisely the same time. (a) What is the energy output in ergs? (b) This process can be repeated every 10^{-4} s. What is the energy output in erg/s and in kcal/s? (c) The specific heat of solid and liquid iron averages 0.12 cal/(g °C), and its boiling point is 3000 °C. Can the laser raise the temperature of 10 g of iron to the boiling point from 25 °C in 10^{-4} s? Units: 4.2×10^7 ergs = 1 cal.

48 Electronic structure (a) Write the electronic structure for $_{16}S$, $_{22}Ti$, $_{26}Fe$, and $_{28}Ni$. (b) How many unpaired electrons are in each of these atoms? (c) Use Fig. 6.13, page 198, to predict the electronic structures of $_{29}Cu$, $_{32}Ge$, $_{35}Br$, and $_{46}Pd$.

Diagram for Problem 42

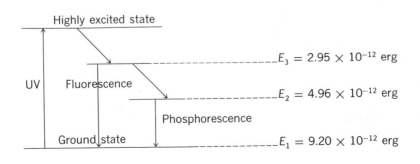

49 (a) How many s, p, and d electrons are in $_{20}Ca$, $_{22}Ti$, and $_{27}Co$? (b) An atom has its KL shells filled. What is its atomic number?

50 An atom has seven electrons. What is its (a) atomic number, (b) electronic structure, (c) number of s, p and d electrons, (d) number of unpaired electrons, (e) number of protons in its nucleus, (f) approximate atomic weight, (g) mass number, (h) number of neutrons in its nucleus?

51 What is the maximum number of electrons that can be put into each of the following subshells: $4d$, $5d$, $5f$, $6f$, $7p$, $8s$?

52 Paramagnetism Which of the following isolated particles possess paramagnetic properties?
(a) $_{21}Sc^+$, $KL3s^2\,3p^6\,3d^1\,4s^1$; (b) $_{21}Sc^{2+}$, $KL3s^2\,3p^6\,3d^1$;
(c) $_{21}Sc^{3+}$, $KL3s^2\,3p^6$; (d) $_{27}Co^+$, $KL3s^2\,3p^6\,3d^8$;
(e) $_{39}Y^+$, $KLM4s^2\,4p^6\,5s^2$; (f) $_{10}Ne$, $1s^2\,2s^2\,2p^6$;
(g) $_{10}Ne^+$, $1s^2\,2s^2\,2p^5$.

53 (a) The magnetic properties of $_{26}Fe^{2+}$ correspond to four unpaired electrons. Write the electronic structure of this ion. (b) How many unpaired electrons are there in $_{10}Ne$, $_{10}Ne^+$, and $_{10}Ne^{4+}$?

54 Pick the isolated atom that is not paramagnetic: $_{11}Na$, $_{12}Mg$, $_{13}Al$, $_{14}Si$, $_{15}P$, $_{16}S$, $_{17}Cl$.

55 Vision The human eye can detect one photon in the dark. Calculate (a) the energy of a photon of green light, 5.33×10^{-5} cm, and (b) the temperature rise for an eye with a mass of 3.0 g and specific heat of 0.90 cal/(g °C). See Problem 30 for equations and constants. 4.2×10^7 ergs = 1 cal.

56 (a) The human eye receives an 11.91×10^{-18} joule signal consisting of photons with $\lambda = 5.00 \times 10^{-5}$ cm. How many photons hit the eye? See Problem 30. 1 joule = 10^7 ergs. (b) An advertisement reads, "Special Film: It sees heat, not light." Explain.

57 Chlorophyll The emission spectrum of chlorophyll exhibits four lines in the visible range (red, yellow, blue, purple). Does chlorophyll absorb all wavelengths or only specific wavelengths of light? What colors will chlorophyll absorb? The Mg in the molecule is actually present as the ion Mg^{2+}. Mg^{2+} alone absorbs photons in the invisible ultraviolet range, but as part of the chlorophyll molecule, it absorbs photons in the visible range. Does the portion* of the molecule surrounding Mg^{2+} increase or decrease the energy differences between the energy states in Mg^{2+}? Explain.

58 Pollution (a) Rickets, the earliest air-pollution disease, was first described in England, about 1650, when soft coal was introduced. The black coal smoke produced sunless streets, blocking the sun's ultraviolet photons (2.92×10^{-5} cm) needed for the body to synthesize the hormone calciferol, $C_{28}H_{44}O$, which prevents rickets.* Find the energy difference between the two energy states resulting in the absorption of these photons. See Problem 30 for equations and constants. (b) Dyes fade and white skin "tans" under the influence of sunlight. Explain.

59 Experiment vs. theory Which of the following are observable? (a) position of electrons in atoms; (b) position of planets; (c) radiation emitted by atoms, molecules, and ions; (d) magnetic properties of matter; (e) electron spin; (f) energy states; (g) a photon; (h) a water wave; (i) a light wave.

60 Quantum mechanics (a) Did anyone prove that atoms and subatomic particles must obey classical mechanics? (b) Has anyone proved that an electron is shapeless? (c) Pick the correct statement: orbital shapes are (i) calculated from theory, (ii) established by experiment. (d) In studying the movements of an ordinary watch, is it possible to observe the exact positions of the moving parts at any instant? (e) Explain: (i) Quantum mechanics does *not* assign a definite position to a particle of known energy. (ii) In classical mechanics, the movement of an object is described; in quantum mechanics, the movement of a particle is not described. (iii) The energy of electrons moving about a nucleus cannot take on any random value.

61 Matter is quantized. Electricity is quantized. Light is quantized. Magnetism is quantized. Motion is quantized. Would you be shocked to learn that gravitation is also quantized? In simplest terms, how would you visualize quantized gravitation?

62 Library Read one of the following:

(a) "Physics in the Twentieth Century," Victor Weisskopf, *Science*, volume 168, 1970, pages 923–925.
(b) "The Light Side of Smog," Arie J. Haagen-Smit, *Chemical Technology*, June 1972, page 330.
(c) "What is Matter?" Erwin Schroedinger, *Scientific American*, September 1953, pages 52–57.
(d) "Microwave Radiation Hazards," William Mun-

---

*Known as *porphyrin*, a portion of many molecules such as hemoglobin and chlorophyll, it is so vital to life that the discovery of porphyrins in moon rocks or meteorites would be accepted as evidence of the existence of life outside of our world. A porphyrin molecule has been definitely identified (1970) in outer space.

---

*Rickets is not a dietary deficiency disease resulting from a lack of "vitamin D"; it results from a lack of sunlight. Readers interested in this subject are referred to an article by William Loomis in *Scientific American*, December 1970, page 77. Excessive vitamin D can result in hypercalcemia, too much calcium in the blood.

ford, *Proceedings of the Institute of Radio Engineers,* February 1961, pages 427–463.

(e) "Structure of the Atom," Ernest Rutherford, *Proceedings of the Royal Society,* Series 6, volume 27, 1914, page 488.

(f) "The Existence of a Neutron," James Chadwick, *Proceedings of the Royal Society,* volume A136, 1932, page 692.

(g) "Magnetic Fields of the Human Body," David Cohen, *Physics Today,* August 1975, page 35.

(h) "Biochemical Effects of Excited States of Molecular Oxygen," Jeffery Bland, *Journal of Chemical Education,* volume 53, May 1976, page 274.

(i) "Lasers: A Renaissance in Optics Research," Nicolaas Bloemberger, *American Scientist,* volume 63, Jan./Feb. 1975, page 63.

(j) "Operating with Light," Lois Wingerson, *The Sciences,* Aug./Sept. 1975, page 27; and "Lasers in Biomedicine: Analyzing and Sorting Cells," *Science,* volume 188, 1975, page 821.

ADDITIONAL PROBLEMS

63 Thales of Miletus (600 B.C.) believed, "There is but one basic stuff out of which all physical things are made." Praise and criticize this belief.

64 An electron in a hydrogen atom in the ground state has the quantum numbers $n = 1$, $l = 0$. Excitation changes the quantum numbers to $n = 4$, $l = 1$. What is the shape of the orbital occupied by the electron in the ground and excited states?

65 Write the electronic structures for the following atoms and ions: Ar, Cl^-, S^{2-}, and O^{2-}.

66 Given: (a) 138 kcal removes one electron from each atom in 1 mole of Al atoms. Find the ionization energy of Al in kcal/electron and in joules/electron. (b) Given: 2.79×10^{-18} joule excites one electron of the F atom from its ground state to infinity. Calculate the ionization energy of fluorine in J/atom, kcal/atom, kcal/mole F. See App. III.

67 The energy states in impure solid zinc sulfide,* ZnS, may be represented as shown below. ZnS absorbs photons, $hf = 5.0 \times 10^{-12}$ erg/photon. It then fluoresces (see Problem 42) in the visible range, $hf =$

4.4 $\times$ 10^{-12} erg/photon, and phosphoresces at 3.3 $\times$ 10^{-12} erg/photon. Assign energy values to E_2, E_3, and E_4. If an impurity separates E_2 further from E_1, will phosphorescence occur at the same, or shorter, or longer wavelength?

68 (a) Explain the absorption and emission of radiation (energy) by a hydrogen atom. (b) 104 kcal/mole H_2 (Chap. 9) are required to pull the H atoms apart in an H_2 molecule. Should a photon of red light, $\lambda = 650$ nm, break up the molecule? See App. III.

69 Chlorophyll absorbs blue light, $\lambda = 460$ nm, and emits red light, $\lambda = 660$ nm. Find the quantity of energy that chlorophyll dissipates in other ways, in ergs and kcal per mole of photons absorbed.

70 Explain in your own words: "The difference of quantum theory from classical theory is not that electrons do not possess definite particle properties like position and energy but rather that they lack laws that determine the future values of these properties." (Leslie Ballantine, 1975.)

71 (a) Explain how terpenes, hydrocarbons that evaporate into the air from plants and trees, may act as a natural sink (page 310) for ozone. (b) Would this action tend to reduce irritant production? (c) Explain: In some locations (*e.g.,* Los Angeles), air pollution problems can result even without automobiles.

---

*The coating on a television screen is ZnS "doped" with traces of a few metals. When hit by high-speed electrons, photons in the visible range are emitted. The metals used as the impurities influence the color emitted. Coatings on television "color sets" are more complex mixtures, but the principle is identical.

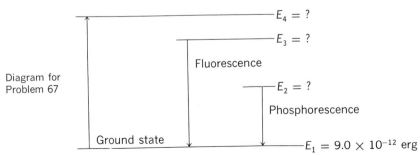

Diagram for Problem 67

$E_4 = ?$

$E_3 = ?$

Fluorescence

$E_2 = ?$

Phosphorescence

Ground state

$E_1 = 9.0 \times 10^{-12}$ erg

MINUTES	NO	NO$_2$	PROPENE, C$_3$H$_6$	PAN	O$_3$
0	0.450	0.050	0.500	0	0
17.1	0.245	0.245	0.409	0	0.0163
42.9	0.123	0.335	0.325	0.00409	0.0573
51.4	0.0785	—	—	—	0.0785
62.1	0.0573	0.349	0.278	0.0122	0.0900
98.6	0.0245	0.318	0.196	0.0245	0.196
180	0.0122	0.172	0.0785	0.0785	0.376
227	0.0122	0.106	0.0434	0.106	0.434
279	—	0.0573	—	0.131	0.458
360	0.0122	0.0327	0.0122	0.123	0.450

DATA FOR PROBLEM 76

72 The photon energy required for the photosynthesis reaction of water is 7.92×10^{-12} erg/molecule H$_2$O. Calculate the energy of a photon with $\lambda = 7.00 \times 10^{-5}$ cm (red). However, only 35 % of this energy is effectively used in photosynthesis. Find the minimum number of photons needed per H$_2$O molecule to drive the reaction.*

73 The visual receptors of a boa snake pass a signal to the brain when the radiation, $\lambda = 800$ nm, reaches an energy level of 2×10^{-14} joule/(μm^2 millisecond). (a) Find the smallest number of photons/(μm^2 millisecond) that must reach the receptors for vision. See App. II. (b) Would the human brain "see" such a radiation?

74 Some crystals, such as anthracene,** C$_{14}$H$_{10}$, have unusual energy states that cause two photons to combine without loss of energy. If two photons, $\lambda = 4.00 \times 10^{-5}$ cm and $\lambda = 3.50 \times 10^{-5}$ cm, are so combined, calculate the energy of the photon produced. Other crystals, such as tetracene, C$_{18}$H$_{12}$, permit one photon to split into two, each having about half the original energy. A photon, $\lambda = 4.60 \times 10^{-5}$ cm, splits into two. Find the energy of each photon.

75 3.0×10^4 joules/s of electricity have been transmitted one mile without the use of wires. The electricity is converted to photons, $f = 2.40 \times 10^9$ s^{-1}, beamed to a receiver, and reconverted to electricity. (a) Find the number of moles of photons transmitted per second. This transmission is similar, in principle, to what common appliances? What does this suggest regarding use of solar energy? (b) How many such photons per day would have to be beamed (100 % efficiency) to meet the needs of New York City, 4.3×10^{14} joules/day? See App. III. (c) If the efficiency of the solar energy collector is only 15 %, how many photons would have to be collected per day?

76 The results of a typical photochemical (about 340 nm) experiment carried out in a chamber are summarized in ppm by pressure of five initial substances as a function of time. See Table above. For each substance plot on the same graph paper the ppm (y-axis) as a function of time (x-axis). Describe the general features of the graphs. What substance(s) might serve as a source of PAN and ozone?

77 (a) Give the number of electrons occupying each of the subshells for which $n = 6$. (b) Give the values of n and l for each of the following subshells: (i) 1s, (ii) 2s, (iii) 2p, (iv) 3p, (v) 4s, (vi) 4d, (vii) 4f, (viii) 3d, (ix) 6d, (x) 7s, (xi) 6f. (c) An electron is assigned the following quantum numbers: $n = 3$, $l = 2$, $m_l = 0$, $m_s = +\frac{1}{2}$. Give the shell and subshell designation of the orbital occupied by the electron.

78 Answer each of the following as true or false: (a) All electrons in a given shell have the same energy. (b) All electrons in a given shell have the same distribution in space. (c) All electrons in a given orbital have the same energy. (d) All electrons in a given subshell have the same energy in the absence of a magnetic field. (e) An orbital in any given shell cannot be occupied by more than two electrons. (f) A subshell is occupied by the same maximum number of electrons independent of its principal quantum number.

---

*The energy relationships involving biochemical compounds are referred to as **bioenergetics.** All chemical and physical principles apply to biochemical reactions, even without the use of special labels.

**Used in the manufacture of dyes, drugs, perfumes, explosives, and plastics.

ANSWERS

4 no, nucleus

5 16, 16; 16, 17; 16, 18; 16, 20

7 (a) (b) 2.42×10^{-12} erg/atom; (c) 19.37×10^{-12} erg/atom

8 (c) 3s, 7s, 11s, 105s

9 (a) 175 ergs; (b) increased 175 ergs; (c) 175 ergs

10 (a) 4.576×10^{-12} erg/atom; (b) 20.92×10^{-12} erg/atom

11 (a) 1, 3, 5, 7, 9; (b) 25

12 5.875×10^{-5} cm

13 photon

14 3.381×10^{-12} erg/photon

15 wire at 1000 °C

16 4.576×10^{-12} erg/atom

17 (a) ten lines; (b) one

18 $2p$, $3s$, $3p$, $4s$, $3d$, $4p$, $5s$

19 $1s^2\, 2s^2\, 2p^5$

20 $1s^2\, 2s^2\, 2p^6\, 3s^2\, 3p^5$

21 $1s^2\, 2s^2\, 2p^6\, 3s^2\, 3p^6\, 4s^2\, 3d^7$

22 2, 2, 6, 6, 10, 10

23 Ne

24 $KL3s^2 3p^6 \underset{}{\underline{\downarrow\uparrow}}\ \underset{}{\underline{\downarrow\uparrow}}\ \underset{3d}{\underline{\downarrow\uparrow}\ \underline{\downarrow}\ \underline{\downarrow}}\ \underset{4s}{\underline{\downarrow\uparrow}}$; 2

26 (a) (i) 62 neutrons (n) 50 protons (p); 65n 50p; 68n 50p; 74n 50p; (ii) 34n 30p; 36n 30p; 42n 30p; (b) 23, 17, 52, 19n; (c) $^{210}_{84}$Po or $^{210}_{84}$Po$^+$, $^{214}_{84}$Po, $^{218}_{84}$Po; 126n 84p; 130n 84p; 134n 84p

27 (a) 112n 78p; 116n 78p; 118n 78p; 120n 78p; (b) $^{197}_{79}$Au

28 (a) electrical; (c) zero

29 1.51×10^3 m/min, 90.6 km/h

30 (a) 2.152×10^{15} s^{-1}; 1.426×10^{-11} erg/photon; (b) 0.333 cm, 5.97×10^{-16} erg/photon

31 (a) 5.97×10^{14} s^{-1}, 3.96×10^{-12} erg/photon, 3.96×10^{-9} erg; (b) 3.11×10^2 cm, 6.38×10^{-19} erg/photon

32 (a) 1.65×10^{-10} mole, 9.93×10^{13} photons, 8.33×10^{14} s^{-1}; (b) 6.03×10^{12} s^{-1}, 4.00×10^{-14} erg/photon

33 4.5579×10^{-12} erg/atom

34 (a) 21.79×10^{-12} erg/atom, 1.312×10^{13} erg/mole, 313.6 kcal/mole, 1.312×10^6 J/mole; (b) 6.053×10^{-12} erg/atom, 3.645×10^{12} erg/mole

35 6.42×10^{-12} erg/ion

36 (a) 1.976×10^{-15} erg/atom; (b) 1.976×10^{-15} erg/atom, 1.190×10^9 ergs/mole

37 (a) $n = 3$, 3 lines; (b) E_4, 6 lines

38 (a) 1.816×10^{-12} erg; (b) 21.79×10^{-12} erg

39 (a) 4 photons; (b) 21.79348×10^{-12} erg; (c) no

40 2 excited (plus ground) states

41 9.496×10^{-6} cm

42 6.40×10^{14} s^{-1}; 4.68×10^{-5} cm

44 Be

46 (b) s

47 (a) 3.0×10^{11} ergs; (b) 3.0×10^{15} ergs/s, 7.1×10^4 kcal/s; (c) yes

48 (b) 2, 2, 4, 2 unpaired; (c) $4s^2 3d^9$, $4s^2 4p^2$, $4s^2 4p^5$, $5s^2 4d^8$; see App. IV for Cu and Pd correct structures

49 (a) 8, 12; 8, 12, 2; 8, 12, 7; (b) 10

50 (a) 7; (b) $1s^2\, 2s^2\, 2p^3$; (c) 4, 3, 0; (d) 3; (e) 7; (f) 14; (g) 14; (h) 7

51 10, 10, 14, 14, 6, 2

52 (a) (b) (d) (g)

53 (a) $3d^6 4s^0$; (b) 0, 1, 2

54 $_{12}$Mg

55 (a) 3.73×10^{-12} erg; (b) 3.3×10^{-20} °C

56 30 photons

57 red, yellow, blue, purple; decrease

58 6.80×10^{-12} erg

59 (b) (c) (d) (h)

60 (a) (b) no; (c) (i); (d) yes

64 s, p

65 Ar, Cl$^-$, S^{2-}: $KL3s^2\, 3p^6$; O^{2-}: KL

66 (a) 2.29×10^{-22} kcal/electron, 9.58×10^{-19} J/electron; (b) 2.79×10^{-18} J/atom, 6.67×10^{-22} kcal/atom, 402 kcal/mole

67 $E_4 = 4.0 \times 10^{-12}$, $E_3 = 4.6 \times 10^{-12}$, $E_2 = 5.7 \times 10^{-12}$ erg; shorter

68 no

69 7.89×10^{11} ergs/mole, 18.8 kcal/mole

71 (b) no

72 2.84×10^{-12} erg/photon, 8 photons

73 (a) 8×10^4 photons/(μm^2 ms); (b) no

74 (a) 10.65×10^{-12} erg/photon; (b) 2.16×10^{-12} erg/photon

75 (a) 3.14×10^4 mole/s wireless telegraphy, T.V., radio; (b) 2.7×10^{38} photons/day; (c) 1.8×10^{39} photons/day

76 PAN (C_3H_6, NO, NO_2); O_3 (NO, NO_2)

77 (a) $6s^2$, $6p^6$, $6d^{10}$, $6f^{14}$, $6g^{18}$, $6h^{22}$; (b) 1,0; 2,0; 2,1; 3,1; 4,0; 4,2; 4,3; 3,2; 6,2; 7,0; 6,3; (c) $3d$

78 (a) (b) false; (c) (d) (e) (f) true

GLOSSARY

atomic number The number of protons in the nucleus of an atom.

atomic nucleus The extremely small region of matter at the center of an atom in which practically all of the mass of the atom is located. Protons and neutrons make up the nucleus.

atomic orbital The region of space about an atomic nucleus in which an electron has a comparatively high chance of being found. Typical atomic orbitals have the letter designations s, p, and d. An orbital can house only two electrons.

electronic structure of atoms The number of electrons in an atom is the same as the number of protons in its nucleus. The electronic structure shows the distribution of these electrons in atomic orbitals by listing the occupied orbitals ($s, p, d, \ldots$) and their principal quantum number, n. The number of electrons housed is written as a superscript to the right of the orbital letter, for example, $_{11}$Na, $1s^2\, 2s^2\, 2p^6\, 3s^1$.

element A substance composed of atoms with the same atomic number.

energy state diagram A set of characteristic energy states (see **energy states**).

energy states A set of characteristic energy values available to a particular atom or molecule, or to an electron in an atom or molecule. These energy values are the energies needed to ionize the atom or molecule. See **quantization of energy.**

excited state The energy state in which at least one electron of an atom or molecule is not in the lowest energy state available to it. Less energy is needed to ionize an atom or molecule in an excited state than in the ground state. Excited states are unstable with respect to the ground state.

ground state The energy state in which all of the electrons of an atom or molecule are in the lowest energy states available to them.

mass number The sum of the number of protons and neutrons in the nucleus of an atom, the nearest whole number to the atomic weight of an atom.

neutron An electrically neutral particle with nearly the same mass as a proton, mass number 1.

nuclear atom An atomic nucleus (see **atomic nucleus**) surrounded by electrons (see **electronic structure of atoms**).

Pauli exclusion principle No more than two electrons can occupy an orbital.

photochemistry Chemical reactions of excited substances resulting from the interactions of matter and radiation.

photon The "atom of light"; its energy is given by $h \times f$, Planck's constant times the frequency of the light.

photosynthesis The manufacture of sugars, starch, cellulose, and other complex compounds from CO_2 and H_2O by plants capable of using sunlight as an energy source.

quantization of energy The energy of atoms or molecules is restricted to certain values; see **energy states.**

quantum mechanics The mathematical equation which, when solved, gives the chances of finding a particle such as an electron in a given region of space about the atomic nucleus, an *orbital*, and the characteristic energy of the particle in that particular (orbital) region of space.

quantum numbers Four natural numbers, symbolized as n, l, m_l, m_s, that determine the energy of electrons in atoms; n is called the *principal quantum number* because, in the absence of an external magnetic field, it determines the energy of an electron in an atom for all practical purposes.

shell The set of atomic orbitals having the same principal quantum number, n, called the K shell when $n = 1$, L when $n = 2$, and so on.

smog, photochemical The production of harmful and irritating pollutants by the action of sunlight on auto and industrial emissions.

spectrum A pattern of characteristic wavelengths produced by electron transitions between two energy states. An *emission spectrum* is the spectrum obtained when light is emitted from a source. A *line spectrum,* consisting of several colored lines, and a *continuous spectrum,* consisting of a continuous band of colors from red to violet, are typical emission spectra.

subshell The set of atomic orbitals having the same principal quantum number, n, and the same orbital letter designation. For example, the M shell has three subshells: the one $3s$ orbital, the three $3p$ orbitals, and the five $3d$ orbitals.

ставляемаго мною начала ко всей совокупности элементовъ, пай
которыхъ извѣстенъ съ достовѣрностію. На этотъ разъ я и желалъ
преимущественно найдти общую систему элементовъ. Вотъ этотъ
опытъ:

		Ti=50	Zr=90	?=180.
		V=51	Nb=94	Ta=182.
		Cr=52	Mo=96	W=186.
		Mn=55	Rh=104,4	Pt=197,4
		Fe=56	Ru=104,4	Ir=198.
		Ni=Co=59	Pl=106,6	Os=199.
H=1		Cu=63,4	Ag=108	Hg=200.
Be=9,4	Mg=24	Zn=65,2	Cd=112	
B=11	Al=27,4	?=68	Ur=116	Au=197?
C=12	Si=28	?=70	Sn=118	
N=14	P=31	As=75	Sb=122	Bi=210
O=16	S=32	Se=79,4	Te=128?	
F=19	Cl=35,5	Br=80	I=127	
Li=7 Na=23	K=39	Rb=85,4	Cs=133	Tl=204
	Ca=40	Sr=87,6	Ba=137	Pb=207.
	?=45	Ce=92		
	?Er=56	La=94		
	?Yt=60	Di=95		
	?In=75,6	Th=118?		

а потому приходится въ разныхъ рядахъ имѣть различное измѣненіе разностей,
чего нѣтъ въ главныхъ числахъ предлагаемой таблицы. Или же придется предпо-
лагать при составленіи системы очень много недостающихъ членовъ. То и
другое мало выгодно. Мнѣ кажется притомъ, наиболѣе естественнымъ составить
кубическую систему (предлагаемая есть плоскостная), но и попытки для ея образо-
ванія не повели къ надлежащимъ результатамъ. Слѣдующія двѣ попытки могутъ по-
казать то разнообразіе сопоставленій, какое возможно при допущеніи основнаго
начала, высказаннаго въ этой статьѣ.

Li	Na	K	Cu	Rb	Ag	Cs	—	Tl
7	23	39	63,4	85,4	108	133		204
Be	Mg	Ca	Zn	Sr	Cd	Ba	—	Pb
B	Al	—	—	—	Ur	—	—	Bi?
C	Si	Ti	—	Zr	Sn	—	—	—
N	P	V	As	Nb	Sb	—	Ta	—
O	S	—	Se	—	Te	—	W	
F	Cl	—	Br	—	J			

REGULARITIES IN THE PROPERTIES OF ELEMENTS

7

Before the nineteenth century, chemists had performed many experiments and developed considerable information about the approximately 60 elements then known. During these years, the discovery of each new element was a problem of reaching into the unknown. Chemists had no way to predict the existence of elements. They also had no way to foretell the general chemical and physical properties of newly discovered elements. Each new element apparently had unique properties that distinguished it from any other element. Nevertheless, although no two elements are exactly alike, certain similarities among some of the elements were observed. Chemists began to look for some scheme to link elements together.

One objective of scientific research is to attempt to find order in nature. Classification, or arrangement of known facts, is one way to recognize this order. This search for order has benefited many fields of knowledge. Biologists, for example, have developed schemes to classify living organisms into such groups as fishes, reptiles, mammals, insects, and flowers. Schemes have also been devised in art so that the artists may be classified as belonging to certain schools.

In the nineteenth century, chemists looked for a system that would classify known elements into related groups. A general method of classification took advantage of the distinction between metals and nonmetals. The chemical behavior of metals will be discussed later (Chap. 20), but their ability to conduct heat and electricity is well known. Since there are many more metals than nonmetals, this classification into two groups was not very helpful. However, the idea began to emerge that there did exist a scheme for distinguishing groups of elements that depended on their atomic weights.

As early as 1820, it was observed that substances with similar properties could be

221

grouped together. In these classifications, relationships were established between two elements (pairs), or three elements (triads).*

By about 1860, Avogadro's law (page 135) was generally accepted. The combining power or valence (page 148) of elements was also known. For example, 1 atom of sodium combines with 1 atom of chlorine to form sodium chloride (NaCl), but 1 atom of calcium combines with 2 atoms of chlorine to yield calcium chloride ($CaCl_2$). However, the compilation of reliable atomic weights provided the starting point for a more useful grouping of elements.

7.2 —————— CLASSIFICATION OF THE ELEMENTS: THE PERIODIC TABLE

Evaluation of available information gradually led to the concept that elements form groups in which the members have closely related chemical and physical properties. As happens with many significant innovations, the necessary information was available, but it had to wait for someone with sufficient imagination and ingenuity to piece it all together, to correlate the data.

Such correlation was attempted by several scientists, but the most useful classifications evolved from the ideas of John Newlands (1864), and Dmitrii Mendeleev and Julius Lothar Meyer (1869).

Newlands proposed that if elements were arranged according to increasing atomic weights, the chemical and physical properties of a particular element would be similar to those of the elements seven places before and seven places after it. For example, he noted that lithium, the second element in his list, had properties similar to sodium, the ninth in the list, and potassium, the sixteenth element. Thus, these three similar elements were related by the numbers 2, 9, and 16, which show intervals of seven [2 (+7), 9 (+7), 16]. This same orderly arrangement occurred with other elements. For example, beryllium, magnesium, and calcium—the third, tenth, and seventeenth elements in his list—were also separated by regular intervals of seven—3, 10, 17. The resemblance to the musical scale led Newlands, who was interested in music, to name his arrangement the law of octaves.**

The Royal Society of London honored Newlands with the Davy Medal five years after Mendeleev and Meyer received the medal.

Although the law of octaves was originally ridiculed, years later Newlands received the Davy Medal for his contribution. The Newlands classification did indeed have very limited application. However, his arrangement of the elements into a repeating pattern was a major breakthrough.

---

*In 1829, Johann Döbereiner made an important first step toward a systematic classification by arranging elements into groups of three (triads). He noticed that the atomic weight of the middle element of the group was midway between the atomic weights of the other two. He also concluded that the same midpoint relationship held for the physical properties of these elements. Two of his "triads" are illustrated:

Element	Approximate Atomic Weight	Average Atomic Weight of 1st and 3rd Element in the Triad
Lithium	7	
Sodium	23	$\frac{7 + 39}{2} = 23$
Potassium	39	
Chlorine	36	
Bromine	80	$\frac{36 + 127}{2} = 82$
Iodine	127	

**The musical scale, "do, re, mi, fa, sol, la, ti, do," known as an octave, also has seven notes before the "do" is repeated. Modern developments in quantum mechanics have shown that the relationships of Newland's classification of the elements to the musical scale is not so far fetched. Sounds made by musical instruments are known to have sound spectra analogous to the line spectra of atoms. Like the wavelengths emitted by atoms, the wave-like vibrations of a guitar string are also quantized.

In 1869, Meyer and Mendeleev attempted to organize the available data into some reasonable arrangement for the textbooks that they were writing. Although approaching the problem differently, they independently arrived at a similar classification of the then-known elements. While examining relationships between atomic weights and data on the physical and chemical properties of elements, Mendeleev and Meyer were impressed by the periodicity of properties; that is, *the appearance of similar properties, again and again, at regular intervals.* Although both chemists are acknowledged for their descriptions of the classification of the elements, the Mendeleev approach proved more successful and is explained here. He summarized his conclusions in the **Periodic law;** the chemical properties of elements change in an orderly way with the atomic weight.

Mendeleev also did not achieve instant recognition for his accomplishments. In 1880, opposition of conservative members prevented his election to the St. Petersburg Academy of Science. His involvement with students in their extracurricular activities as well as with their studies led him to deliver a petition, on their behalf, to the ministry of education. As a result, he was politely asked to resign from a teaching position at the University where he had taught for more than thirty years. "At his death from heart failure, students followed his funeral to the Volkov Cemetery in St. Petersburg carrying the periodic table of the elements high above the procession as the fitting emblem of Mendeleev's career."

RELATIONSHIP OF CHEMICAL PROPERTIES TO ATOMIC WEIGHTS _____ 7.3

Mendeleev based his periodic arrangement on valence, the number describing the capacity of an element to combine with other elements. In his textbook, Men-

TABLE 7.1
PERIODIC TABLE OF THE ELEMENTS
(ADAPTED FROM MENDELEEV, 1871)*

Groups:	I		II		III		IV		V		VI		VII		VIII
General formulas:	R_2O		RO		R_2O_3		RH_4		RH_3		RH_2		RH		RO_4
	RCl		RCl_2		RCl_3		RO_2		R_2O_5		RO_3		R_2O_7		
Family:	A	B	A	B	A	B	A	B	A	B	A	B	A	B	
1		H													
2	Li		Be		B		C		N		O		F		
3		Na		Mg		Al		Si		P		S		Cl	
4	K		Ca				Ti		V		Cr		Mn		Fe, Co, Ni
5		Cu		Zn						As		Se		Br	
6	Rb		Sr		Yt?		Zr		Nb		Mo				Ru, Rh, Pd
7		Ag		Cd		In		Sn		Sb		Te		I	
8	Cs		Ba		Di?		Ce?								
9															
10					Er?		La?		Ta		W				Os, Ir, Pt
11		Au		Hg		Tl		Pb		Bi					
12							Th				U				

*The A and B subdivisions, not important for the moment, are discussed on page 227.

deleev organized the chapters according to a regular increase and decrease in valence; for example, valence of 1 for lithium, 2 for beryllium, 3 for boron, 4 for carbon, 5 and 3 for nitrogen, 6 and 2 for oxygen, 7 and 1 for fluorine, and then starting again with 1 for sodium. In this way, elements with similar valences and similar chemical properties were grouped together. In this attempt to relate these valences and properties to physical properties, his main emphasis was on atomic weights. Therefore, he arranged the elements in the order of increasing atomic weights in horizontal rows and vertical columns, as shown in Table 7.1.

From his table, Mendeleev concluded that the chemical properties of the elements are periodic; that is, the properties repeat at regular intervals. Thus, we see that elements in a given vertical column, called a **group,** have the same valence. They also have similar chemical properties. For example, lithium and cesium both displace hydrogen from water, although the speed of the reaction differs. The horizontal rows emphasize the differences in the chemical behavior of each element with increasing atomic weight.

Examine Table 7.1 and notice the gaps—for example, those following zinc in series 5. If the gaps were closed by moving arsenic, As, selenium, Se, and bromine, Br, two spaces to the left, arsenic would fall under aluminum. But the chemical reactions of arsenic are more like those of phosphorus. Therefore, arsenic belongs in Group V. Mendeleev tried to avoid such inconsistencies in his table. Besides placing the known elements where they apparently belonged, he boldly predicted that elements would be discovered to fill the gaps. He further predicted the properties that these undiscovered elements would have.

A tribute was paid to Mendeleev (1955) when the synthesized element 101 was named mendelevium.

Mendeleev's predictions proved amazingly accurate. For example, when germanium was discovered, its properties were found to be remarkably close to those predicted by Mendeleev for *eka*-silicon (Table 7.2). He also predicted the existence and properties of gallium (*eka*-aluminum) and scandium (*eka*-boron).

eka is Sanskrit for one below; eka-silicon is one below silicon.

A successful scientific theory (page 4) has to accomplish three objectives:

TABLE 7.2
PREDICTED AND OBSERVED PROPERTIES
OF GERMANIUM

| PROPERTY | "EKA-SILICON"—GERMANIUM (Ge) | | |
	PREDICTED IN 1871 BY MENDELEEV	REPORTED IN 1886 BY CLEMENS WINKLER	CURRENTLY ACCEPTED
Atomic weight	72	72.32	72.59
Density	5.5	5.47	5.35
Melting point	High	—	947 °C
Specific heat, cal/(g °C)	0.073	0.076	0.074
Molar volume*	13	13.22	13.6
Color	Dark gray	Grayish white	Grayish white
Valence	4	4	4
Reaction with HCl and NaOH	Es will be slightly attacked by acids such as HCl, but will resist attack by NaOH	Ge is not dissolved by either HCl or dilute NaOH, but is dissolved by concentrated NaOH	Ge is not dissolved by either HCl or dilute NaOH, but is dissolved by concentrated NaOH
Density of GeO$_2$	4.7	4.703	4.228
Boiling point of GeCl$_4$	100 °C	86 °C	84 °C

*The volume occupied by 1 mole of solid element, cm^3/mole.

Its agreement with experimental observations must be acceptable. For example, Table 7.2 shows the close agreement between predicted and observed values.

It must tie together seemingly unrelated observations; for example, atomic weight and chemical properties.

It must successfully predict future discoveries or stimulate scientists to perform experiments not previously conceived. Validation of a prediction provides strong support for a theory. Although it increases its acceptance, it does not prove the theory, since theories are modified by the acquisition of new knowledge. The end of this process is never achieved.

Mendeleev's views on periodicity were not immediately accepted. However, they rapidly gained favor when gallium was discovered and its properties were shown to be very similar to the predicted values.

Periodicity is still useful for predicting properties of yet-to-be discovered elements. In recent years, Glenn Seaborg and his co-workers have synthesized the so-called transuranic elements (elements heavier than uranium) by nuclear reactions (Chap. 17) and accurately predicted the properties of these elements based on their positions in the periodic table.

MODERN PERIODIC TABLE _____ 7.4

Mendeleev's table, modified to include later developments, was in use until about 1950, at which time the so-called long-period form, shown in Table 7.3, was formulated. This is the form that is now used by most scientists. A major modification is the arrangement of elements in order of increasing atomic numbers rather than increasing atomic weights.

Interestingly, this form of the periodic table was originally prepared by Julius Thomsen in 1895.

Advantages of the Periodic Table   The major advantage of the periodic table is its usefulness in systematizing chemistry. Elements are grouped to show similarities and differences and even to reveal trends in properties. Instead of listing separate details about each element, similar properties of each group of elements can be learned. The periodic table thus simplifies the study of the properties of the elements.

In the early years, because of its relationship to atomic weights, the table could not account for the properties of the elements in terms of the nuclear charges of atoms. Chemical reactions, we believe, are dependent on the electronic structure of the atoms (Chap. 8). Atoms with similar electronic structures should therefore behave similarly. When elements are arranged so that those with the same electronic structure are grouped together, periodicity becomes evident. For example, fluorine and chlorine each have seven electrons in their highest shell, and they are chemically alike. Both elements, for example, combine with hydrogen and sodium to form similar types of compounds: $HF(g)$ and $HCl(g)$, $NaF(c)$ and $NaCl(c)$.

The modern periodic table shows electronic as well as chemical relationships. The long form shows not only the position of the element in the periodic table, but also the number of electrons in the shells as well as the nuclear charge. In this form of the table elements appear in blocks. In each block, elements are filling s, p, d, or f orbitals (Table 7.4). The s block contains two groups in which the last electron entering the atom goes into the s orbital. The p block is six elements wide; the last entering electron is in a p orbital. Similarly, the d block is 10 elements wide, and the f block is 14 elements wide.

Table 7.3 has 16 vertical columns (groups), labeled IA, IIA, IIIB and so on to 0. These groups, also called **families,** consist of elements with closely related physical

TABLE 7.3
PERIODIC TABLE, THE LONG-PERIOD FORM*

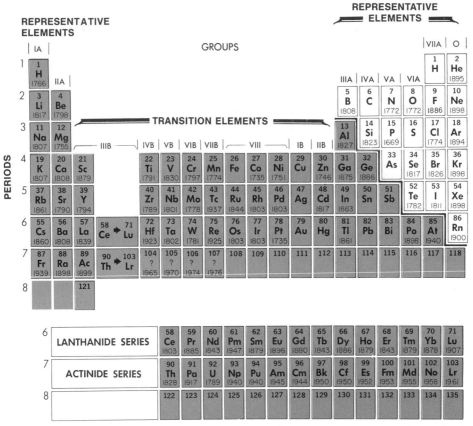

*The heavy line approximately separates the metallic elements, to the left, from the nonmetallic elements, to the right. Elements 104, 105, 106, and 107 have not been officially named by the International Union of Pure and Applied Chemistry (page 147). Besides the atomic numbers, the dates of discovery of the elements are given. The elements with no given dates were known to the ancients.

and chemical properties. The horizontal rows of elements are called **periods** and are numbered from the top to the bottom. The properties of elements within a period vary gradually from those having a highly metallic character, meaning a tendency to form a positive ion like Na $\longrightarrow$ Na$^+$ + e^-, at the left side, to those with a highly nonmetallic (electronegative) character, meaning a tendency to form a negative ion like Cl + e^- $\longrightarrow$ Cl$^-$, at the right side.

The heavy black line drawn in Table 7.3 separates the metallic from the non-metallic elements, but the division is not sharp. In fact, the elements along the line are known as *semiconductors,* and show both metallic and nonmetallic characteristics. Silicon and germanium are typical semiconductors whose distinctive features are discussed later (Chap. 20).

Derived from metallon, *the Greek word for mine.*

Although *metal* is a commonly used word, its usage in science is restricted to those elements that are good heat and electrical conductors (Chap. 20). Chemically, metals are also characterized by their tendency to give up electrons to form positively charged ions; metals are therefore referred to as *electropositive* elements. Boron, for example, has a lesser tendency than aluminum, Group IIIA, to form a positive ion and is said to be less electropositive.

TABLE 7.4
THE *s, p, d,* AND *f* BLOCKS OF THE PERIODIC TABLE*

*n is the principal quantum number, page 184. See App. IV for disagreement between predicted and experimental electronic structures.

On the other hand, because the nonmetallic elements tend to gain electrons, they are referred to as *electronegative* elements. In general, metallic character increases from top to bottom within a group.

To gain an insight into the reasons for the gradual change in properties, the so-called trends across and down the table, we shall study the table in some detail.

Group IB (Cu ⟶ Au) and Group IIB (Zn ⟶ Hg) are exceptions.

DIVISIONS OF THE PERIODIC TABLE————————7.5

Special names are given to sections of the table. Since chemists are not yet in complete agreement regarding these names and arrangements, we list below only those most often used (also see Tables 7.3 and 7.4).

NAME	PROPERTIES
Representative Elements	Electron enters an *s* or *p* subshell. This subgroup is designated A.
Transition Elements	Electron enters a *d* or *f* subshell. These elements are designated B.
Lanthanide and Actinide Series	Electron enters an *f* subshell. The lanthanides, elements 58 to 71, are built up by addition to the 4*f* subshell, while the actinides, elements 90 to 103, are built up by addition to the 5*f* subshell.

In comparison with the representative elements, the change in properties among the transition elements is not as great. For example, the transition elements, scandium, Sc, to zinc, Zn, in period 4 are rather closely related to each other, and all are metals. On the other hand, the representative elements in period 3 are not related to each other; sodium, Na, is a typical metal while chlorine, Cl, is a typical nonmetal.

Another characteristic feature of the transition elements is their ability to form compounds in which they have different valences; for example, the oxides of vanadium include VO, V_2O_3, VO_2, and V_2O_5.

The lanthanides (elements 58 to 71), in the sixth period, are very closely related to each other. For example, the electronic structure for cerium, $_{58}Ce$ (App. IV), includes $4f^2 5s^2 5p^6 6s^2$, and for samarium $_{62}Sm$, $4f^6 5s^2 5p^6 6s^2$. This similarity in electronic structure makes these elements so much alike in properties that it was very difficult to identify and separate them until recent times.

All of the actinides in the seventh period are radioactive (Chap. 17); only uranium and thorium are found naturally in significant amounts.

PROBLEM 1 Use the periodic table to classify the following elements as representative, transition, lanthanide, or actinide: Na, Cs, Sr, Ba, Zr, Xe, Ce, Al, C, O, I, F, Ni, U. Name these elements.

7.6 _____ GROUP IA ELEMENTS

The Group IA elements, also known as the **alkali metals,** are listed below:

ELEMENT	PERIOD NUMBER	SYMBOL	CHARACTERISTIC ELECTRONIC STRUCTURE	M.P.	B.P.
Lithium	2	$_3Li$	$2s^1$	180.54 °C	1347 °C
Sodium	3	$_{11}Na$	$3s^1$	97.81 °C	882.9 °C
Potassium	4	$_{19}K$	$4s^1$	63.65 °C	774 °C
Rubidium	5	$_{27}Rb$	$5s^1$	38.89 °C	688 °C
Cesium	6	$_{55}Cs$	$6s^1$	28.40 °C	678.4 °C
Francium	7	$_{87}Fr$	$7s^1$	(27 °C)	(677 °C)

These elements are characterized by an s^1 electronic structure, one electron in their highest shell. Their valence is therefore 1 and they generally form ionic compounds (Chap. 8) that are very soluble in water. These elements are the most reactive metals. For example, they react very rapidly with cold water, producing hydrogen and hydroxides while generating dangerous amounts of heat:

$$2Na(c) + 2H_2O(l) \longrightarrow H_2(g) + 2NaOH(aq)$$

The resulting hydroxide solutions are said to be "basic." This means that they make the skin feel slippery, "a soapy feeling," and they turn red litmus, a natural dye, blue. Acids and bases are discussed in Chap. 13.

The alkali metals also react violently with nonmetallic elements like fluorine and chlorine, forming fluorides and chlorides:

$$2Na(c) + F_2(g) \longrightarrow 2NaF(c)$$

In the gaseous state, they form diatomic molecules like Li_2 and K_2.

The alkali metals are soft enough to be easily cut with a knife. They must, however, be held with tongs since the moisture on fingers is sufficient to cause a reaction.* These metals readily emit electrons under the impact of light:

$$Cs(c) + hf \longrightarrow Cs^+(c) + e^-$$

In particular, cesium is widely used in photoelectric cells (page 232).

GROUP IB ELEMENTS _____ 7.7

ELEMENT	PERIOD NUMBER	SYMBOL	CHARACTERISTIC ELECTRONIC STRUCTURE	M.P.	B.P.
Copper	4	$_{29}Cu$	$3d^{10}\,4s^1$	1083.4 °C	2567 °C
Silver	5	$_{47}Ag$	$4d^{10}\,5s^1$	961.93 °C	2212 °C
Gold	6	$_{79}Au$	$5d^{10}\,6s^1$	1064.4 °C	2807 °C

The elements in this group are named the **coinage metals** because of their comparative lack of reactivity. Their attractive finish, relative scarcity, and resistance to corrosion make them useful for jewelry and coinage systems. Gold is also used for coating the surface of electrical equipment designed for space exploration. These metals are relatively soft and can be pounded so thin that, for example, gold leaf can be made to transmit light.

Silver coins were first struck about 650 B.C. in the Asia Minor kingdom of Lydia.

The nonreactivity of these elements differs radically from the activity of the alkali metals. Their properties, in fact, are more like those of transition metals. Their properties differ from those of the alkali metals because the d^{10} electrons may participate in chemical reactions (Chap. 8).

While $Ag^+(aq)$ is colorless, $Cu^{2+}(aq)$ is pale blue. White $CuSO_4(c)$, green $CuCl_2(c)$, and brown $CuBr_2(c)$ dissolve in water producing $Cu(H_2O)_4^{2+}$, characterized by a pale blue color. Addition of ammonia changes the color of the solution to a deep blue, a characteristic property of $Cu(NH_3)_4^{2+}$. The color of $Cu(NH_3)_4^{2+}$ is therefore used to test for the presence of $Cu^{2+}(aq)$.

The origin of these color changes is discussed in Chap. 21.

GROUP IIA ELEMENTS _____ 7.8

ELEMENT	PERIOD NUMBER	SYMBOL	CHARACTERISTIC ELECTRONIC STRUCTURE	M.P.	B.P.
Beryllium	2	$_4Be$	$2s^2$	1278 °C	2970 °C
Magnesium	3	$_{12}Mg$	$3s^2$	648.8 °C	1090 °C
Calcium	4	$_{20}Ca$	$4s^2$	839 °C	1484 °C
Strontium	5	$_{38}Sr$	$5s^2$	769 °C	1384 °C
Barium	6	$_{56}Ba$	$6s^2$	725 °C	1640 °C
Radium	7	$_{88}Ra$	$7s^2$	700 °C	1140 °C

---

*Warning: Never handle alkali metals with bare fingers, and never add them to water. Alkali metals are usually stored in a vacuum or under kerosene to protect the metal from air and moisture.

This group is named the **alkaline earth metals.** In the early days of chemistry, insoluble solid oxides, called "earths," were discovered. These compounds remain unchanged in a fire and have properties in common with the hydroxides of the alkali metals. Lime, CaO, used in the preparation of mortar to lay bricks and stones since prehistoric times, is a typical "earth." When the oxide is mixed with water, the hydroxide is formed:

$$CaO(c) + H_2O(l) \longrightarrow Ca(OH)_2(aq)$$

Magnesia, MgO, is another typical Group IIA oxide.

The alkaline earth metals are quite reactive, although they do not generally react as rapidly as the alkali metals. Characterized by an s^2 electronic structure, with two electrons in their highest shell, they generally form 2^+ ions when two electrons are removed:

$$Ba(c) + 2H_2O(l) \longrightarrow H_2(g) + Ba(OH)_2(aq)$$
$$Ba(c) + F_2(g) \longrightarrow BaF_2(c)$$

These metals have a grayish-white luster when freshly cut but readily tarnish on exposure to air. At high temperatures, they react at dangerous speeds with the release of much heat:

$$2Mg(c) + O_2(g) \longrightarrow 2MgO(c)$$

However, the thin oxide coating formed on beryllium and magnesium is sufficiently strong and adhering (difficult to remove and does not break or crumble) to protect the metal, at ordinary temperatures, from further attack by oxygen. This stability of the coating accounts for the use of magnesium as a structural material.

Compared with compounds of the alkali metals, many compounds of the alkaline earth metals are relatively insoluble (App. VII).

PROBLEM 2   Write (a) the formulas of the products, and (b) the balanced equation for each reaction:

$$\mathbf{Cs}(c) + \mathbf{H_2O}(l) \longrightarrow$$
$$\mathbf{Na}(c) + \mathbf{Cl_2}(g) \longrightarrow$$
$$\mathbf{Ca}(c) + \mathbf{F_2}(g) \longrightarrow$$
$$\mathbf{Mg}(c) + \mathbf{Br_2}(g) \longrightarrow$$

7.9 _____ GROUP IIIA ELEMENTS

ELEMENT	PERIOD NUMBER	SYMBOL	CHARACTERISTIC ELECTRONIC STRUCTURE	M.P.	B.P.
Boron	2	$_5B$	$2s^2\, 2p^1$	2300 °C	2550 °C (sublimes)
Aluminum	3	$_{13}Al$	$3s^2\, 3p^1$	660.37 °C	2467 °C
Gallium	4	$_{31}Ga$	$4s^2\, 4p^1$	29.78 °C	2403 °C
Indium	5	$_{49}In$	$5s^2\, 5p^1$	156.61 °C	2080 °C
Thallium	6	$_{81}Tl$	$6s^2\, 6p^1$	303.5 °C	1457 ± 10 °C

In this group, boron is a nonmetallic solid while the other members are metals. They generally exhibit a valence of 3, associated with their electron structure.

Aluminum, a reactive metal, like magnesium, forms a protective oxide coating of Al_2O_3 that makes possible its use in cooking utensils, tank-car containers, and electrical equipment, and as a structural material. High strength aluminum alloys protected the Apollo moon rockets. Aluminum oxide, Al_2O_3, found in nature as *corundum*, is sufficiently hard to be used as an abrasive in grinding wheels and emery powders.

Breakage of the Al_2O_3 film in a tank truck carrying liquid oxygen resulted in the death of the driver.

Like the alkali and alkaline earth metals, aluminum displaces hydrogen from acid solutions, provided that a protective oxide coating does not form:

$$2Al(c) + 6HCl(aq) \longrightarrow 2AlCl_3(aq) + 3H_2(g)$$

Interestingly, aluminum does not displace hydrogen from water because of the formation of the protective oxide coating. However, the addition of alkali hydroxides liberates hydrogen as these hydroxides dissolve the protective coating:

$$2Al(c) + 3H_2O(l) \longrightarrow Al_2O_3(\text{protective coating}) + 3H_2(g)$$
$$Al_2O_3(\text{protective coating}) + 6NaOH(aq) + 3H_2O(l) \longrightarrow 2Na_3Al(OH)_6(aq)$$

so that the observed reaction is

$$2Al(c) + 6NaOH(aq) + 3H_2O(l) \longrightarrow 2Na_3Al(OH)_6(aq) + 3H_2(g)$$

The low melting point and high boiling point of gallium make it a liquid over a very large temperature range. It is therefore used in the construction of special thermometers.

GROUP IVA ELEMENTS ————————— 7.10

ELEMENT	PERIOD NUMBER	SYMBOL	CHARACTERISTIC ELECTRONIC STRUCTURE	M.P.	B.P.	
Carbon	2	$_6$C	$2s^2\,2p^2$	3730 °C	4830 °C	*Data for diamond*
Silicon	3	$_{14}$Si	$3s^2\,3p^2$	1410 °C	2355 °C	
Germanium	4	$_{32}$Ge	$4s^2\,4p^2$	937.4 °C	2380 °C	
Tin	5	$_{50}$Sn	$5s^2\,5p^2$	231.96 °C	2270 °C	
Lead	6	$_{82}$Pb	$6s^2\,6p^2$	327.5 °C	1740 °C	

The elements of Group IVA show a transition from nonmetallic carbon, to the semiconductors silicon and germanium, to metallic tin and lead. Characterized by an s^2p^2 electronic structure, they generally exhibit valences of 2 and 4.

Carbon forms the backbone of most compounds (except water) found in living matter. Coke (page 269), a relatively pure form of carbon, is used in the extraction of metals from minerals, particularly iron (Chap. 20).

From carbo, the Latin word for coal.

When lead is attacked by acids, the resulting compounds, generally insoluble in acids, form a strong protective film. Lead is therefore used as an "acid-proof material" (Chap. 13).

7.11 _____ GROUP VA ELEMENTS

Data for white phosphorus

ELEMENT	PERIOD NUMBER	SYMBOL	CHARACTERISTIC ELECTRONIC STRUCTURE	M.P.	B.P.
Nitrogen	2	$_7$N	$2s^2\,2p^3$	-209.86 °C	-195.8 °C
Phosphorus	3	$_{15}$P	$3s^2\,3p^3$	44.1 °C	280 °C
Arsenic	4	$_{33}$As	$4s^2\,4p^3$	817 °C	613 °C (sublimes)
Antimony	5	$_{51}$Sb	$5s^2\,5p^3$	630.7 °C	1750 °C
Bismuth	6	$_{83}$Bi	$6s^2\,6p^3$	271.3 °C	1560 °C

Nitrogen gas and solid phosphorus are nonmetallic; arsenic and antimony are semiconductors; and bismuth is metallic. These elements generally form trivalent and pentavalent compounds (Chap. 8).

Nitrogen and phosphorus compounds have long been used as fertilizers (Chap. 19). An early source of phosphate was animal bones (page 614). During the early 19th century, the need for bones was so great in England that old battlefields were searched. It was not until the middle of the 19th century that the English turned to other phosphate sources.

7.12 _____ GROUP VIA ELEMENTS

ELEMENT	PERIOD NUMBER	SYMBOL	CHARACTERISTIC ELECTRONIC STRUCTURE		M.P.	B.P.
Oxygen	2	$_8$O	$2s^2\,2p^4$		-218.4 °C	-182.96 °C
Sulfur	3	$_{16}$S	$3s^2\,3p^4$	rhombic	112.8 °C	444.7 °C
				monoclinic	119 °C	
Selenium	4	$_{34}$Se	$4s^2\,4p^4$		217 °C	684.9 °C
Tellurium	5	$_{52}$Te	$5s^2\,5p^4$		449.5 °C	989.8 °C
Polonium	6	$_{84}$Po	$6s^2\,6p^4$		254 °C	962 °C

These elements generally exhibit a valence of 2. Oxygen is the most reactive element in this group; it combines with all the other elements except some of the Group 0 gases. Oxygen atoms also combine with one another to form the peroxides, of which hydrogen peroxide, HOOH (H_2O_2), is typical.

Sulfur readily forms sulfides with many elements, comparable to the oxides: Na_2S and Na_2O, MgS and MgO. But, unlike oxygen, it forms compounds like SCl_4 and SF_6 (page 270).

Selenium resembles sulfur in its various physical forms as well as in its compounds. Unlike sulfur, selenium (which is a semiconductor) easily emits electrons when exposed to light. Its electrical conductance increases with increased illumination, a property that accounts for its use in photoelectric cells, instruments in which the electric current varies with the intensity of incident light. This property also accounts for the use of selenium in Xerox photocopying machines (page 270).

ELEMENT	PERIOD NUMBER	SYMBOL	CHARACTERISTIC ELECTRONIC STRUCTURE	M.P.	B.P.
Fluorine	2	$_9F$	$2s^2\,2p^5$	-219.62 °C	-188.14 °C
Chlorine	3	$_{17}Cl$	$3s^2\,3p^5$	-100.98 °C	-34.6 °C
Bromine	4	$_{35}Br$	$4s^2\,4p^5$	-7.2 °C	58.78 °C
Iodine	5	$_{53}I$	$5s^2\,5p^5$	113.5 °C	184.35 °C
Astatine	6	$_{85}At$	$6s^2\,6p^5$	302 °C	337 °C

These elements, known as the **halogens,** react with hydrogen to form hydrogen halides, typical of which is hydrogen chloride. In particular, the reactions with fluorine and chlorine tend to be explosively rapid. These halides dissolve in water to form acid solutions (Chap. 13).

Derived from the Greek words hals and gennalin, meaning salt producer.

The halogens react with most metals to form **halide salts,** typical of which are sodium chloride, NaCl, and zinc bromide, $ZnBr_2$.

$$Zn(c) + Br_2(l) \longrightarrow ZnBr_2(c)$$

The halogens are very *toxic, corrosive,* and *reactive* and therefore are extremely dangerous to handle. Because of their reactivity, the halogens are found naturally only in combination with metals. Many of these halides are soluble in water (App. VII) and therefore are components of sea water. With the exception of fluorine, each of the halogens forms several oxyacids (pages 152 and 420).

Only HOF is known.

Fluorine is a yellow gas, chlorine is a greenish-yellow gas, and bromine is a dark-red volatile liquid. Iodine is a volatile black solid with a metallic appearance; its vapor is violet. Astatine is radioactive and, although it has not yet been thoroughly investigated, it is known to form an astatide ion, At^-.

THE POSITION OF HYDROGEN_____7.14

The first period contains two gaseous elements, hydrogen and helium, with widely differing properties. Hydrogen is a reactive gas which forms explosive mixtures with oxygen and other elements. It is widely used to convert vegetable oils into solid fats (margarine) and also to convert hydrocarbons obtained as a by-product from petroleum refineries into more useful automobile fuels. On the other hand, helium (Group 0), found in natural gas wells in the southwestern United States, strongly resists chemical combination. It is therefore used as an artificial atmosphere (page 69) and for filling observation and weather balloons. Although denser than hydrogen (He $= 4$ g/mole, $H_2 = 2$ g/mole), it is still less dense than air (about 29 g/mole) and much safer to use than hydrogen.

Because of its electronic structure, $1s^1$, hydrogen is generally placed in Group IA with the alkali metals. Hydrogen, under usual conditions, does form the positive ion, H^+. But, like the halogens, it also forms a negative ion, H^-, characteristic of the hydride salts of which sodium hydride, NaH, is typical. It is therefore sometimes also placed in Group VIIA with the halogens.

THE GROUP 0 ELEMENTS

ELEMENT	PERIOD NUMBER	SYMBOL	CHARACTERISTIC ELECTRONIC STRUCTURE		M.P.	B.P.
Helium	1	$_2$He	$1s^2$	below	−272.2 °C (26 atm)	−268.93 °C
Neon	2	$_{10}$Ne	$2s^2\, 2p^6$		−248.67 °C	−246.05 °C
Argon	3	$_{18}$Ar	$3s^2\, 3p^6$		−189.2 °C	−185.7 °C
Krypton	4	$_{36}$Kr	$4s^2\, 4p^6$		−156.6 °C	−152.30 °C
Xenon	5	$_{54}$Xe	$5s^2\, 5p^6$		−111.9 °C	−107.1 °C
Radon	6	$_{86}$Rn	$6s^2\, 6p^6$		−71 °C	−61.8 °C

These elements, known as the **noble gases,** are characterized by filled subshells. The resistance of these elements to chemical combination is generally so strong that originally it was believed that their participation in chemical reactions was impossible. In fact, they were identified and discovered by spectral (page 191) rather than chemical means. They were therefore called the "inert gases," but compounds of some of these elements have since been prepared (page 273).

Helium enjoys a number of uses (page 69). Neon, argon, krypton, and xenon are largely used in electric lighting appliances and photographic flash bulbs. Argon is also used to provide an inert atmosphere in arc welding. Neon is beginning to replace helium in artificial atmospheres (page 69) because the speed of sound is slower in neon and speech is less distorted.

7.16 PERIODIC TRENDS IN PROPERTIES OF ATOMS

The chemical properties of elements are dependent on at least three properties of their atoms. These include the tightness with which an electron is bound to an atom and the energy released when electron is added to an atom. These properties, in turn, are generally related to the size of the atom.

Periodic trends—that is, the change in these properties within a group and a period—will now be discussed.

Atomic Radius—Size of Atoms The actual size of an atom cannot be experimentally determined because it is not a definite quantity. The concept of a definite size for an atom is not consistent with our theoretical view of an atom. The atom consists of a positively charged nucleus surrounded by an electron cloud without a sharp, well-defined boundary (page 181). In molecules, the radius of an atom may also be affected by its neighboring atoms or ions. The radii of ions, however, remain fairly constant; they are largely indifferent to their neighbors.

It is possible to measure the distance between nuclei in molecules and ionic solids. These distances are called **bond lengths.** From these measurements, it is possible to assign a radius to each atom and ion. Table 7.5 gives the *atomic radii,* the radius assigned to an atom. These radii are commonly expressed in ångström units; one ångström unit, symbolized Å, equals exactly 10^{-8} cm.

1 Å = 10 nm

The fluorine atom, one of the smallest atoms, has a radius of 0.71 Å, while one of the largest atoms, cesium, has a radius of 2.35 Å.

In general, within a given period, the atomic radius decreases across the table from left to right. This decrease is due to the attractive effect of increasing the nuclear charge without adding another shell. For example, in period 3, the nuclear charge increases from +11 in sodium to +17 in chlorine without adding another shell.

Within a given group, in general, the atomic radius increases downward from the

TABLE 7.5
COVALENT* AND IONIC RADII, IN ÅNGSTRÖM UNITS

	IA	IIA	IIIA	IVA	VA	VIA	VIIA	
1	**H** H 0.28 to 0.38 H⁻ 2.08							
2	**Li** Li 1.3 Li⁺ 0.60	**Be** Be 0.90 Be²⁺ 0.31	**B** B 0.80 B³⁺ 0.23	**C** C 0.77 C⁴⁺ 0.16 C⁴⁻ 2.60	**N** N 0.73 N³⁻ 1.71	**O** O 0.74 O²⁻ 1.40	**F** F 0.71 F⁻ 1.36	
3	**Na** Na 1.54 Na⁺ 0.95	**Mg** Mg 1.36 Mg²⁺ 0.65	**Al** Al 1.25 Al³⁺ 0.50	**Si** Si 1.15 Si⁴⁺ 0.42	**P** P 1.1 P³⁻ 2.12	**S** S 1.02 S²⁻ 1.84	**Cl** Cl 0.99 Cl⁻ 1.81	
4	**K** K 1.96 K⁺ 1.33	**Ca** Ca 1.74 Ca²⁺ 0.99	**Ga** Ga 1.26 Ga³⁺ 0.62	**Ge** Ge 1.22 Ge⁴⁺ 0.53	**As** As 1.19 As³⁻ 2.22	**Se** Se 1.16 Se²⁻ 1.98	**Br** Br 1.14 Br⁻ 1.95	
5	**Rb** Rb 2.16 Rb⁺ 1.48	**Sr** Sr 1.92 Sr²⁺ 1.13	**In** In 1.44 In³⁺ 0.81	**Sn** Sn 1.41 Sn⁴⁺ 0.71	**Sb** Sb 1.38 Sb³⁻ 2.45	**Te** Te 1.35 Te²⁻ 2.21	**I** I 1.33 I⁻ 2.16	
6	**Cs** Cs 2.35 Cs⁺ 1.69	**Ba** Ba 1.98 Ba²⁺ 1.35	**Tl** Tl 1.48	**Pb** Pb 1.47 Pb⁴⁺ 0.84	**Bi** Bi 1.46 Bi⁵⁺ 0.74	**Po**	**At**	
7	**Fr**	**Ra** Ra²⁺ 1.52						

	IIIB	IVB	VB	VIB	VIIB		VIII		IB	IIB
4	**Sc** Sc 1.44 Sc³⁺ 0.81	**Ti** Ti 1.32 Ti⁴⁺ 0.68	**V** V 1.22 V⁵⁺ 0.59	**Cr** Cr 1.18 Cr⁶⁺ 0.52	**Mn** Mn 1.17 Mn⁷⁺ 0.46	**Fe** Fe 1.17 Fe³⁺ 0.67	**Co** Co 1.16 Co³⁺ 0.29	**Ni** Ni 1.15 Ni³⁺ 0.35	**Cu** Cu 1.17 Cu⁺ 0.96	**Zn** Zn 1.25 Zn²⁺ 0.74
5	**Y** Y 1.62	**Zr** Zr 1.45	**Nb** Nb 1.34	**Mo** Mo 1.30	**Tc** Tc 1.27	**Ru** Ru 1.25	**Rh** Rh 1.25	**Pd** Pd 1.28	**Ag** Ag 1.34 Ag⁺ 1.26	**Cd** Cd 1.48 Cd²⁺ 0.97
6	**La**	**Hf**	**Ta**	**W**	**Re**	**Os**	**Ir**	**Pt**	**Au** Au 1.34 Au⁺ 1.37	**Hg** Hg 1.49 Hg²⁺ 1.10

*Covalent radii (taken mostly from Table of Interatomic Distances, London, Chem. Soc., Special Publ., 1958) are applicable only to single-bonded atoms in mainly covalent molecules (Chap. 8). Crystal (ionic) radii are from the publications of Linus Pauling.

top to the bottom of the table. Although the atomic number increases downward in a group, this tendency to decrease the radius is more than counterbalanced by the effect of adding another shell. The greater the number of shells, the larger the atom. In summary,

$$_3\text{Li} \quad \xrightarrow[\substack{\textit{nuclear charge increases} \\ n = 1 \text{ and 2 shells only}}]{\text{radius decreases}} \quad _9\text{F}$$
$$1s^2\, 2s^1 \qquad\qquad\qquad 1s^2\, 2s^2\, 2p^5$$

radius increases ↓ *addition of shells dominates over effect of increase in nuclear charge*

$$_{55}\text{Cs}$$
$$n = 1, 2, 3, 4, 5, \text{ and 6 shells}$$

n is the principal quantum number. Electron structure is abbreviated to emphasize addition of shells. Cs is KLM 4s² 4p⁶ 4d¹⁰ 5s² 5p⁶ 6s¹.

Notice that in the transition elements in Table 7.5 the change in radius across a period is small, only from 1.44 Å in $_{21}$Sc to 1.25 Å in $_{30}$Zn, and from 1.65 Å in $_{58}$Ce to 1.56 Å in $_{71}$Lu. These small changes are associated with the special feature of the electronic structure of the transition elements; namely, the addition of electrons to an *inner shell* without changing the number of electrons in the outer shell. The nucleus attracts the outer electrons but the inner electrons repel them. Thus, the addition of electrons to the inner *d* and *f* subshells nearly cancels the effect of the increase in the nuclear charge; the result is a small decrease in radius.

Commonly referred to as a "screening effect."

Size of Ions   There is a marked difference between the size of a neutral atom and its corresponding ion. A positive ion is always smaller than the neutral atom, while a negative ion is always larger than the atom from which it was formed.

In forming a positive ion, the atom loses an electron. The electron cloud of the positive ion now consists of fewer electrons. Thus, the nucleus exerts a greater attraction on the remaining electrons and draws them closer. The radius of a sodium atom, for example, is 1.54 Å, while its ion, Na^+, is 0.95 Å. Table 7.5 gives some typical **ionic radii,** the radius assigned to ions.

The radius for ions of the same charge increases downward in a group; for example, Li^+, radius 0.60 Å, to Cs^+, radius 1.69 Å; and F^-, radius 1.36 Å, to I^-, radius 2.16 Å. The increase is due to the addition of shells.

Known as isoelectronic ions, derived from isos, the Greek word for equal.

Ions having the same number of electrons have the same electronic structure; for example, Li^+, $1s^2$, and Be^{2+}, $1s^2$. Their radii decrease across a period from left to right, since the number of shells remains the same as the nuclear charge increases, illustrated in Table 7.6.

The electron cloud of the negative ion contains more electrons than the neutral atom. Repulsion between the electrons is therefore greater, the electrons are spread further apart, and the electron cloud becomes larger; for example, F atom, 0.71 Å, F^- ion, 1.36 Å. Ion charge and size are important in determining solubilities (Chap. 10).

PROBLEM 3   **In each series, pick the atom or ion with (a) the smallest and (b) the largest radius:**

(i)   **B, Al, Ga, In, Tl**
(ii) **Na, Mg, Al, Si, P, S, Cl**
(iii) **Li^+, Na^+, K^+, Rb^+, Cs^+**
(iv) **N^{3-}, O^{2-}, F^-**
(v)   **B, B^{3+}**
(vi) **S^{2+}, S, S^{2-}**

Ionization Energy   The formation of a positive ion from a neutral atom by the loss of an electron is not a spontaneous process. It involves the removal of an electron

TABLE 7.6
**CHANGE IN IONIC RADII FOR IONS HAVING THE SAME
ELECTRONIC STRUCTURES**

Ion	Na^+	Mg^{2+}	Al^{3+}	Si^{4+}	P^{5+}	S^{6+}	Cl^{7+}
Nuclear charge (increases)	+11	+12	+13	+14	+15	+16	+17
Number of electrons (same)	10	10	10	10	10	10	10
Same electronic structure	$1s^2\,2s^2\,2p^6$	$1s^2\,2s^2\,2p^6$	$1s^2\,2s^2\,2p^6$	$1s^2\,2s^2\,2p^6$	$1s^2\,2s^2\,2p^6$	$1s^2\,2s^2\,2p^6$	$1s^2\,2s^2\,2p^6$
Radius, Å (decreases)	0.95	0.65	0.50	0.42	0.35	0.30	0.27

from the attractive force of a nucleus and therefore occurs only when sufficient energy
is available:

$$M(g) + \text{ionization energy} \longrightarrow M^+(g) + e^-$$

neutral gaseous atom | positive gaseous ion + electron

The energy required to remove an electron from the neutral gaseous atom of an
element in the ground state is called the **ionization energy.** Table 7.7 lists the ionization energies of some elements.

In general, the ionization energy increases across a period from left to right as the
number of shells remains the same and the nuclear charge increases.

Ionization energy is given in kilocalories per mole of atoms.

The ionization energy may be related to the size of the atom. The smaller the
radius, the closer the electron cloud is to the nucleus, the greater the attraction, and
the more difficult it is to remove the electron;* for example, Li = 124 kcal/mole, and
F = 402 kcal/mole.

Within a group, the ionization energy, in general, decreases from top to bottom;
for example, Li = 124 kcal/mole and Cs = 89.7 kcal/mole. Again, the decrease in
ionization energy follows the increase in the size of the atom. Thus, electrons further
away from the nucleus are easier to remove.

Note that thallium, Tl, has a higher ionization energy than indium, In.

Trends in ionization energy are related to other properties of an element. For
example, metallic character, related to the tendency to form positive ions, increases
with a decrease in ionization energy. The smaller the ionization energy of an element,
the greater is its ability to lose electrons, and the greater is its metallic character.

---

*However, some irregularities do occur. For example, boron $2s^2 2p^1$ has a smaller ionization energy
than beryllium $2s^2$, and oxygen $2s^2 2p^4$ has a smaller ionization energy than nitrogen $2s^2 2p^3$. It is easier to
remove an electron from a p orbital than from an s orbital in the same shell; therefore, a decrease occurs in
going from Be to B. In going from N to O, the electron-electron repulsion in the fully occupied p orbital in
O makes its ionization easier (Problem 38, page 240).

TABLE 7.7
FIRST IONIZATION ENERGIES, kcal/mole

1	**H** $1s^1$ 314							**He** $1s^2$ 567
2	**Li** $2s^1$ 124	**Be** $2s^2$ 215	**B** $2s^2 2p^1$ 191	**C** $2s^2 2p^2$ 260	**N** $2s^2 2p^3$ 336	**O** $2s^2 2p^4$ 314	**F** $2s^2 2p^5$ 402	**Ne** $2s^2 2p^6$ 497
3	**Na** 119		**Al** 138				**Cl** 300	
4	**K** 100		**Ga** 138				**Br** 273	
5	**Rb** 96.3		**In** 133				**I** 241	
6	**Cs** 89.8		**Tl** 141					

1 kcal = 4.184 kJ

Source: National Standard Reference Data System, National Bureau of Standards
Publication Number 26, 1969.

PROBLEM 4   In each series, pick the atom with (a) the largest radius, and (b) the smallest ionization energy:

(i) Li, Be, B, O, F
(ii) F, Cl, Br, I

Electron Affinity   Neutral atoms have some attraction for electrons. Electron affinity is a measure of the energy change that occurs when a gaseous atom in the ground state accepts an electron to become a negative ion:

$$X(g) + e^- \longrightarrow X^-(g) + \text{energy released}$$

neutral	negative
gaseous	gaseous
atom	ion

The value of the electron affinity is a good indicator of the relative ease with which an atom forms a negative ion. The greater the amount of energy released, the more easily is the negative ion formed. Values of electron affinities are expressed in kilocalories per mole of atoms; for example:

$$Cl(g) + e^- \longrightarrow Cl^-(g), \text{ 83 kcal/mole } released$$

We should expect that the smaller the atom, the greater the attraction of the nucleus for the electron, and the greater the electron affinity:

$$I \xrightarrow[\substack{\text{greater electron attraction} \\ \text{greater electron affinity}}]{\text{decreasing radius}} F$$

Thus, the electron affinity should increase from left to right across a period and should decrease downward within a group.

Unfortunately, electron affinities are generally difficult to measure directly. But measurements (Problem 33, page 240) that have been made do not show the expected trends across a period or down a group. Trends are generally erratic. The reliable data available for the halogen family, for example, do not show the expected relationship between size and electron affinity:

	I	Br	Cl	F
		decreasing radius $\longrightarrow$		
electron affinity	70.59	77.58	83.37	78.38 kcal/mole *released*

Nevertheless, as we shall learn in the next chapter, when different atoms are brought together, both of these atomic properties, ionization energy and electron affinity, determine the tendency of these atoms to form ions.

EPILOG from *Scientific American,* February, 1924 ⸻

"The recent discovery of hafnium, the latest addition to the list of chemical elements, was the result of investigations based on the latest and most advanced conceptions of atomic structure. The list of elements arranged in the order of their atomic number showed a break after No. 71, the element lutecium. No. 72 was lacking. D. Coster and George de Hevesy, working in Copenhagen, deduced that the unknown element would probably show great resemblance to element No. 40, zirconium, to which, according to the theory of Niels Bohr, it must be closely related. The two investigators examined the X-ray spectra of all zirconium minerals and in each case found, in addition to the characteristic lines of the known element, lines of another, unknown element in the position where the lines of element No. 72 should be. The two scientists succeeded in separating the new element from the zirconium and named it in honor of Copenhagen (called Hafnia in its Latin form).”

“At a recent session of the French Academy of Sciences, M. Wurtz presented a communication from M. Lecoq, announcing the discovery of a new simple body, a metal analogous and allied to zinc and cadmium, and found in blende or sulphide of zinc in Spain. The existence of the substance was revealed by spectral analysis, two lines appearing which could not be traced to any other element. The new metal has not been reduced from its combinations, so that its physical characteristics remain undetermined. The discoverer patriotically names the new element gallium.”

PROBLEMS

5 Vocabulary Define the following terms: (a) group, (b) period, (c) representative elements, (d) transition elements, (e) lanthanides, (f) ionization energy, (g) electron affinity.

6 Mendeleev's table What is the significance of blank spaces in Mendeleev's periodic table?

7 Periodic table What is meant by the following statement: "Properties of the elements are periodic functions of their atomic numbers"?

8 Periodic table Locate the following groups in the periodic table: (a) the alkali metals, (b) the halogens, (c) the alkaline earth metals, (d) the coinage metals, (e) the noble gases.

9 Periodic table List some identifying characteristics of the groups in Problem 8.

10 Periodic table Which elements are nonmetals?

11 Periodic table What is the fundamental difference in electronic structure between the Group IA elements and the Group IB elements?

12 Periodic table Iodine, I, rather than tellurium, Te, is placed in Group VII even though the atomic weight of tellurium is higher than that of iodine. Explain.

13 Atomic size Select the larger atom from each pair: (a) Li, Na; (b) K, Se; (c) Cl, Br; (d) F, I.

14 Select the pair of atoms with nearly identical radii: (a) Fe, Mn; (b) C, Ac; (c) F, B.

15 Select the larger ion from each pair: (a) K^+, Mg^{2+}; (b) Mg^{2+}, Ba^{2+}; (c) Li^+, K^+; (d) Cl^-, Br^-.

16 Ionization energy From each pair, select the element with the higher ionization energy: (a) Al, Cl; (b) Na, Si; (c) Ar, Rn.

17 How does the ionization energy generally vary within a given (a) group, and (b) period?

18 Bond length The distance between the nuclei of atoms in a molecule is known as *bond length*. The sum of the assigned radii for the individual atoms equals the bond length (internuclear distance). What is the bond length for (a) C—Br, (b) Ca^{2+}—S^{2-}? See Table 7.5, page 235.

19 Explain the variation in size in the following sets of isoelectronic ions: (a) Na^+, Mg^{2+}; (b) Se^{2-}, Br^-; (c) Rb^+, Sr^{2+}.

20 Bond length Arrange the following sets in order of increasing bond length:
(a) HBr, HCl, HF, HI
(b) Cl_2, Br_2, I_2, F_2

21 Do metals or nonmetals, in general, have the higher (a) ionization energy, (b) electron affinity?

22 What is the relationship between the size of an atom and the ionization energy?

23 From each of the following groups, pick (a) the most metallic element, and (b) the element with the largest atomic radius: (i) Br, Ca, As; (ii) S, Se, Te; (iii) Al, Si, P; (iv) Ga, Al, B.

24 Arrange the elements in Group VIIA in the order of (a) increasing atomic radius and (b) increasing ionization energy. (Put the element with the smallest value first.)

25 In the given isoelectronic series of ions, pick the ion with the smallest radius: $_{16}S^{2-}$, $_{17}Cl^-$, $_{18}Ar$, $_{19}K^+$, $_{20}Ca^{2+}$, $_{21}Sc^{3+}$.

26 Explain the increase and decrease in radius that occur in forming negative and positive ions.

27 Rearrange the following elements in the order of increasing ionization energy: F, Na, Cs, Ne.

28 (a) Pick the atom with the smallest radius: K, Ca, Ge, As, Br. (b) Pick the atom with the largest radius: Cu, Zn, Co, Fe, Sc.

29 (a) Give the group number of the atoms having each of the following characteristic electronic structures: s^1, s^2p^1, s^2p^4, s^2p^6. (b) Which of these structures

239

corresponds to a noble gas? (c) Pick an element from each of the other groups and write the most probable formula for its oxide.

30 From the given characteristic electronic structures, pick the one associated with the transition elements: s^1p^2, s^2p^2, s^2p^5, s^2d^2.

31 (a) Use Fig. 6.13, page 198, to write the electronic structure and to identify each of the following elements as representative or transition: atomic numbers 32, 38, 44, 50, and 53. (a) Are any of these elements in the same group?

32 In what portion of the periodic table would you expect to find: (a) the metals, (b) the nonmetals, (c) the semiconductors?

33 **Electron affinity** Given the following recommended values for electron affinities of elements* in kcal/mole; <0 means less than zero (App. II), that is, heat is absorbed rather than evolved.

H						
17.4						
Li	Be	B	C	N	O	F
14.3	<0	6.45	29.2	<0	33.7	78.38
Na	Mg	Al	Si	P	S	Cl
12.6	<0	10.6	31.9	17.1	47.9	83.37
K						Br
11.6						77.58
Rb						I
11.2						70.59

*Source: H. Hotop and W. C. Lineberger, *Journal of Physical and Chemical Reference Data,* volume 4, 1975, page 539.

Cs
10.9

Plot the Li $\longrightarrow$ F and Na $\longrightarrow$ Cl data (on the *y*-axis) against the group number. Plot the Li $\longrightarrow$ Cs and F $\longrightarrow$ I data against the period number. Can you draw definite conclusions regarding periodicity of electron affinities?

34 **Library** Read one of the following:
(a) In *Chemistry,* volume 43, January 1970, pages 6–9, Glenn Seaborg discusses the extension of the periodic table by synthesis of heavy elements. Read this article so that you can discuss the application of the periodic table to the prediction of properties of these "yet-to-be-synthesized" elements.
(b) Elements lying along a diagonal line in the periodic table, such as Be and Al, also show a periodic relationship. William Allen discusses such relationships in *Chemistry,* volume 43, April 1970, pages 22–74. Read this article and discuss trends in atomic radii along diagonals in the periodic table.
(c) "From Periodic Table to Production," Thomas Midgley, Jr., *Industrial Engineering Chemistry,* volume 29, 1937, reprinted in *Chemical Technology,* June 1976, page 364.
(d) "A Pattern of Chemistry, 100 Years of the Periodic Table," F. Greenway, *Chemistry in Britain,* volume 5, 1965, page 97.
(e) "A Newly Arranged Periodic Chart," J. F. Hyde, *Chemistry,* September 1976, pages 15–18.
(f) "The Experimental Values of Atomic Electron Affinities," E. Chen and W. Wentworth, *Journal of Chemical Education,* volume 52, August 1975, page 486. (In reading this, note that 1 eV/atom = 23.1 kcal/mole.)

ADDITIONAL PROBLEMS

35 The removal of one electron from a neutral atom, $A(g) \longrightarrow A^+(g) + e^-$, requires the addition of an amount of energy known as the **first ionization energy.** The energy required to remove a second electron, $A^+(g) \longrightarrow A^{2+}(g) + e^-$, is called the **second ionization energy.** Given are some typical data.

ATOM	FIRST IONIZATION ENERGY	SECOND IONIZATION ENERGY
Ne	497 kcal/mole	1445 kcal/mole
Ar	360	1001
Kr	323	889

Inspection of these data shows that more energy is always required to remove the second electron. Explain. Account for the decrease in ionization energy as one moves downward in Group 0.

36 When a beam of light shines on a metal, electrons are knocked out of its surface. This is the basis of photoelectric cells ("electric eyes") used to trigger a signal or hold a door open. Pick the element (see Table 7.7, page 237) that you would recommend for use in such devices: Al, Be, Li, or Cs. Explain.

37 The discovery of the alkali and alkaline earth metals was generally delayed (Table 7.3, page 226), while the coinage metals have been known since prehistoric times. Explain.

38 The N atom has three $2p$ electrons, one in each orbital: $\underline{\downarrow}$ $\underline{\downarrow}$ $\underline{\downarrow}$. The O atom has four $2p$ electrons, making it necessary to put two electrons in the *same* orbital: $\underline{\downarrow\uparrow}$ $\underline{\downarrow}$ $\underline{\downarrow}$. Is the repulsion between two electrons in the same orbital greater than, less than, or the same as between two electrons in separate orbitals? On the basis of your answer, should the ionization energy of oxygen be greater than or less than that of nitrogen? Check your answer against Table 7.7, page 237.

39 Plot the ionization energies (on the y-axis) of magnesium against the ionization number (on the x-axis) corresponding to each of the first ten ionization steps. Identify the $1s$, $2s$, $2p$, and $3s$ electrons.

1st	2nd	3rd	4th	5th	6th
Mg^+	Mg^{2+}	Mg^{3+}	Mg^{4+}	Mg^{5+}	Mg^{6+}
7.6	15	80	109	141	187

7th	8th	9th	10th	11th
Mg^{7+}	Mg^{8+}	Mg^{9+}	Mg^{10+}	Mg^{11+}
225	266	328	367	1761

(Data are given in electron volts per atom, eV/atom; 1 eV/atom = 23.06 kcal/mole.)

ANSWERS

1 Representative   Transition

Na	Al	Zr
Cs	C	Ni
Sr	O	
Ba	I	
Xe	F	

Lanthanide   Actinide

Ce   U

3 (i) (a) B, (b) Tl
(ii) (a) Cl, (b) Na

(iii) (a) Li^+, (b) Cs^+
(iv) (a) F^-, (b) N^{3-}
(v) (a) B^{3+}, (b) B
(vi) (a) S^{2+}, (b) S^{2-}
4 (i) (a) (b) Li
(ii) (a) (b) I
13 (a) Na, (b) K, (c) Br, (d) I
14 Fe, Mn
15 (a) K^+, (b) Ba^{2+}, (c) K^+, (d) Br^-
16 (a) Cl, (b) Si, (c) Ar
18 (a) 1.91 Å, (b) 2.83 Å
20 (a) HF, HCl, HBr, HI
(b) F_2, Cl_2, Br_2, I_2

21 (a) (b) nonmetals
23 (a) (b) (i) Ca, (ii) Te, (iii) Al, (iv) Ga
24 (a) F, Cl, Br, I
(b) I, Br, Cl, F
25 Sc^{3+}
27 Cs, Na, F, Ne
28 (a) Br
(b) Sc
29 (a) IA, IIIA, VIA, 0
(b) $s^2 p^6$
(c) Na_2O, Al_2O_3, SO_3
30 $s^2 d^2$
38 greater, less

GLOSSARY

actinides   Elements 90 to 103 following actinium, $_{89}Ac$, in the seventh period in the periodic table. An electron enters the $5f$ subshell as the atomic number increases.

alkali metals   The Group IA family of elements, characterized by an s^1 electronic structure.

alkaline earth metals   The Group IIA family of elements, characterized by an s^2 electronic structure.

atomic radius   The radius assigned to an atom.

bond length   The measured distance between nuclei in molecules and ionic solids.

coinage metals   The Group IB family of relatively unreactive metals, characterized by a $d^{10} s^1$ electronic structure.

family   See **group**.

group   A set or family of elements occupying a vertical column in the periodic table, with similar characteristic electronic structures, such as Group IVA ($s^2 p^2$) and Group IVB ($s^2 d^2$).

halogen   A member of the Group VIIA family of very toxic, corrosive, reactive elements, characterized by an $s^2 p^5$ electronic structure.

ionization energy   The energy required to remove an electron from the neutral gaseous atom of an element in the ground state.

lanthanides   Elements 58 to 71 following lanthanum, $_{57}La$, in the sixth period of the periodic table. An electron enters the $4f$ subshell as the atomic number increases.

metallic elements (metals)   Elements that are good conductors of heat and electricity. They tend to form positive ions, and are therefore also known as electropositive elements. They are characterized by comparatively low ionization energies and low electron affinities.

noble gases   Elements of Group 0, characterized by filled subshells.

nonmetallic elements (nonmetals)   Elements that tend to form negative ions, and are therefore also known as electronegative elements. They are characterized by comparatively high ionization energies and high electron affinities, and are poor conductors of heat and electricity.

period   The set of elements in a row of the periodic table. See **periodic table**.

periodic table   A table in which the elements are arranged in the order of increasing atomic number in columns, called Groups, and rows, called Periods, so that elements with similar chemical properties fall in the same column (Group).

representative elements   The elements in the A subgroups in the periodic table. An element enters an s or p subshell as the atomic number increases.

semiconductors   Elements, like silicon, that are on the border between metallic elements, like aluminum, and nonmetallic elements, like phosphorus, in the periodic table. They have both metallic and nonmetallic properties.

transition elements   The elements in the B subgroups in the periodic table. An electron enters a d or f subshell as the atomic number increases.

CHEMICAL BONDING: FORCES BETWEEN ATOMS AND MOLECULES

8

Matter is made up of discrete particles, atoms or molecules. Atoms and molecules are made up of positively charged nuclei and electrons arranged in definite energy states. We now consider the following questions: What are the forces that hold—*bond*—atoms together in molecules? We have studied three types of attractive forces: gravitational, electric, and magnetic. All are undoubtedly involved, but are the three forces equally important in chemical bonding, or is one force sufficient? And, will the answer to this question also explain differences in the properties of matter? Solid copper and silver are excellent conductors of electricity, while solid diamond is a typical nonconductor. Sodium and fluorine combine in the atomic ratio of 1 to 1 to produce sodium fluoride, NaF, a colorless solid, melting point 990 °C, boiling point 1700 °C, while carbon and fluorine combine in the ratio of 1 to 4 to produce carbon tetrafluoride, CF_4, a colorless gas, freezing point −184 °C, boiling point −128 °C. Table 4.1, page 116, illustrates the range of boiling points among the common chlorides of the representative elements (page 227). Notice the tendency of the boiling points to decrease as we move across the periodic table from left to right (for example, NaCl $\longrightarrow$ BrCl) and to increase as we move down the table (for example, CCl_4 $\longrightarrow$ $SnCl_4$). Sodium fluoride, NaF, calcium fluoride, CaF_2 (b.p. 2500 °C), sodium chloride, NaCl, calcium chloride, $CaCl_2$, and calcium oxide CaO (b.p. 2850 °C) are typical of the many compounds that are composed of positively and negatively charged particles (ions) rather than atoms or molecules. The attractive force between atoms or ions is called a *chemical bond*. The nature of this force is of fundamental importance in the study of chemistry, since all chemical changes essentially involve an alteration of chemical bonds.

Under room conditions, the atoms of most elements prefer companionship—they like to be bonded together. For example, many gases—hydrogen, oxygen, nitrogen, the halogens (fluorine $\longrightarrow$ iodine)—exist as diatomic molecules. White solid phosphorus and phosphorus vapor exist as P_4 molecules. Sulfur exists as S_8 in liquid sulfur (below 160 °C) and in yellow crystal forms (rhombic and monoclinic), but as S_6, S_4, and S_2 in the gaseous state, depending upon the temperature. Solid red phosphorus, solid carbon (graphite and diamond), and most metals are composed of countless atoms connected together.

On the other hand, at high temperatures (above about 1000 °C), in electric discharge tubes (page 118), or under exposure to high energy photons, molecules and metals tend to separate into atoms. At extremely high temperatures (sun and stars), atoms become largely ionized and exist mainly as individual nuclei separated from their electrons.

Known as the plasma state of matter.

At high pressures (10^5 to about 10^6 atm) many nonmetallic substances—for example, wood, calcium carbonate (chalk), $CaCO_3$, phosphorus, iodine, and benzene—behave like metals in that they become good conductors of electricity.

In addition, many molecules do not like the way in which they were formed and very quickly (in less than 0.001 s) react or rearrange to form other molecules. This is an extremely important phenomenon in determining the course of a chemical reaction. However, in our discussion of chemical bonding, we will mainly deal with molecules that last a long time under more or less familiar conditions.

8.2 THE KIND OF FORCE BETWEEN ATOMS

Speculation about interatomic forces has been traced back more than 2500 years. Atoms originally were visualized as particles of various shapes with hooks by which one atom could bond to another, as illustrated in Fig. 8.1. However, the invention of forces made possible a more quantitative investigation of the nature of the force. When atoms combine, energy (heat) is evolved. The strength of interatomic forces is measurable (page 294). But studies show that gravitational and magnetic forces are much too weak to account for interatomic forces. *Only electric forces are strong enough to account for these interatomic forces.* We may then visualize a chemical bond as an electrical attractive force.

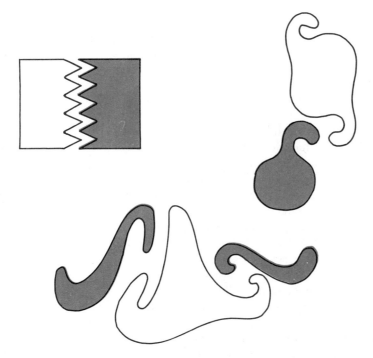

FIGURE 8.1 An unrealistic view of chemical bonding. Atoms form bonds by attachment of hooks or by meshing teeth. (Adapted from Leslie Holliday, *Scientific American*, page 117, May, 1970.)

LEWIS SYMBOLS _____ 8.3

Symbols are an indispensable crutch for scientists. Lewis symbols are very useful in describing the formation of chemical bonds and, hence, are used to represent atoms and ions. A Lewis symbol consists of the chemical symbol of the element and dots to *represent* the **valence electrons.** The valence electrons are the electrons in the highest (outermost) shell. They are called valence electrons because they are usually involved in bonding when elements combine. Thus, in lithium, $1s^2 2s^1$, the 2 electrons in the $1s$ orbital are so strongly attracted by the nucleus that they do not play a major role in the chemistry of lithium. Lithium therefore has one valence electron, $2s^1$, and its Lewis symbol is Li·. For the representative elements, the number of valence electrons equals the group number (page 226). For example, the electronic structure for carbon is $_6$C $1s^2 2s^2 2p^2$. There are 4 electrons in its highest shell and carbon is in Group IVA. Its Lewis symbol is thus ·C̤·. $_{20}$Ca $1s^2 2s^2 2p^6 3s^2 3p^6 4s^2$, in Group IIA, has 2 electrons in its highest shell. Its Lewis symbol is Ca·. No distinction is made among these valence electrons except that *after 4 electrons have been placed* around the chemical symbol, *electron dots are paired off.* For example, the Lewis symbol for sulfur, $_{16}$S $1s^2 2s^2 2p^6 3s^2 3p^4$, with 6 electrons in its highest shell, is :S̈·. When necessary, the charge of the ion is shown. For example, when a sulfur atom picks up 2 electrons, its Lewis symbol becomes :S̈:$^{2-}$

*Named after Gilbert
Lewis, who used
"electron dot"
formulas (1916) to
explain chemical
bonding.*

$$·\ddot{S}: + 2e^- \longrightarrow :\ddot{S}:^{2-}$$

Lewis symbols and group numbers for the first 10 elements and a few of their ions are given:

*Transition elements
(page 228 and Chap.
21) may use electrons
in more than one
shell. For example,
bonding in titanium,
$_{22}$Ti KL $3s^2 3p^6 3d^2 4s^2$,
may involve $3d^2$ and
$4s^2$ electrons.*

I	II	III	IV	V	VI	VII	VIII
H·							He:
H:⁻							He²⁺
H⁺							
Li·	Be·	·B·	·C̤·	·N̈·	·Ö:	:F̈·	:N̈e:
Li⁺	Be²⁺			:N̈:³⁻	:Ö:²⁻	:F̈:⁻	

PROBLEM 1   Consult the periodic table, page 227. Write the Lewis symbols for argon, chlorine, chloride ion, Cl⁻, and aluminum. How many unpaired electrons appear in each symbol?

THE BOND BETWEEN IONS— _____ 8.4
THE IONIC BOND

In the years from 1893 to 1898, the noble gases—argon (*inert*), helium (*sun*), neon (*new*), krypton (*hidden*), xenon (*stranger*)—were discovered by William Ramsey and Morris Travers. These gases constituted a new periodic group. The common feature of these gases is their resistance to chemical combination. Strangely, this chemical inertness served as an important key to the understanding of chemical reactions. The relationship between the bonding of atoms and the electronic structure of noble gases was noted independently by Walter Kossel and Gilbert Lewis (1916), and by Irving Langmuir (1919). They concluded that *atoms react by changing the*

*Based on the work of
Henry Cavendish
(1785), Pierre Janssen
and Joseph Lockyer
(1868), William
Hillebrand (1891), and
James Dewar (1895).*

From the Greek word okto, for eight. Exceptions to the octet rule are discussed on pages 250 and 270.

number of their electrons so as to acquire the electronic structure of a noble gas. Each noble gas, except helium, has 8 electrons, s^2p^6, in its highest shell (page 234). Helium has a $1s^2$ electronic structure. Since an 8-electron structure is mainly involved, this generalization is named the **octet rule.**

In chemical changes, the number of protons and neutrons in the nucleus of an atom is not changed. However, an atom may change the number of its electrons by giving up or gaining electrons. When electrons are transferred from one atom to another, ions are formed, and the resulting bond is said to be ionic. For example, in forming sodium chloride, sodium, $_{11}Na$, with 1 valence electron, Na·, transfers 1 electron to chlorine, $_{17}Cl$, with 7 valence electrons, $:\ddot{C}l\cdot$. The sodium atom thus becomes positively charged because of the loss of an electron. The chlorine atom becomes negatively charged because of the gain of an electron. The sodium ion, Na^+, now has the same electronic structure as neon, $_{10}Ne$, and the chloride ion, $:\ddot{C}l:^-$, has the same electronic structure as argon, $_{18}Ar$. Each ion now has an octet in its highest shell. In summary,

$$Na\overset{\frown}{} + \quad \cdot\ddot{C}l: \quad \longrightarrow \quad Na^+ \quad + \quad :\ddot{C}l:^-$$

$$1s^2\,2s^2\,2p^6\,3s^1 \quad 1s^2\,2s^2\,2p^6\,3s^2\,3p^5 \qquad 1s^2\,\underset{octet}{\underline{2s^2\,2p^6}} \quad 1s^2\,2s^2\,2p^6\,\underset{octet}{\underline{3s^2\,3p^6}}$$

$$\qquad\qquad\qquad Ne \qquad\qquad\qquad Ar$$

$$\qquad\qquad 1s^2\,\underset{octet}{\underline{2s^2\,2p^6}} \quad 1s^2\,2s^2\,2p^6\,\underset{octet}{\underline{3s^2\,3p^6}}$$

The oppositely charged ions attract each other, forming an **ionic bond,** the electrical attraction between positive and negative ions.

Since compounds are electrically neutral, *in the formation of an ionic bond, the number of electrons gained and lost must be equal.* The following examples illustrate the transfer of *all available valence electrons* of the atoms of the elements of Groups IA, IIA, and IIIA. This procedure predicts the correct empirical (simplest) formula of ionic compounds as found at room conditions.

Li· + ·$\ddot{O}$:, the oxygen atom requires 2 electrons to form an octet, while the lithium atom has only 1 electron to give up. Thus, 2 lithium atoms are needed to satisfy the oxygen atom:

$$Li\overset{\frown}{\cdot} + Li\overset{\frown}{\cdot} + \overset{\frown}{\cdot}\ddot{O}: \longrightarrow \quad 2Li^+ + :\ddot{O}:^{2-}$$

$$Li_2O, \textit{ lithium oxide}$$
$$\text{white solid, b.p. over } 2000°C$$

$\dot{C}a\cdot$ + H·, the hydrogen atom may accept 1 electron to acquire the electronic structure of helium, $1s^2$. But the calcium atom has 2 electrons to give up. Thus, 2 hydrogen atoms are needed to satisfy the calcium atom:

$$\dot{C}a\overset{\frown}{\cdot} + H\overset{\curvearrowright}{\cdot} + H\cdot \longrightarrow \quad Ca^{2+} + 2H:^-$$

$$CaH_2, \textit{ calcium hydride}$$
$$\text{white solid, decomposes above } 600°C$$

$\dot{M}g\cdot$ + ·$\dot{N}$·, the nitrogen atom requires 3 electrons to form an octet, while the magnesium atom has 2 electrons to give up. The simplest ratio necessary to satisfy the nitrogen and magnesium is 3 magnesium atoms and 2 nitrogen atoms:

$$\text{Mg·} + \text{Mg·} + \text{Mg·} + \cdot\ddot{\text{N}}\cdot + \cdot\ddot{\text{N}}\cdot \longrightarrow \qquad 3\text{Mg}^{2+} + 2\,:\!\ddot{\text{N}}\!:^{3-}$$

Mg_3N_2, *magnesium nitride*
green-yellow solid, decomposes at 1500°C

$\dot{\text{Al}}\cdot + \cdot\ddot{\text{F}}\!:$, 3 fluorine atoms are required for each aluminum atom:

$$\text{Al·} + \cdot\ddot{\text{F}}\!: + \cdot\ddot{\text{F}}\!: + \cdot\ddot{\text{F}}\!: \longrightarrow \qquad \text{Al}^{3+} + 3\,:\!\ddot{\text{F}}\!:^{-}$$

AlF_3, *aluminum fluoride*
colorless solid, sublimes at 1291°C

We see that *in forming an ionic bond, the number of electrons gained or lost by an atom is equal to its common valence* (page 149).

PROBLEM 2 **(a) Use the Lewis symbols for lithium and nitrogen to represent the formation of ionic lithium nitride, consistent with the octet rule. A typical ionic nitride, it reacts with water to form ammonia and lithium hydroxide, LiOH. Write the empirical formula of lithium nitride. (b) Predict, from Lewis symbols, the empirical formula for cesium sulfide, a typical ionic sulfide that dissolves in water to form hydrogen sulfide, H_2S, and the metal hydroxide.**

THE BOND BETWEEN ATOMS— _____ 8.5
THE COVALENT BOND

Most chemical bonds are *not* ionic. For example, there is absolutely no experimental evidence to indicate the presence of an ionic bond in the hydrogen molecule, H_2. It is, in fact, impossible to invent even a theoretical basis to suppose that one of the two combined hydrogen atoms should have a preference for an additional electron. Further, chlorine and fluorine form negative ions, $:\!\ddot{\text{Cl}}\!:^{-}$ and $:\!\ddot{\text{F}}\!:^{-}$. Ionic bond formation requires oppositely charged ions; similarly charged ions repel each other. Therefore, the bond in the known compound, chlorine fluoride, ClF,* cannot be ionic.

How do such atoms acquire the electronic structure of a noble gas? Each hydrogen atom needs 1 electron to become like a helium atom. So, instead of transferring electrons, the hydrogen atoms in H_2 *share* their electrons. The shared pair belongs to each atom. It is the common property of the two atoms, so that we can say each atom has acquired the helium electronic structure. Electrical forces so bond the two atoms (page 562) that an electric charge *does not develop* on either atom. This sharing of a pair of electrons produces a **covalent bond,** represented as a pair of dots,

$$\textcircled{H}\cdot + \cdot\text{H} \longrightarrow \text{H}\!:\!\text{H}$$

More usually, a dash, H—H, is used to represent a pair of electrons.

In a similar manner, the chlorine fluoride molecule forms a covalent bond. By sharing a pair of electrons, each atom acquires an octet:

$$:\!\overset{\cdot\cdot}{\text{Cl}}\cdot + \cdot\ddot{\text{F}}\!: \longrightarrow :\!\ddot{\text{Cl}}\!:\!\ddot{\text{F}}\!:$$

"Co" means together, jointly, and "valent" means having the power to combine, used here in the sense of atoms combining by sharing electrons.

---

*ClF, a colorless gas, is a typical **interhalogen compound,** a compound formed from different halogens. In general, the interhalogen compounds are very reactive, tending to attack most elements to produce a mixture of halides.

The electron dot formula of a molecule is known as an **electronic formula** or **structural formula.** The number of covalent bonds formed by an atom is usually equal to its common valence, the number of unpaired electrons appearing in its Lewis symbol. Examples, some of which are not consistent with the octet rule, are given in the table on page 249.

PROBLEM 3   Use Lewis symbols to represent the formation of the covalent compound nitrogen trifluoride (page 116) from the elements nitrogen and fluorine. Write the electronic formula for the compound.

Example 1

Write the electronic formula for the combination C_2H_7N, consistent with the octet rule and common valences.

Answer

The common valences are carbon, 4, —C̣—; nitrogen, 3, —N̈—; and hydrogen,

1, H—. It may be possible to combine these atoms in more than one way. Let us try

$$C—C—N$$

Then, let us add the number of bonds required to satisfy the common valences:

$$—\overset{|}{\underset{|}{C}}—\overset{|}{\underset{|}{C}}—\overset{..}{\underset{|}{N}}—$$

number of bonds   4   4   3

Now, complete the molecule by combination with H atoms, $H—\overset{H}{\underset{H}{C}}—\overset{H}{\underset{H}{C}}—\overset{..}{\underset{H}{N}}—H$

and we finish with C_2H_7N. This electronic formula is therefore acceptable. It is the formula for ethylamine, a colorless liquid smelling much like ammonia. Next, let us try

$$C—N—C$$

Then, add the number of bonds required to satisfy the common valences:

$$—\overset{|}{\underset{|}{C}}—\overset{..}{\underset{|}{N}}—\overset{|}{\underset{|}{C}}—$$

number of bonds   4   3   4

Now, complete the molecule by combination with H atoms, $H—\overset{H}{\underset{H}{C}}—\overset{..}{\underset{H}{N}}—\overset{H}{\underset{H}{C}}—H$

and again we finish with C_2H_7N. This electronic formula is also acceptable.

The formula for dimethylamine, a colorless "fishy" smelling gas with many industrial applications. This kind of behavior is treated in Chap. 22.

Suppose we try something like C—H—C—H—N or C—H—H—C—N? However, the mistake should be quickly spotted because hydrogen has a valence of 1, not the valence of 2 assigned to it in these incorrect combinations. The chemistry of hydrogen is determined by the number of electrons in one shell, the $1s$, which cannot take more than 2 electrons. Thus, the hydride ion H: ⁻, or H: H, or H: Cl: is possible. But :H: corresponds to $1s^4$, an impossible situation. In fact, while water and hydrogen sulfide exist as H—O̤—H and H—S̤—H molecules, molecules like H—H—O̤: or H—H—S̤: have never been detected (Chap. 24).

ATOM	GROUP NUMBER	NUMBER OF UNPAIRED ELECTRONS IN LEWIS SYMBOL	COMMON VALENCE	NUMBER OF COVALENT BONDS	TYPICAL COVALENT COMPOUND
H·	1	1	1	1	HCl

$$H + \cdot \ddot{Cl}{:} \longrightarrow H{:}\ddot{Cl}{:}$$

hydrogen chloride; b.p. −84°C

ATOM	GROUP NUMBER	NUMBER OF UNPAIRED ELECTRONS IN LEWIS SYMBOL	COMMON VALENCE	NUMBER OF COVALENT BONDS	TYPICAL COVALENT COMPOUND
Be·	2	2	2	2	$BeCl_2$

$$Be + \cdot \ddot{Cl}{:} + \cdot \ddot{Cl}{:} \longrightarrow {:}\ddot{Cl}{-}Be{-}\ddot{Cl}{:}$$

beryllium dichloride
colorless, poisonous solid;
b.p. 520°C

ATOM	GROUP NUMBER	NUMBER OF UNPAIRED ELECTRONS IN LEWIS SYMBOL	COMMON VALENCE	NUMBER OF COVALENT BONDS	TYPICAL COVALENT COMPOUND
·B·	3	3	3	3	BF_3

$$\cdot B\cdot + \cdot\ddot{F}{:} + \cdot\ddot{F}{:} + \cdot\ddot{F}{:} \longrightarrow$$

(boron trifluoride structure with F atoms bonded to B)

boron trifluoride
colorless gas;
b.p. −101°C

*In this chapter, the
student need not be
concerned with the
angles between atoms.*

ATOM	GROUP NUMBER	NUMBER OF UNPAIRED ELECTRONS IN LEWIS SYMBOL	COMMON VALENCE	NUMBER OF COVALENT BONDS	TYPICAL COVALENT COMPOUND
·C·	4	4	4	4	CH_4

$$\cdot C\cdot + H + H + H + H \longrightarrow$$

(methane structure with C bonded to four H)

methane
b.p. −184°C

ATOM	GROUP NUMBER	NUMBER OF UNPAIRED ELECTRONS IN LEWIS SYMBOL	COMMON VALENCE	NUMBER OF COVALENT BONDS	TYPICAL COVALENT COMPOUND
·Si·	4	4	4	4	(silicon tetrabromide structure with Si bonded to four Br)

silicon tetrabromide
colorless, fuming liquid;
b.p. 153°C

ATOM	GROUP NUMBER	NUMBER OF UNPAIRED ELECTRONS IN LEWIS SYMBOL	COMMON VALENCE	NUMBER OF COVALENT BONDS	TYPICAL COVALENT COMPOUND
·N·	5	3	3	3	(ammonia structure N bonded to three H)

ammonia

ATOM	GROUP NUMBER	NUMBER OF UNPAIRED ELECTRONS IN LEWIS SYMBOL	COMMON VALENCE	NUMBER OF COVALENT BONDS	TYPICAL COVALENT COMPOUND
·S:	6	2	2	2	H—S̤—H

*Extremely toxic, more
poisonous than HCN
(page 269), H_2S is a
colorless, flammable
gas with a
characteristic "rotten
egg" odor.*

hydrogen sulfide

ATOM	GROUP NUMBER	NUMBER OF UNPAIRED ELECTRONS IN LEWIS SYMBOL	COMMON VALENCE	NUMBER OF COVALENT BONDS	TYPICAL COVALENT COMPOUND
·I:	7	1	1	1	H—Ï:

hydrogen iodide
colorless, poisonous gas;
b.p. −35°C

PROBLEM 4 Write the electronic formula for CH_5N consistent with the octet rule and common valences.

8.6 CHANGING VALENCE

Notice (page 249) that the two molecules $BeCl_2$ and BF_3 have atoms with less than an octet associated with them. Indeed, the octet rule is a useful guide in that it does correctly describe hundreds of thousands of covalent compounds. But there are exceptions to this rule that are worthy of our attention (page 270). Nevertheless, the drive to obtain an octet explains the formation of ions from neutral molecules. Typical examples are

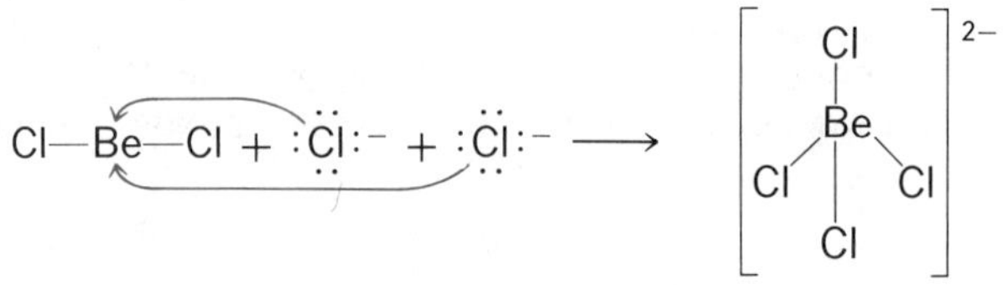

beryllium dichloride + chloride ions ⟶ beryllium tetrachloride ion

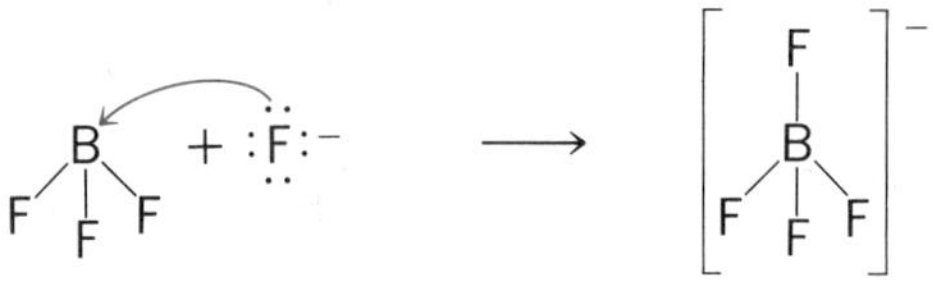

boron trifluoride + fluoride ion ⟶ boron tetrafluoride ion

In these ions, the beryllium and boron atoms are now associated with an octet. All bonds in $BeCl_4^{2-}$ are identical; it is impossible to assign the charges to any two Cl atoms. Hence we write

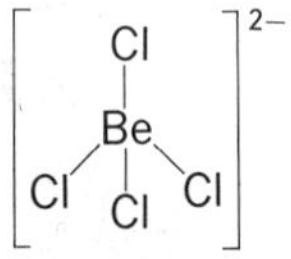

or $[BeCl_4]^{2-}$

and *not*

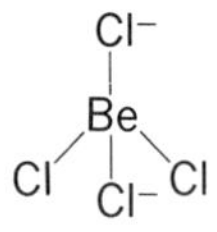

An atom in a molecule with an unshared pair of electrons usually is willing to share it with an atom, molecule, or ion that needs a pair of electrons to complete an octet (or the "duet" in hydrogen):

From the Italian word due, for two.

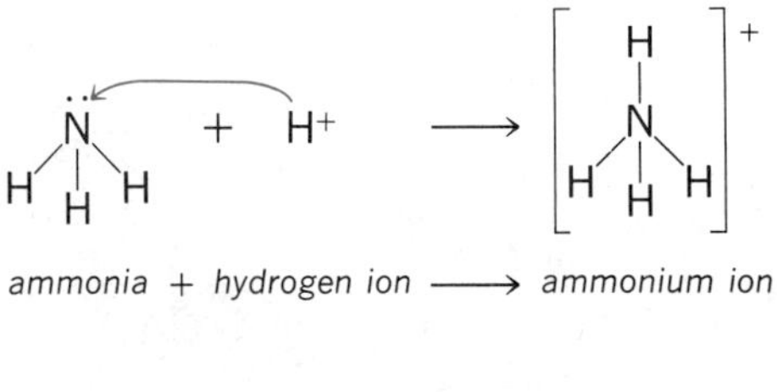

ammonia + hydrogen ion ⟶ ammonium ion

ammonia + boron trifluoride ⟶ ammonia-boron trifluoride
white solid; m.p. 163 °C

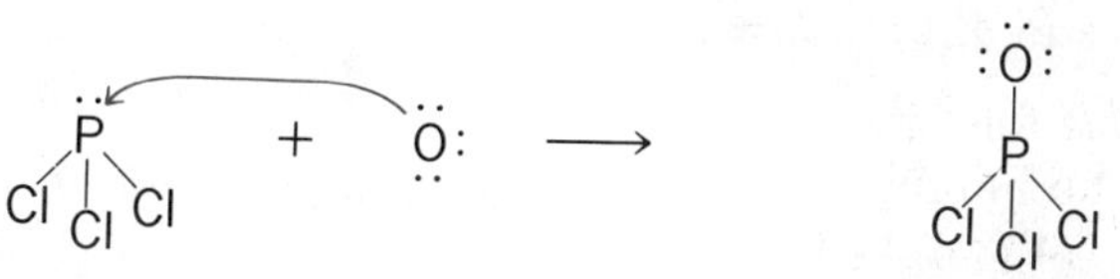

phosphorus trichloride + oxygen ⟶ phosphorus oxychloride
poisonous fuming liquid,   colorless, fuming liquid; b.p. 105 °C
b.p. 76 °C

Discovered by Gay-Lussac (1809) during his study of gases involved in chemical changes (page 135), $H_3N:BF_3$ is soluble in water but does not react with it.

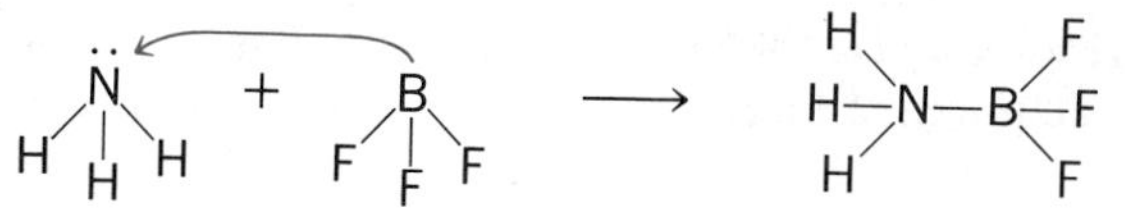

These illustrations are consistent with the octet rule, but the number of covalent bonds does not correspond to the common valence. The common valence of beryllium is 2, but it forms 4 covalent bonds in $BeCl_4^{2-}$. Oxygen, common valence 2, forms 1 covalent bond in $OPCl_3$. *The reader will, therefore, be specifically informed when an atom in a molecule or an ion does not have its common valence.*

PROBLEM 5 **(a) Write the electronic formula for each reactant and the product in the reaction $AlCl_3 + NCl_3 \longrightarrow$ product. (b) How many covalent bonds does aluminum form in $AlCl_3$ and in the product? (c) How many covalent bonds does nitrogen form in the product?**

Example 2

Draw the electronic formula consistent with the octet rule for the sulfate, SO_4^{2-}, and perchlorate, ClO_4^-, ions. The oxygen atoms in such ions are arranged around and singly bonded to the other ("central") atom.

Answer

Since the oxygen atoms are singly bonded to the S and Cl atoms, we write

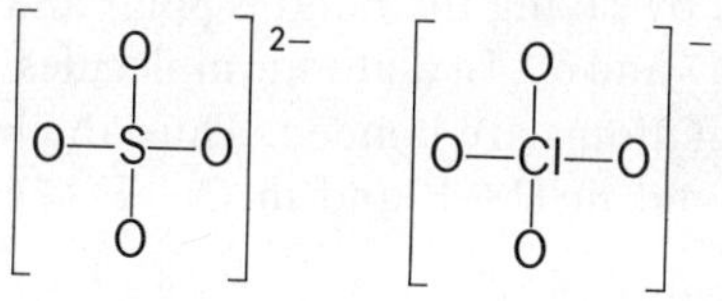

yielding octets only for the S and Cl atoms. The addition of 6 electrons to each O atom satisfies the octet rule,

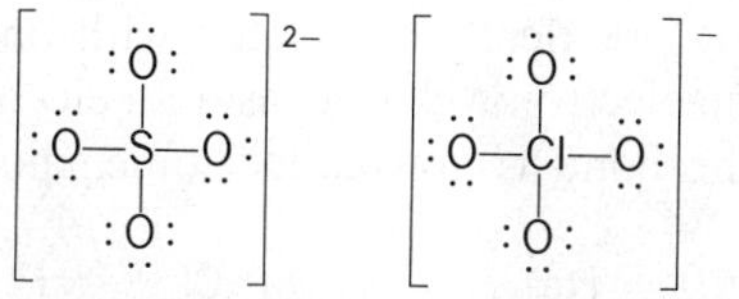

However, it is wise to check our answer by comparing the number of electrons used with the number available. For each formula, 32 electrons were used. The number of electrons available equals the group number for each atom, VI for S

and for O, and VII for Cl, *plus* the charge on the ion. The sulfate ion has a 2−
charge. Hence, it acquired 2 electrons while the perchlorate ion acquired 1
electron:

electrons available for SO_4^{2-}
$$= \text{group number for S} + 4 \times \text{group number for O} + \text{ion charge}$$
$$= 6 + (4 \times 6) + 2 = 32$$

electrons available for ClO_4^{-}
$$= \text{group number for Cl} + 4 \times \text{group number for O} + \text{ion charge}$$
$$= 7 + (4 \times 6) + 1 = 32$$

In general, the atoms in ions and molecules of the type XY_z are arranged so that the
Y atoms are bonded to the X atom, as in SO_4^{2-}, SF_6 (page 270), PO_4^{3-}, PCl_3, BF_4^{-},
and sulfuryl fluoride, SO_2F_2 (a chemically unreactive colorless gas, unaffected by
water at high temperatures).

PROBLEM 6   **Draw the electronic formula consistent with the octet rule for the ion
$AlCl_4^{-}$ and for the silicate ion, SiO_4^{4-}. Check the number of electrons used with the number of
electrons available, 32 for each ion. Check that there are indeed 32 electrons available.**

8.7 _____ PROPERTIES OF THE COVALENT BOND

No doubt, we have left the student with the false idea that the ionic bond and the
covalent bond are fundamentally different. Actually, the situation is akin to the
various tints obtained when white paint is added to blue paint. The tints gradually
blend from a pure blue to a pure white. Identical atoms, H—H or F—F, attract
electrons equally. But if the two bonded atoms are not alike, one atom is likely to
attract electrons more strongly than the other. That is, *the sharing of the electron pair
is not equal.* The distribution of the electron pair between the two bonded atoms is
not the same. The atoms which more strongly attracts the electron pair acquires more
of the charge and develops what is called a **partial negative charge,** a part of an
electronic charge. The other atom develops a **partial positive charge** of the same
magnitude. The molecule is, of course, electrically neutral, but more of the negative
charge sits on one end; the density of the electron cloud is greater around one atom.
This situation is described by saying the bond is **polar** and by designating the partial
charges with the symbols δ^+ and δ^-. In diatomic molecules, polarity may develop only
when two *different kinds* of atoms are bonded. Thus, the bond in H—H and in F—F
is called **nonpolar.** The bond in H—F and in Cl—F is called **polar,** shown as

*δ, the Greek letter
"delta," corresponds
to our letter "d" and
is used to mean "a
small part of."*

δ° δ°	δ° δ°	δ^+ δ^-	δ^+ δ^-
H—H	F—F	H—F	Cl—F
covalent bond	covalent bond	covalent bond	covalent bond
nonpolar	nonpolar	polar	polar

In some molecules, Cs—F, Na—F, Na—Cl, the unequal sharing of the electron pair is
so extreme that the pair is practically associated with only one atom. The partial
charge now approaches the electronic charge, as if an electron were transferred from
one atom to another.* The bond is now called ionic, shown as

Cs^+ F^-	Na^+ F^-	Na^+ Cl^-	F^- Ca^{2+} F^-
ionic bond	ionic bond	ionic bond	ionic bond

_____

*Ionic bonding is about 97 % complete in NaCl and practically 100 % complete in CsF. (From *Journal
of Chemical Physics,* B. P. Dailey and C. H. Townes, volume 23, 1955, page 122.)

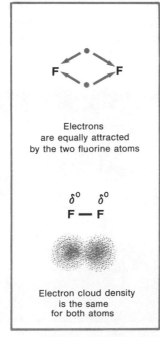

Electrons
are equally attracted
by the two fluorine atoms

$\delta^0 \quad \delta^0$
F — F

Electron cloud density
is the same
for both atoms

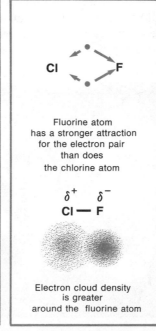

Fluorine atom
has a stronger attraction
for the electron pair
than does
the chlorine atom

$\delta^+ \quad \delta^-$
Cl — F

Electron cloud density
is greater
around the fluorine atom

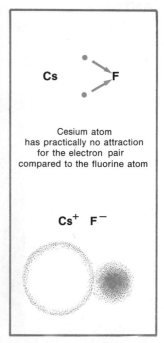

Cesium atom
has practically no attraction
for the electron pair
compared to the fluorine atom

$Cs^+ \quad F^-$

FIGURE 8.2 Representation of the unequal attraction of atoms in molecules for the electron pair.

and illustrated in Fig. 8.2. Thus, H—H, a typical *nonpolar covalent bond,* and Cs^+F^-, a typical *ionic bond, are extreme cases of the distribution of an electron pair* between two atoms. There are many variations of polar covalent bonds between these extreme distributions.

PROBLEM 7   **Pick the molecules you would expect to have a polar bond: Si—Cl, Cl—Cl, C—Cl, Cs—Br, Br—Br, Al—Cl.**

Dipole Moment   Let us represent a polar molecule like $\overset{\delta^+ \quad \delta^-}{\text{H—Cl}}$ as ⊕—⊖. The kinetic energy of gaseous molecules keeps them in motion and tends to keep them in disorder. That is, the charged ends will not point in any particular direction:

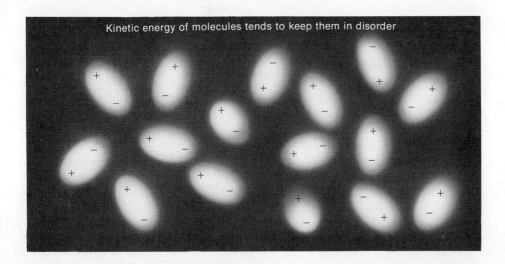

Kinetic energy of molecules tends to keep them in disorder

But we see that because opposite charges attract each other, the charged ends in molecules can make them line up in an electric field. So, if hydrogen chloride, HCl(g), is placed between two charged plates, the positive ends tend to line up toward the negative plate while the negative ends tend to line up toward the positive plate:

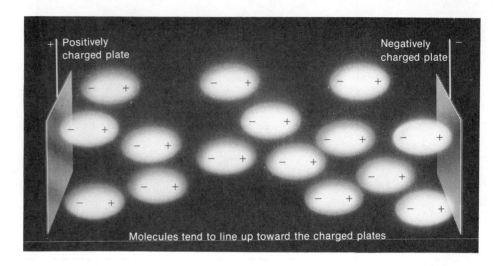

Molecules tend to line up toward the charged plates

Measurements based on this tendency to line up in an electric field are used to calculate the polarity of molecules. Such molecules are said to possess a **dipole moment,*** a measure of the amount of charge attracted to one end of a molecule and the distance between the oppositely charged ends. A dipole moment is usually shown with an arrow like so, H ⟶ Cl.

It is possible for a molecule with *more than one polar bond*, for example, gaseous beryllium dichloride, $\overset{\delta^-}{Cl}—\overset{\delta^+}{Be}—\overset{\delta^-}{Cl}$, to have a zero dipole moment. The entire molecule is nonpolar; it has no tendency to line up in an electric field, and *experimentally* it shows no polarity. The situation is similar to two horses of *equal strength* pulling a cart in opposite directions; the horses strain but the cart does not move. In BeCl$_2$, Cl ⟵ Be ⟶ Cl, the moment in one direction cancels the moment of equal strength but in the exact opposite direction. Therefore, BeCl$_2$ is *not* a polar molecule.

PROBLEM 8   From the following molecules, all of which have polar bonds, pick the one(s) that behave(s) like a polar molecule: (a) N—N ⟶ O, (b) H ⟶ I, (c) O ⟵ C ⟶ O.

The polarity of molecules is very important to our understanding of intermolecular attractive forces (page 257), the shapes of molecules (Chap. 18), and the formation of ions in solution (Chap. 10).

Electronegativity   Although the polarity of molecules can be experimentally determined, no one has yet devised an experiment to measure directly the tendency of a bonded atom to attract an electron pair. The ability of an atom in a molecule to

---

* Di, from *dyo,* the Greek word for two; hence, "two poles." However, "dipole" is used here to signify two partially charged ends as found in polar molecules. Peter Debye derived (1912) the equation from which dipole moments are calculated and developed theories to explain the behavior of polar molecules.

attract electrons to itself is named **electronegativity.** Electronegativity values are obtained from a variety of data and from a variety of assumptions. For example, one set of values is based on the average of the ionization energy—the energy required to pull off an electron (page 236)—and the electron affinity—the energy evolved when an electron is added to an atom (page 238). A small ionization energy and a small electron affinity for an atom mean a small desire to hold or to acquire an electron and, therefore, imply a small electronegativity value. Conversely, a high ionization energy and a high electron affinity for an atom imply a high electronegativity value.

The Russians prefer the term electrophily, from the Greek words meaning electron loving.

Table 8.1 lists the electronegativities of the representative elements. Notice that *electronegativities increase from left to right in a period* and, with exceptions, *decrease from top to bottom in a group.* Note that fluorine (high ionization energy and high electron affinity) and oxygen are the most electronegative elements, while the alkali metals, Group IA (low ionization energy, low electron affinity), are among the least electronegative elements.

Electronegativities were first derived by Linus Pauling (1932) from bond energy data (Chap. 9), and by Robert Mulliken (1934) from ionization energy and electron affinity data.

A question that frequently "bugs" the student is, "How do I know if a compound is ionic or covalent?" Table 8.1 permits us to predict with some confidence which bonds are ionic or covalent and which bonds are polar. The larger the difference in the electronegativities of two bonded atoms, the greater is the opportunity to form an ionic bond. For example, cesium, Cs (0.86), and fluorine, F (4.1), form an ionic bond. The F atom has a much greater attraction for the electron pair. On the other hand, chlorine, Cl (2.8), and bromine, Br (2.7), with nearly equal electronegativities, form a covalent bond. These conclusions are in agreement with the observation that the alkali (Group IA) and the alkaline earth (Group IIA) metals generally form ionic bonds with Group VIA and Group VIIA (halogen) elements, while nonmetallic

**TABLE 8.1
ELECTRONEGATIVITIES OF THE
REPRESENTATIVE ELEMENTS***

IA	IIA	IIIA	IVA	VA	VIA	VIIA
H 2.1						
Li 0.97	Be 1.5	B 2.0	C 2.5	N 3.0	O 3.5	F 4.1
Na 1.0	Mg 1.2	Al 1.5	Si 1.9	P 2.2	S 2.4	Cl 2.8
K 0.91	Ca 1.0	Ga 1.8	Ge 2.0	As 2.2	Se 2.5	Br 2.7
Rb 0.89	Sr 0.99	In 1.5	Sn 1.7	Sb 2.1	Te 2.0	I 2.2
Cs 0.86	Ba 0.97	Tl 1.4	Pb 1.6	Bi 2.2	Po 1.8	At 2.0

* Electronegativity values of most elements are not constant; for example, carbon has different values in CH_4, C_2H_4, and C_2H_2, because the nature of the bond differs in these compounds (pages 581–583). Nevertheless, these values, calculated by A. L. Allred and Eugene Rochow (1958, 1961) are a useful guide. The values for noble gases are not necessarily zero but they are too uncertain for inclusion in this table. Scale is arbitrary. These values do not represent absolute electronegativities or atomic constants like atomic weights or ionization energies.

elements combine with each other by covalent bonding. We content ourselves with the generalization that a difference of 1.5 or more produces an ionic bond; a difference of less than 1.5 produces a covalent bond.*

Example 3

Use Table 8.1 to pick the ionic and covalent compounds from the following list: MgO, Rb_2S, AlF_3, $AlBr_3$, and $SiCl_4$.

Answer

First represent each compound with the appropriate number of bonds—one in MgO, two in Rb_2S, three in AlF_3 and $AlBr_3$, four in $SiCl_4$—and next to each atom place its electronegativity value as shown:

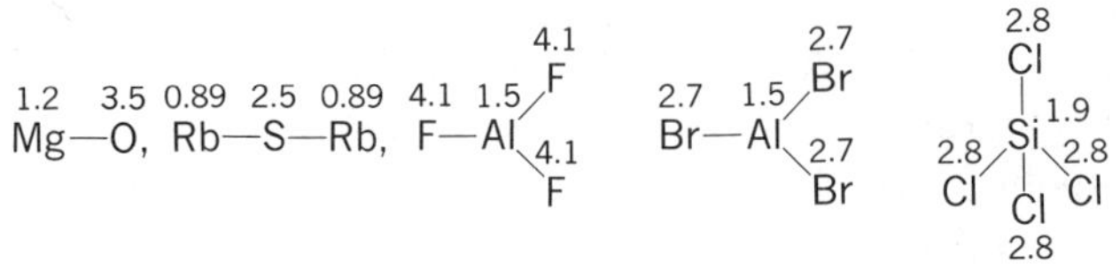

$$
\begin{array}{ccccc}
& & & & \overset{4.1}{F} \\
\underset{Mg}{1.2}-\underset{O}{3.5} & \underset{Rb}{0.89}-\underset{S}{2.5}-\underset{Rb}{0.89} & \underset{F}{4.1}-\overset{1.5}{Al}\diagdown & \overset{2.7}{Br} \\
\end{array}
$$

Mg—O, Rb—S—Rb, F—Al (4.1 F, 1.5, 4.1 F), Br—Al (2.7 Br, 1.5, 2.7 Br), Si (2.8 Cl, 1.9, 2.8 Cl, 2.8 Cl, 2.8 Cl)

Then, take the difference in the electronegativities between two bonded atoms. Since the two Rb—S bonds in Rb_2S are similar, *one subtraction* operation suffices. The same applies to AlF_3, $AlBr_3$, and $SiCl_4$. If the difference is less than 1.5 the bond is covalent:

Mg—O, $3.5 - 1.2 = 2.3$ ionic bond; MgO, ionic compound
Rb—S, $2.5 - 0.89 = 1.6$ ionic bond; Rb_2S, ionic compound
Al—F, $4.1 - 1.5 = 2.6$ ionic bond; AlF_3, ionic compound
Al—Br, $2.7 - 1.5 = 1.2$ covalent bond; $AlBr_3$ covalent compound
Si—Cl, $2.8 - 1.9 = 1.1$ covalent bond; $SiCl_4$ covalent compound

---

PROBLEM 9 Use Table 8.1 to pick the covalent compounds from the following list: CaI_2, $BeBr_2$, BeF_2, CCl_4, PH_3, and OF_2.

Bond polarity results when atoms with different electronegativities are bonded. The greater the difference in the electronegativities of two bonded atoms, the greater is the bond polarity. The more electronegative atom will acquire a partial negative charge while the other atom acquires a partial positive charge. We content ourselves with the conclusion that *when the difference is zero, the bond is nonpolar*.

Example 4

Use Table 8.1 to pick the polar bonds from the following list of bonds: O—Cl, F—Cl, Br—Cl, and Sb—H. Indicate the atoms which acquire a partial charge.

Answer

If the difference in the electronegativities of the two bonded atoms is not zero, then the bond is polar:

---

*Some exceptions: Hydrides of Group IA (LiH $\longrightarrow$ CsH) and Group IIA (BeH$_2$ $\longrightarrow$ BaH$_2$) are ionic although electronegativity differences are less than 1.5. C—F and H—F are covalent bonds although electronegativity differences are greater than 1.5.

3.5 2.8
O—Cl, 3.5 − 2.8 = 0.7, polar $\overset{\delta^+}{Cl}$—$\overset{\delta^-}{O}$

4.1 2.8
F—Cl, 4.1 − 2.8 = 1.3, polar $\overset{\delta^+}{Cl}$—$\overset{\delta^-}{F}$

2.7 2.8
Br—Cl, 2.8 − 2.7 = 0.1, polar $\overset{\delta^+}{Br}$—$\overset{\delta^-}{Cl}$

2.1   2.1
Sb—H, 2.1 − 2.1 = 0.0, nonpolar

PROBLEM 10   Use Table 8.1 to pick the polar bonds from the following list of bonds: N—H, Al—Cl, F—F, C—H, and C—Br. Indicate the atoms which acquire a partial charge.

PROPERTIES OF IONIC AND COVALENT SUBSTANCES _____ 8.8

We have just considered electronegativity (page 255) as a basis for distinguishing between ionic and covalent compounds. The distinction may also be made on the basis of melting and boiling points, because these properties are related to the type of bonding. However, the boiling point is a more reliable standard than the melting point.

Covalent Substances   Covalent substances, such as hydrogen, H_2, carbon monoxide, CO, ammonia, NH_3, and hydrogen chloride, HCl, *consist of individual molecules. The atoms in these molecules are held together by strong covalent bonds,* but *the forces between the molecules,* the intermolecular (van der Waals) forces, *are comparatively weak.* The attraction between molecules results from the electrical attractive force between the partially charged portions of the molecules, illustrated below:

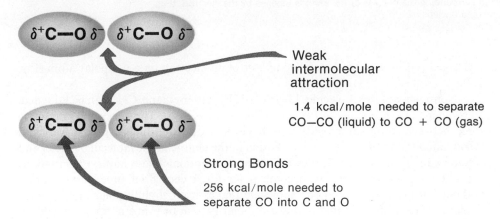

Weak intermolecular attraction

1.4 kcal/mole needed to separate CO—CO (liquid) to CO + CO (gas)

Strong Bonds

256 kcal/mole needed to separate CO into C and O

This kind of intermolecular attractive force is known as a **dipole force** and is responsible for holding molecules in liquids and solids. It also plays a major role in determining solubilities (page 325). This electric attraction is weaker than the attraction between charged ions because the partial charges are much less than the unit charges (1, 2, or 3) on the ions.

The effect of a polar molecule on a nonpolar molecule is the same as the effect of

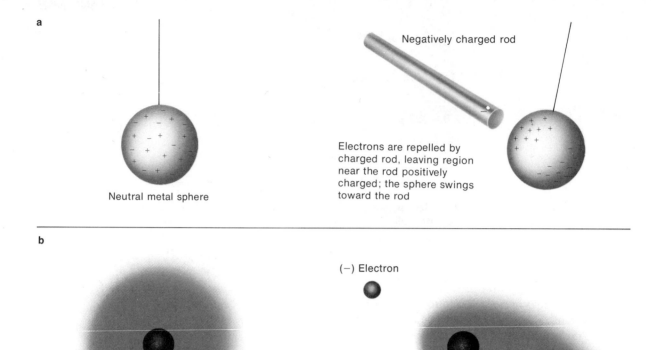

a

Neutral metal sphere

Negatively charged rod

Electrons are repelled by charged rod, leaving region near the rod positively charged; the sphere swings toward the rod

b

(−) Electron

Neutral nonpolar atom

Atom becomes polarized when approached by a negative charge

FIGURE 8.3 (a) Since electrons can move and redistribute themselves, an attractive force develops between a charged rod and a neutral metal body. (b) Polarization of a neutral atom of boron by an electron. The electron cloud surrounding the nucleus of the atom is repelled by the electron, thus exposing the positively charged nucleus.

a charged rod on a neutral metal sphere or of an electron on a nonpolar atom (Fig. 8.3).

Nonpolar gaseous molecules like He, H_2, F_2, and methane, CH_4, can be liquefied. This means that *attractive forces must exist in these gases*. The very weak attractive force between nonpolar molecules is believed to result from a spontaneous and instantaneous unbalance in the distribution of the charge in the molecule. Nuclei and electrons in atoms and molecules are always in motion. These natural fluctuations cause a nonpolar molecule to become polar for a very brief time period. Thus, without outside help, a nonpolar molecule makes itself slightly polar and, in turn, "polarizes" its neighbors; that is, it causes polarity to appear in a nonpolar neighbor, illustrated below:

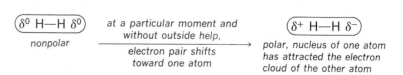

δ^0 H—H δ^0

nonpolar

at a particular moment and without outside help,

electron pair shifts toward one atom

δ^+ H—H δ^-

polar, nucleus of one atom has attracted the electron cloud of the other atom

$$\left(\delta^+ \; H\!-\!H \; \delta^-\right) + \left(\delta^0 \; H\!-\!H \; \delta^0\right) \xrightarrow{\;polarization\;} \left(\delta^+ \; H\!-\!H \; \delta^-\right) + \left(\delta^+ \; H\!-\!H \; \delta^-\right)$$

polar   nonpolar   polar   polar

neighbor   neighbor

These self-made polar bonds, resulting from the natural fluctuation of electrons, hold the molecules together in liquids and solids. These weak forces are known as **London forces,** named after Fritz London, who developed (1928) the quantum mechanical basis for this explanation.* London forces appear to be roughly related to the number of electrons in a molecule. The more electrons in a molecule, the greater the force. For example, the intermolecular attractive (London) force is greater in liquid neon, $_{10}Ne$, with 10 electrons, than in liquid helium, $_2He$, with 2 electrons.

PROBLEM 11   **Look up the atomic numbers of the Group 0 elements, inside the front cover, and arrange them in the order of increasing intermolecular attractive force.**

Since intermolecular attractive forces are comparatively weak, the molecules are easily separated. Not much heat is required to overcome these intermolecular forces. In general, the stronger the attractive forces, the greater the heat energy required to overcome them. When solid covalent compounds melt or liquid covalent compounds boil, *molecules separate.* Hence, at room conditions, *covalent substances* are generally gases, or volatile liquids, or solids with comparatively *low melting points and boiling points.* Very few covalent substances boil above 600 °C. See Fig. 8.4.

Network Covalent Substances   Let us next consider the effect on the melting and boiling points of a *covalent substance,* such as silicon carbide, SiC, *that cannot exist as individual molecules* in the solid or liquid states.

Silicon carbide (*carborundum*), ranked next below diamond in hardness,** is manufactured in an electric furnace from sand and carbon

Pure sand (silica) is pulverized quartz, SiO_2. Opal is an amorphous form of silica.

---

    *Experimental confirmation is found in the fact that the attraction between two metal, *electrically neutral* spheres is very slightly (but measurably) greater than the attraction due only to gravitational attraction.

    The hardest substance known, diamond is one of the standards used for measuring hardness. The **Mohs-Wooddell hardness scale measures resistance to grinding under standardized conditions. It ranges from talc (hardness 1) to diamond (42.5).

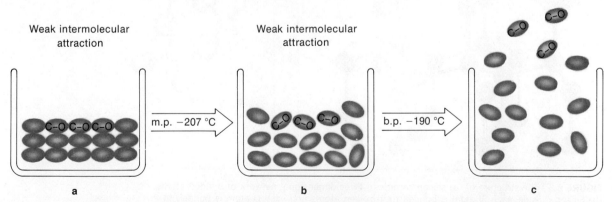

FIGURE 8.4 Representation of the melting and boiling of a covalent substance involving the separation of molecules held together by weak intermolecular forces.

$$SiO_2(c) + 3C(excess\ coke) \longrightarrow SiC(c) + 2CO(g)$$

and is used to manufacture cutting and polishing tools.

In silicon carbide, the silicon and carbon atoms, $\cdot \overset{\cdot}{Si} \cdot$ and $\cdot \overset{\cdot}{C} \cdot$, are bonded, conforming to the octet rule. The common valence of 4 for silicon is satisfied as shown:

$$
\begin{array}{c}
\cdot \overset{\cdot\cdot}{C} \cdot \\
| \\
\cdot \overset{\cdot\cdot}{C} - Si - \overset{\cdot\cdot}{C} \cdot \\
| \\
\cdot \overset{\cdot\cdot}{C} \cdot
\end{array}
$$

The common valence of 4 for carbon is also satisfied as shown:

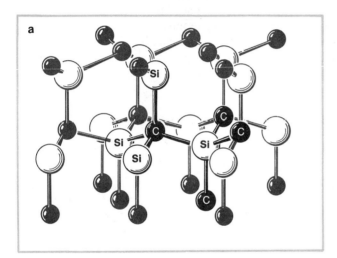

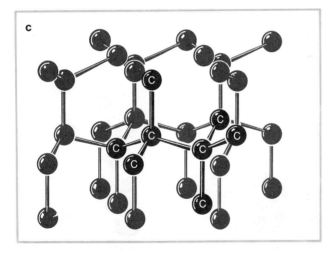

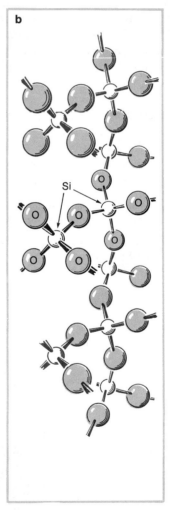

FIGURE 8.5 The structure of (a) silicon carbide, a three-dimensional network of bonded atoms. (b) Silicon dioxide, each Si atom is bonded to 4 oxygen atoms and each O atom is bonded to 2 silicon atoms, forming a three-dimensional network of bonded atoms. (c) Diamond, each C atom is bonded to 4 other carbon atoms, forming a three-dimensional network of bonded atoms.

```
            ·         ·
            ·Si—C—Si·
            |   |   |
   ·Si—C—Si—C—Si·
      |   |   |
     ·Si—C—Si·
            ·         ·
```

*SiC has a three-
dimensional structure,
Fig. 8.5(a).*

But we can still add carbon and silicon atoms without violation of any rules:

```
         ·C—Si—C—Si—C·
         |   |   |   |
·C—Si—C—Si—C—Si—C·
    |   |   |   |
   ·C—Si—C—Si—C·
    |   |   |
  ·Si—C—Si—C—Si·
```

Actually, we can continue to extend the molecule as long as we wish. There is no end
to this molecule. Silicon carbide is thus a network of covalently bonded atoms to
which the usual concept of a molecule is not applicable. Unlike individual H—Cl
molecules, no one atom can be said to be exclusively bonded to another one atom.
Rather, each Si atom is bonded to 4 C atoms and each C atom is bonded to 4 Si
atoms. However, we can regard any one crystal of silicon carbide, regardless of size, as
a **"giant molecule."** The structure of silicon carbide is shown in Fig. 8.5(a).

Silicon carbide is a typical **network covalent substance.** Other examples shown in
Fig. 8.5 are silicon dioxide (quartz), SiO_2, and diamond, C. It is usually the nonme-

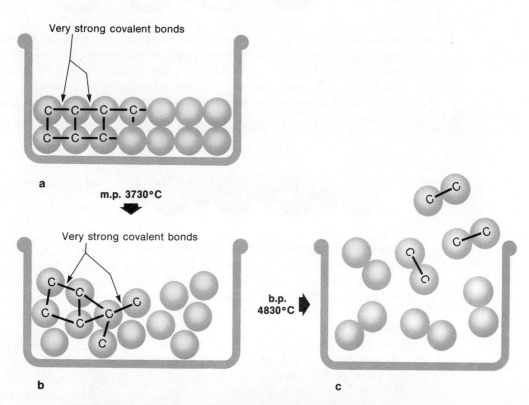

FIGURE 8.6 Representation of the melting and boiling of a network covalent substance involving
the separation of atoms held together by very strong covalent bonds.

tallic elements in the center of the periodic table, Groups IVA and VA, that form network covalent solids.

The attractive forces between the atoms in these network covalent substances are *very strong*. For example, while only 4.1 kcal/mole are required to separate the molecules in solid HCl, HCl(c) $\longrightarrow$ HCl(g), 171 kcal/mole are required to separate a collection of bonded carbon atoms in diamond, C(*diamond*) $\longrightarrow$ C(g). The atoms are, therefore, very difficult to separate. When network covalent substances melt or boil, *atoms separate*. Considerable heat is required to break the covalent bond between these atoms. Hence, at room conditions, *network covalent substances* are solids with *very high melting and boiling points*. Silicon dioxide melts at 1710 °C and boils at 2590 °C; diamond melts at 3730 °C and boils at 4830 °C. See Fig. 8.6.

In the vapor state.

Ionic Substances   When ionic (highly polar) molecules* such as Na$^+$Cl$^-$ and Cs$^+$F$^-$ solidify, they do not condense as individual molecules or atoms. Rather, they form an *ionic solid, a solid composed of ions in which no positive ion can be said to be bonded to any one negative ion*. For example:

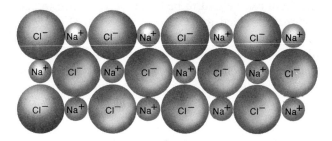

Sodium chloride is thus a network of bonded ions. As in silicon carbide, individual molecules do not exist, and any one crystal of sodium chloride may be called a giant molecule. The structure of sodium chloride is shown in Fig. 8.7. Each Na$^+$ ion is bonded to 6 Cl$^-$ ions and each Cl$^-$ ion is bonded to 6 Na$^+$ ions.

The attractive forces between the ions in these ionic solids are strong. For example,

Strong bonds

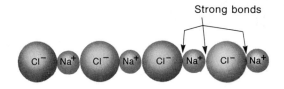

183 kcal/mole are needed to separate a collection of bonded Na$^+$Cl$^-$ ions into individual Na$^+$ and Cl$^-$ ions

much heat is required to break these ionic bonds. The ions are, therefore, difficult to separate. When these solids melt or boil, *ions are separated*. Hence, at room conditions, ionic compounds are solids, generally with high melting and boiling points, but not as high as those of the network covalent substances. For example, NaCl melts at 801 °C and boils at 1413 °C; NaOH melts at 318 °C and boils at 1390 °C. See Fig. 8.8.

The boiling points given in Table 4.1, page 116, nicely correlate with the character of the bonding. The ionic character decreases from left to right in a period and the boiling point generally decreases from left to right: LiCl (*ionic, b.p.* 1382 °C) $\longrightarrow$ ClF (*covalent, b.p.* -101 °C). The ionic character increases from top to bottom in a group and the boiling point generally increases from top to bottom: CCl$_4$ (*covalent, b.p.* 77 °C) $\longrightarrow$ PbCl$_2$ (*ionic, b.p.* 950 °C).

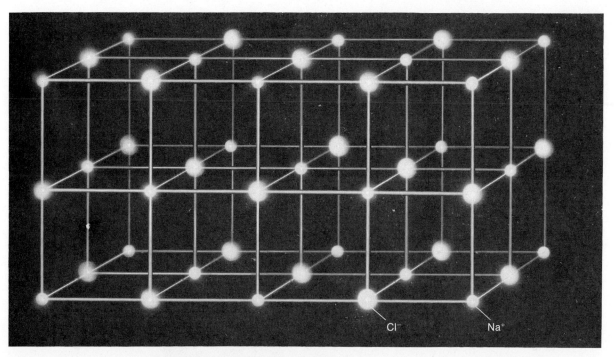

FIGURE 8.7 The structure of sodium chloride, a face-centered cubic network of bonded ions, page 85. Actually, the ions are very closely packed.

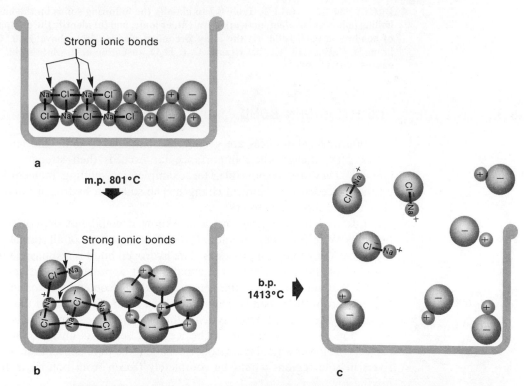

FIGURE 8.8 Representation of the melting and boiling of an ionic substance involving the separation of ions held together by strong ionic bonds. (Model of molten salt after L. V. Woodcock, *Nature, Physical Science,* volume 232, 1971, page 63.)

TABLE 8.2

A COMPARISON OF THE PROPERTIES OF COVALENT, NETWORK COVALENT, AND IONIC SUBSTANCES

	COVALENT	IONIC	NETWORK COVALENT	METAL
Unit Particle in Solid	molecule	ion	atom	atom
Bonding Force in Solid	intermolecular	ionic	covalent	metallic
Electrical Conductivity				
Solid	no	no*	no	yes
Liquid	no*	yes	no	yes
Approximate Range of Boiling Points	−270 °C to 600 °C	700 °C to 3600 °C**	2000 °C to 6000 °C	650 °C to 6000 °C

* A few exceptions exist. For example, covalent solid SbF_3 conducts when melted; ionic solid KAg_4I_5 ($K^+ + 4Ag^+ + 5I^-$) conducts.
** A covalent compound, $C_{42}H_{18}$, whose flat, electron-rich molecules fit together perfectly, develops such strong London forces that it boils above 700 °C. Beryllium oxide, an ionic solid but with considerable network covalent character, boils at about 3900 °C. Overlap of boiling points is expected since few compounds are purely ionic or purely covalent (page 252).

However, the property that most clearly identifies an ionic compound is its ability to conduct an electric current when melted. Ions carry an electric current by moving through a liquid (Chap. 11). In the liquid state, the ions can move. On the other hand, an ionic solid is generally a poor conductor because the ions are too strongly bonded to move about freely.

Table 8.2 summarizes the differences in the properties of covalent, network covalent, and ionic substances. (Metals, Chap. 20, are included *only* for comparison.)

PROBLEM 12 **(a) Use Table 8.2 to classify the following solids on the basis of the given boiling points as covalent, network covalent, or ionic, and (b) identify the unit particle and type of bonding in each solid: (i) the alloy zirconium nitride, ZrN, above 3600 °C; (ii) calcium bromide, $CaBr_2$, 810 °C; (iii) vitamin C, $C_6H_8O_6$ (ascorbic acid, white solid, whose absence causes scurvy), 300 °C.**

8.9 THE HYDROGEN BOND

Intermolecular forces are very weak compared to ionic and covalent bonding forces. Nevertheless, their importance far exceeds their strength and cannot be ignored. They are responsible, for example, for guiding molecules into crucial positions needed for chemical changes. The so-called hydrogen bond falls into the class of intermolecular forces.

Life and the environment as we know it could not exist without hydrogen bonding. Water, without question, is the most important of all simple substances for biological and geological processes. The hydrogen bond is responsible for the unique property of water that makes it expand as it approaches the freezing point and freezes. Water has its maximum density at 3.98 °C; cooled below or heated above this temperature, water expands. The volume of a gram of ice is larger than the volume of a gram of water at 0 °C. Ice, less dense than water, consequently floats. Ice thus forms at the top of a body of water. The ice layer serves as an insulating blanket and protects the lower water layers from freezing. If ice were denser than water, lakes and rivers in cold regions would be completely frozen from bottom to top, killing all marine life.

The large molecules—proteins and enzymes (Chap. 23)—necessary to all life processes must line up in a definite orderly manner before they can do their necessary

Ice
0 °C
4 °C

Freezing of water
in a lake

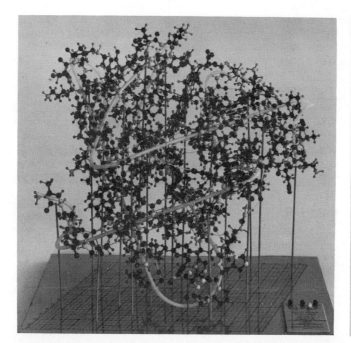

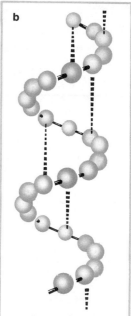

FIGURE 8.9 (a) A long protein molecule (myoglobin,* 18 × 10³ g/mole). (Photo courtesy John Kendrew, University of Cambridge, and Herman Watson, University of Bristol.)

(b) "Corkscrew coiled" (helix) portion of a long protein molecule held in a specific arrangement through hydrogen bonds, represented by broken lines. Nature does not permit such molecules to flop into any haphazard position. These bonds hold the molecule in the three-dimensional compact form necessary for biological activity. If the hydrogen bonds are broken, activity is lost, even though the composition of the molecule is not changed. Such structures were first proposed by Linus Pauling and Robert Corey (1950), based on the work of William Astbury (1930), Maurice Huggins (1943), and others.

The first three-dimensional structure of a protein molecule showing atomic detail as in (a) was worked out by John Kendrew (1959) from the reflection of X-ray photons impinged upon the crystals of myoglobin.

*Myoglobin is found in muscle tissue. Like hemoglobin it contains Fe^{2+} and is therefore an oxygen-carrier. It serves as an oxygen reservoir. When the partial pressure of oxygen is too low for hemoglobin to hold oxygen, the myoglobin supplies the necessary oxygen to the tissues. Therefore, with hemoglobin, it is classified as a respiratory protein.

work. Hydrogen bonding serves as the "policeman" in maintaining order in the biological world of living cells. An illustration is given in Fig. 8.9. It is also believed that hydrogen bonding is responsible for the action of local anesthetics, such as procaine. General anesthetics induce unconsciousness by breaking hydrogen bonds, causing certain proteins to alter their shapes and become inactive.

The hydrogen bond is an unusually strong intermolecular bond. It is generally stronger than the bonds due to ordinary intermolecular forces (dipole or London forces), but weaker than most covalent or ionic bonds. The hydrogen bond is *formed between molecules in which hydrogen is bonded to a highly electronegative atom,* particularly, fluorine, oxygen, or nitrogen. *The electronegative atom must have at least one pair of unshared electrons,* as in ammonia, $\ddot{N}H_3$, or water, $H\ddot{O}H$. The hydrogen atom can be visualized as a bridge that connects molecules together. The electronegative atom attracts the partially positive hydrogen atom of another molecule

Water is the primary stuff of life. "A boy weighing 100 lb is 60 lb water; the rest is 'boy'."

The molecules are hooked up in a definite pattern,

$$F—H---F\\ \qquad\qquad H$$

$$:\!\ddot{F}\!—H \longleftrightarrow \overset{\delta^-\;\;\delta^+}{:\!\ddot{F}\!—H} \longrightarrow \overset{\delta^-\;\;\delta^+}{:\!\ddot{F}\!—H}\cdots:\!\ddot{F}\!—H$$
Hydrogen bond

265

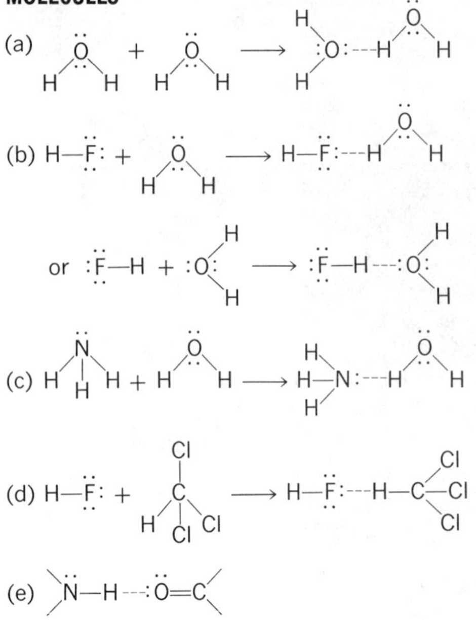

(a)

(b)

or

(c)

(d)

(e)

FIGURE 8.10 Examples of hydrogen bonding represented by broken lines: (a) two water molecules bonded, (b) a hydrogen fluoride and a water molecule bonded, (c) an ammonia molecule and a water molecule. (The hydrogen bonding is sufficiently strong so that the molecular state of NH_3 in water may be represented as $NH_3 \cdot H_2O$ or NH_4OH, depending on personal preference.) (d) A hydrogen fluoride and a chloroform molecule bonded through hydrogen bonding. (e) The $\geq$N—H---O=C$\leq$ hydrogen bond is largely responsible for the three-dimensional structures of all proteins. Ionic bonds and London forces are also involved in stabilizing protein structures. The meaning of the two dashes between the C and O atoms is considered in the next section.

and so bridges the molecules together. This type of bond in which the hydrogen atom sits between two other atoms (two pairs of electrons) is called the **hydrogen bond.** In the hydrogen difluoride ion, HF_2^-, the hydrogen atom is between the two fluorine atoms, so that this ion is regarded as two fluoride (negative) ions bridged by a proton:

The hydrogen bond is therefore also known as a "bridge bond."

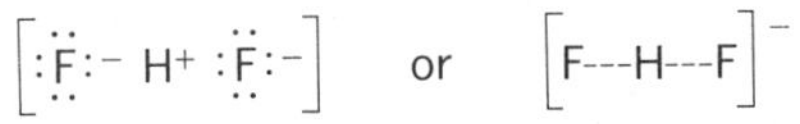

$$\left[:\ddot{F}:^- \ H^+ \ :\ddot{F}:^- \right] \quad or \quad \left[F\text{---}H\text{---}F \right]^-$$

Other examples of hydrogen bonding are given in Fig. 8.10.

In general, *the higher the electronegativity of the atoms* being bridged, *the stronger the bond;* F, O, and N form strong hydrogen bonds, while Br and C form weak hydrogen bonds.

The size of the atom and the angle at which the hydrogen bond forms also influence bond strength.

Hydrogen bonding accounts for the unexpected sharp rise in the boiling point of water in the Group VIA series, H_2Te, H_2Se, H_2S, H_2O, and in the boiling point of hydrogen fluoride in the Group VIIA series, HI, HBr, HCl, HF, illustrated in Fig. 8.11. The hydrogen bond makes it more difficult to separate H_2O and HF molecules in liquid HF and water.

PROBLEM 13 Consult Table 8.1, page 255. (a) Pick the compound in which you would expect strong hydrogen bond formation: hydrogen sulfide, $H_2\ddot{S}:$, ammonia, $\dot{N}H_3$, or phosphine,

Phosphine, a very toxic gas, burns readily in air and explodes in pure oxygen.

$\ddot{P}H_3$. (b) Show how $R—N\overset{\textstyle H}{\underset{\textstyle H}{<}}$ and $R—\ddot{O}—H$ may be combined through hydrogen bonding.

(c) Is hydrogen bonding possible in CH_4? in CH_3F?

In ice, each oxygen atom is bonded to 4 other oxygen atoms by hydrogen bonds as shown in Fig. 8.12(a).

The oxygen atoms are arranged in the same way as the carbon atoms in diamond (Fig. 8.5, page 260). Nevertheless, ice is very much softer and has a much lower melting point because the hydrogen bonds are much weaker than the C—C covalent bonds in diamond. Also, the distance between the oxygen atoms is much larger than

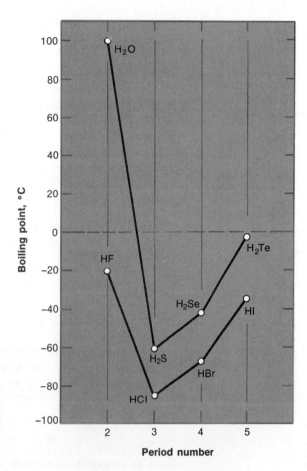

FIGURE 8.11 Boiling points of hydrides of Groups VIA and VIIA plotted against the period number. Hydrogen bonding is weak in these hydrides, except in H_2O and HF. Very foul-smelling, H_2Se and H_2Te are extremely toxic.

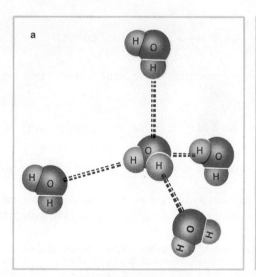 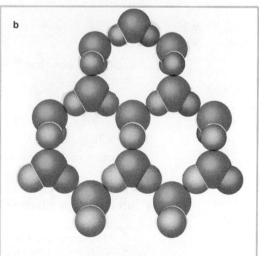

FIGURE 8.12 The structure of ice. Each oxygen atom is connected ("bridged") to four other oxygen atoms by hydrogen bonds, shown for one water molecule in (a). A hydrogen atom whose position is not exactly fixed sits nervously between two oxygen atoms.

The representation in (b) makes the hexagonal pattern, the six-membered oxygen rings characteristic of snow crystals, more evident. For better clarity of the open spaces characteristic of ice, all oxygen atoms connected to any one oxygen atom by hydrogen bonds are not shown.

Almost twice the distance. The hydrogen bond energy is about 5 kcal/mole; the C—C bond energy is 171 kcal/mole.

the C—C distance. This makes the empty spaces in ice much larger than those in diamond. This gives ice an open framework (Fig. 8.12(b)).* When ice melts, some hydrogen bonds are broken. The "bridges" and the open framework collapse, causing water molecules to fall into the empty spaces. This close packing of molecules makes the liquid occupy a smaller volume than the ice, and the density increases. However, some hydrogen bonding is still present in liquid water, so that the structure of liquid water at 0 °C is more like that of ice than it is of the liquid at 100 °C. Above 0 °C, the collapse of hydrogen bridges continues and the volume continues to decrease until the temperature 3.98 °C is reached. Above this temperature, the kinetic energy of the molecules suffices to spread the molecules apart. This increasing movement of the molecules increases the space between them, causing expansion of the liquid.** Water vapor above 100 °C consists of individual water molecules.

PROBLEM 14 Explain the change that should occur in the volume and density when ice melts at 0 °C (a) if molecular motion increases the distance between *all* H_2O molecules at 0 °C; (b) if *all* hydrogen bonds break at 0 °C. (c) Liquid water has its maximum density at 3.98 °C. Which effect is more important in water between 0 °C and 3.98 °C? Above 3.98 °C?

8.10 DOUBLE AND TRIPLE BONDS

In many covalent compounds, atoms share more than one pair of electrons to satisfy the octet rule. This kind of bonding also explains the chemistry of covalent compounds. For example, if the nitrogen molecule, N_2, is written with one bond

$$\cdot \ddot{N} \cdot \ + \ \cdot \ddot{N} \cdot \ \longrightarrow \ \cdot \ddot{N} : \ddot{N} \cdot \quad \textit{(not correct)}$$

each atom has only 6 valence electrons associated with it. If we write a second bond between the two atoms

$$\cdot \ddot{N} \cdot \ + \ \cdot \ddot{N} \cdot \ \longrightarrow \ \cdot \ddot{N} :: \ddot{N} \cdot \quad \textit{(not correct)}$$

each atom now has 7 valence electrons. If we write a third bond between the two atoms

$$\cdot \ddot{N} \cdot \ + \ \cdot \ddot{N} \cdot \ \longrightarrow \ \ddot{N} ::: \ddot{N} \quad \text{or} \quad \ddot{N} \equiv \ddot{N} \quad \textit{(correct)}$$

the octet rule is now satisfied. The sharing of 3 pairs of electrons is called a **triple bond.**

Ethylene, C_2H_4, is a gaseous hydrocarbon that is largely obtained as a by-product in the manufacture of gasoline. It combines very quickly with many substances

---

*The empty spaces are large enough, for example, to accommodate atoms and molecules such as radon, Rn, and chlorine, Cl_2. The resulting compounds, $Rn(H_2O)_6$ and $Cl_2(H_2O)_8$, are known as **"cage compounds"** (or **clathrates**) from the Latin word *clathratus,* meaning enclosed by crossbars.

** This explanation of the maximum density of water was first offered (1892) by Wilhelm Röntgen (of X-ray fame), and John Bernal and Ralph Fowler (1933). The concept of hydrogen bonds was invented by Tom Moore and Thomas Winmill (1912) and largely applied by Linus Pauling. In spite of the study of water from all presently known theoretical points of view, all is not quiet on the "water front." The structure of liquid water is still largely unknown and the prospects that theoretical calculations will give us useful information about a complex liquid like water are presently remote.

and finds many industrial applications. For example, it is used in the manufacture of ethylene dibromide, a component of antiknock ("lead") gasoline (page 378):

$$C_2H_4(g) + Br_2(l) \longrightarrow C_2H_4Br_2(l)$$

colorless   red   ethylene dibromide,
colorless

Reminder; bromine is very toxic and corrosive.

If we write the molecule with single bonds

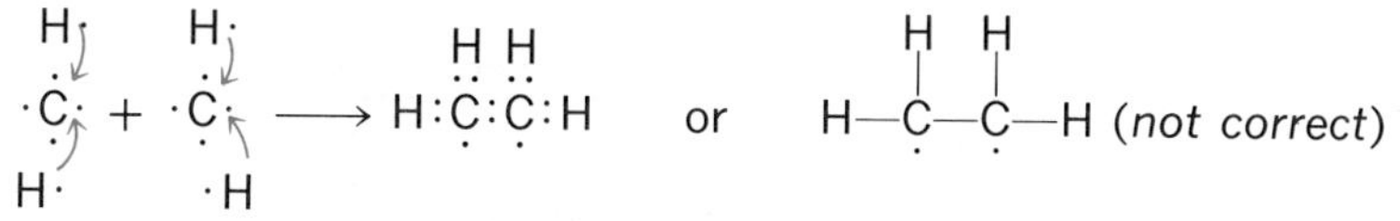

$$\cdot \overset{H}{\underset{H}{C}} + \cdot \overset{H}{\underset{H}{C}} \longrightarrow H : \overset{H}{\underset{H}{C}} : \overset{H}{\underset{H}{C}} : H \quad \text{or} \quad H - \overset{H}{\underset{H}{C}} - \overset{H}{\underset{H}{C}} - H \; (\textit{not correct})$$

each H atom has a duet, but each C atom has only 7 valence electrons. The addition of a second bond between the C atoms

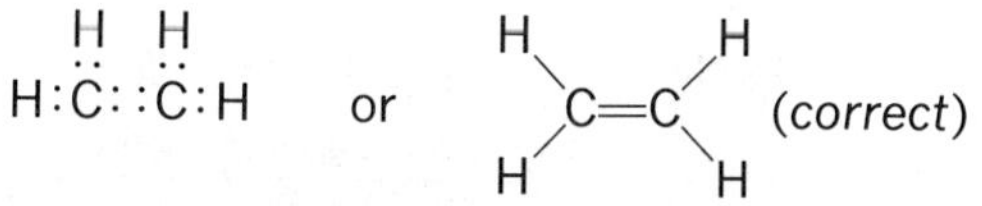

$$H : \overset{H}{\underset{H}{C}} : : \overset{H}{\underset{H}{C}} : H \quad \text{or} \quad \underset{H}{\overset{H}{C}} = \underset{H}{\overset{H}{C}} \; (\textit{correct})$$

satisfies the octet rule. The sharing of 2 pairs of electrons is called a **double bond.** Examples of molecules containing double and triple bonds are

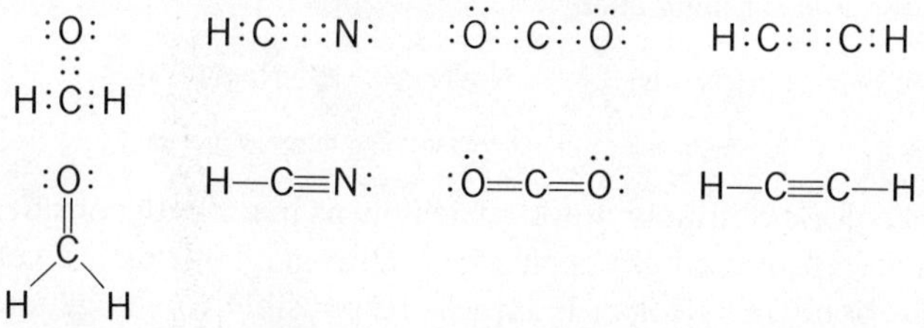

:O:
::
H:C:H

$$:O: \\ \parallel \\ \underset{H}{\overset{}{C}} {\diagdown} H$$

formaldehyde

H:C:::N:

H—C≡N:

hydrogen
cyanide

:Ö::C::Ö:

:Ö=C=Ö:

carbon
dioxide

H:C:::C:H

H—C≡C—H

acetylene

None of these molecules are paramagnetic.

Note that in these compounds the atoms have their common valences: the number of covalent bonds for carbon is 4, the same as in CH_4; 3 for nitrogen as in NH_3; and 2 for oxygen as in H_2O.

Hydrogen cyanide is a *very poisonous,* colorless gas with a bitter almond smell. It is evolved when cyanides are treated with acids. It combines very rapidly with the Fe^{2+} ion in hemoglobin (Chap. 21), displacing oxygen molecules and thus depriving body cells of the necessary oxygen. Acetylene is a colorless gas manufactured from calcium carbonate (*limestone,* oyster shells), carbon (coke), and water:

$$CaCO_3(c) \xrightarrow{\text{heated}} CaO(c) + CO_2(g)$$

$$CaO(c) + 3C \text{ (coke)} \xrightarrow[\text{furnace}]{\text{electric}} CaC_2(l) + CO(g)$$

$$CaC_2(c) + 2H_2O(l) \longrightarrow H-C \equiv C-H(g) + Ca(OH)_2(c)$$

Acetylene is used in oxyacetylene torches for welding and cutting metals and in the manufacture of plastics and synthetic fibers.

Notice that carbon dioxide has two double bonds. With few exceptions, *only C, N, O, and S form double or triple bonds* with themselves or other atoms.

PROBLEM 15   Write the electronic formula, consistent with the octet rule and common valences, for chloroacetylene, C_2HCl, a gas that explodes at $-30\,°C$.

For the same pair of bonded atoms, *the larger the number of bonds, the shorter is the distance between the bonded atoms* (page 234) and the *larger is the bond energy* (page 295), the energy needed to break the bond. This is illustrated by the following data:

increasing number of bonds $\longrightarrow$

	ethane	ethylene	acetylene
	$H_3C—CH_3$	$H_2C{=}CH_2$	$HC{\equiv}CH$

CC *bond length* 1.54×10^{-8} cm 1.33×10^{-8} cm 1.20×10^{-8} cm

decreasing bond length $\longrightarrow$

CC *bond energy*   83 kcal/mole   143 kcal/mole   194 kcal/mole

increasing bond energy $\longrightarrow$

Natural gas contains about 10 % ethane, used principally as a fuel.

PROBLEM 16   From the following set of bonds, pick the one with (a) the longest bond length and (b) the highest bond energy:

$$H_2\ddot{N}—\ddot{N}H_2 \qquad :N{\equiv}N: \qquad H—\ddot{N}{=}\ddot{N}—H$$

hydrazine   *nitrogen*   *nitrogen hydride*

*Acetylene is reactive
because its reactions
(page 690), unlike
those of N_2, do not
require triple bond
breakage, $C_2H_2 \longrightarrow$
$2CH_2$.*

Hydrazine is a colorless fuming liquid which burns in air with considerable evolution of heat and is therefore used as a rocket fuel. Nitrogen hydride is a very unstable gas.

The triple bond in nitrogen is largely responsible for its general resistance to chemical change, because the triple bond must be broken ($N_2 \longrightarrow 2N$) *before* reaction occurs.

8.11 ———————— EXCITING ELECTRONS TO HIGHER ORBITALS

In Section 8.6 (page 250) molecules having atoms with less than an octet were discussed. However, no one has yet been able to prepare compounds composed of the elements of the second period, Li $\longrightarrow$ F, in which these atoms in molecules have more than an octet. But many known compounds of the elements in the higher periods—for example, S, As, I, Bi—are composed of molecules in which atoms have *more* than an octet. The following molecules are typical:

*These molecules are
three-dimensional.*

SF₆
sulfur hexafluoride
6 bonds = 6 × 2 = 12 electrons
associated with the S atom

PCl₅
phosphorus pentachloride
5 bonds = 5 × 2 = 10 electrons
associated with the P atom

IF₇
iodine heptafluoride
7 bonds = 7 × 2 = 14 electrons
associated with the I atom

Sulfur hexafluoride is a very inert, colorless gas; it does not react with steam at 500 °C or with oxygen even in the presence of an electric discharge. It is therefore used as an insulator in high voltage electrical equipment.

Phosphorus pentachloride is a yellowish-white, poisonous, corrosive solid which readily fumes in the presence of water vapor and may be used to prepare phosphoric acid:

$$PCl_5(c) + 4H_2O(l) \longrightarrow H_3PO_4(aq) + 5HCl(g)$$

Iodine heptafluoride is a colorless liquid, extremely dangerous to handle because of its activity as a fluorinating agent (tendency to add fluorine to other compounds).

A fundamental difference between the elements of the second period, Li $\longrightarrow$ F, and those of the higher periods lies in the electronic structure of the elements. Nitrogen and phosphorus are typical:

$$_7N \ 1s^2 \ 2s^2 \ 2p^3 \ \cdot \overset{\cdot\cdot}{\underset{\cdot}{N}} \cdot \qquad _{15}P \ 1s^2 \ 2s^2 \ 2p^6 \ 3s^2 \ 3p^3 \ 3d^0 \ \cdot \overset{\cdot\cdot}{\underset{\cdot}{P}} \cdot$$

Notice that the nitrogen atom *does not have a d orbital available* to accept electrons. The phosphorus atom *has a d orbital available,* and therefore may have *more* than an octet.

d orbitals play an essential role in chemical bonding.

The properties of these elements are definitely related to the energy needed to excite an electron to the *next available orbital.* For example, helium, $_2He\ 1s^2$, is very inert, while beryllium, $_4Be\ 1s^2\ 2s^2\ 2p^0$, is reactive. Both atoms have paired electrons in an *s* orbital. However, unpaired electrons are required for these atoms to form a covalent bond. One unpaired electron corresponds to one combining capacity for the element. Thus, an electron in He $1s^2$ has to be excited to a *higher shell,* 2s. But in Be $1s^2\ 2s^2\ 2p^0$ the electron can be excited within the *same shell;* the electron is excited from a 2s to 2p orbital. In beryllium this requires little energy (Fig. 6.13, page 198), but helium requires about 10^4 times as much energy:

He $\underset{1s}{\downarrow\uparrow}$ $\xrightarrow{\text{excited to}}$ He $\underset{1s}{\downarrow}$ $\underset{2s}{\downarrow}$

ground state
no unpaired electrons

excited state
two unpaired electrons

unreactive $\xrightarrow{\text{much energy}}$ *reactive*

Be $\underset{1s}{\downarrow\uparrow}$ $\underset{2s}{\downarrow\uparrow}$ $\underset{2p}{\underline{\quad\quad}}$ $\xrightarrow{\text{excited to}}$ Be $\underset{1s}{\downarrow\uparrow}$ $\underset{2s}{\downarrow}$ $\underset{2p}{\downarrow}$ $\underline{\quad}$

ground state
no unpaired electrons

excited state
two unpaired electrons

unreactive $\xrightarrow{\text{little energy}}$ *reactive*

Therefore, helium is unreactive while beryllium is reactive. It can use an *s* and a *p* electron (orbital) to form 2 covalent bonds with 2 chlorine atoms.

Similarly, too much energy is required to excite electrons in the nitrogen atom to the 3s orbital,

The energy used in exciting electrons is more than balanced by the energy evolved when B̈e · forms $BeCl_2$.

$_7N$ $\underset{1s}{\downarrow\uparrow}$ $\underset{2s}{\downarrow\uparrow}$ $\underset{2p}{\downarrow}$ $\underset{}{\downarrow}$ $\underset{}{\downarrow}$ $\xrightarrow{\text{much energy}}$ $_7N$ $\underset{1s}{\downarrow\uparrow}$ $\underset{2s}{\downarrow}$ $\underset{2p}{\downarrow}$ $\underset{}{\downarrow}$ $\underset{}{\downarrow}$ $\underset{3s}{\downarrow}$

Nitrogen forms $\ddot{N}Cl_3$; it does not form NCl_5. Also, the d orbitals in the N atom are not as easily reached as they are in the P atom. Exciting electrons within the same shell in the P atom requires little energy:

$$_{15}P \; KL \; \frac{\downarrow\uparrow}{3s} \; \frac{\downarrow}{} \frac{\downarrow}{} \frac{\downarrow}{3p} \; - - \; \frac{}{} - - - \; \frac{}{3d} - - - \xrightarrow[\text{energy}]{\text{little}} \; _{15}P \; KL \; \frac{\downarrow}{3s} \; \frac{\downarrow}{} \frac{\downarrow}{} \frac{\downarrow}{3p} \; \frac{}{} - \frac{\downarrow}{} - \; \frac{}{3d} - -$$

Phosphorus can use these 5 unpaired electrons to form 5 covalent bonds; therefore, it forms PCl_5 as well as PCl_3.

In sulfur, $\cdot\ddot{S}:$, 2 electrons may be excited within the same shell, yielding an atom with 6 unpaired electrons:

$$_{16}S \; KL \; \frac{\downarrow\uparrow}{3s} \; \frac{\downarrow\uparrow}{} \frac{\downarrow}{} \frac{\downarrow}{3p} \; - - \; \frac{}{} - \; \frac{}{3d} - - \longrightarrow \; _{16}S \; KL \; \frac{\downarrow}{3s} \; \frac{\downarrow}{} \frac{\downarrow}{} \frac{\downarrow}{3p} \; \frac{\downarrow}{} - \frac{\downarrow}{} - \; \frac{}{3d} - -$$

Sulfur may thus form SF_6.

In iodine, $:\ddot{I}\cdot$,

$$\frac{\downarrow\uparrow}{5s} \; \frac{\downarrow\uparrow}{} \frac{\downarrow\uparrow}{} \frac{\downarrow}{5p} \; - - - \; \frac{}{} - - \; \frac{}{5d} - -$$

3 electrons may be excited, yielding an atom with 7 unpaired electrons:

$$\frac{\downarrow}{5s} \; \frac{}{} - \frac{\downarrow}{} \frac{\downarrow}{} \frac{\downarrow}{5p} \; \frac{\downarrow}{} - \frac{\downarrow}{} - \frac{\downarrow}{5d} - - \; \frac{}{} - -$$

Iodine may thus form IF_7.

Example 5

How many unpaired electrons in the I atom are needed to form (a) ICl, (b) ICl_3, and (c) IF_5? How many electrons in the $:\underline{I}\cdot$ atom, $5s^2 \, 5p^5 \, 5d^0$, are excited to higher orbitals to form these molecules? Write the electronic structure of the atom in the excited state.

Answer

(a) To form ICl, 1 unpaired electron is needed. Therefore, excitation to a higher orbital is not necessary. (b) To form ICl_3, 3 unpaired electrons are needed. Exciting 1 electron yields $5s^2 \, 5p^4 \, 5d^1$ with 3 unpaired electrons. (c) To form IF_5, 5 unpaired electrons are needed. Exciting 2 electrons yields $5s^2 \, 5p^3 \, 5d^2$ with 5 unpaired electrons.

PROBLEM 17 **(a) How many electrons (0, 1, or 2) are excited to higher orbitals in the carbon atom, $_6C \; K \; \frac{\downarrow\uparrow}{2s} \; \frac{\downarrow}{} \frac{\downarrow}{2p}$ —, to form (i) methylene*, CH_2, and (ii) ethylene, C_2H_4? (b) How many electrons are excited to higher orbitals in the tellurium atom, $_{52}Te \; 5s^2 \, 5p^4 \, 5d^0$,**

---

* Produced from diazomethane, a poisonous yellow gas, $CH_2N_2 + hf\,(\text{photon}) \longrightarrow CH_2$, methylene is so reactive that it is gone within about 10^{-6} s. Nevertheless, much is known about its shape (page 592), bond energy, and chemistry.

to form TeF_6, a colorless gas with an unpleasant odor that reacts with water to form telluric acid, H_2TeO_4, and hydrofluoric acid, HF? In each case, how many unpaired electrons are needed to form the molecule? Write the electronic structure of the atom in the excited state.

Similarly, the existence of compounds of the noble gases may be explained. Compared to helium (Fig. 6.13, page 198), not much energy is required to excite electrons in krypton, Kr, and xenon, Xe, to higher orbitals. KrF_4, with 4 covalent bonds, requires 4 unpaired electrons. Exciting 2 electrons from the $4p$ to the $4d$ orbitals,

$$_{36}Kr\ KLM\ \underset{4s}{\downarrow\uparrow}\ \underset{4p}{\downarrow\uparrow\ \downarrow\uparrow\ \downarrow\uparrow}\ \xrightarrow{\text{excited to}}\ _{36}Kr\ KLM\ \underset{4s}{\downarrow\uparrow}\ \underset{4p}{\downarrow\uparrow\ \downarrow\ \downarrow}\ \underset{4d}{\downarrow\ \downarrow}\ \underline{\quad}\ \underline{\quad}$$

yields the 4 unpaired electrons. Similarly, exciting 2 electrons from the $5p$ orbitals to the $5d$ orbitals explains the formation of XeF_4.

EPILOG

The subject of electron excitation to higher orbitals brings us back to the beginning of the chapter, the invention of the octet rule as a basis for explaining chemical reactions. It was originally believed that the noble gases were completely inert chemically. In fact, the noble gas family (He $\longrightarrow$ Rn) was called the "inert" gases, assigned the periodic table group number "0," meaning zero valence, no tendency to combine. This apparent inertness gave such strong support to the validity of the octet rule that very few chemists ventured to study the chemistry of these gases. One of the few, Don Yost, for many years attempted, without success, to prepare the fluorides of the noble gases. But with improved techniques and instrumentation, many fluorides of xenon have since been prepared by the Yost method.* However, the concept that the noble gases are inert first became unbelievable when Neil Bartlett prepared (1962) xenon hexafluoroplatinate, $XePtF_6$, an ionic, yellow solid. He observed that oxygen reacts with platinum hexafluoride, PtF_6, a reddish-black, volatile solid, to form dioxygen(1+) hexafluoroplatinate, O_2PtF_6, an ionic solid. Since the ionization energy of molecular oxygen, $O_2 \longrightarrow O_2^+ + e^-$, 282 kcal/mole, is practically the same as that of xenon, Xe $\longrightarrow Xe^+ + e^-$, 280 kcal/mole, he predicted that xenon should also react with PtF_6.* Mixed with PtF_6 vapor, xenon immediately formed a yellow solid:

$$\overset{..}{:}\overset{..}{Xe}\overset{..}{:}(g) + PtF_6(g) \longrightarrow :\overset{..}{Xe}\overset{.+}{}PtF_6^-(c)$$

$$\text{colorless} \qquad \text{red} \qquad\qquad \text{yellow}$$

These discoveries notwithstanding, the octet rule is still a useful tool for correlating many chemical reactions of the representative elements. No compounds of helium, neon, or argon have yet been prepared.

---

*Electrically sparking xenon and fluorine mixtures. Other methods are also used.

*The high electron affinity of PtF_6 is also an important factor in stabilizing these compounds.

PROBLEMS

18 Vocabulary Define and illustrate (a) valence electron, (b) Lewis symbol, (c) octet rule, (d) ionic bond, (e) polar bond, (f) nonpolar bond, (g) electronegativity, (h) dipole force, (i) London force, (j) giant molecule, (k) covalent substance, (l) network covalent solid, (m) ionic solid, (n) hydrogen bond, (o) triple bond, (p) double bond, (q) single bond, (r) covalent bond.

19 From the following forces, pick the one that plays the major role in all chemical bonding without exception: gravitational force, weak nuclear force, magnetic force, electrical force, quantum force, or nuclear force.

20 What is the force that holds CO_2 (nonpolar) molecules together in the liquid state? Answer the same question for ammonia, NH_3, nitrogen, N_2, molten diamond, and cesium chloride, CsCl.

21 Illustrate in terms of this chapter the statement of Robert Boyle (of gas law fame) that "chemical combination takes place under the mutual attractive force of the elements."

22 Lewis symbols What is the relationship between the Lewis symbol and the periodic table group number of the representative elements?

23 Bonds Use Lewis symbols to represent the formation of the compound, consistent with the octet rule and common valences, formed from each given pair of elements. Use the electronegativity generalization on page 256 to determine the type of bond formed, ionic or covalent. Write the simplest formula of the compound. (a) Ba, Br; (b) P, Cl; (c) Br, F; (d) Cs, S; (e) K, O; (f) Ca, N; (g) Be, O; (h) C, I; (i) C, H (at least two different compounds).

24 See Table 8.1, page 255. Pick the compounds that form ionic bonds: KCl, PH_3, BeS, AgF, CdS, $C*F_2Cl_2$. Electronegativities: Ag, 1.4; Cd, 1.5.

25 Predict the nature of the bond between each pair of atoms: (a) C, N; (b) Li, N; (c) Li, P; (d) As, Cl; (e) Ca, Cl; (f) K, Bi.

26 Use Lewis symbols and electronegativities** to show the formation of the hydrogen compounds (hydrides) of Li, Be, B, C, N, O, F, Na, and Mg consistent with the octet rule and common valences.

27 Electronic formula Write the electronic formula for each of the following covalently bonded compounds or ions. (a) Octet rule and common valences are followed in each: (i) CF_2Cl_2; (ii) $C_2H_2Cl_4$; (iii) $C_2H_4OCl_2$; (iv) H_2O_2; (v) C_3H_8; (vi) C_2H_6S; (vii) CH_5N; (viii) CH_3OCl; (ix) C_2H_6NCl; (x) CH_4S; (xi) O_4†; (xii) $HOCl$; (xiii) $C_2N_2H_6F_2$. (b) Octet rule (but not common valences) is followed in each: (i) BrO_4^-; (ii) BrO_3^-; (iii) AsO_4^{3-}; (iv) OH^-; (v) IO_2^-; (vi) SeO_4^{2-}; (vii) ClF_2^+; (viii) RnF^+; (ix) PCl_4^+; (x) CH_3^-.

28 Electronic formula (a) Chloroethanol, C_2H_5ClO, a substance present in foodstuffs sterilized by exposure to ethylene oxide, $(CH_2)_2O$, is mutagenic (changes the genes) for bacteria. Write the electronic formula for chloroethanol consistent with the octet rule and common valences. (b) In 1919, Irving Langmuir published the "constitution" of the ions of the ten known sulfur acids from sulfurous to peroxydisulfuric, $H_2S_2O_8$. The "constitutions" of three of the acids are

thiosulfuric acid $\begin{bmatrix} O & S \\ & S \\ O & O \end{bmatrix}^{2-}$,

pyrosulfuric (disulfuric) $\begin{bmatrix} & O & & O & \\ O-S-O-S-O \\ & O & & O & \end{bmatrix}^{2-}$,

and

pentathionic $\begin{bmatrix} & O & & & & O & \\ O-S-S-S-S-S-O \\ & O & & & & O & \end{bmatrix}^{2-}$,

the last being an unstable acid decomposing rapidly into sulfur, sulfur dioxide, and sulfuric acid. Find the number of electrons available for each formula. Are these formulas consistent with the octet rule?

29 Predict the empirical formula of the compound resulting from the combination of each of the following pairs of atoms: (a) Li, P; (b) Ca, Cl; (c) K, Bi.

30 Polar bonds Pick the polar molecules from the following and indicate partial charges with δ^+ and δ^- where they exist: (a) P_2; (b) ClI; (c) AlF; (d) CN; (e) OH; (f) F_2.

31 (a) Classify the following bonds as polar or nonpolar (See Table 8.1, page 255): N—O, C—O, P—I, Sb—H, Al—N, Se—Cl. (b) From Table 8.1, pick at least two pairs of elements that should not form a polar bond.

32 Dipole moment The following molecules have polar bonds. Pick the ones that do not behave like polar molecules: (a) N ⟵ C—C ⟶ N; (b) F ⟵ O ⟶ F; (c) N—N ⟶ O; (d) H ⟶ C ⟶ N; (e) Br ⟵ C≡C ⟶ Cl; (f) KCl(g).

33 Carbon dioxide, CO_2, consists of polar bonds. But it is not a polar molecule. Explain.

34 The calculated partial charges for the atoms in the molecule HF are $+0.27$ and -0.27. To which atom is the negative charge nearer? Would you expect the partial charges in the molecule LiF to be the same as, or smaller or larger than, the charges in HF? Explain.

35 Properties and bonds Pick (a) the substance with the lowest boiling point: CS_2, CO_2, O_2, CH_4, PbF_2 (Pb electronegativity, 1.44), C_2H_6; (b) the substance with the highest boiling point from the same group.

---

*See footnote on page 256.
**See footnote on page 256.
†The molecules $(NO)_2(g)$ and (l), formed from NO; and $(O_2)_2(g)$, formed from O_2, have definitely been identified by IR and UV spectra (Chap. 24).

36 Properties and bonds Classify the following substances as covalent, network covalent, or ionic: (a) beryllium oxide, BeO, b.p. about 3900 °C, molten liquid does not conduct electricity; (b) ethyl chloride, C_2H_5Cl, used as a local (topical) anesthetic, a colorless volatile liquid, b.p. 13 °C, that does not conduct electricity; (c) calcium oxide, CaO, b.p. 2850 °C, liquid conducts electricity.

37 (a) Complete the following table:

Substance	NiO, ionic	AlN, network covalent	CS₂, covalent
Unit particle in solid			
Bonding force between unit particles			
Electrical conductivity: Solid			
Liquid			

(b) Which compound should have the (i) highest, (ii) lowest boiling point? (c) Of the bonding forces noted, which one is the weakest?

38 Which should be easier to vaporize: solid CO_2 or solid oxonium antimony hexafluoride, $H_3O^+ SbF_6^-$? Explain. (H_3O^+ originates from $H_2O + H^+$, Problem 49.)

39 Intermolecular forces (a) *Assume* we have a camera capable of photographing the two electrons and the nucleus in a helium atom (*no such instrument exists*). Further, *assume* the following photographs are obtained:

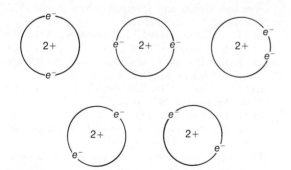

Pick the atom(s) that would show polarity; which end(s) would develop a negative charge? (b) Arrange the noble gases (Group 0) in the order of increasing boiling points. What is the basis of your order?

(c) The following molecules do not have a dipole moment; they are nonpolar molecules: C_4H_{10}, CH_4, C_3H_8, C_2H_6. Arrange them in the order of increasing boiling points.

40 Intermolecular forces Pick the force that makes the greatest contribution to the intermolecular forces in liquid ammonia, NH_3.

41 Magnetism is *not* involved in the so-called "magnetic" photo albums (holds photos without use of stickers). Pick the kind of force(s) most likely involved: (a) gravitation; (b) nuclear force; (c) London force; (d) ionic; (e) covalent; (f) dipole force.

42 Hydrogen bond (a) Pick the substance in which hydrogen bonding influences the boiling point: Cl_2, F_2, HCl, SiF_4, CCl_4. (b) In which of the following compounds is hydrogen bonding impossible? (Disregard

; concentrate on the *essential features* of the hydrogen bond.)

$H-C\equiv N$, $\overset{H}{\underset{H}{C}}=O$, CH_3OH, , CH_4, CHF_3, , $CHCl_3$, and SiH_4.

(c) HF boils at 19 °C while ClF, with more electrons per molecule, boils at −101 °C. Explain.

43 (a) Explain the high heat of vaporization of water (liquid ⟶ vapor) compared to the other hydrides of Group VIA:

	H_2O	H_2S	H_2Se	H_2Te
kcal/mole at b.p.	9.7	4.2	4.7	5.4

(b) If hydrogen bonding did not exist in water,

would water be a gas (vapor) or a solid at room temperature? Explain.

44 (a) Show how HOH and ethyl alcohol, C_2H_5OH, in which one C_2H_5 group replaces an H in HOH, form a hydrogen bond. Would you expect weak or strong hydrogen bonding between HOH and C_2H_6, in which an H replaces the OH group in C_2H_5OH? (b) Pick the pair of molecules between which the strongest hydrogen bond should form: $CH_3\overset{\text{O}}{\overset{\|}{C}}CH_3$, $CHCl_3$, (b) H_2O, NH_3, (c) HI, HI, (d) SiH_4, SiF_4.

45 Hydrogen bonding plays a major role in biological reactions. (a) Draw dashed lines between the atoms of a biochemical compound (to the left) and an enzyme (page 728) that can bind it through hydrogen bonding:

(b) Amino acids are the basic units of which all proteins are constructed (Chap. 23). One such acid, asparagine, may be represented as

What is the maximum number of strong hydrogen bonds that may be formed by one molecule of this acid?

46 On the basis of the number of electrons per molecule, arrange the acids HF, HCl, HBr, and HI in the order of increasing boiling points. See Fig. 8.11, page 267, and explain the high boiling point of HF.

47 **Open structure** Most rocks are composed of silicate compounds, some of which are comparatively simple like *olivine*, Mg_2SiO_4 and Fe_2SiO_4, composed of Mg^{2+} and Fe^{2+} ions interspersed among SiO_4^{4-} ions, while others are endless arrangements in which oxygen atoms are shared between Si atoms (clay, *kaolin*, $Al_2Si_2O_7$, mica, *muscovite*, $K_2Al_6Si_6O_{22}$), giving rise to three-dimensional open networks. When rocks melt, would you expect these various silicates to separate? If so, which should rise to the surface of the molten (lava) rock? Explain.

48 **Double and triple bonds** Write the electronic formula, consistent with the octet rule and common valences, for each of the following: (a) formaldehyde, CH_2O; (b) carbon oxyselenide, COSe; (c) P_2; (d) azomethane, $(CH_3)_2N_2$; (e) ketene, C_2H_2O; (f) tetrafluoroethylene, C_2F_4; (g) arsenic nitride, AsN; (h) carbon oxysulfide, OCS; (i) cyanide ion, CN^-; (j) Grignard reagent,* C_2H_3MgBr; (k) cyanoethylene (acrylonitrile), C_3H_3N, from which *Orlon* and *Acrilan* fibers are manufactured; (l) red copper(I) acetylide, Cu_2C_2, which explodes on heating; (m) cyanate ion, NCO^- (ammonium cyanate warmed in water changes to urea); (n) urea, $(NH_2)_2CO$, excreted in the urine, the main end product of metabolism of proteins; (o) formamide, CH_3ON, used to break down a chain of carbon atoms one C atom at a time; (p) thiocyanate ion, NCS^-, used in testing for Fe^{3+} ion (page 400); (q) propyne, C_3H_4, used to prepare vinyl acetate, from which chewing gums and self-sealing wrapping materials are manufactured by polymerization (Chap. 23); (r) cyanodiacetylene, C_5HN, largest molecule detected in space; (s) silaethylene, CH_2SiH_2.

49 For each reaction, write the electronic formula of the product, consistent with the octet rule but not with common valences. Clearly show how you arrive at your electronic formula. (a) $NF_3 + BH_3$; (b) $CH_3^- + BF_3$; (c) $H_2O + H^+$; (d) $CH_3^+ + GaCl_4^-$; (e) $AlH_3 + H^-$.

50 In each given atom, how many unpaired electrons are needed to form the molecule? How many electrons are excited to higher orbitals in each of the given atoms? Write the electronic structure of these atoms in the excited state. (a) Se in $SeBr_4$; (b) Br in BrF_3; (c) Kr in KrF_6; in KrF_2; (d) Xe in XeF_4; (e) Sb in SbF_5.

51 **Library** Read one of the following:
(a) "A Comprehensive Treatise on Inorganic and Theoretical Chemistry," J. W. Mellor, Longmans, Green and Company, New York, 1922, volume 1, pages 225–226.
(b) "The Chemical Bond," J. J. Lagowski, Houghton Mifflin Company, New York, 1966, pages 1–29.
(c) "Early Views on Forces Between Atoms," *Scientific American,* May 1970, page 116.
(d) "The Catalyst," G. R. Yohe, *Chemistry,* volume 46, September 1973, page 8.
(e) "Isaac Newton's Theory of Matter," G. D. Goehring, *Journal of Chemical Education,* volume 53, July 1976, page 423.
(f) "Water, the Unique Chemical," F. Franks, *Chemistry in Britain,* volume 12, 1976, page 278.

---

*Important in the synthesis of organic compounds, it was developed (1900) by Philippe Barbier and Victor Grignard.

52 Write the electronic formula for ethylene oxide (Problem 28), C_2H_4O, in which the carbon and oxygen atoms are hooked up in the form of a ring.

53 Write the product of the reaction between $(CH_3)_2O$ and BF_3.

54 C_2H_5OH, an alcohol, and $CH_3{-}O{-}CH_3$, an ether, have the same number of atoms of the same kind (C_2H_6O), the same number of electrons, and practically the same dipole moments; yet the alcohol boils at 79 °C and the ether at −24 °C. Explain.

55 A drop of a *nonpolar* liquid is attracted to an electrically charged rod. Explain.

56 Criticize the electronic formula $\ddot{\text{O}}::\text{C}:\ddot{\text{O}}:$ for CO_2.

57 An alcohol consisting of large molecules, $C_{14}H_{31}OH$, when carefully spread over the surface of water in a pan, prevents the water from evaporating. Explain.

58 Solid HF does not float on liquid HF, while solid H_2O floats on liquid H_2O. Explain.

59 Show how NH_3 and H_2O may be hydrogen bonded in two different ways (empirical composition of the product is NOH_5).

60 The first compound made with a xenon-nitrogen bond is $\text{FXeN}\begin{smallmatrix}\diagup \text{SO}_2\text{F}\\ \diagdown \text{SO}_2\text{F}\end{smallmatrix}$. Check the number of electrons used and the number available.

61 Find the number of bonds (single, double, triple) formed by carbon, oxygen, sulfur, and nitrogen atoms in each of the following molecules in which common valences are followed: (a) C_2Cl_4; (b) CS_2; (c) C_2N_2; (d) $C_2Cl_4(CN)_2$; (e) CCl_2H_2; (f) N_2F_2; (g) C_4H_6; (h) C_2F_3CN.

62 Some molecules can be represented as circular, and others tend to be linear, as crudely shown for molecules composed of the same number of the same kinds of atoms:

For the same number of electrons, which compound, circular or linear, should have a higher boiling point? Explain.

63 Obtain the boiling points of NH_3, PH_3, AsH_3, and SbH_3 from the Handbook of Chemistry and plot against the period number. Do the same for CH_4, SiH_4, GeH_4, and SnH_4. Explain the difference in the two graphs.

64 As solid $AlCl_3$ approaches its melting point, its electrical conductivity increases rapidly. When it melts, the conductivity suddenly drops to zero and the density decreases sharply. What does the solid consist of, ions or molecules? What does the liquid consist of, ions or molecules? Explain the sharp decrease in density.

65 (a) The vapors of the trihalides of Al consist of Al_2Cl_6, Al_2Br_6, and Al_2I_6 molecules. Write the electronic formula for any one of these molecules, in which the octet rule is followed but in which Al forms four bonds while two of the six halide atoms form two bonds. (At higher temperature, they break down to AlX_3 molecules.) (b) In the vapor state, some formic acid, HCOOH, molecules combine through hydrogen bonding. Show how two formic acid molecules may so combine.

66 The heavy metal halides SnI_4, UF_6, $SbCl_3$, WCl_6, and PuF_6 form molecular crystals—solids consisting of molecules. Vaporization involves a separation against what forces? Should you expect a high or a low heat of vaporization compared to NaCl or SiO_2?

67 Arrange the following set of bonds in the order of (a) increasing bond length and (b) increasing bond energy: $-\text{C}\equiv\text{N},\ \diagdown\!\text{C}-\text{N}\diagup,\ \diagup\!\text{C}=\text{N}-.$

68 Write the electronic formula for the fulminate ion, CNO^-. Mercury(II) fulminate is used in percussion caps to detonate high explosives.

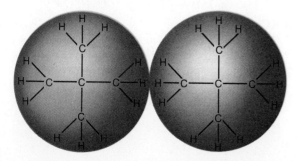

and

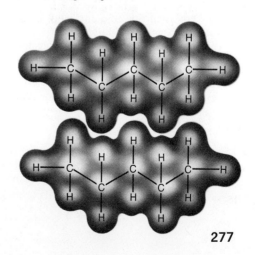

69 (a) Explain the formation of the known ions IF_6^- and SbF_6^-. (b) An ionic noble gas halide has been observed from its spectrum (but it has not been isolated). Write the electronic formula for Xe^+I^-. Should it be paramagnetic, unlike Na^+Cl^-?

70 Given N^+, N^{3-}, N, and N_2. (a) Are these particles identical? (b) Do they have identical properties? (c) How are the first three related to N_2? (d) Which particle is most likely to pick up an electron? Explain.

ANSWERS

1 $:\ddot{Ar}:$, $\cdot\ddot{Cl}:$, $:\ddot{Cl}:^-$, $\cdot Al\cdot$

2 (a) Li_3N; (b) Cs_2S

3 $F:\ddot{N}:F$
$\quad\;\; F$

4
```
   H  H
   |  |
H—C—N—H
   |
   H
```

5 (a)
```
       Cl
        \
Cl—Al       + Cl—N—Cl  ⟶
        /          |
       Cl          Cl
```
```
Cl         Cl
 \          |
Cl—N—Al—Cl; (b) 3, 4; (c) 4
 /          |
Cl         Cl
```

6 $\left[\begin{array}{c} :\ddot{Cl}: \\ :\ddot{Cl}:Al:\ddot{Cl}: \\ :\ddot{Cl}: \end{array}\right]^-$ $\left[\begin{array}{c} :\ddot{O}: \\ :\ddot{O}:Si:\ddot{O}: \\ :\ddot{O}: \end{array}\right]^{4-}$

7 All except Cl_2 and Br_2

8 HI, N_2O

9 CaI_2, $BeBr_2$, CCl_4, PH_3, OF_2

10 $\overset{\delta^-\;\;\delta^+}{N-H}$, $\overset{\delta^+\;\;\delta^-}{Al-Cl}$, $\overset{\delta^-\;\;\delta^+}{C-H}$, $\overset{\delta^+\;\;\delta^-}{C-Br}$

11 $_2$He, $_{10}$Ne, $_{18}$Ar, $_{36}$Kr, $_{54}$Xe, $_{86}$Rn

12 (i) ZrN, network covalent solid, atoms, covalent (ii) $CaBr_2$, ionic solid, ions, ionic (iii) vitamin C, covalent solid, molecules, intermolecular

13 (a) $\ddot{N}H_3$; (b) $RH_2\ddot{N}:$---$H-\ddot{O}R$ or $RH\ddot{N}H$---$:\overset{\textstyle H}{\underset{\textstyle R}{\ddot{O}}}:$;

(c) CH_4, no; CH_3F, yes

14 (a) volume increases, density decreases; (b) volume decreases, density increases; (c) breakdown of H bonds; increase in molecular motion above 3.98 °C.

15 $H-C\equiv C-\ddot{Cl}:$

16 (a) hydrazine; (b) nitrogen

17 (a) (i) none, 2 unpaired, $2s^2\,2p^2$; (ii) one, 4 unpaired, $2s^1\,2p^3$; (b) two, 6 unpaired, $5s^1\,5p^3\,5d^2$

19 electrical

20 CO_2, intermolecular, largely London forces; NH_3, intermolecular, largely H bonding; N_2, intermolecular, London forces; C, covalent; CsCl, ionic

23 (a) $\dot{Ba}\cdot + 2\cdot\ddot{Br}: \longrightarrow Ba^{2+} + 2:\ddot{Br}:^-$, 1.7, $BaBr_2$

(b) $:\dot{P}\cdot + 3\cdot\ddot{Cl}: \longrightarrow :\ddot{Cl}:\ddot{P}:\ddot{Cl}:$, 0.6, PCl_3
$\qquad\qquad\qquad\qquad\qquad\; :\ddot{Cl}:$

(c) $:\ddot{Br}\cdot + \cdot\ddot{F}: \longrightarrow :\ddot{Br}:\ddot{F}:$, 1.4, BrF

(d) $2Cs\cdot + \cdot\ddot{S}: \longrightarrow 2Cs^+ + :\ddot{S}:^{2-}$, 1.5, Cs_2S

(e) $2K\cdot + \cdot\ddot{O}: \longrightarrow 2K^+ + :\ddot{O}:^{2-}$, 2.6, K_2O

(f) $3\dot{Ca}\cdot + 2\cdot\dot{N}\cdot \longrightarrow 3Ca^{2+} + 2:\ddot{N}:^{3-}$, 2.0, Ca_3N_2

(g) $\dot{Be}\cdot + \cdot\ddot{O}: \longrightarrow Be^{2+} + :\ddot{O}:^{2-}$, 2.0, BeO

(h) $\cdot\dot{C}\cdot + 4\cdot\ddot{I}: \longrightarrow :\ddot{I}:\overset{\textstyle :\ddot{I}:}{\underset{\textstyle :\ddot{I}:}{\ddot{C}:}}\ddot{I}:$, 0.3, CI_4

(i) $\cdot\dot{C}\cdot + 4\cdot H \longrightarrow H:\overset{\textstyle H}{\underset{\textstyle H}{C}}:H$, 0.4, CH_4

$2\cdot\dot{C}\cdot + 4\cdot H \longrightarrow H:\overset{\textstyle H}{C}::\overset{\textstyle H}{C}:H$, C_2H_4

$2\cdot\dot{C}\cdot + 2\cdot H \longrightarrow H:C:::C:H$, C_2H_2

24 KCl, AgF

25 (a)(c)(d)(f) covalent; (b)(e) ionic

26 $Li\cdot + \cdot H \longrightarrow Li^+ + :H^-$

$\dot{Be}\cdot + 2\cdot H \longrightarrow Be^{2+} + 2:H^-$

$\dot{B}\cdot + 3\cdot H \longrightarrow \overset{\textstyle H}{\underset{\textstyle H}{B}}-H$

$\cdot \ddot{C} \cdot + 4 \cdot H \longrightarrow H-\underset{\underset{H}{|}}{\overset{\overset{H}{|}}{C}}-H$

$\cdot \ddot{N} \cdot + 3 \cdot H \longrightarrow H-\underset{\underset{H}{|}}{N}-H$

$\cdot \ddot{\ddot{O}} : + 2 \cdot H \longrightarrow H-\ddot{\ddot{O}}-H$

$: \ddot{\ddot{F}} \cdot + \cdot H \longrightarrow H-\ddot{\ddot{F}} :$

$Na \cdot + \cdot H \longrightarrow Na^+ + : H^-$

$\dot{Mg} \cdot + 2 \cdot H \longrightarrow Mg^{2+} + 2 : H^-$

27 (a) (i) $F-\underset{\underset{Cl}{|}}{\overset{\overset{Cl}{|}}{C}}-F$; (ii) $H-\underset{\underset{H}{|}}{\overset{\overset{Cl}{|}}{C}}-\underset{\underset{Cl}{|}}{\overset{\overset{Cl}{|}}{C}}-Cl$;* (iii) $H-\underset{\underset{H}{|}}{\overset{\overset{H}{|}}{C}}-\underset{\underset{H}{|}}{\overset{\overset{Cl}{|}}{C}}-\ddot{\ddot{O}}-Cl$;*

(iv) $H-\ddot{\ddot{O}}-\ddot{\ddot{O}}-H$; (v) $H-\underset{\underset{H}{|}}{\overset{\overset{H}{|}}{C}}-\underset{\underset{H}{|}}{\overset{\overset{H}{|}}{C}}-\underset{\underset{H}{|}}{\overset{\overset{H}{|}}{C}}-H$; (vi) $H-\underset{\underset{H}{|}}{\overset{\overset{H}{|}}{C}}-\ddot{\ddot{S}}-\underset{\underset{H}{|}}{\overset{\overset{H}{|}}{C}}-H$;*

(vii) $H-\underset{\underset{H}{|}}{\overset{\overset{H}{|}}{C}}-N\overset{\diagup H}{\diagdown H}$; (viii) $H-\underset{\underset{H}{|}}{\overset{\overset{H}{|}}{C}}-\ddot{\ddot{O}}-Cl$; (ix) $H-\underset{\underset{H}{|}}{\overset{\overset{H}{|}}{C}}-\underset{\underset{H}{|}}{\overset{\overset{H}{|}}{C}}-\underset{\underset{H}{|}}{N}-Cl$;*

(x) $H-\underset{\underset{H}{|}}{\overset{\overset{H}{|}}{C}}-\ddot{\ddot{S}}-H$; (xi) $: \overset{\cdots}{O}-\overset{\cdots}{O} :$; (xii) $H-\ddot{\ddot{O}}-Cl$; (xiii) $H-\underset{\underset{H}{|}}{\overset{\overset{H}{|}}{C}}-\underset{\underset{H}{|}}{\overset{\overset{H}{|}}{C}}-\underset{\underset{H}{|}}{N}-\underset{\underset{F}{\diagdown}}{N}\overset{\diagup F}{}$*

(b) $\left[: \overset{\cdot\cdot}{\underset{\cdot\cdot}{O}}-Br-\ddot{\ddot{O}} : \right]^-$; $\left[: \ddot{\ddot{O}}-Br-\ddot{\ddot{O}} : \right]^-$; $\left[: \overset{\cdots}{\underset{\underset{: \overset{\cdot\cdot}{\underset{\cdot\cdot}{O}} :}{|}}{O}}-As-\ddot{\ddot{O}} : \right]^{3-}$; $\left[: \ddot{\ddot{O}}-H \right]^-$; $\left[: \ddot{\ddot{O}}-I-\ddot{\ddot{O}} : \right]^-$;

$\left[: \overset{\cdots}{\underset{\underset{: \overset{\cdot\cdot}{\underset{\cdot\cdot}{O}} :}{|}}{O}}-Se-\ddot{\ddot{O}} : \right]^{2-}$; $\left[: \ddot{\ddot{F}}-\ddot{Cl}-\ddot{\ddot{F}} : \right]^+$; $\left[: Rn-\ddot{\ddot{F}} : \right]^+$; $\left[: \overset{\cdots}{\underset{\underset{: \overset{\cdot\cdot}{\underset{\cdot\cdot}{Cl}} :}{|}}{Cl}}-P-\ddot{Cl} : \right]^+$; $\left[\underset{\underset{H}{|}}{\overset{\overset{H}{|}}{C}}-H \right]^-$

28 (a) $H-\underset{\underset{H}{|}}{\overset{\overset{: \ddot{Cl} : H}{|}}{C}}-\underset{\underset{H}{|}}{C}-\ddot{\ddot{O}}-H$;* (b) $S_2O_3{}^{2-}$, 32 electrons; $S_2O_7{}^{2-}$, 56; $S_5O_6{}^{2-}$, 68; yes

29 (a) Li_3P; (b) $CaCl_2$; (c) K_3Bi

30 $\overset{\delta^-}{Cl}-\overset{\delta^+}{I}, \overset{\delta^+}{Al}-\overset{\delta^-}{F}, \overset{\delta^+}{C}-\overset{\delta^-}{N}, \overset{\delta^-}{O}-\overset{\delta^+}{H}$

31 (a) nonpolar: PI, SbH

32 (a)(b)

34 nearer F; larger

35 (a) O_2; (b) PbF_2

36 (a) network covalent; (b) covalent; (c) ionic

37 (a) See Table 8.2, page 264; (b) (i) AlN, (ii) CS_2; (c) intermolecular

38 CO_2

39 (a) the third one; electron cloud density greater at the right end; (b) order of increasing atomic numbers; (c) CH_4, C_2H_6, C_3H_8, C_4H_{10}

40 H bonding

41 (c)(f)

* More than one formula acceptable.

42 (a) HCl; (b) CH_4, SiH_4

43 (b) gas (vapor)

44 (a)

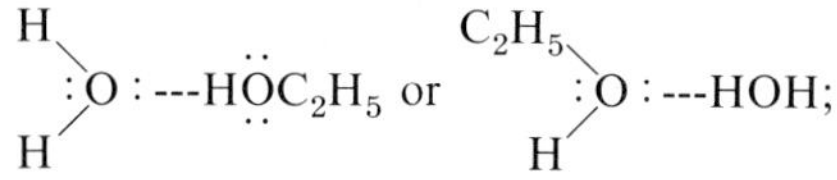

H
:O: ---HÖC$_2$H$_5$ or
H

C$_2$H$_5$
:O: ---HOH; weak;
H

(b) NH_3—H_2O

45 (a) in order of top to bottom: O---HN, NH---O, O---HO; (b) nine

46 HF, HCl, HBr, HI

47 clays and micas float

48 (a)

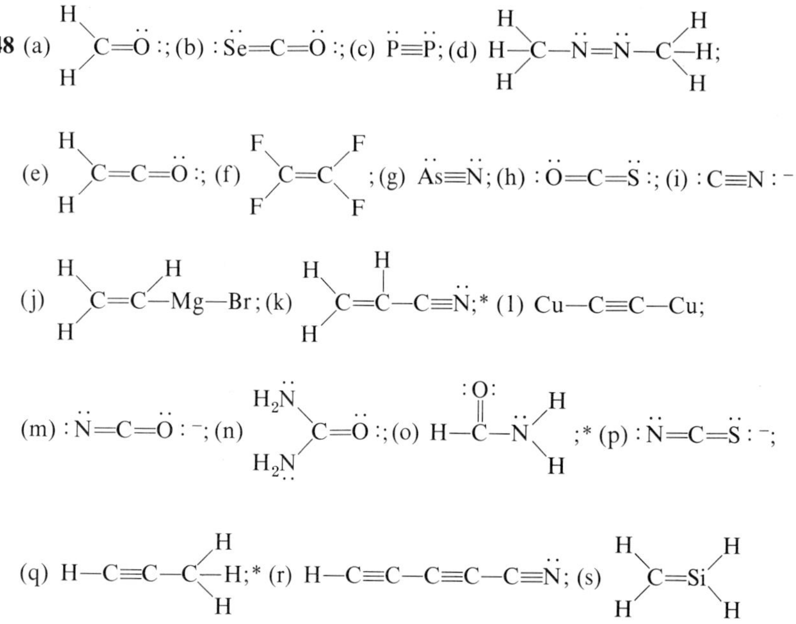

H
C=Ö:; (b) :Se=C=Ö:; (c) P≡P; (d) H—C—N=N—C—H;
H

(with H substituents on the two carbons)

(e)

H
C=C=Ö:; (f)
H

F
C=C
F

F
F
; (g) As≡N; (h) :Ö=C=S:; (i) :C≡N:⁻

(j)

H
C=C—Mg—Br; (k)
H

H
C=C—C≡N;* (l) Cu—C≡C—Cu;
H

(with H substituents)

(m) :N=C=Ö:⁻; (n)

H$_2$N
C=Ö:; (o)
H$_2$N

:O:
H—C—N
H
;* (p) :N=C=S:⁻;

(with H on N)

(q)

H
H—C≡C—C—H;* (r) H—C≡C—C≡C—C≡N; (s)
H

H
C=Si
H

H
H
;

49 (a) F$_3$N : BH$_3$ (b) [H$_3$C : BF$_3$]⁻; (c)

[H—Ö—H]⁺

H

; (d) H$_3$C : Cl—Ga—Cl;

Cl
Cl

(e)

[H :Al—H]⁻

H
H

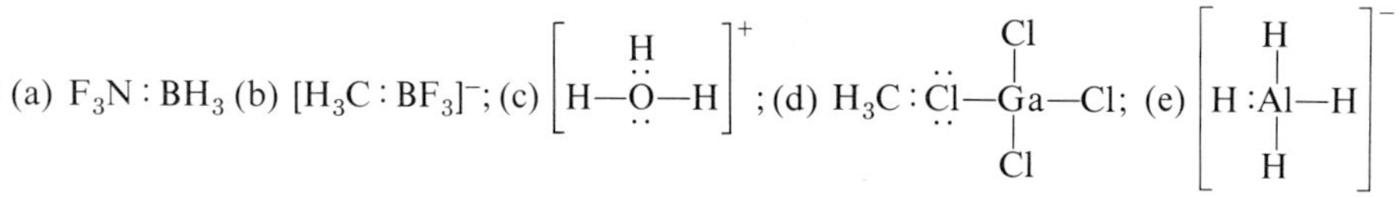

50 (a) 4 unpaired, 1, $s^2 p^3 d^1$; (b) 3 unpaired, 1, $s^2 p^4 d^1$;
(c) 6 unpaired, 3, $s^2 p^3 d^3$; 2 unpaired, 1, $s^2 p^5 d^1$;
(d) 4 unpaired, 2, $s^2 p^4 d^2$; (e) 5 unpaired, 1, $s^1 p^3 d^1$

52

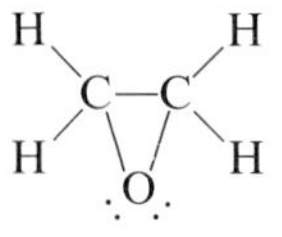

H
C—C
H

H
H

:O:

53

H$_3$C
:O : B—F
H$_3$C

F
F

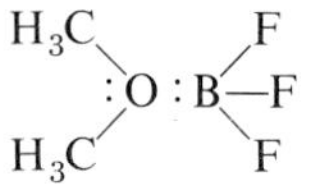

54 difference in H bonding

55 polarization

56 octet rule not satisfied for C

59 H$_3$N:---HOH, H$_2$O:---HNH$_2$

60

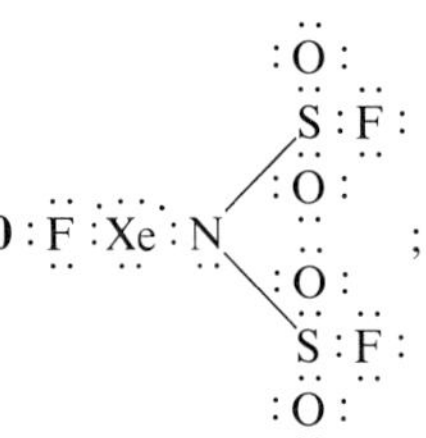

:O:
S : F:
:O:
:F : Xe : N
:O:
S : F:
:O:

; 70 electrons

61 (a) 1 double, 4 single; (b) 2 double; (c) 1 single, 2 triple; (d) 7 single, 2 triple; (e) 4 single; (f) 2 single, 1 double; (g) 8 single, 1 triple; (h) 4 single, 1 double, 1 triple

62 linear

64 solid, ions; liquid, molecules; open structure molecules

*See footnote on page 279.

65 (a)

$$\begin{array}{ccc} :\ddot{X}: & \ddot{X} & \ddot{X}: \\ & Al & Al \\ :\ddot{X}: & \ddot{X} & \ddot{X}: \end{array} \;;$$

(b) $\text{H}-\overset{\overset{\displaystyle O}{\|}}{\text{C}}-\text{OH}\text{---}\text{O}=\overset{\overset{\displaystyle H}{}}{\underset{\text{OH}}{\text{C}}}$

66 Intermolecular forces; low

67 (a) C≡N, C=N, C—N; (b) C—N, C=N, C≡N

68 $:\ddot{\text{C}}=\text{N}=\ddot{\text{O}}:^-$ or $:\text{C}\equiv\text{N}-\ddot{\text{O}}:^-$

69 (a) I^-, $s^2 p^6 \longrightarrow s^2 p^3 d^3$; Sb^-, $s^2 p^4 \longrightarrow s^1 p^3 d^2$;
(b) $:\ddot{\text{X}}\text{e}\cdot{}^+\cdot\ddot{\text{I}}:^-$, yes

70 (a)(b) no; (c) $\text{N}_2 \longrightarrow 2\text{N}$, $\text{N} \longrightarrow \text{N}^+ + e^-$,
$\text{N} + 3e^- \longrightarrow \text{N}^{3-}$; (d) N^+

covalent bond A chemical bond resulting from the sharing of electrons between the bonded atoms, $:\ddot{\text{Cl}}:\ddot{\text{Cl}}:$, $\text{H}:\ddot{\text{N}}:\text{H}$

covalent substance A substance consisting of molecules held together by intermolecular attractive forces; examples: H_2, CO_2, H_2O, gasoline, Vaseline; see **dipole force, London force,** and **hydrogen bond.** Such substances may exist as gas, liquid, or solid at room conditions.

dipole force An intermolecular electrical attractive force resulting from the presence of partially charged atoms in molecules. The strength of this force determines whether a substance exists as a gas, liquid, or solid at room conditions.

dipole moment Polar compounds whose molecules tend to line up in an electric field are said to have a dipole moment; $\overset{\delta^+}{\text{C}}\rightarrow\overset{\delta^-}{\text{O}}$ has a dipole moment, $\overset{\delta^-}{\text{O}}\leftarrow\overset{\delta^+}{\text{C}}\rightarrow\overset{\delta^-}{\text{O}}$ does not.

double bond A chemical bond consisting of two shared pairs of electrons, $\text{C}::\text{O}::\text{O}$.

electronegativity The ability of a bonded atom to attract electrons.

electronic formula A chemical formula showing the electrons in the highest shell of each atom,

$$:\ddot{\text{Cl}}:$$
$$\text{H}:\ddot{\text{C}}:\text{C}:::\text{N}:$$
$$\text{H}$$

(A dash may be used to represent a pair of electrons.)

hydrogen bond An intermolecular attractive force in which a hydrogen atom serves as a bridge between highly electronegative atoms, $\overset{\delta^-}{\text{O}}-\overset{\delta^+}{\text{H}}\cdots\overset{\delta^-}{\text{O}}$.

ionic bond A chemical bond in which the attractive force is the electrical attraction between positive and negative ions, $\text{Ca}^{2+} + 2:\ddot{\text{F}}:^-$, formed by a transfer of electrons.

ionic substance A substance consisting of an endless orderly arrangement of ions,

$$\begin{array}{cccc} -\text{Cl}^- & -\text{Na}^+ & -\text{Cl}^- & -\text{Na}^+ - \\ -\text{Na}^+ & -\text{Cl}^- & -\text{Na}^+ & -\text{Cl}^- - \\ -\text{Cl}^- & -\text{Na}^+ & -\text{Cl}^- & -\text{Na}^+ - \end{array}$$

held together by strong electrical attractive forces.

The concept of a molecule does not apply to an ionic solid, although any piece of it may be called a *giant molecule.* Such substances are always solids at room conditions.

Lewis formula Same as electronic formula.

Lewis symbol The chemical symbol for an element with the number of electrons in its highest shell shown as dots, $\cdot\ddot{\text{N}}\cdot$, $:\ddot{\text{N}}:^{3-}$.

London force A very weak intermolecular electrical attractive force naturally developed between nonpolar molecules.

network covalent substance A substance consisting of an endless orderly arrangement of covalently bonded atoms,

$$\begin{array}{cccc} -\text{Si}- & \text{C}- & \text{Si}- & \text{C}- \\ -\text{C}- & \text{Si}- & \text{C}- & \text{Si}- \\ -\text{Si}- & \text{C}- & \text{Si}- & \text{C}- \end{array}$$

The concept of a molecule does not apply to a network covalent substance, although any piece of it may be called a *giant molecule.* Such substances are always comparatively hard solids at room conditions.

nonpolar bond A chemical bond in which the shared electron pair is equally distributed between the two bonded atoms, $\overset{\delta^0}{\text{Cl}}-\overset{\delta^0}{\text{Cl}}$, $\overset{\delta^0}{\text{Sb}}-\overset{\delta^0}{\text{H}}$.

octet rule The generalization (to which there are important exceptions) that atoms combine to acquire the electronic structure of a noble gas, eight electrons (octet) in their highest shells, $\ddot{\text{N}}:::\ddot{\text{N}}$, $:\ddot{\text{O}}:^{2-}$.

polar bond A chemical bond between two atoms in which each atom has a partial charge, $\overset{\delta^+}{\text{H}}-\overset{\delta^-}{\text{Cl}}$, resulting from an unequal distribution of the shared electron pair between the two bonded atoms.

polar compound A compound consisting of polar molecules that tend to line up in an electric field, $\overset{\delta^+}{\text{H}}-\overset{\delta^-}{\text{F}}$, $\underset{\delta^+}{\text{H}}\overset{\delta^-}{\underset{\;\;\;\text{H}}{\text{O}}}{}_{\delta^+}$

single bond A chemical bond consisting of one shared pair of electrons, $\text{H}:\ddot{\text{Cl}}:$, $:\ddot{\text{F}}:\ddot{\text{O}}:\ddot{\text{F}}:$

structural formula Same as electronic formula.

triple bond A chemical bond consisting of three shared pairs of electrons, $:\text{C}:::\text{N}:$

valence electrons The electrons in the highest (outermost) shell of an atom.

ENERGY CHANGES IN CHEMICAL REACTIONS

9

INTRODUCTION ————— 9.1

The energy thirst of modern society, satisfied at the end of a pipe or a wire, is gigantic. The combustion of coal, oil, and natural gas, known as *fossil fuels,*• the basis of thermal• (heat) electric power plants, remains our major energy source. Hydro (falling water) electric power generates only 4 % and nuclear power (Chap. 17) 9 % of our electric supply. The combustion of liquid and solid substances (propellants) in rocket engines produces the thrust, the push necessary to send vehicles into space. Liquid hydrogen and liquid oxygen were used to operate the engines in the second and third stages of the Apollo (moon) flights, while gasoline and air drive our automobiles. An insect (the bombardier beetle) ejects an explosive discharge at 100 °C, making capture with the naked hand impossible. These are all energy changes accompanying chemical changes.

In chemical changes, atoms are conserved, but they are redistributed during the chemical reaction. This rearrangement, however, means that the bonds holding atoms together in the reactant molecules must be broken and that new bonds must form in the product molecules. For the reaction $H_2(g) + Cl_2(g) \longrightarrow 2HCl(g)$ to occur, the H—H and Cl—Cl bonds must be broken and the H—Cl bond must form. But *energy must be absorbed to break a bond; in separating the atoms, work must be done against the forces that hold atoms together.* Conversely, *when a bond forms, energy is evolved.* The energy needed to break a bond and the energy ejected (evolved, released, liberated, thrown out) when a bond forms are definite and characteristic for each bond (page 295). The energy of the product molecules may therefore be greater or smaller than the energy of the reactant molecules. Hence, chemical changes are always accompanied by energy changes. These energy changes are known as **heats of reaction,** the net result of breaking and making chemical bonds. **Thermochemistry** deals with the measurement of the heats of reaction. It has, however, been developed into an indispensable tool for the study of chemistry, biology, biochemistry, and space science. Living cells utilize nutrients (chemicals) to obtain the heat vital for warm-blooded animals. Thermochemistry provides a method to predict heats of reaction, a characteristic property of chemical reactions and a major factor in determining the extent of the reaction (Chaps. 12 and 15).

•*Produced by the decay of prehistoric plants and animals buried in mud and rock.*
•*From therme, the Greek word for heat.*

283

Heat transfer is always from a warmer (higher temperature) to a neighboring cooler (lower temperature) object (page 21). Heat transfer occurs because of a temperature difference. The SI unit of energy is the joule, J, and 1 calorie is by definition 4.184 J (exactly). A calorie suffices to raise the temperature of 1 g of water from 14.5 °C to 15.5 °C (page 25). The quantity of heat transferred (gained or lost) is determined by the temperature difference, the mass, and the specific heat of a substance (page 89).

From the Latin words calor (heat) and metrum (measure).

The heat of a reaction is measured by mixing known quantities of reactants in an apparatus called a calorimeter. The general idea is to determine the rise or lowering of the temperature produced in a known mass of water; water is chosen because its specific heat (page 89) is accurately known. The heat of reaction is then directly obtained from the mass of water, its temperature change, and its specific heat. The essential parts of a calorimeter are shown in Fig. 9.1.

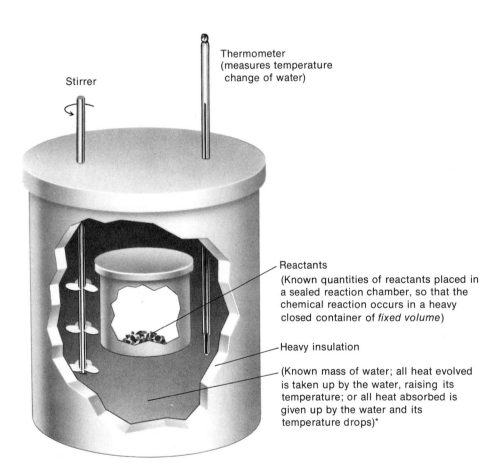

Stirrer

Thermometer
(measures temperature
change of water)

Reactants
(Known quantities of reactants placed in a sealed reaction chamber, so that the chemical reaction occurs in a heavy closed container of *fixed volume*)

Heavy insulation

(Known mass of water; all heat evolved is taken up by the water, raising its temperature; or all heat absorbed is given up by the water and its temperature drops)*

*More accurately, the heat evolved by the reaction is absorbed not only by the water but also by the stirrer, the thermometer, the reaction chamber and its contents.

FIGURE 9.1 Representation of a calorimeter. The stirrer maintains uniform temperature. Insulation minimizes heat leakage in or out of the calorimeter.

Example 1

The combustion of 1.00 g of liquid benzene, C_6H_6

$$C_6H_6(l) + 7\tfrac{1}{2}\, O_2(g) \longrightarrow 3H_2O(l) + 6CO_2(g)^*$$

in a closed container raises the temperature of 3835 g of water 2.609 °C. (This includes the heat absorbed by the other parts of the calorimeter.) Calculate the heat evolved in kilocalories (a) by 1.00 g of liquid C_6H_6; (b) by 1.00 mole of liquid C_6H_6, 78.1 g/mole. The specific heat of water is 0.9983 cal/(g °C); 1000 cal = 1 kilocalorie (kcal).

Answer

(a) Heat energy and temperature are related but they are not the same. Experimentally, the same heat energy, measured in calories, produces different temperature changes in the same mass of different substances. While 1.0 cal raises 1.0 g of water 1.0 °C, 1.0 cal raises 1.0 g of iron 9.1 °C. For each substance, the heat energy and temperature are related by specific heat values (page 89). The rise in temperature of the given mass of water then measures the heat energy evolved by the combustion of the 1.00 g of liquid C_6H_6,

specific heat of water, $\dfrac{cal}{g\,°C} \times$ water mass, $g \times$ water temperature change, $°C$

= heat absorbed by water, cal

= heat evolved by C_6H_6

$0.9983\, \dfrac{cal}{g\,°C} \times 3835\, g \times 2.609\, °C = 9989\ cal = 9.989\ kcal$

9.989 kcal = 41.79 kJ

The heat evolved by the combustion of 1.00 g of liquid C_6H_6 is 9.989 kcal. Experimentally, *it is the quantity of heat that would have to be removed to restore the reaction products to the original temperature of the reactants.* (b) The heat absorbed or evolved depends on the quantity of reactants. It is therefore customary to express heats of reaction on the basis of 1 mole. To convert 1 mole of benzene (78.1 g) to kcal of heat evolved, we need a conversion factor (page 9) of kcal per gram of C_6H_6. The conversion factor is therefore $\dfrac{9.989\ kcal}{1\ g\ C_6H_6}$

and the heat evolved by 1 mole is

$$78.1\ g\ C_6H_6 \times \dfrac{9.989\ kcal}{1\ g\ C_6H_6} = 780\ kcal^{**}$$

780 kcal = 3264 kJ

The combustion of C_6H_6 is a typical **exothermic** reaction, a chemical reaction that *evolves* heat to the surroundings. If the heat is *not removed,* the *temperature* of the

---

*Reminder: the equation is read (page 153) as

1 mole C_6H_6 + $7\tfrac{1}{2}$ moles $O_2 \longrightarrow$ 3 moles H_2O + 6 moles CO_2,

and $7\tfrac{1}{2}\, O_2$ is the same as $^{15}/_2 \times 2 = 15$ oxygen atoms.
  **Data source for this chapter: mainly from "Selected Values of Chemical Thermodynamic Properties," National Bureau of Standards Technical Notes 270–3, 4, 5, 6, 7, and IR76–1034 (1968–1976).

Calorimeters come so close to doing this that the error is negligible.

surroundings *increases*. The object of the calorimeter experiment is to remove that quantity of heat necessary to restore the reaction products to the original temperature of the reactants. Effectively, the experiment, for all purposes, is carried out at constant temperature.

Since energy is evolved, the energy of the reaction products, $E_{product}$, of an exothermic reaction must be less than that of the reactants, $E_{reactant}$. From experiment, for the combustion of benzene, $E_{product}$, the energy of 3 moles of $H_2O(l)$ and 6 moles of $CO_2(g)$, is 780 kcal *less* than $E_{reactant}$, the energy of 1 mole of $C_6H_6(l)$ and $7\frac{1}{2}$ moles of $O_2(g)$. These measured energy differences, the heat evolved or absorbed at *constant volume* and *constant temperature,* are sufficiently important properties of chemical reactions to have a special symbol, **ΔE,** called "delta E." * By convention, these differences are *always* taken by subtracting the *reactant* quantity from the *product* quantity, so that ΔE, the difference in energy resulting from a chemical change, is

$$\Delta E = \text{energy of products} - \text{energy of reactants}$$
$$\Delta E = E_{product} - E_{reactant}$$

For the combustion of 1 mole of $C_6H_6(l)$, $E_{product}$ is smaller than $E_{reactant}$ by 780 kcal; ΔE then takes a *negative sign:*

$$\Delta E = -780 \text{ kcal} = -3264 \text{ kJ}$$

The **thermochemical equation** for the combustion of $C_6H_6(l)$ is thus written as

$$C_6H_6(l) + 7\frac{1}{2}\,O_2(g) \longrightarrow 3H_2O(l) + 6CO_2(g)$$

exothermic reaction
$\Delta E = -780 \text{ kcal}$
volume and temperature constant

ΔE gives us the difference in the energy of products and reactants. No attempt is made to define the separate values of $E_{product}$ and $E_{reactant}$, because these values cannot be experimentally determined. We concern ourselves only with the difference because this can be experimentally measured in a calorimeter.

An energy state diagram (page 185) summarizes this discussion:

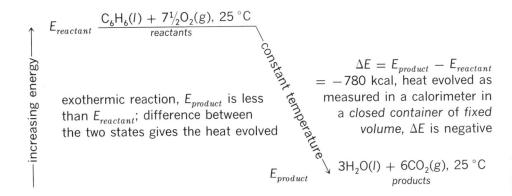

$E_{reactant}$ $\quad$ $C_6H_6(l) + 7\frac{1}{2}O_2(g), 25\,°C$
reactants

increasing energy →

exothermic reaction, $E_{product}$ is less than $E_{reactant}$; difference between the two states gives the heat evolved

constant temperature

$\Delta E = E_{product} - E_{reactant}$
$= -780$ kcal, heat evolved as measured in a calorimeter in a *closed container* of *fixed volume,* ΔE is negative

$E_{product}$ $\quad$ $3H_2O(l) + 6CO_2(g), 25\,°C$
products

---

*The Greek letter Δ, named delta, equivalent to our D, in scientific notation denotes a "difference" in various measurable quantities. Δt, for example, denotes the time it takes for a certain event to occur; a plane leaves New York at t_1, 6:00 AM, and arrives in Washington, D.C., at t_2, 8:35 AM, $\Delta t = t_2 - t_1 = 8:35 - 6:00 = 2$ h 35 min.

Example 2

The decomposition of 0.10 g of ammonia-boron trifluoride (page 251), $H_3NBF_3(c) \longrightarrow NH_3(g) + BF_3(g)$, in a closed vessel (constant volume) at constant temperature absorbs 0.0483 kcal. Calculate the heat absorbed by 1 mole of solid H_3NBF_3, 85 g/mole.

Answer

To convert 1 mole of H_3NBF_3(85 g) to kcal of heat absorbed, we need a conversion factor of kcal per gram. Therefore the conversion factor is $\dfrac{0.0483 \text{ kcal}}{0.10 \text{ g}}$.
Hence, the number of kcal absorbed by 85 g is

$$85 \text{ g} \times \frac{0.0483 \text{ kcal}}{0.10 \text{ g}} = 41 \text{ kcal}$$

The decomposition of $H_3NBF_3(c)$ is a typical **endothermic** reaction, a chemical reaction that *absorbs* (takes in, gains) heat from the surroundings.* If heat is not added, the temperature of the surroundings decreases. In an experiment, the calorimeter adds that quantity of heat needed to restore the reaction products to the original temperature of the reactants. Similar to an exothermic reaction, the experiment is effectively carried out at constant temperature. Since energy is absorbed, the energy of the reaction products, $E_{product}$, of an endothermic reaction must be greater than that of the reactants, $E_{reactant}$. For the decomposition of $H_3NBF_3(c)$, the energy of 1 mole of $NH_3(g)$ and 1 mole of $BF_3(g)$ is 41 kcal *more* than the energy of 1 mole of $H_3NBF_3(c)$. The difference in energy, ΔE, is $E_{product} - E_{reactant}$; but $E_{product}$ is larger than $E_{reactant}$. ΔE, therefore, takes a *positive sign;* namely, $\Delta E = +41$ kcal. The thermochemical equation for the decomposition reaction is

$$H_3NBF_3(c) \longrightarrow NH_3(g) + BF_3(g)$$

endothermic reaction
$\Delta E = +41$ kcal
volume and temperature constant

and its energy state diagram is

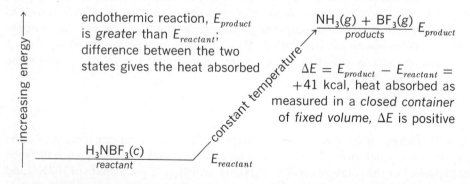

---

*Marcellin Berthelot, a founder of thermochemistry, introduced (1879) the terms exothermic and endothermic, derived from the Greek words *exo* (outside), *endon* (inside), and *therme* (heat), used in the sense of producing and absorbing heat.

The energy of a substance depends on its temperature and physical condition. For example, the energy of water vapor, $H_2O(g)$, at 25 °C is greater than that of liquid water, $H_2O(l)$, at 25 °C because heat is absorbed during vaporization (page 90):

$$H_2O(l),\ 25\ °C \longrightarrow H_2O(g),\ 25\ °C \qquad \begin{array}{c}\textit{endothermic}\\ \Delta E = +9.9\ \text{kcal}\\ \textit{volume and temperature constant}\end{array}$$

Thus, when $H_2O(l)$ and $H_2O(g)$ form, the heat evolved is not the same:

$$H_2(g) + \tfrac{1}{2}\,O_2(g) \longrightarrow H_2O(l) \qquad \Delta E = -67.4\ \text{kcal}$$
$$H_2(g) + \tfrac{1}{2}\,O_2(g) \longrightarrow H_2O(g) \qquad \Delta E = -57.5\ \text{kcal}$$

The state of each reactant and product must therefore be clearly indicated.

Data in this text, unless otherwise stated, are for substances in their natural condition at 25 °C and 1 atm pressure; for example, H_2(g), H_2O(l), Fe(c).

PROBLEM 1   **(a) The combustion of 0.200 g of ethyl alcohol, $C_2H_5OH(l)$ + $3O_2(g) \longrightarrow 2CO_2(g) + 3H_2O(l)$, in a closed container (volume constant), raises the temperature of 3.000×10^3 g of water 0.473 °C. Calculate the heat evolved in kcal (i) by 0.200 g and (ii) by 1.00 mole of $C_2H_5OH(l)$. (b) The decomposition of 0.300 g of potassium perchlorate, $KClO_4(c) \longrightarrow KCl(c) + 2O_2(g)$, in a closed vessel at constant temperature, absorbs 0.221 kcal. Calculate the heat absorbed when 1.00 mole of $KClO_4$ decomposes. (c) Write the thermochemical equation for each reaction.**

9.3 HEAT OF REACTION; CONSTANT PRESSURE AND CONSTANT TEMPERATURE

Known as a bomb calorimeter.

Although thermochemical measurements are generally made for convenience in a closed container of fixed volume, reactions most frequently occur in apparatus open to the atmosphere, and therefore occur at constant (barometric) pressure. In going from reactants to products, the volume may change (page 135), but the pressure exerted by the atmosphere remains practically constant. Experimentally, however, the heat of reaction measured at constant pressure and constant temperature frequently differs from that measured at constant volume and constant temperature. In a closed container, gases can neither expand nor contract. For example, when 1 mole of $C_6H_6(l)$ is burned in an open vessel (constant pressure), the heat evolved is 781 kcal, not 780 kcal. This difference is real; it is small but not due to experimental error.

In the same way that ΔE denotes the heat of a reaction under specific experimental conditions of *constant volume, constant temperature*, "delta H," ΔH, is used to denote the heat of reaction under the experimental conditions of *constant pressure and constant temperature*. ΔH, called the "difference in **enthalpy**" resulting from a chemical change, is equal to the enthalpy of the products, $H_{product}$, minus the enthalpy of the reactants, $H_{reactant}$

From enthalpo, the Greek word for warming up. Formerly known as "heat content," this obsolete and misleading term accounts for the symbol H.

$$\Delta H = H_{product} - H_{reactant}$$

As with energy values (page 286), enthalpies of products and reactants cannot be experimentally determined. We content ourselves only with the difference between enthalpies. For the combustion of $C_6H_6(l)$, the enthalpy of the 3 moles of $H_2O(l)$ and the 6 moles of $CO_2(g)$ is 781 kcal *less* than the enthalpy of 1 mole of $C_6H_6(l)$ and $7\tfrac{1}{2}$ moles of $O_2(g)$. The thermochemical equation for the combustion of $C_6H_6(l)$ may then be written as

$$C_6H_6(l) + 7\tfrac{1}{2}\,O_2(g) \longrightarrow 3H_2O(l) + 6CO_2(g)$$

exothermic reaction
$\Delta H = -781$ kcal
pressure and temperature constant

and its enthalpy state diagram is

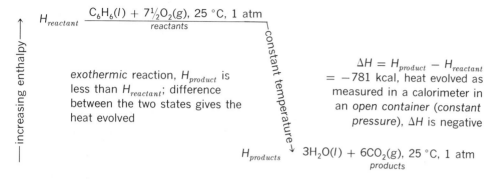

The thermochemical equation for the decomposition of H_3NBF_3 (page 287) may be written as

$$H_3NBF_3(c) \longrightarrow NH_3(g) + BF_3(g)$$

endothermic reaction
$\Delta H = +42$ kcal
pressure and temperature constant

and its enthalpy state diagram is

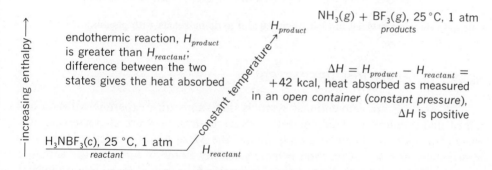

PROBLEM 2 Write the thermochemical equation in terms of ΔE or ΔH from the following experimental data (25 °C). (a) The decomposition of 1 mole of calcium hydride, $CaH_2(c)$, to calcium and hydrogen (i) in a closed container absorbs 43.9 kcal; (ii) in an open vessel absorbs 44.5 kcal. (b) The explosion of 1 mole of xenon trioxide, $XeO_3(c) \longrightarrow Xe(g) + 1\tfrac{1}{2}\,O_2(g)$, evolves (i) 95.6 kcal in an open vessel; (ii) 97.1 kcal in a closed container. (c) The reaction occurring in a polluted atmosphere, $O_3(g) + SO_2(g) \longrightarrow SO_3(g) + O_2(g)$, evolves the same quantity of heat, 57.7 kcal, in (i) an open vessel; (ii) a closed container.

Reactions involving only solids and liquids usually undergo very small volume changes; expansions and contractions are negligible. However, if gases are involved, large volume changes may result when a reaction occurs at constant pressure (recall that 1 mole of gas at STP occupies 22.4 liters). Pushing back the atmosphere requires work, so a difference between the heat of a reaction measured at constant volume (ΔE) and that measured at constant pressure (ΔH) results from volume changes that may accompany a reaction.

Example 3

Given the thermochemical equation

$$H_2(g) + \tfrac{1}{2} O_2(g) \longrightarrow H_2O(l) \qquad \Delta H = -68.3 \text{ kcal}$$

How much heat in kcal is evolved when 50.0 g H_2 is burned to water in an open-end rocket?

Answer

To convert 50.0 g H_2 to kcal of heat, we need a conversion factor of kcal per g H_2. The equation states that 1 mole, 2.02 g H_2, evolves 68.3 kcal. The conversion factor is then $\dfrac{68.3 \text{ kcal}}{2.02 \text{ g } H_2}$ and the quantity of heat evolved by 50.0 g H_2 is given by

$$50.0 \text{ g } H_2 \times \frac{68.3 \text{ kcal}}{2.02 \text{ g } H_2} = 1691 = 1.69 \times 10^3 \text{ kcal}$$

PROBLEM 3   **For the hydrogen bonding reaction in liquid carbon tetrachloride between phenol (carbolic acid), C_6H_5OH, a highly poisonous substance used to prevent infections, and pyridine, NC_5H_5, a liquid solvent obtained from coal tar, the thermochemical equation is**

$$C_6H_5OH + NC_5H_5 \longrightarrow C_6H_5OH\text{---}NC_5H_5 \qquad \Delta H = -7.3 \text{ kcal}$$

Calculate the heat evolved in kcal when 5.0 g of pyridine reacts with phenol.

9.4 _____ HEATS OF REACTION PREDICTED

ΔE and ΔH are conventional symbols that summarize experimental data obtained under definitely fixed conditions. Nevertheless, they are characteristic of a chemical reaction and can be used to predict the ΔE or ΔH of a reaction. However, information on heats of reaction is most generally stored in terms of the enthalpy change, ΔH, in kcal/mole, as the **heat of formation.** The heat of formation is the heat evolved or absorbed when 1 mole of a substance is formed from the most stable form of its elements. Data are also stored as the **heat of combustion,** in kcal/mole, the heat evolved when 1 mole of a substance is burned in oxygen. Typical examples are the formation of silver nitrate

Reminder: At 25 °C and 1 atm.

$$Ag(c) + \tfrac{1}{2} N_2(g) + \tfrac{3}{2} O_2(g) \longrightarrow AgNO_3(c) \qquad \Delta H = -29.4 \text{ kcal}$$

and the combustion of C_6H_6 (page 289).

All available experimental data show that ΔH (or ΔE) for a given reaction is *independent* of the method used to change the reactants to products. The heat of a reaction does not depend on the method by which the reaction is made to take place. This generalization, known as **Hess's law,** means that thermochemical equations, like any other mathematical equations, may be added or subtracted. For example, the addition of the two thermochemical equations

Discovered by Germain Hess (1840).

$$C(graphite) + \tfrac{1}{2} O_2(g) \longrightarrow \cancel{CO}(g) \qquad \Delta H = -26.4 \text{ kcal}$$
$$\cancel{CO}(g) + \tfrac{1}{2} O_2(g) \longrightarrow CO_2(g) \qquad \Delta H = -67.6 \text{ kcal}$$

predicts that the heat of combustion of carbon, C(*graphite*), to carbon dioxide is

$$C(graphite) + O_2(g) \longrightarrow CO_2(g) \qquad \Delta H = -26.4 \text{ plus } -67.6 = -94.0 \text{ kcal}$$

In canceling CO, we merely recognize that 1 mole of CO produced in the first reaction is consumed in the second. A substance will not appear in the final equation if it is produced and consumed (or consumed and produced) in equal quantities. The experimentally determined heat of combustion is

$$C(graphite) + O_2(g) \longrightarrow CO_2(g) \qquad \Delta H = -94.0428 \text{ kcal}$$

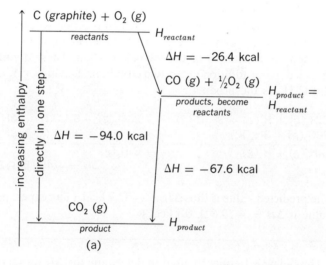

(a)

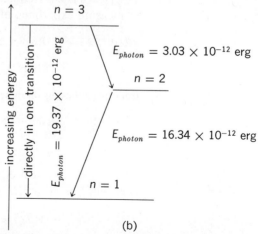

(b)

FIGURE 9.2 (a) The heat of combustion of graphite is the same whether the reaction occurs in one step or in two steps. Similarly, in (b), the energy of the photon emitted by a hydrogen atom (Color Plate V(C)) in one transition ($n_3 \to n_1$) is the same as the sum of the energies of the two photons emitted in two transitions ($n_3 \to n_2$, $n_2 \to n_1$).

An enthalpy (or energy) state diagram, shown in Fig. 9.2, helps us visualize that ΔH (or ΔE) for a given reaction must be the same whether it occurs in one or several steps.

Example 4

Predict ΔH for the addition of hydrogen to 1 mole of ethylene, C_2H_4, forming ethane, C_2H_6

$$C_2H_4(g) + H_2(g) \longrightarrow C_2H_6(g) \qquad \Delta H = ?$$

from the following thermochemical equations:

$$C_2H_4(g) + H_2(g) + 3\tfrac{1}{2}\,O_2(g) \longrightarrow 2CO_2(g) + 3H_2O(l) \qquad \Delta H = -405.5 \text{ kcal}$$
$$2CO_2(g) + 3H_2O(l) \longrightarrow C_2H_6(g) + 3\tfrac{1}{2}\,O_2(g) \qquad \Delta H = +372.8 \text{ kcal}$$

Answer

The $3\tfrac{1}{2}$ moles of O_2 consumed in the first reaction is regenerated in the second reaction; the 2 moles of CO_2 and the 3 moles of H_2O produced in the first reaction are consumed in the second reaction. These quantities are therefore canceled in the addition of the two equations, leaving C_2H_4 and H_2 as reactants and C_2H_6 as the product:

$$C_2H_4(g) + H_2(g) + \cancel{3\tfrac{1}{2}\,O_2(g)} \longrightarrow \cancel{2CO_2(g)} + \cancel{3H_2O(l)} \qquad \Delta H = -405.5 \text{ kcal}$$
$$\cancel{2CO_2(g)} + \cancel{3H_2O(l)} \longrightarrow C_2H_6(g) + \cancel{3\tfrac{1}{2}\,O_2(g)} \qquad \Delta H = +372.8 \text{ kcal}$$

$$C_2H_4(g) + H_2(g) \longrightarrow C_2H_6(g)$$
$$\Delta H = -405.5 + 372.8 = -32.7 \text{ kcal}$$

The predicted value is thus $\Delta H = -32.7$ kcal. (The experimentally determined value is $\Delta H = -32.6 \pm 0.1$ kcal.)

Hess's law is frequently used to determine the ΔH for reactions that are difficult to measure experimentally.

PROBLEM 4   **Predict ΔH for the reaction**

$$Mg(c) + 2HCl(g) \longrightarrow MgCl_2(c) + H_2(g) \qquad \Delta H = ?$$

from the following thermochemical equations:

$$Mg(c) + Cl_2(g) \longrightarrow MgCl_2(c) \qquad \Delta H = -153.3 \text{ kcal}$$
$$2HCl(g) \longrightarrow H_2(g) + Cl_2(g) \qquad \Delta H = +44.1 \text{ kcal}$$

Thermochemical equations may be reversed; the sign of ΔH (or ΔE) is then changed. For example, on reversing

$$H_2(g) + \tfrac{1}{2}\,O_2(g) \longrightarrow H_2O(l) \qquad \Delta H = -68.3 \text{ kcal}$$

the sign of ΔH is changed:

$$H_2O(l) \longrightarrow H_2(g) + \tfrac{1}{2}\,O_2(g) \qquad \Delta H = +68.3 \text{ kcal}$$

This means that the heat (energy), no matter how supplied, required to decompose 1 mole of $H_2O(l)$ must equal the heat evolved in its formation.

The combustion of glucose, the reverse of photosynthesis (page 195) and the energy source for living organisms, is another example:

$$C_6H_{12}O_6(c) + 6O_2(g) \longrightarrow 6H_2O(l) + 6CO_2(g) \qquad \Delta H = -670 \text{ kcal}$$

Electrolysis (electrical work), Chap. 15, or heat from a hydrogen bomb, Chap. 17.

However, the reaction does not occur wastefully in one step, but rather transfers the energy to *adenosine triphosphate, ATP,* found in muscle tissue. A compound of great biochemical importance, ATP absorbs heat when formed from ADP and releases it only on demand when other biochemical reactions require it for muscle movement (biological work):

adenosine triphosphate, ATP

adenosine diphosphate, ADP

The heat evolved exactly equals the heat absorbed. ATP thus serves as a "biological energy storage tank."

Example 5

Use the thermochemical equations

$$\tfrac{1}{2} H_2(g) + \tfrac{1}{2} I_2(g) \longrightarrow HI(g) \qquad \Delta H = \quad -1.1 \text{ kcal} \qquad (1)$$
$$2H(g) \longrightarrow H_2(g) \qquad \Delta H = -104.2 \text{ kcal} \qquad (2)$$
$$\tfrac{1}{2} I_2(g) \longrightarrow I(g) \qquad \Delta H = \quad +18.1 \text{ kcal} \qquad (3)$$

to predict ΔH for the formation of hydrogen iodide gas from gaseous atomic hydrogen and gaseous atomic iodine:

$$H(g) + I(g) \longrightarrow HI(g) \qquad \Delta H = ? \qquad (4)$$

Answer

First, manipulate the given chemical equations so as to eliminate the substances not appearing in the desired reaction (Equation 4). Observe in Equation 4 that $I(g)$ is a reactant and that only 1 mole of $H(g)$ appears as a reactant. Hence,

---

*The reader need not be concerned with the complex composition of these biochemical molecules. Readers interested in the thermodynamics of ATP are referred to articles in the *Journal of Chemical Education* by Robert Alberty, volume 46, October 1969, page 713, and by Joel Kirschbaum, volume 45, January 1968, page 28. The chemical reactions of the muscle-contraction cycle are outlined on page 64, *Scientific American*, February 1974. Joseph Fourier founded (1809) thermodynamics (from the Greek words *therme*, heat, and *dynamikos*, work), the study of the relations between heat and work.

multiply Equation 2 by $\frac{1}{2}$ and reverse Equation 3 to obtain Equations 5 and 6 below. Notice that reversing Equation 3 changes the sign of ΔH, and that multiplying a chemical equation multiplies its ΔH (or ΔE) by the same number; the heat evolved by $\frac{1}{2}$ mole of H_2 is one-half the heat evolved by 1 mole:

$$\frac{1}{2}\,H_2(g) + \frac{1}{2}\,I_2(g) \longrightarrow HI(g) \qquad \Delta H = -1.1\ \text{kcal} \qquad (1)$$

$$H(g) \longrightarrow \frac{1}{2}\,H_2(g) \qquad \Delta H = -52.1\ \text{kcal} \qquad (5)$$

$$I(g) \longrightarrow \frac{1}{2}\,I_2(g) \qquad \Delta H = -18.1\ \text{kcal} \qquad (6)$$

Secondly, addition of Equations 1, 5, and 6 yields the desired Equation 4:

$$H(g) + I(g) \longrightarrow HI(g) \qquad \Delta H = -1.1 - 52.1 - 18.1 = -71.3\ \text{kcal}$$

PROBLEM 5   **Predict ΔH for the reaction**

$$H(g) + Cl(g) \longrightarrow HCl(g) \qquad \Delta H = ?$$

from the given thermochemical equations:

$$2Cl(g) \longrightarrow Cl_2(g) \qquad \Delta H = -58\ \text{kcal}$$

$$\frac{1}{2}\,H_2(g) + \frac{1}{2}\,Cl_2(g) \longrightarrow HCl(g) \qquad \Delta H = -22\ \text{kcal}$$

$$\frac{1}{2}\,H_2(g) \longrightarrow H(g) \qquad \Delta H = +52\ \text{kcal}$$

9.5 _____ CHEMICAL BONDS AND HEATS OF REACTION

Visualization of chemical change as the breakage of bonds in the reactants and the formation of bonds in the products makes possible the prediction of the heats of reactions. Example 5 illustrates this for the reaction $H(g) + I(g) \longrightarrow HI(g)$. We visualize the breaking of the H—H(g) and I—I(g) bonds into gaseous atoms:

This scheme takes advantage of Hess's law to predict heats of reaction. It does not show how reactants change to products, the subject of Chap. 16.

$$H{-}H(g) \longrightarrow H(g) + H(g) \qquad \Delta H = +104.2\ \text{kcal}$$

$$I{-}I(g) \longrightarrow I(g) + I(g) \qquad \Delta H = +\ \ 36.2\ \text{kcal}$$

This *breakage* requires 140.4 (104.2 + 36.2) kcal. Next we visualize the formation of HI(g) from the gaseous atoms

$$H(g) + I(g) \longrightarrow H{-}I(g) \qquad \Delta H = -71.3\ \text{kcal}$$

The *formation* of two H—I(g) bonds *evolves* 142.6 (2 × 71.3) kcal. Breaking bonds

TABLE 9.1

BOND ENERGIES, EXPRESSED AS ΔH IN KCAL/MOLE, FOR THE REACTION IN WHICH ONE BOND PER MOLECULE IS BROKEN

HF	135	F_2	37.8	C—H	99.3	C—C (single)	83
HCl	103	Cl_2	58.2	C—F	116	C=C (double)	143
HBr	87.5	Br_2	46.1	C—Cl	78	C≡C (triple)	194
HI	71.3	I_2	36.1	C—Br	68	N_2	226.0

$NF_3 \longrightarrow NF_2 + F$	58	$CH_4 \longrightarrow CH_3 + H$	103
$NF_2 \longrightarrow NF + F$	76	$CH_3 \longrightarrow CH_2 + H$	113

absorbs 140.4 kcal, while forming bonds *evolves* 142.6 kcal. More heat is evolved than absorbed; the reaction is therefore exothermic with an *emission* of 2.2 kcal (142.6 − 140.4). This discussion is summarized in the enthalpy state diagram:

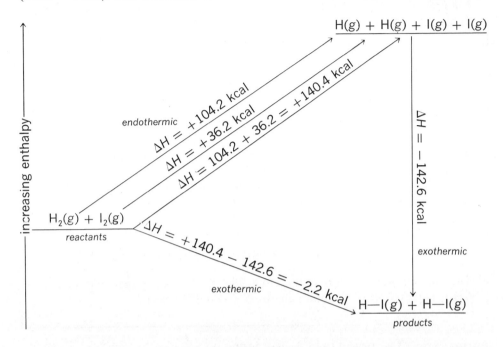

The energy required to break one bond in a gaseous molecule into two gaseous products is called the **bond energy,** expressed as ΔH in kcal per mole (Table 9.1). These values may be calculated as shown in Example 5 and Problem 5. However, methane, CH_4, and carbon tetrafluoride, CF_4, typical of molecules containing more than two atoms, invariably require different quantities of energy to detach the atoms one by one. The difference develops because an atom may change the type of atomic orbital it uses in bonding as other atoms are detached (Chap. 18). In these cases, an *average bond energy* is assigned to the bond. For example, experimentally, 397.2 kcal/mole is required to detach the 4 H atoms from CH_4

Sometimes called polyatomic molecules, derived from the Greek word polys, meaning many.

$$H-\underset{\underset{H}{|}}{\overset{\overset{H}{|}}{C}}-H(g) \longrightarrow C(g) + 4H(g) \qquad \Delta H = +397.2 \text{ kcal}$$

Since 4 C—H bonds are being broken, the average energy required to break one C—H bond is then one-fourth of +397.2 kcal: $\frac{397.2}{4} = 99.3$ kcal per mole of C—H bonds. Average bond energies usually are simply called bond energies, some of which are given in Table 9.1.

This assignment of bond energies makes it possible to calculate the heats of reaction for which experimental data are not available. A small number of bond energies, about 20 bonds, make it possible to predict the heats of reaction of about a million organic compounds undergoing an almost limitless number of reactions. We stress that such calculations are based on the assumption that bond energies are independent of the nature of the molecule.

With an error of about 10 % or less; but with refinements, accuracy can be improved to 0.1 %.

Example 6

Chloromethane, CH_3Cl, a colorless gas, is a useful organic reagent. Using Table 9.1, calculate the heat of the reaction

$$H-\underset{\underset{H}{|}}{\overset{\overset{Cl}{|}}{C}}-H(g) \longrightarrow C(g) + 3H(g) + Cl(g) \qquad \Delta H = ?$$

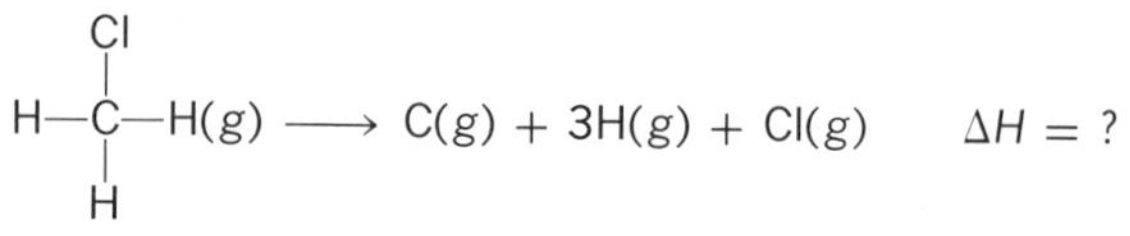

Answer

We *assume* that a bond between a given pair of atoms does not depend on the particular molecule of which it is a part. The data in Table 9.1 may then be used to predict the energy required to break (dissociate) any molecule. In the given reaction, three C—H bonds and one C—Cl bond are broken:

Breaking three C—H bonds requires 3×99.3 kcal = 298 kcal

Breaking one C—Cl bond requires 78 kcal = 78 kcal

The ΔH for the reaction is therefore $298 + 78 = +376$ kcal per mole of $CH_3Cl(g)$. (The experimental value is $\Delta H = +375.8$ kcal.)

PROBLEM 6 Use Table 9.1 to calculate ΔH for the reaction

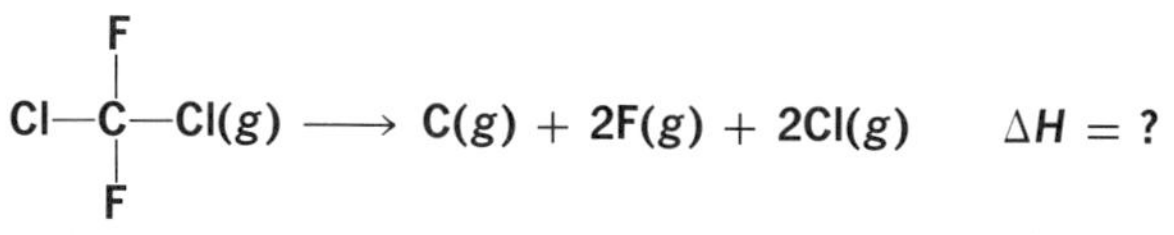

$$Cl-\underset{\underset{F}{|}}{\overset{\overset{F}{|}}{C}}-Cl(g) \longrightarrow C(g) + 2F(g) + 2Cl(g) \qquad \Delta H = ?$$

Freon-12

Example 7

Use Table 9.1 to calculate the heat of the reaction

$$H-\underset{\underset{H}{|}\,\underset{H}{|}}{\overset{\overset{H}{|}\,\overset{H}{|}}{C-C}}-H(g) + Br_2(g) \longrightarrow H-\underset{\underset{H}{|}}{\overset{\overset{H}{|}}{C}}-Br(g) + H-\underset{\underset{H}{|}}{\overset{\overset{H}{|}}{C}}-Br(g)$$

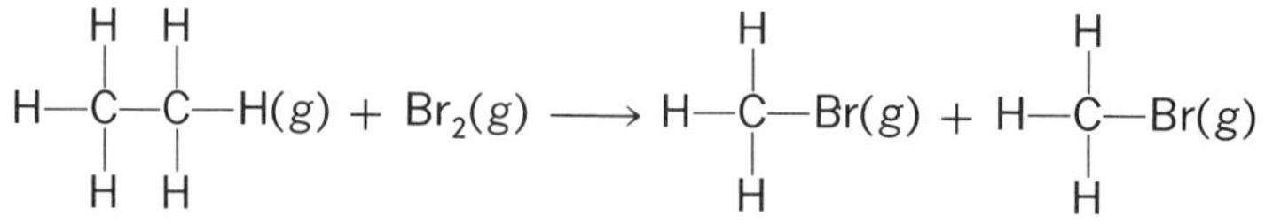

ethane   bromomethane

Answer

In the given reaction, the number of C—H bonds is the same before and after the reaction; however, one C—C (single) bond and one Br—Br bond are broken, while two C—Br bonds form:

Breaking one C—C bond requires   83   kcal
Breaking one Br—Br bond requires   46.1   kcal
Bond breaking thus requires   129.1   kcal
Forming two C—Br bonds evolves $2 \times 68 = 136$ kcal

More heat is evolved than absorbed; the reaction is therefore exothermic:

$$C_2H_6(g) + Br_2(g) \longrightarrow 2CH_3Br(g) \qquad \Delta H = +129 - 136 = -7 \text{ kcal}$$

PROBLEM 7   Use Table 9.1 to calculate the heat of the reaction

Occasionally, a significant difference is found between the ΔH of a reaction as calculated (in Examples 6 and 7) and the experimental ΔH. These differences force the student to re-examine the assumption that the energy required to break a bond is independent of the make-up of the molecule. However, this re-examination will actually lead us (Chaps. 18 and 22) to a better understanding of the nature of bonds in molecules.

Thermal and Bond Stability   The higher the bond energy, the greater the **bond stability.** The C=C (double) bond (Table 9.1), for example, is more stable than the C—C (single) bond; this means more energy is needed to break the C=C bond. **Thermal stability** refers to the resistance of a substance to decomposition when heated in a vacuum. Water and bromine, for example, are thermally stable; at 2000 °C only about 0.01 % of water decomposes to hydrogen and oxygen, while only about 5 % of bromine decomposes to atoms. On the other hand, potassium chlorate, $KClO_3$, may be completely decomposed to the chloride, KCl, and oxygen, O_2, at about 360 °C. Chlorates are *dangerous* chemicals, frequently exploding in the presence of impurities. The student is advised to heat substances only when so instructed and never to heat substances in closed containers.

Decomposition temperatures are sufficiently characteristic to identify substances by thermal analysis, a study of the changes in the mass of a substance as its temperature is increased in the absence of oxygen.

Thermal stability and bond stability should not be confused with **reactivity,** the tendency to react (Chap. 16). An unreactive substance has little tendency to undergo chemical changes, under given conditions, *with itself or other substances*. High bond stability or high thermal stability does not necessarily mean the molecule is unreactive. Thus, bromine, Br_2, is thermally stable, but it is nevertheless very reactive; it easily reacts with other elements and compounds to form bromides. It is, in fact, a very deadly element since it readily attacks body tissues, causing hideous burns. And, as we shall study later (Chap. 22), a carbon-carbon double bond is more reactive than a single bond even though the double bond has greater bond stability.

PROBLEM 8   (a) Sodium azide, NaN_3, decomposes smoothly at 300 °C, while the thermal decomposition of hydrogen fluoride requires very high temperatures. Liquid hydrazoic acid, HN_3, decomposes (*explosively*) above about 40 °C. (i) Which substance has the highest thermal stability? (ii) Does it follow, without further information, that this substance is also the least reactive? (b) The triple bond, C≡C, has a greater bond stability, Table 9.1, than a single bond. Does this mean that the single bond must be more reactive?

Enthalpy changes are largely stored as heats of formation, ΔH_f, expressed as kcal/mole of compound formed from its most stable elements at 25 °C and 1 atm (page 290). An element formed at 25 °C and 1 atm is exactly the same as the state in which it naturally exists at 25 °C and 1 atm. Therefore, by definition, the heat of formation of any element at 25 °C and 1 atm is zero. If an element exists in different compositions or different bonding, then the most stable form at 25 °C and 1 atm is assigned zero heat of formation. Examples of typical heats of formation follow:

$$H_2(g) + \tfrac{1}{2}O_2(g) \longrightarrow H_2O(l) \qquad \Delta H_f = -68.3 \text{ kcal} \qquad (7)$$

$$C(graphite) + O_2(g) \longrightarrow CO_2(g) \qquad \Delta H_f = -94.0 \text{ kcal} \qquad (8)$$

$$C(graphite) + 2H_2(g) \longrightarrow CH_4(g) \qquad \Delta H_f = -17.9 \text{ kcal} \qquad (9)$$

$$O_2(g) \longrightarrow O_2(g) \qquad \Delta H_f = 0 \qquad (10)$$

$$1\tfrac{1}{2}O_2(g) \longrightarrow O_3(g) \qquad \Delta H_f = +34.1 \text{ kcal} \qquad (11)$$

$$C(graphite) \longrightarrow C(graphite) \qquad \Delta H_f = 0 \qquad (12)$$

$$C(graphite) \longrightarrow C(diamond) \qquad \Delta H_f = +0.453 \text{ kcal} \qquad (13)$$

At 25 °C and 1 atm, O_2 is more stable than O_3 and graphite is more stable than diamond.

Let us now use these heats of formation to calculate the heat of the reaction for the combustion of natural gas, which is mostly methane:

$$CH_4(g) + 2O_2(g) \longrightarrow CO_2(g) + 2H_2O(l) \qquad \Delta H = ?$$

CO_2 and H_2O are the *products*. Notice that the addition of Equations 7 and 8, the heats of formation, yields CO_2 and H_2O as *products*. Therefore, we add Equations 7 amd 8, being careful to multiply Equation 7 by 2:

$$
\begin{array}{lll}
C(graphite) + O_2(g) \longrightarrow CO_2(g) & \Delta H_f = -94.0 \text{ kcal} & \\
2H_2(g) + O_2(g) \longrightarrow 2H_2O(l) & \Delta H_f = -68.3 \times 2 = -136.6 \text{ kcal} & \\
\hline
C(graphite) + 2H_2(g) + 2O_2(g) \longrightarrow CO_2(g) + 2H_2O(l) & \Delta H_f = -230.6 \text{ kcal} & (14)
\end{array}
$$

CH_4 and O_2 are the *reactants*. Notice that *reversing* Equation 9 properly places CH_4 as a *reactant*. Therefore, we *reverse* Equation 9, being careful to change the sign of ΔH_f from $-$ to $+$, and then add it to Equation 10:

$$
\begin{array}{ll}
CH_4(g) \longrightarrow C(graphite) + 2H_2(g) & \Delta H_f = +17.9 \text{ kcal} \\
O_2(g) \longrightarrow O_2(g) & \Delta H_f = 0 \\
\hline
CH_4(g) \longrightarrow C(graphite) + 2H_2(g) & \Delta H_f = +17.9 \text{ kcal} \qquad (15)
\end{array}
$$

Addition of Equations 14 and 15 yields the desired answer:

$$
\begin{array}{lll}
C(graphite) + 2H_2(g) + 2O_2(g) \longrightarrow CO_2(g) + 2H_2O(l) & \Delta H_f = -230.6 \text{ kcal} & (14) \\
CH_4(g) \longrightarrow C(graphite) + 2H_2(g) & \Delta H_f = +17.9 \text{ kcal} & (15) \\
\hline
CH_4(g) + 2O_2(g) \longrightarrow CO_2(g) + 2H_2O(l) & \Delta H = -212.7 \text{ kcal} & (16)
\end{array}
$$

What have we done? We *added the heats of formation of the products* for the number of moles in the chemical equation as written. But by reversing and changing the sign, we *subtracted the heats of formation of the reactants*:

$$
\begin{aligned}
\Delta H_{reaction} &= \Delta H_{f\,products} && - \Delta H_{f\,reactants} \\
&= (\Delta H_{CO_2} + 2 \times \Delta H_{H_2O}) && - (\Delta H_{CH_4} + 2 \times \Delta H_{O_2}) \\
&= (-94.0 \text{ kcal} + 2 \times -68.3 \text{ kcal}) && - (-17.9 \text{ kcal} + 0) \\
&= -230.6 \text{ kcal} && + 17.9 \text{ kcal} \qquad = -212.7 \text{ kcal}
\end{aligned}
$$

Example 8

Use heats of formation to find the heat of the reaction

$$C(diamond) + O_2(g) \longrightarrow CO_2(g) \qquad \Delta H = ?$$

Answer

$$\Delta H_{reaction} = \Delta H_{f\,products} - \Delta H_{f\,reactants}$$
$$= \Delta H_{CO_2} - (\Delta H_{C(diamond)} + \Delta H_{O_2})$$

From the heats of formation, Equations 8 and 13,

$$\Delta H_{reaction} = -94.0 \text{ kcal} - (+0.453 \text{ kcal} + 0)$$
$$= -94.0 \text{ kcal} - 0.453 \text{ kcal} = -94.5 \text{ kcal}$$

PROBLEM 9   From the heats of formation, $\Delta H_{C_2H_4(g)} = +12.49\text{ kcal}$, $\Delta H_{CO_2(g)} = -94.0\text{ kcal}$, $\Delta H_{H_2O(l)} = -68.3\text{ kcal}$, and $\Delta H_{O_2} = 0$, find the heat of the reaction for the combustion of ethylene, $C_2H_4(g) + 3O_2(g) \longrightarrow 2CO_2(g) + 2H_2O(l)$, $\Delta H = ?$

Actually, by common consent, we have set up an arbitrary relative enthalpy scale based on heats of formation at 25 °C and 1 atm, as illustrated (not to scale):

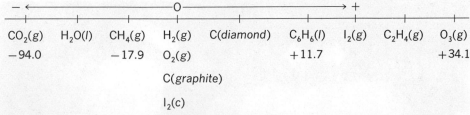

A table of heats (enthalpies) of formation is given in Appendix VI.

HEAT, PHOTONS, AND MOLECULAR MOTION_____9.7

The statement, "Heat is molecular motion," (page 66) is a classic expression. Like electricity (electrical energy), matter, and light, *heat energy is quantized*. Electricity consists of individual electrons, matter consists of individual atoms or molecules, light consists of photons in the wavelength range $(4 \text{ to } 7) \times 10^{-5}$ cm, and heat consists of individual photons in the IR range, above 7×10^{-5} to 0.05 cm (page 191). Like light, the absorption and emission of heat involves electron (atomic or molecular) transitions between two energy states (page 193). The greater the difference, the greater the energy and the higher the photon frequency (Fig. 9.3 a).

The absorption and emission of heat photons by atoms and molecules are associated with motion. Molecular motion always increases with temperature. Atoms—monatomic molecules—undergo only translational (linear) motion. Diatomic and more complex molecules, like H_2 and H_2O, can also rotate and vibrate (Fig. 9.3 b). The more atoms in a molecule, the greater the number of ways in which the molecule can rotate and vibrate. These motions are related to temperature. As the

First experimental proof of the theory that heat is motion is due to B. Thompson (1798).

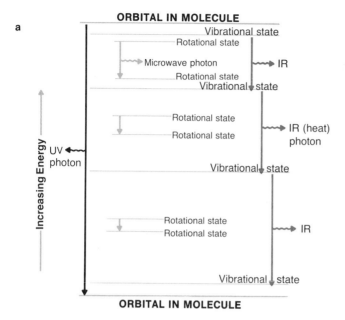

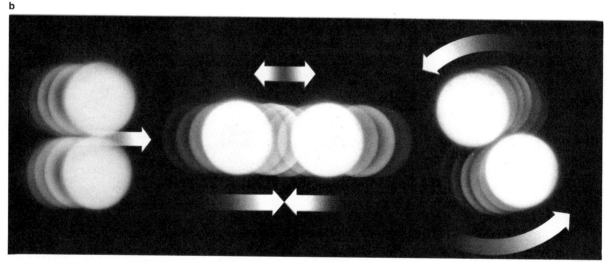

Translational motion

Center of molecule moves; the whole molecule moves through space

Vibrational motion

Center of molecule does not move, but atoms move relative to each other; atoms move away from and return toward center of molecule.

Rotational motion

Center of molecule does not move, but the whole molecule rotates; the atoms rotate about the center of the molecule.

FIGURE 9.3 (a) Typical energy state diagram of a molecule (not to scale). Transitions between orbitals in molecules (Chap. 18) require photons of the highest frequency, while transitions between rotational states require photons of the smallest frequency. (b) Typical molecular motions.

temperature is raised, more and more photons are absorbed, molecules move faster, rotate faster, and vibrate more violently. These vibrations may cause molecules to decompose or dissociate. But molecules vibrate and rotate only with *definite and characteristic amounts of energy;* vibrational and rotational energy states are quantized. Hence, like atoms, molecules may be identified by the frequency of absorbed photons in the UV, IR, or microwave range, the subject of Chap. 24.

It is theoretically possible to watch molecular motion with laser beams and so study biological molecules in living tissues with little damage. Experiments with such lasers may soon demonstrate the feasibility of making motion pictures of important processes, such as the synthesis of proteins in living cells (page 733). Laser surgery on individual parts (organs) of a single living cell is possible because photons of a specific frequency focused on a spot about 10^{-6} cm in diameter are converted to molecular vibrational motions which alter or destroy the molecular structure. Frequent and prolonged exposure to microwave photons ("microwave ovens") has been linked to cataracts in man and blood damage in animals. Such photons can also break down toxic organic (insecticide) compounds into harmless simpler compounds.

Cytology, from the Greek word kytos for cell, is the branch of biology that studies the functions of the tiny organs of living plant and animal cells.

Collisions and Vibrations   In many chemical reactions, the products are stabilized by the removal of excessive vibrational energy. In photochemical smog, for example, absorption of light breaks one N—O bond in NO_2, forming a highly reactive oxygen atom (page 196):

$$NO_2 + hf\ (about\ UV) \longrightarrow NO + O$$

These O atoms may collide with (air) oxygen molecules, forming ozone:

$$O + O_2 \longrightarrow unstable\ O_3\ (excess\ vibrational\ energy)$$

However, the O_3 formed contains large quantities of vibrational energy. Unless this energy is quickly removed, the O_3 decomposes back to $O + O_2$. Therefore, a third molecule, M, must participate in the reaction:

$$unstable\ O_3 + M \longrightarrow stable\ O_3 + M + hf\ (IR)$$

Actually, a "three-body" reaction occurs:
$O + O_2 + M \longrightarrow$
$O_3 + M$

M represents a nitrogen, N_2, molecule or some other molecule that removes the excess vibrational energy and so stabilizes the O_3 molecule.

CONSERVATION OF MATTER REVISITED: INTERCHANGING MATTER AND ENERGY _____ 9.8

Man learns about the behavior of nature only bit by bit, not in big jumps but by small quanta of knowledge. Consequently, to understand experimental knowledge, the scientific model of today requires a modification tomorrow; and for many models, tomorrow is actually today. So, let us reword our conservation law (page 109) in terms of our present knowledge.

Atoms are conserved. They are not destroyed or created in chemical changes. But in the rearrangement the *mass of atoms may increase or decrease.* If energy is *absorbed,* the mass *increases;* conversely, if energy is *evolved,* the mass *decreases.* Expressed in grams, instead of the traditional units of calories or ergs (page 66) the quantity of energy absorbed or evolved is *exactly equal* to the change in the mass of the atoms, also expressed in grams. Regardless of the classification used—physical reaction, phase change, ordinary chemical change, chemical change, nuclear reaction—changes in matter involve *the change of matter to energy* if the reaction *evolves energy,* and *the change of energy to matter* if the reaction *absorbs energy.* Energy and matter are thus interchangeable. The scope of the conservation principle is therefore enlarged to include energy as a form of matter or matter as a form of energy.

We have not been educated to regard energy as matter, but matter and energy do possess common properties. Like matter, visible light and heat—photons—*are attracted by gravity,* but unlike matter, photons travel at the speed of light. Photons with frequencies a billion times higher than visible light photons exhibit properties in common with neutrons.

In summary,

$$\text{atoms} \quad + \quad \text{energy} \quad \longrightarrow \quad \text{molecules} \qquad \Delta H = +x \text{ kcal}$$
$$\text{mass of atoms} + \text{mass of energy} \quad = \quad \text{mass of molecules}$$

$$\text{atoms} \quad \longrightarrow \quad \text{molecules} \quad + \quad \text{energy} \qquad \Delta H = -y \text{ kcal}$$
$$\text{mass of atoms} \quad = \quad \text{mass of molecules} + \text{mass of energy}$$

$$\text{atoms} \quad \longrightarrow \text{different atoms} + \quad \text{energy} \qquad \Delta H = -z \text{ kcal}$$
$$\text{mass of atoms} \quad = \quad \text{mass of atoms} \quad + \text{mass of energy}$$

The interchangeability of matter and energy is given by $\Delta E = \Delta m\, c^2$, predicted by Albert Einstein in 1905. ΔE is the energy evolved or absorbed in ergs, Δm is the quantity of matter in grams changed, and c is the speed of light, 3.00×10^{10} cm/s. An erg has the dimensions of $\text{g} \dfrac{\text{cm}^2}{\text{s}^2}$. The quantity c^2, 9.0×10^{20} cm^2/s^2, is so large that even a very small conversion of matter corresponds to a tremendous amount of energy.

1 joule = 10^7 ergs

Two experiments demonstrate the meaning of the ("matter-energy") conservation principle and the Einstein equation. The first, shown in Fig. 9.4a, is not a real experiment, but it follows experiments that have been performed on a smaller (and safer) scale: Exactly 100 g of a substance is placed in a perfectly insulated can weighing exactly 500 g, so that the total initial mass is exactly 600 g at 25 °C:

$$matter + can = 600 \text{ g } (exactly)$$

A reaction is allowed to occur in which heat is evolved. The temperature inside the can reaches 10^6 °C but the heat is contained in the can—no heat is lost to the outside (surroundings). The total mass of the can and its contents is still exactly 600 g:

$$matter + can + heat = 600 \text{ g } (exactly)$$

After allowing the heat to escape until the temperature is restored to 25 °C, the can is reweighed. The mass of the can and its contents is now *less* than 600 g, but the loss in mass exactly equals the mass of heat evolved:

$$matter + can = 598 \text{ g } (exactly)$$
$$matter\ destroyed = heat\ evolved = \quad 2 \text{ g } (exactly)$$
$$total\ mass = 600 \text{ g } (exactly)$$

a

Before reaction	After reaction	After reaction
	(heat not allowed to escape)	(heat released from can) 2 g heat escape

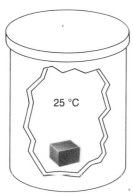

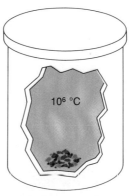

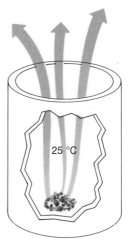

mass of can = 500 g
mass of reactant = 100 g
total mass = 600 g

mass of can = 500 g
mass of products = 98 g
heat produced = matter destroyed = 2 g

total mass = 600 g

mass of can = 500 g
mass of products = 98 g
matter released as heat = 2 g

Total mass = 600 g

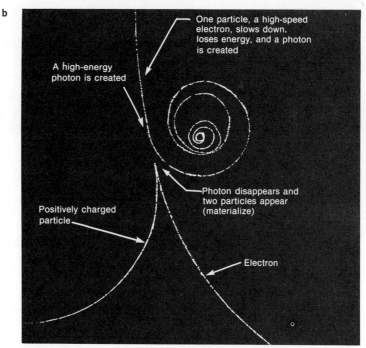

FIGURE 9.4 Illustrating the meaning of the matter-energy conservation principle.

(a) An ideal experiment in which heat is evolved.

(b) An experiment, performed and photographed by Luis Alvarez, in which (kinetic) energy of an electron, entering at the top, is converted to a photon, which in turn is converted to two oppositely charged particles. (Photography involved is explained in Chap. 17; the photon does not show because it is uncharged.)

Example 9

In the above experiment the quantity of matter decreases by 2.00 g. Calculate the heat evolved in grams, in ergs, and in joules. $1 J = 10^7$ ergs.

Answer

The quantity of energy evolved, expressed in grams, equals the quantity of matter destroyed. Therefore, the heat evolved is 2.00 g. The Einstein equation, $\Delta E = \Delta m \, c^2$, expresses this quantity in ergs—it tells us how to change the unit from grams to ergs:

$$\Delta m, \text{ the quantity of matter destroyed} = 2.00 \text{ g}$$
$$c = 3.00 \times 10^{10} \text{ cm/s}$$

Then

$$\Delta E = 2.00 \text{ g} \times \left(3.00 \times 10^{10} \frac{cm}{s}\right)^2 = 2.00 \text{ g} \times 9.00 \times 10^{20} \frac{cm^2}{s^2}$$

$$= 18.0 \times 10^{20} \text{ g} \frac{cm^2}{s^2}$$

Since $1 \text{ erg} = 1 \text{ g} \dfrac{cm^2}{s^2}$

$$\Delta E = 18.0 \times 10^{20} \text{ ergs}$$

There are 10^7 ergs in 1 J; then

$$\Delta E = 18.0 \times 10^{20} \text{ ergs} \times \frac{1 \text{ J}}{10^7 \text{ ergs}} = 1.80 \times 10^{14} \text{ J}$$

1.80 × 10¹⁴ J, equal to the quantity of heat generated by the combustion of 4 × 10³ tons of gasoline.

In a second experiment, shown in Fig. 9.4b, a high-speed electron slows down and so loses kinetic energy. This energy appears as a photon. In turn, this photon condenses ("materializes") to form matter—two particles, an electron and a positively charged particle (positron, Chap. 17).

Example 10

In this experiment (Fig. 9.4b), the energy of the created photon is 1.64×10^{-6} erg, the energy lost when the high-speed electron is slowed down. What is the mass in grams of the two particles formed when the photon disappears?

Answer

The mass of the two particles is related to the energy of the photon by the Einstein equation, $\Delta E = \Delta m \, c^2$, which merely changes the unit erg to the unit gram:

$$\Delta E = 1.64 \times 10^{-6} \text{ erg and } c = 3.00 \times 10^{10} \frac{cm}{s}$$

so that

$$1.64 \times 10^{-6} \text{ erg} = \Delta m \times \left(3.00 \times 10^{10} \frac{cm}{s}\right)^2$$

from which

$$\Delta m = \frac{1.64 \times 10^{-6} \text{ erg}}{9.00 \times 10^{20} \frac{\text{cm}^2}{\text{s}^2}} = 0.182 \times 10^{-26} = 1.82 \times 10^{-27} \text{ erg} \frac{\text{s}^2}{\text{cm}^2}$$

Since $1 \text{ erg} = 1 \text{ g} \frac{\text{cm}^2}{\text{s}^2}$

$$\Delta m = 1.82 \times 10^{-27} \text{ g} \frac{\cancel{\text{cm}^2}}{\cancel{\text{s}^2}} \frac{\cancel{\text{s}^2}}{\cancel{\text{cm}^2}} = 1.82 \times 10^{-27} \text{ g}$$

Thus, 1.82×10^{-27} g is the quantity of matter formed when the photon disappears.

In agreement with experiment: mass of electron = 9.11×10^{-28} g = mass of positron; $2 \times 9.11 \times 10^{-28}$ g = 1.82×10^{-27} g.

Example 11

In an explosion of a hydrogen-oxygen mixture, 63×10^6 joules are evolved:

$$\text{hydrogen} + \text{oxygen} \longrightarrow \text{water} \qquad \Delta E = -63 \times 10^6 \text{ J}$$

Calculate the decrease in matter in grams accompanying this reaction.

Answer

The mass of the product is less by the amount given by the Einstein equation, $\Delta E = \Delta m \, c^2$:

$$\Delta E = 63 \times 10^6 \text{ J and } c = 3.00 \times 10^{10} \frac{\text{cm}}{\text{s}}$$

so that

$$63 \times 10^6 \text{ J} = \Delta m \times \left(3.00 \times 10^{10} \frac{\text{cm}}{\text{s}}\right)^2$$

Since there are 10^7 ergs in 1 joule,

$$63 \times 10^6 \cancel{\text{J}} \times 10^7 \frac{\text{ergs}}{\cancel{\text{J}}} = \Delta m \times \left(3.00 \times 10^{10} \frac{\text{cm}}{\text{s}}\right)^2$$

$$63 \times 10^{13} \text{ ergs} = \Delta m \times 9.00 \times 10^{20} \frac{\text{cm}^2}{\text{s}^2}$$

from which

$$\Delta m = \frac{63 \times 10^{13} \text{ ergs}}{9.00 \times 10^{20} \frac{\text{cm}^2}{\text{s}^2}} = 7.0 \times 10^{-7} \text{ erg} \frac{\text{s}^2}{\text{cm}^2}$$

Since $1 \text{ erg} = 1 \text{ g} \frac{\text{cm}^2}{\text{s}^2}$

$$\Delta m = 7.0 \times 10^{-7} \text{ g} \frac{\cancel{\text{cm}^2}}{\cancel{\text{s}^2}} \frac{\cancel{\text{s}^2}}{\cancel{\text{cm}^2}} = 7.0 \times 10^{-7} \text{ g}$$

Thus, 7.0×10^{-7} g is the quantity of matter converted to heat and evolved to the surroundings.

So small is this quantity that we can correctly say that the total mass of matter undergoing a phase change or a chemical change is *practically* constant. The change in mass is less than can be detected with the best available balances. The statement is not, however, true for high-speed particles or nuclear reactions (Chap. 17). While chemical bond energies involve kilocalories, nuclear bond energies involve billions of calories. The conversion of matter into energy is the source of all heat and light that reach us from the sun.

PROBLEM 10   **The combustion of 11.0 moles of methyl (wood) alcohol releases 8.41 × 10^6 joules. Calculate the decrease in matter in grams accompanying this reaction.**

9.9 _____ POPULATION, POWER, AND POLLUTION

Power to the people! More and more people demand more and more power. A trillion-dollar economy is a giant (monster?), capable of pioneering technological, social, and economic advances in many directions. But neither science nor technology can decide the direction to follow. Society, to make wise decisions and to plan its future with wisdom, must do its homework, always recalling that the problem of population, energy, economics, employment, and pollution are too closely related to be treated separately. Is economic and technological growth undesirable; is "that" power plant necessary; should we shift from littering to recycling, should the emphasis be on leisure and living rather than competitiveness and making a living; should the United Nations restrain the growth of underdeveloped countries; should taxation be used to discourage energy consumption; should protection of the environment take precedence over new jobs, profits, and tax dollars? Delaware recently became the first state to enact a law prohibiting all heavy industry from its entire coastline. Some people prefer clams and crabs to supertankers. On the other hand, a slowdown would cause additional unemployment, making it impossible for more people to enjoy the preserved environment. The health of our economy cannot be ignored in discussions of the health of our environment. In addition, sociological patterns still have not made natural public areas freely available. What would be the effect of a slowdown on the estimated 30 million people living below the poverty level? But environmental protection will create new jobs; trained personnel—technicians, scientists, engineers—will be needed to control pollution.

Such as paper and cellulose mills, chemical plants, metallurgical plants, oil refineries.

Notwithstanding, independent forecasts by several sources indicate a 25 % to 300 % increase in energy consumption in the United States by the year 2000. The International Atomic Energy Agency predicts that world energy consumption will increase at the rate of 7 % per year. The consumption of coal, 6 × 10^8 ton/year, petroleum oil, 1.6 × 10^7 barrel/day (2.5 × 10^9 ton/day), and natural gas, 2.7 × 10^9 ft^3/hour, still constitutes our major energy souce. Oil and gas satisfy about 80 % of the energy requirement. But oil and gas are also the source of practically all manufactured organic compounds (Chap. 22) currently in use. However, unlike coal, the natural supply of oil and gas is comparatively limited.* This compels the conclusion that the energy crisis is not a problem only for today. It will persist for decades; we may be headed for a major disaster. While public consumption of electricity and gasoline continues to increase, domestic production of oil and natural gas decreases.

Depends on many assumptions concerning population growth, per capita consumption, and income.

---

*Major world production sources of oil and gas: Africa, 10.6 %, 0.3 %; Middle East, 38.1 %, 0.4 %; North America, 20.7 %, 64 %; South America, 8.4 %, 8 %; Western Europe, 1.4 %, 5 %; USSR and Eastern Europe, 17.1 %, 21 %; Southwest Pacific, 3.7 %, 1.3 %. Estimates are that at the present rate of use, the natural supply of coal in the United States may last through 2650, that of natural gas and oil to 2025.

Since 1973, the U.S. has become more dependent on foreign oil; more than 45 % of our oil needs are imported. The only satisfactory solution to the shortage is conservation, maximum efficient use of energy, and development of other energy sources.

Gasification of coal,* production of synthetic oil from coal, production of petroleum from oil shales and tar sands, improved batteries and fuel cells (Chap. 15), geothermal sources (natural steam and hot water generated in the interior of the Earth), windmills, and the use of solar energy are new sources under development. But they are not expected to make significant contributions in the near future. The production cost of synthetic fuel gas from coal, and of oil from oil shales, still makes foreign oil a better buy. Current information projected into the future indicates the need for coal and nuclear power plants to satisfy energy deficiencies, particularly in the form of electricity.** A nuclear breeder (Chap. 17) plant development program has therefore been initiated by the United States Government. But it lags badly behind Russian and European developments.

An equally fundamental long-range problem involves the economics of energy sources. The projected amount of capital investment required for the development of new sources for the next decade is large enough to disrupt the financial needs of other industries. The U.S. Energy Research and Development Administration was therefore established (1975) to promote commercial applications of new energy sources. Most prominent American scientists believe that the solution rests in conservation measures and in the much greater use of coal and nuclear energy, accompanied by strict regulations; they also believe that nuclear fusion (Chap. 17) and solar power are the most likely candidates for the Twenty-first Century.

The production of energy is a principal source of air pollution. The combustion of coal and oil releases millions of tons of colorless, irritating sulfur dioxide gas (Table 9.2), causing considerable damage to health and property. A convincing collection of evidence indicates that human health is endangered as sulfur dioxide levels increase (Problem 46(1), page 316), especially among those suffering from heart or respiratory disease. But laboratory animals (guinea pigs and monkeys) exposed to sulfur dioxide and smoke particle levels higher than those found in city atmospheres showed no ill effects. However, very little is known about the effects of exposure to low levels of SO_2 over long periods of time; the claim is made that the minimum level of air

Temperature at which coal melts, about 200–400 °C, without becoming a hard plastic is very important in new processes for coal utilization.

Like water in a sponge, after an oil field is pumped "dry," 2.5 times as much oil remains bound by surface tension in fine pores in rocks. Theoretically, oil recovery is possible by washing with detergents.

---

*Steam, air, and coal react at high temperatures to produce combustible gases, which must then be upgraded to the quality of natural gas, largely methane, CH_4. Some of these reactions are exothermic while others are endothermic, making temperature control in the reaction zones very critical:

$$\text{volatile matter in coal} \xrightarrow{700\,°C} CH_4(g) + C(amorph)$$

$$C + H_2O \xrightarrow{\text{above } 925\,°C} CO + H_2$$
$$CO + H_2O \longrightarrow CO_2 + H_2$$
$$CO_2 + H_2 \longrightarrow CO + H_2O$$
$$C + 2H_2 \xrightarrow{925\,°C} CH_4$$

Then, in a separate container, the methane content is increased by reaction on a nickel catalyst (Chap. 16):

$$CO + 3H_2 \xrightarrow{370\,°C} CH_4 + H_2O$$

Readers interested in this subject are referred to "Gasification of Coal," Harry Perry, *Scientific American,* March 1974, page 19, and "Evaluation of Coal-Gasification Technology, National Research Council, National Academy of Engineering, 1973.

**For an examination of the history of energy consumption and projections of consumption through the year 2000, the reader is referred to "Energy in Perspective," L. Gaucher, *Chemical Technology,* March 1971, pages 153–158.

Coal gasification demonstration plants handling about 3000 ton coal/day are under construction in Illinois and Ohio under ERDA contracts.

pollution over extended periods is more significant than occasional high levels.* Pollution effects are probably reinforced by additional health stresses, such as cigarette smoking.

The sulfur dioxide eventually (in roughly one week) forms sulfuric acid (page 621), which may react further with atmospheric matter to form ammonium sulfate particles:

$$H_2SO_4(aq) + 2NH_3(aq) \longrightarrow (NH_4)_2SO_4(c)$$

The major source of sulfur dioxide is the coal used for electric power plants. Coal contains about 2.5 % sulfur. Compounds released by bacteria in mud are another major source of atmospheric sulfur. The sulfur content of oil varies considerably with the source; for example, Venezuela produces high-sulfur oils, now subjected to desulfurization processes, while Africa produces low-sulfur oils. New York City has prohibited the use of fuels having more than 1 % sulfur, and the United States Government has expanded and accelerated its study of sulfur dioxide control technologies to remove the gas from the stack gases of power and industrial plants. We can therefore look forward to cleaner air and increases in energy prices (Problem 20, page 313). Yet, individual research studies may discover radically new competitive energy sources. For example, the generation of electricity based on magnetohydrodynamics (MHD), the passage of ionized gases through magnetic fields, has been developed in the United States by Avco Everett Research Laboratory. This type of generator is being evaluated in a demonstration plant in the USSR.

321 ml per million ml of air in 1969, compared to 290 ml in 1869. However, the oceans may slowly absorb the excess CO_2.

Carbon dioxide is a major product of the combustion of fossil fuels. Nature releases CO_2 into the atmosphere at a rate five times greater than our output. Nevertheless, our output is enough to disturb the natural equilibrium between carbon dioxide production by animal life, fuel consumption, and plant material decomposition, and its consumption by plant life (page 195). The greatest concern, however, is the possibility first suggested by John Tyndall (1863) and Svante Arrhenius (1896) that the increase may lead to a significant rise in the Earth's temperature and cause melting of polar ice, resulting in the submersion of coastal cities. Carbon dioxide has a strong tendency to absorb photons in the infrared (heat) region. But this is the region in which most of the heat of the Earth's surface is radiated into outer space. The carbon dioxide may thus reduce the rate at which heat is lost by the Earth. However, this climatic effect may be more than counterbalanced by smoke particles, sulfate particles, and dust, which tend to reflect sunlight back into outer space and so decrease the Earth's temperature. On the other hand, these particles also absorb radiation and so may increase the temperature.

Known as the "greenhouse effect," after green (glass) houses, which confine heat and water vapor.

See Problem 42, page 315.

Although the causes of changes in the Earth's surface temperature are not yet completely explained, current studies conclude that atmospheric carbon dioxide and thermal pollution (discussed below) are increasingly competing with natural factors, forcing a net increase in temperature. Conversely, the surface temperature drops rapidly with increasing atmospheric particle concentration. Therefore, a definite evaluation of the effects of man-made carbon dioxide and airborne particles on natural temperature changes cannot now be made. Concern is also expressed about the effect of chlorocarbon (e.g., CCl_4, CH_2Cl_2, volatile colorless liquids used as grease solvents) and chlorofluorocarbon (e.g., CF_2Cl_2, $CFCl_3$, volatile colorless liquids used as refrigerants, insecticides, and propellants in spray cans) compounds. Like carbon

---

*Readers interested in the effect of air pollution on health are referred to "Mineral Resources and Environment," National Academy of Sciences, Washington, D.C., 1975, Chapter X.

dioxide, they tend to increase temperature. Theoretical studies show that an increase from the present value, 0.1 ml per billion ml of air, to 2.5 ppb may increase the Earth's surface temperature by about 0.5 °C.

Man emits fewer particles than are added to the atmosphere from natural sources (dust storms, volcanoes, evaporation of ocean sprays). Water vapor condenses on these particles (page 101) and so affects rainfall on a *local scale*. The global rainfall effect is a matter of debate, but it may be significant.*

Nature emits more than twice our output.

*Science, volume 183, 8 March 1974, page 909.

The hydrocarbons and nitrogen oxides, released mainly by automobiles (Table 9.2), photochemically react to produce the photochemical smog; nitrogen dioxide strongly absorbs photons in the UV range (pages 196, 386) and initiates reactions that produce irritating smog. It can also produce nitric acid and solid nitrate particles:

$$3NO_2(g) + H_2O(g) \longrightarrow 2HNO_3(aq) + NO(g)$$
$$NO(g) + \tfrac{1}{2} O_2(g) \longrightarrow NO_2(g)$$
$$HNO_3(aq) + NH_3(aq) \longrightarrow NH_4NO_3(c).$$

Natural emissions of nitrogen compounds (page 610) greatly exceed pollution sources.

The thermal (heat) energy presently rejected by power plants into rivers and lakes also constitutes a major problem, named *thermal pollution*. Regardless of the nature of the fuel, the object of a power plant is to form, at the *highest possible temperature,* steam, which drives the shaft (turbine) that turns the electric generator, and to exhaust the steam at the *lowest possible temperature*. Independent of all other features, the efficiency of a power plant is determined merely by two factors: the initial temperature and the final temperature of the steam. The greater this temperature difference, the greater the efficiency in converting the heat energy into work that the shaft does in driving the generator. But nature makes it extremely difficult for man to convert heat into electricity; even with the best technologically available

Known as the Second Law of Thermodynamics,

$$\text{efficiency} = \frac{T_2 - T_1}{T_2},$$

in which T_2 is the high temperature and T_1 is the low temperature.

TABLE 9.2
POLLUTANTS IN MILLIONS OF TONS EMITTED IN THE UNITED STATES IN 1968[1]

	SMOKE PARTICLES	SULFUR OXIDES	NITROGEN OXIDES	CARBON MONOXIDE	HYDROCARBONS
Power and heating	8.9	24.4	10.0	1.9	0.7
Transportation[2]	1.2	0.8	8.1	63.8	16.6
Refuse disposal	1.1	0.1	0.6	7.8	1.6
Industry	7.5	7.3	0.2	9.7	4.6
Miscellaneous[3]	9.6	0.6	1.7	16.9	8.5
Total	28.3	33.2	20.6	100.1	32.0
Relative Importance[4]	49.6%	27.2%	12.3%	4.1%	6.8%

[1] From "Man's Impact on the Global Environment," sponsored by Massachusetts Institute of Technology, MIT Press, Cambridge, Massachusetts, 1970, pages 296-297.

[2] Includes autos, trucks, railroads, aircraft, and so forth, but gasoline constitutes the main transportation pollution source.

[3] Includes such sources as agriculture, and forest and building fires. The quantity of mercury released by the burning of coal is estimated to be about 600 tons per year, compared to about 230 tons per year released by natural chemical reactions. A study (*Science*, volume 173, 16 July 1971, page 233) of 51 elements between lithium and uranium shows that the quantity per year released into the atmosphere by the combustion of coal and oil is generally less than that released by natural chemical reactions; for example, by volcanic reactions and eruptions. Another study (*Science*, volume 171, 29 January 1971, page 381) concludes that emissions from power plants contributed only a modest percentage of the yearly average sulfur dioxide concentration at ground level in the most polluted areas of Cook County, Illinois.

[4] Relative importance is *not* based only on the mass of pollutants; some are more toxic than others. It is based on the mass and toxicity of a pollutant. (Data source: Lyndon Babcock, Jr., and Niren Nagda, 1972.)

designs, power plants operate at efficiencies of about 40 %. This means that for 1 cal of fuel energy, 0.40 cal appears as *electricity* and 0.60 cal is *wasted*. Look at it this way: Heat is molecular motion (page 299). But it is a random kind of motion, related to the entropy (page 102) of the gas (steam). Unlike a hail of bullets aimed in one direction, the molecules do not move in one direction, in the direction moving the shaft that drives the generator. There is no preferred direction. The result is a waste of heat (motion). This waste—the difference between the work available and the work actually obtained—results from an increase in the disorder (entropy) of the gas and its surroundings as it expands against a shaft or a piston. The entropy change thus measures the quantity of energy that is impossible to harness in any kind of real machine. Thus, 2150 kcal of heat produces 860 kcal (2150 $\times$ 0.40) of electricity and the remainder, 1290 kcal (2150 − 860) of heat, is rejected to the surroundings. Something in the surroundings must absorb and dissipate the rejected heat. Unfortunately, water is the most practical coolant available. In the United States roughly 8000 km^3 (5000 cubic miles) of water are warmed 20 °C in absorbing the heat rejected by power plants in one year. For comparison, the *rivers of the world* are estimated to carry about 10,500 km^3 (6500 cubic miles) of water per year to the oceans. Evidently, the multiplication of power plants could cause a thermal pollution crisis. Higher water temperatures decrease the quantity of dissolved oxygen, depriving fish of their required oxygen, decreasing the rate at which waste matter is decomposed, and promoting the growth of undesirable parasites and aquatic plants. Gas bubble disease of fish is caused by supersaturation of gases (page 324) in the heated water. In addition, areas of thermal pollution ("heat islands") affect local climate; uncontrolled, it might affect the global climate. Therefore, cooling towers, which cool by evaporation (an endothermic phase change), are being installed. Also, technological studies are seeking ways to recycle the rejected heat to preheat water before it enters the boiler, or to use the rejected heat for distillation and other industrial operations, or for operating evaporators to desalt water. With proper studies and planning, it should be possible to find beneficial uses for discharged hot water.*

Carbon monoxide (Table 9.2), produced by the incomplete combustion of fossil fuels or by the reaction of carbon with carbon dioxide

$$C(amorph) + \tfrac{1}{2} O_2(g) \longrightarrow CO(g)$$
$$CO_2(g) + C(amorph) \longrightarrow 2CO(g)$$

causes more than 1000 deaths per year in the United States. There is, for example, a definite relationship between the carbon monoxide concentration and mortality in Los Angeles County. However, at comparatively low concentrations, cigarette smoking outweighs the contribution made by traffic to the formation of carboxyhemoglobin (page 205). Natural sources, the major source of atmospheric CO, include the production of carbon monoxide in clouds due to photochemical reactions with organic matter. Nature, however, also provides for the removal of carbon monoxide. Soil bacteria serve as a "natural sink" for carbon monoxide—they reduce a concentration of 120 ml per million ml of air to nearly zero within 3 hours. It is estimated that the soil surface in the United States can remove seven times the annual national

860 kcal of electricity is a kilowatt-hour of electricity, sufficient to operate a 1000-watt toaster for 1 hour or a 100-watt bulb for 10 hours.

In cooling towers, both air and water serve as coolants.

Waste heat from a nuclear power plant in Kincardine, Ont., Canada, will be used for greenhouse heating and fish farming.

Named by analogy to a kitchen sink which drains water, the word "sink" is used in science to mean the opposite of source.

---

*For example, the *Nuplex* concept is a design for a huge unified complex that would generate power (nuclear plants) and at the same time manufacture chemicals and fertilizers, desalinate sea-water, and so support farm lands and fish farms. A power-water desalting farm complex, built by the University of Arizona's Environmental Research Laboratory in the desert of Abu Dhabi (Arabian Peninsula) is in successful operation.

production of carbon monoxide. There is therefore no buildup of carbon monoxide in the general atmosphere.

While nature also puts out substances called pollutants, the concern of the scientist is the evaluation of the changes from the natural situation caused by human activities.

From *Scientific American,* January 1870

"Henry St. Claire Deville has conducted a series of experiments on the possible use of petroleum for fuel, and he has succeeded in inventing a furnace that satisfactorily accomplishes the object. This may be regarded as one of the most important inventions of the year."

From Gould Inc., Rolling Meadows, Illinois

"The last 35 years have yielded much more than advanced technology—they have produced an advanced technological bureaucracy.

During four consecutive decades—through hot and cold wars, space competition and energy shortfalls—the federal government has been mobilizing the nation's technological resources.

During the 1940s, the War Department organized the secret Manhattan Project as it raced against Axis powers to explode the first atomic bomb.

During the 1950s, the Pentagon began to develop highly complex military systems—some ground-based, some airborne and, subsequently, some undersea—to detect and deter a potential enemy attack.

During the 1960s, the National Aeronautics and Space Administration perfected the powerful Saturn booster rocket and launched (among other things) the Apollo lunar missions that asserted the nation's supremacy in space.

During the 1970s, the government has been shifting toward the public needs. For the rest of the present decade at least, the Federal Energy Research and Development Corporation will spend $2.5 billion a year to explore alternatives to the nation's dwindling supply of fossil oil.

All these projects were necessary, for they responded to an external threat to the nation's security and prestige. Virtually all captured the public imagination as scientists probed deeper than before into inner and outer space. Many spawned new technologies that literally reshaped our world.

And yet, for all their urgency, we see today a clear-cut danger in letting government dominate our research and development. For the plain fact is that now, only a few years after we put man on the moon, our technology faces serious trouble—mainly because it is losing its vitalizing link with the needs of the marketplace.

We can shuttle astronauts between earth and space. But we still can't move masses of people efficiently between their homes and their jobs.

We can study rocks recovered from the surface of the moon. But we still can't economically extract many essential materials from their low-grade ores.

We can provide the most diligent medical treatment for astronauts returning to earth. But we have not done enough to dramatically improve the productivity of our doctors in the delivery of public health care.

Our satellites and spacecraft have cells to provide all the energy they need. But our development of breeder reactors for nuclear energy stutters along while both the Russians and French have units in operation.

In short, the projects sponsored by government often take off on a course all their own. But they fail to bridge the gap between scientific endeavor and everyday needs.

While the nation focused on the moon and weaponry, it neglected energy, communications, mass transit, health care, the environment and raw materials. As a result, we still lead the world in areas of high technology. But we are struggling for survival in such basic industries as steelmaking, shipbuilding, mining, metal refining and surface transportation.

A committee of the National Academy of Engineering summed up the dilemma. It observed that the welter of federally funded programs "has not resulted in widespread 'spin-offs' of secondary or additional applications of practical products, processes and services that have an impact on the nation's economic growth, industrial productivity, employment gains and foreign trade."

And yet those are precisely the areas—growth,

productivity, employment, trade—which our technology must address if our economy is to remain healthy in today's interdependent world. As time goes by, the nation's security will depend less upon long-range missiles equipped with warheads than upon the state of its technology and how well it satisfies the demands of the domestic and global marketplace."

PROBLEMS

11 Vocabulary Define or illustrate (a) fossil fuel, (b) exothermic reaction, (c) endothermic reaction, (d) thermochemical equation, (e) conditions under which ΔE and ΔH are measured, (f) meaning of $\Delta H = -100$ cal, $\Delta H = +100$ cal, (g) bond energy, (h) bond stability, (i) thermal stability, (j) molecular motion, (k) heat of formation, (l) heat of combustion.

12 Vocabulary For each of the following: (a) ΔE is negative, (b) ΔE is positive, (c) ΔH is negative, (d) ΔH is positive, pick the correct word(s) from (i) exothermic or endothermic, (ii) constant volume or constant pressure, (iii) constant temperature or temperature changes, (iv) energy increases or energy decreases, (v) enthalpy increases or enthalpy decreases, (vi) mass increases or mass decreases, (vii) heat evolved or heat absorbed, (viii) depends on path or does not depend on path chosen to change reactants to products.

13 Heat of reaction (a) *This is a thought experiment, not to be performed.* A pellet of solid white sodium hydroxide, NaOH (very caustic poison), reacts with moisture and feels hot in the hand. Are the hand and the hydroxide at a higher or lower temperature than the rest of the body? To restore the hand to normal body temperature, should heat be added or removed? Is the reaction, $NaOH(c) + H_2O \longrightarrow$ solution, exothermic or endothermic? (b) An alcohol, a volatile liquid, feels cold to the hand. Are the alcohol and the hand at a higher or lower temperature than the rest of the body? To restore the hand to normal body temperature, should heat be added or removed? Is the reaction, liquid $\longrightarrow$ vapor, exothermic or endothermic?

14 Methyl alcohol, CH_3OH, the "new fuel" obtainable from coal, burns cleanly and has a high octane rating. (a) 3.66 g of graphite reacts with water vapor at constant pressure, absorbing 9.56 kcal. Find ΔH for $C(graphite) + H_2O(g) \longrightarrow CO(g) + H_2(g)$. (b) 1.01 g of hydrogen reacts with carbon monoxide at constant pressure, evolving 5.39 kcal. Find ΔH for $CO(g) + 2H_2(g) \longrightarrow CH_3OH(g)$. (c) The combustion of 0.200 g of the alcohol at constant pressure raises the temperature of 1.000 kg water 1.14 °C. Calculate ΔH for $CH_3OH(g) + 1\frac{1}{2} O_2(g) \longrightarrow CO_2(g) + 2H_2O(l)$.

15 (a) When 0.524 g of potassium bromate dissolves in water, 0.252 kcal is evolved. Find ΔH for

$KBrO_3(c) + H_2O \longrightarrow KBrO_3(aq)$. (b) 0.980 kcal is evolved when 4.00 g of water combines with zinc bromide. Find ΔH for $ZnBr_2(c) + 2H_2O(l) \longrightarrow ZnBr_2(H_2O)_2(c)$.

16 (a) Solid-fuel rockets are reliable and comparatively simple to construct, but no adjustments can be made once one is in operation. Liquid propellants involve a complex of valves, pumps, and tanks, but they can be controlled from stop to full throttle and are therefore generally favored for spaceships. Given the following data:

$$H_2(g) + \frac{1}{2} O_2(g) \longrightarrow H_2O(l)$$
$$\Delta H = -68.3 \text{ kcal}$$

$$Mg(c) + \frac{1}{2} O_2(g) \longrightarrow MgO(c)$$
$$\Delta H = -136.10 \text{ kcal}$$

$$2Al(c) + 1\frac{1}{2} O_2(g) \longrightarrow Al_2O_3(c)$$
$$\Delta H = -399 \text{ kcal}$$

Pick the best and the poorest rocket fuel on the basis of kcal/g. (b) Write ΔH for $MgO(c) \longrightarrow Mg(c) + \frac{1}{2} O_2(g)$.

17 Calorimeter The principle of a calorimeter was first used by Joseph Black (1761), who used an ice calorimeter in which a quantity of heat is measured by how much ice it melts. Strontium and hydrochloric acid (1 molar), enclosed in a container of fixed volume at 0 °C in a block of ice at 0 °C, evolved sufficient heat to melt 8.226 g of ice at 0 °C on forming 0.112 liter (STP) of $H_2(g)$. The heat of fusion of ice is 79.7 cal/g. (a) How many calories are needed to melt the ice? (b) How many calories are evolved when the H_2 forms? (c) Write the thermochemical equation of $Sr(c) + 2HCl(aq) \longrightarrow SrCl_2(aq) + H_2(g)$. (d) Is ΔE or ΔH measured in this experiment?

18 Calorie saver (a) The heat of combustion of sucrose, table sugar ($C_{12}H_{22}O_{11}$, 342 g/mole) is 1350 kcal/mole, while the heat of combustion of sodium cyclamate ($C_6H_{12}NSO_3Na$, 201 g/mole) is 771 kcal/mole. Find the savings in kcal when 1.0 g of cyclamate* is substituted for 30.0 g of sucrose. (b) The

---

*1 kcal = 1 large Calorie, calorie spelled with a capital C, the energy unit used in nutrition. Cyclamates were banned by the FDA in 1969 after tests indicated that large doses might produce tumors in the bladders of mice.

average American consumes 47 kg of sucrose per year. Aldoxime, $C_6H_7(CH_2OCH_3)(HCNOH)$, a new sweetening agent, is 450 times sweeter than sucrose on a weight basis. Find the annual and daily savings in calories if aldoxime, 156 g/mole, heat of combustion (estimated from bond energies) 1360 kcal/mole, is substituted for sucrose. (Use 365 days/year.)

19 Chocolate drinks A high quality popular chocolate drink mix ranks highest in quality with 11 g protein (4.1 kcal/g), 36 g carbohydrate (3.9 kcal/g), plus 8 oz fresh whole milk (11.6 kcal/oz) per serving. Calculate the number of kcal in one serving.

20 Hess's law (a) A scheme proposed for stack-gas desulfurization involves the reaction, $SO_2(g) + \frac{1}{2}O_2(g) + H_2O(g) \longrightarrow H_2SO_4(l)$. Find ΔH for this reaction from the following data:

$$SO_2(g) \longrightarrow S(c) + O_2(g)$$
$$\Delta H = +70.9 \text{ kcal}$$
$$H_2SO_4(l) \longrightarrow H_2(g) + S(c) + 2O_2(g)$$
$$\Delta H = +194.5 \text{ kcal}$$
$$H_2(g) + \frac{1}{2}O_2(g) \longrightarrow H_2O(g)$$
$$\Delta H = -57.8 \text{ kcal}$$

(b) The estimated minimum cost of desulfurization is 5 mills/kilowatt hour (1 mill = 0.10 cent). The average (New Jersey) consumer uses 720 kilowatt hours per month at an average cost of 0.0677 dollar/kilowatt hour. Estimate the additional cost per month and the percentage increase in the cost of electricity if this process is put into operation at a power plant.

21 Predict ΔH for the combustion of trimethylpentane, C_8H_{18}, a high-octane hydrocarbon, $C_8H_{18}(l) + 12\frac{1}{2}O_2(g) \longrightarrow 8CO_2(g) + 9H_2O(l)$, from the given data:

$$8C(graphite) + 9H_2(g) \longrightarrow C_8H_{18}(l)$$
$$\Delta H = -52.1 \text{ kcal}$$
$$C(graphite) + O_2(g) \longrightarrow CO_2(g)$$
$$\Delta H = -94.0 \text{ kcal}$$
$$H_2(g) + \frac{1}{2}O_2(g) \longrightarrow H_2O(l)$$
$$\Delta H = -68.3 \text{ kcal}$$

22 Hot beetle (a) Hydroquinone-quinone is involved in many essential biochemical reactions and has been isolated from many living organisms. The chemical reaction responsible for the defensive explosive discharge of the bombardier beetle is

$$C_6H_4(OH)_2(aq) + H_2O_2(aq) \longrightarrow$$
hydroquinone
$$C_6H_4O_2(aq) + 2H_2O(l) \quad \Delta H = ?$$
quinone

Calculate ΔH from

$$C_6H_4(OH)_2(aq) \longrightarrow C_6H_4O_2(aq) + H_2(g)$$
$$\Delta H = +42.4 \text{ kcal}$$
$$H_2(g) + O_2(g) \longrightarrow H_2O_2(aq)$$
$$\Delta H = -45.7 \text{ kcal}$$
$$H_2(g) + \frac{1}{2}O_2(g) \longrightarrow H_2O(g)$$
$$\Delta H = -57.8 \text{ kcal}$$
$$H_2O(l) \longrightarrow H_2O(g)$$
$$\Delta H = +12.9 \text{ kcal}$$

(b) Use your answer to calculate (i) the heat in cal evolved by 1.0×10^{-5} mole of hydroquinone and (ii) the temperature rise for 5.4 milligrams of water caused by the absorption of this heat.

23 (a) Predict ΔH for the reaction

$$O(g) + H(g) \longrightarrow OH(g) \quad \Delta H = ?$$

from

$$\frac{1}{2}O_2(g) + \frac{1}{2}H_2(g) \longrightarrow OH(g)$$
$$\Delta H = +9.31 \text{ kcal}$$
$$H(g) \longrightarrow \frac{1}{2}H_2(g)$$
$$\Delta H = -52.095 \text{ kcal}$$
$$O(g) \longrightarrow \frac{1}{2}O_2(g)$$
$$\Delta H = -59.553 \text{ kcal}$$

(b) What is the bond energy of OH in kcal/mole?

24 Bond energy Calculate the bond energy of CN in kcal/mole from

$$CN(g) \longrightarrow C(graphite) + \frac{1}{2}N_2(g)$$
$$\Delta H = -109 \text{ kcal}$$
$$C(g) \longrightarrow C(graphite)$$
$$\Delta H = -171 \text{ kcal}$$
$$\frac{1}{2}N_2(g) \longrightarrow N(g)$$
$$\Delta H = +113 \text{ kcal}$$

25 (a) From the given data for the reactions in the gaseous state:

$$NH_3 \longrightarrow NH_2 + H \quad \Delta H = +104 \text{ kcal}$$
$$NH_2 \longrightarrow NH + H \quad \Delta H = +90$$
$$NH \longrightarrow N + H \quad \Delta H = +86$$

Calculate ΔH for $NH_3(g) \longrightarrow N(g) + 3H(g)$. (b) How many N—H bonds are broken? (c) Assign a bond energy value to the N—H bond. (d) Use your assigned bond energy value to calculate ΔH for $NH_3(g) \longrightarrow N(g) + 3H(g)$. Does your answer agree with your answer to part (a)? (e) What thermochemical equations are needed to find ΔH for $\frac{1}{2}N_2(g) + \frac{3}{2}H_2(g) \longrightarrow NH_3(g)$?

26 Use Table 9.1, page 295, to calculate ΔH for each of the following reactions:

(a)

$$H\text{—}\underset{\underset{H}{|}}{\overset{\overset{H}{|}}{C}}\text{—}\underset{\underset{H}{|}}{\overset{\overset{H}{|}}{C}}\text{—}H(g) + 3Br_2(g) \longrightarrow$$

ethane

$$H\text{—}\underset{\underset{Br}{|}}{\overset{\overset{Br}{|}}{C}}\text{—}\underset{\underset{H}{|}}{\overset{\overset{Br}{|}}{C}}\text{—}H(g) + 3HBr(g)$$

tribromoethane

(b) $H\text{—}C\equiv C\text{—}H(g) + 2Cl_2(g) \longrightarrow$

acetylene

$$H\text{—}\underset{\underset{Cl}{|}}{\overset{\overset{Cl}{|}}{C}}\text{—}\underset{\underset{Cl}{|}}{\overset{\overset{Cl}{|}}{C}}\text{—}H(g)$$

tetrachloroethane

(c) $2HBr(g) + F_2(g) \longrightarrow 2HF(g) + Br_2(g)$

(d)

$$H\text{—}\underset{\underset{H}{|}}{\overset{\overset{H}{|}}{C}}\text{—}\underset{\underset{H}{|}}{\overset{\overset{H}{|}}{C}}\text{—}H(g) + 2F_2(g) \longrightarrow$$

ethane

$$H\text{—}\underset{\underset{H}{|}}{\overset{\overset{F}{|}}{C}}\text{—}F(g) + F\text{—}\underset{\underset{H}{|}}{\overset{\overset{H}{|}}{C}}\text{—}H(g) + HF(g)$$

difluoromethane   fluoromethane

27 ΔH_f Calculate ΔH for each given reaction from heats of formation given here and in App. VI:

(a) $C_2H_2(g) + 3H_2(g) \longrightarrow 2CH_4(g)$

(b) $NH_3(g) + CO(g) \longrightarrow HCN(g) + H_2O(g)$

(c) $N_2H_4(l) + 2N_2O_5(g) \longrightarrow$
    $2HNO_3(l) + 2NO_2(g) + 2NH(g)$

(d) $Fe_2O_3(c) + 3CO(g) \longrightarrow 2Fe(c) + 3CO_2(g)$

(e) $BaCl_2(c) + F_2(g) \longrightarrow BaF_2(c) + Cl_2(g)$

(f) $Na(c) + H_2O(l) \longrightarrow NaOH(aq) + \frac{1}{2} H_2(g)$

(g) $CdCl_2(aq) + H_2S(aq) \longrightarrow$
    $2HCl(aq) + yellow\ CdS(c)$

(h) $CuO(c) + H_2(g) \longrightarrow Cu(c) + H_2O(l)$

(i) $CaCO_3(c) \longrightarrow CaO(c) + CO_2(g)$

(j) $H_2O(g) + Cl_2(g) \longrightarrow 2HCl(g) + \frac{1}{2} O_2(g)$

$\Delta H_{HCN(g)} = +32.3$ kcal, $\Delta H_{N_2H_4(l)} = +12.10$ kcal,

$\Delta H_{N_2O_5(g)} = +2.7$ kcal, $\Delta H_{HNO_3(l)} = -41.61$ kcal,

$\Delta H_{NO_2(g)} = +7.93$ kcal, $\Delta H_{NaOH(aq)} = -112.36$ kcal,

$\Delta H_{F_2O_3(c)} = -197.0$ kcal, $\Delta H_{BaF_2(c)} = -288.5$ kcal,

$\Delta H_{NH(g)} = +79$ kcal, $\Delta H_{CdCl_2(aq)} = -98.04$ kcal,

$\Delta H_{H_2S(aq)} = -9.5$ kcal, $\Delta H_{HCl(aq)} = -39.95$ kcal,

$\Delta H_{CuO(c)} = -40.3$ kcal, $\Delta H_{CaCO_3(c)} = -288.46$ kcal,

$\Delta H_{CaO(c)} = -151.79$ kcal.

28 Stability Cyanogen, C_2N_2, a colorless, poisonous, water-soluble gas, decomposes above 800 °C: $N\equiv C\text{—}C\equiv N(g) \longrightarrow 2C(g) + 2N(g)$ ($\Delta H = +415$ kcal), and undergoes a number of chemical reactions at ordinary temperatures. With respect to C_2N_2, is the bond stability high or low? Is it thermally stable? Is it chemically reactive?

29 The temperature at which the following substances start to decompose is given in parentheses: potassium perchlorate, $KClO_4$ (655 °C), a substance that tends to explode at ordinary temperatures; copper(I) oxide, Cu_2O (145 °C), a non-explosive substance. Pick the more thermally stable substance.

30 Molecular motion, entropy (a) Which molecule, C_2H_6, Kr, or CO, would you expect to have (i) the largest number of molecular motions (translational, vibrational, and rotational), (ii) the largest disorder (page 102), (iii) the largest entropy at a given temperature? (b) The increase in the average (translational) kinetic energy for 1 degree temperature rise is the same for *all* molecules. Make a guess. For the same number of molecules, will the number of calories required to raise the temperature 1 degree be the same for a simple molecule with only translational motion as it is for a more complex molecule which also vibrates and rotates? What is the basis of your guess?

31 $\Delta E = \Delta mc^2$ (a) 10.0 mg of each of the following substances is converted to heat: plutonium, helium, zinc, cobalt oxide. Is the energy evolved in each case the same? If so, calculate the energy evolved in ergs and in kilojoules. If not, explain. (b) When a substance is cooled, its mass is decreased. Find the decrease in the mass of copper when a sample is cooled by removal of 200 joules.

32 About 1.5×10^6 kJ is evolved in the explosion of 500 lb of TNT (trinitrotoluene, $(NO_2)_3C_6H_2CH_3$). Calculate the quantity of matter in grams converted to heat in this explosion.

33 An electron, mass 9.11×10^{-28} g (matter), and the identical particle with a positive electric charge, 9.11×10^{-28} g (antimatter), are annihilated on contact, forming a gamma photon. Find the energy of the photon in grams, ergs, and joules. (Actually, two photons are created.)

34 Find the number of grams of hydrogen and oxygen required to produce 1.5×10^6 cal by the reaction $H_2(g) + \frac{1}{2} O_2(g) \longrightarrow H_2O(l)$, $\Delta E = -67.4$ kcal. Calculate the percentage of matter destroyed.

35 Hydrogen bond The energy of the H bond in water varies with the geometry (Chap. 18) of the bond and the number of bonds formed by a given H_2O molecule. In liquid water, the energy is about 2.58 kcal/mole H bond. Calculate the number of (a) calories and (b) joules required to break 3.26×10^{20} H bonds.

36 Energy Fill in the correct word: Heat is the movement of _____. Light (radiation) is the movement of _____. Electricity is the movement of _____. Mechanical energy (work) is the movement of _____.

37 Russia and Ireland have significant numbers of peat-fired electric generating plants. **Peat** is the first stage in the slow transformation from plant (vegetation) to coal. World peat deposits are equivalent to a depth of 6 feet covering 3.8×10^8 acres; peat has a density of 0.023 ton/ft³. The heat of the reaction, $C(peat) + O_2(g) \longrightarrow CO_2(g)$, is $\Delta H = -60$ kcal. (a) Calculate the heat in kcal obtainable from peat. (b) The mass of oil reserves is about half that of peat, but its heat of combustion per gram is about twice that of peat. What statement can you make about the heat value of the known available peat and oil reserves? 1 acre = 4356 ft², 10^6 g = 1 ton.

38 Energy consumption The world's energy consumption for 1967 was 5.0×10^{16} kcal. The total energy consumption for 1975 in U.S. was 7.11×10^{16} BTU (British Thermal Units). 1 BTU = 1055 J. Compare, by percentage, the U.S. (1975) consumption with the world's (1967) consumption. (b) The U.S. sits on about 1.3×10^{12} tons of readily recoverable coal,* with a heat value of 7.3 kcal/g. Assuming that this is the only available source of energy, how long would

*Coal composition varies. Approximate carbon content of coal: ("hard") anthracite, 70 to 98 %; ("soft") bituminous, 40 to 80 %; lignite, 30 to 40 %.

it supply energy needs at the U.S. 1975 consumption rate? 1 ton = 10^6 g.

39 Energy consumption (a) Plot the energy consumption (y-axis), given as the number of BTU (British Thermal Units) consumed per person per day, against the date (x-axis):

	BTU/PER-SON-DAY	DATE
Primitive man	8×10^3	10^6 B.C.
Hunting man	20×10^3	10^5 B.C.
Primitive agricultural man	48×10^3	5000 B.C.
Advanced agricultural man	103×10^3	1400 A.D.
Industrial man	308×10^3	1875
Technological man	913×10^3	1970

Is there a relationship between "cultural" development and energy consumption? (b) Explain: Improvement of deplorable conditions in slums and poverty in this country as well as in underdeveloped countries translates into energy consumption. (1 BTU = 252 cal.)

40 Muscle work When doing work, a muscle uses about 5×10^{-4} mole ATP/g muscle-minute. Find the heat output for 50.0 lb of muscle working over a period of one hour. See page 293 for heat of ATP reaction.

41 Cosmic rays, composed of high-energy electrons and nuclei of the entire periodic table, have measured energies as high as 1.6×10^8 erg/particle. Calculate the energy of such particles in kilojoules and kcal per mole. Compare this with the heat of formation of $H_2O(l)$, given on page 293.

42 Pollution and climate (a) Plot the following data (surface temperature on the y-axis against relative number of particles per liter on the x-axis), obtained from a theoretical model:

EARTH'S SURFACE TEMPERATURE, °C	RELATIVE NUMBER OF SMOKE PARTICLES PER LITER
9.5	5.0
11.5	4.0
12.8	3.0
14.0	2.0
15.0 (present average)	1.0 (present relative amount)
15.5	0.5

(b) Plot aerosol (liquid or solid particles suspended in air) cloud height (y-axis) expressed as air pressure, against the change in the Earth's surface temperature (x-axis). Data are for an aerosol whose particle density is twice the U.S. Federal Standard and are obtained from a theoretical model:

	HEIGHT, ATM	SURFACE TEMPERATURE CHANGE, °C
(sea level)	1.00	−0.5
	0.85	−0.4
	0.60	−0.2
	0.40	−0.2
(about 15 km)	0.10	−0.2

(c) Plot the year (y-axis) against CO_2 atmospheric content (x-axis), expressed in parts per million by molecule, and against global temperature change (x-axis):

YEAR	CO_2 CONTENT, PPM	TEMPERATURE CHANGE, °C
1900	295	+0.02
1920	299	+0.07
1940	305	+0.11
1960	314	+0.21
1970	322	+0.29
1980*	335	+0.42
2000	373	+0.80
2010	403	+1.10

*Assumes an increase of CO_2 of 3% per year after 1975.

(i) Make a statement regarding the effect of CO_2 and smoke (aerosol) particles on the Earth's surface temperature. (ii) Which appears to have a greater effect on temperature, CO_2 or aerosol particles? (iii) Can a definite statement be made about the net climatic effect of CO_2 and aerosols?

43 Explain: "One man's conservation may be another man's job."

44 Pollution A supersonic transport plane (SST) at supersonic cruising speed consumes 1.15×10^5 lb of kerosene/hour. The heat of combustion may be represented as

$$C_{10}H_{22}(l) + 15\tfrac{1}{2} O_2(g) \longrightarrow 10CO_2(g) + 11H_2O(l)$$
$$\Delta H = -1632 \text{ kcal}$$

Calculate the heat consumption in kcal/h and CO_2 output in lb/h. (For comparison, a 747 jet plane consumes 1.2×10^4 lb kerosene/h.)

45 Thermal pollution The Federal Fish and Wildlife Service calculates that if there were no restrictions imposed, the heat input into Lake Michigan would increase 10 times by the year 2000 and ruin the lake's fish and plant life. A power plant on the lakefront is restricted to a discharge of 5.0×10^{11} cal/hour. If the cooling water is pumped at the rate of 1.5×10^7 gal/hour, calculate the rise in temperature for the cooling water. 1 gal water = 3.8×10^3 g. (b) A hurricane precipitates 2 inches of rain over an area 1500 miles × 1000 miles. How many calories are released to the atmosphere by this condensation? 6.63×10^4 inch = 1 mile; 4.1×10^{15} ml = 1 cubic mile; heat of vaporization = 582 cal/g. (c) Compare this answer with the plant discharge in part (a). What is the basic difference between these two kinds of heat discharge?

46 Library Read one of the following:

(a) *Energy and Matter,* Charles Bazzoni, The University Society, New York, 1937, Chapter 1, pages 1–11.

(b) *Count Rumford,* Physicist Extraordinary,* Sanborn Brown, Anchor Books, Doubleday and Company, Garden City, New York, 1962, Chapter 12 ("Contributions to the Theory of Heat").

(c) *Order and Chaos,* Stanley Angrist and Loren Hepler, Basic Books, Inc., New York, 1967, pages 55–64 ("Bookkeeper's Delight").

(d) *The Smoake of London, Two Prophecies. Fumifugium: On the Inconvenience of the Aer and Smoake of London Dissipated,* John Evelyn, 1661, reprinted 1933 by National Smoke Abatement Society, Manchester, England, pages 7–9 and 25–27.

(e) "Foreign Technology and the U.S. Economy (Declining U.S. Technology)," Sherman Gee, *Science,* volume 187, 21 February 1975, page 622.

(f) "Carbon Dioxide and Climate: The Uncontrolled Experiment," *American Scientist,* volume 65, 1977, page 310.

(g) "Energy Policy: Independence by 1985 May be Unreachable Without BTU Tax," *Science,* volume 191, 13 February 1976, page 546.

(h) "Synthetic Fuels: Prices, Prospects, and Prior Art," Ogden Hammond and Robert Baron, *American Scientist,* volume 64, July/August 1976, page 407; or in the same issue, page 424, "The Long Range Prospects for Solar Energy," William Pollard.

(i) "Social Impact of Pollution Control Legislation," Wallace Johnson, *Science,* volume 192, 14 May 1976, page 629.

(j) "Ecology, Energy, and Economics," J. N. Pitts, Jr. and coauthors, *Chemistry in Britain,* volume 11, July 1975, page 247.

(k) "Agricultural Production and Energy Resources," G. H. Heichel, *American Scientist,* volume 64, January/February 1976, page 64.

(l) "Effects of Sulfur Oxides, Particles and Nitrogen Dioxide," Proceedings of Conference

---

* Born Benjamin Thompson, a poor farm boy in Woburn, Mass.

on Health Effects of Air Pollutants, National Academy of Sciences, U.S. Government Printing Office, Washington, D.C., 1973, pages 207–215, 227–252, 263–275, 363–380, 407–428.

(m) "The Origin and Influence of Airborne Particulates," Paul Fennelly, *American Scientist,* volume 64, January/February 1976, page 46.

(n) "Management, Key to Energy Conservation," Ernest Critzer, *Chemical Technology,* April 1976, page 255.

(o) "A Southwest Power Plant Saga," Stan Miller, *Environmental Science and Technology,* volume 10, June 1976, page 532.

(p) "The Necessity of Fission Power," H. A. Bethe, *Scientific American,* January 1976, page 21.

(q) "Drilling, Tankers, and Oil Spills on the Atlantic Outer Continental Shelf," William Travers and Percy Luney, *Science,* volume 194, 19 November 1976, page 791.

ADDITIONAL PROBLEMS

47 Reports of cataracts occurring in persons exposed to *microwaves* have been published. Approximately how many photons with a wavelength of 12 cm must be absorbed by the eye of a rabbit to raise its temperature 3.0 °C? Assume that the mass of the eye is 10 g and its specific heat is 1.0 cal/(g °C).

48 The gas-burning cooking stove was invented by B. Giles in 1875. A 0.50 ℓ tank of butane, C_4H_{10}, at 20 °C and 5.0 atm feeds a stove. How many liters of water at 20 °C may be heated to, and vaporized at, 100 °C? Assume ideal gas behavior; the reaction is $C_4H_{10}(g) + 6\frac{1}{2} O_2(g) \longrightarrow 4CO_2(g) + 5H_2O(g)$, $\Delta H = -635$ kcal. Hint: What is the pressure in the "empty" tank?

49 A scheme proposed to utilize solar energy as an energy source involves a catalyst, Z (Chap. 16), and photon absorption:

$$Z + H_2O(l) + hf \longrightarrow ZO + H_2(g)$$
$$\Delta H = 70.0 \text{ kcal} \quad (17)$$
$$ZO \longrightarrow Z + \frac{1}{2} O_2(g)$$
$$\Delta H = ? \quad (18)$$

$$\overline{H_2O(g) + hf \longrightarrow H_2(g) + \frac{1}{2} O(g)}$$
$$\Delta H = 68.3 \text{ kcal}$$

If only one photon out of five is absorbed, (a) find the number of photons ($\lambda = 4.20 \times 10^{-5}$ cm) needed to produce 0.500 mole of $H_2(g)$; (b) find the heat in kcal evolved when 0.150 g of H_2 is burned to $H_2O(l)$; and (c) find ΔH for Reaction 18.

50 Production of sugar from sugar beets requires an input of 40 MJ/kg sugar beet. A farm produces 5×10^3 tons of sugar beets. Calculate the number of gallons of fuel oil needed for this production. Fuel oil: heat of combustion = 10.5 kcal/g; 8 lb/gal; 10^6 g/ton. 1 MJ = 10^6 J.

51 Given the following heats of formation: difluoroethane, $C_2H_4F_2(g)$, $\Delta H = -114.3$ kcal; hydrogen iodide, HI(g), $\Delta H = +6.33$ kcal; difluoroethyl radical, $CH_3\dot{C}F_2(g)$, $\Delta H = -72.3$ kcal. Find the heat of formation of atomic iodine, $\frac{1}{2} I_2(g) \longrightarrow I(g)$, from the reaction

$$CH_3CF_2H(g) + I(g) \longrightarrow CH_3\dot{C}F_2(g) + HI(g)$$
$$\Delta H = +22.80 \text{ kcal}$$

52 Water may hydrogen bond to ammonia, $H_3N: + H\ddot{O}H \longrightarrow H_3N:\text{---}H\ddot{O}H$, $\Delta E = -5.9$ kcal; or ammonia may hydrogen bond to water, $H_2\ddot{N}H + :\ddot{O}H_2 \longrightarrow H_2\ddot{N}H\text{---}:\ddot{O}H_2$, $\Delta E = -4.1$ kcal. (a) Are the products' compositions identical? (b) Which atom, nitrogen or oxygen, more strongly accepts the H atom in forming a hydrogen bond? Explain.

53 (a) In a microwave oven, food gets hot but the oven remains cool. Explain. (b) Laser beam sterilization of water has been developed. "The effect on bacteria is to tear them apart physically." Explain.

54 (a) The relation between food and muscular work was not always clear. But in 1875, scientists doing research on the conservation of energy concluded that the work is produced by "the energy stored in the carboniferous food and set free by oxidation." Explain in your own words. (b) The leg muscle of a kangaroo is highly elastic (almost perfect elasticity compared to man). Compare the conversion of kinetic energy to heat when (i) a kangaroo bounces off the ground, (ii) a molecule bounces off a wall, and (iii) an ordinary rubber ball bounces off the ground by listing them in the order of increasing heat evolved. Which one does not evolve any heat?

55 A person weighing 70 kg walking at 1.75 meter/s has a metabolic rate of 452 J/s. If each serves as the only energy source, find the number of grams of (a) table sugar, sucrose, $C_{12}H_{22}O_{11}$, heat of combustion = 5648 kJ/mole, and (b) fat, heat of combustion = 38 kJ/g, consumed in one hour.

56 Horsepower is a measurement of work (energy) devised by James Watt. A horsepower-hour, the work done by 1 horsepower in 1 hour, equals 2.68×10^6 joules. A British Thermal Unit (BTU) is the heat needed to raise the temperature of a pound of water 1 °F. (a) Find the number of calories in 1 BTU. (b) How many horsepower-hours and BTU are there in 1 barrel of fuel oil? Fuel oil: 10.6 kcal/g; 1 barrel = 42.0 gal; density 7.7 lb/gal.

57 (a) Matter is a form of energy. Explain. (b) In 1925, Albert Einstein concluded that "a tremendous amount of heat may be created at the expense of a slow decrease in mass." Explain.

58 Which is more desirable as a cooling agent in an automobile, a liquid with a small or large specific heat, or is the specific heat of the liquid of no importance?

59 An atmosphere contains 2.9×10^3 micrograms (μg) of SO_2 per cubic meter. (a) If one out of five SO_2 molecules is converted to $(NH_4)_2SO_4(c)$ aerosol, calculate the mass of the aerosol in μg/m³. (b) The density of $(NH_4)_2SO_4$ is 1.77 g/ml and the volume of an $(NH_4)_2SO_4$ aerosol particle is 8.64×10^{-7} nanoliter. Calculate the number of $(NH_4)_2SO_4(c)$ particles per m³. 1 nℓ = 10^{-9} liter.

60 Explain the distinction among the terms "demand," "consumption," and "need," and their relation to the life style of a society.

ANSWERS

1 (a) (i) 1.42 kcal, (ii) 327 kcal;
(b) 102 kcal; (c) $C_2H_5OH(l) + 3O_2(g) \longrightarrow$
$2CO_2(g) + 3H_2O(l)$, $\Delta E = -327$ kcal;
$KClO_4(c) \longrightarrow KCl(c) + 2O_2(g)$,
$\Delta E = +102$ kcal

2 (a) (i) $\Delta E = +43.9$ kcal,
(ii) $\Delta H = +44.5$ kcal,
(b) (i) $\Delta H = -95.6$ kcal,
(ii) $\Delta E = -97.1$ kcal
(c) (i) (ii) $\Delta E = \Delta H =$
-57.7 kcal

3 0.46 kcal

4 $\Delta H = -109.2$ kcal

5 $\Delta H = -103$ kcal

6 $\Delta H = +388$ kcal

7 $\Delta H = -114$ kcal

8 (a) (i) HF, (ii) no
(b) no

9 $\Delta H = -337.1$ kcal

10 9.34×10^{-8} g

12 (a) exothermic, constant volume, constant temperature, energy decreases, mass decreases, heat evolved, does not
(b) endothermic, constant volume, constant temperature, energy increases, mass increases, heat absorbed, does not
(c) exothermic, constant pressure, constant temperature, enthalpy decreases, mass decreases, heat evolved, does not
(d) endothermic, constant pressure, constant temperature, enthalpy increases, mass increases, heat absorbed, does not

13 (a) higher, remove, exothermic
(b) lower, add, endothermic

14 (a) $\Delta H = +31.3$ kcal
(b) $\Delta H = -21.5$ kcal
(c) $\Delta H = -182$ kcal

15 (a) $\Delta H = -80.3$ kcal
(b) $\Delta H = -8.82$ kcal

16 (a) H_2, Mg; (b) $\Delta H = +136.10$ kcal

17 (a) (b) 655 cal; (c) (d) $Sr(c) +$
$2HCl(aq) \longrightarrow SrCl_2(aq) + H_2(g)$,
$\Delta E = -131$ kcal

18 (a) 114 kcal; (b) 1.85×10^5
kcal/yr, 5.1×10^2 kcal/day

19 278 kcal

20 (a) $\Delta H = -65.8$ kcal
(b) \$3.60/month, 7.39%

21 $\Delta H = -1315$ kcal

22 (a) $\Delta H = -53.3$ kcal
(b) (i) 0.53 cal, (ii) 98 °C

23 (a) $\Delta H = -102.34$ kcal
(b) 102.34 kcal/mole

24 175 kcal/mole

25 (a) $\Delta H = 280$ kcal; (b) three;
(c) 93.3 kcal; (d) $\Delta H = 280$ kcal;
(e) $\frac{1}{2} N_2 \longrightarrow N$, $\frac{3}{2} H_2 \longrightarrow 3H$

26 (a) -30.3; (b) -85;
(c) -103; (d) -225 kcal

27 (a) -89.91, (b) $+11.9$,
(c) $+73$, (d) -5.8, (e) -83.3,
(f) -44.05, (g) -11.1, (h) -28.0,
(i) $+42.63$, (j) $+13.68$ kcal

28 high bond stability, thermally stable, reactive

29 $KClO_4$

30 (a) (i)(ii)(iii) C_2H_6;
(b) no, greater for complex molecules

31 (a) yes, 9.00×10^{18} ergs,
9.00×10^8 kJ; (b) 2.22×10^{-12} g

32 1.7×10^{-5} g

33 1.82×10^{-27} g, 1.64×10^{-6} erg,
1.64×10^{-13} J

34 44.5 g H_2, 356 g O_2, 1.7×10^{-7} %

35 (a) 1.40 cal, (b) 5.85 J

36 molecules (atoms), photons, electrons, matter

37 (a) 1.1×10^{18} kcal; (b) about the same
38 (a) 36 %, (b) 530 years
40 6×10^3 kcal
41 9.6×10^{21} kJ/mole, 2.3×10^{21} kcal/mole, 3.4×10^{19} greater
42 (ii) aerosols, greater effect; (iii) no
44 6.00×10^8 kcal/h, 3.56×10^5 lb/h
45 (a) 8.8 °C; (b) 1.1×10^{20} cal
47 1.2×10^2 mole

48 0.085 ℓ
49 (a) 1.51×10^{24} photons; (b) 5.07 kcal; (c) -1.7 kcal
50 1.3×10^6 gal
51 $+25.53$ kcal
52 (a) yes (NOH_5); (b) N atom
54 (b) molecule, kangaroo, ball; molecule
55 (a) 98.6 g/h; (b) 43 g/h
56 (a) 252 cal; (b) 2.4×10^3 hp-h
58 large
59 (a) 1.2×10^3 μg, (b) 7.8×10^8 particles

GLOSSARY

bond energy The energy required to break one bond in a gaseous molecule forming two gaseous products. Examples: $HF(g) \longrightarrow H(g) + F(g)$, $\Delta H = +135$ kcal; $AlF_3(g) \longrightarrow AlF_2(g) + F(g)$, $\Delta H = +156$ kcal.

bond stability The energy required to break a bond (see **bond energy**); the higher the bond energy, the greater the bond stability.

calorimeter An instrument for measuring the quantity of heat evolved or absorbed in a chemical reaction at constant temperature.

combustion A chemical reaction—burning—evolving heat and light (flames).

endothermic reaction A chemical reaction in which heat is absorbed, thereby cooling the surroundings.

energy change ΔE The heat of a reaction carried out at constant volume and constant temperature, the difference in energy resulting from a chemical change; ΔE = energy of products − energy of reactants. For an endothermic reaction, ΔE takes a positive sign; for an exothermic reaction, ΔE takes a negative sign.

enthalpy change ΔH The heat of a reaction carried out at constant pressure and constant temperature, the difference in enthalpy resulting from a chemical change. For an endothermic reaction, ΔH takes a positive sign; for an exothermic reaction, ΔH takes a negative sign.

entropy change A measure of the quantity of energy that is impossible to convert to useful work in any kind of real machine.

exothermic reaction A chemical reaction in which heat is evolved, thereby warming the surroundings.

fuel, fossil Fuels—peat, coal, petroleum, natural gas—produced by the decay of prehistoric plants and animals.

fuel, synthetic Petroleum or combustible gas manufactured from coal.

greenhouse effect The strong tendency of CO_2 in the atmosphere to absorb heat, minimizing loss of heat from the Earth's surface and thereby causing an increase in the Earth's temperature.

heat Photons in the wavelength range from roughly 7×10^{-5} to 7×10^{-3} cm produce motion—linear, vibrational, and rotational—of molecules; it is thermal energy, usually measured in joules or calories.

heat of combustion The quantity of heat evolved when 1 mole of a substance is burned in oxygen at 25 °C and 1 atm; for example, $CO(g) + \frac{1}{2} O_2(g) \longrightarrow CO_2(g)$, $\Delta H = -67.6$ kcal.

heat of formation The quantity of heat evolved or absorbed when 1 mole of a substance is formed from its elements at 25 °C and 1 atm. Examples: $Ca(c) + \frac{1}{2} O_2(g) \longrightarrow CaO(c)$, $\Delta H = -152$ kcal; $\frac{1}{2} N_2(g) + O_2(g) \longrightarrow NO_2(g)$, $\Delta H = +7.93$ kcal.

heat of reaction The energy change, the quantity of heat absorbed or evolved, that accompanies a chemical reaction as written.

Hess's law The quantity of heat evolved or absorbed is independent of the method used to change reactants into products; the quantity of heat is the same whether the reaction occurs in one step or in several steps.

sink Used in science to mean the opposite of source.

thermal pollution The increase in the temperature of natural waters—rivers, lakes, and so forth—or air used to absorb the heat energy rejected by electric power plants; more generally, the addition of heat to any part of the environment causing an increase in its temperature.

thermal stability The resistance of a substance to decomposition when heated in a vacuum; the higher the temperature required for decomposition, the greater the thermal stability.

thermochemical equation A chemical equation showing the quantity of heat evolved or absorbed during the reaction as written. Examples: $H_2(g) + \frac{1}{2} O_2(g) \longrightarrow H_2O(l)$, $\Delta H = -68.3$ kcal; $H_2O(l) \longrightarrow H_2(g) + \frac{1}{2} O_2(g)$, $\Delta H = +68.3$ kcal; $2H_2(g) + O_2(g) \longrightarrow 2H_2O(l)$, $\Delta H = -136.6$ kcal.

thermochemistry Deals with energy changes that accompany chemical reactions and physical changes such as melting, evaporation, and boiling.

thermodynamics Deals with the laws relating the transformation of heat and work from one to the other.

SOLUTIONS　10

IMPORTANCE OF SOLUTIONS_____ 10.1

The importance of solutions may already be evident, since many of the chemical reactions previously discussed take place in solution. Solution chemistry is even involved in our daily living. Almost all processes in the body occur in some kind of liquid solution. For example, a salt solution of nutrients (chemicals) in water bathes and nourishes body cells.

The effectiveness of a drug in curing sickness is strongly influenced by the solubility of the drug in aqueous and nonaqueous solvents. The drug must be soluble in the fatty (nonaqueous) portion of cell membranes to enter the cell, while its solubility in water determines how quickly the drug is removed from the body by way of the urinary system.

Minute variations in solubility can sometimes mean the difference between life and death. Sickle cell anemia, for example, is a disease that results from changes in

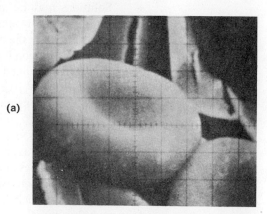
(a)

(b)

FIGURE 10.1 (a) Normal red blood cells, doughnut-shaped. (b) Genetic abnormality, sickled red blood cells.

the solubility of unoxygenated hemoglobin (page 205). When it becomes insoluble, hemoglobin crystallizes and distorts the cells into a "sickle" shape (Fig. 10.1) with a tough, inflexible membrane. The insoluble hemoglobin no longer functions as an oxygen carrier. In addition, the inflexible sickled cells cannot squeeze through small blood vessels. They thus become trapped in small capillaries and veins, blocking the flow of blood and deforming normal red blood cells. This hereditary disease, responsible for much pain and many deaths, occurs mainly in areas of the world, such as Africa, India, and the Mediterranean, that are subject to the malaria parasite.

Over 50,000 Americans suffer from this disease.

10.2 —————————— TYPES OF SOLUTIONS

Typical solutions include *liquid solutions,* such as salt-water or sugar-water mixtures; *gaseous solutions,* such as air, a mixture of several gases; and *solid solutions,* such as a solution of copper in silver (sterling silver). For our purposes, liquid solutions are emphasized.

A solution is a homogeneous mixture of particles—ions, atoms, or molecules—of two or more different substances. *Homogeneous* in this definition means that the properties and the appearance of all parts of the solution are uniform. That is, no boundary between particles is visible with or without the aid of instruments. In a solution, the particles are of atomic, molecular, or ionic size, about 5 nm or less in diameter.

10^9 nm = 1 m

Solutions are usually discussed in terms of **solvent** and **solute.** In general, the substance present in the greater amount is referred to as the solvent, while the other substance is called the solute.

Solutions may be made by dissolving gases, liquids, or solids in a liquid or a solid. When gases or solids are dissolved in a liquid, the liquid is ordinarily referred to as the solvent while the other component is the solute. When liquids are dissolved in liquids, the distinction is not always so clear. Thus, if 10 g of liquid ethyl alcohol and 90 g of water are mixed forming a solution, the water is clearly the solvent. If the solution consists of 10 g of water and 90 g of alcohol, the alcohol is the solvent.

Since all gaseous mixtures are homogeneous (page 63), any mixture of gases is a gaseous solution.*

Solid solutions made by dissolving a gas in a solid—for example, hydrogen dissolved in the metal palladium—are not very common. However, solids dissolved in solids, which includes *alloys,* are in general use. For example, *yellow gold;* an alloy of copper and gold, *brass,* an alloy of copper and zinc; *bronze,* an alloy of copper and tin; *monel* metal (nickel, copper, iron, and manganese); and *steel* (iron and carbon) are typical solid solutions.

Pure gold equals 24 carats; so 14 carat jewelry contains 14/24 or 58 % gold.

Liquid mercury dissolves many metals, but the resulting solution, called an *amalgam,* may be liquid or solid, depending on the relative amounts used. Silver amalgams are used for dental fillings.**

---

*However, at temperatures and pressures above the critical temperature and pressure (page 76), gases may separate into different gas phases. For example, at temperatures and pressures above the critical temperature and pressure of NH_3, a gaseous solution of N_2 and NH_3 separates into two gas phases. At these pressures, the molecules, squeezed together, form various clusters of molecules due to intermolecular attractive forces.

**Mercury vapor is a dangerous poison. But it is generally believed that mercury vapor from dental fillings does not constitute a health hazard. However, at room temperature, the vapor pressure of liquid mercury is high enough to be toxic. Readers interested in problems of mercury contamination are referred to the *Journal of the American Dental Association,* volume 81, October 1970, page 923; and to *Scientific American,* May 1971, page 15.

COMPOSITION OF SOLUTIONS_____ 10.3

The properties of solutions depend on their composition, the quantity of solute in a given quantity of solvent. For example, the hardness, melting point, and vapor pressure of a dental filling depend on the quantity of metal dissolved in the mercury. Some people prefer more sugar in their coffee than others. The term *concentration* of a solution is also used to express relative quantities of solute and solvent. The intensity of the pink color of an aqueous potassium permanganate solution depends on its concentration.

When a relatively large amount of solute is present, the solution is said to be concentrated. It is called dilute when a relatively small amount of solute is present. These terms, however, have no precise quantitative significance.

Another way of describing the amount of dissolved solute is by stating whether the solution is *saturated, unsaturated,* or *supersaturated.* When a solute—say, sodium chloride, NaCl—is continually added in small amounts to a given quantity of water at a given temperature, the concentration of the sodium chloride solution increases. Eventually, however, a *concentration is reached which remains constant;* even with the further addition of sodium chloride, the solid now remains undissolved. The solid sodium chloride in contact with the solution, but which does not appear to dissolve, is called the *excess solute.* The rate at which the excess solute dissolves equals the rate at which the dissolved solute crystallizes. Thereafter, an equilibrium (page 92) is established between solid sodium chloride and its aqueous solution:

$$\text{NaCl(c)} \rightleftharpoons \text{NaCl(aq)} \text{ (temperature constant)}$$

The solution in equilibrium with the excess solute is said to be **saturated.** The concentration of the saturated solution is known as the **solubility** of the solute in the given solvent at a specific temperature:

$$\text{excess solute} \rightleftharpoons \text{saturated solution (temperature constant)}$$
$$\updownarrow$$
equilibrium concentration is called solubility

Solubility is a characteristic property of substances, generally expressed as grams of solute dissolved in 100 g solvent. For example, the solubility of sodium bromide, NaBr, an ingredient of some headache powders (page 152), in water is 116.0 g per 100 g of water at 50 °C. This means that the addition of 117 g of NaBr to 100 g of water at 50 °C produces a saturated solution with 1 g of NaBr in excess.

Sodium bromide is said to be a very soluble substance, but it is common to refer to very slightly soluble substances as "*insoluble.*"

A solution of sodium bromide containing less than the equilibrium concentration (116.0 g per 100 g of H_2O at 50 °C) is called an **unsaturated** solution. However, the term unsaturated is not very definite, since an unsaturated solution may contain any amount of solute less than the amount required for the saturated solution.

It is also possible to prepare solutions with solute concentrations higher than the equilibrium concentration. This kind of solution, analogous to supercooled (page 101) and superheated liquids (page 101), is called a **supersaturated** solution. Supersaturation is not a stable state. Supersaturated solutions are not stable with respect to the solute that is present in the saturated solution. For example, a solution containing 116.1 g of NaBr in 100 g water at 50 °C is a supersaturated solution. It is unstable with respect to solid sodium bromide. This means that the excess solute (0.1 g) may quickly crystallize to attain the equilibrium condition of the saturated solution. As observed in supercooled liquids (page 101), the supersaturated condition may be relieved by the presence of nuclei around which the excess solute may crystallize. A tiny crystal or a dust particle may serve as a nucleus. Supersaturation of gases in body fluids is associated with the "bends" (page 69) and gas bubble disease in fish (page 310).

A supersaturated solution is generally prepared by heating a solution in contact with solute until all of it dissolves. Then, cooling the solution slowly, without stirring, produces a supersaturated solution. Very soluble salts, especially sodium thiosulfate, $Na_2S_2O_3$, sodium acetate, CH_3COONa, and sodium sulfate, Na_2SO_4, easily form supersaturated solutions.

PROBLEM 1 The solubility of table salt, sodium chloride, NaCl, is 35.7 g per 100 g of water at 0 °C. (a) What is the composition of a saturated solution of table salt in water at 0 °C? (b) Give a possible composition for (i) an unsaturated, (ii) a supersaturated solution of table salt in water at 0 °C.

Like gases, many pairs of liquids are completely **miscible.** They do not form saturated solutions; rather, they dissolve in one another in all proportions. Ethyl alcohol and water, for example, never form two layers. They completely dissolve in each other. They are mutually soluble regardless of the quantities mixed. Other liquid pairs, however, have definite solubilities; they are only **partially miscible.** For example, when benzene and water are shaken at 50 °C, two layers form (Fig. 10.2); one layer is a saturated solution of benzene in water, and the other is a saturated solution of water in benzene.

When the solubilities of liquids are so small that they cannot be measured, the liquids are said to be **immiscible.** For example, mercury and water at 20 °C are said to be immiscible.

PROBLEM 2 Water and methyl alcohol mixed in any proportion at 20 °C always form one liquid layer. At 20 °C, after the addition of 1.0 g of chloroform, $CHCl_3$, to 100 g of water, two layers form. Which pair of liquids is completely miscible? Which is partially miscible?

10.4 THE SOLUTION PROCESS

In our discussion of the nature of the dissolving process, we shall concentrate on two points of view: the polar nature of the solvent, and the heat of solution—the heat absorbed or evolved in the interaction between solute and solvent.

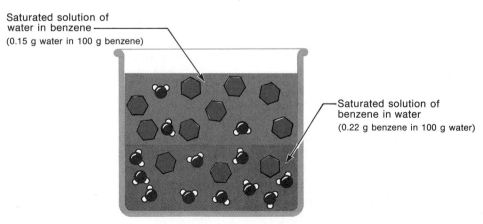

Saturated solution of water in benzene
(0.15 g water in 100 g benzene)

Saturated solution of benzene in water
(0.22 g benzene in 100 g water)

FIGURE 10.2 An example of partially miscible liquids at 50 °C.

Polar Nature of the Solvent   "Like dissolves like" is a common expression among chemists. Although there are many exceptions to this rule, it does find theoretical justification. In terms of our model of solids and liquids, substances in which the nature of the forces between molecules or ions is similar are more likely to enjoy one another's company. The more nearly alike the particles, the more likely they are to exchange places. The solute particle must find an accommodating spot in the solvent or be rejected by the solvent particles. Thus, water is composed of polar molecules bound by hydrogen bonding (page 265). Ammonia, ethyl alcohol, and hydrogen fluoride are also polar molecules bound by hydrogen bonding. Water is very happy to accommodate these molecules. At 0 °C, 90 g of ammonia dissolve in 100 g of water, ethyl alcohol is completely miscible with water, and practically an infinite amount of hyrogen fluoride dissolves in 100 g of water. On the other hand, carbon monoxide, CO, and octane (a component of gasoline), largely nonpolar molecules not participating in hydrogen bonding, are largely rejected by water and by ethyl alcohol. But gasoline is a good solvent for oils and greases, which also have largely nonpolar molecules that do not participate in hydrogen bonding.

Solubilities in 100 g water at 20 °C: CO, 0.0028 g; octane, 0.0015 g.

PROBLEM 3   Pick the substances most likely to dissolve (a) in water, (b) in gasoline: (i) methyl alcohol, CH_3OH, polar, participates in hydrogen bonding; (ii) methane, CH_4, nonpolar, no appreciable hydrogen bonding; (iii) methanethiol, CH_3SH, practically nonpolar, no appreciable hydrogen bonding.

The harmful effects of the insecticide DDT are a consequence of its solubility properties. DDT (page 696), a largely nonpolar molecule, is insoluble in polar solvents but soluble in nonpolar solvents. Once deposited in soil, it is not easily removed by solution in rain water but is "washed" into rivers and streams. When it is consumed as contaminated food by fish, birds, or other animals, it becomes concentrated in fatty tissues. Since nerve tissue is fatty, a considerable amount of the ingested DDT is localized in nerve tissue, where it interferes with normal biological reactions. In addition, because of its extreme stability it presents the danger of long-term storage in living organisms.

Absorption and Evolution of Heat   Ionic molecules (page 262) such as Na^+Cl^- and Cs^+F^- are extremely polar and therefore are predicted to be more soluble in water than in gasoline or benzene, C_6H_6 (nonpolar); experimentally, they are more soluble in water. The use of Hess's law makes it possible for us to develop a model for the process of solution.

Potassium fluoride is a typical ionic solid in which strong attractive forces exist between the K^+ and F^- ions. To break up and dissolve solid K^+F^-, the ions must be separated. The separation (bond breaking) is therefore an endothermic reaction:

$$K^+F^-(c) \longrightarrow K^+(g) + F^-(g) \qquad \Delta H = +190 \text{ kcal}$$

This is a rather "expensive" process, absorbing much heat. Hence, we should not expect solution unless some compensation occurs by making new bonds, an exothermic process (page 285). An ion, however, has a great attraction for a polar solvent like water, $H \overset{\overset{\displaystyle \cdots^{\delta-}}{O}}{{}_{\delta+}_{\delta+}} H$, or liquid ammonia. The positive ion attracts the negative end of the polar solvent molecules, while the negative ion attracts the positive end:

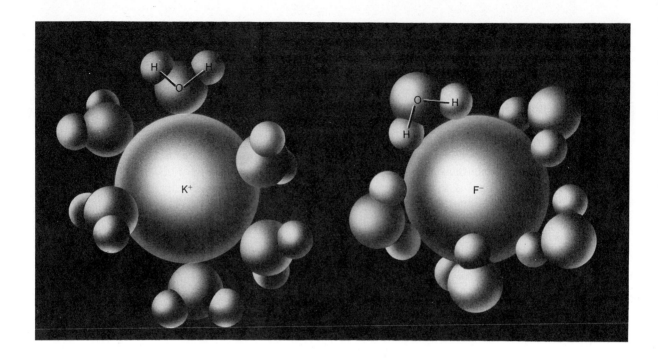

A typical ion-dipole
interaction, the
number of bonded
water molecules per
ion can be only
indirectly measured;
recent methods
indicate that the
number generally
ranges from 3 to 6.

In making these bonds, the ions are said to be **solvated;** when the solvent is water, the ions are said to be **hydrated.**

Hydration or solvation (bond forming) is an exothermic reaction:

$$K^+(g) + F^-(g) + H_2O \longrightarrow K^+(aq) + F^-(aq) \qquad \Delta H = -194 \text{ kcal}$$

The actual process of solution of solid KF is then the addition of the above two steps: *vaporization of the solid*

$$K^+F^-(c) \longrightarrow K^+(g) + F^-(g) \qquad \Delta H = +190 \text{ kcal}$$

and *solvation of the ions*

$$K^+(g) + F^-(g) + H_2O \longrightarrow K^+(aq) + F^-(aq) \qquad \Delta H = -194 \text{ kcal}$$

solution of the solid:

$$K^+F^-(c) + H_2O \longrightarrow K^+(aq) + F^-(aq)$$
$$\Delta H = 190 \text{ kcal} - 194 \text{ kcal} = -4 \text{ kcal (exothermic)}$$

The larger the number of water molecules attached to an ion and the stronger the ionic charge, the larger is the amount of heat evolved (Problem 85, page 350). Solution of K^+F^- is an exothermic reaction. However, in other cases the heat of solution may be positive:

$$Na^+Cl^-(c) + H_2O \longrightarrow Na^+(aq) + Cl^-(aq) \qquad \Delta H = +0.91 \text{ kcal}$$

Further discussed on
page 488.

In the application of this model, ion hydration (solution) is the crucial step. As the attraction of the solvent molecules for the ions decreases, the solubility of the solid most likely also decreases. Thus K^+F^- and Na^+Cl^- are soluble in water (polar), are less soluble in liquid ammonia (less polar) and are insoluble in benzene (nonpolar).

PROBLEM 4   In which of the given solvents is sodium iodide, Na^+I^-, likely to be (a) most soluble, (b) least soluble: (i) liquid benzene (nonpolar); (ii) liquid ammonia, NH_3 (polar); (iii) ethyl ether (slightly polar)?

In fact, solvation may be so strong that polar covalent molecules are frequently broken into solvated ions. Hydrogen chloride, HCl, and acetic acid, CH_3COOH, are typical examples:

$$HCl(aq) + H_2O \longrightarrow H^+(aq) + Cl^-(aq)$$
$$CH_3COOH(aq) + H_2O \rightleftharpoons H^+(aq) + CH_3COO^-(aq)$$

HCl, NaCl, and KF are typical **strong electrolytes.** This means that they exist in dilute aqueous solutions largely as ions; merely a way of saying that they react (dissociate) almost completely in water to form ions:

$$Na^+Cl^-(aq) \longrightarrow Na^+(aq) + Cl^-(aq)$$

We can also say that the tendency of the ions to combine in dilute solutions is practically zero.*

All ionic solids are strong electrolytes. Many covalent substances, for example, $AlCl_3$, HCl, HBr, HI, HNO_3, H_2SO_4, and $HClO_4$, are also strong electrolytes.

Acetic acid is a typical **weak electrolyte.** This means it exists in dilute aqueous solutions largely as molecules; merely a way of saying that the tendency of the molecules to form ions (ionize) is very small.

$$CH_3COOH(aq) \rightleftharpoons H^+(aq) + CH_3COO^-(aq)$$

The quantity of $H^+(aq)$ and $CH_3COO^-(aq)$ in solution compared to the quantity of $CH_3COOH(aq)$ is very small.

Hydrogen fluoride is another typical weak electrolyte:

$$HF(aq) \rightleftharpoons H^+(aq) + F^-(aq)$$

In a dilute solution, only about 8 % of the HF reacts as shown.

Many water-soluble covalent molecules are weak electrolytes. However, most polar or nonpolar covalent molecules are **nonelectrolytes:** the molecules have no measurable tendency to form ions in water. Methane, CH_4, glucose, $C_6H_{12}O_6$, and sucrose, $C_{12}H_{22}O_{11}$, are typical nonelectrolytes.

Solubilities depend, as we have just discussed, on the nature of the solvent and the nature of the solute. The generalization "like dissolves like" has been translated into the generalization "polar solvents dissolve polar solutes, nonpolar solvents dissolve nonpolar solutes."

PROBLEM 5   From the following list, pick the strong electrolytes, the electrolytes that exist in water mostly as ions: (i) lithium hydroxide, Li^+OH^-; (ii) calcium chloride, $Ca^{2+}(Cl^-)_2$; (iii) ethyl alcohol, C_2H_5OH (polar covalent); (iv) chloroform, $CHCl_3$ (polar covalent); (v) cadmium chloride, $CdCl_2$ (nonpolar covalent).

General, but useful, rules for the solubilities of common salts are summarized in App. VII.

---

*In more concentrated solutions, the ions will stick together long enough to be considered an **"ion pair."** While an ion pair exists, it behaves as one particle.

The strong electrostatic attraction between polar water molecules and ions frequently results in such strong bonding that when the solid crystallizes, it contains a definite number of water molecules. Such substances are called **hydrates.** Many of the ions of the transition metals from hydrates,* such as $FeCl_3(H_2O)_6$, $CrBr_3(H_2O)_6$, and $CuSO_4(H_2O)_5$. Other examples include $Na_2SO_4(H_2O)_{10}$ and $CaSO_4(H_2O)_2$. Most hydrates are thermally unstable and release water when heated.

10.5   METHODS OF EXPRESSING COMPOSITION

Mass Percent   Several methods are used by chemists for expressing solution compositions. One method is based on the **mass percent of solute** present in a solution. The percentage by mass is the mass in grams of solute present in 100 g of solution. For example, a 5.0 % NaCl aqueous solution by mass contains 5.0 g of NaCl and 95 g of H_2O per 100 g of solution.

Also known as weight percent.

The mass percentage of solute is given by the mass fraction of solute $\times$ 100, or

$$\text{mass percent} = \text{mass fraction} \times 100\ \% = \frac{\text{mass of solute, g}}{\text{mass of solution, g}} \times 100\ \%$$

or

$$= \frac{\text{mass of solute, g}}{\text{mass of solute, g} + \text{mass of solvent, g}} \times 100\ \% \text{ solution}$$

Thus, a 10 % aqueous solution of sodium bromide, NaBr, by mass is prepared by dissolving 10 g of sodium bromide in 90 g of water.

Example 1

Express the percentage of sodium chloride by mass in a solution weighing 400 g and containing 50.0 g of sodium chloride.

Answer

$$\text{mass percent} = \frac{\text{mass of solute, g}}{\text{mass of solution, g}} \times 100\ \% \text{ solution}$$

$$= \frac{50.0\ \text{g NaCl}}{400\ \text{g solution}} \times 100\ \% \text{ solution} = 12.5\ \% \text{ NaCl}$$

Example 2

How many grams of sodium sulfate, Na_2SO_4, are in 230 g of a 15.0 % solution of Na_2SO_4 by mass?

Answer

$$\text{mass percent} = \frac{\text{mass of solute, g}}{\text{mass of solution, g}} \times 100\ \% \text{ solution}$$

---

*International Union of Pure and Applied Chemistry (IUPAC) nomenclature for hydrates minimizes memorization. The name of the hydrate is formed by connecting the name of the individual compound with water and indicating the number of molecules; for instance, sodium carbonate-water (1/10) means $Na_2CO_3(H_2O)_{10}$ and cadmium sulfate-water (3/8) means $(CdSO_4)_3(H_2O)_8$.

From the given data:

$$15.0 \% \ Na_2SO_4 = \frac{mass \ of \ solute}{230 \ g \ solution} \times 100 \% \ solution$$

$$\frac{15.0 \% \ Na_2SO_4}{100 \% \ solution} \times 230 \ g \ solution = mass \ of \ solute$$

$$34.5 \ g \ Na_2SO_4 = mass \ of \ solute$$

Example 3

What mass of water is needed to prepare a 15.0 % solution of copper(II) sulfate, $CuSO_4$, by mass to contain 90.0 g of $CuSO_4$?

Answer

$$mass \ percent = \frac{mass \ solute, \ g}{mass \ solution, \ g} \times 100 \% \ solution$$

From the given data:

$$15.0 \% \ CuSO_4 = \frac{90.0 \ g \ CuSO_4}{mass \ of \ solution} \times 100 \% \ solution$$

from which

$$15.0 \% \ CuSO_4 \times mass \ of \ solution = 90.0 \ g \ CuSO_4 \times 100 \% \ solution$$

$$mass \ of \ solution = 90.0 \ g \ CuSO_4 \times \frac{100 \% \ solution}{15.0 \% \ CuSO_4} =$$

$$600 \ g \ solution$$

600 g is the mass of solution. This problem, however, seeks the number of grams of solvent (water). We therefore subtract the mass of the solute (90 g) from the mass of the solution:

600 g solution − 90 g solute = 510 g solvent, the required mass of water

PROBLEM 6   What is the mass percent of sugar in a solution consisting of 30.0 g of sugar in 200 g of water?

PROBLEM 7   (a) What is the mass of H_2O_2 in 140 g of a 3.0 % solution of H_2O_2 by mass? (b) What mass of water is needed to prepare a 2.55 % solution of $KMnO_4$ by mass to contain 35.0 g of $KMnO_4$?

Example 4

A solution of hydrochloric acid contains 37.23 % HCl by mass. Calculate the mass of hydrogen chloride in 100.0 ml of the acid. The density of the solution* is 1.19 g/ml.

*Commercial labels commonly use "*specific gravity*," a comparison of the masses of equal volumes of the liquid and water at a specific temperature. Since the density of water is close to 1.00 g/ml, the specific gravity of a liquid is practically the same as its density in g/ml.

329

Answer

Since this is a mass percentage problem, the mass of the solution is first determined from its volume and density:

$$100 \text{ ml solution} \times 1.19 \, \frac{\text{g solution}}{\text{ml solution}} = 119 \text{ g solution}$$

Then,

$$37.23 \% \text{ HCl} = \frac{\text{mass of solute}}{119 \text{ g solution}} \times 100 \% \text{ solution}$$

from which

$$\frac{37.23 \% \text{ HCl}}{100 \% \text{ solution}} \times 119 \text{ g solution} = \text{mass of solute} = 44.3 \text{ g HCl}$$

PROBLEM 8   Calculate the mass of H_3PO_4 in 250 ml of concentrated phosphoric acid solution, density 1.82 g/ml, which contains 96.0 % H_3PO_4 by mass.

Mole Fraction   Very frequently, the mass quantities of solute and solvent are expressed in terms of number of moles, because several properties of solutions depend on the *number of particles,* regardless of their masses. One such measure is the **mole fraction,** the fraction of the number of *moles of a substance* divided by the *total number of moles in the solution,* the number of moles of a solute plus the number of moles of solvent:

$$\text{mole fraction of A} = \frac{\text{moles of A}}{\text{moles of A} + \text{moles of B}}$$

or

$$= \frac{\text{moles of A}}{\text{total number of moles in solution}}$$

For example, in a solution containing 1 mole of sugar and 9 moles of water, the mole fraction of sugar is

$$\frac{1 \text{ mole}}{1 \text{ mole} + 9 \text{ mole}} = 0.1 \text{ mole fraction of sugar}$$

and

$$\frac{9 \text{ mole}}{1 \text{ mole} + 9 \text{ mole}} = 0.9 \text{ mole fraction of water}$$

Accepted abbreviations for mole fraction and other molecular quantities are given in App. II.

Notice that the sum of the mole fractions of all the substances in a solution must equal 1.

Example 5

Calculate the mole fraction of ethyl alcohol, C_2H_5OH, and of water in a solution containing 23.0 g ethyl alcohol, 46.0 g/mole, and 72.0 g water, 18.0 g/mole.

Answer

The mole fraction of a substance is merely its mass fraction (page 328) changed to the amounts in moles. Recall (page 123) that an amount in grams is converted to the amount in moles by multiplying by the proper conversion factor, $\frac{\text{mole}}{\text{g}}$. Thus, mass fraction of alcohol ——————— changed to ——————→ mole fraction

$$\frac{23.0\text{ g}}{23.0\text{ g} + 72.0\text{ g}} \quad \xrightarrow[\text{factor, } \frac{\text{mole}}{\text{g}}]{\substack{\text{multiply each} \\ \text{amount by its}}} \quad \frac{23.0\text{ g} \times \frac{1\text{ mole}}{46.0\text{ g}}}{23.0\text{ g} \times \frac{1\text{ mole}}{46.0\text{ g}} + 72.0\text{ g} \times \frac{1\text{ mole}}{18.0\text{ g}}}$$

from which

$$\text{mole fraction of ethyl alcohol} = \frac{0.500\text{ mole}}{0.500\text{ mole} + 4.00\text{ mole}} = \frac{0.500}{4.50} = 0.111$$

$$\text{mole fraction of water} = \frac{\text{moles of water}}{\text{moles of alcohol} + \text{moles of water}}$$

$$= \frac{4.00\text{ mole}}{4.50\text{ mole}} = 0.889$$

Or more simply, mole fraction of water $= 1.000 - 0.111 = 0.889$

PROBLEM 9 What is the mole fraction of sugar, $C_{12}H_{22}O_{11}$, in a solution containing 60.0 g of sugar and 600 g of water?

Molality Scientists, especially chemists and biologists, find it necessary to compare several solution properties on the basis of a *fixed mass of solvent*. The amount chosen is 1 kg (1000 g) of solvent. The number of moles of solute in 1 kg of solvent is called the **molality** of the solution, denoted by the letter m:

$$m_A = \frac{\text{moles of A}}{\text{kg of solvent}}$$

Example 6

Calculate the molality of NaCl, 58.5 g/mole, prepared by dissolving 14.7 g NaCl in 500 g H_2O.

Answer

$$m_{\text{NaCl}}, \text{ molality of NaCl} = \frac{\text{moles of NaCl}}{\text{kg water}}$$

and

$$\text{moles of NaCl} = 14.7\text{ g} \times \frac{1\text{ mole}}{58.5\text{ g}} = 0.251\text{ mole}$$

$$\text{kg water} = 500\text{ g} \times \frac{1\text{ kg}}{1000\text{ g}} = 0.500\text{ kg}$$

Hence

$$m_{\text{NaCl}} = \frac{0.251\text{ mole}}{0.500\text{ kg}} = 0.502\ \frac{\text{mole}}{\text{kg}}$$

PROBLEM 10 Calculate the molality of potassium bromide in a solution containing 4.28 g of KBr in 500 g of H_2O.

Molarity Chemists and biologists are also concerned with the quantities of substances involved in chemical reactions. Particularly for analytical purposes they separate, identify, and determine the quantity of different substances; for example, amino acids in bread, sulfur in oil, and mercury in fish. Definite molar qualities are involved in chemical reactions (page 156). Hence, it is also convenient to express solution compositions in terms of **concentration:** the number of moles divided by the volume of the solution in liters. The concentration is commonly called the **molarity,** abbreviated M, meaning the *number of moles of solute per liter of solution:*

$$M_A, \text{ molarity of solute A} = \frac{\text{moles of solute}}{\text{liters of solution}} = \frac{\text{mole}}{\text{liter}}$$

For example, 0.020 mole of hydrochloric acid, HCl, in 0.100 ℓ of solution has a molarity of 0.20:

$$M_{HCl} = \frac{\text{moles of HCl}}{\text{liter of solution}} = \frac{0.020 \text{ mole}}{0.100 \; \ell} = 0.20 \frac{\text{mole}}{\ell}$$

We can say that the concentration or the molarity of the hydrochloric acid is 0.20; or, equally correct, we can say that the solution of hydrochloric acid is 0.20 M (0.20 molar); or, we can simply write $M_{HCl} = 0.20$ mole/ℓ.

The advantage of this system is that the chemist can measure out a definite volume of the solution and immediately know the number of moles of reactant (solute) in the measured volume (page 160):

volume of solution, liters × molarity of solution, mole/liter = number of moles

The disadvantage of this scheme is that, unlike the previously discussed methods based on mass-mass relationships, the volume of a solution changes slightly with temperature. If a temperature change increases the volume, the molarity of the solution decreases.

Solutions of a desired molarity are prepared in a volumetric flask by adding enough water to a known mass of solute so that the solution exactly fills the flask.

Volumetric flasks are calibrated to contain a definite volume of liquid at a definite temperature (page 14).

Example 7

0.230 g of ethyl alcohol, C_2H_5OH, 46.06 g/mole, is dissolved in 200 ml of solution. Calculate the molarity of ethyl alcohol.

Answer

By definition, M, molarity of solute, is the number of moles of solute divided by number of liters of solution. From the data:

$$\text{moles of alcohol} = 0.230 \; g \times \frac{1 \text{ mole}}{46.1 \; g} = 0.00499 \text{ mole}$$

$$\text{liters of solution} = 200 \; ml \times \frac{1 \text{ liter}}{1000 \; ml} = 0.200 \; \ell$$

Therefore

$$M_{alcohol} = \frac{0.00499 \text{ mole}}{0.200 \; \ell} = 0.0250 \text{ mole}/\ell$$

Since molarity is frequently symbolized as [A], we can also write

$$[C_2H_5OH] = 0.0250$$

PROBLEM 11 0.324 g of sulfuric acid, H_2SO_4, 98.1 g/mole, is dissolved in 500 ml of solution. Calculate the molarity of H_2SO_4 in the solution.

Example 8

How many grams of hydrogen chloride, HCl, 36.5 g/mole, are needed to prepare 5.00 ℓ of 4.00 M HCl in water?

Answer

To obtain the number of grams, we need the number of moles of HCl. This is given to us by the volume and molarity of the solution:

$$\text{volume of solution, liter} \times \text{molarity of solution,} \frac{\text{mole}}{\text{liter}} = \text{mole}$$

$$5.00\ \ell \times 4.00\ \frac{\text{mole}}{\ell} = 20.0\ \text{mole}$$

Then, the number of grams is obtained from the number of moles:

$$\text{mole} \times \text{molecular weight,} \frac{g}{\text{mole}} = g$$

$$20.0\ \text{mole} \times 36.5\ \frac{g}{\text{mole}} = 730\ g\ \text{HCl}$$

Thus, 730 g of HCl dissolved in sufficient water to make 5.00 ℓ of solution yields 4.00 M HCl solution.

PROBLEM 12 How many grams of sodium carbonate, Na_2CO_3, are needed to make 3.50 ℓ of a 0.400 M Na_2CO_3 solution?

Example 9

A sulfuric acid solution contains 98.00 % of H_2SO_4, 98.08 g/mole, by mass, and its density is 1.836 g/ml at 20 °C. Calculate the molarity of H_2SO_4 in this solution.

Answer

By definition, the molarity is the number of moles of H_2SO_4 per liter of solution. We therefore first calculate the number of grams of H_2SO_4 in 1 liter and then convert this quantity to the number of moles.

The mass of 1 liter of solution, as in previous examples, is obtained from its density:

$$\text{volume, ml} \times \text{density,} \frac{g}{\text{ml}} = g$$

$$1000\ \frac{\text{ml}}{\ell} \times 1.836\ \frac{g\ \text{solution}}{\text{ml solution}} = 1836\ \frac{g\ \text{solution}}{\ell\ \text{solution}},$$

the mass of 1 liter of solution. But the solution contains 98.00 % H_2SO_4 by mass.

This means that there are 98.00 g of H_2SO_4 in 100.0 g of solution. Then, the mass of H_2SO_4 in 1 liter is given by

$$\text{mass of } H_2SO_4 = \frac{1836 \text{ g solution}}{1 \text{ } \ell \text{ solution}} \times \frac{98.00 \text{ g } H_2SO_4}{100.0 \text{ g solution}} = \frac{1799 \text{ g } H_2SO_4}{\ell \text{ solution}}$$

The mass of H_2SO_4 in 1 liter of solution is thus 1799 g. Then

$$M_{H_2SO_4} = \frac{\text{moles of } H_2SO_4}{\text{liter of solution}} = \frac{1799 \text{ g } H_2SO_4}{\ell \text{ solution}} \times \frac{1 \text{ mole } H_2SO_4}{98.08 \text{ g } H_2SO_4} = 18.34 \frac{\text{mole}}{\ell}$$

PROBLEM 13 **A solution of hydrochloric acid, HCl, 36.5 g/mole, contains 36.0 % HCl by mass, and its density is 1.18 g/ml. Calculate the molarity of HCl in this solution.**

In many procedures, only very small volumes of solution are required; in fact, instruments are available that accurately deliver solutions in units of microliters (10^{-3} ml) and nanoliters (10^{-6} ml). We shall, however, content ourselves with the units of liters, moles, grams, and *milliliters,* ml, *millimoles,* mmol, and *milligrams,* mg.

These units are related to one another in the same sense as 1 meter and 100 centimeters. The unit g/mole is the same as mg/mmol, and mole/liter is the same as mmol/ml. This is true because there are 10^3 mg in 1 g, 10^3 mmol in 1 mole, and 10^3 ml in 1 liter. For example, 18 g/mole is the same as 18 mg/mmol,

$$18 \frac{g}{\text{mole}} \times 10^3 \frac{mg}{g} \times \frac{1 \text{ mole}}{10^3 \text{ mmol}} = 18 \frac{mg}{\text{mmol}}$$

and 0.20 mole/ℓ is the same as 0.20 mmol/ml:

$$0.20 \frac{\text{mole}}{\ell} \times 10^3 \frac{\text{mmol}}{\text{mole}} \times \frac{1 \ell}{10^3 \text{ ml}} = 0.20 \frac{\text{mmol}}{ml}$$

In switching units, essentially, we divide and multiply by 1000. To avoid confusion, use g/mole with mole/liter, and use mg/mmol with mmol/ml. Like meters and centimeters, the use of either set of units is dictated by convenience.

Example 10

Calculate the molarity of silver nitrate, $AgNO_3$, in a solution containing 6.0 millimoles, mmol, of $AgNO_3$ in 30 ml.

Answer

By definition,

$$M, \text{ molarity of solute} = \frac{\text{mmol of solute}}{\text{ml of solution}} = \frac{6.0 \text{ mmol}}{30 \text{ ml}} = 0.20 \frac{\text{mmol}}{ml} = 0.20 \frac{\text{mole}}{\ell}$$

Example 11

How many (a) mmol, (b) mg, and (c) g of nitric acid, HNO_3, 63.0 g/mole, are in 13.0 ml of 0.0872 M HNO_3 solution?

Answer

As in the previous examples

(a)
$$\text{volume, } ml \times \text{molarity, } \frac{mmol}{ml} = mmol$$

$$13.0 \, ml \times 0.0872 \, \frac{mmol}{ml} = 1.13 \, mmol$$

(b) to convert mmol to mg, we multiply by the molecular weight in mg/mmol:

$$1.13 \, mmol \times \frac{63.0 \, mg}{mmol} = 71.2 \, mg \, HNO_3$$

(c) Although balances calibrated in milligram units are available, most balances are still calibrated in gram units. Hence, it becomes necessary to convert milligrams to grams:

$$71.2 \, mg \times \frac{1 \, g}{1000 \, mg} = 0.0712 \, g$$

PROBLEM 14   **What is the mass (a) in mg, and (b) in g of cadmium nitrate, $Cd(NO_3)_2$, in 24.7 ml of 0.221 M $Cd(NO_3)_2$?**

The *dilution* of solutions, the addition of more solvent to a given solution, is a common procedure. Drug solutions, for example, are frequently diluted before injection into patients. This operation does not change the amount (mmol) of solute present in the entire solution. The increase in volume only decreases the concentration. This means that the product of the molarity and volume—the number of mmol—remains constant. For example, 1.0 ml of 0.10 M solution contains 0.10 mmol of solute:

This is a constant source of concern; incorrect dilutions—for example, by misplacing the decimal point—could result in more than mere patient discomfort.

$$1.0 \, ml \times 0.10 \, \frac{mmol}{ml} = 0.10 \, mmol$$

Adding more solvent to dilute the solution to 2.0 ml does not add or remove solute, but the molarity is decreased:

$$M \text{ solute} = \frac{0.10 \, mmol}{2.0 \, ml} = 0.050 \, \frac{mmol}{ml}$$

We can also see that the amount of solute remains constant during dilution by calculating the number of mmol in the diluted solution,

$$2.0 \, ml \times 0.050 \, \frac{mmol}{ml} = 0.10 \, mmol$$

which is the same as in the original solution. Thus, the product of the molarity and volume of the original solution must equal the product of the molarity and volume of the diluted solution.

Example 12

1.50 ml of 0.24 M solution of codeine (an analgesic, "pain-killer" drug) is diluted to 4.50 ml. What is the molarity of the diluted drug solution?

Answer

The original solution contains 0.36 mmol of codeine,

$$1.50 \text{ ml} \times 0.24 \frac{\text{mmol}}{\text{ml}} = 0.36 \text{ mmol}$$

which remains unchanged during dilution. The molarity of the diluted solution is therefore

$$M = \frac{\text{mmol of solute}}{\text{ml of solution}} = \frac{0.36 \text{ mmol}}{4.50 \text{ ml}} = 0.080 \frac{\text{mmol}}{\text{ml}}$$

PROBLEM 15 **What is the molarity of a solution prepared by diluting 16.0 ml of 0.250 M HCl to 54.0 ml?**

10.6 NUMBER OF SOLUTE PARTICLES, AND SOLUTION PROPERTIES

The addition of a solute to a solvent to form a solution alters some properties of the solvent. In this section, we shall study the effect of solute particles on the vapor pressure of a liquid solvent. We shall see that the vapor pressure of the solvent is decreased ("lowered, depressed") by the presence of the solute particles. As a consequence, the properties of the solvent, such as freezing and boiling points, that are dependent on the vapor pressure (Chap. 3) are also changed. We shall see that the freezing point is decreased ("lowered, depressed") while the boiling point is increased ("elevated"). The change in the vapor pressure is also responsible for the so-called osmotic pressure of solutions.

We shall also learn that these changes in dilute solutions for a given quantity of solvent depend only on the *number of solute particles*, independent of mass and charge.* Ions, atoms, and molecules have the same effect, regardless of origin. A molecule of glucose, 180 g/mole, has the same effect as an H^+ ion, 1.0 g/mole, or a heavy negative iodide ion, 127 g/mole.

*These changes are known as colligative properties, from colligare, Latin for bind together, used here to mean a principle bringing facts together.

Vapor Pressure of Solutions Let us imagine the following experiment at constant temperature, 25 °C. One flask, connected to a mercury plug (page 54), contains water, as shown in Fig. 10.3(a). Pure liquids have a characteristic vapor pressure at a given temperature (page 92). However, a second, similar flask, shown in Fig. 10.3(b), containing 1 mole of glucose, $C_6H_{12}O_6$, 180 g/mole, dissolved in 1 kg of water shows a lower vapor pressure than pure water. This is indicated by the difference in the heights of the mercury columns. Equally important, a third flask containing 1 mole of sucrose, $C_{12}H_{22}O_{11}$, 342 g/mole, as in Fig. 10.3(c), shows exactly the same decrease in vapor pressure as the glucose solution. The common feature of

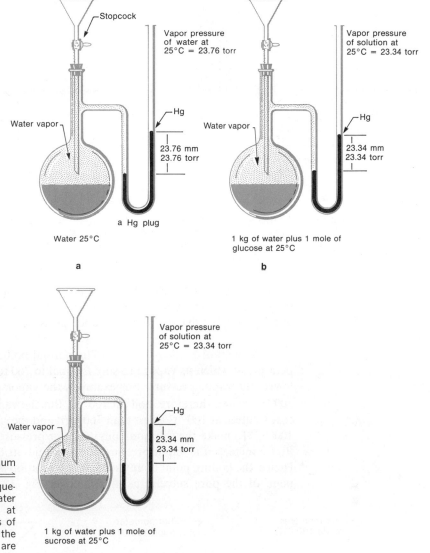

FIGURE 10.3 (a) Water in equilibrium with water vapor, liquid water ⇌ water vapor, at 25 °C. (b) and (c) Aqueous solutions in equilibrium with water vapor, solution ⇌ water vapor, at 25 °C. The difference in the heights of the mercury columns shows that the vapor pressures of the solutions are lower by 0.42 torr.

Stopcock

Vapor pressure
of water at
25°C = 23.76 torr

Water vapor

Hg

23.76 mm
23.76 torr

a Hg plug

Water 25°C

a

Vapor pressure
of solution at
25°C = 23.34 torr

Water vapor

Hg

23.34 mm
23.34 torr

1 kg of water plus 1 mole of
glucose at 25°C

b

Vapor pressure
of solution at
25°C = 23.34 torr

Water vapor

Hg

23.34 mm
23.34 torr

1 kg of water plus 1 mole of
sucrose at 25°C

c

these two solutions is the presence of the same number of moles of solute, the same number of solute particles, in the same number of moles of solvent. From the results of many such experiments involving a variety of liquids and solutes, François Raoult (1886) concluded that *the decrease in the vapor pressure of a solvent is determined by the mole fraction of solute dissolved in it.* The solutions in which the components at all possible mole fractions have vapor pressures in agreement with Raoult's law are known as **ideal solutions.** *Many solutions are nearly ideal; none is exactly ideal.*

Known as Raoult's law.

The explanation for this decrease in vapor pressure is associated with the number of solvent molecules at the surface of the liquid. The vapor pressure of a liquid depends on the number of solvent molecules that escape from the surface. The number of solvent molecules present at the surface, however, is reduced by the presence of solute particles. Consequently, the number of solvent molecules escaping is correspondingly reduced, and the vapor pressure of the solvent is decreased, as

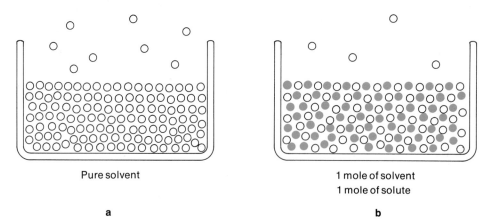

FIGURE 10.4 Illustrating the decrease in vapor pressure. (a) Escape (evaporation) of molecules from the surface of pure solvent. (b) In solution, solute particles (color) also occupy part of the surface area and so reduce the number of water molecules at the surface. Hence, the number of solvent molecules that evaporate (escape) is reduced.

shown in Fig. 10.4. We can also say that the solute merely lowers the concentration of the solvent in the solution, compared with the concentration in pure solvent. This dilution of the solvent lowers its vapor pressure.

Elevation of Boiling Point The normal boiling point of a liquid is the temperature at which its vapor pressure is equal to 760 torr. But the presence of a solute lowers the vapor pressure. For example, the vapor pressure of water is 760 torr at 100 °C; water, therefore, boils at 100 °C. But the vapor pressure of an aqueous glucose solution at 100 °C is less than 760 torr, and the solution therefore will not boil at 100 °C. To make the solution boil, its vapor pressure must be increased to 760 torr. But to increase the vapor pressure of any liquid, its temperature must be increased. Hence, the boiling point of any solvent in a solution is always higher than the boiling point of the pure solvent, as illustrated in Fig. 10.5. Like the decrease in vapor

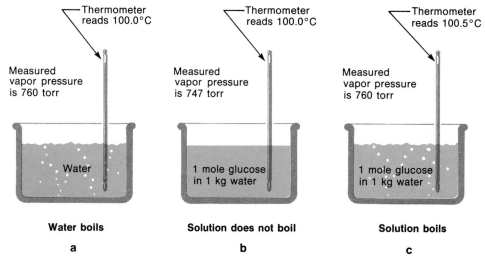

FIGURE 10.5 Illustrating the increase (elevation) in the boiling point; barometric pressure is 760 torr. The solution does not boil at 100 °C because its vapor pressure is less than 760 torr. It boils at the higher temperature because its vapor pressure has been increased to 760 torr.

pressure, the boiling point elevation depends on the nature of the solvent and the number of solute particles in a given amount of solvent. A solution of 1 mole of glucose in 1 kg of water boils at 100.512 °C at 1 atm pressure.

Lowering of Freezing Point   While an increase in boiling point accompanies a decrease in vapor pressure, experiments show that the freezing point of a solution is *lower* than that of the pure solvent. This is shown in Fig. 10.6.

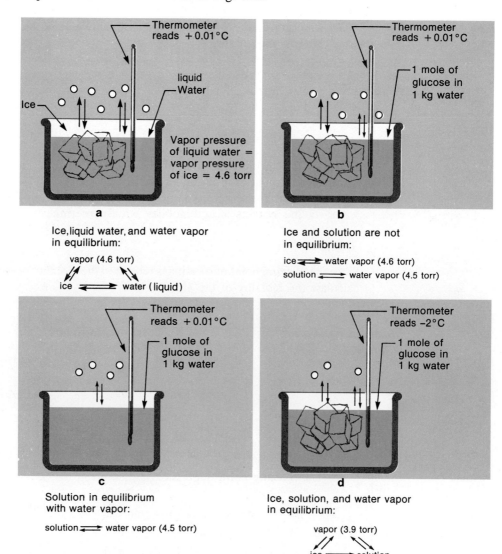

FIGURE 10.6 The lowering of the freezing point of water in solution. At the triple point (Fig. 3.12, page 100), (a) ice, water, and water vapor are in equilibrium with one another; the ice and the water have the same vapor pressure (4.6 torr). The freezing point of water at its own vapor pressure (4.6 torr) is +0.01 °C.

(b) The solution, however, at the same temperature, *has a lower vapor pressure, while the vapor pressure of the pure ice remains the same;* the ice thus has a higher vapor pressure than the solution. Consequently, while the ice evaporates, water vapor condenses on the surface of the solution. This is another way of saying that the ice now melts at +0.01 °C, shown in (c). However, to freeze the solution, ice must reappear. But for ice to reappear, the temperature must be lowered, as shown in (d). Raising the temperature of water can never freeze it. The lowering of the freezing point at 1 atm pressure is the same as that observed at the triple point.

Experimentally, it has been determined that one mole of solute particles in 1 kg of water lowers the freezing point of water 1.86 °C. This experimental observation is generalized into the following language: we call 1.86 °C the **freezing point lowering (depression) constant** and write it with the units °C kg/mole. Thus, the freezing point depression constant for water is 1.86 °C kg/mole, while that for benzene is 5.12 °C kg/mole. For convenience, a table of freezing point depression and boiling point elevation constants is given in App. VIII. These constants depend on the nature of the solvent.

The lowering of the freezing point is directly related to the molality of the solution. We can then write

$$\text{lowering of freezing point} = \text{freezing point depression constant}, \frac{°C\ kg}{mole} \times \text{molality of solute}, \frac{mole}{kg}$$

Example 13

Calculate (a) the freezing point depression, and (b) the freezing point of a solution containing 45 g of ethylene glycol $(CH_2OH)_2$, 62 g/mole, in 600 g of water. Ethylene glycol is in common use as an additive ("antifreeze") to protect water-cooling systems of automobiles against freezing.

Answer

Since the freezing point depression is related to the molality of the solution, first calculate the molality of the glycol:

$$m_{glycol} = \text{molality of glycol} = \frac{\text{moles of glycol}}{\text{kg water}}$$

$$\text{moles of glycol} = 45\ g \times \frac{1\ mole}{62\ g} = 0.73\ mole$$

$$\text{kg of water} = 600\ g \times \frac{1\ kg}{1000\ g} = 0.60\ kg$$

Hence

$$m_{glycol} = \frac{0.73\ mole}{0.60\ kg} = 1.2\ \frac{mole}{kg}$$

(a) The freezing point depression is then given by

$$\text{lowering of freezing point} = 1.86\ \frac{°C\ kg}{mole} \times 1.2\ \frac{mole}{kg} = 2.2\ °C$$

(b) The freezing point of the aqueous solution is therefore the freezing point of the solvent minus the depression, or 0 °C − 2.2 °C = −2.2 °C.

PROBLEM 16 Calculate (a) the freezing point depression, and (b) the freezing point of a solution containing 82.0 g of glucose, 180 g/mole, in 400 g of water.

This generalization is true only for dilute solutions, particularly when applied to solutions of electrolytes in which each ion acts like an individual particle in its effect on the freezing point of the solution.

In extremely cold climates, preventing water from freezing in car radiators and house water pipes is an important problem. But fish in icy waters (Arctic and Antarctic) also require protection. A combination of sugars and proteins (glycoproteins) serves as the biological antifreeze.

DETERMINATION OF MOLECULAR WEIGHT_____10.7

The major reason for studying the depression of the freezing point is that it provides a relatively simple laboratory method for the determination of molecular weights of nonelectrolytes, such as glucose and sucrose, that cannot be determined by modern methods (Chap. 4). Unlike the electrolytes (page 355), nonelectrolytes do not ionize—do not form ions while dissolving in water.

A solution containing a known mass of nonelectrolyte in a known amount of solvent is prepared. The freezing point depression is then experimentally determined. From the known freezing point depression constant of the solvent, the molality of the solute can be calculated. In turn, from the known quantity of solute present and the calculated molality, the molecular weight can be determined.

The instrument Cryette measures freezing point of solutions with a precision of ± 0.001 °C at the rate of 1 min per determination of molecular weight.

Example 14

1.00 g of a nonelectrolyte solute dissolved in 50.0 g of benzene lowered the freezing point of benzene 0.400 °C. The freezing point depression constant of benzene is 5.12 °C kg/mole. Find the molecular weight of the solute.

Answer

This method rests on the fact that the number of grams of solute in 1 kg of solvent can be calculated from the known composition of the solution, as shown:

$$50.0 \text{ g solvent} \times \frac{1 \text{ kg}}{1000 \text{ g}} = 0.0500 \text{ kg solvent}$$

$$\text{mass of solute in 1 kg solvent} = \frac{1.00 \text{ g}}{0.0500 \text{ kg}} = 20.0 \frac{\text{g}}{\text{kg}}$$

and that the molality of the solute can be calculated from the measured depression and the known depression constant, as shown:

$$\text{lowering of freezing point} = \text{depression constant} \times \text{molality of solute}$$

$$0.400 \text{ °C} = 5.12 \frac{\text{°C kg}}{\text{mole}} \times m_{\text{solute}}$$

$$m_{\text{solute}} = 0.400 \text{ °C} \times \frac{1 \text{ mole}}{5.12 \text{ °C kg}} = 0.0781 \frac{\text{mole}}{\text{kg}}$$

This then tells us that 0.0781 mole of the solute has a mass of 20.0 g. Then, the molecular weight of the solute, the mass of 1 mole, is given by

$$\frac{20.0 \text{ g}}{0.0781 \text{ mole}} = 256 \frac{\text{g}}{\text{mole}} \quad \text{or} \quad 20.0 \frac{\text{g}}{\text{kg solvent}} \times \frac{\text{kg solvent}}{0.0781 \text{ mole}} = 256 \frac{\text{g}}{\text{mole}}$$

PROBLEM 17   Calculate the molecular weight of a nonelectrolyte if 4.32 g dissolved in 600 g of benzene lowers the freezing point of benzene 0.340 °C; the freezing point depression constant of benzene is 5.12 °C kg/mole.

10.8 _____ OSMOSIS AND OSMOTIC PRESSURE

From osmos, the Greek word for impulse, to push.

Other membranes may allow solvent molecules to pass through along with ions and molecules.

Osmosis is the transfer of solvent molecules through a barrier—a semipermeable membrane—in that direction which tends to equalize the concentrations of solutions on both sides of the membrane. A semipermeable membrane permits the passage only of solvent molecules. Solvent always flows from pure solvent into solution, or from solutions of lower concentration to solutions of higher concentration. Osmosis is a process of prime importance in living organisms. Cell membranes in plants and animals are permeable to water and some solutes. For example, animal blood cells contain many solutes, including sodium chloride.

The salt concentration in blood plasma is the same as 0.9 % NaCl(*aq*) by mass. If blood cells are placed in pure water, water molecules rapidly move into the cell in an attempt to equalize the concentration. The transfer of water molecules into the cell dilutes the salt content. The blood cells therefore swell and may burst. Hence, care is always exercised to insure that solutions that flow into the blood stream are of the same osmotic pressure as the blood itself.* Sodium ions, Na⁺, and potassium ions, K⁺, are mainly responsible for maintaining proper osmotic pressure balance inside and

_____

*Solutions having the same osmotic pressure are known as **isotonic solutions,** derived from *isos* and *tonos,* the Greek words for same tone, used here in the sense of having equal pressures.

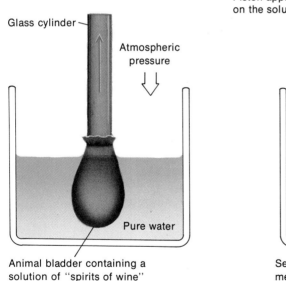

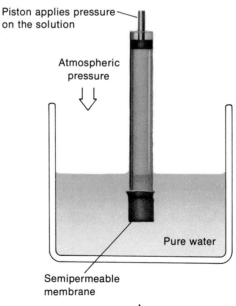

Glass cylinder

Atmospheric pressure

Piston applies pressure on the solution

Atmospheric pressure

Pure water

Pure water

Animal bladder containing a solution of "spirits of wine"

Semipermeable membrane

a

b

FIGURE 10.7 (a) An animal bladder containing an aqueous solution of "spirits of wine" (ethyl alcohol) is placed in pure water. The animal bladder allows only water molecules, no solute molecules, to pass through. The rise in the level of the solution in the tube indicates the passage of water from the pure water side through the animal bladder into the solution.

(b) The principle of measuring osmotic pressure. The pressure in excess of atmospheric pressure that must be applied to the solution to prevent it from rising in the tube—to prevent the flow of solvent molecules into the solution—is the osmotic pressure of the solution.

outside of the cells of organisms. Osmosis is also critically involved in the functioning of the kidneys. Fish satisfy their needs for water, which may be as much as 30 % of their body weight, by osmosis rather than by drinking.

The **osmotic pressure** of a solution is the excess pressure which must be applied to the solution to prevent osmosis, to stop the passage of solvent through a semipermeable membrane into the solution. This is illustrated in Fig. 10.7. At this pressure, equilibrium is established between solvent molecules on both sides of the membrane. The rate of flow into the solution is the same as the rate of flow out of the solution. The osmotic pressure of human blood, due primarily to proteins, is approximately 25 torr.

The osmotic pressure of a solution depends only on the number of solute particles in a given volume of solution. Therefore, it is very useful for determining the molecular weights of solutes such as proteins, polymers (Chap. 23), and other large molecules in the molecular weight range of several thousand.

Osmotic pressure was first studied in 1748 by Jean Nollet, who enclosed a solution of "spirits of wine" in a glass cylinder with an animal bladder.

COLLOIDS _____ 10.9

Some properties of substances are dependent upon particle size. For example, silver chloride crystals are colorless, but appear milky white when formed as a fine suspension. All suspended materials, including black carbon, may be made to appear white by proper reduction of the particle size, so that all photons in the visible range (page 191) are scattered. Finely divided solids usually dissolve to a greater extent than relatively coarse particles. The vapor pressure of a tiny drop of liquid is greater than the vapor pressure of the same liquid in bulk; a drop of water, diameter of 4×10^{-6} cm, boils at about 99 °C.

In solutions, the solute and solvent are distributed as atoms, molecules, or ions. **Suspensions,** such as finely divided clay in water, on the other hand, consist of particles that are much larger than individual molecules; these aggregates of molecules are so large that they settle out. Clay particles settle to the bottom, but milkfat particles, less dense than water, float to the top.

Between solutions and suspensions there is a particle size known as **colloidal particles.** This region of particle size is also known as the **colloidal state** or simply a **colloid.** Colloids include such familiar mixtures as glue, blood, beer, milk, and jellies. The process of digestion and such diverse applications as the dyeing of cloth, glassmaking, and the grinding of paints are associated with the colloidal state.

Colloidal particles range in diameter from roughly 5 nm, the size range of protein molecules, to 200 nm, the limit of visibility with the aid of a microscope. The dispersed particles are not large enough to settle out at appreciable rates. They are, however, sufficiently large to scatter visible light much more efficiently than molecular or dissolved particles in solution. When a light beam is passed through colloidal particles in a gas or a liquid, the beam of light, viewed from the side, is clearly visible. Passed through clean air, pure liquid, or solution, the light beam is not visible. Known as the Tyndall effect, this phenomenon is accepted as a method of detecting the colloidal state (Fig. 10.8).

The individual colloidal particles may be seen as light dots with the aid of a microscope. The particles, too small to be seen, scatter light and so appear as light dots moving in a random zig-zag fashion, known as Brownian movement. This erratic motion results from the collisions of liquid (or gas) molecules in which the colloidal particles are dispersed. Brownian motion is also partly responsible for the exceedingly slow settling of colloidal particles in liquids.

From kolla, the Greek word for glue. Colloids are also called colloidal suspensions or colloidal solutions.

For example, the diameter of a hemoglobin molecule (page 665) is 6.4 nm.

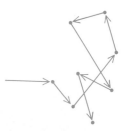

Random motion of Brownian movement, first noted by Robert Brown in 1827.

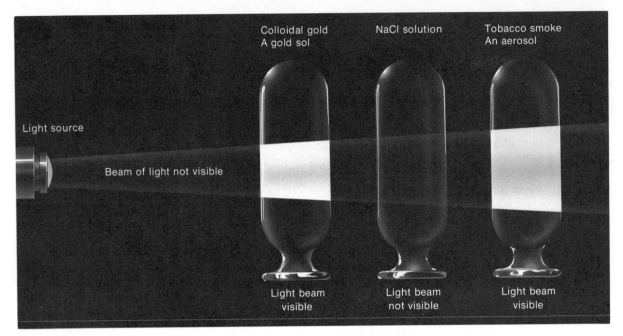

Colloidal gold
A gold sol

NaCl solution

Tobacco smoke
An aerosol

Light source

Beam of light not visible

Light beam
visible

Light beam
not visible

Light beam
visible

FIGURE 10.8 The presence of colloidal particles is easily detected with the aid of a light beam.

The rate of Brownian motion is proportional to T, evidence that kinetic energy of molecules is proportional to T (page 65).

The most important colloids are the **sols, gels, emulsions,** and **aerosols.** A sol consists of a solid dispersed in a liquid, such as particles of magnesium hydroxide dispersed in water (*milk of magnesia*). An emulsion consists of a liquid dispersed in a liquid, such as oils in water (mayonnaise), or butterfat in water (milk). On the other hand, a gel consists of liquid particles dispersed in a solid; a pearl, gelatin, and jellies are examples of gels. Aerosols consist of solid particles (smoke) or liquid particles (fog) dispersed in a gas.

George Bredig method, invented in 1898.

In general, colloidal particles are made by breaking large particles or by growing small particles to colloidal sizes. For example, an electric arc between two platinum electrodes under a very dilute solution of sodium chloride breaks down the metal, forming colloidal platinum. The addition of small amounts of dilute sulfuric acid to a dilute solution of sodium thiosulfate causes the growth of sulfur particles.

Known as a thixotropic gel, derived from thixis and trope, the Greek words meaning touch and turning.

Non-drip paint is an interesting type of gel. It has the special property of becoming fluid when shaken. That is, when the paint is subjected to the mechanical force of brushing, it becomes fluid and spreads easily. However, when the brushing is stopped, the fluid immediately gels. This kind of action also occurs in quicksand, a gel composed of water in some kinds of sand.

Napalm, the incendiary bomb, is a gel made from gasoline and a sticky aluminum soap (aluminum naphthenate). Canned heat (*Sterno*) is also a gel made by the addition of alcohol to an aqueous calcium acetate solution. The technique for gelling oil in distressed tankers may reduce oil spills.

In cosmetics, "vanishing cream" is an emulsion of an oil dispersed in water; when rubbed on the skin, the cream "vanishes" because most of the emulsion consists of water. A "cold cream," on the other hand, leaves an oil residue because it is an emulsion of water dispersed in oil so that most of the emulsion consists of oil.

From detergere, the Latin word for cleansing agent.

Cleansing Agents   The main function of a cleansing agent, a detergent, is to reduce oily and greasy dirt to colloidal particles. Detergents are therefore known as **emulsifying agents.** These are molecules or ions that consist of two parts: a long hydrocarbon and a polar part. The hydrocarbon portion is soluble in oil, and the polar portion is soluble in water (page 327). Examples of typical detergents are

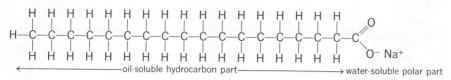

sodium stearate, a typical soap

sodium lauryl sulfate, a synthetic detergent

The oily-greasy dirt is emulsified in such a manner that the oil-soluble (nonpolar) part of the detergent dips (dissolves) in the oil (nonpolar), while the water-soluble (polar) part dips (dissolves) in the water (polar) as shown:*

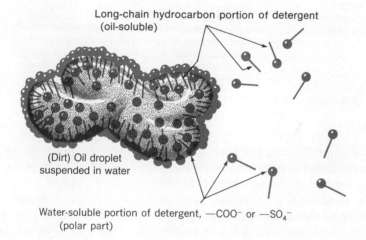

Long-chain hydrocarbon portion of detergent (oil-soluble)

(Dirt) Oil droplet suspended in water

Water-soluble portion of detergent, —COO⁻ or —SO₄⁻ (polar part)

Repulsion of the like charges, $—COO^-$ or $—SO_4^-$, covering each droplet prevents their growth. The removal of dirt from a fabric is illustrated in Fig. 10.9.

When first used on a large scale, the synthetic detergents were foreign to natural microorganisms (bacteria) that normally decomposed sewage. As a result, foaming and contamination became evident in much of our water supply. However, the research chemist solved this problem by changing the structure of the molecule to make it acceptable to the bacteria. However, another serious detergent problem, the phosphate problem (Chap. 19), still remains unsolved.

---

*Cleansing agents also serve to reduce the surface tension at the boundary between oil droplets and water (called *interfacial tension*), making it easier to break down the greasy dirt to particles of colloidal size. It also reduces the surface tension between the greasy dirt and the cloth, making it easier to displace the dirt from the cloth.

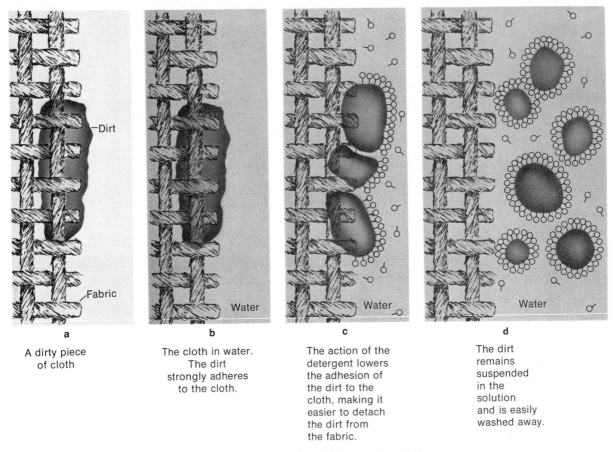

a	b	c	d
A dirty piece of cloth	The cloth in water. The dirt strongly adheres to the cloth.	The action of the detergent lowers the adhesion of the dirt to the cloth, making it easier to detach the dirt from the fabric.	The dirt remains suspended in the solution and is easily washed away.

FIGURE 10.9 Illustrating the action of a detergent in removing dirt from a piece of cloth.

Bile salts, produced in the liver, serve to emulsify fats. Breaking up large fat particles into smaller ones increases the surface area available to enzymes (Chap. 23) responsible for the proper metabolism of fats.

Liquid membranes are a recently discovered class of artificial membranes. They consist of an emulsion suspended in a liquid that does not destroy the emulsion. If a substance is soluble in the emulsion, it readily passes through the membrane. If the substance is not soluble in the emulsion, it does not pass through the membrane. Rather, it is trapped in it. Such membranes may therefore find applications in the purification and separation of mixtures. Many poisons, for example, can be trapped in them for safe elimination from the body.

Stability of Colloids   The particles of a colloid generally carry a charge that repels similarly charged particles, thus preventing the build-up of a particle large enough to settle out rapidly. The origin of the charge is not a settled question. However, it is known that sols require the presence of a small but definite amount of an electrolyte for their preparation. It is therefore concluded that a particle forms which behaves as a strong electrolyte. For example, in the presence of potassium chloride, gold forms particles whose composition may be $K_x^+[Au_y(AuCl^-)]_x$, which completely dissociates as follows:

$$K_x^+[Au_y(AuCl^-)]_x \longrightarrow xAu_y(AuCl^-) \ colloidal \ particle + xK^+$$

Iron(III) oxide forms positively charged colloidal particles in dilute hydrochloric acid solution.

Other colloidal particles, particularly the gels and protein solutions, are stabilized by hydration in addition to an electric charge. A protein particle literally covers itself with a water shield that prevents mutual contact and growth (coagulation). In acid solutions, protein molecules are positively charged

$$R{<}^{COOH}_{NH_2(aq)} + H^+(aq) + Cl^-(aq) \longrightarrow R{<}^{COOH}_{NH_3^+(colloidal)} + Cl^-(aq)$$

| protein | acid | positively charged particle |

but they are negatively charged in a less acidic solution:

$$R{<}^{COOH}_{NH_2(aq)} + Na^+(aq) + OH^-(aq) \longrightarrow R{<}^{COO^-}_{NH_2(colloidal)} + H_2O + Na^+(aq)$$

| protein | hydroxide | negatively charged particle |

The electrical charge on colloidal particles may be demonstrated by **electrophoresis,** the migration of colloidal particles in an electric field. The gold particles in a gold sol migrate toward the positive electrode and move away from the negative electrode. They are, therefore, negatively charged. Accurate measurements of the rate of migration can be made. Thus, for example, protein molecules in blood serum can be separated and identified. Linus Pauling definitely demonstrated that hemoglobin prepared from patients with sickle cell anemia (page 321) migrates at a distinctly lower rate than does hemoglobin from normal individuals.

The stability of an aerosol is determined mainly by the particle size; the smaller the particle, the slower the settling rate (determined in still air), and the greater the stability. In the Cottrell process used for smoke pollution control, the aerosol particles passed between oppositely charged electrodes in a smokestack acquire charges; when passed through a second electric field, these charged particles are deposited on the oppositely charged electrodes. Relatively clean gas is thus discharged into the atmosphere.

A 0.1 mm sand particle (10^5 nm) settles in still air at a rate of about 130 cm/s, while a colloidal particle (10 nm) settles at a rate of 1.3 × 10^{-6} cm/s.

PROBLEMS

18 Vocabulary Define and illustrate: (a) solute, (b) solvent, (c) solubility, (d) saturated solution, (e) unsaturated solution, (f) supersaturated solution, (g) hydration, (h) hydrate, (i) miscibility of liquids, (j) molarity, (k) molality, (l) mole fraction, (m) strong electrolyte, (n) weak electrolyte, (o) electrolyte and nonelectrolyte, (p) vapor pressure depression, (q) freezing point depression, (r) osmosis, (s) osmotic pressure, (t) colloid, (u) aerosol, (v) emulsion, (w) Tyndall effect.

19 Solution How would you experimentally determine whether a given solution is saturated, unsaturated, or supersaturated?

20 Solubility (a) Ethyl alcohol, C_2H_5OH, is miscible with water while carbon tetrachloride, CCl_4, is not. Explain. (b) Butanol, C_4H_9OH, polar, participates in hydrogen bonding, but butane, C_4H_{10}, nonpolar, does not. Which one is more soluble in (i) water, (ii) gasoline? (c) In which solvent is cesium chloride,

Cs^+Cl^-, likely to be (i) most soluble, (ii) least soluble: liquid SO_2 (slightly polar); liquid hydrogen cyanide, HCN (very highly polar), liquid carbon disulfide, CS_2 (nonpolar)? (d) Which solute, C_2H_5F or C_2H_5I, is likely to be more soluble in water? (Consult table of electronegativities, page 255.) (e) Which solvent, water (polar) or carbon tetrachloride (nonpolar), is more likely to dissolve lithium chloride, Li^+Cl^-; bacon fat?

21 (a) Three substances, gasoline, water, and methyl alcohol, CH_3OH, are used in automobiles. Pick the pair that are mutually soluble. Explain. (b) In which liquid is NaCl more likely to dissolve: octane, a component of gasoline, or ethyl alcohol, C_2H_5OH? (c) What is the nature of the force (i) between H_2O and CH_3OH, (ii) between H_2O and CsF?

22 (a) Methane, CH_4, does not dissolve in H_2O, while methyl alcohol, CH_3OH, does. Explain. (b) Many organic molecules do not dissolve in water, but the widely used antifreeze, ethylene glycol, $(CH_2OH)_2$, dissolves in water. Explain.

23 Calcium hydroxide, $Ca(OH)_2$, solution is used for the treatment of *oxalism,* poisoning by oxalic acid, $H_2C_2O_4$. The solubility at room temperature is 0.190 g $Ca(OH)_2$ per 100 ml solution. Express the solubility in mole/liter.

24 **Mass percent** Express the mass percent of calcium hydroxide, $Ca(OH)_2$, in a solution weighing 248 g and containing 17.0 g of $Ca(OH)_2$.

25 How many grams of sodium carbonate, Na_2CO_3, are in 143.0 g of a 12.0 % solution of sodium carbonate by mass?

26 What mass of water would you use to prepare a 14.0 % solution of sodium nitrite, $NaNO_2$, by mass, containing 34.0 g $NaNO_2$?

27 A chemist needs 10.0 g of NaOH. A stock solution, 7.85 % NaOH by mass, is available. How many grams of the solution should be used?

28 How many grams and moles of NaOH are in 50.0 ml of NaOH solution, density 1.53 g/ml, that contains 50.0 % NaOH by mass?

29 (a) How many grams of water are required to dissolve 30.0 g of Na_2CO_3 to make a 12.0 % solution of Na_2CO_3 by mass? (b) How many grams of Na_2CO_3 are in 150 g of a 5.00 % solution of Na_2CO_3 by mass?

30 A solution of hydrochloric acid, density 1.15 g/ml, contains 29.13 % HCl by mass. Calculate the mass of HCl in 50.0 ml of the solution. (b) Calculate the molarity of HCl in the solution.

31 **Mole fraction** Intravenous transfusions of isotonic solutions (see the footnote on page 342) are used to replenish body fluids. These solutions contain 0.90 g NaCl per 100 g H_2O. What is (a) the mass percent and (b) mole fraction of NaCl in an isotonic solution?

32 Intravenous glucose solutions contain 5.1 g of glucose per 100 g H_2O. What are the mass percent and mole fraction of glucose, $C_6H_{12}O_6$, in this solution?

33 Approximately 41 g of urea, NH_2CONH_2, per liter of urine is excreted as a product of protein metabolism. The density of urine is 1.02 g/ml. What is the mole fraction of urea in urine? (Consider only urea and water.)

34 (a) What is the mole fraction of ethylene glycol, $(CH_2OH)_2$, in a solution containing 45.0 g of ethylene glycol and 380 g of H_2O? (b) What is the molality of this solution?

35 (a) A solution contains 600 g of water and 8.40 g of glycerine, $C_3H_8O_3$. Calculate the mole fraction of (i) water and (ii) glycerine. (b) What is the mole fraction of (i) H_2O and (ii) glycerine in an 8.00 % solution by mass of glycerine in water?

36 **Molality** Calculate the molality of the solution in Problem 35(a).

37 Two tablespoons (approximately 12.5 g) of sodium bicarbonate, $NaHCO_3$, in a glass of water (200 g H_2O) are often taken as an antacid for an upset stomach. (a) What is the molality of this solution? (b) What is the molarity of this solution if the volume of the solution is 200 ml?

38 **Molarity** Calculate the mass of solute in each given solution: (a) 200 ml of 0.300 M potassium chromate, K_2CrO_4; (b) 3.25 ℓ of 0.110 M sodium nitrate, $NaNO_3$, and (c) 350 ml of 0.100 M phosphoric acid, H_3PO_4.

39 Find the number of grams of solute needed to prepare 100.0 ml of each of the following 0.125 M solutions: (a) mercury(II) chloride, $HgCl_2$ (colorless), used as a skin disinfectant; (b) potassium permanganate, $KMnO_4$ (pink), used as an internal and external disinfectant; (c) silver nitrate, $AgNO_3$ (colorless), used as an antiseptic for the prevention of gonorrheal eye infections in babies.

40 A solution of $MgCl_2$, density 1.05 g/ml, contains 6.00 % $MgCl_2$ by mass. Calculate the molarity of $MgCl_2$ in the solution.

41 (a) Calculate the molarity of H_2SO_4 in a solution containing 147.4 g of H_2SO_4 dissolved in 400 ml of solution. (b) How many grams of sulfuric acid are needed to prepare 4.50 ℓ of 2.15 M H_2SO_4? (c) What is the mass (i) in mg, and (ii) in g of barium hydroxide in 36.4 ml of 0.111 M $Ba(OH)_2$?

42 What is the molarity of a solution consisting of 7.90 g of potassium iodide, KI, in 54.0 ml of solution?

43 Calculate the concentration of copper(II) sulfate prepared by dissolving 4.32 g of $CuSO_4$ in 150 ml of solution.

44 Calculate the number of moles of lithium chloride in 2.50 ℓ of 0.805 M LiCl.

45 How would you prepare 500 ml of a 0.250 M NaOH solution?

46 How would you prepare 150 ml of a 0.0400 M NaBr solution?

47 What is the mass (a) in mg and (b) in g of KI in 54.2 ml of 0.25 M KI?

48 A concentrated sulfuric acid solution contains 62.0 % H_2SO_4 by mass. The density of the solution is 1.52 g/ml. (a) Calculate the mass of H_2SO_4 in 200 ml of the acid. (b) Calculate the molarity of H_2SO_4.

49 (a) What is the mass of HCl in 350 ml of commercial hydrochloric acid (36.0 % HCl by mass), with a density of 1.18 g/ml? (b) Calculate the molarity of HCl.

50 What is (a) the mass and (b) the molarity of NH_3 in 225 ml of concentrated ammonia (28.0 % by mass), with a density of 0.900 g/ml?

51 Calculate the number of (a) mmol, (b) mg, and (c) g of magnesium bromide in 25.6 ml of a 0.0320 M $MgBr_2$ solution.

52 (a) An automobile battery contains 2.02 g of H_2SO_4 in 10.0 ml of solution. Calculate the molarity of H_2SO_4. (b) The solution in a fully charged battery contains 35 % H_2SO_4, density 1.26 g/ml. Calculate the molarity of H_2SO_4.

53 The molarity of household *Clorox* solution is about 0.55 M NaOCl. How many grams of NaOCl are needed to prepare 2.00 ℓ of the solution?

54 Dilution What is the final molarity of 50.0 ml of a 0.500 M H_2SO_4 solution when it is diluted to 450 ml?

55 250 ml of a 3.20 M solution of hydrochloric acid is diluted to 900 ml. What is the molarity of the diluted solution?

56 Freezing point (a) Benzene freezes at 5.5 °C. Its freezing point depression constant is 5.12 °C kg/mole. Calculate the freezing point depression of a solution containing 3.74 g of naphthalene, $C_{10}H_8$, in 350 g of benzene. (b) A 9.00 g sample of *p*-dichlorobenzene, moth repellant, $C_6H_4Cl_2$, is added to 60.0 g of benzene. What is (i) the freezing point depression, and (ii) the freezing point of this solution?

57 Calculate the molecular weight of the sugar arabinose if a solution made by dissolving 22.5 g of the sugar in 250 g of water freezes at −1.13 °C.

58 (a) What is the molality of a solution made by dissolving 45.0 g of glucose, $C_6H_{12}O_6$, in 500 g of water? (b) Calculate the freezing point of the solution.

59 The empirical formula of an antifreeze is CH_3O. In 100 g of benzene (freezing point depression constant 5.12 °C kg/mole), 0.0310 g of this compound lowers the freezing point 0.0256 °C. Calculate the molecular formula of the antifreeze.

60 Molecular weight Because of its exceptionally large freezing point depression constant, 40.0 °C kg/mole, camphor ($C_{10}H_{16}O$, m.p. 179.8 °C) is used in micromethods for determining molecular weights. It is found that 8.906 mg of morphine dissolved in 10.00 g of camphor lowers the freezing point 0.125 °C. Find the molecular weight of morphine.

61 3.572 g of a nonelectrolyte dissolved in 250.0 g of benzene lowers the freezing point 0.246 °C. Calculate the molecular weight of the solute. Freezing point depression constant is 5.12 °C kg/mole.

62 Osmosis A semipermeable membrane is between (a) pure water and 0.01 M NaCl(*aq*), (b) 0.02 M NaCl(*aq*) and 0.05 M NaCl(*aq*). In each case, predict the direction of the flow of water across the membrane.

63 Colloid A solution appears clear and colorless to the naked eye. Describe the experiment you would perform to determine whether the solution contains colloidal particles.

64 Heat of solution From the following data, calculate the heat of solution. Is the process of solution exothermic or endothermic?

$$Mg^{2+}(g) + 2F^-(g) \longrightarrow Mg^{2+}(aq) + 2F^-(aq)$$
$$\Delta H = -698.33 \text{ kcal}$$

$$MgF_2(c) \longrightarrow Mg^{2+}(g) + 2F^-(g)$$
$$\Delta H = +694.1 \text{ kcal}$$

65 Entropy A solution has a higher entropy (greater disorder) than the separate solute and solvent. Given pure liquid water, an aqueous sugar solution, and water vapor, for which liquid state will the water vapor have a preference, the pure water or the solution? Explain.

66 Library Read one of the following:

(a) "Order from Chaos, Regular Solutions," Joel Hildebrand, *Science,* volume 150, 22 October 1965, pages 441–450.
(b) "Sickle Cell Anemia: Unwise Blood," *The Sciences,* December 1971, pages 6–10.

ADDITIONAL PROBLEMS

67 A magnesium citrate solution, $MgC_5H_6O_7$, used as a mild cathartic, contains 2.00 % $MgC_5H_6O_7$ and 98.0 % water, density 1.01 g/ml. Calculate (a) the mole fraction, (b) the molality, and (c) the molarity of $MgC_5H_6O_7$.

68 Sodium thiosulfate is used in photography (page 667) and to remove excess chlorine in many industrial processes. A stock solution is prepared by dissolving 350 g of the hydrate, $Na_2S_2O_3(H_2O)_5$ ("hypo"), in 2.00 ℓ of solution. Find the molarity of $Na_2S_2O_3$.

69 How many moles and what weight of silver nitrate, $AgNO_3$, must be taken to prepare 350 ml of a solution containing 0.0400 mole of Ag^+ per liter? $AgNO_3$ is a strong electrolyte.

70 What volume of 0.00100 M lead(II) nitrate, $Pb(NO_3)_2$, solution could be made from 10.00 g lead(II) nitrate?

71 Find the number of liters (STP) of HCl that must be distilled into water to prepare 600 ml of 0.155 M hydrochloric acid solution.

72 What is the mole fraction of acetic acid, CH_3COOH, in vinegar? Vinegar is approximately a 5 % solution of acetic acid in water.

73 Calculate the number of moles of Ca^{2+} in 150 ml of a 0.40 M $CaCl_2$ (a strong electrolyte) solution.

74 Aluminum sulfate, $Al_2(SO_4)_3$, is used as an astringent (shrinks tissues). A stock solution, 26.0 % by mass, has a density of 1.31 g/ml. Find the volume of stock solution that you would dilute to prepare 200 ml of 0.200 M $Al_2(SO_4)_3$ solution.

75 On the basis of 1.00 g each of NaCl, $CaCl_2$, and CH_3OH, which one should be most efficient in melting ice on streets? Show your calculations. NaCl and $CaCl_2$ are strong electrolytes.

76 It is necessary to prepare 125 ml of a 23.1 % solution of nitric acid, HNO_3, density 1.13 g/ml. The stock solution available is 32.0 % HNO_3, density 1.16 g/ml. What volume of the stock solution should you use?

77 Lithium chloride, LiCl, is a strong electrolyte.

(a) Find the number of moles of ions in aqueous solution per mole LiCl. (b) The molality of a LiCl(*aq*) solution is 0.0109 mole/kg. Calculate its freezing point.

78 The flavor of *Provolone* cheese may be imitated by the following mixture by mass: 50 % butyric acid, C_3H_7COOH; 30 % hexanoic acid, $C_5H_{11}COOH$; 10 % octanoic acid, $C_7H_{15}COOH$; and 10 % decanoic acid, $C_9H_{19}COOH$. Find the mole fraction of each acid in the mixture.

79 How would you prepare 350 ml of a 0.250 M KOH solution from a 18.6 % KOH solution, density 1.162 g/ml?

80 How would you prepare 350 ml of 0.25 M NH_3 from 15 M NH_3?

81 If you are given 18 M H_2SO_4 in your laboratory, how would you prepare 800 ml of a 0.40 M H_2SO_4 solution?

82 The volume fraction of a liquid in a liquid solution is the volume of the pure liquid divided by the volume of the solution. The *proof number** of an ethyl alcohol (pages 373, 697) aqueous solution is twice the volume percent (volume fraction × 100) of ethyl alcohol in it. The volume of pure ethyl alcohol in a liter of gin is 400 ml. Calculate the (a) volume fraction, (b) volume percent, and (c) proof number.

83 The volume of pure ethyl alcohol obtainable from a liter of an "86 proof" (Problem 82) Scotch whisky is 430 ml. The density of pure alcohol is 0.80 g/ml. Find the concentration of ethyl alcohol, C_2H_5OH, in mole/liter in this Scotch.

84 Assume that you have 12 kg of water in your automobile radiator. What volume in liters of antifreeze, ethylene glycol, $C_2H_6O_2$, should you use to protect it from freezing at −20 °F? The density of ethylene glycol is 1.11 g/ml.

85 In hydration reactions (page 326), the heat evolved is mainly determined by the *charge density* on the ion. Charge density = ionic charge/ionic radius. Calculate the charge densities for Na^+, Cs^+, Mg^{2+}, and Al^{3+} from the data on pages 235–236 to predict the ions with the largest and smallest heat of hydration. Experimental values in kcal/mole of ion for the

---

*The term *proof* is derived from the early British test in which whiskey and gun powder were mixed and ignited. If the mixture burned, it was "above proof."

reaction, ion(g) $\longrightarrow$ ion(aq), are Na$^+$ (203), Cs$^+$ (167), Mg^{2+} (672), Al^{3+} (1438). Are your predictions in agreement with experiment? Should H$^+$ have a larger or smaller heat of hydration compared to Na$^+$? Explain.

86 How many grams of H$_2$ form when 200 ml of 0.200 M HCl reacts with Mg?

$$Mg + 2HCl \longrightarrow MgCl_2 + H_2$$

87 What volume of H$_2$ at STP forms when 100 ml of 0.100 M H$_2$SO$_4$ reacts with Al?

$$2Al(c) + 3H_2SO_4(l) \longrightarrow 3H_2(g) + Al_2(SO_4)_3(c)$$

88 What volume of 0.100 M HCl must react with Zn to provide 10.0 ℓ of H$_2$ at STP?

$$Zn + 2HCl \longrightarrow ZnCl_2 + H_2$$

ANSWERS

1 (a) 35.7 g per 100 g H$_2$O
  (b) less than 35.7 g per 100 g H$_2$O
  (c) more than 35.7 g per 100 g H$_2$O
2 water and methyl alcohol—completely; water and chloroform—partially
3 water—CH$_3$OH
  gasoline—CH$_4$, CH$_3$SH
4 (a) ii; (b) (i)
5 LiOH, CaCl$_2$
6 13.0 %
7 (a) 4.2 g H$_2$O$_2$; (b) 1338 g H$_2$O
8 437 g H$_3$PO$_4$
9 0.00524
10 0.0720 mole/kg
11 0.00660 M
12 148 g
13 11.6 M
14 1.29 × 10^3 mg; 1.29 g
15 0.0741 M
16 (a) 2.12 °C; (b) −2.12 °C
17 108 g/mole
20 (b) butanol in water, butane in gasoline
  (c) (i) HCN most soluble;
    (ii) CS$_2$ least soluble
  (d) C$_2$H$_5$F
  (e) LiCl, water; bacon fat, CCl$_4$
21 (a) water and methyl alcohol
  (b) ethyl alcohol
  (c) (i) hydrogen bonding;
    (ii) polar or dipole
23 0.0257 M
24 6.85 %
25 17.2 g
26 209 g water
27 127 g
28 38.3 g NaOH, 0.956 mole
29 (a) 220.0 g H$_2$O
  (b) 7.50 g Na$_2$CO$_3$
30 (a) 16.7 g HCl
  (b) 9.15 M
31 0.89 % NaCl; 0.0027
32 4.9% glucose; 0.0051

33 0.012
34 (a) 0.0333
  (b) 1.91 mole/kg
35 (a) (i) 0.997 mole fraction of water
    (ii) 0.00273 mole fraction of glycerine
  (b) (i) 0.983 mole fraction H$_2$O
    (ii) 0.0167 mole fraction C$_3$H$_8$O$_3$
36 0.152 mole/kg
37 (a) 0.745 mole/kg
  (b) 0.745 mole/liter
38 (a) 11.6 g K$_2$CrO$_4$
  (b) 30.4 g NaNO$_3$
  (c) 3.43 g H$_3$PO$_4$
39 (a) 3.40 g HgCl$_2$
  (b) 1.98 g KMnO$_4$
  (c) 2.13 g AgNO$_3$
40 0.661 M
41 (a) 3.76 M
  (b) 949 g H$_2$SO$_4$
  (c) (i) 0.691 g; (ii) 691 mg Ba(OH)$_2$
42 0.881 mole/liter
43 0.180 M
44 2.01 moles
45 Add water to 5.00 g NaOH to make 500 ml solution
46 Add water to 0.618 g NaBr to make 150 ml solution
47 (a) 2.2 × 10^3 mg, (b) 2.2 g KI
48 (a) 188 g H$_2$SO$_4$; (b) 9.58 mole/ℓ
49 (a) 149 g HCl; (b) 11.7 mole/ℓ
50 (a) 56.8 g NH$_3$; (b) 14.8 mole/ℓ
51 (a) 0.82 mmol MgBr$_2$
  (b) 151 mg MgBr$_2$
  (c) 0.151 g MgBr$_2$
52 (a) 2.06 mole/ℓ
  (b) 4.5 mole/ℓ
53 82 g
54 0.0556 mmol/ml
55 0.889 M
56 (a) 0.427 °C
  (b) (i) 5.22 °C; (ii) 0.3 °C
57 148 g/mole
58 (a) 0.500 mole/kg
  (b) −0.93 °C

59 $C_2H_6O_2$
60 285 g/mole
61 298 g/mole
62 (a) pure water to solution
   (b) 0.02 M to 0.05 M
64 −4.2 kcal, exothermic
65 the solution
67 (a) 0.00182
   (b) 0.101 mole/kg
   (c) 0.100 M
68 0.705 mole/ℓ
69 0.0140 mole $AgNO_3$, 2.38 g $AgNO_3$
70 30.2 ℓ
71 2.08 ℓ (STP)
72 0.0155
73 0.060 mole Ca^{2+}
74 40.2 ml
75 NaCl
76 87.9 ml
77 (a) 2 moles
   (b) −0.0406 °C

78 0.595, 0.271, 0.0727, 0.0609
79 Dilute 22.7 ml of the 18.6 % solution
   to 350 ml with stirring
80 Dilute 5.8 ml of 15 M NH_3 solution
   to 350 ml
81 Dilute 18 ml of 18 M H_2SO_4 solution
   to 800 ml
82 (a) 0.400
   (b) 40.0 %
   (c) 80.0 proof
83 7.48 mole/ℓ
84 11 ℓ $C_2H_6O_2$
85 (Largest) $Al^{3+} > Mg^{2+} > Na^+ > Cs^+$
   Prediction correct.
   Same charge but proton is smaller than
   Na^+; therefore, H^+ should have the
   larger heat of hydration.
86 0.0404 g
87 0.224 ℓ (STP)
88 8.93 ℓ

GLOSSARY

aerosol Consists of colloidal particles, liquid or solid, dispersed in a gas.

alloys Solutions in which solids are dissolved in solids, such as yellow gold, an alloy of copper and gold.

amalgam A solution containing liquid mercury and another metal.

boiling point elevation The amount by which the boiling point of a solvent is increased by the addition of a solute. The increase is due to the lowering of the vapor pressure of the solvent by the solute, and is related to the molality of the solution.

Brownian movement The rapid random motion of colloidal particles, resulting from bombardment by high-speed molecules of the gas or liquid in which the particles are suspended.

colloid (colloidal state) A mixture containing particles intermediate in size between those in solutions and those in suspensions.

colloidal particles Particles larger than atoms, molecules, or ions but not large enough to separate out as rapidly as particles in a suspension.

electrolytes Compounds that form ions in water. Strong electrolytes, such as NaCl and KBr, exist largely as ions in dilute aqueous solutions. Weak electrolytes, such as CH_3COOH, exist largely as molecules in dilute aqueous solutions.

electrophoresis The migration of colloidal particles in an electric field.

emulsion Consists of a liquid dispersed in a liquid, such as milk, an emulsion of butterfat in water.

freezing point depression The amount by which the freezing point of a solvent is lowered by the addition of a solute. The depression is due to the lowering of the vapor pressure of the solvent by the solute, and is related to the molality of the solution.

freezing point depression constant The number of degrees the freezing point of a solvent is lowered by one mole of solute particles in 1 kg of the solvent is constant for a given solvent. For water, it is 1.86 °C; the freezing point depression constant for water is then said to be 1.86 °C kg/mole.

hydrate A crystalline solid containing combined water in a constant composition, such as $CuSO_4(H_2O)_5$ and $Na_2SO_4(H_2O)_{10}$.

ideal solution A solution whose vapor pressures are in agreement with Raoult's law at all possible mole fractions. See **Raoult's law**.

mass percent of solute The mass in grams of solute present in 100 g of solution.

miscible liquids Liquids that completely dissolve in one another in all proportions.

molality The number of moles of solute in 1 kg of solvent; units are mole/kg.

molarity The number of moles of solute in 1 liter of solution; units are mole/liter.

mole fraction The fraction formed by dividing the number of moles of a substance present in a solution by the total number of moles of all substances in the solution.

nonelectrolytes Compounds, such as methane, CH_4, and sucrose, $C_{12}H_{22}O_{11}$, that do not form ions in water.

osmosis The transfer of solvent molecules through a semipermeable membrane so as to equalize the concentrations of the solutions on both sides of the membrane. The solvent flow is always from the solution of lower concentration to the solution of higher concentration.

osmotic pressure The excess pressure which must be applied to the solution of higher concentration to prevent osmosis. See **osmosis.**

polar solvent A solvent composed of polar molecules.

Raoult's law The decrease in the vapor pressure of a solvent is proportional to the mole fraction of solute dissolved in it. See **ideal solution.**

saturated solution A solution in which an equilibrium exists between excess undissolved solute and its solution.

semipermeable membrane A membrane that permits the passage of solvent molecules only.

sol A colloid consisting of a solid dispersed in a liquid. Milk of magnesia, magnesium hydroxide dispersed in water, is a typical sol.

solubility The equilibrium concentration of solute in a saturated solution.

solute The substance dissolved in a solution, usually present in a smaller amount than the solvent. See **solvent.**

solution A homogeneous mixture of ions, atoms, or molecules of two or more different substances.

solvent The substance in which the solute dissolves forming a solution, usually present in a greater amount than the solute. See **solute.**

supersaturated solution A solution containing more solute than the saturated solution at the same temperature. See **saturated solution.**

suspension A heterogeneous mixture containing particles that are much larger than individual molecules and rapidly separate out.

Tyndall effect The scattering of light by colloidal particles, making a beam of light visible.

unsaturated solution A solution containing less solute than the saturated solution at the same temperature. See **saturated solution.**

IONIC SOLUTIONS,   11
OXIDATION AND
REDUCTION

An introduction to solution chemistry and its importance was presented in Chapter 10. But solution chemistry also involves an understanding of the properties of ions in solutions and how solutions of ions are related to electricity. We shall also be concerned in this chapter with the apparent exchange of electrons between reactants and how we keep track of these electrons in balancing such chemical equations.

EXPERIMENTAL DIFFERENCE BETWEEN
ELECTROLYTES AND NONELECTROLYTES_____ 11.1

Compounds which form ions while dissolving in water are called **electrolytes.** Compounds which do not form ions while dissolving in water are called *nonelectrolytes.* Ionic solids when melted also form liquids composed of ions. The presence of these ions is easily detected with an apparatus consisting of two electrodes, an electric light bulb, and a source of electricity. When the electrodes are placed in pure water, as shown in Fig. 11.1(a), the bulb does not light; water is practically a nonconductor of electricity. However, when the two electrodes are placed in 0.10 M HCl(*aq*) or 0.10 M NaCl(*aq*), the bulb glows brightly (Fig. 11.1(b)), showing that the solutions are good conductors of electricity. They are typical strong electrolytes. When the electrodes are placed in 0.10 M acetic acid, $CH_3COOH(aq)$, the bulb glows dimly (Fig. 11.1(c)), showing that this solution is a poor conductor of electricity. Acetic acid is a typical weak electrolyte. When the electrodes are placed in 0.10 M sugar or ethyl alcohol, $C_2H_5OH(aq)$, solution, the bulb does not light (Fig. 11.1(d)), showing that these solutions are nonconductors of electricity. Sugar and ethyl alcohol are typical nonelectrolytes.

Electrodes are metallic or graphite rods through which an electric current enters and leaves a liquid.

PROBLEM 1   **Experiments (Fig. 11.1) yield the following results with aqueous solutions of the substances given: (a) KCl, bulb glows brightly; (b) $HgCl_2$, bulb glows dimly; (c) $AlCl_3$, bulb glows brightly; (d) NH_3, bulb glows dimly; (e) sucrose, $C_{12}H_{22}O_{11}$, bulb does not light. Classify these substances (i) as electrolytes and nonelectrolytes, (ii) as strong or weak electrolytes.**

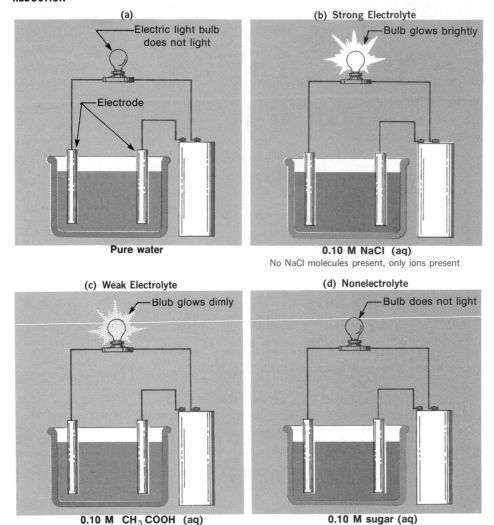

(a)

Electric light bulb does not light

Electrode

Pure water

(b) Strong Electrolyte

Bulb glows brightly

0.10 M NaCl (aq)
No NaCl molecules present, only ions present

(c) Weak Electrolyte

Blub glows dimly

0.10 M CH_3COOH (aq)
Mostly molecules present, with some ions

(d) Nonelectrolyte

Bulb does not light

0.10 M sugar (aq)
Only molecules present

FIGURE 11.1 Representation of an experiment* to determine the presence of ions in solution.

*Electrical conductivities of salt solutions were first studied by Henry Cavendish (1777). Accurate measurements were made by Friedrich Kohlrausch in 1874.

Ionic Electrolytic Conduction   The electrical conductivity of solutions of electrolytes was first successfully explained by Svante Arrhenius in 1887.* In a metal, the electric current is a flow of electrons (page 118). However, when a source of

*When Arrhenius proposed his theory of electrolytic dissociation (ionization) in his formal discussion for his Ph.D. degree, he created an intellectual storm that brewed for several years. When Wilhelm Ostwald, recognized as a founding father of theoretical chemistry, received a copy of the discussion, he wrote "that he got on the same day this discussion, a toothache, and a nice daughter, and that was too much for one day. The poorest was the discussion, for the others developed quite normally."

However, largely through the support of Ostwald, Raoult (page 337), and Walther Nernst (page 470), Arrhenius's theory became generally accepted. Most scientists objected to the idea that ions—*oppositely* charged particles—remain apart and free to move. The forces between oppositely charged ions, they reasoned, should attract and hold the ions together. However, this attractive force between ions is overcome by the *attraction of the solvent molecules* for each of the oppositely charged ions. If ions are not hydrated (solvated) they cannot exist apart, and the solution will not conduct electricity. Thus, in water, H^+ and Cl^- ions are hydrated, but benzene has no attraction for these ions. Hence, in benzene HCl is a nonelectrolyte.

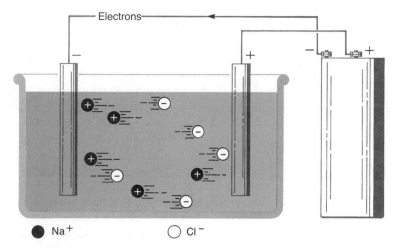

FIGURE 11.2 The motion of ions through a solution is an electric current and accounts for ionic (electrolytic) conduction of solutions.

● Na$^+$ ○ Cl$^-$

electricity is applied to a solution containing ions, it is the migration—the movement—of the ions that constitutes the electric current in the solution. The positive ions move toward the electrode with a negative charge, and the negative ions move toward the electrode with a positive charge. The number of positive charges moving in one direction is the same as the number of negative charges moving in the opposite direction. But a metal requires one, and only one, charged particle, the negative electron, for conductance. A solution or a molten ionic compound, however, requires the presence of both negative and positive ions (Fig. 11.2). The greater the number of ions present per liter of solution and the greater the speed with which they move, the greater is the electrical conductivity of the solution.

PROBLEM 2   **Increasing the temperature of a solution of an electrolyte increases the speed with which the ions move. Should the conductivity decrease, remain the same, or increase as the temperature of the solution is increased?**

This subject is further discussed in Chapter 15.

IONIC EQUATIONS_____11.2

The close relationship between electricity and chemistry is shown by the existence of atoms, molecules, and ions. Ions exist not only in the gas phase (Chap. 4) and in ionic solids (Chap. 8), but also in solutions. Consequently, it is not uncommon for chemists to describe chemical reactions between electrolytes in terms of ions. For example, the reaction between silver nitrate and sodium chloride

$$AgNO_3(aq) + NaCl(aq) \longrightarrow AgCl(c) + NaNO_3(aq)$$

may be written as

$$Ag^+(aq) + \cancel{NO_3^-}(aq) + \cancel{Na^+}(aq) + Cl^-(aq) \longrightarrow AgCl(c) + \cancel{Na^+}(aq) + \cancel{NO_3^-}(aq)$$

because $AgNO_3(aq)$, $NaCl(aq)$, and $NaNO_3(aq)$ are strong electrolytes. They exist only as ions in (dilute) aqueous solutions. Now, observe that Na^+ and NO_3^- appear on both sides of the equation. This means that Na^+ and NO_3^- ions do not participate in this reaction. They are innocent bystanders. The only reaction is the combination of

Recall footnote on page 327.

357

Ag^+ and Cl^- ions to form insoluble silver chloride. We can therefore rewrite the equation simply as

$$Ag^+(aq) + Cl^-(aq) \longrightarrow AgCl(c) \tag{1}$$

This is known as an **ionic equation.** The advantage of showing the chemical reaction this way is that it emphasizes the fact that the chloride ion, regardless of the soluble chloride it comes from—NaCl, KCl, or $CaCl_2$—pairs off with the silver ion, regardless of the soluble silver salt it comes from—$AgNO_3$ or CH_3COOAg (silver acetate).

On the other hand, carbon tetrachloride is a nonelectrolyte. It does not form chloride ions in aqueous solutions. Therefore, the silver ion does not react with carbon tetrachloride. In fact, the reaction between ions is the basis for a comparatively old-fashioned (but educationally useful) method of detecting ions in aqueous solutions. The formation of a white suspension of insoluble silver chloride ("precipitate") is used to test for the presence of chloride or silver ions in solution.

The reaction between the strong electrolytes iron(III) chloride and sodium hydroxide

$$FeCl_3(aq) + 3NaOH(aq) \longrightarrow Fe(OH)_3(c) + 3NaCl(aq)$$

may be written as

$$Fe^{3+}(aq) + 3OH^-(aq) \longrightarrow Fe(OH)_3(c) \tag{2}$$

However, weak electrolytes, since they exist largely as molecules in solution, are represented by their molecular formulas. Thus, the reaction between acetic acid, a weak electrolyte, and sodium hydroxide

$$CH_3COOH(aq) + NaOH(aq) \longrightarrow CH_3COONa(aq) + H_2O$$

is written as

$$CH_3COOH(aq) + OH^-(aq) \longrightarrow CH_3COO^-(aq) + H_2O \tag{3}$$

When writing such ionic equations it is very important to note that the *electric charges on both sides of the equation must also balance.* Thus, in Equation 1

$$1^+ \text{ charge} + 1^- \text{ charge} = \text{neutral (0)}$$
$$(1^+) + (1^-) = 0$$

while in Equation 2

$$3^+ \text{ charges} + 3^- \text{ charges} = \text{neutral (0)}$$
$$(3^+) + (3^-) = 0$$

and in Equation 3

$$\text{neutral (0)} + 1^- \text{ charge} = 1^- \text{ charge} + \text{neutral (0)}$$
$$0 + (1^-) = (1^-) + 0$$

PROBLEM 3   **Write the ionic equation for the reaction**

$$Pb(NO_3)_2(aq) + 2NaBr(aq) \longrightarrow PbBr_2(c) + 2NaNO_3(aq)$$

Recall (page 327) the generalizations about substances that are strong and weak electrolytes; nitrates and bromides are ionic solids.

TRANSFER OF ELECTRONS _____ 11.3

Many atoms, molecules, and ions in solution participate in reactions in which it appears that a transfer of electrons occurs. Such reactions are classified as oxidation-reduction reactions. A typical example of an oxidation-reduction reaction is

$$Zn(c) + 2HCl(aq) \longrightarrow ZnCl_2(aq) + H_2(g)$$

or

$$Zn(c) + 2H^+(aq) \longrightarrow Zn^{2+}(aq) + H_2(g) \qquad (4)$$

Chemists frequently analyze such reactions as two **half-reactions,** as shown:

$$Zn(c) \longrightarrow Zn^{2+}(aq) \quad (incomplete)$$

and

$$2H^+(aq) \longrightarrow H_2(g) \quad (incomplete)$$

Notice that electrically neutral zinc, $Zn(c)$, loses 2 electrons in changing to Zn^{2+}. It is therefore rewritten as

$$Zn(c) \longrightarrow Zn^{2+}(aq) + 2e^- \quad (half\text{-}reaction\ balanced) \qquad (5)$$

Also notice that H^+ ions gain electrons in changing to $H_2(g)$. It is therefore rewritten as

$$2H^+(aq) + 2e^- \longrightarrow H_2(g) \quad (half\text{-}reaction,\ balanced) \qquad (6)$$

The addition of the half-reactions (5 and 6) yields the overall reaction (4).

Oxidation is defined as the loss of electrons. **Reduction** is defined as a gain of electrons. The substance that gains electrons is reduced and oxidizes another substance; it is therefore called an **oxidizing agent.** The substance that loses electrons is oxidized and reduces another substance; it is therefore called a **reducing agent.** This language is summarized and illustrated as follows:

Oxidation originally referred only to the reaction of oxygen with another substance. Reduction originally referred only to removal of oxygen from a compound, as in the reduction of Fe_2O_3 to Fe. These terms are redefined in terms of oxidation numbers on page 364.

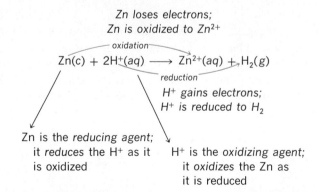

Zn loses electrons;
Zn is oxidized to Zn^{2+}

oxidation

$$Zn(c) + 2H^+(aq) \longrightarrow Zn^{2+}(aq) + H_2(g)$$

reduction

H^+ gains electrons;
H^+ is reduced to H_2

Zn is the *reducing agent;*
it *reduces* the H^+ as it
is oxidized

H^+ is the *oxidizing agent;*
it *oxidizes* the Zn as
it is reduced

PROBLEM 4   For the reaction $Zn(c) + Cl_2(aq) \longrightarrow Zn^{2+}(aq) + 2Cl^-(aq)$ **(a) write the oxidation half-reaction and the reduction half-reaction. (b) Indicate what is oxidized, what is reduced, the oxidizing agent, and the reducing agent.**

In chemical reactions, oxidation is *always* accompanied by reduction; neither oxidation nor reduction can occur without the other. This is another way of saying that electrons are conserved.

11.4 BALANCING OXIDATION-REDUCTION EQUATIONS

We shall illustrate one method of balancing equations for oxidation-reduction reactions in aqueous solution. The method considers only the ionic equations and is therefore known as the *ion-electron method*. For example, let us consider a reaction used to determine the quantity of iron in solution, the reaction of an acid solution of potassium permanganate, $KMnO_4$, with iron(II) sulfate, $FeSO_4$. The ionic equation is

Since these reactions occur in aqueous solution, unless stated otherwise, notation is simplified by not using (aq).

$$Fe^{2+} + MnO_4^- + H^+ \longrightarrow Fe^{3+} + Mn^{2+} + H_2O \quad \textit{(unbalanced, incomplete)} \quad (7)$$

First, *carefully observe* products and reactants to detect which ions, molecules, or atoms are oxidized or reduced. Examination of our unbalanced Equation 7 shows that Fe^{2+} changes to Fe^{3+} and that MnO_4^- changes to Mn^{2+}. We therefore write our two half-reactions as

$$Fe^{2+} \longrightarrow Fe^{3+} \quad \textit{(unbalanced, incomplete)} \quad (8)$$

and

$$MnO_4^- \longrightarrow Mn^{2+} \quad \textit{(unbalanced, incomplete)} \quad (9)$$

Half-reaction 8 appears to be balanced. It is, but only with respect to conservation of matter (atoms). We have the same number of Fe atoms on each side. Nature, however, also demands conservation of charge, or electrical balance (page 120). The sum of electric charges after any change must equal the sum of the charges before the change occurs. In changing from 2^+ to 3^+, one electron must be given up. Since electrons are given up, the change of Fe^{2+} to Fe^{3+} corresponds to oxidation:

$$Fe^{2+} \underset{\textit{atom balance}}{\longrightarrow} Fe^{3+} + 1e^- \quad \textit{(oxidation, balanced)} \quad (10)$$

charge balance $(2^+) = (3^+) + (1^-)$

$$2^+ = 2^+$$

Observe that Half-reaction 9 is neither atomically nor electrically balanced. It is therefore necessary *first* to balance the number of atoms on each side. We have 4 O atoms on the left side and none on the right. In this method, we *assume* that all unbalanced O atoms are balanced by *adding water molecules to one side or the other*. We therefore balance the 4 O atoms on the left side with 4 H_2O molecules on the right

$$\underset{\textit{atom balance}}{\overset{\textit{atom balance}}{MnO_4^- \longrightarrow Mn^{2+} + 4H_2O}} \quad \textit{(unbalanced, incomplete)} \quad (11)$$

But this introduces H atoms, which must also be balanced. In this method, we *assume* all unbalanced H atoms are balanced by *adding H^+ ions to one side or the other*. We therefore balance the 8 H atoms on the right with 8 H^+ ions on the left:

$$\overbrace{MnO_4^- + 8H^+ \longrightarrow Mn^{2+} + 4H_2O}^{atom\ balance} \quad \text{(atomically balanced, electrically unbalanced)} \qquad (12)$$

Secondly, we balance the number of charges on each side. The charge on the right is 2^+. On the left the charge is $(1^-) + (8^+) = 7^+$:

$$MnO_4^- + 8H^+ \longrightarrow Mn^{2+} + 4H_2O$$
$$(1^-) + (8^+)\ does\ not\ equal\ (2^+) + 0$$

Therefore, we add 5 electrons to the left side to balance this half-reaction electronically:

$$\overbrace{MnO_4^- + 8H^+ + 5e^- \longrightarrow Mn^{2+} + 4H_2O}^{atom\ balance} \quad \text{(reduction, balanced)} \qquad (13)$$

$$charge\ balance\ (1^-) + (8^+) + (5^-) = (2^+)$$
$$2^+ = 2^+$$

Finally, the addition of the balanced Half-reactions 10 and 13 gives us the balanced equation for Reaction 7. However, reaction between ions does not charge the solution; it remains electrically neutral. This means that the *number of electrons given up* in the oxidation half-reaction *must equal* the *number of electrons picked up* in the reduction half-reaction.

In this reaction, 1 electron is given up by 1 Fe^{2+} ion while 5 electrons are picked up by 1 MnO_4^- ion. Thus, for each MnO_4^- ion changed to Mn^{2+} ion, 5 Fe^{2+} ions must change to 5 Fe^{3+} ions. We therefore rewrite Half-reaction 10 as 10' and add it to Half-reaction 13:

$$5Fe^{2+} \longrightarrow 5Fe^{3+} + 5e^- \quad \text{(oxidation, balanced)} \qquad (10')$$
$$MnO_4^- + 8H^+ + 5e^- \longrightarrow Mn^{2+} + 4H_2O \quad \text{(reduction, balanced)} \qquad (13)$$

$$\text{atom balance } 5Fe^{2+} + MnO_4^- + 8H^+ \longrightarrow 5Fe^{3+} + Mn^{2+} + 4H_2O \quad \text{(balanced)}$$

$$\text{charge balance } 5 \times (2^+) + (1^-) + (8^+) = 5 \times (3^+) + (2^+) + (0)$$
$$(10^+) + (1^-) + (8^+) = (15^+) + (2^+)$$
$$17^+ = 17^+$$

It is wise to test the final balanced equation by checking the atom balance and the charge balance as shown above.

We shall now review and summarize this method by balancing the equation for the reaction between the dichromate ion, $Cr_2O_7^{2-}$, and sulfur dioxide in acid solution:

$$Cr_2O_7^{2-} + SO_2 + H^+ \longrightarrow Cr^{3+} + HSO_4^- + H_2O$$

Observe the products and reactants to detect what is oxidized or reduced:

$$Cr_2O_7^{2-} \longrightarrow Cr^{3+} \quad \text{(unbalanced)} \qquad (14)$$
$$SO_2 \longrightarrow HSO_4^- \quad \text{(unbalanced)} \qquad (15)$$

Balance Half-reaction 14 atomically, recalling that O atoms are balanced with H_2O molecules, while the H atoms are balanced by supplying H^+ ions:

$$Cr_2O_7{}^{2-} + 14H^+ \longrightarrow 2Cr^{3+} + 7H_2O \quad \textit{(atomically balanced, electrically unbalanced)} \qquad (16)$$

Balance Half-reaction 16 electrically:

$$Cr_2O_7{}^{2-} + 14H^+ \longrightarrow 2Cr^{3+} + 7H_2O$$
$$(2^-) + (14^+) \textit{ does not equal } 2 \times (3^+) + (0)$$
$$12^+ \textit{ does not equal } 6^+$$

Therefore, add 6 electrons to the left side:

$$Cr_2O_7{}^{2-} + 14H^+ + 6e^- \longrightarrow 2Cr^{3+} + 7H_2O \quad \textit{(reduction, balanced)} \qquad (17)$$
$$\text{charge balance } (2^-) + (14^+) + (6^-) = (6^+)$$
$$6^+ = 6^+$$

Balance Half-reaction 15 atomically:

$$SO_2 + 2H_2O \longrightarrow HSO_4{}^- + 3H^+ \quad \textit{(atomically balanced, electrically unbalanced)} \qquad (18)$$

Balance Half-reaction 18 electrically:

$$SO_2 + 2H_2O \longrightarrow HSO_4{}^- + 3H^+$$
$$(0) + (0) \textit{ does not equal } (1^-) + (3^+)$$
$$0 \textit{ does not equal } 2^+$$

Therefore, add 2 electrons to the right side:

$$SO_2 + 2H_2O \longrightarrow HSO_4{}^- + 3H^+ + 2e^- \quad \textit{(oxidation, balanced)} \qquad (19)$$
$$\text{charge balance } (0) + (0) = (1^-) + (3^+) + (2^-)$$
$$0 = 0$$

Make the number of electrons given up in the oxidation (19) *equal the number of electrons picked up* in the reduction (17) by multiplying Half-reaction 19 by 3:

$$3SO_2 + 6H_2O \longrightarrow 3HSO_4{}^- + 9H^+ + 6e^- \quad \textit{(oxidation, balanced)} \qquad (19')$$

Add balanced Half-reactions 17 and 19' to obtain the balanced equation for the reaction:

$$Cr_2O_7{}^{2-} + 14H^+ + \cancel{6e^-} \longrightarrow 2Cr^{3+} + 7H_2O \quad \textit{(reduction, balanced)} \qquad (17)$$
$$\underline{3SO_2 + 6H_2O \longrightarrow 3HSO_4{}^- + 9H^+ + \cancel{6e^-} \quad \textit{(oxidation, balanced)} \qquad (19')}$$
$$Cr_2O_7{}^{2-} + 14H^+ + 3SO_2 + 6H_2O \longrightarrow 2Cr^{3+} + 3HSO_4{}^- + 7H_2O + 9H^+ \quad \textit{(balanced)}$$

In this reaction,* 6 moles of H_2O are consumed but 7 moles of H_2O are produced, leaving 1 mole of H_2O on the right side. Also, 14 moles of H^+ are consumed while 9 moles of H^+ are produced, leaving 5 moles of H^+ on the left side:

$$Cr_2O_7^{2-} + 5H^+ + 3SO_2 \longrightarrow 2Cr^{3+} + 3HSO_4^- + H_2O \ (balanced) \qquad (20)$$

$$charge \ balance \ (2^-) + (5^+) + 0 = 2 \times (3^+) + 3 \times (1^-) + 0$$
$$(2^-) + (5^+) = (6^+) + (3^-)$$
$$3^+ = 3^+$$

Check the balanced equation for atom and charge balances as shown.

PROBLEM 5 **Balance each of the following equations (first balance the half-reactions):**
(a) $Fe^{3+} + Sn^{2+} \longrightarrow Fe^{2+} + Sn^{4+}$; (b) in acid solution: $ClO_3^- + C_2O_4^{2-} + H^+ \longrightarrow Cl^- + CO_2 + H_2O$.

In some reactions, the number of electrons given up and the number of electrons picked up may consist of odd and even numbers. Typical is the oxidation of metals by nitric acid:

$$Zn \longrightarrow Zn^{2+} + 2e^- \quad (oxidation, \ balanced) \qquad (21)$$
$$NO_3^- + 4H^+ + 3e^- \longrightarrow NO + 2H_2O \quad (reduction, \ balanced) \qquad (22)$$

The simplest way to equalize the number of electrons lost and gained is to multiply Half-reaction 21 by 3, and Half-reaction 22 by 2 before the addition:

$$3Zn \longrightarrow 3Zn^{2+} + \cancel{6e^-} \quad (oxidation, \ balanced)$$
$$\underline{2NO_3^- + 8H^+ + \cancel{6e^-} \longrightarrow 2NO + 4H_2O \quad (reduction, \ balanced)}$$
$$3Zn + 8H^+ + 2NO_3^- \longrightarrow 3Zn^{2+} + 2NO + 4H_2O \quad (balanced)$$

The scheme used here may also be used for reactions in solutions that are not acidic. They may occur in basic (NaOH) solutions. For example, the equation for the oxidation of sulfite ion by the chromate ion in basic solution in which the yellow chromate ion is reduced to the green chromite ion

$$CrO_4^{2-} + SO_3^{2-} \longrightarrow CrO_2^- + SO_4^{2-}$$

may be balanced in the same way as an acid solution, as shown:

$$CrO_4^{2-} + 4H^+ + 3e^- \longrightarrow CrO_2^- + 2H_2O \quad (reduction, \ balanced)$$
$$SO_3^{2-} + H_2O \longrightarrow SO_4^{2-} + 2H^+ + 2e^- \quad (oxidation, \ balanced)$$

Equalize the number of electrons lost and gained

$$2CrO_4^{2-} + 8H^+ + 6e^- \longrightarrow 2CrO_2^- + 4H_2O \quad (reduction, \ balanced)$$
$$3SO_3^{2-} + 3H_2O \longrightarrow 3SO_4^{2-} + 6H^+ + 6e^- \quad (oxidation, \ balanced)$$

---

*Like all other methods, the ion-electron method does not tell us how the oxidation-reduction reaction actually takes place, the subject of Chap. 16. It does, however, give correctly balanced equations for the overall reaction.

and add

$$2CrO_4{}^{2-} + 8H^+ + 3SO_3{}^{2-} + 3H_2O \longrightarrow$$
$$2CrO_2{}^- + 4H_2O + 3SO_4{}^{2-} + 6H^+ \quad (balanced)$$

In this reaction, 3 moles of H_2O are consumed while 4 moles of H_2O are produced, leaving 1 mole of H_2O on the right side. Also, the number of moles of H^+ consumed (8) and produced (6) leaves 2 moles of H^+ on the left side:

$$2CrO_4{}^{2-} + 2H^+ + 3SO_3{}^{2-} \longrightarrow 2CrO_2{}^- + H_2O + 3SO_4{}^{2-} \quad (balanced) \quad (23)$$

Then, all H^+ ions appearing in the balanced Equation 23 are changed to HOH molecules by adding the required number of OH^- *ions to both sides* of the balanced equation, as shown:

$$2CrO_4{}^{2-} + 2H^+ + 2OH^- + 3SO_3{}^{2-} \longrightarrow$$
$$2CrO_2{}^- + 3SO_4{}^{2-} + H_2O + 2OH^- \quad (balanced)$$

$$2CrO_4{}^{2-} + 2H_2O + 3SO_3{}^{2-} \longrightarrow$$
$$2CrO_2{}^- + 3SO_4{}^{2-} + H_2O + 2OH^- \quad (balanced)$$

$$2CrO_4{}^{2-} + H_2O + 3SO_3{}^{2-} \longrightarrow 2CrO_2{}^- + 3SO_4{}^{2-} + 2OH^- \quad (balanced)$$

Unless told otherwise, the reader may assume that oxidation-reduction reactions given in this chapter occur in acidic solutions.

11.5 OXIDATION NUMBER

Another scheme, the assignment of an oxidation number to atoms in molecules and to ions, is also useful for keeping track of apparent electron transfers (page 359). The oxidation number also plays a very important role in naming simple and complex compounds (page 150). For example, tin(II) chloride means $SnCl_2$ (a white solid), tin(IV) chloride means $SnCl_4$ (a colorless liquid), and uranium(V) chloride means UCl_5 (a dark green-gray solid that decomposes at 120 °C). The oxidation number of the iron atom in hemoglobin (page 269) is important: iron(II), oxidation number 2, carries oxygen molecules from the lungs to the body cells, but iron(III), oxidation number 3, does *not* carry oxygen.

The **oxidation number** is a *fictitious charge assigned* to covalently bonded atoms. The assignment of an oxidation number is based on the *arbitrary assumption that all bonding electrons belong to the more electronegative atom*. Thus, in the polar molecule $\overset{\delta^+\ \ \delta^-}{H:\overset{..}{\underset{..}{Cl}}:}$, the electron pair making up the covalent bond is *assigned* to the Cl atom *as if* HCl consisted of separate ions.

If we assign the bonding pair of electrons to Cl in HCl, $H:\overset{..}{\underset{..}{Cl}}: \xrightarrow{\text{arbitrarily}}$ $H^+ + :\overset{..}{\underset{..}{Cl}}:^-$, then the Cl atom will have 8 valence electrons and the H atom none. We then say that the oxidation number of the Cl atom is -1 and that of the H atom is $+1$. Thus, unlike the electronic charge or the charge on ions, oxidation numbers are *not* experimentally determined quantities. Since a molecule is electrically neutral, the sum of the oxidation numbers of all atoms in the molecule must equal zero. But for an ion, the sum must equal the charge on the ion. In methane, CH_4, the carbon atom is more electronegative than the hydrogen atom (Table 8.1, page 255). Each hydrogen atom has an oxidation number of $+1$, as if the hydrogen atom, $H\cdot$, had lost 1 electron; the 4 hydrogen atoms total $+4$. Therefore, the oxidation number of the carbon atom in methane is -4, as if the carbon atom, $\cdot\overset{\cdot}{\underset{\cdot}{C}}\cdot$, had gained 4 electrons:

$$
\begin{array}{c}
\text{H} \\
\text{H}\!:\!\overset{\cdot\cdot}{\underset{\cdot\cdot}{C}}\!:\!\text{H} \\
\text{H}
\end{array}
\xrightarrow{\ arbitrarily\ }
\begin{array}{c}
\text{H}^+ \\
\text{H}^+\!:\!\overset{\cdot\cdot}{\underset{\cdot\cdot}{C}}\!:\!{}^{-4}\text{H}^+ \\
\text{H}^+
\end{array}
$$

In ethylene, C_2H_4, the 4 hydrogen atoms total $+4$. But there are 2 carbon atoms in one molecule; therefore, each C atom in ethylene is assigned an oxidation number of -2.

PROBLEM 6   (a) What is the total oxidation number of the hydrogen atoms in (i) ethane, C_2H_6, and (ii) acetylene, C_2H_2? (b) What is the number of carbon atoms in one molecule of (i) ethane, and (ii) acetylene? (c) What is the oxidation number of the carbon atoms in (i) ethane, and (ii) acetylene?

However, in carbon dioxide, CO_2, the oxygen atom is more electronegative than the carbon atom (Table 8.1, page 255). The bonding electrons are thus assigned to the oxygen atom:

$$
:\!\overset{\cdot\cdot}{\underset{\cdot\cdot}{O}}\!:^{-2}\text{C}^{+4}\!:\!\overset{\cdot\cdot}{\underset{\cdot\cdot}{O}}\!:^{-2}
$$

The oxidation number of each oxygen atom is -2, and the oxidation number of the carbon is now $+4$.

PROBLEM 7   See Table 8.1. What is the oxidation number of the carbon atom in carbon tetrafluoride, CF_4,

$$
\begin{array}{c}
\text{F} \\
\text{F}\!:\!\overset{\cdot\cdot}{\underset{\cdot\cdot}{C}}\!:\!\text{F} \quad ? \\
\text{F}
\end{array}
$$

An atom in its elementary state—for example, Cl_2, H_2, C—is assigned an oxidation number of zero; neither atom in Cl_2 or in H_2 can be said to be more electronegative than the other atom.

The following table can be used to calculate oxidation numbers directly from formulas for most molecules and ions:

Element	Assigned Oxidation Number		
Li $\longrightarrow$ Cs	$+1$	$\left.\vphantom{\begin{array}{c}a\\a\\a\end{array}}\right\}$	no exceptions; corresponds to the group number
Be $\longrightarrow$ Ra	$+2$		
B $\longrightarrow$ Tl	$+3$		
H	$+1$		except when combined with the above metals; for example, H atom is -1 in sodium hydride, NaH
F	-1		no exceptions; F is the most electronegative of all elements*

*In hypofluorous acid, HOF, F is assigned an oxidation number of -1, and hydrogen is assigned $+1$, leaving oxygen with an oxidation number of zero, $H^+\!:\!\overset{\cdot\cdot}{\underset{\cdot\cdot}{O}}\!:\!\overset{\cdot\cdot}{\underset{\cdot\cdot}{F}}\!:^{-1}$.

Recently synthesized compounds in which the oxidation number of alkali metals is -1 (page 673) need not concern us here.

Cl $\longrightarrow$ I	-1	except when combined with an O atom or one another; oxygen is the second strongest electronegative element; in ClF, Cl is $+1$, but in bromine chloride, BrCl, an unstable gas, Cl is -1
O	-2	except in the peroxides, in which it is assigned -1; for example, hydrogen peroxide, $H^+ : \overset{..}{\underset{..}{O}}{}^{-1} - \overset{..}{\underset{..}{O}} : {}^{-1} H^+$
Transition metals such as Fe, Co, Cr, Mn, W		variable, but generally combined with halogens (-1) or oxygen (-2)

In the examples that follow, the oxidation number is written over the symbol for the element:

$$\overset{0}{Cl_2} \qquad \overset{+1\ -2\ +1}{H_2O,\quad H:\overset{..}{\underset{..}{O}}:H} \qquad \overset{-1\ +2\ -1}{CaH_2,\quad H:Ca:H} \qquad \overset{+1\ -3\ +1}{NH_3,\quad H:\overset{..}{N}:H} \qquad \overset{-1\ +3\ -1}{NF_3,\quad F:\overset{..}{N}:F}$$

$$\underset{\text{chlorine}}{} \qquad \underset{\text{water}}{} \qquad \underset{\text{calcium hydride}}{} \qquad \underset{\text{ammonia}}{\overset{H\ +1}{}} \qquad \underset{\text{nitrogen trifluoride}}{\overset{F\ -1}{}}$$

Example 1

Find the oxidation number of the Mn atom (a) in permanganate ion, MnO_4^-, whose aqueous solution possesses a characteristic pink color, and (b) in K_2MnO_4, a dark green solid.

Answer

(a) Oxidation number -2 is assigned to the O atom. This gives the four oxygen atoms a total oxidation number of -8 ($4 \times -2 = -8$). The charge on the ion is -1. Then the Mn atom must have an oxidation number of $+7$ (-8 for the O atoms, $+7$ for the Mn atom $= -1$, the charge on the ion). Thus, the oxidation number for the Mn atom in MnO_4^- is $+7$. In summary, let Mn represent the oxidation number of manganese in MnO_4^-; then

$$Mn \longleftarrow \overset{MnO_4^-}{\big|\quad\big|} \longrightarrow 4 \times -2 = -8$$

$$\text{sum of oxidation numbers} = \text{ion charge}$$
$$Mn - 8 = -1$$
$$Mn = +8 - 1 = +7$$

(b) The oxidation number -2 is assigned to the O atom and $+1$ is assigned to the K atom. The four oxygen atoms have a total oxidation number of -8 ($4 \times -2 = -8$). For K, the total oxidation number is $+2$ ($2 \times +1 = +2$). The compound is electrically neutral, so the oxidation number of Mn must be $+6$ ($+2 + Mn - 8 = 0$, from which $Mn = +6$), or in summary:

$$K_2MnO_4$$

$$2 \times +1 = +2 \quad \lefthalfcup \quad \rightarrow 4 \times -2 = -8$$

$$\rightarrow Mn$$

sum of oxidation numbers = zero, compound is electrically neutral

$$+2 + Mn - 8 = 0$$
$$Mn = +8 - 2 = +6$$

PROBLEM 8 Na_2SO_4, a colorless solid obtained as a by-product in the manufacture of hydrochloric acid from sodium chloride and sulfuric acid, is used in the production of paper, glass, dyes, and detergents. Find the oxidation number of S in Na_2SO_4.

Example 2

Find the oxidation number of Cr in the dichromate ion, $Cr_2O_7^{2-}$.

Answer

Assign -2 oxidation number to O. Then

$$Cr_2O_7^{2-}$$

$$2Cr \quad \lefthalfcup \quad \rightarrow 7 \times -2 = -14$$
$$2Cr - 14 = -2, \text{ the ion charge}$$
$$2Cr = -2 + 14 = +12, \text{ the total oxidation number}$$
$$\text{for two Cr atoms}$$

$$Cr = \frac{+12}{2} = +6$$

The oxidation number of Cr in $Cr_2O_7^{2-}$ is $+6$.*

PROBLEM 9   Show that the oxidation number of N in the ammonium ion, NH_4^+, is -3.

PROBLEM 10   Find the oxidation number of C in each of the following: CH_4, CCl_4, chloroform, $CHCl_3$, and formaldehyde, H_2CO.

The fictitious oxidation number has its origin in the proposal (1819) by J. J. Berzelius that all chemical bonding is ionic in nature.

Oxidation-Reduction and Oxidation Numbers   Many reactions, for example, the fermentation (page 697) of glucose (grape sugar) to alcohol

$$C_6H_{12}O_6(aq) \longrightarrow 2C_2H_5OH(aq) + 2CO_2(g)$$

may not, at first, appear to be an oxidation-reduction reaction. Let us determine the

---

*Chemists frequently call the oxidation number the **oxidation state.** Thus in $Cr_2O_7^{2-}$, Cr is in the $+6$ oxidation state and O is in the -2 oxidation state.

oxidation numbers of C, H, and O atoms among the reactants and products by assigning oxidation number -2 to O atoms and $+1$ to H atoms

$$C_6H_{12}O_6 \longrightarrow C_2H_5OH + CO_2$$

$6C \quad \hookleftarrow \quad \hookrightarrow 6 \times -2 = -12 \qquad 2C \hookleftarrow \hookrightarrow 6 \times +1 = +6 \quad C \hookleftarrow \hookrightarrow 2 \times -2 = -4$

$\hookrightarrow 12 \times +1 = +12 \qquad\qquad \hookrightarrow 1 \times -2 = -2$

$$6C + 12 - 12 = 0 \qquad 2C + 6 - 2 = 0 \qquad C - 4 = 0$$
$$6C = 0 \qquad 2C = +2 - 6 = -4 \qquad C = +4$$
$$C = 0 \qquad C = -2$$

We now see that the oxidation number of carbon changes from 0 in the reactant molecule to -2 and $+4$ in the product molecules:

$$\overset{0}{C} \longrightarrow \overset{-2}{C} + \overset{+4}{C}$$

An increase in oxidation number, $\overset{0}{C} \longrightarrow \overset{+4}{C}$, *is called oxidation. A decrease in oxida-tion number,* $\overset{0}{C} \longrightarrow \overset{-2}{C}$, *is called reduction. The oxidizing agent* is the substance that contains the atom showing a *decrease in oxidation number. The reducing agent* is the substance that contains the atom showing an *increase in oxidation number.* In this reaction, the sugar, $C_6H_{12}O_6$, serves as both the oxidizing agent and the reducing agent.

Example 3

Aqueous solutions of permanganate, MnO_4^-, may be prepared from manga-nous salts, Mn^{2+}, and lead dioxide, PbO_2, a brown solid used in batteries (page 478):

$$2Mn^{2+}(aq) + 5PbO_2(c) + 4H^+(aq) \longrightarrow 2MnO_4^-(aq) + 5Pb^{2+}(aq) + 2H_2O$$

From changes in oxidation numbers, determine what is oxidized and reduced, and which substances act as oxidizing and reducing agents.

Answer

First, find the oxidation number of each atom involved in the reaction by proper assignment of oxidation numbers:

$$Mn^{2+} + PbO_2 + H^+ \longrightarrow MnO_4^- + Pb^{2+} + H_2O$$

$\qquad\qquad \downarrow \quad \downarrow \hookrightarrow 2 \times -2 = -4 \qquad \downarrow \quad \downarrow \hookrightarrow 4 \times -2 = -8 \qquad \downarrow \quad \downarrow \hookrightarrow -2$

$\quad +2 \quad +4 \qquad\qquad\qquad +1 \quad +7 \qquad\qquad\qquad +2 \quad 2 \times +1 = +2$

We now note the changes in oxidation numbers:

$$\overset{+2}{Mn} \xrightarrow{\text{increase}} \overset{+7}{Mn} \qquad \overset{+4}{Pb} \xrightarrow{\text{decrease}} \overset{+2}{Pb}$$

We therefore conclude that Mn^{2+} is oxidized to MnO_4^- and that PbO_2 is reduced to Pb^{2+}. Further, PbO_2 acts as the oxidizing agent while Mn^{2+} acts as the reducing agent.

PROBLEM 11 **By assignment of oxidation numbers, find (a) the substances oxidized and reduced, and (b) the oxidizing and reducing agents in the reaction for the preparation of nitric acid (page 608):**

$$3NO_2(g) + H_2O \longrightarrow 2HNO_3(aq) + NO(g)$$

_____ PROBLEMS

12 Vocabulary Define and illustrate: (a) electrolyte, (b) nonelectrolyte, (c) oxidation, (d) reduction, (e) oxidizing agent, (f) reducing agent, (g) oxidation number.

13 Ionic equations Write the balanced ionic equation for each of the following reactions:
(a) $HCl(aq) + NH_3(aq) \longrightarrow NH_4Cl(aq)$
(b) $Sn(c) + HCl(aq) \longrightarrow$
$SnCl_2(aq) + H_2(g)$
(c) $Pb(NO_3)_2(aq) + NaCl(aq) \longrightarrow$
$PbCl_2(c) + NaNO_3(aq)$
(d) $CuSO_4(aq) + K_4Fe(CN)_6(aq) \longrightarrow$
$K_2SO_4(aq) + Cu_2Fe(CN)_6(c)$
(e) $Fe(NO_3)_3(aq) + NaOH(aq) \longrightarrow$
$Fe(OH)_3(c) + NaNO_3(aq)$
(f) $FeCl_2(aq) + H_2S(aq) \longrightarrow$
$FeS(c) + HCl(aq)$
(g) $Al(NO_3)_3(aq) + NaOH(aq) \longrightarrow$
$Al(OH)_3(c) + NaNO_3(aq)$
(h) $BaCO_3(c) + HCl(aq) \longrightarrow$
$BaCl_2(aq) + CO_2(g) + H_2O$
(i) $MgCl_2(aq) + KOH(aq) \longrightarrow$
$Mg(OH)_2(c) + KCl(aq)$
(j) $BaCl_2(aq) + Na_2CrO_4(aq) \longrightarrow$
$BaCrO_4(c) + NaCl(aq)$
(k) $BaCl_2(aq) + Na_2SO_3(aq) \longrightarrow$
$BaSO_3(c) + NaCl(aq)$
(l) $AgNO_3(aq) + NaCNS(aq) \longrightarrow$
$AgCNS(c) + NaNO_3(aq)$

14 Oxidation number Write the oxidation number of each element in each of the following compounds:
(a) $NaCl$, (b) Na_2S, (c) K_2SO_4, (d) $NaHSO_4$, (e) H_2O, (f) H_2O_2, (g) Fe_2S_3, (h) FeS, (i) $KMnO_4$, (j) Na_2CrO_4, (k) $Na_2Cr_2O_7$, (l) HNO_3, (m) Br_2, (n) $NaClO_3$, (o) $RbTeF_4$, (p) Mg_2SiO_4.

15 Oxidation-reduction Balance each of the following

half-reactions and state whether it is an oxidation or reduction:
(a) $Zn \longrightarrow Zn^{2+}$
(b) $Cu^{2+} \longrightarrow Cu$
(c) $Mn^{2+} \longrightarrow MnO_4^-$
(d) $NO_2^- \longrightarrow NO_3^-$
(e) $SO_3^{2-} \longrightarrow SO_4^{2-}$
(f) $NO_3^- \longrightarrow NH_3$
(g) $Bi \longrightarrow BiO^+$

16 Balance each of the following equations by the ion-electron method:
(a) $Al(c) + H^+(aq) \longrightarrow Al^{3+}(aq) + H_2(g)$
(b) $Al(c) + Ag^+(aq) \longrightarrow Ag(c) + Al^{3+}(aq)$
(c) $Al(c) + Cu^{2+}(aq) \longrightarrow$
$Al^{3+}(aq) + Cu(c)$
(d) $Ce^{4+}(aq) + AsO_2^-(aq) + H_2O \longrightarrow$
$AsO_4^{3-}(aq) + Ce^{3+}(aq) + H^+(aq)$
(e) $Fe^{2+}(aq) + Ce^{4+}(aq) \longrightarrow$
$Fe^{3+}(aq) + Ce^{3+}(aq)$
(f) $Fe^{2+}(aq) + NO_3^-(aq) + H^+(aq) \longrightarrow$
$Fe^{3+}(aq) + NO(g) + H_2O$
(g) $Fe^{3+}(aq) + Zn(c) \longrightarrow$
$Fe(c) + Zn^{2+}(aq)$
(h) $Fe^{2+}(aq) + Cr_2O_7^{2-}(aq) + H^+(aq) \longrightarrow$
$Cr^{3+}(aq) + Fe^{3+}(aq)$
(i) $HAsO_2(c) + I_2(aq) + H_2O \longrightarrow$
$H_2AsO_4^-(aq) + I^-(aq) + H^+(aq)$
(j) $C_2O_4^{2-}(aq) + MnO_4^-(aq) + H^+(aq) \longrightarrow$
$CO_2(g) + Mn^{2+}(aq) + H_2O$
(k) $ClO_3^-(aq) + Cl^-(aq) + H^+(aq) \longrightarrow$
$Cl_2(g) + H_2O$
(l) $ClO^-(aq) + As(c) + H_2O \longrightarrow$
$Cl^-(aq) + AsO_4^{3-}(aq) + H^+(aq)$
(m) $Cu^{2+}(aq) + I^-(aq) \longrightarrow Cu(c) + I_2(c)$
(n) $Cu^{2+}(aq) + S_2O_4^{2-}(aq) + H_2O \longrightarrow$
$Cu(c) + SO_3^{2-}(aq) + H^+(aq)$
(o) $Co^{2+}(aq) + SO_4^{2-}(aq) + H_2O \longrightarrow$
$Co^{3+}(aq) + SO_3^{2-}(aq) + OH^-(aq)$ _(basic solution)_

(p) $Mn^{2+}(aq) + PbO_2(c) + H^+(aq) \longrightarrow$
$MnO_4^-(aq) + Pb^{2+}(aq) + H_2O$

(q) $BrO_3^-(aq) + I^-(aq) + H^+(aq) \longrightarrow$
$Br^-(aq) + I_2(c) + H_2O$

(r) $MnO_2(c) + Fe^{2+}(aq) + H^+(aq) \longrightarrow$
$Mn^{2+}(aq) + Fe^{3+}(aq) + H_2O$

(s) $Zn(c) + NO_3^-(aq) + H^+(aq) \longrightarrow$
$Zn^{2+}(aq) + NH_4^+(aq) + H_2O$

(t) $PbS(c) + H^+(aq) + NO_3^-(aq) \longrightarrow$
$Pb^{2+}(aq) + S(c) + NO(g) + H_2O$

(u) $Cl_2(g) + OH^-(aq) \longrightarrow$
$Cl^-(aq) + ClO_3^-(aq) + H_2O$ (basic solution)

(v) $Cl^-(aq) + H^+(aq) + MnO_4^-(aq) \longrightarrow$
$Mn^{2+}(aq) + Cl_2(g) + H_2O$

(w) $V(OH)_4^+(aq) + U(c) + H^+(aq) \longrightarrow$
$VO^{2+}(aq) + UO_2^{2+}(aq) + H_2O$

(x) $CeOH^{3+}(aq) + Br^-(aq) \longrightarrow$
$Ce^{3+}(aq) + BrO_3^-(aq)$

(y) $NaClO_3(aq) + HCl(aq) \longrightarrow$
$ClO_2(g) + NaCl(aq) + H_2O + Cl_2$

(z) $CH_4(g) + O_2(g) + OH^-(aq) \longrightarrow$
$CO_3^{2-}(aq) + H_2O$ (basic solution)

(z') $Cr_2O_7^{2-}(aq) + Sn^{2+}(aq) + H^+(aq) \longrightarrow$
$Cr^{3+}(aq) + Sn^{4+}(aq) + H_2O$

17 Pollution (a) About 8×10^6 tons of sulfuric acid seep into streams from United States coal mines (active and abandoned), destroying them as a source of drinking water and aquatic life. The acid results from the air (O_2) oxidation of *pyrite,* FeS_2:

$$FeS_2(c) + O_2(g) + H_2O \longrightarrow$$
$$Fe^{2+}(aq) + H^+(aq) + SO_4^{2-}(aq)$$

Balance the equation. (b) "Dead air," oxygen-deficient air, recently caused the deaths of construction workers in Japan working in a tunnel dug in a soil containing Fe^{2+} compounds. Explain the formation of "dead air."

18 Library Read one of the following:
(a) "Redox Reactions and the Acid-Base Properties of Solvents," *Chemistry,* January 1970, page 18.
(b) "Fundamentals of Chemistry," Brescia, Arents, Meislich, and Turk, Academic Press, Inc., New York, 3rd Edition, 1975, pages 230–232 ("Conductivity and Equivalent Conductance").

ADDITIONAL PROBLEMS

19 Balance each of the following equations by the ion-electron method:
(a) $Fe^{3+}(aq) + SnCl_4^{2-}(aq) + Cl^-(aq) \longrightarrow$
$Fe^{2+}(aq) + SnCl_6^{2-}(aq)$
(b) $MnO_4^-(aq) + SnO_2^{2-}(aq) + H_2O \longrightarrow$
$MnO_2(c) + SnO_3^{2-}(aq) + OH^-(aq)$

20 Determine the oxidation number (a) of Sb in $[Sb_3F_{16}]^-$, (b) of N in $[N_2F_5]^+$, (c) of Mn in $BaMnF_4$, and (d) of Fe in $LiMgFeF_6$.

21 Find the changes in the oxidation number of nitrogen (a) when it is "fixed" by natural electric discharges (thunderstorms) and atmospheric reactions:
$N_2 \longrightarrow NO \longrightarrow NO_2 \longrightarrow NO_2^- \longrightarrow NO_3^-$;
(b) when hydrazine (page 270) and nitrogen dioxide are used in a reaction to propel rockets into space:
$2N_2H_4 + N_2O_4 \longrightarrow 3N_2 + 4H_2O$

22 Is $[HgCl_4]^{2-} + 2SO_2 + 2H_2O \longrightarrow [Hg(SO_3)_2]^{2-} + 4Cl^- + 4H^+$ an oxidation-reduction reaction?

23 Black hydrated nickel oxide, NiO_2, is a sufficiently strong oxidizing agent to oxidize water in acid solution. Balance: $NiO_2(c) + H_2O \longrightarrow Ni^{2+}(aq) + O_2(g)$

24 Certain very difficult to dissolve chromium steels can be dissolved in hot boiling **(dangerous)** perchloric acid. Balance: $Cr(c) + HClO_4(aq) + H_2O \longrightarrow Cl_2(g) + Cr_2O_7^{2-}(aq) + H^+(aq)$

25 Copper metal is dissolved by hot dilute (6 M) nitric acid. Balance: $Cu(c) + NO_3^-(aq) + H^+(aq) \longrightarrow Cu^{2+} + NO_2(g) + H_2O$

26 Fe^{2+} ion may be analyzed by a reaction in which Fe^{2+} is oxidized to Fe^{3+}. Balance: $Fe^{2+}(aq) + H^+(aq) + Cr_2O_7^{2-}(aq) \longrightarrow Fe^{3+}(aq) + Cr^{3+}(aq) + H_2O$

ANSWERS

1 (i) all electrolytes except sucrose
(ii) KCl, $AlCl_3$, strong electrolytes;
$HgCl_2$, NH_3 weak electrolytes
2 conductivity should increase
3 $Pb^{2+}(aq) + 2Br^-(aq) \longrightarrow PbBr_2(c)$

4 Zn oxidized, reducing agent
Cl_2 reduced, oxidizing agent
5 (a) 2, 1, 2, 1; (b) 1, 3, 6, 1, 6, 3
6 (a) (i) $+6$, (ii) $+2$; (b) (i)(ii) 2;
(c) (i) -3, (ii) -1

7 +4

8 +6

10 −4, +4, +2, 0

11 (a) NO_2 is oxidized to HNO_3 and reduced to NO; (b) NO_2 is oxidizing and reducing agent

14 (a) +1, −1; (b) +1, −2; (c) +1, +6, −2; (d) +1, +1, +6, −2; (e) +1, −2; (f) +1, −1; (g) +3, −2; (h) +2, −2; (i) +1, +7, −2; (j) +1, +6, −2; (k) +1, +6, −2; (l) +1, +5, −2; (m) 0; (n) +1, +5, −2; (o) +1, +3, −1; (p) +2, +4, −2

15 a, c, d, e, g, oxidation; b, f, reduction

16 (a) 2, 6, 2, 3; (b) 1, 3, 3, 1; (c) 2, 3, 2, 3; (d) 2, 1, 2, 1, 2, 4; (e) 1, 1, 1, 1; (f) 3, 1, 4, 3, 1, 2; (g) 2, 3, 2, 3; (h) 6, 1, 14, 2, 6, 7; (i) 1, 1, 2, 1, 2, 3; (j) 5, 2, 16, 10, 2, 8; (k) 1, 5, 6, 3, 3;

(l) 5, 2, 3, 5, 2, 6; (m) 1, 2, 1, 1; (n) 1, 1, 2, 1, 2, 4; (o) 2, 1, 1, 2, 1, 2; (p) 2, 5, 4, 2, 5, 2; (q) 1, 6, 6, 1, 3, 3; (r) 1, 2, 4, 1, 2, 2; (s) 4, 1, 10, 4, 1, 3; (t) 3, 8, 2, 3, 3, 2, 4; (u) 3, 6, 5, 1, 3; (v) 10, 16, 2, 2, 5, 8; (w) 6, 1, 8, 6, 1, 16; (x) 6, 1, 6, 1, 3; (y) 2, 4, 2, 2, 2, 1; (z) 1, 2, 2, 1, 3; (z′) 1, 3, 14, 2, 3, 7

17 2, 2, 7, 2, 4, 4

19 (a) 2, 1, 2, 2, 1; (b) 2, 3, 1, 2, 3, 2

20 (a) +5, (b) +3, (c) +2, (d) +3

21 (a) 0, +2, +4, +3, +5; (b) −2, +4, 0

22 No, no change in oxidation number

23 $2NiO_2 + 4H^+ \rightarrow 2Ni^{2+} + 2H_2O + O_2$

24 14, 12, 1, 6, 7, 14

25 1, 2, 4, 1, 2, 2

26 6, 14, 1, 6, 2, 7

---

electrodes The metallic or graphite rods at which an electric current enters or leaves a liquid.

electrolytic conduction The movement of ions constituting an electric current in a solution. Aqueous solutions of strong electrolytes contain comparatively high concentrations of ions and are therefore good conductors of electricity. Aqueous solutions of weak electrolytes contain comparatively low concentrations of ions and are therefore poor conductors of electricity. Aqueous solutions of nonelectrolytes contain no ions and therefore do not conduct electricity.

half-reaction The oxidation or reduction part of an oxidation-reduction reaction. For ease of interpretation, a reaction is divided into two half-reactions which may be examined separately. The combined half-reactions yield the overall reaction.

ionic equation An equation for a reaction in solution that shows only the ions and molecules participating in the reaction, excluding the ions that do not participate in the reaction.

oxidation The loss of electrons by a reactant in a chemical reaction; an increase in oxidation number. It is always accompanied by reduction of another reactant. See **reduction**.

oxidation number A fictitious number assigned to the atoms in ions or molecules on the arbitrary assumption that all bonding electrons belong to the more electronegative atom. The sum of the oxidation numbers of all the atoms in a molecule is zero; for an ion, the sum equals the charge of the ion.

oxidizing agent The substance that gains electrons and oxidizes another substance. It is the substance containing the atom that decreases in oxidation number. The oxidizing agent is always reduced by the reducing agent.

reduction The gain of electrons by a reactant in a chemical reaction; a decrease in oxidation number. It is always accompanied by oxidation of another reactant. See **oxidation**.

reducing agent The substance that loses electrons and reduces another substance. It is the substance containing the atom that increases in oxidation number. The reducing agent is always oxidized by the oxidizing agent.

CHEMICAL EQUILIBRIUM

12

In this chapter we shall seek answers and explanations to questions like "To what extent will the two pollutants hydrogen sulfide, H_2S and sulfur dioxide, SO_2, react to form sulfur:

$$2H_2S(g) + SO_2(g) \longrightarrow 3S(c) + 2H_2O(l) \qquad \Delta H = -55.8 \text{ kcal} \qquad (1)$$

"On mixing H_2S and SO_2 in the molar ratio of 2 to 1 at 25 °C and 1 atm, what fraction of SO_2 will react? Practically none? 10 %? 90 %? 100 %? If the extent of the reaction is too small to be economically feasible, can the chemist change the reaction conditions to increase the fraction of SO_2 that reacts?" Another question, will ethylene, C_2H_4, a cheap available gas (12 cents/lb), react with water to produce ethyl alcohol, C_2H_5OH (colorless, intoxicating liquid, 17 cents/lb)?

Annual C_2H_4 production: 2×10^7 tons

$$C_2H_4(g) + H_2O(g) \longrightarrow C_2H_5OH(l) \qquad \Delta H = -21.1 \text{ kcal} \qquad (2)$$

Before developing the explanations, let us first note some experimental observations:

(a) Nickel, Ni, a comparatively inert metal, is used mainly in the manufacture of stainless steels. Nickel is purified by the **Mond process:** crude nickel is treated with carbon monoxide, CO, at about 75 °C, forming volatile nickel tetracarbonyl, $Ni(CO)_4$ (colorless flammable toxic liquid, b.p. 43 °C)

After Ludwig Mond, co-discoverer (1890) of $Ni(CO)_4$, who developed this process.

$$Ni(c) + 4CO(g) \longrightarrow Ni(CO)_4(g) \qquad \Delta H = -39.1 \text{ kcal} \qquad (3)$$

leaving solid impurities behind. The carbonyl compound is then decomposed at about 200 °C, depositing pure Ni,

$$Ni(CO)_4(g) \longrightarrow Ni(c) + 4CO(g) \qquad \Delta H = +39.1 \text{ kcal} \qquad (4)$$

The released CO is recirculated for reuse.

If Ni and CO are enclosed at some intermediate temperature, the two reactions oppose each other and a mixture of Ni(c), CO(g), and $Ni(CO)_4(g)$ is obtained. *The composition of the mixture does not change with time.* In this mixture it appears that Ni and CO do not combine and $Ni(CO)_4$ does not decompose. For all practical production purposes, the reaction has stopped. What is the explanation for this stoppage?

TABLE 12.1
PROGRESS OF THE GAS REACTION, $N_2 + 3H_2 \longrightarrow 2NH_3$, AT 350 °C, IN TWO EXPERIMENTS

TIME, HOURS	H_2, MOLE/LITER		N_2, MOLE/LITER		NH_3, MOLE/LITER	
	(1)	(2)	(1)	(2)	(1)	(2)
0	3.00	1.03	1.00	0.39	0.00	0.00
1	1.95	0.71	0.65	0.29	0.70	0.21
2	1.35	0.56	0.45	0.24	1.11	0.31
3	1.05	0.47	0.35	0.21	1.30	0.37
4	0.90	0.44	0.30	0.20	1.40	0.39 ⎫ reaction stops
100	0.90	0.44	0.30	0.20	1.40	0.39 ⎭ after 4 hours

(b) Nature is not capable of furnishing our intensively cultivated farmlands with the quantities of fertilizers necessary to grow the required amounts of food. Farmers therefore supplement soil minerals with manufactured fertilizers. One vital soil nutrient, ammonia, NH_3, transported as liquid NH_3 by pipelines to major farmlands in the midwest, is manufactured from nitrogen, N_2, a comparatively inert gas, and hydrogen:

$$N_2(g) + 3H_2(g) \longrightarrow 2NH_3(g) \qquad \Delta H = -22.1 \text{ kcal} \qquad (5)$$

But in the actual manufacturing process, 3.3 moles H_2 to 1.0 mole N_2 are used at 500 °C and 450 atm instead of 3.0 moles H_2 to 1.0 mole N_2 at atmospheric temperature and pressure. The process thus at first sight appears to be wasteful and expensive. It is costly to operate at conditions other than the natural surroundings. Even worse, experiment shows that the conversion of N_2 and H_2 to NH_3 is incomplete; all of the N_2 and H_2 do not react. In one experiment, 3.00 moles H_2 and 1.00 mole N_2 were mixed in a vessel at 350 °C. In a second experiment, 1.03 moles of H_2 and 0.39 mole of N_2 were mixed. The contents were analyzed hourly. The results, shown in Table 12.1, reveal that after 4 hours, no further reaction occurs in spite of the presence of substantial quantities of unused N_2 and H_2. How can we explain this apparent waste?

12.2 REVERSIBLE REACTIONS AND EQUILIBRIUM

We now consider the principles involved in answering the questions raised in the previous section.

At the start of one experiment, $Ni(CO)_4$ is added to a container at 125 °C. The $Ni(CO)_4$ decomposes as shown in Reaction 4. At the start of another experiment, $Ni(c)$ and $CO(g)$ are added to a container at the same temperature, 125 °C. The nickel and the carbon monoxide combine as shown in Reaction 3.

This fact is expressed by saying that Reaction 3 or 4 is **reversible*** and by writing it with a double arrow:

$$Ni(CO)_4(g) \rightleftharpoons Ni(c) + 4CO(g) \qquad \Delta H = +39.1 \text{ kcal}$$

This means that in any mixture of $Ni(CO)_4(g)$, $Ni(c)$, and $CO(g)$, reactions 3 and 4 will take place at the same time. The decomposition of $Ni(CO)_4$ is referred to as the

---

*Claude Berthollet invented this concept in 1799 while explaining the formation of natural deposits of sodium carbonate in Egypt by the reaction $CaCO_3(c) + 2NaCl(aq) \longrightarrow Na_2CO_3(c) + CaCl_2(aq)$.

forward reaction, while the formation of $Ni(CO)_4$ is called the reverse reaction. On the other hand, if the chemical equation is written as

$$Ni(c) + 4CO(g) \rightleftharpoons Ni(CO)_4(g) \qquad \Delta H = -39.1 \text{ kcal}$$

the formation of $Ni(CO)_4$ becomes the forward reaction and the decomposition of $Ni(CO)_4$ becomes the reverse reaction.

Reactions 1, 2, and 5 also illustrate reversible reactions:

$$2H_2S(g) + SO_2(g) \rightleftharpoons 3S(c) + 2H_2O(l) \qquad \Delta H = -55.8 \text{ kcal} \qquad (1)$$

$$C_2H_4(g) + H_2O(g) \rightleftharpoons C_2H_5OH(l) \qquad \Delta H = -21.1 \text{ kcal} \qquad (2)$$

$$N_2(g) + 3H_2(g) \rightleftharpoons 2NH_3(g) \qquad \Delta H = -22.1 \text{ kcal} \qquad (5)$$

The significance of a reversible reaction lies in the fact that if the products of the reaction are not removed, they react to re-form the initial reactants. Eventually, a state is reached where there will be *no further net change* in the composition of the reaction mixture. For all practical purposes, the reaction has stopped. This dynamic

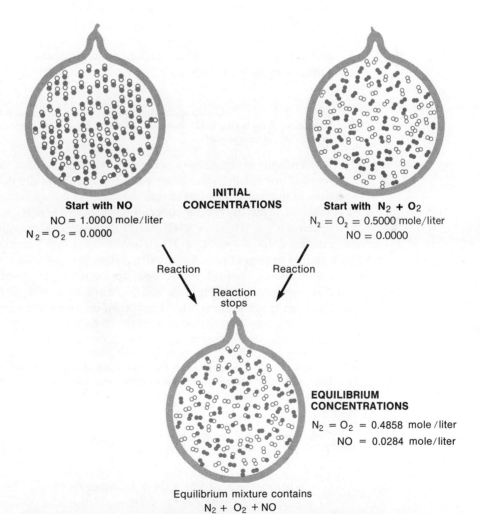

Start with NO
NO = 1.0000 mole/liter
$N_2 = O_2 = 0.0000$

**INITIAL
CONCENTRATIONS**

Start with $N_2 + O_2$
$N_2 = O_2 = 0.5000$ mole/liter
NO = 0.0000

Reaction

Reaction

Reaction
stops

**EQUILIBRIUM
CONCENTRATIONS**
$N_2 = O_2 = 0.4858$ mole/liter
NO = 0.0284 mole/liter

Equilibrium mixture contains
$N_2 + O_2 + NO$

FIGURE 12.1 Representation of an experimental approach to equilibrium (2400 °C) from opposite directions.

condition is referred to as **chemical equilibrium,** or simply as **equilibrium.** This important property of chemical reactions is illustrated with reversible Reaction 5 in Table 12.1 in two experiments. After 4 hours, no further changes in composition occur. The quantities of the three gases are constant; therefore, equilibrium has been attained. The concentrations of the reacting substances in an equilibrium mixture are called **equilibrium concentrations.**

Similar results are obtained starting with NH_3. The NH_3 decomposes; after a period of time a mixture of H_2, N_2, and NH_3, whose composition does not change with time, is obtained. An illustration involving N_2, O_2, and NO is given in Fig. 12.1.

Another *significant conclusion* is that all reversible reactions eventually come to equilibrium and, therefore, are incomplete. The data in Table 12.1 are illustrative. Appreciable quantities of both reactants and products are present in the equilibrium mixture. However, some reactions reach equilibrium after the formation of only extremely small amounts of the products. In other reactions, equilibrium is attained after practically all of the initial reactants are converted to products. In any case, the chemical equation gives the *relative quantities,* and *not* absolute quantities, of reactants and products reacting and forming (page 153). For example, no matter what quantities of ammonia, nitrogen, and hydrogen may be mixed, 3 molecules of hydrogen react for every 1 molecule of nitrogen that reacts, forming 2 molecules of ammonia. Of course, from the known quantity of any one substance that reacts, the absolute quantities of other reactants and products may be calculated from the chemical equation (Chap. 5).

PROBLEM 1   Unknown quantities of N_2 and H_2 are added to 0.110 mole of NH_3. An instrument detects that 0.025 mole of N_2 formed. How many moles and grams (i) of H_2 formed, (ii) of NH_3 decomposed?

This explanation was given by Alexander Williamson in 1850.

The state of equilibrium may be described in terms of the speed of a reaction. As we shall see in Chap. 16, the speed of a reaction usually increases as the concentrations of the reactants increase, and decreases as the concentrations decrease. Thus, in Table 12.1, the decreasing concentrations of N_2 and H_2 result in a slowing of the reaction $N_2 + 3H_2 \longrightarrow 2NH_3$, while the rising concentration of NH_3 speeds up the reaction $2NH_3 \longrightarrow N_2 + 3H_2$. The faster reaction becomes slower, and the slower reaction becomes faster. Eventually, a state of equilibrium will be reached when the two reactions, forward and reverse, are occurring at the same speed: molecules of NH_3 are decomposing into H_2 and N_2, while N_2 and H_2 molecules are combining at the same speed to form NH_3. From then on, there will be no further change in the composition of the reaction mixture. A balance of opposing reactions has been achieved.

PROBLEM 2   A broken salt (NaCl) crystal of a given mass is placed in a liquid. After 36 hours, the crystal repairs itself but its mass is unchanged. Is the crystal in equilibrium with the liquid? What substance must be present in the liquid?

12.3 THE LAW OF CHEMICAL EQUILIBRIUM: THE EQUILIBRIUM CONSTANT

What are the experimental conditions at which equilibrium will be attained? Can we predict these conditions? Is there a definite relationship among the equilibrium concentrations of the reacting substances? We shall answer these questions with a generalized reaction and then apply the answer to specific cases.

Suppose the ideal gases A, B, C, and D undergo, at constant temperature, the reaction

$$aA + bB \rightleftharpoons cC + dD$$

where a, b, c, and d are the number of moles of each substance in the balanced chemical equation *as written*. Now, we write a **concentration term** in terms of molar concentrations as shown:

$$\frac{(\text{Concentration of C})^c \times (\text{Concentration of D})^d}{(\text{Concentration of A})^a \times (\text{Concentration of B})^b} = \frac{[C]^c \times [D]^d}{[A]^a \times [B]^b} = \frac{[C]^c[D]^d}{[A]^a[B]^b}$$

where [A], [B], [C], [D] are the concentrations in moles per liter of the gases in the reaction mixture. Experimentally, we find that equilibrium is reached at a given temperature when the concentration term equals a constant value:

$$\frac{[C]^c[D]^d}{[A]^a[B]^b} = \text{a constant value} = K \qquad (6)$$

By convention, a bracket, [ ], is used as an abbreviation for moles/liter, and multiplication signs are omitted.

K_c, the approved symbol for the equilibrium constant in terms of concentration, is simplified to K in this text.

This statement is known as the **law of chemical equilibrium** and the constant value is called the **equilibrium constant**, K for the reaction. Equation 6 is called the **equilibrium condition** for the reaction.* The value of K is a characteristic property of the given reaction.

In words, K is obtained when the equilibrium concentration of C, raised to the power c, is multiplied by the equilibrium concentration of D, raised to the power d, and this multiplication product is divided by the equilibrium concentration of A, raised to the power a, times the equilibrium concentration of B, raised to the power b. By convention, the concentrations of the reaction products are written in the numerator, and the concentrations of the initial reactants are written in the denominator. At equilibrium, *an infinite number of values* are possible for each concentration of A, B, C, and D, but the value of K remains constant. It does not depend upon the quantities of A, B, C, and D that are mixed, nor on the volume of the container in which they are mixed. The value for K changes *only* with changes in temperature. This condition is the same as saying that a constant is the product of two numbers, for example, the constant 18. There is then an infinite number of pairs whose product is 18—9.0 × 2.0 = 18, 6.0 × 3.0 = 18, 5.5 × 3.3 = 18, 7.5 × 10⁻⁶ × 2.4 × 10⁶ = 18, and so forth.

The equilibrium constant, like the concentration term, is a quotient, the result of dividing one number (the numerator) by another (the denominator); numerator/denominator = quotient.

PROBLEM 3   **Write three more different pairs of numbers whose product is 18.**

If the reaction is written backward, $cC + dD \rightleftharpoons aA + bB$, the equilibrium condition becomes

$$\frac{[A]^a[B]^b}{[C]^c[D]^d} = K' = \frac{1}{K}$$

Reversing the chemical equation changes the equilibrium constant from K to $1/K$. Therefore, to avoid unnecessary confusion, one should write the chemical equation *before* writing its equilibrium condition.

---

*The existence of such a relationship was first suspected by Claude Berthollet (1803) and formulated by Cato Guldberg and Peter Waage (1864). The theoretical (thermodynamic) basis for the law of chemical equilibrium was provided by Josiah Gibbs (1874–1878) and Jacobus Van't Hoff (1886).

For the gas reaction, $N_2 + 3H_2 \rightleftharpoons 2NH_3$, the equilibrium condition is

$$K = \frac{[NH_3]^2}{[N_2][H_2]^3}$$

From Table 12.1, the equilibrium concentrations are $[N_2] = 0.30$, $[H_2] = 0.90$, and $[NH_3] = 1.41$ mole/liter for Experiment 1 and $[N_2] = 0.20$, $[H_2] = 0.44$, and $[NH_3] = 0.39$ mole/liter for Experiment 2. Then K at 350 °C is

$$K = \frac{(1.40)^2}{0.30 \times (0.90)^3} = \frac{(0.39)^2}{0.20 \times (0.44)^3} = 9.0$$

In agreement with the law of chemical equilibrium, the concentration term is constant at equilibrium at a given temperature.

PROBLEM 4   **Write the equilibrium condition for the formation of nitrous acid from air pollutants:**

$$NO(g) + NO_2(g) + H_2O(g) \rightleftharpoons 2HNO_2(g)$$

K measures the extent to which a given reaction goes as written before equilibrium is attained. The *larger* the K, the *larger the quantities of products* compared to the reactants in the equilibrium mixture, and the *more complete* is the reaction as written. For example, a reaction involved in exhausting lead products from gasoline engines as comparatively volatile lead dichloride, $PbCl_2(c)$ (white, b.p. 950 °C), is

$$PbO(c) + C_2H_4Cl_2(l) \rightleftharpoons PbCl_2(c) + CO(g) + CH_4(g) \qquad \Delta H = -38.4 \text{ kcal}$$

for which $K = 1 \times 10^{38}$ at 25 °C. The conversion of lead(II) oxide, PbO (yellow solid), and dichloroethane, $C_2H_4Cl_2$ (colorless liquid, b.p. 84 °C), to $PbCl_2$, CO, and methane, CH_4, will be practically complete before equilibrium is established. The reverse reaction, however, is negligible.

A feeling for the relation between the value of K and the completeness of a reaction is helpful in appreciating its significance. For a value of K equal to about 10, not a very large number, a reaction like $H_2CO(g) \longrightarrow CO(g) + H_2(g)$ is practically complete; about 90 % of the H_2CO reacts and only 10 % remains unreacted at equilibrium, an engineer's paradise.

PROBLEM 5   **Oxygen, the most abundant element in the earth's crust, is obtained from air by liquefaction and distillation from other components. However, in General Chemistry laboratories it is generally prepared by thermal (use of heat) decomposition of oxygen compounds.* Pick (a) the compound most suitable, and (b) the compound least suitable as a laboratory source of O_2. Explain in terms of the K values.**

$$2KBrO_3(aq) \rightleftharpoons 2KBr(aq) + 3O_2(g) \qquad K = 2.20 \times 10^{14}$$
$$KClO_4(c) \rightleftharpoons KCl(c) + 2O_2(g) \qquad K = 4.19 \times 10^{20}$$
$$2KClO_3(c) \rightleftharpoons 2KCl(c) + 3O_2(g) \qquad K = 2.6 \times 10^{40}$$
$$2Fe_2O_3(c) \rightleftharpoons 4Fe(c) + 3O_2(g) \qquad K = 5.95 \times 10^{-265}$$

---

* This problem is not presented as an experiment to be performed by the student without supervision. Chlorates and perchlorates are particularly dangerous chemicals that frequently explode in the presence of impurities. Also, one must not heat materials in closed containers.

For the reaction

$$2CO_2(g) \rightleftharpoons 2CO(g) + O_2(g) \qquad \Delta H = +135.4 \text{ kcal}$$

$K = 3.2 \times 10^{-8}$ at 1550 °C. Because of the very small value of K, CO_2 will produce practically zero quantities of CO and O_2 before equilibrium is established. But the reverse reaction is practically complete. For this reason, a mixture of CO and O_2 is explosive.

The chemist would say, "CO_2 is **thermodynamically stable.**" This means that CO_2 has very little desire to decompose. The chemist would also say, "A mixture of CO and O_2 is **thermodynamically unstable.**" This means that CO and O_2 have a large tendency to form CO_2. Water is thermodynamically stable

$$2H_2O(g) \rightleftharpoons 2H_2(g) + O_2(g) \qquad K = 1.35 \times 10^{-11} \text{ at } 1430 \text{ °C}$$

but a mixture of H_2 and O_2 is not (the mixture is dangerously explosive).

PROBLEM 6 **(a) Commercially, ozone is prepared by passing air through a silent electric discharge (*ozonizer*):**

$$3O_2(g) \rightleftharpoons 2O_3(g) \qquad K = 1.65 \times 10^{-56}$$

Pick the substance, O_2 or O_3, that is thermodynamically stable. (b) Which molecule, O_2 or O, is thermodynamically stable?

$$2O(g) \rightleftharpoons O_2(g) \qquad K = 3.87 \times 10^{82}$$

EQUILIBRIA INVOLVING SOLIDS AND LIQUIDS*————————12.5

For the reaction

$$Ni(CO)_4(g) \rightleftharpoons Ni(c) + 4CO(g)$$

the equilibrium condition is

$$K'' = \frac{[Ni][CO]^4}{[Ni(CO)_4]}$$

in which [Ni] refers to the concentration of Ni in solid nickel. However, *at a given temperature,* the concentration of a pure solid or a pure liquid, unlike the concentration of a gas, is a constant, independent of the quantity present. The concentration of a solid is directly related to its density;** it is not altered by the chemical reaction, nor

---

*When chemical equilibrium is established in a mixture of gases or in a liquid solution (page 322), we have a case of homogeneous equilibrium (only one phase is involved, page 6). When chemical equilibrium is established between a gas and a solid, a gas and a liquid, or a liquid and a solid, the equilibrium is said to be heterogeneous (more than one phase is involved, page 28).

**The density, g/ml, at a given temperature, remains the same for any given quantity of a pure solid or liquid and so fixes the concentration:

$$\frac{\text{density}}{\text{molecular wt}} \times \frac{10^3 \text{ ml}}{\text{liter}} = \frac{g}{ml} \times \frac{\text{mole}}{g} \times \frac{10^3 \text{ ml}}{\text{liter}}$$

is it sensitive to pressure changes. We can then incorporate the constant concentration of Ni into the equilibrium constant to give a new constant:

$$\frac{[CO]^4}{[Ni(CO)_4]} = \frac{K''}{[Ni]} = K$$

K is just as good a constant as K'', provided the temperature is fixed and the solid (regardless of the quantity) is present. Thus, *whenever a reaction involves pure solids or pure liquids, they do not appear in the equilibrium condition or in the concentration term*. Then, the equilibrium condition for the reaction

$$4H_2O(g) + 3Fe(c) \rightleftharpoons 4H_2(g) + Fe_3O_4(c) \qquad \Delta H = -35.8 \text{ kcal}$$

is

$$K = \frac{[H_2]^4}{[H_2O]^4}$$

This procedure greatly simplifies the writing of equilibrium conditions.

PROBLEM 7   **Write the equilibrium condition for the formation of silver tarnish (silver sulfide):**

$$2Ag(c) + H_2S(g) \rightleftharpoons H_2(g) + Ag_2S(c)$$

12.6 _____ DIRECTION OF THE REACTION

For the gas reaction, $N_2 + 3H_2 \rightleftharpoons 2NH_3$, the concentration term is

$$\frac{[NH_3]^2}{[N_2][H_2]^3} \qquad \text{and} \qquad K = 9.0 \text{ at } 350 \text{ °C}$$

When the concentration term equals 9.0, equilibrium has been attained. When the concentration term does *not* equal K, the mixture is *not* at equilibrium, and a chemical change (either the forward or the reverse reaction) will occur until equilibrium is re-established.

When the concentration term is less than K, $[NH_3]$ is smaller than it should be at equilibrium. Equally correct, we may say that $[N_2]$ and $[H_2]$ are greater than they should be at equilibrium. Under these conditions, the only possible direction of the reaction is the direction that makes $[NH_3]$ larger and makes $[N_2]$ and $[H_2]$ smaller; namely, the reaction goes from left to right. N_2 and H_2 are thus consumed and NH_3 is formed. We describe this reaction by saying, "*When the concentration term is less than K, the reaction goes from left to right.*" Similarly, when the concentration term is greater than K, the $[NH_3]$ is too great or $[N_2]$ and $[H_2]$ are too small. In this case, the only possible direction of the reaction is from right to left—the formation of more N_2 and H_2 with the consumption of NH_3. *When the concentration term is greater than K, the reaction goes from right to left*. In general, *the reaction goes in that direction that makes the concentration term equal K*. When the concentration term equals K, equilibrium has been re-established.

Example 1

For the gas reaction, $CO + H_2O \rightleftharpoons CO_2 + H_2$, $K = 0.628$ at 986 °C. A mixture   contains $[H_2O] = 0.0120$, $[H_2] = 0.0141$, $[CO_2] = 0.0100$,

[CO] = 0.0105 mole/liter. Is the reaction at equilibrium? If not, in which direction will the reaction go?

Answer

First calculate the concentration term from the given initial concentrations:

$$\frac{[CO_2][H_2]}{[CO][H_2O]} = \frac{0.0100 \times 0.0141}{0.0105 \times 0.0120} = 1.12$$

We see that the concentration term does not equal K; therefore, the reaction is not at equilibrium. Since the concentration term is greater than K, the reaction goes from right to left. The concentrations of CO_2 and H_2 decrease while the concentrations of CO and H_2O increase until the concentration term equals 0.628.

PROBLEM 8 **(a) Calculate the concentration term from the composition of the mixture given for each of the following reactions; (b) K is also given. For each reaction state whether it is at equilibrium. If it is not at equilibrium, state the direction in which the reaction will go.**

(i) Manufacture of lime:
$$CaCO_3(c) \rightleftharpoons CaO(c) + CO_2(g) \qquad K = 5.76 \times 10^{-25}$$
$$[CO_2] = 1.01 \times 10^{-3}\,mole/\ell$$

(ii)
$$NO(g) + NO_2(g) + H_2O(g) \rightleftharpoons 2HNO_2(g) \qquad K = 26.7$$
$$[NO] = 0.100,\ [NO_2] = 0.150,\ [H_2O] = 4.00 \times 10^{-3},\ [HNO_2] = 0.0400\,mole/\ell$$

(iii) Manufacture of methyl (wood) alcohol:
$$CO(g) + 2H_2(g) \rightleftharpoons CH_3OH(g) \qquad K = 1.36 \times 10^7$$
$$[CO] = 0.0100,\ [H_2] = 0.0300,\ [CH_3OH] = 0.0200\,mole/\ell$$

EQUILIBRIUM CALCULATIONS —————————————— 12.7

The most important calculation involving equilibrium is the calculation of the equilibrium constant from experimental data. When the equilibrium concentrations are known, this calculation involves merely a substitution of these numbers into the equation for the equilibrium condition (see page 378 for an example).

PROBLEM 9 **From the given equilibrium concentrations, $[N_2O_4] = 0.69$ and $[NO_2] = 0.62\,mole/\ell$ at 40 °C, calculate K for $N_2O_4(g) \rightleftharpoons 2NO_2(g)$ at 40 °C.**

More frequently, however, it is necessary to calculate equilibrium concentrations.

There is scarcely a product whose manufacture does not involve the use of sulfur* in some manner. The production of sulfuric acid, known as "the life blood of the chemical industry," serves as a measure of industrial, and thus, economic activity. It is used in such basic industries as the manufacture of fertilizers, chemicals, paints and pigments, paper, coal tar products, and industrial explosives, the processing of textiles, the refining of petroleum, the fabrication of iron and steel, and other metallurgical processes.

Sulfuric acid, H_2SO_4 (colorless, corrosive liquid), is manufactured from waste

---

*Also known as *brimstone* (from Old English *brinnen,* to burn, and *ston,* stone). More than 100 lb are used each year for each person in the United States, although sulfur itself is rarely seen by most persons.

H_2S and waste SO_2, or the mineral *pyrite* (*fool's gold*), FeS_2 (yellow), or sulfur, S, obtained from underground sulfur deposits. But the crucial step in making H_2SO_4 is the reversible gas reaction

$$2SO_2 + O_2 \rightleftharpoons 2SO_3 \qquad (7)$$

Such as platinum, Pt, or divanadium pentoxide, V_2O_5 (yellow-red solid), but the presence of a catalyst (Chap. 16) need not concern us here.

The reaction is extremely slow under room conditions but proceeds very rapidly above 500 °C in the presence of a catalyst. This reaction is also the basis of a commercial method for the conversion of about 90 % of the SO_2 in exhaust (stack) gases to SO_3, recovered as H_2SO_4.

Recall (page 156) the warning that a mixture of reactants in the proper proportions does not necessarily react completely, leaving only traces of the initial reactants unreacted. Equation 7 *does not* tell us that 1 mole of O_2 *must* react with 2 moles of SO_2 to produce 2 moles of SO_3. However, the equation does give us the *relative amounts that react* (page 376); it tells us that for every 1 mole of O_2 consumed, 2 moles of SO_2 must also be consumed to produce 2 moles of SO_3. This means that if we start with any given quantity of O_2—say, 3.50 moles—and we find *from experiment* that only 0.22 mole of O_2 reacts, then 0.44 mole of SO_2 must also be consumed and 0.44 mole of SO_3 must be produced. This is the same as using conversion factors to find how many moles of SO_2 react with 0.22 mole of O_2 and how many moles of SO_3 form from 0.22 mole of O_2

$$0.22 \text{ mole } O_2 \times \frac{2 \text{ mole } SO_2}{1 \text{ mole } O_2} = 0.44 \text{ mole } SO_2$$

$$0.22 \text{ mole } O_2 \times \frac{2 \text{ mole } SO_3}{1 \text{ mole } O_2} = 0.44 \text{ mole } SO_3$$

Or, if x moles is the change in oxygen, then $2x$ must be the change for SO_2 and SO_3, the same as writing

$$x \text{ mole } O_2 \times \frac{2 \text{ mole } SO_2}{1 \text{ mole } O_2} = 2x \text{ mole } SO_2$$

$$x \text{ mole } O_2 \times \frac{2 \text{ mole } SO_3}{1 \text{ mole } O_2} = 2x \text{ mole } SO_3$$

Example 2

3.00 moles of SO_2 and 1.50 moles of O_2 are introduced into an empty 2.0-liter container at 1350 °K. We find, by experiment, that 0.90 mole of O_2 is present at equilibrium. Calculate K.

Answer

We start with 1.50 moles of O_2. But only 0.90 mole of O_2 is present at equilibrium. This means that 0.60 mole of O_2 (1.50 mole − 0.90 mole) reacts. Hence, 1.20 moles of SO_2 is consumed and 1.20 moles of SO_3 is produced as shown:

$$0.60 \text{ mole } O_2 \times \frac{2 \text{ mole } SO_2}{1 \text{ mole } O_2} = 1.20 \text{ mole } SO_2$$

$$0.60 \text{ mole } O_2 \times \frac{2 \text{ mole } SO_3}{1 \text{ mole } O_2} = 1.20 \text{ mole } SO_3$$

This leaves 1.80 moles of SO_2 (initial 3.00 moles − 1.20 moles consumed) at equilibrium. Or, let x = the number of moles of O_2 *consumed* = 0.60 mole. Then

$2x$ = the number of moles of SO_2 *consumed* = 2×0.60 = 1.20 moles

and

$2x$ = the number of moles of SO_3 *produced* = 1.20 moles

The numbers of moles present at equilibrium, then, are SO_2, 3.00 − 1.20; O_2, 1.50 − 0.60; SO_3, 1.20. A summary follows:

	$2SO_2$	+	O_2	$\rightleftharpoons$	$2SO_3$
Initial number of moles, from data	3.00		1.50		0
Change in moles, from chemical equation (7)	$-2x$		$-x$		$+2x$
Moles at equilibrium (sum of first two lines)	$3.00 - 2x$		$1.50 - x$		$0 + 2x$
From the data, $x = 0.60$ mole, then					
Moles at equilibrium	$3.00 - 1.20 = 1.80$		$1.50 - 0.60 = 0.90$		$0 + 1.20 = 1.20$
Volume, from data = 2.0 l					
[ ] at equilibrium	$\dfrac{1.80}{2} = 0.90$		$\dfrac{0.90}{2} = 0.45$		$\dfrac{1.20}{2} = 0.60$

The equilibrium condition is

$$K = \frac{[SO_3]^2}{[SO_2]^2[O_2]} = \frac{(0.60)^2}{(0.90)^2 \times 0.45} = 0.99 \text{ at } 1350 \text{ }^\circ K$$

Example 3

1.24 moles of H_2 and 5.08 moles of N_2 were introduced into an empty 10.0-liter container at 400 °C. When equilibrium was attained, 0.159 mole of NH_3 was formed. Calculate K for $N_2 + 3H_2 \rightleftharpoons 2NH_3$.

Answer

Let x = the number of moles of N_2 *consumed*. Then, according to the chemical equation, for every 1 mole of N_2 consumed, 3 moles of H_2 are *consumed*, and 2 moles of NH_3 must *form*. Therefore, $3x$ is equal to the number of moles of H_2 consumed and $2x$ is equal to the number of moles of NH_3 formed. This is the same as writing

$$x \text{ mole } N_2 \times \frac{3 \text{ mole } H_2}{1 \text{ mole } N_2} = 3x \text{ mole } H_2$$

$$x \text{ mole } N_2 \times \frac{2 \text{ mole } NH_3}{1 \text{ mole } N_2} = 2x \text{ mole } NH_3$$

A summary follows:

	N_2	+	$3H_2$	$\rightleftharpoons$	$2NH_3$
Initial number of moles, from data	5.08		1.24		0
Change in moles, from chemical equation	$-x$		$-3x$		$+2x$
Moles at equilibrium (sum of first two lines)	$5.08 - x$		$1.24 - 3x$		$0 + 2x$

From the data, $2x = 0.159$ mole, then
$x = 0.0795$ and $3x = 0.239$

Moles at equilibrium	$5.08 - 0.080 = 5.00$	$1.24 - 0.239 = 1.00$		0.159

Volume, from data $= 10.0\ \ell$
[ ] at equilibrium

$$\frac{5.00}{10.0} = 0.500 \qquad \frac{1.00}{10.0} = 0.100 \qquad \frac{0.159}{10.0} = 0.0159$$

The equilibrium condition is

$$K = \frac{[NH_3]^2}{[N_2][H_2]^3} = \frac{(0.0159)^2}{0.500 \times (0.100)^3} = 0.506 \text{ at } 400\ °C$$

PROBLEM 10 When **1.082 mole of N_2, 1.164 mole of O_2, and 1.082 mole of F_2 are mixed in an empty 10.0-liter container at 627 °C, a reaction occurs leaving 1.000 mole of N_2 at equilibrium. Find K for $N_2(g) + 2O_2(g) + F_2(g) \rightleftharpoons 2NO_2F(g)$, nitryl fluoride, at 627 °C.**

Example 4

6.00 moles of nickel tetracarbonyl, $Ni(CO)_4$, were introduced into an empty 3.00-liter container at 399 °K. After 10.0 % of the $Ni(CO)_4$ decomposed to Ni and CO, equilibrium was established. (a) How many moles of Ni were produced? (b) Calculate K for $Ni(CO)_4(g) \rightleftharpoons Ni(c) + 4CO(g)$ at 399 °K.

Answer

Let $x =$ the number of moles of Ni *produced*. Then, according to the chemical equation, for every 1 mole of Ni formed, 4 moles of CO must also *form*, and 1 mole of $Ni(CO)_4$ must be *consumed*. Then $4x$ is equal to the number of moles of CO formed,

$$x \text{ mole Ni} \times \frac{4 \text{ mole CO}}{1 \text{ mole Ni}} = 4x \text{ mole CO}$$

and x is equal to the number of moles of $Ni(CO)_4$ consumed:

$$x \text{ mole Ni} \times \frac{1 \text{ mole Ni (CO)}_4}{1 \text{ mole Ni}} = x \text{ mole Ni (CO)}_4$$

From the data, only 10.0 % of the 6.00 moles of the $Ni(CO)_4$ decomposes; this means that 0.600 mole $\left(\frac{10}{100} \times 6.00 \text{ moles} = 0.600 \text{ mole}\right)$ decomposes. Hence $x = 0.600$ mole. In summary,

	$Ni(CO)_4(g)$ $\rightleftharpoons$	$Ni(c)$ +	$4CO(g)$
Initial number of moles, from data	6.00	0	0
Change in moles, from chemical equation	$-x$	$+x$	$+4x$
Moles at equilibrium (sum of first two lines)	$6.00 - x$	$0 + x$	$0 + 4x$
From the data, $x = 0.600$ mole, then			
Moles at equilibrium	$6.00 - 0.600 = 5.40$	0.600	2.40
Volume, from data $= 3.00\ \ell$			
[ ] at equilibrium	$\dfrac{5.40}{3.00} = 1.80$		$\dfrac{2.40}{3.00} = 0.800$
Moles of Ni produced $= 0.600$			

The equilibrium condition is

$$K = \frac{[CO]^4}{[Ni(CO)_4]} = \frac{(0.800)^4}{1.80} = 0.228$$

PROBLEM 11   0.816 mole of methyl alcohol is added to a 5.00-liter flask at 100 °C. Equilibrium is established after 18 % of the alcohol dissociates (decomposes) into CO and H_2. Calculate K for $CH_3OH(g) \rightleftharpoons CO(g) + 2H_2(g)$ at 100 °C.

When the value of K and the initial concentrations are known, the composition of the equilibrium mixture can be calculated. This is illustrated in Example 5, page 386, with the reaction $N_2(g) + O_2(g) \longrightarrow 2NO(g)$. NO, nitrogen oxide, is a color-less gas. It is formed in all combustion processes that occur in air. It is, therefore, one of the pollutants (page 309) emitted by internal combustion engines (trucks, auto-mobiles, and planes) and tobacco or grass smokers. It rapidly undergoes further reaction (page 169) with O_2 (air), producing NO_2, nitrogen dioxide (reddish-brown gas). NO_2 is a deadly poison; its great danger is often unappreciated. Exposure may cause inflammation of the lungs with only slight pain, but death may occur a few days later from the resulting edema.• Continuous exposure to concentrations as low as 5×10^{-4} ml per ml of air may be fatal in 48 hours. NO_2 is therefore of great significance in air pollution. It is involved in a series of atmospheric reactions leading to smog formation (page 169). Cigarette smoke* (filtered or unfiltered) contains about 3×10^{-4} ml NO_2 per ml of air; pipe tobacco smoke and cigar smoke contain higher concentrations.

•Swelling due to the accumulation of water in the intercellular spaces of the body.

Pollution control schemes cover radical redesigns of boiler combustion zones and auto engines** and the firing of fuel so as to reduce the amount of excess air required for combustion. Presently, no practical scheme is available to remove nitrogen oxides from waste gases.

Environmental problems associated with high-flying supersonic aircraft (SST) result from the chemical reaction of engine-exhausted NO with ozone:

---

*Cigarette smoke sufficiently alters the structure of the mitochondria—the cell sites where many chemical reactions occur to extract energy from food and make it available to the cell—to cause the death of cells in respiratory passages. Readers interested in the subject are referred to "Health Consequences of Smoking," Surgeon General Report: 1972, H.E.W. Department, U.S. Govt. Printing Office, Washington, D.C.

**Such as the Rankine engine based on the principle of William Rankine's steam engine (1859); and the engine (*Scientific American*, August 1972, page 14) invented by Felix Wankel (1954), based on the principle of a rotating engine.

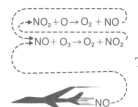

$$NO \text{ (exhaust)} + O_3 \longrightarrow NO_2 + O_2 \qquad (8)$$
$$NO_2 + O \longrightarrow NO + O_2 \qquad (9)$$

The addition of these two equations yielding

$$O_3 + O \longrightarrow 2O_2 \qquad (10)$$

clearly shows that comparatively small amounts of NO can in time destroy large amounts of ozone. The NO molecule consumed in Equation 8 is regenerated in Equation 9 and can again be used to change ozone, O_3, to oxygen, O_2 (Equation 10).

About 25–30 km high.

The (non-smog) air we normally breathe contains about 2×10^{-8} ml O_3 per ml air. But in the upper atmosphere, a layer of ozone of much higher concentration exists. Presumably, nature was aware of our existence when she formed this layer of ozone, because it makes life possible on earth. Its presence protects us from ultraviolet (UV) photons that cause severe damage to body cells. It prevents these UV photons generated in outer space from reaching the earth's surface by absorbing them and then emitting harmless photons in the IR (heat) range:

$$hf(UV) + O_3 \text{ (ground state)} \longrightarrow O_3 \text{ (excited state)}$$
$$O_3 \text{ (excited state)} \longrightarrow O_2 + O \text{ (excited state)}$$
$$O \text{ (excited state)} \longrightarrow O \text{ (ground state)} + hf(IR)$$
$$\overline{hf(UV) + O_3 \longrightarrow O_2 + O + hf(IR)}$$

In turn, O_2 and O are converted back to O_3, so that the concentration of O_3 remains more or less constant.

Thus, a disastrous upset of the natural ozone balance with the subsequent destruction of the protective shield against serious UV biological damage is possible. The National Academy of Sciences concludes that the danger of ozone destruction due to emissions of nitrogen oxides by high altitude (SST) aircraft is real. Although current operations are not a significant threat, any large scale operation should be preceded by a binding commitment to strict engine emission standards.* However, more recent research on the reaction between chlorine oxide, ClO (page 518), and NO predicts a decrease of roughly 30 % in the calculated ozone destruction by SST emissions. Further, molecules like HO_2 may rapidly convert NO to NO_2 before the NO has a chance to react with O_3.

HO_2 is formed at high altitudes, and

$$HO_2 + NO \xrightarrow{fast} ON + NO_2$$

Example 5

In an experimental combustion chamber at 1800 °K, the initial concentrations are $[N_2] = 2.2$ and $[O_2] = 0.060$ mole/ℓ. K for the reaction $N_2(g) + O_2(g) \rightleftharpoons 2NO(g)$ is 1.2×10^{-4} at 1800 °K. Find the equilibrium concentrations of N_2, O_2, and NO.

Answer

Since concentrations are given in mole per liter, we can assume we have initially 2.2 moles N_2 and 0.060 mole O_2 in a 1-liter chamber. Let x = number of moles

---

*"Environmental Impact of Stratospheric Flight," Report of Climatic Impact Committee, National Academy of Sciences, Washington, D.C., 1975, and "Biological Impacts of Increased Intensities of Solar Ultraviolet Radiation," National Academy of Sciences, Washington, D.C., 1973.

of N_2 *consumed* in reaching equilibrium. Then, according to the chemical equation, x is also the number of moles of O_2 consumed, and $2x$ is the number of moles of NO formed. In summary,

	N_2	$+$ O_2	$\rightleftharpoons$ 2NO
Initial number of moles, from data	2.2	0.060	0
Change in moles, from chemical equation	$-x$	$-x$	$+2x$
Moles at equilibrium (sum of first two lines)	$2.2 - x$	$0.060 - x$	$0 + 2x$
Volume, from data = 1.00 ℓ			
[ ] at equilibrium	$2.2 - x$	$0.060 - x$	$2x$

The equilibrium condition is

$$\frac{[NO]^2}{[N_2][O_2]} = \frac{(2x)^2}{(2.2 - x)(0.060 - x)} = 1.2 \times 10^{-4} \qquad (11)$$

We can avoid the labor of solving this quadratic equation by assuming that x is so small compared to 0.060 (and, therefore, also small compared to 2.2) that it can be discarded without introducing a serious error into our calculation. But what constitutes a serious error? For our purposes, we will *discard* a quantity which is not larger than *0.1 of the initial quantity.* Equation 11 then becomes

$$\frac{(2x)^2}{2.2 \times 0.060} \approx 1.2 \times 10^{-4}$$

(on the *assumption* that x is not larger than 0.006, 0.1 of 0.060). Now, solving for x

$$(2x)^2 \approx 1.2 \times 10^{-4} \times 2.2 \times 0.060 \approx 0.16 \times 10^{-4}$$
$$4x^2 \approx 0.16 \times 10^{-4}$$
$$x^2 \approx 0.040 \times 10^{-4} \approx 4.0 \times 10^{-6}$$
$$x \approx 2.0 \times 10^{-3} = 0.002$$

x is not larger than 0.1 of 0.060. We are, therefore, justified in changing $2.2 - x$ to 2.2 and $0.060 - x$ to 0.060 in Equation 11. On the other hand, if x is greater than 0.1 of the initial quantity, it cannot be discarded and Equation 11 cannot be solved by this method.

The equilibrium concentrations are then

$$[NO] = 2x = 2 \times 2.0 \times 10^{-3} = 4.0 \times 10^{-3}$$
$$[N_2] = 2.2 - x = 2.2 - 0.002 = 2.2$$
$$[O_2] = 0.060 - x = 0.060 - 0.002 = 0.058$$

We summarize our recommended procedure for solving quadratic equations:

Make the simplifying assumption that x is not larger than 0.1 of the initial quantity and so discard x.

Solve the simplified equation.

Verify that the assumption is true.

When multiplying, notice that x *cannot* be discarded; it may be discarded in an addition or a subtraction depending on the number of significant figures. For example, in $2.0 - x$ and $2.0x$ let $x = 0.0030$

A quadratic equation is an equation in which the variable (x) is raised to a power no higher than 2.

The symbol $\approx$ means "approximately equal to," App. II.

$$2.0 - x = 2.0 - 0.0030 = 1.9970 = 2.0$$
$$2.0 \times x = 2.0 \times 0.0030 = 0.0060$$

1.9970 is almost equal to 2.0 so that x may be discarded, while 0.0060 does not equal 2.0.

PROBLEM 12   Find the equation concentrations of N_2, O_2, and NO when the initial concentrations are $[N_2] = 0.175$ and $[O_2] = 1.50$ mole/ℓ, and $K = 1.12 \times 10^{-6}$ at 1027 °C for the reaction $N_2(g) + O_2(g) \rightleftharpoons 2NO(g)$.

12.8 PRINCIPLE OF LE CHATELIER: CHANGING THE COMPOSITION OF AN EQUILIBRIUM MIXTURE

Almost everyone is conscious of the tremendous importance and influence of scientific research and development on our society and environment. Science is interwoven throughout the structure of society and government. This situation began during the 18th century, particularly in France, when chemical knowledge stimulated industrial chemistry. As a consequence of World War I, industries and governments recognized the importance of chemistry and physics. They became aware that the conditions under which maximum yield of a chemical product could be obtained, for a given economic input, could be predicted from university (basic) researches. Such conditions, formerly sought through expensive and frequently useless modifications of manufacturing equipment, can be calculated *before* a plant is designed. The prediction of these conditions is the subject of this section.

The vast sums of money, roughly 43 billion dollars for the year 1977, from industry and government, required to support research and development have a massive impact on the nature of our society. This expenditure no longer represents a budgetary fringe benefit. However, according to Donald Hornig, "The question is not whether we should have basic research, whether we should have research and development, or even whether it should continue to grow—but rather in what ways and for what purposes it should be expanded. The answer to this question will have to be supplied by all of us." In the final analysis, it is the manner in which scientific discoveries are applied that will affect our welfare, and the scientist should have no more control over the nature of these applications than any other citizen. But scientists do hold the responsibility of helping governmental policy makers understand technical issues. Science should be viewed as a means of improving the well-being of mankind, but this requires continuous support of basic and applied research. The pursuit of happiness and the pursuit of science are not incompatible in the marriage of science and technology.

We shall now develop some general rules to enable us to predict the chemical reaction that will occur when the composition of an equilibrium mixture is disturbed. The composition of a mixture at equilibrium depends on the quantities of the reactants, on the volume of the container in which they are mixed, and on the temperature. *But only the temperature affects the value of the equilibrium constant.* A change in volume, or the addition or removal of substances, alters the concentrations of the reacting substances, but the value of K remains the same.

Change of Concentration   The addition or removal of any one of the reacting substances at constant volume changes its concentration. If a gas mixture of NH_3, H_2,

Special Science Assistant to the President (1967).

Read, for example, "Physics in Combustion Research," Danny Hartley, Physics Today, December 1975, page 37.

and N_2 ($N_2 + 3H_2 \rightleftharpoons 2NH_3$) is at equilibrium and more H_2 is added at constant volume, the H_2 concentration is increased. This makes the concentration term, $[NH_3]^2/[N_2][H_2]^3$, *smaller* than K. For example, K at 350 °C is 9.0. If in Experiment 1, page 378, $[H_2]$ is increased from 0.90 to—say, 2.0 mole/liter—then

$$\text{concentration term} = \frac{(1.40)^2}{0.30 \times (2.0)^3} = 0.82 \neq 9.0$$

$\neq$ *means "not equal to." See App. II.*

The concentration term is less than K. Hence, the reaction goes from left to right (page 380). When NH_3 is thus produced at the expense of N_2 and H_2, the equilibrium is said to "*shift to the right*." See Fig. 12.2. Similarly, adding N_2 causes a shift to the right. Adding NH_3 causes a shift to the left (more N_2 and H_2 form at the expense of NH_3). The rule is that *increasing the concentration* (or quantity or the pressure at constant volume) of one substance in an equilibrium mixture *causes the reaction to take place in that direction which consumes some of the material added.* Similarly, decreasing the concentration of a substance causes the equilibrium to shift in that

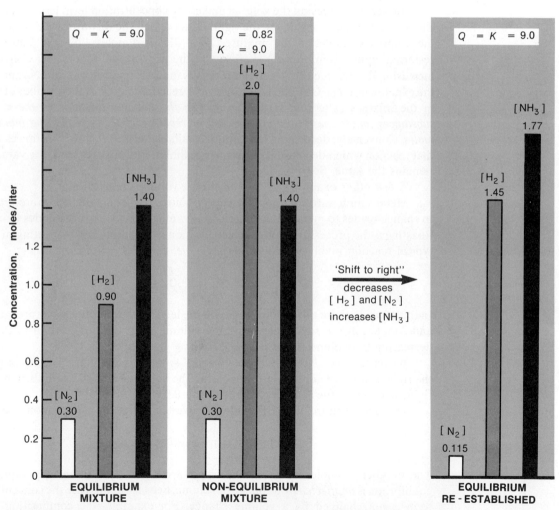

FIGURE 12.2 Representation of the equilibrium "shift to the right" in the gas reaction, $N_2 + 3H_2 \rightleftharpoons 2NH_3$, at 350 °C, resulting from an increase in the quantity (concentration) of H_2. The concentration term is abbreviated as Q.

direction which produces more of that substance. But in either case, the value of K does not change.

The addition or removal of a portion of pure solid or pure liquid involved in a reaction—for example, nickel in $Ni(CO)_4(g) \rightleftharpoons Ni(c) + 4CO(g)$—has no effect because the concentration of pure solids and liquids is not changed (page 379).

Change of Volume (Concentration)   Another way in which to change the concentration is to change the volume of the container available to the reacting gases. When the volume of the container is changed, the concentration of all the gases in it is changed. Thus, for the equilibrium mixture $N_2 + 3H_2 \rightleftharpoons 2NH_3$ at 350 °C, if the volume of the container is decreased—say it is halved—then the concentration of each gas is doubled. (*This also increases the pressure of each gas,* page 51.) In Experiment 1, page 378, the concentration term then becomes

$$\frac{(1.40 \times 2)^2}{(0.30 \times 2)(0.90 \times 2)^3} = \frac{(2.80)^2}{(0.60)(1.80)^3} = 2.2 \neq 9.0$$

In this case, decreasing the volume makes the concentration term less than K (9.0). Therefore, the reaction shifts to the right. Observe that the forward reaction *decreases* the number of moles in the mixture ($N_2 + 3H_2$ is 4 moles, $2NH_3$ is 2 moles). In restoring equilibrium, more NH_3 forms at the expense of N_2 and H_2. Conversely, increasing the volume of the container results in the formation of more N_2 and H_2 at the expense of NH_3. Observe that the reverse reaction *increases* the number of moles in the mixture. The rule is that *increasing the volume available to the reacting substances favors that reaction (forward or reverse) which increases the number of moles.* Conversely, decreasing the volume available to the reacting substances favors that reaction which decreases the number of moles. But in either case, the value of K remains the same. See Fig. 12.3.

A few other examples of the effect of a volume change follow:

Metal sulfides are commonly used as a source of metals. But it is more practical to change oxides to metals. It is therefore advantageous to convert sulfides to oxides. **Roasting** is the process whereby such conversion is accomplished by heating in air. A typical reaction involves zinc sulfide (*zinc blende*), ZnS (colorless):

White when formed as a fine suspension; see page 343.

$$2ZnS(c) + 3O_2(g) \rightleftharpoons 2ZnO(c) + 2SO_2(g) \qquad \Delta H = -217.8 \text{ kcal}$$

In this reaction there are 3 moles of gas on the left (recall that pure solids are ignored) and 2 moles on the right. Increasing the volume shifts the equilibrium to the left; decreasing the volume shifts it to the right.

In the reaction, $Ni(CO)_4(g) \rightleftharpoons Ni(c) + 4CO(g)$, there are 4 moles of gas on the right and 1 mole on the left. Increasing the volume shifts the equilibrium to the right; decreasing the volume shifts it to the left.

In a blast furnace, iron(III) oxide is converted to iron by carbon monoxide, CO,

$$Fe_2O_3(c) + 3CO(g) \rightleftharpoons 2Fe(l) + 3CO_2(g)$$

The number of moles of gas is the *same,* 3 on each side of the equation. This equilibrium is *unaffected* by a change in volume, because in this case the concentration term is not changed by a volume change. For example, the composition of an equilibrium mixture at about 400 °C is $[CO] = 0.010$ and $[CO_2] = 0.0215$ mole/ℓ, so that

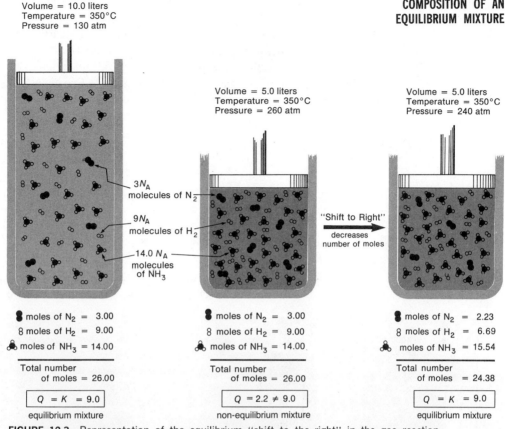

FIGURE 12.3 Representation of the equilibrium "shift to the right" in the gas reaction, $N_2 + 3H_2 \rightleftharpoons 2NH_3$, at 350 °C, resulting from a decrease in volume (increase in pressure): the number of moles of N_2 and H_2 decreases, while the number of moles of NH_3 increases, resulting in a decrease in the total number of moles. Concentration term is abbreviated as $Q\cdot$. *Pressure values are assumed.*

$$K = \frac{(0.0215)^3}{(0.010)^3} = 9.9$$

If the volume of the blast furnace is doubled to prolong contact between CO and Fe_2O_3, then [CO] = 0.010/2 and $[CO_2]$ = 0.0215/2. However, the concentration term still equals K:

$$\text{concentration term} = \frac{(0.0215/2)^3}{(0.010/2)^3} = \frac{(0.0215)^3 \times 2^3}{(0.010)^3 \times 2^3} = 9.9 = K$$

This equilibrium is thus not affected by volume changes.

Change of Temperature   An equilibrium constant stays constant only *if the temperature is not changed.* A change in temperature changes the composition of an equilibrium mixture by changing the equilibrium constant. This effect can be predicted from the thermochemical equation. The rule is that *increasing the temperature favors that reaction which absorbs heat; decreasing the temperature favors that reaction which emits heat.* In forming NH_3, heat is emitted:

Unless otherwise stated, K values are at 25 °C.

$$N_2 + 3H_2 \rightleftharpoons 2NH_3 \qquad \Delta H = -22.1 \text{ kcal} \qquad (12)$$

Therefore, raising the temperature shifts the equilibrium to the left, *decreasing K*; lowering the temperature shifts the equilibrium to the right, *increasing K*. For example, for this reaction $K = 4.0 \times 10^8$ at 25 °C but equals 9.0 at 350 °C.

These rules are summarized by **Le Chatelier's Principle:*** *When a change is made in an equilibrium mixture, the equilibrium shifts; the equilibrium will shift in the direction that tends to oppose or counteract the change.*

Example 6

An equilibrium mixture of the gases, N_2, H_2, and NH_3 ($N_2 + 3H_2 \rightleftharpoons 2NH_3$) is changed by (a) adding H_2 at constant volume, (b) decreasing the volume (the same as increasing the pressure), (c) raising the temperature. Show how the equilibrium shifts oppose these changes.

---

*Henry Le Chatelier formulated this principle in 1888. Essentially the same principle was independently recognized by Ferdinand Braun in 1887, as a result of his work on solubility (page 397).

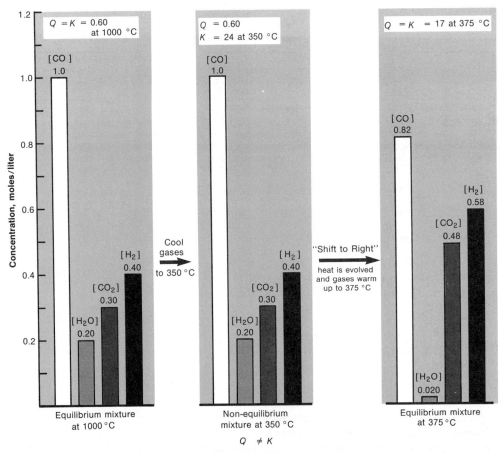

FIGURE 12.4 Representation of the equilibrium "shift to the right" in the gas reaction, $CO + H_2O \rightleftharpoons CO_2 + H_2$, $\Delta H = -10$ kcal, resulting from a decrease in temperature. However, the heat evolved makes the decrease in temperature less than it would be in the absence of an equilibrium shift. The concentration term is abbreviated as Q.

Answer

(a) The *addition* of H_2 increases the concentration of H_2, but the shift of the equilibrium to the right *consumes* some of the H_2 and decreases the concentration; see Fig. 12.2 (page 389). (b) Decreasing the volume causes an *increase in the pressure* of the gases, but the equilibrium shift to the right decreases the number of moles of gas; decreasing the number of moles of gas *decreases the pressure* (page 127); see Fig. 12.3, page 391.

When the number of moles of gas is the same on each side of the chemical equation, the equilibrium mixture is not changed by a change in volume because the forward or the reverse reaction *cannot oppose* an increase or a decrease in pressure by changing the number of molecules in the container.*

(c) The temperature is raised, but the equilibrium shift to the left absorbs heat. Absorption of heat has a cooling effect (page 287). This heat absorption thus makes the rise in temperature less than it would be in the absence of the shift. See Fig. 12.4 for an illustration.

PROBLEM 13 **For the tarnishing of silver**

$$2Ag(c) + H_2S(g) \rightleftharpoons H_2(g) + Ag_2S(c) \qquad K = 3.60, \Delta H = -2.86 \text{ kcal}$$

(a) State the effect (increase, decrease, no change) of the following changes on the number of moles of $Ag_2S(c)$ at equilibrium. Temperature and volume are constant unless otherwise stated. Consider each change separately: (i) decreasing the volume of the container (the same as increasing the pressure of the gases); (ii) adding $Ag(c)$; (iii) adding H_2; (iv) adding H_2S; (v) removing H_2; (vi) removing H_2S; (vii) lowering the temperature. (b) What is the effect of each of the following changes on K? (i) raising the temperature; (ii) increasing the volume (the same as decreasing the pressure of the gases); (iii) adding $Ag(c)$; (iv) removing H_2.

EQUILIBRIUM AND SPEED OF REACTION _____ 12.9

An apparent contradiction requires an explanation. For Reaction 12 (page 392), K is much larger at 25 °C than at 500 °C. This tells us that much more NH_3 will form (for a given quantity of H_2 and N_2 in the molar ratio of 3 : 1) at 25 °C than at 500 °C. Yet, the temperature used at T.V.A. (Tennessee Valley Authority) for NH_3 production is 500 °C!

Annual NH_3 production: 2×10^7 tons

K only gives us information about the completeness of a reaction; it tells us *nothing* about the speed of the reaction. K does not answer the question, "How much time is required to reach equilibrium?" In some reactions, equilibrium is attained in hours, in other reactions it may be quickly attained, but there are also reactions that will not attain equilibrium even after millions of years. Typical of such extremely slow reactions is the formation of NH_3 at 25 °C. So, in synthesizing (manufacturing) any desired substance, two factors must be considered: K and the speed of the reaction.

This subject is treated more extensively in Chap. 16.

The time required to reach equilibrium is decreased by raising the temperature. The reason for this (Chap. 16) is that an increase in temperature speeds up *both* the forward and reverse reactions. But only rarely are both reactions speeded up equally. In this particular case, the decomposition of NH_3 speeds up more than the formation of NH_3; thus, less NH_3 is present when equilibrium is restored (the speeds again become equal). The tendency of NH_3 to decompose thus increases as the temperature

---

*An alternate explanation is that in this case, the concentration term is independent of the volume of the container. See blast furnace reaction (page 390) for an example.

is raised. On the other hand, a catalyst (Chap. 16) speeds up the forward and reverse reactions equally, so that the composition of the equilibrium mixture is not changed by the catalyst. So, in the presence of a catalyst, the reaction speed becomes commercially feasible at 500 °C. But *only* 0.0013 mole NH_3 is formed from 3 moles H_2 and 1 mole of H_2 at a pressure of 1 atm. Hence, to shift the equilibrium to the right, an excess of H_2 is used (molar ratio of H_2 to N_2 is made larger than 3 : 1) and the pressure is increased (container made smaller) to 350 atm. The nitrogen is obtained from air (page 43), and the hydrogen is obtained from water by the following series of reactions:

Water gas, a mixture of CO and H_2, is industrially produced by the action of steam on coke or any carbonaceous (carbon-containing) matter:

Known as the Haber process, after Fritz Haber, who developed this process in 1905; about 50 % of the N_2 is converted to NH_3.

$$C(graphite) + H_2O(g) \xrightarrow{\text{1000 °C}} CO(g) + H_2(g) \qquad \Delta H = +41.9 \text{ kcal}$$

$$(natural \ gas) \ CH_4(g) + H_2O(g) \xrightarrow{\text{925 °C}} CO(g) + 3H_2(g) \quad \Delta H = +59.8 \text{ kcal}$$

More H_2 may be obtained by further treatment of the products with steam:

$$CO(g) + H_2O(g) \xrightarrow{\text{475 °C}} CO_2 + H_2 \qquad \Delta H = +0.68 \text{ kcal}$$

The CO_2 is frozen to "Dry Ice." H_2 is also produced by the decomposition of hydrocarbons, compounds that contain only carbon and hydrogen; a representative reaction is

Carbon black is used in the manufacture of rubber tires, inks, paints, enamels, and polishes.

$$CH_4(g) \xrightarrow{\text{1200 °C}} C(carbon \ black) + 2H_2 \qquad \Delta H = +17.9 \text{ kcal}$$

However, ammonia has been produced at room temperature and pressure (Eugene van Tamelin, 1969) from air and hydrogen compounds, using titanium compounds as a catalyst. These experiments show promise of a more efficient industrial pathway to ammonia.

PROBLEM 14   **Answer this question from the point of view of an industrial chemist to whom cost of operation is of paramount importance. A catalyst is available to make the speed of the reaction $C_2H_4(g) + H_2O(g) \rightleftharpoons C_2H_5OH(l)$, $\Delta H = -21.1$ kcal, commercially feasible at 80 °C. $K = 1.8 \times 10^3$ at 80 °C and 1.9×10^5 at 25 °C. With respect to C_2H_5OH production, would you recommend (a) 80 °C, or a higher or lower temperature? (b) atmospheric pressure, or higher or lower? (c) 1 mole C_2H_4 to 1 mole H_2O, or some other ratio? Explain.**

12.10 _____EQUILIBRIUM IN LIQUID SOLUTIONS

The principles of chemical equilibrium are applicable to all chemical reactions independent of the medium in which they occur. Difficulties arise, however, when the concentrations of the reacting substances are too large to be treated as ideal. (The law of chemical equilibrium as used here assumes the presence of ideal gases.) In the same sense that *dilute* gases are assumed to behave ideally, *dilute solutions* may similarly be treated. The equilibrium condition in terms of concentrations may, therefore, be applied only to dilute solutions. A dilute solution is one in which the quantity of every component except one—called the solvent—is very small in comparison with the quantity of solvent. For example, a solution containing 0.17 mole ethyl alcohol, C_2H_5OH, 0.17 mole acetic acid, CH_3COOH, 0.33 mole ethyl acetate, $CH_3COOC_2H_5$ (colorless liquid, sweet-smelling component of plants), and 0.33 mole

From the Latin solvens, meaning to loosen, not crowded.

H_2O is not an ideal solution. On the other hand, a solution containing 0.17 mole CH_3COOH, 0.33 mole $CH_3COOC_2H_5$, 0.33 mole H_2O, and 60 moles C_2H_5OH may be treated as ideal; in this solution C_2H_5OH is called the solvent. A solution containing 0.17 mole each of C_2H_5OH and CH_3COOH, 0.33 mole $CH_3COOC_2H_5$, and 60 moles H_2O is also treated as ideal; in this solution, H_2O is called the solvent.*

In making the solution dilute, we achieve another objective: the solvent, although not pure, is *sufficiently pure* to be omitted from the equilibrium condition (page 379). For example, the equilibrium condition for the reaction

$$CH_3COOC_2H_5 + H_2O \rightleftharpoons C_2H_5OH + CH_3COOH \tag{13}$$

ethyl acetate   solvent   ethyl alcohol   acetic acid

in a dilute solution of water is

$$K_{13} = \frac{[C_2H_5OH][CH_3COOH]}{[CH_3COOC_2H_5]}$$

The subscript on K refers to the number of the corresponding reaction.

To show that water is the solvent, it is customary (page 156) to write the reaction as

$$CH_3COOC_2H_5(aq) + H_2O \rightleftharpoons C_2H_5OH(aq) + CH_3COOH(aq) \tag{13}$$

For the same reaction in a dilute solution of ethyl alcohol

$$CH_3COOC_2H_5 + H_2O \rightleftharpoons C_2H_5OH + CH_3COOH \tag{14}$$

solvent

the equilibrium condition is

$$K_{14} = \frac{[CH_3COOH]}{[CH_3COOC_2H_5][H_2O]}$$

K_{13} will not equal K_{14}; K for reactions in liquid solution depends *on the identity of the solvent*. For example, the equilibrium constant for the biologically important reaction** in water solutions

$$CO_3{}^{2-}(aq) + H^+(aq) \rightleftharpoons HCO_3{}^-(aq)$$

carbonate   acid   hydrogen carbonate

$$K = \frac{[HCO_3{}^-]}{[H^+][CO_3{}^{2-}]}$$

may be drastically changed by the addition of substances, such as sodium chloride or ethyl alcohol, that apparently do not participate in the reaction.

PROBLEM 15   **Write the equilibrium condition for the reaction (page 293)**

$$\text{ATP}(aq) + H_2O \rightleftharpoons \text{ADP}(aq) + H_3PO_4(aq)$$

---

*Since the density of water is 1.0 g/ml, the volume of 60 moles is 1.1 liter:

$$60 \text{ moles} \times 18 \frac{g}{mole} \times \frac{ml}{1 g} \times \frac{liter}{10^3 ml} = 1.1 \text{ liter}$$

**This reaction is essential in maintaining the acidity of the blood within the narrow range required to avoid death. The disease called cholera destroys this $CO_3{}^{2-}$—$HCO_3{}^-$ system, causing the blood acidity to increase dangerously.

The principle of Le Chatelier is the same for reactions in solution as it is for the other cases we have studied.

Example 7

Known as kwashiorkor, these deficiencies affect DNA duplication and protein synthesis (Chap. 23).

Amino acids are essential for the proper growth of all living organisms (anything that is alive). They are the "stuff" of which all proteins (Chap. 23) are composed. The most critical type of malnutrition results from amino acid deficiencies (page 727). A typical amino acid is glycine (*aminoacetic acid*), NH_2CH_2COOH (white solid), which may be synthesized from NH_3 and chloroacetic acid, $ClCH_2COOH$ (colorless solid), in two steps:

$$3NH_3 + ClCH_2COOH \rightleftharpoons NH_2CH_2COONH_4 + NH_4Cl \qquad \Delta H = +10 \text{ kcal} \quad (15)$$
$$NH_2CH_2COONH_4 + HCl \rightleftharpoons NH_2CH_2COOH + NH_4Cl$$

How would you shift Equilibrium 15 to increase the quantity of products?

Answer

This would require a shift of the reaction to the right. Therefore, add NH_3 and raise the temperature.

Example 8

The efficiency of tin(II) fluoride, SnF_2 (page 163), in decreasing dental decay is well established. One of the products of the reaction of SnF_2 in the dental enamel is CaF_2, a colorless solid. Typical of many solids that are only slightly soluble in water, the solution of CaF_2 may be represented by the equation

$$CaF_2(c) \rightleftharpoons Ca^{2+}(aq) + 2F^-(aq)$$

(a) Write the equilibrium condition for the reaction. (b) At 26 °C, the equilibrium concentrations are $[Ca^{2+}] = 2.3 \times 10^{-4}$, $[F^-] = 8.00 \times 10^{-4}$ mole/ℓ; calculate K. (c) By addition of soluble solid NaF, the fluoride ion concentration is increased so that $[F^-] = 8.50 \times 10^{-4}$ mole/ℓ. Is the reaction at equilibrium? If not, in which direction will the reaction go?

Answer

Recall (page 379) that the concentration of a pure solid is fixed at a given temperature; $CaF_2(s)$ therefore does not appear in K.

(a) The equilibrium condition is
$$K = [Ca^{2+}][F^-]^2$$
(b) $$K = 2.3 \times 10^{-4} \times (8.00 \times 10^{-4})^2 = 1.5 \times 10^{-10}$$
(c) concentration term = $2.3 \times 10^{-4} \times (8.50 \times 10^{-4})^2 = 1.7 \times 10^{-10}$
Since the concentration term does not equal K, the reaction is not at equilibrium. Since the concentration term is greater than K, the reaction goes from right to left; solid CaF_2 will form at the expense of Ca^{2+} and F^- ions. Since CaF_2 and NaF have the F^- ion in common, this shift of the equilibrium is usually named the *common ion effect*, but there is nothing special about it. The common ion effect is merely an application of Le Chatelier's principle.

PROBLEM 16   Calculate the concentration term for the mixture given and state the direction in which the reaction will go:

$$Cu(OH)_2(c) \rightleftharpoons Cu^{2+}(aq) + 2OH^-(aq) \qquad K = 2.2 \times 10^{-22}$$
$$[Cu^{2+}] = 0.15 \qquad [OH^-] = 0.10$$

It is common to symbolize the equilibrium constant with various subscripts such as "K_a," "K_b," "K_{sp}," "K_{this}," and "K_{that}" (Chaps. 13 and 14), depending on the type of the reaction. However, the law and principles of chemical equilibrium are independent of symbols and apply with equal force to *any* equilibrium condition for *any* reaction.

Solubility and Le Chatelier's Principle   In the previous chapter, we concluded that "polar solvents dissolve polar solutes, nonpolar solvents dissolve nonpolar solutes." Solubility, however, is merely another word for equilibrium concentration and is therefore subject to temperature and pressure changes.

The effect of pressure (temperature constant) on the solubility of gases is very noticeable, while its effect on the solubility of other solutes is negligible. When a gas dissolves in a liquid, equilibrium is established between the excess gas and the solution; for example,

$$CO_2(g) + H_2O \rightleftharpoons CO_2(aq) \qquad \Delta H = -4.8 \text{ kcal}$$

If at constant temperature the volume of the $CO_2(g)$ is decreased, its pressure is increased, and its concentration increases. Consequently, the reaction that consumes $CO_2(g)$, the forward reaction, occurs. The solubility of carbon dioxide therefore

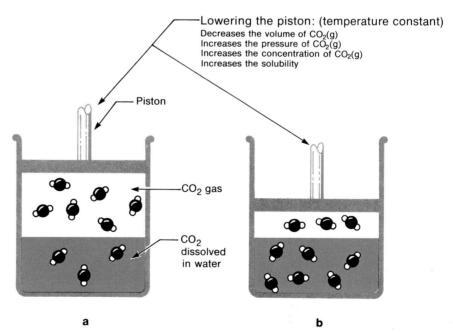

FIGURE 12.5 Solution of a gas in a liquid (a) at equilibrium; the rate of escape of the gas from solution equals the rate of gas dissolving. (b) Increasing the pressure of a gas increases its solubility.

The properties of a substance are those characteristics which help to identify it. All substances are unique in that each has a particular set of properties, such as color, density, odor, composition, melting point, and boiling point, which differentiate it from all other substances. Although color alone would not necessarily help us to identify a substance, we can see in the Color Plate how important a factor it can be when we consider it along with the other distinguishing properties of the substance. (The student need not here be concerned about the chemical formulas and nomenclature.) See following page for identification. (Courtesy of Sargent-Welch Scientific Company.)

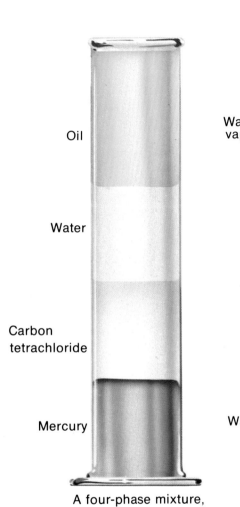

Oil

Water

Carbon
tetrachloride

Mercury

A four-phase mixture,
each phase in the
liquid state.

a

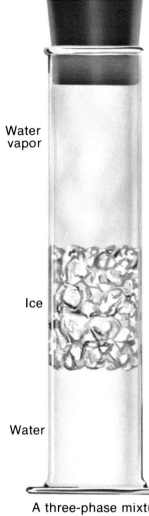

Water
vapor

Ice

Water

A three-phase mixture,
each phase in a
different state.

b

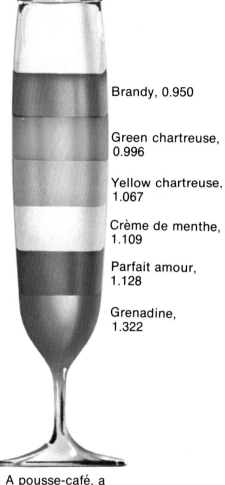

Brandy, 0.950

Green chartreuse,
0.996

Yellow chartreuse,
1.067

Crème de menthe,
1.109

Parfait amour,
1.128

Grenadine,
1.322

A pousse-café, a
six-phase mixture,
each phase in the
liquid state.

c

1. Cobalt(II) chloride, $CoCl_2$
2. Sodium chloride, $NaCl$
3. Lead sulfide, PbS
4. Sulfur, S
5. Zinc, Zn
6. Marble chips, $CaCO_3$
7. Logwood chips
8. Charcoal, C
9. Mercury(II) iodide, HgI_2
10. Pyrite, FeS_2
11. Chromium(III) oxide, Cr_2O_3
12. Iron(II) sulfate, $FeSO_4$
13. Sodium sulfite, Na_2SO_3
14. Rosin

15. Sodium thiosulfate, $Na_2S_2O_3$
16. Iron filings, Fe
17. Aluminum, Al
18. Potassium hexacyanoferrate, $K_3Fe(CN)_6$
19. Chromium potassium sulfate, $Cr_2K_2(SO_4)_4$
20. Menthol, $C_{10}H_{19}OH$
21. Potassium permanganate, $KMnO_4$
22. Ammonium nickel sulfate, $(NH_4)_2Ni(SO_4)_2$
23. Copper(II) sulfate hydrate, $CuSO_4(H_2O)_5$
24. Sodium chromate, Na_2CrO_4
25. Trilead tetraoxygen, Pb_3O_4
26. Hydroquinone, $C_6H_4(OH)_2$
27. Copper, Cu

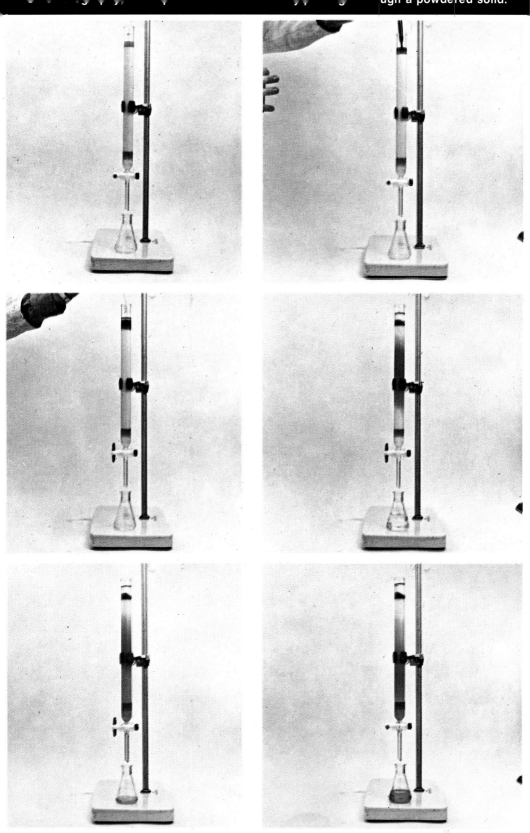

PLATE IV

A glass sphere, 0.020 mm diameter, is shown suspended (levitated) in air by a beam of green light. (Courtesy of Arthur Ashkin, Bell Laboratories.)

PLATE V

This monument, representing the rain god, was found buried at the site of the Olmec Civilization, the oldest known civilization (1200 B.C.) in Southern Mexico and Central America. It is typical of many discoveries made with a magnetometer, an instrument based on the magnetism of cesium atoms, $6s^1$, which detects the extremely small differences in the magnetic properties of ordinary soil and buried artifacts. (Courtesy of Sheldon Breiner and Michael Coe, *American Scientist, 60,* Sept.–Oct., 1972.)

PLATE VI

The separation of light emitted by selenium into its spectrum in the visible range, separated colored lines on a black background. Wavelengths are so separated that each wavelength (color) may be distinctly identified. The line separation in this case is so wide and the light intensity so great that three spectra can be seen. (Photograph by Fritz Goro, courtesy of William Siefvast, Bell Laboratories, and *Scientific American*, February 1973, cover.)

PLATE VII

Absorption and emission of photons by chlorophyll. Blue light enters from the top and is absorbed by chlorophyll (dissolved in ether). Some of the energy is emitted as red light (see Problems 57 and 69, pp. 215 and 216). The natural green color of chlorophyll is seen at the bottom of the container. (Photograph by Fritz Goro, courtesy of *Scientific American,* December 1974, page 68.)

PLATE VIII

Top. Liquid oxygen attracted and held between the poles of an electromagnet. The paramagnetism of oxygen is due to two unpaired electrons in the O_2 molecule. Notice the blue color of liquid oxygen. (Courtesy of Robert Doman, SUNY at Farmingdale.) *Bottom left.* The blue color of the solution is due to the alkali metal anion Na^- (see Chapter 21 Epilog). The golden film on the inside of the flask is crystalline $(NaC_{18}H_{36}O_6N_2)^+Na^-$ formed by evaporation of the solution at low temperature. *Bottom right.* Crystals of disodium cryptate, $Na_2C_{18}H_{36}O_6N_2$, in which sodium exists as Na^+ and Na^-. (Courtesy of James L. Dye, Michigan State University, and *Scientific American*, July 1977, page 93. Photographs by Ralph Morse.)

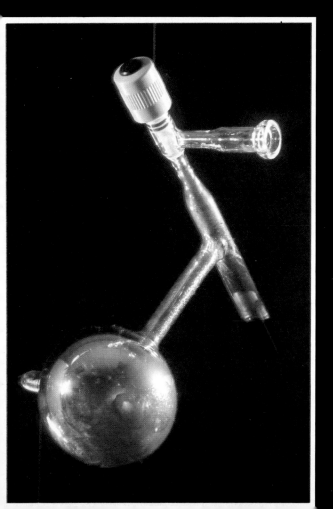

PLATE IX

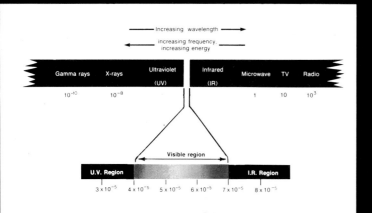

Frequency range of radiation. All wavelengths are given in centimeters (approximate and not to scale). The visible region is only a small portion of the entire range.

A typical (emission) line spectrum in the visible region, the emission spectrum of hydrogen. Separated colored lines on a black background.

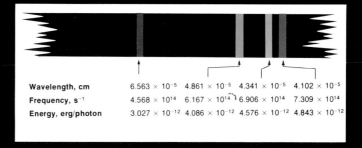

Wavelength, cm	6.563×10^{-5}	4.861×10^{-5}	4.341×10^{-5}	4.102×10^{-5}
Frequency, s^{-1}	4.568×10^{14}	6.167×10^{14}	6.906×10^{14}	7.309×10^{14}
Energy, erg/photon	3.027×10^{-12}	4.086×10^{-12}	4.576×10^{-12}	4.843×10^{-12}

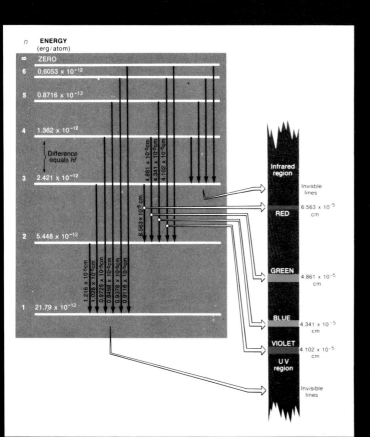

Energy state diagram used to predict the spectrum of hydrogen. The wavelengths (frequencies, energies) of the lines (photons) emitted or absorbed are given by the energy differences between any two energy states. These differences are usually represented by arrows, as shown. The greater the difference, the greater the energy and frequency of the photon, and the smaller its wavelength. A comparison between the predicted and measured wavelengths is made for four lines in the visible region of the hydrogen spectrum.

PLATE X

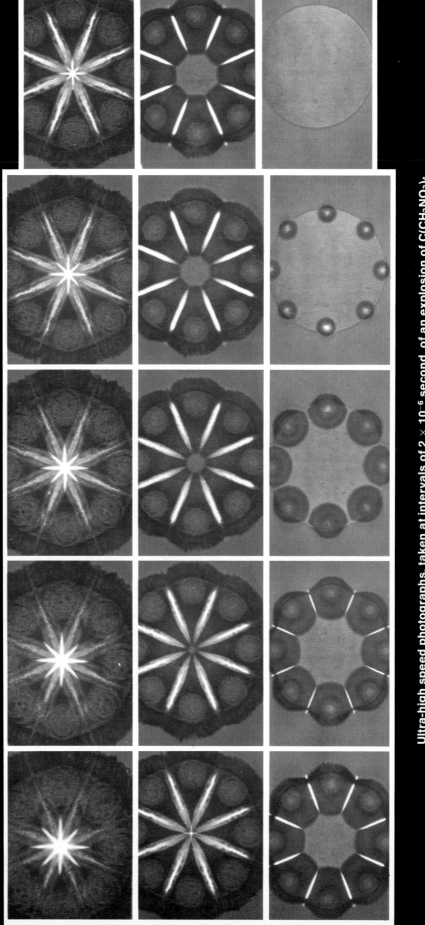

Ultra-high speed photographs, taken at intervals of 2×10^{-6} second, of an explosion of $C(CH_2NO_3)_4$, a tetrahedral molecule related to methane. A sheet of the explosive was mounted on plywood (first frame). It was then detonated at eight separate points at the same time. The course of the reaction,

$$C(CH_2NO_3)_4(c) \rightarrow 4H_2O(g) + 2CO(g) + 3CO_2(g) + 2N_2(g) \qquad \Delta H = -856 \text{ kcal}$$

is complete in less than 3×10^{-5} second, as shown in the remaining frames. The intense light results from the ionization of air. (Courtesy of the U.S. Naval Laboratory, Dahlgren, Virginia.)

PLATE XI

Thermoluminescence illustrated. (a) Limestone quartz and (b) calcite, chiefly $CaCO_3$, exposed to X-rays, photographed under room light. Light emission from the same piece of (c) limestone quartz and (d) calcite, photographed upon heating in a dark room. (e) Thermoluminescence from colorless LiF, "doped" with very small amounts of Mg^{2+} and Ti^{2+}, used in radiation dosimeters. (Courtesy of Larry A. DeWerd, *American Scientist,* volume 60, page 303, 1972.)

a

b

c

d

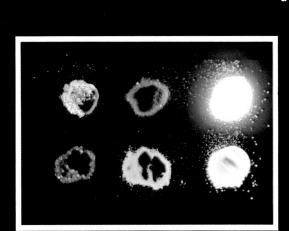

PLATE XII

A display of colors appearing in the sky (an aurora) produced by a high-altitude nuclear explosion, 9 July 1962. The deep brilliant red color, characteristic of lithium, shows that lithium hydride was used in the "hydrogen bomb." Photographed 645 miles from the explosion site. (Courtesy of the University of California, Los Alamos Scientific Laboratory.)

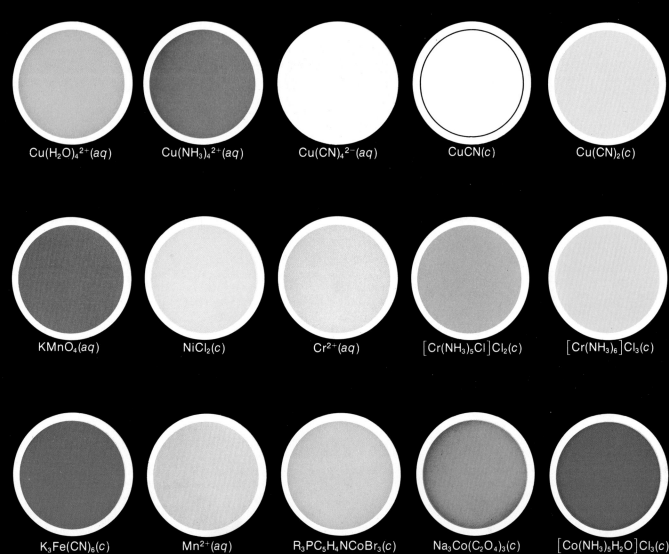

| $Cu(H_2O)_4^{2+}(aq)$ | $Cu(NH_3)_4^{2+}(aq)$ | $Cu(CN)_4^{2-}(aq)$ | $CuCN(c)$ | $Cu(CN)_2(c)$ |

| $KMnO_4(aq)$ | $NiCl_2(c)$ | $Cr^{2+}(aq)$ | $[Cr(NH_3)_5Cl]Cl_2(c)$ | $[Cr(NH_3)_6]Cl_3(c)$ |

| $K_3Fe(CN)_6(c)$ | $Mn^{2+}(aq)$ | $R_3PC_5H_4NCoBr_3(c)$ | $Na_3Co(C_2O_4)_3(c)$ | $[Co(NH_3)_5H_2O]Cl_3(c)$ |

Typical compounds and ions of the transition metals

increases with increasing pressure, as shown in Fig. 12.5. In general, the solubility of gases increases as the pressure of the gas above the solution is increased. Conversely, decreasing the pressure decreases the solubility. When a "soda" (carbonated beverage) bottle is opened, the $CO_2(g)$ pressure decreases, its solubility decreases, and CO_2 bubbles escape from the beverage (the soda "fizzes"). The bends (page 69) result from the tendency of nitrogen to form supersaturated solutions in blood. In expelling excess nitrogen, bubbles form in the blood stream.

The effect of temperature on solubility can also be predicted from Le Chatelier's principle. If, *at or near equilibrium conditions*, the heat of solution is exothermic (ΔH is negative; heat is evolved), the solubility decreases with increasing temperature. Conversely, if the heat of solution at or near equilibrium is endothermic (ΔH is positive; heat is absorbed), the solubility increases with increasing temperature.

Since the solution of gases is usually exothermic, the solubility of gases usually decreases as the temperature of the solution is increased (pressure constant).

PROBLEM 17 **From the following, pick the solute(s) whose solubility will increase with increasing temperature:**

$$BaSO_4(c) \rightleftharpoons BaSO_4(aq) \qquad \Delta H = +6.0 \text{ kcal}$$
$$MgSO_3(H_2O)_6(c) \rightleftharpoons MgSO_3(aq) \qquad \Delta H = -1.13 \text{ kcal}$$
$$Na_2SO_4(c) \rightleftharpoons Na_2SO_4(aq) \qquad \Delta H = -511 \text{ cal}$$
$$C_{10}H_8(c) \rightleftharpoons C_{10}H_8(benzene) \qquad \Delta H = +4.60 \text{ kcal}$$

In this text we shall deal only with dilute aqueous solutions, solutions in which water is the solvent, unless otherwise specified.

EPILOG from René J. Dubos, The Bulletin of Arthur D. Little, Inc., January–February, 1971

"A society that blindly accepts the decisions of experts is a sick society on its way to death. The time has come when we must produce, alongside specialists, another class of scholars and citizens who have broad familiarity with the facts, methods, and objectives of science and thus are capable of making judgments about scientific policies. Persons who work at the interface of science and society have become essential simply because almost everything that happens in society is influenced by science."

PROBLEMS

18 Vocabulary Illustrate (a) reversible reaction, (b) equilibrium, (c) equilibrium concentration, (d) the distinction between concentration term and K, (e) thermodynamic stability, (f) "shifting" the equilibrium (Le Chatelier's principle).

19 K Write the equilibrium condition for each of the following reactions:
(a) *Ostwald process for producing NO in the manufacture of nitric acid:*
$$4NH_3(g) + 5O_2(g) \rightleftharpoons 4NO(g) + 6H_2O(g)$$

(b) *Laboratory preparation of chlorine:*
$$MnO_2(c) + 4HCl(aq) \rightleftharpoons$$
$$MnCl_2(aq) + Cl_2(g) + 2H_2O$$
(c) *Electrolysis of water:*
$$2H_2O(l) \rightleftharpoons 2H_2(g) + O_2(g)$$
(d) *Decomposition of nitric acid:*
$$4HNO_3(l) \rightleftharpoons 4NO_2(g) + 2H_2O(g) + O_2(g)$$
(e) *Solution reaction:*
$$Al(OH)_3(c) + 3NaOH(aq) \rightleftharpoons$$
$$Al(OH)_6^{3-}(aq) + 3Na^+(aq)$$
(f) *Solution reaction:*
$$BaF_2(c) \rightleftharpoons Ba^{2+}(aq) + 2F^-(aq)$$

20 Significance of K From the following reactions, pick the one that is (a) most complete, and (b) least complete:

(i) $PbCl_2(c) \rightleftharpoons Pb^{2+}(aq) + 2Cl^-(aq)$
$$K = 1.7 \times 10^{-5}$$
(ii) $CaF_2(c) \rightleftharpoons Ca^{2+}(aq) + 2F^-(aq)$
$$K = 1.5 \times 10^{-10}$$
(iii) $Ag_2CrO_4(c) \rightleftharpoons 2Ag^+(aq) + CrO_4^{2-}(aq)$
$$K = 1.1 \times 10^{-10}$$
(iv) $Cu(OH)_2(c) \rightleftharpoons Cu^{2+}(aq) + 2OH^-(aq)$
$$K = 2.2 \times 10^{-22}$$

21 Carbon disulfide, CS_2, is more expensive than carbon dioxide. Pick the reaction you would recommend for the manufacture of carbon tetrachloride. Explain your choice:

(a) $CO_2(g) + 2\frac{1}{2} Cl_2(g) \rightleftharpoons$
$$CCl_4(g) + ClO_2(g) \qquad K = 6.51 \times 10^{-79}$$
(b) $CS_2(g) + 3Cl_2(g) \rightleftharpoons$
$$CCl_4(g) + S_2Cl_2(g) \qquad K = 1.6 \times 10^7$$

22 Pick the more suitable reaction for the preparation of hydrogen chloride. Explain your choice.
(a) $NaCl(c) + H_3PO_4(aq) \rightleftharpoons NaH_2PO_4(c) + HCl(g) \quad K = 5.23 \times 10^{-9}$
(b) $NaCl(c) + H_2SO_4(aq) \rightleftharpoons NaHSO_4(c) + HCl(g) \quad K = 7.23 \times 10^{-5}$

23 Equilibrium Pick the correct statement(s): (a) Without outside assistance, an equilibrium mixture will never change. (b) The addition of a catalyst to an equilibrium mixture will speed up the reaction and change the equilibrium concentrations. (c) $CaCO_3(c) \rightleftharpoons CaO(c) + CO_2(g)$, $K = [CO_2]$; this means that at any given temperature there can be one and only one concentration (pressure) of CO_2 in equilibrium with two solids. (d) Changes in volume or concentration in an equilibrium mixture at constant temperature alter the value of K. (e) If the temperature of an equilibrium mixture is changed, the value of K changes.

24 The equation for the formation of nitrogen dioxide is $N_2(g) + 2O_2(g) \rightleftharpoons 2NO_2(g)$. Pick the correct statement(s): The equation tells us that (a) the equilibrium mixture consists of 20 mole percent NO_2

$$\left(\frac{1 \text{ mole}}{1 \text{ mole} + 2 \text{ moles} + 2 \text{ moles}} \times 100\% = 20 \text{ mole} \right.$$

$\left. \text{percent} \right)$; (b) for every 1 mole of N_2 that reacts, 2 moles of O_2 reacts to form 2 moles of NO_2; (c) 1 mole of N_2 and 2 moles of O_2 must react; (d) 2 moles of NO_2 forms; (e) 2 volumes of O_2 must be added to 1 volume of N_2; (f) 0.10 mole of N_2 reacts with 0.20 mole of O_2 to form 0.20 mole of NO_2.

25 Thermodynamic stability From the following data at 25 °C
$$2NO_2(g) \rightleftharpoons N_2(g) + 2O_2 \qquad K = 6.7 \times 10^{16}$$
$$2NO(g) \rightleftharpoons N_2(g) + O_2(g) \qquad K = 2.2 \times 10^{30}$$
$2N_2O$(*dinitrogen oxide,* colorless, "laughing gas")
$$\rightleftharpoons 2N_2(g) + O_2(g) \qquad K = 3.5 \times 10^{33}$$
$2N_2O_5$(*dinitrogen pentoxide,* white, corrosive solid)
$$\rightleftharpoons 2N_2(g) + 5O_2(g) \qquad K = 1.2 \times 10^{34}$$
select (a) the most and (b) the least thermodynamically stable oxide of nitrogen.

26 From the following data at 700 K, pick (a) the most and (b) the least thermodynamically stable oxide of sodium with respect to the elements of which they are composed:
disodium monoxide
$$Na_2O(c) \rightleftharpoons 2Na(l) + \frac{1}{2}O_2(g) \; K = 1.84 \times 10^{-25}$$
sodium monoxide
$$NaO(g) \rightleftharpoons Na(l) + \frac{1}{2}O_2(g) \qquad K = 2.12 \times 10^{-5}$$
sodium peroxide (disodium dioxide)
$$Na_2O_2(c) \rightleftharpoons 2Na(l) + O_2(g) \; K = 4.93 \times 10^{-29}$$
sodium superoxide (sodium dioxide)
$$NaO_2(c) \rightleftharpoons Na(l) + O_2(g) \qquad K = 2.76 \times 10^{-14}$$

27 K calculation Calculate K for $2HI(g) \rightleftharpoons H_2(g) + I_2(g)$ at 500 K from the given equilibrium concentrations, $[HI] = 0.125$, $[H_2] = 5.50 \times 10^{-3}$, $[I_2] = 0.0222 \text{ mole}/\ell$.

28 From the equilibrium concentrations at 10^4 K, $[As_2] = 1.71 \times 10^{-2}$, $[Cl_2] = 0.150$, $[AsCl_3] = 2.40 \times 10^{-5} \text{ mole}/\ell$, calculate K for $As_2(g) + 3Cl_2(g) \rightleftharpoons 2AsCl_3(g)$.

29 (a) A critical reaction in the commercial production of hydrogen (page 394) is $CO(g) + H_2O(g) \rightleftharpoons CO_2(g) + H_2(g)$. At 1000 K, 0.750 mole of CO and 1.50 mole of H_2O are mixed in a 10.0-liter container. At equilibrium, the mixture contains 0.62 mole of H_2. Find K for the reaction as written. (b) The experiment is repeated at the same temperature with the same quantities of CO and H_2O in a 5.00-liter container. Find K for the reaction as written in (a). (c) If the same answer is obtained in (a) and (b), explain.

30 (a) After 0.59 mole of CF_3Cl (chlorotrifluoromethane) and 7.0×10^{-7} mole of OH (hydroxyl molecules) are added to a 3.0-liter container, $4.0 \times$

10^{-11} mole of HOCl is detected at equilibrium. Find K for $CF_3Cl(g) + OH(g) \rightleftharpoons HOCl(g) + CF_3(g)$. (b) In repeating the experiment, the same quantities of CF_3Cl and OH are mixed in a 2.0-liter container. Within the experimental error, the same quantity of HOCl, 4.0×10^{-11} mole, is detected at equilibrium. Find K for the same reaction as written in (a). (c) If the same answer is obtained for (a) and (b), explain.

31 Check the composition of the equilibrium mixture in Fig. 12.1, page 375, by calculating K for $2NO \rightleftharpoons N_2 + O_2$, using the data for the reverse and forward reactions.

32 Phosphorus pentachloride, PCl_5, decomposes as shown: $PCl_5(g) \rightleftharpoons PCl_3(g) + Cl_2(g)$. The addition of 0.300 mole of PCl_5 into a 1.00-liter container at 400 K produces an equilibrium mixture after 18.0 % of the PCl_5 dissociates. Calculate K for the dissociation of PCl_5.

33 2.000 moles of HCl is added to a 1.000-liter container at 3000 K. Equilibrium is established after 2.20 % dissociates as shown: $2HCl(g) \rightleftharpoons H_2(g) + Cl_2(g)$. Find K for the dissociation (decomposition) of HCl.

34 Potassium cyanate, KNCO, appears to be useful in the treatment of sickle-cell anemia (pages 321, 608). In solution, urea, the chief end-product of protein metabolism, is in equilibrium with NH_4^+ and NCO^- ions: $NH_2CONH_2(aq) \rightleftharpoons NH_4^+(aq) + NCO^-(aq)$. In a slightly basic solution, 0.167 molar urea established an equilibrium mixture at 37 °C (body temperature) after 3.0 % dissociated as shown. Calculate K for the dissociation of urea.

35 (a) The presence of $Fe^{3+}(aq)$ is detected by the addition of thiocyanate ion, SCN^-, forming a deep red solution owing to the presence of $FeSCN^{2+}$ ions: $Fe^{3+}(aq) + SCN^-(aq) \rightleftharpoons FeSCN^{2+}(aq)$. A solution containing 1.00×10^{-3} M Fe^{3+} and 0.100 M SCN^- reaches equilibrium after 99 % of the Fe^{3+} reacts as shown. Find K for the formation of $FeSCN^{2+}$. (b) Equilibrium is reached after 1.33 % of a 0.1000 M solution of acetic acid dissociates to H^+ and CH_3COO^-. Calculate K for the reaction $CH_3COOH(aq) \rightleftharpoons CH_3COO^-(aq) + H^+(aq)$.

36 Starting with 0.550 mole/ℓ N_2 and 0.200 mole/ℓ H_2, 0.126 mole/ℓ NH_3 forms at equilibrium at 127 °C. Find K for $N_2(g) + 3H_2(g) \rightleftharpoons 2NH_3(g)$.

37 The addition of tin to a solution containing 0.0823 molar Pb^{2+} results in the formation of 0.0268 molar Sn^{2+} at equilibrium. Find K for the reaction $Sn(c) + Pb^{2+}(aq) \rightleftharpoons Pb(c) + Sn^{2+}(aq)$.

38 A solution contains 0.200 mole/ℓ Fe^{2+} and 0.300 mole/ℓ Hg_2^{2+} [Hg(I) or mercurous ion].

After the reaction $2Fe^{2+}(aq) + Hg_2^{2+}(aq) \rightleftharpoons 2Hg(l) + 2Fe^{3+}(aq)$ occurs, 0.250 mole/ℓ Hg_2^{2+} remains at equilibrium. Find K for the reaction as written.

39 A solution is prepared containing 0.100 mole/ℓ acetate ion, CH_3COO^- (from the strong electrolyte sodium acetate). The acetate ion reacts with water, $CH_3COO^-(aq) + H_2O \rightleftharpoons CH_3COOH(aq) + OH^-(aq)$, and at equilibrium 7.48×10^{-6} mole/ℓ OH^- is measured. Calculate K for the reaction as written.

40 Equilibrium concentration The initial concentration of silicon monoxide, SiO, in a container at 2000 K is 0.350 mole/ℓ. SiO dissociates: $2SiO(g) \rightleftharpoons 2Si(l) + O_2(g)$, $K = 9.62 \times 10^{-13}$. Find (a) the equilibrium concentrations of SiO and O_2; (b) the number of moles of $Si(l)$ present at equilibrium.

41 Methyl mercaptan (methanethiol), CH_3SH, is a foul-smelling gas associated with paper-pulp mills and spoiled foods. In solution at 100 °C, it dissociates as shown: $CH_3SH(aq) \rightleftharpoons CH_3S^-(aq) + H^+(aq)$, $K = 4.30 \times 10^{-11}$. Find the equilibrium concentrations of CH_3S^-, H^+, and CH_3SH in a solution initially containing 0.400 mole/ℓ CH_3SH.

42 The initial concentration of gaseous methyl alcohol, CH_3OH, in a container is 0.300 mole/ℓ. Calculate the concentration of each gas at equilibrium: $CH_3OH(g) \rightleftharpoons CO(g) + 2H_2(g)$, $K = 7.37 \times 10^{-8}$.

43 (a) Ammonium chloride crystals are enclosed in a 1.00-liter flask. Calculate the concentrations of NH_3 and HCl after equilibrium is established in the presence of $NH_4Cl(c)$ by the reaction $NH_4Cl(c) \rightleftharpoons NH_3(g) + HCl(g)$, $K = 1.77 \times 10^{-19}$. (b) Find the equilibrium concentration of HCl in the flask when the equilibrium concentration of NH_3 is 8.00×10^{-10} mole/ℓ. (c) Explain the decrease in [HCl] in terms of Le Chatelier's principle.

44 A solution is prepared, initially containing 0.15 M $FeSCN^{2+}$ (Problem 35), which dissociates as shown: $FeSCN^{2+}(aq) \rightleftharpoons Fe^{3+}(aq) + SCN^-(aq)$, $K = 9.4 \times 10^{-4}$. Find [$FeSCN^{2+}$], [Fe^{3+}], and [SCN^-] at equilibrium.

45 (a) When a solution initially containing 0.100 mole/ℓ ATP (page 293) is allowed to react with water, 2.15 % of the ATP is converted to ADP at equilibrium. Calculate K for the reaction $ATP(aq) + H_2O \rightleftharpoons ADP(aq) + H_3PO_4(aq)$. (b) Find [ADP] and [$H_3PO_4$] at equilibrium for a solution initially containing 0.0100 M ATP.

46 (a) Several enzymes (Chap. 23) catalyze the change (oxidation) of glucose, $C_6H_{12}O_6$, a sugar, to vitamin C, ascorbic acid, $C_6H_8O_6$, by a pathway involving the formation of gluconic acid. This acid dissociates as shown:

$$C_5H_{11}O_5COOH(aq) \rightleftharpoons$$

gluconic acid

$$H^+(aq) + C_5H_{11}O_5COO^-(aq)$$

hydrogen   gluconate ion
ion

$$K = 1.4 \times 10^{-4} \text{ at } 25 \text{ °C}$$

If the equilibrium concentrations are $[C_5H_{11}O_5COOH] = 0.105$ and $[C_5H_{11}O_5COO^-] = 6.50 \times 10^{-5}$ mole/ℓ, find $[H^+]$ at equilibrium. (b) Calculate the concentration of nitrogen in an equilibrium mixture at 127 °C containing $[NH_3] = 0.250$ and $[H_2] = 0.120$ mole/ℓ. The reaction is $N_2(g) + 3H_2(g) \rightleftharpoons 2NH_3(g)$, $K = 2.5 \times 10^4$.

47 Direction of reaction Calculate the concentration term and state the direction in which the reaction goes:

(a) $AgCl(c) \rightleftharpoons Ag^+(aq) + Cl^-(aq)$

$$K = 1.77 \times 10^{-10}$$

(i) $[Ag^+] = 1.0 \times 10^{-2}$; $[Cl^-] = 2.5 \times 10^{-5}$; (ii) $[Ag^+] = 1.0 \times 10^{-6}$, $[Cl^-] = 2.5 \times 10^{-5}$; (iii) $[Ag^+] = [Cl^-] = 1.33 \times 10^{-5}$; (iv) $[Ag^+] = [Cl^-] = 1.0 \times 10^{-4}$.

(b) $2Ag(c) + 2H^+(aq) + 2Cl^-(aq) \rightleftharpoons H_2(g) + 2AgCl(c)$ $K = 3.1 \times 10^{-8}$

(i) $[H^+] = [Cl^-] = [H_2] = 1.5 \times 10^{-2}$; (ii) $[H^+] = [Cl^-] = [H_2] = 3.1 \times 10^{-8}$; (iii) $[H^+] = [Cl^-] = 1.50$, $[H_2] = 1.2 \times 10^{-7}$.

48 Chlorofluoromethanes (page 518), like NO_2, may destroy the natural ozone layer. Hydroxyl, OH, molecules, also present in the upper atmosphere (Problem 48, page 000), react with chlorofluoromethanes, for example, $CF_3Cl(g) + OH(g) \rightleftharpoons HOCl(g) + CF_3(g)$, $K = 3.9 \times 10^{-15}$. From the given information, calculate the concentration term and state the direction in which the reaction should go:
(a) $[CF_3Cl] = 1.0 \times 10^{-6}$, $[OH] = 1.0 \times 10^{-14}$, $[HOCl] = [CF_3] = 1.0 \times 10^{-16}$.
(b) $[CF_3Cl] = 2.5 \times 10^{-4}$, $[OH] = 1.1 \times 10^{-14}$, $[HOCl] = [CF_3] = 1.0 \times 10^{-17}$.

49 Equilibrium and reaction speed Given:

$$N_2 + O_2 \rightleftharpoons 2NO \quad K = 4.5 \times 10^{-31} \text{ at } 25 \text{ °C},$$
$$K = 3.4 \times 10^{-3} \text{ at } 2400 \text{ °C}$$

(a) For the same initial concentration of NO, at which temperature (i) will NO decompose faster, (ii) will more NO form? (b) Is the reaction as written

endothermic or exothermic? Explain. (c) The hotter the (engine or boiler) combustion zone, or the greater the amount of excess air, the higher the nitrogen oxide, NO, emission. Explain.

50 Two reactions under study for the removal of SO_2 from power plant stack gases* are given:

(a) $Na_2CO_3(l) + SO_2(g) + \frac{1}{2}O_2(g) \rightleftharpoons Na_2SO_4(l) + CO_2(g)$ $K = 4.9 \times 10^{16}$ at 800 K
(b) $FeO(c) + SO_2(g) + \frac{1}{2}O_2(g) \rightleftharpoons FeSO_4(c)$ $K = 9.2 \times 10^{23}$ at 800 K

At 800 K, (a) is fast while (b) is slow. Pick the reaction you would recommend. Explain.

51 Pollution control Removal of SO_2 from power plant stack gases by limestone ($CaCO_3$ or CaO) scrubbing appears to be controlled by the following equilibrium reaction: $MgSO_4(aq) + CaSO_3(H_2O)_{0.5}(c) + \frac{3}{2}H_2O \rightleftharpoons MgSO_3(aq) + CaSO_4(H_2O)_2(c)$.   (a) Write the equilibrium condition. (b) Would you maintain a high or low concentration of (i) $MgSO_4(aq)$, (ii) $MgSO_3(aq)$ for maximum process efficiency?

52 Pollution In the absence of hydrocarbons (page 196), oxygen and nitrogen dioxide in the atmosphere roughly maintain a balance with ozone and nitrogen oxide so that, effectively, little if any reaction occurs. Show that this statement is true by adding the following gaseous reactions:

$$NO_2 + hf \rightleftharpoons NO + O \qquad K = 6.8 \times 10^{-49}$$
$$O_2 + O \rightleftharpoons O_3 \qquad K = 2.52 \times 10^{13}$$
$$O_3 + NO \rightleftharpoons NO_2 + O_2 \qquad K = 5.82 \times 10^{34}$$

53 Le Chatelier principle Sodium carbonate, Na_2CO_3 (soda ash, white solid), an industrial chemical used in the manufacture of glass, paper, soap, other chemicals, water softeners, and cleansers, is obtained from the mineral trona (Na_2CO_3, $NaHCO_3$, H_2O) and from the thermal decomposition of sodium hydrogen carbonate**:

$$2NaHCO_3(c) \rightleftharpoons Na_2CO_3(c) + H_2O(g) + CO_2(g)$$
$$\Delta H = +30.6 \text{ kcal}, \ K = 2.46 \times 10^{106}$$

State the effect (increase, decrease, no change) of the following changes on the number of moles of $Na_2CO_3(c)$ at equilibrium. Temperature and volume

*Readers interested in this subject are referred to "Air Quality and Stationary Source Emission Control," Commission on Natural Resources, National Academy of Sciences, U.S. Government Printing Office, Washington, D.C. 20402, March 1975; "Health Effects," pages 58–149; "Ecological Effects," pages 170–182; "Desulfurization," pages 193–231 and 385–456.
**$Na_2CO_3(H_2O)_{10}$ is known as washing soda (sal soda). $NaHCO_3$, known as baking soda or bicarbonate of soda, is manufactured from sodium chloride, ammonia, and carbon dioxide.

are constant unless otherwise stated: (a) removing CO_2, (b) removing H_2O, (c) adding H_2O, (d) adding CO_2, (e) adding $NaHCO_3(c)$, (f) lowering the temperature. (g) Which of these changes alter the value of K?

54 For the reaction

$$Cu(OH)_2(c) \rightleftharpoons Cu^{2+}(aq) + 2OH^-(aq)$$
$$\Delta H = +13.0 \text{ kcal}, \quad K = 2.2 \times 10^{-22}$$

state and explain the effect (increase, decrease, no change) of the following changes. Unless otherwise stated, temperature and volume are constant. (a) On the number of moles of $Cu(OH)_2(c)$ at equilibrium: (i) adding OH^-, (ii) removing OH^-, (iii) adding Cu^{2+}, (iv) removing Cu^{2+}, (v) raising the temperature, (vi) increasing the volume by the addition of water so that $[Cu^{2+}]$ and $[OH^-]$ decrease. (b) On the number of moles of OH^- at equilibrium: (i) removing Cu^{2+}, (ii) removing some $Cu(OH)_2(c)$. (c) On the number of moles of Cu^{2+} at equilibrium: (i) adding $Cu(OH)_2(c)$, (ii) adding OH^-.

55 Phosphorus, chlorine, and phosphorus trichloride are in equilibrium in a container of fixed volume at 10^4 K following the reaction $P_2(g) + 3Cl_2(g) \rightleftharpoons 2PCl_3(g)$. $\Delta H = -171$ kcal at 700 K. On cooling, how will each of the following quantities change (increase or decrease)? (a) $[PCl_3]$, (b) $[Cl_2]$, (c) $[P_2]$, (d) temperature.

56 (a) Hemoglobin, Hb (Chap. 21), has four Fe atoms per molecule that, on the average, pick up roughly 3 molecules of O_2:

$$Hb(aq) + 3O_2(g) \rightleftharpoons Hb(O_2)_3(aq)$$

Discuss mountain or space sickness in terms of this equilibrium. (b) Is the following statement true or false? At constant temperature, the state of equilib-

rium can be disturbed only by changing the concentrations of reactants or products. Explain. (c) Hydrogen iodide (colorless) is in equilibrium with hydrogen and iodine (violet) at 600 K: $H_2(g) + I_2(g) \rightleftharpoons 2HI(g)$. On lowering the temperature, the violet color fades (becomes less intense). Is the reaction as written exothermic or endothermic? Explain.

57 An equilibrium mixture at 1300 K of molecular and atomic iodine contains $[I_2] = 3.46$ and $[I] = 0.0700$ mole/ℓ. Find K for the reaction $I_2(g) \rightleftharpoons 2I(g)$. The equilibrium concentration of I_2 is increased to 3.90 moles/ℓ. Predict the effect on the equilibrium concentration of I. Verify your prediction by calculating $[I]$ in the second equilibrium mixture.

58 Library Read one of the following:
(a) Page v and Chapter 1 ("The Scope of Thermodynamics") in the book *Thermodynamics,* by Gilbert Lewis and Merle Randall, revised by Kenneth Pitzer and Leo Brewer, 2nd Edition, McGraw-Hill Book Company, New York, 1961. Thermo (heat) dynamics (work) is the study of the relations between heat and work.
(b) "Social Control of Science and Technology," Michael Baram, *Science,* volume 172, 1971, pages 535–539.
(c) "Contribution of Research and Development to Economic Growth in U.S.A.," Edwin Mansfield, *Science,* volume 175, 1972, page 487.
(d) "The Community of Science and the Search for Peace," Paul Doty, *Science,* volume 173, 1971, pages 998–1002.
(e) "Reduction of Stratospheric Ozone by Nitrogen Oxide from Supersonic Transport Exhaust," Harold Johnston, *Science,* volume 173, 1971, page 571.
(f) "SO_2 and Coal Processing," *Chemical Engineering Progress,* volume 70, June 1974, pages 45–69.

ADDITIONAL PROBLEMS

59 See Problem 14, page 394. Find the number of moles per liter and the percentage of ethylene, C_2H_4, converted to C_2H_5OH, starting with 1.000 mole/ℓ of each reactant at 80 °C.

60 The NO_x ($NO + NO_2$) Federal automobile emission standard is 2.0 g/mile for California and 3.1 g/mile for the other 49 States. If the initial NO concen-

tration is 1.21×10^{-7} g/ml and the initial O_2 concentration is 2.36×10^{-4} g/ml at 25 °C, find the equilibrium concentration of NO_2: $2NO(g) + O_2(g) \rightleftharpoons 2NO_2(g)$, $K = 3.3 \times 10^{-13}$.

61 Given the data for two gaseous reactions:

$$N_2 + 2O_2 \rightleftharpoons 2NO_2 \qquad K_1 = 1.49 \times 10^{-17}$$
$$2NO \rightleftharpoons N_2 + O_2 \qquad K_2 = 2.2 \times 10^{30}$$

Prove that the equilibrium constant for the net reaction, $2NO + O_2 \rightleftharpoons 2NO_2$, is the product, $K_1 \times K_2$, and not the sum, $K_1 + K_2$.

2 At 25 °C, 550.0 g of deuterium oxide, D_2O (20.0 g/mole; density 1.10 g/ml), and 498.5 g of H_2O (18.0 g/mole; density 0.997 g/ml) are mixed. The volumes are additive. 47.0 % of the H_2O reacts to form HDO. Calculate K for the reaction $H_2O + D_2O \rightleftharpoons 2HDO$ at 25 °C.

63 Glycogen, made from thousands of glucose molecules, and stored in muscle tissue and liver, serves as a biological storage tank for glucose, the source of energy for muscular activity (page 293). In its utilization, glycogen is first cleaved by a phosphate ion to glucose phosphate:

$$O_5H_{11}C_6-O-C_6H_{10}O_5R(aq) + PO_4{}^{3-}(aq) \rightleftharpoons$$
glycogen

$$C_6H_{10}O_5PO_4{}^{3-}(aq) + C_6H_{11}O_6R(aq)$$
glucose phosphate

In a mixture of 0.100 mmol glycogen and 1.00 mmol $PO_4{}^{3-}$ in 100 ml of solution at the acidity of muscle tissue, 77 % of the glycogen is cleaved. (a) Find K. The composition of R is not necessary for this calculation. (b) In muscle, the mole ratio of $PO_4{}^{3-}$/glucose phosphate is more than 100. Does this favor the forward or the reverse reaction? Explain.

64 (a) See Problem 49. Pollution studies indicate that the addition of hydrogen to gasoline in the carburetor permits engine operation at lower temperatures. Are these studies worthy of support? Explain. (b) NO molecules rapidly remove Cl from ClO: $NO + ClO \rightleftharpoons Cl + NO_2$, $K = 7.2 \times 10^4$. Can this reaction cause destruction of the ozone layer or does it tend to protect the layer? Explain. (c) Highly energetic electrons produced by cosmic rays (page 315) may lead to the following reactions in the upper atmosphere:

$$N_2 + e^- \longrightarrow 2N(excited) + e^-$$
$$N(excited) + O_2 \longrightarrow NO + O$$

What is the importance of these natural reactions with respect to the ozone layer in the upper atmosphere?

65 Calculate the heat of solution from the given data. Is the process of solution exothermic or endothermic? Does the solubility increase or decrease with increasing temperature? Does the K for the reaction as written increase or decrease with increasing temperature?

$$AgCl(c) \rightleftharpoons Ag^+(g) + Cl^-(g)$$
$$\Delta H = +215.2 \text{ kcal}$$
$$Ag^+(g) + Cl^-(g) \rightleftharpoons Ag^+(aq) + Cl^-(aq)$$
$$\Delta H = -199.6 \text{ kcal}$$

ANSWERS

1 (a) 0.075 mole, 0.15 g;
(b) 0.050 mole, 0.85 g
2 yes, salt
3 $4.5 \times 4.0 = 18$, $5.0 \times 3.6 = 18$,
$1.8 \times 10 = 18$, and so on
4 $K = \dfrac{[HNO_2]^2}{[NO][NO_2][H_2O]}$
5 (a) $KClO_3(c)$; (b) $Fe_2O_3(c)$
6 (a)(b) O_2
7 $K = \dfrac{[H_2]}{[H_2S]}$
8 (a)(i) 1.03×10^{-3}, (ii) 26.7,
(iii) 2.22×10^3; (b)(i)
reverse, (ii) equilibrium,
(iii) forward
9 0.56
10 2.69

11 7.6×10^{-4}
12 $[NO] = 2x = 5.42 \times 10^{-4}$,
$[N_2] = 0.175$, $[O_2] = 1.50$
13 (a)(i)(ii) no change,
(iii) decrease, (iv)(v)
increase, (vi) decrease,
(vii) increase; (b)(i)
decrease, (ii)(iii)(iv)
no change
14 (a) 80 °C; (b) atmospheric;
(c) 1 to 1
15 $\dfrac{[H_3PO_4][ADP]}{[ATP]} = K$
16 1.5×10^{-3}, reverse
17 $BaSO_4$, $C_{10}H_8$
19 (a) $\dfrac{[H_2O]^6[NO]^4}{[NH_3]^4[O_2]^5} = K$

12 / CHEMICAL EQUILIBRIUM

(b) $\dfrac{[Cl_2][MnCl_2]}{[HCl]^4} = K$

(c) $[H_2]^2[O_2] = K$

(d) $[NO_2]^4[H_2O]^2[O_2] = K$

(e) $\dfrac{[Na^+]^3[Al(OH)_6^{3-}]}{[NaOH]^3} = K$

(f) $[Ba^{2+}][F^-]^2 = K$

20 (a) i; (b) iv
21 (b)
22 (b)
23 (a)(c)(e)
24 (b)(f)
25 (a) NO_2, (b) N_2O_5
26 (a) Na_2O_2, (b) NaO
27 7.81×10^{-3}
28 9.98×10^{-6}
29 (a)(b) 3.4
30 (a)(b) 3.9×10^{-15}
31 2.93×10^2
32 0.0119
33 1.27×10^{-4}
34 1.5×10^{-4}
35 (a) 1×10^3, (b) 1.79×10^{-5}
36 2.4×10^4
37 0.483
38 4.00
39 5.60×10^{-10}
40 (a) $[SiO] = 0.350$, $[O_2] = 1.18 \times 10^{-13}$; (b) 2.36×10^{-13} mole
41 $[CH_3SH] = 0.400$, $[CH_3S^-] = [H^+] = 4.15 \times 10^{-6}$
42 $[CH_3OH] = 0.298$, $[CO] = 1.77 \times 10^{-3}$, $[H_2] = 3.54 \times 10^{-3}$
43 (a) $[NH_3] = [HCl] = 4.21 \times 10^{-10}$ (b) $[HCl] = 2.21 \times 10^{-10}$

44 $[FeSCN^{2+}] = 0.14$, $[Fe^{3+}] = [SCN^-] = 0.012$
45 (a) 4.72×10^{-5} (b) $[ATP] = 9.9 \times 10^{-3}$ $[ADP] = [H_3PO_4] = 6.87 \times 10^{-4}$
46 (a) $[H^+] = 0.23$, (b) $[N_2] = 1.4 \times 10^{-3}$
47 (a)(i)(iv) reverse, (ii) forward, (iii) equilibrium; (b)(i)(ii) reverse, (iii) forward
48 (a) reverse, (b) forward
49 (a)(i)(ii) 2400 °C; (b) endothermic
50 reaction a
51 (a) $\dfrac{[MgSO_3]}{[MgSO_4]} = K$; (b) (i) high, (ii) low
53 (a)(b) increase; (c)(d)(f) decrease; (e) no change; (g) only (f)
54 (a) (i)(iii) increase, (ii)(iv)(v)(vi) decrease; (b) (i) increase, (ii) no effect; (c) (i) no effect, (ii) decrease
55 (a) increase; (b)(c)(d) decrease
56 (b) true; (c) exothermic
57 $K = 1.42 \times 10^{-3}$, increase, $[I] = 7.44 \times 10^{-2}$
59 0.976, 98 %
60 2.0×10^{-13}
62 3.17
63 0.28; forward
65 $\Delta H = +15.6$ kcal, endothermic, increase, increase

GLOSSARY

concentration term The ratio of the concentrations of products to the concentrations of reactants, each raised to a power determined by the coefficients in the chemical equation as written.

equilibrium A condition in which the reverse reaction takes place at the same speed as the forward reaction so that no net chemical change is observed; see **reversible reaction.**

equilibrium concentrations The concentrations of the substances in an *equilibrium mixture,* a mixture of substances at equilibrium; see **equilibrium.**

equilibrium constant, *K* The value of the constant obtained when equilibrium concentrations are used

to calculate the concentration term; see **concentration term.** Only changes in temperature change the value of *K*.

heterogeneous equilibrium An equilibrium involving more than one phase, such as $CaCO_3(c) \longrightarrow CaO(c) + CO_2(g)$.

law of chemical equilibrium The state or the condition of equilibrium is reached when the concentration term is constant at a given temperature. The *equilibrium condition* for a reaction, $aA \rightleftharpoons bB$, is thus given by $\dfrac{[B]^b}{[A]^a} = K$, temperature fixed.

Le Chatelier's principle When a change is made in the

temperature, concentration, or volume of an equilibrium mixture, the equilibrium shifts in the direction that tends to oppose the change. (The so-called *common-ion effect* is merely an application of this principle to a concentration change.)

reversible reaction A chemical reaction in which the *reverse reaction,* right to left as written, occurs at the same conditions as the *forward reaction,* left to right as written, as in $2SO_2(g) + O_2(g) \rightleftharpoons 2SO_3(g)$.

thermodynamic stability The natural tendency of a chemical reaction to occur, determined by the value of the equilibrium constant. The larger the value, the greater the tendency for the given reaction to occur as written, the smaller the stability.

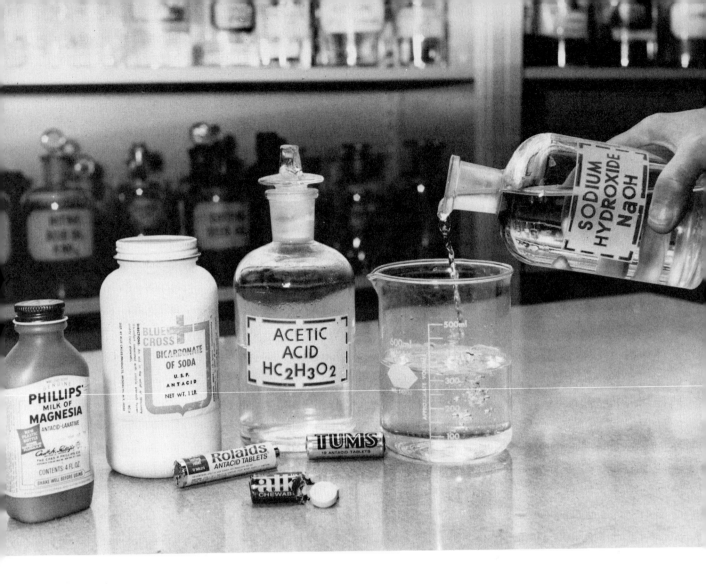

ACIDS AND BASES   13

INTRODUCTION _____ 13.1

Acids and bases have been recognized by chemists for several hundred years. The early definitions of these substances were based entirely on observed properties. Acids were first characterized by Robert Boyle in 1680. According to Boyle, an acid is a substance that changes the color of the natural dye litmus from blue to red but loses this ability when brought in contact with substances known as bases.

By the eighteenth century, the definition of an acid was modified to a substance that has a sour or tart taste and liberates carbon dioxide when placed in contact with limestone, $CaCO_3$.

In 1787, Antoine Lavoisier attempted to relate the composition of acids to their known properties. Lavoisier proposed that acids are compounds that contain oxygen. In fact, Lavoisier so named oxygen, derived from the Greek words *oxys* and *gennan* meaning acid-producer, because of the mistaken idea that oxygen was a constituent of all acids.

This theory was disproved in 1810 when Humphrey Davy showed that hydrochloric acid consists of only hydrogen and chlorine. Davy's work led to the conclusion that acids are compounds which necessarily contained hydrogen rather than oxygen.

In a similar fashion, bases (also referred to as *alkali*)* originally were defined in terms of observable properties. Thus, a base was considered to be a substance which turns red litmus blue and whose aqueous solution makes skin feel slippery ("soapy feeling").

The discovery by Michael Faraday (1834) that aqueous solutions of acids and bases are electrolytes (page 355) led to the first scientifically useful definitions of acids and bases.

From the Latin acidus, *meaning sour.*

Acetic acid, the main component of vinegar, oxalic acid in rhubarb, citric acid in lemon and grapefruit, and tartaric acid in grape possess a sour taste.

Most common acids contain oxygen; for example, sulfuric acid, H_2SO_4, nitric acid, HNO_3.

THE ARRHENIUS THEORY _____ 13.2

In 1884, Svante Arrhenius proposed that water dissociates very slightly into hydrogen, H^+, and hydroxide, OH^-, ions:

$$H_2O \rightleftharpoons H^+(aq) + OH^-(aq) \qquad K = K_w = 1.008 \times 10^{-14}$$

Then, he suggested that the acid properties of aqueous acid solutions were due

Since water is the most commonly used solvent, its K is commonly written as K_w. Data are at 25 °C.

---

* Alkali comes from the Arabic word *alqili,* meaning plant ash. The ashes of burnt plants were one of the first sources of bases. It was common practice to extract the alkali from wood ashes in iron pots. Thus, the two common alkalis produced by this method were called "potash" (potassium carbonate, K_2CO_3) and "caustic potash" (potassium hydroxide, KOH). These were used to change animal fat into soap (page 704).

407

primarily to the dissociation of the parent acid into hydrogen ions.* Similarly, the basic properties of aqueous alkaline solutions were attributed to the hydroxide ion. Thus, according to the Arrhenius theory, an *acid* is a hydrogen-containing substance that dissociates in water to form hydrogen ions. Correspondingly, a *base* is a hydroxy compound that dissociates in water to yield hydroxide ions.

The reaction of an acid with a base leads to the formation of water, a neutral molecule. This union of hydrogen and hydroxide ions is called **neutralization:**

$$H^+(aq) + OH^-(aq) \longrightarrow HOH \quad \Delta H = -13.35 \text{ kcal}$$
$$\text{acid} \qquad \text{base} \qquad \text{water}$$

The neutralization reaction also includes the combination of the other ions to form **salts.** A neutralization reaction, according to the Arrhenius theory, always results in the formation of water and a salt:

$$\text{neutralization} \quad \text{Acid} + \text{Base} \longrightarrow \text{Salt} + \text{Water}$$
$$CH_3COOH(aq) + NaOH(aq) \longrightarrow CH_3COONa(aq) + H_2O$$

The salt generally exists as hydrated ions in the water, and it may be obtained in solid form by evaporating the solution.

PROBLEM 1   **(a) Give the formulas of the acid and base you would use to prepare (i) a solution of potassium chloride, KCl, and (ii) solid KCl. (b) Write equations for these reactions.**

In 1905, Edward Franklin showed that water is not alone in its ability to serve as a solvent for acid-base reactions. He postulated a general solvent theory that extended Arrhenius' aqueous acid-base theory to similar reactions in other (nonaqueous) solvents. Just as the dissociation of the solvent water into a positive ion leads to acidic properties, the dissociation of other solvents into positive ions also leads to acidic properties. Correspondingly, the negative ion formed in the dissociation is a base:

$$\text{Solvent} \rightleftharpoons \text{Acid} + \text{Base}$$
$$H_2O \rightleftharpoons H^+ + OH^-$$
$$NH_3 \rightleftharpoons H^+ + NH_2^-$$

13.3 BRÖNSTED-LOWRY THEORY

Based on the ideas of Arrhenius and Franklin, Johannes Brönsted and Thomas Lowry in 1923 proposed a more general concept of acids and bases.

According to the Brönsted-Lowry theory, an **acid** *is a proton donor* while a **base** *is a proton acceptor.* An acid gives up a proton, while a base accepts a proton. The advantage of this theory is that *neither an acid nor a base is restricted to neutral molecules.* Acids and bases can be either neutral molecules or ions. For example,

*The highly concentrated positive charge of the hydrogen ion, a proton, about 10^{-13} cm in diameter, makes it very attractive to the negatively charged electron clouds of atoms and molecules. Hence, ions like KrH$^+$ and H(H$_2$O)$^+$ easily form. The ion H(H$_2$O)$^+$ or H$_3$O$^+$ is called a **hydronium ion.** A proton bonded to six water molecules, H$^+$(H$_2$O)$_6$, has been detected in a mass spectrometer and in certain solutions, but the proton in liquid water is believed to be associated mainly with four water molecules, H$_3$O$^+$(H$_2$O)$_3$ or H$_9$O$_4^+$. Hydronium compounds have been prepared (page 275).

hydrochloric acid, a typical *strong acid,* has a large equilibrium constant. This means that ionization in water is practically complete or that the transfer of H from HCl to H_2O is practically complete, as shown by the longer arrow pointing to the right:

$$\text{Acid} + \text{Base}$$

$$HCl(aq) + H_2O \rightleftharpoons H_3O^+(aq) + Cl^-(aq) \qquad K \approx 10^7$$

For ammonium ion, a typical *weak acid,* the equilibrium constant is small. This means that the transfer of H^+ from NH_4^+ to H_2O is very incomplete, as shown by the longer arrow pointing to the left:

$$NH_4^+(aq) + H_2O \rightleftharpoons H_3O^+(aq) + NH_3(aq) \qquad K = 5.68 \times 10^{-10}$$

Other examples of Brönsted-Lowry acids are

$$HSO_4^-(aq) + H_2O \rightleftharpoons H_3O^+(aq) + SO_4^{2-}(aq)$$

$$HCl(aq) + NH_3(aq) \rightleftharpoons NH_4^+(aq) + Cl^-(aq)$$

$$HCO_3^- + NH_3 \underset{NH_3}{\overset{\text{in liquid}}{\rightleftharpoons}} NH_4^+ + CO_3^{2-}$$

This theory requires that an acid contain a *transferable hydrogen.* However, the theory offers a greater freedom in defining what constitutes a base. It also explains acid-base reactions in solutions other than aqueous. In fact, acid-base reactions can even occur without a solvent present. Some examples of Brönsted-Lowry bases are

$$\text{Base} + \text{Acid}$$

$$O^{2-}(aq) + H_2O \rightleftharpoons OH^-(aq) + OH^-(aq)$$

$$NH_3(aq) + H_2O \rightleftharpoons OH^-(aq) + NH_4^+(aq)$$

$$CO_3^{2-}(aq) + H_2O \rightleftharpoons OH^-(aq) + HCO_3^-(aq)$$

$$NH_3(g) + HCl \underset{\text{benzene}}{\overset{\text{in}}{\rightleftharpoons}} NH_4^+Cl^- \text{ (solid in benzene)}$$

$$OH^-(aq) + NH_4^+(aq) \rightleftharpoons NH_3(aq) + H_2O$$

From the examples given, it becomes apparent that *when an acid has donated its proton, the remaining portion of the molecule or ion is a base.* Also notice that *when a base accepts a proton, it forms an acid.* Typical examples are

$$\text{Acid} + \text{Base} \rightleftharpoons \text{Acid} + \text{Base}$$

$$HCl + H_2O \rightleftharpoons H_3O^+ + Cl^-$$

$$H_2O + NH_3 \rightleftharpoons NH_4^+ + OH^-$$

The base formed from an acid is referred to as the **conjugate base of the acid.** Correspondingly, the acid formed from a base is called the **conjugate acid of the base.** Thus, the conjugate acid differs from its conjugate base by one proton. The conjugate base of HCl, acid$_1$, is Cl$^-$, base$_1$, while the conjugate acid of NH$_3$, base$_2$, is the ammonium ion, acid$_2$:

$$HCl + NH_3 \rightleftharpoons NH_4^+ + Cl^-$$
$$acid_1 + base_2 \rightleftharpoons acid_2 + base_1$$

The conjugate acid always has one more proton than its conjugate base.

PROBLEM 2   **(a) Write the formula of (i) the conjugate acid of the base NO$_3^-$, (ii) the conjugate base of the acid HBr. (b) For the reaction**

$$HClO_4 + NH_3 \rightleftharpoons NH_4^+ + ClO_4^-$$

label the conjugate acid-base pairs as acid$_1$, base$_1$, acid$_2$, base$_2$.

This theory emphasizes the dependence of an acid and a base upon each other. *A base must be present for the acid to act as an acid; an acid must be present for a base to act as a base.*

Amphoteric Compounds   Many substances—for example, water and bicarbonate ion, HCO$_3^-$ (obtained from sodium hydrogen carbonate, NaHCO$_3$)—may act either as acids or as bases:

Water as an acid

$$H_2O + NH_3 \rightleftharpoons OH^- + NH_4^+$$
$$acid_1 + base_2 \rightleftharpoons base_1 + acid_2$$

Water as a base

$$HCl + H_2O \rightleftharpoons H_3O^+ + Cl^-$$
$$acid_1 + base_2 \rightleftharpoons acid_2 + base_1$$

Hydrogen carbonate (bicarbonate) as an acid

$$HCO_3^- + NH_3 \rightleftharpoons NH_4^+ + CO_3^{2-}$$
$$acid_1 + base_2 \rightleftharpoons acid_2 + base_1$$

Hydrogen carbonate (bicarbonate) as a base

This reaction accounts for the use of baking soda, NaHCO$_3$, as an "antacid."*

$$HCl + HCO_3^- \rightleftharpoons H_2CO_3 + Cl^-$$
$$acid_1 + base_2 \rightleftharpoons acid_2 + base_1$$

From the Greek word amphoteros, meaning both.

Substances which exhibit both acidic and basic properties are called **amphoteric.**

13.4——————   STRENGTH OF BRÖNSTED-LOWRY ACIDS AND BASES

The strength of an acid or a base is measured by its tendency to lose or gain protons. A strong acid is a substance which loses a proton easily to a base. Conse-

*Readers interested in the subject of stomach acidity, heartburn, and remedies, are referred to *Consumer Reports,* volume 38, September 1973, page 584, and *Naval Research Reviews,* volume 26, March 1973, page 8.

quently, *the conjugate base of a strong acid is a weak base, since it has little tendency to pick up a proton:*

$$HCl + H_2O \longrightarrow H_3O^+ + Cl^-$$

strong acid   weak base

Conversely, *the conjugate base of a weak acid is a strong base:*

$$HS^- + H_2O \rightleftharpoons H_3O^+ + S^{2-}$$

weak acid   strong base

A strong base like S^{2-} has a strong attraction for a proton. Therefore, *the conjugate acid of such a strong base has little tendency to lose a proton and is a weak acid:*

$$S^{2-} + H_3O^+ \rightleftharpoons HS^- + H_2O$$

strong base   weak acid

A weak base like Cl^- has little attraction for a proton. *The conjugate acid of such a weak base,* therefore, *has a great tendency to lose a proton and is a strong acid:*

$$Cl^- + H_3O^+ \rightleftharpoons HCl + H_2O$$

weak base   strong acid

PROBLEM 3   **HCl and HI are strong acids; HCO_3^- and CH_3COOH are weak acids. Write the formulas of the corresponding (conjugate) bases and indicate the two stronger bases.**

The ability of an acid to lose a proton (*acid strength*) is experimentally measured by its equilibrium constant (page 377), also known as an acid constant, K_{acid}:

$$HA(aq) + H_2O \rightleftharpoons H_3O^+(aq) + A^-(aq)$$

$$K = K_{acid} = K_a = \frac{[H_3O^+][A^-]}{[HA]}$$

Water is the base most generally used to determine acid strength.

The larger the value of the equilibrium constant, K_a, the *more complete* the reaction as written, the *higher* the concentration of H_3O^+, and the *stronger* is the acid. Any acid whose equilibrium constant, K_a, is 1 or larger is a strong acid. They exist only as ions in dilute solutions.

Example 1

For acetic acid, CH_3COOH, $K_a = 1.79 \times 10^{-5}$. For hydrocyanic acid, HCN, $K_a = 7.2 \times 10^{-10}$. Which is the stronger acid?

Answer

Since acetic acid has the larger K_a, it is the stronger acid.

The equilibrium constant of an acid, like any other equilibrium constant, can be determined from the fraction or percentage of the acid that ionizes or dissociates (page 384).

The general principle employed to compare acidities is also used to compare basicities. The bases ammonia, $\ddot{N}H_3$, and hydroxide ion, $:\ddot{O}H^-$, can compete for a proton:

$$\ddot{N}H_3 + H\ddot{O}H \rightleftharpoons NH_4^+ + :\ddot{O}H^-$$

$$\text{base}_1 + \text{acid}_2 \rightleftharpoons \text{acid}_1 + \text{base}_2$$

To determine which direction is preferred, the equilibrium constant for the reaction is determined:

$$K = K_{base} = K_b = \frac{[NH_4^+][OH^-]}{[NH_3]} = 1.76 \times 10^{-5}$$

The equilibrium constant for a base is commonly written as K_{base}, abbreviated K_b. The small value of K_b indicates that the formation of OH^- is not favored in this reaction. Thus, the hydroxide ion, OH^-, must be a stronger base than ammonia, NH_3. Table 13.1 shows the relative strengths in water of representative acids and bases. For our purposes, the three oxyacids $HClO_4$, H_2SO_4, and HNO_3 and the three hydrogen halides HI, HBr, and HCl may be considered as the *only common strong acids,* acids which ionize completely in dilute aqueous solution. All other acids—neutral, negatively charged, or positively charged—may be considered *weak.*

TABLE 13.1
RELATIVE STRENGTH OF ACIDS AND
BASES IN WATER

	ACID		CONJUGATE BASE		
	Name	*Formula*	*Formula*	*Name*	
	Perchloric acid	$HClO_4$	ClO_4^-	Perchlorate ion	
	Sulfuric acid	H_2SO_4	HSO_4^-	Hydrogen sulfate ion	
	Hydriodic acid	HI	I^-	Iodide ion	
	Hydrobromic acid	HBr	Br^-	Bromide ion	
	Hydrochloric acid	HCl	Cl^-	Chloride ion	
	Nitric acid	HNO_3	NO_3^-	Nitrate ion	
	Hydrogen sulfate ion	HSO_4^-	SO_4^{2-}	Sulfate ion	
	Phosphoric acid	H_3PO_4	$H_2PO_4^-$	Dihydrogen phosphate ion	
	Nitrous acid	HNO_2	NO_2^-	Nitrite ion	
	Hydrofluoric acid	HF	F^-	Fluoride ion	
	Acetic acid	CH_3COOH	CH_3COO^-	Acetate ion	
	Carbonic acid**	H_2CO_3	HCO_3^-	Hydrogen carbonate ion	
	Hydrogen sulfide	H_2S	HS^-	Hydrosulfide ion	
	Ammonium ion	NH_4^+	NH_3	Ammonia	
	Hydrocyanic acid	HCN	CN^-	Cyanide ion	
	Ammonia	NH_3	NH_2^-	Amide ion	

Increasing Acid Strength (left side, arrow up) / *Increasing Base Strength* (right side, arrow down)

* Acids enclosed within this bracket are the strong acids.
** When CO_2 dissolves in water, most of the dissolved CO_2 is present as hydrated CO_2 and not as H_2CO_3; only less than 1 % reacts to form H_2CO_3:

$$CO_2 + H_2O \rightleftharpoons H_2CO_3$$

However, it is common practice to represent dissolved CO_2 by the formula H_2CO_3; H_2CO_3 therefore represents the total concentration of CO_2 and H_2CO_3.

ACIDIC, BASIC, AND NEUTRAL SOLUTIONS 13.5

The **acidic, basic** (alkaline), or **neutral** character of an aqueous solution is determined by the relative concentrations of the hydrogen, H^+, and the hydroxide, OH^-, ions. In pure water they are equal, $[H^+] = [OH^-]$.

Neutral as used here means that the solution is neither acidic nor basic. The same word is also used to indicate electrical neutrality, neither positively nor negatively charged.

An acidic solution is one in which the concentration of the hydrogen ion exceeds that of the hydroxide ion:

$$[H^+] > [OH^-] \qquad \textit{acidic solution}$$

A basic solution is a solution in which the hydroxide ion concentration exceeds the hydrogen ion concentration:

$>$ is an abbreviation for "greater than," while $<$ is an abbreviation for "less than"; App. II.

$$[OH^-] > [H^+] \qquad \textit{basic solution}$$

A neutral solution is one in which the hydrogen and hydroxide ions have equal concentrations:

$$[H^+] = [OH^-] \qquad \textit{neutral solution}$$

REACTIONS OF IONS WITH WATER 13.6

The Brönsted-Lowry theory explains many types of reactions, previously assigned specific names, and unifies them in terms of the transfer of a proton. For example, the term *neutralization* has been extended to include all reactions between the conjugate acid and conjugate base of any solvent. Thus, *in water*

$$\xrightarrow{\textit{neutralization}}$$
$$H_3O^+ + OH^- \rightleftharpoons H_2O + H_2O$$
$$\textit{acid}_1 + \textit{base}_2 \rightleftharpoons \textit{base}_1 + \textit{acid}_2$$
$$\xleftarrow{\textit{ionization}}$$

and *in liquid ammonia*

$$\xrightarrow{\textit{neutralization}}$$
$$NH_4^+ + NH_2^- \rightleftharpoons NH_3 + NH_3$$
$$\textit{acid}_1 + \textit{base}_2 \rightleftharpoons \textit{base}_1 + \textit{acid}_2$$
$$\xleftarrow{\textit{ionization}}$$

PROBLEM 4 **Write the equation for the neutralization reaction between (a) nitric acid, HNO_3, and potassium hydroxide, KOH, in water; (b) ammonium nitrate, NH_4NO_3, and potassium amide, KNH_2, in liquid ammonia.**

Another important type of reaction, the reaction of ions with water, is still referred to as **hydrolysis,** even though the reaction is merely the transfer of a proton.

From the Greek words hydro meaning water, and lysis meaning loosening, used here in the sense of the splitting of water by an ion.

Reaction of Negative Ions with Water A typical hydrolysis is the reaction of the conjugate base of a weak acid (see Table 13.1) with water to *form hydroxide ions.*

Thus, acetate ions, obtained from sodium acetate, CH_3COONa (strong electrolyte), and cyanide ions, obtained from sodium cyanide, NaCN (strong electrolyte), react with water to form hydroxide (basic) solutions:

$$CH_3\overset{\frown}{C}OO^- + H_2O \rightleftharpoons CH_3COOH + OH^- \qquad K_b = 5.6 \times 10^{-10}$$

$$\overset{\frown}{C}N^- + H_2O \rightleftharpoons HCN + OH^- \qquad K_b = 1.4 \times 10^{-5}$$

Just like a solution of ammonia, these reactions produce OH^- ions, making $[OH^-]$ greater than $[H^+]$ in the solution. Aqueous solutions of acetate and cyanide ions are therefore basic.

On the other hand, *the conjugate base of a strong acid does not react* with water to form hydroxide ions. For example, Cl^- ions, obtained from sodium chloride, form a neutral solution:

no H^+
transfer
$$Cl^- + H_2O \longrightarrow \text{NO REACTION} \qquad K_b \approx 0$$

Since OH^- ions are not produced, $[H^+] = [OH^-]$ and the solution remains neutral.

PROBLEM 5   **Refer to Table 13.1. From the following, pick the ions that will react with water to form a basic solution: Br^-, NO_3^-, HS^-, F^-.**

Extent of Hydrolysis   The extent of hydrolysis of a negative ion can be predicted from the equilibrium constant for the reaction. The *larger* the equilibrium constant for the reaction with water, the *greater* the hydroxide ion concentration and the *higher* the basicity of the solution.

The equilibrium condition for the reaction of acetate ion with water is

$$K_b = \frac{[CH_3COOH][OH^-]}{[CH_3COO^-]} = 5.6 \times 10^{-10} \qquad (1)$$

However, this equilibrium constant is related to the equilibrium constant for the conjugate acid, CH_3COOH, by the relationship

$$K_{base} \times K_{conjugate\,acid} = K_w$$

This relationship is proved as follows:
The equilibrium condition for the reaction

$$CH_3COOH + H_2O \rightleftharpoons H_3O^+ + CH_3COO^-$$

is

$$K_{conjugate\,acid} = \frac{[H_3O^+][CH_3COO^-]}{[CH_3COOH]} \qquad (2)$$

Multiplying Equations 1 and 2 gives us

$$K_{conjugate\,acid} \times K_{base} = \frac{[H_3O^+][CH_3COO^-]}{[CH_3COOH]} \times \frac{[CH_3COOH][OH^-]}{[CH_3COO^-]}$$

Thus,

$$K_{conjugate\,acid} \times K_{base} = [H_3O^+][OH^-] = K_w = 1.00 \times 10^{-14} \qquad (3)$$

Equally correct, we can write

$$K_{conjugate\,base} \times K_{acid} = 1.00 \times 10^{-14} \qquad (4)$$

Equation 4 may be used to calculate $K_{conjugate\,base}$ from the known K_{acid} and then an equation like Equation 1 may be used to calculate the $[OH^-]$ resulting from the reaction of negative ions with water. However, the following generalizations allow predictions concerning the acidity or basicity of salt solutions:

1. The conjugate bases of the strong acids, nitric acid, HNO_3, to perchloric acid, $HClO_4$ (Table 13.1), for all practical purposes do not hydrolyze (page 413). Thus, the halide ions, Cl^-, Br^-, I^-, the nitrate ion, NO_3^-, and the perchlorate ion, ClO_4^-, do not react with water to form hydroxide ions. Their corresponding aqueous solutions are, therefore, neutral. The hydrogen sulfate ion, HSO_4^-, does not react with water to form hydroxide ion; but its solutions are acidic (Table 13.1, page 412).

2. The conjugate bases of *all other acids* react with water to form hydroxide ions. Thus, such ions as acetate, CH_3COO^-, fluoride, F^-, and cyanide, CN^-, react with water, and their aqueous solutions are basic.

Reaction of Positive Ions with Water   A typical hydrolysis is the reaction of the ammonium ion, NH_4^+, obtained from ammonium chloride, NH_4Cl, with water to form H_3O^+ ions:

$$NH_4^+ + H_2O \rightleftharpoons H_3O^+ + NH_3 \qquad K_a = 5.68 \times 10^{-10}$$

Since hydrogen ions are produced, the solution is acidic.

With the exception of the metal ions of Group IIA, Be^{2+} to Ra^{2+}, all 2^+ positive ions, such as Zn^{2+} and Fe^{2+}, and all 3^+ positive ions, such as Al^{3+} and Fe^{3+}, react with water to form acidic solutions. None of the 1^+ metal ions, Group IA, Li^+ to Fr^+, and Ag^+, gives acidic aqueous solutions. This behavior is probably associated with the size and charge of the ion. The smaller the ion and the higher the charge, the greater the acidity of the aqueous solution. Thus, Al^{3+}, a comparatively small ion with a comparatively high charge, yields a fairly strong acidic aqueous solution. The Al^{3+} ion strongly attracts the electron clouds of water molecules and becomes highly hydrated. Each aluminum ion combines with 6 molecules of water:

There are exceptions to these generalizations; Be^{2+} hydrolyzes to form an acidic solution.

$$Al^{3+} + 6H_2O \longrightarrow \left[\begin{array}{c} OH_2 \\ H_2O \diagdown \mid \diagup OH_2 \\ Al \\ H_2O \diagup \mid \diagdown OH_2 \\ OH_2 \end{array} \right]^{3+}$$

Then, one or more protons may split off from the water molecules in the ion, forming H_3O^+,

$$Al(H_2O)_6{}^{3+} + H_2O \rightleftharpoons Al(H_2O)_5OH^{2+} + H_3O^+$$

Therefore, the solution is acidic. In dilute solutions of aluminum salts, 3 protons in succession may be transferred, leaving $Al(H_2O)_3(OH)_3$, hydrated aluminum hydroxide, as an insoluble gelatinous material, a gel (page 344). This material is therefore widely used to fix dyes to fabrics. Cloth which is soaked in a hot solution of aluminum acetate becomes impregnated with aluminum hydroxide formed by hydrolysis of the salt. When the hydroxide is formed from a solution containing a dye, the hydroxide binds the dye and acquires a color. Because of its capacity to absorb suspended material, including bacteria, it is also used in the purification of water. Magnesium hydroxide is equally effective in water purification.

PROBLEM 6   From the following, pick the hydrated ions that react with water to form an acidic solution: Li^+, B^{3+}, Fe^{3+}, Mg^{2+}, Cu^{2+}, Ag^+, and Cd^{2+}.

Table 13.2 summarizes the hydrolysis of ions. Notice the influence of size and charge of the ion on its acidity; examine, for example, the pairs Be^{2+} and Mg^{2+}, Fe^{3+} and Fe^{2+}, Sn^{4+} and Sn^{2+}.

Reactions of Salts with Water   We are now in a position to predict the effect of the addition of salts to water. The hydrolysis of the ions obtained from the salts then determines the acidity or basicity of the solution. We consider three cases:

Only the negative ion reacts with water: Potassium nitrite, KNO_2, sodium carbonate, Na_2CO_3, and silver fluoride, AgF, are typical. K^+, Na^+, and Ag^+ do not hydrolyze; they are neutral. But NO_2^-, CO_3^{2-}, and F^- are conjugate bases of weak acids and react with water, forming hydroxide ions. The solutions are, therefore, basic.

Only the positive ion reacts with water: Ammonium nitrate, NH_4NO_3, zinc chloride, $ZnCl_2$, and ferric perchlorate, $Fe(ClO_4)_3$, are typical. NO_3^-, Cl^-, and ClO_4^- do not hydrolyze; they are neutral. But NH_4^+, Zn^{2+}, and Fe^{3+} react with water to form acidic solutions. The solutions are, therefore, acidic.

Neither ion reacts with water: Silver nitrate, $AgNO_3$, sodium chloride, $NaCl$, and lithium iodide, LiI, are typical. Neither Ag^+, Na^+, or Li^+, nor NO_3^-, Cl^-, or I^- reacts with water. Therefore, the solution is neutral.

Zn^{2+} and Fe^{3+} become hydrated, forming $Zn(H_2O)_4^{2+}$ and $Fe(H_2O)_6^{3+}$.

PROBLEM 7   From the following, pick the salts whose aqueous solutions are (a) acidic, (b) basic, or (c) neutral: (i) KCl, (ii) $FeCl_3$, (iii) $Mg(NO_3)_2$, (iv) NH_4Cl, (v) $CuCl_2$, (vi) $MgCO_3$, (vii) KCN, (viii) $NaClO_4$, (ix) Li_2S, (x) CH_3COONa.

TABLE 13.2
REACTION OF COMMON IONS WITH WATER

NO REACTION	WEAK REACTION	STRONG REACTION
	Basic	
Cl^-, Br^-, I^-, NO_3^-, ClO_4^-	CH_3COO^-, F^-, NO_2^-, HCO_3^-, CN^-, SO_4^{2-}, SO_3^{2-}	PO_4^{3-}, S^{2-}, CO_3^{2-}
	Acidic	
$Li^+ \longrightarrow Rb^+$, Mg^{2+}, Ca^{2+}, Ag^+	NH_4^+, Be^{2+}, Zn^{2+}, Cu^{2+}, Cd^{2+}, Fe^{2+}, Sn^{2+}	Fe^{3+}, Bi^{3+}, Sn^{4+}, Al^{3+}

LEWIS ACID-BASE THEORY _____ 13.7

A broader definition of acids and bases was proposed by Gilbert Lewis in 1923. In the Brönsted-Lowry definition the proton is "king." An acid is a molecule or ion that gives up a proton. A base is a molecule or ion that can attract and hold a proton. *The base must have at least one unshared pair of electrons. The proton, H^+, can use (accept) the unshared pair of electrons to form a covalent bond* (page 250):

$$\ddot{N}H_3 + H^+ \longrightarrow \ddot{N}H_3^+ \text{ or } NH_4^+$$

$$:\ddot{O}:^{2-} + H^+ \longrightarrow H:\ddot{O}:^- \text{ or } OH^-$$

Lewis, however, decided to make the unshared pair of electrons more important than the proton. He postulated that the concept of acids and bases could be widely extended by assuming that a pair of unshared electrons is the fundamental characteristic of a base. Thus, *a base is any substance, charged or uncharged, that possesses at least one unshared pair of electrons.* The unshared pair of electrons can form a covalent bond with an ion, atom or molecule. This definition fits all the known Brönsted-Lowry bases as well as the Arrhenius base, the hydroxide ion.

An acid, according to Lewis, *is any substance, charged or uncharged, that can form a covalent bond by accepting an unshared pair of electrons.* This definition includes the proton of the Brönsted-Lowry and Arrhenius theories, as well as many other substances which previously had not been considered as acids. Typical Lewis acid-base reactions include the reaction between boron trifluoride, BF_3, and ammonia, $\ddot{N}H_3$ (page 251):

Acid — Boron trifluoride Base — Ammonia Product — Ammonia-boron trifluoride

and between aluminum trichloride and $:\ddot{Cl}:^-$, forming aluminum tetrachloride ion:

Acid Base Product

POLYPROTIC ACIDS _____ 13.8

Acids may further be classified in terms of the number of protons that can be given to a base. Acids such as hydrochloric, HCl, nitric, HNO_3, and acetic, CH_3COOH, that give up one proton per molecule, are called **monoprotic acids.**

Acids that can give up more than one proton per molecule or ion are referred to

Ionization of polyprotic acids is also discussed in Chap. 19.

as **polyprotic acids.** Thus, sulfuric acid, H_2SO_4, and phosphoric acid, H_3PO_4, are typical polyprotic acids. The reaction of phosphoric acid, H_3PO_4, with water is typical:

First Ionization　　　$H_3PO_4 + H_2O \rightleftharpoons H_3O^+ + H_2PO_4^-$

$$K_1 = \frac{[H_3O^+][H_2PO_4^-]}{[H_3PO_4]} = 7.00 \times 10^{-3}$$

Second Ionization　　$H_2PO_4^- + H_2O \rightleftharpoons H_3O^+ + HPO_4^{2-}$

$$K_2 = \frac{[H_3O^+][HPO_4^{2-}]}{[H_2PO_4^-]} = 6.21 \times 10^{-8}$$

Third Ionization　　　$HPO_4^{2-} + H_2O \rightleftharpoons H_3O^+ + PO_4^{3-}$

$$K_3 = \frac{[H_3O^+][PO_4^{3-}]}{[HPO_4^{2-}]} = 4.73 \times 10^{-13}$$

The first ionization of polyprotic acids always takes place to a greater extent than the subsequent ionizations. K_1 is always larger than K_2, which is always larger than K_3. This makes the dihydrogen phosphate ion, $H_2PO_4^-$, the weakest base and the phosphate ion, PO_4^{3-}, the strongest base in this series. The PO_4^{3-} ion is a stronger base than the hydrogen phosphate ion, HPO_4^{2-}, because its greater negative charge has a greater attraction for a proton. For the same reason, the HPO_4^{2-} ion is a stronger base than the $H_2PO_4^-$ ion.

13.9 ———— PERIODICITY OF BINARY AND OXYACIDS

Binary acids are composed of hydrogen and a nonmetallic element. Actually, only the binary acids of Group VIA and VIIA elements show appreciable acidity in water solution. In general, the acidity of binary acids increases on proceeding down a given group and across a given period from left to right in the periodic table:

Increasing Acidity →

CH$_4$	NH$_3$	H$_2$O	HF
		H$_2$S	HCl
		H$_2$Se	HBr
			HI

Increasing Acidity ↓

"Fundamentals of Chemistry," F. Brescia, J. Arents, H. Meislich, and A. Turk, Academic Press, New York, 2nd Edition, 1971, page 432.

Too many factors, most of which are difficult to evaluate, influence acid strength and make reliable predictions impossible. We have, therefore, elected to offer an explanation based on only one assumption: namely, that basicity of an ion is related to the volume available to the electron, the volume over which an electron can spread. The greater the available volume for a given series of basic ions, the larger the volume over which the electron can spread, the smaller is the electron density (charge/volume). The smaller the electron density, the smaller is the attraction for the proton, and the weaker is the base; the weaker the base, the stronger is the conjugate acid (Table 13.1, page 412). For example, in CH_3^-, the conjugate base of methane, CH_4, the negative charge is on the carbon atom. However, approximately three-fourths of the volume of the carbon atom is overlapped by three hydrogen atoms, as illustrated below in (a):

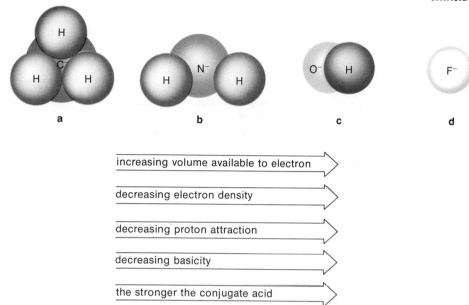

Thus, the negative charge on the carbon exists over approximately one-fourth the volume of the carbon atom. This produces a high electron density, which strongly attracts a proton. CH_3^- is thus a strong base, and the resulting acid, CH_4, is a weak acid. On the other hand, the entire volume of the fluoride ion is available to the negative charge, as illustrated in (d) above. This produces a comparatively small electron density, which weakly attracts a proton. F^- is thus a weaker base and HF is a stronger acid.

Similarly, in the series HF to HI, the volume of the ion increases from F^- to I^-; consequently, the volume available to the electron also increases, electron density decreases, the attraction for a proton decreases, and basicity decreases, as illustrated:

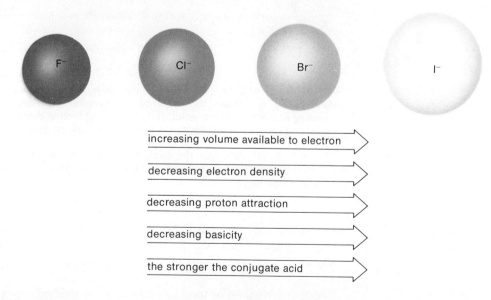

This makes HI the strongest acid in the series, in agreement with the experimental order.

For oxyacids, acids that contain oxygen, acidity increases with increasing oxidation number of the central atom, the atom to which the oxygen atoms are attached. The chlorine oxyacids are typical:

	Acid	Formula	Oxidation Number of Chlorine
Increasing Acidity ↓	Hypochlorous	HClO	+1
	Chlorous	$HClO_2$	+3
	Chloric	$HClO_3$	+5
	Perchloric	$HClO_4$	+7

Hypochlorous acid is least acidic while perchloric acid is most acidic. A reasonable explanation is afforded by the concept of electron density. In this particular series, the electron spreads over the chlorine and oxygen atoms, indicated below by dashed lines. As the number of oxygen atoms increases, the electron spreads over more oxygen atoms and the volume available to it increases. Consequently, electron density decreases, the attraction for a proton decreases, and basicity decreases, as illustrated:

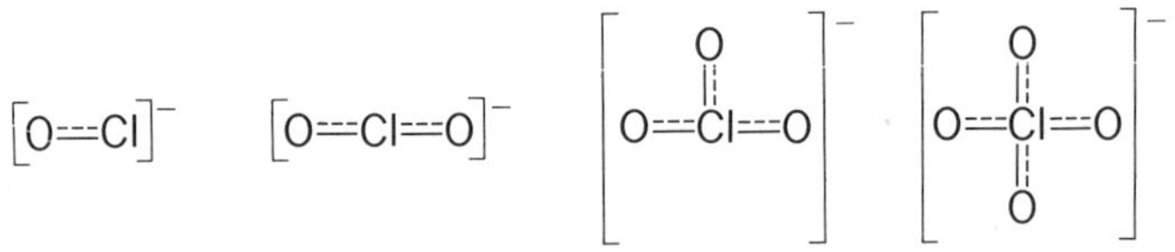

$$[O \text{---} Cl]^- \quad [O \text{---} Cl \text{---} O]^- \quad \begin{bmatrix} O \\ \| \\ O \text{---} Cl \text{---} O \end{bmatrix}^- \quad \begin{bmatrix} O \\ \| \\ O \text{---} Cl \text{---} O \\ \| \\ O \end{bmatrix}^-$$

———— increasing oxidation number of chlorine ————→
———— increasing number of oxygen atoms ————→
———— increasing volume available to electron ————→
———— decreasing electron density ————→
———— decreasing proton attraction ————→
———— decreasing basicity ————→
———— increasing acidity of conjugate acid ————→

This makes $HClO_4$ the strongest acid in the series, in agreement with the experimental order.

PROBLEM 8 List the oxyacids of nitrogen, nitric, HNO_3, hyponitrous, HNO (molecular formula $H_2N_2O_2$), and nitrous, HNO_2, in order of (a) increasing oxidation number of nitrogen, (b) increasing number of oxygen atoms, (c) decreasing electron density, (d) decreasing proton attraction, and (e) decreasing basicity. (f) Pick the weakest and the strongest acid.

PROBLEM 9 (a) Calculate the oxidation number of sulfur in its oxyacids: sulfuric, H_2SO_4, and sulfurous, H_2SO_3. (b) Predict which acid is (i) the weaker and (ii) the stronger. (c) Explain your selection.

13.10 PREPARATION OF ACIDS

Common acids are usually prepared by one of the following general methods:

Direct Combination of the Elements This method is applicable only to the preparation of binary acids. It is used mainly to prepare the halogen acids, especially hydrofluoric acid and hydrochloric acid:

$$H_2(g) + F_2(g) \longrightarrow 2HF(g)$$

The cost of the halogen elements usually makes this method commercially impractical. However, in the reaction of chlorine with organic substances (page 623), HCl is obtained as a by-product.

Reaction of Salts with Strong Acids   A large number of acids may be prepared by this method. Normally, the acid employed is sulfuric acid, since it is cheap, strong, thermally stable (page 297), and nonvolatile. Most of the acids formed by this method are volatile and, thus, are easily separated in pure form:

$$CaF_2(c) + H_2SO_4(l) \longrightarrow CaSO_4(c) + 2HF(g)$$

Reaction of Nonmetal Halides with Water   The halides of most nonmetallic elements hydrolyze to give the oxyacid of the element and the corresponding hydrohalogen acid without a change in oxidation numbers, as illustrated:

Oxidation Number
$$PBr_3(l) + 3H_2O \longrightarrow H_3PO_3(aq) + 3HBr(aq)$$
$$BCl_3(l) + 3H_2O \longrightarrow H_3BO_3(aq) + 3HCl(aq)$$

Oxidation Number
$$PCl_5(l) + 5H_2O \longrightarrow H_3PO_4(aq) + 5HCl(aq)$$

If the halogen is less electronegative than the nonmetal atom, the hydrolysis proceeds in a different fashion. Typical is the hydrolysis of nitrogen triiodide:

Oxidation Number
$$NI_3(c) + 3H_2O \longrightarrow NH_3(aq) + 3HOI(aq)$$

Note that there is no change in the oxidation numbers of the elements involved.

The Action of Water on Nonmetallic Oxides   Nonmetallic oxides, of which sulfur dioxide is typical, react with water to form oxyacids. This method of preparing acids occurs naturally in the air of urban areas and leads to the formation of a solution of sulfurous acid, a serious pollutant:

$$SO_2(g) + H_2O \longrightarrow H_2SO_3(aq)$$

H_2SO_3 has never been isolated, page 620.

The sulfur dioxide results from the combustion of coal and petroleum with a comparatively high sulfur content (page 307).

The decrease of this source of pollution, in the future, will depend very largely on the development and application of a combination of technologies designed to prevent the sulfur in coal and petroleum products from reaching the atmosphere through combustion processes. At present, many processes are being developed to perform this task.

A typical process being developed to combat sulfur dioxide emission from exhaust stacks is the *Cat-Ox Process*. In this process, stack gases are heated to about 500 °C and then passed over a catalyst of divanadium pentoxide (V_2O_5). The resultant gas contains a relatively high percentage of sulfur trioxide, SO_3, and a very low and tolerable percentage of sulfur dioxide, SO_2. This gas mixture is then cooled and passed through water to yield sulfuric acid:

"Fossil Fuel ⟶ Power + Pollution," Chemical Technology, volume 3, 1973, page 53. Also see page 401.

$$H_2O + SO_3(g) \longrightarrow H_2SO_4(aq)$$

Thus, a serious pollutant might be converted into a useful chemical reagent.

A considerable body of practical knowledge now available indicates that lime-stone, $CaCO_3$, and lime, CaO, processes may top the list for flue gas desulfurization. A typical reaction is

$$CaCO_3(slurry) + 2SO_2(aq) + H_2O \longrightarrow (CaSO_3)_2H_2O(c) + 2CO_2(g)$$

or

$$\underset{base}{CO_3^{2-}} + \underset{acid}{2HSO_3^-} \longrightarrow CO_2 + 2SO_3^{2-} + H_2O$$

$$Ca^{2+} + SO_3^{2-} + \tfrac{1}{2} H_2O \longrightarrow CaSO_3(H_2O)_{0.5}(c)$$

PROBLEMS

10 Vocabulary Define and give an example of the following terms: (a) Arrhenius base, (b) Arrhenius acid, (c) Lewis acid, (d) Lewis base, (e) Brönsted-Lowry acid, (f) Brönsted-Lowry base, (g) neutralization, (h) amphoteric compound, (i) hydrolysis, (j) polyprotic acid.

11 Conjugate acid-base pairs (a) Give the conjugate acid of (i) NH_3, (ii) NH_2^-, (iii) PO_4^{3-}, (iv) PH_3, (v) S^{2-}, (vi) NO_3^-, (vii) CO_3^{2-}, (viii) O^{2-}. (b) Give the conjugate base of (i) HCl, (ii) HSO_4^-, (iii) H_2O_2, (iv) HPO_4^{2-}, (v) H_2CO_3, (vi) NH_4^+, (vii) NH_3, (viii) $H_2PO_4^-$.

12 Amphoterism Illustrate with balanced equations the reactions of (a) HS^- and (b) HPO_4^{2-} with OH^- and with H_3O^+.

13 When nitric acid is dissolved in methyl alcohol, the following reaction occurs:

$$HNO_3 + CH_3OH \rightleftharpoons CH_3OH_2^+ + NO_3^-$$

Pick out the conjugate acid-base pairs.

14 Acidity or basicity State whether an aqueous solution of the following substances is acidic, basic, or neutral: (a) HNO_3, (b) KOH, (c) AlI_3, (d) $MgCl_2$, (e) $Ca(OH)_2$, (f) $LiCl$, (g) $AgNO_3$, (h) KI, (i) $Cr(NO_3)_3$.

15 Predict whether the following substances give acidic, basic, or neutral aqueous solutions: (a) $Mg(ClO_4)_2$, (b) KCN, (c) $FeBr_3$, (d) $Al(ClO_4)_3$, (e) $FeCl_2$, (f) NH_4I, (g) $Mg_3(PO_4)_2$, (h) AgI, (i) $LiHSO_4$, (j) $(CH_3COO)_2Ca$.

16 Write ionic equations for the reaction of the compounds in (a) Problem 14 and (b) Problem 15 with water.

17 (a) Pick the compound whose aqueous solution is basic: (i) $LiNO_3$, (ii) Li_2CO_3, (iii) NH_4Br, (iv) $BiCl_3$, (v) $BeCl_2$. (b) Pick the compound whose aqueous solution is acidic: (i) $LiNO_3$, (ii) Li_2CO_3, (iii) NH_4Br, (iv) BaF_2, (v) MgS.

18 (a) Phenol, C_6H_5OH, is a weaker base than ethyl alcohol, C_2H_5OH. Is the percentage dissociation of acetic acid, CH_3COOH, the same, smaller, or greater in phenol compared to ethyl alcohol? Explain. (b) Methylamine, CH_3NH_2 (b.p. $-6.5\ °C$), is a stronger base than water. Explain the observation that hydrochloric acid, HCl, is a stronger acid in methylamine than in water.

19 Base strength Sodium amide (b.p. $400\ °C$), $NaNH_2$, completely reacts with water to form sodium hydroxide and ammonia. Write the ionic equation. Which is the stronger base, OH^- or NH_2^-?

20 When sodium hydrogen sulfate is heated, sulfur trioxide and sodium sulfate result:

$$2NaHSO_4(c) \longrightarrow Na_2SO_4(c) + SO_3(g) + H_2O(g)$$

Show how this reaction can be treated as a Brönsted-Lowry acid-base reaction.

21 Brönsted-Lowry theory (a) Write equations for the following substances reacting as Brönsted-Lowry acids in water: (i) HNO_3, (ii) HPO_4^{2-}, (iii) $H_2PO_4^-$. (b) Write equations for the following substances reacting as Brönsted-Lowry bases in water: (i) $H_2PO_4^-$, (ii) PO_4^{3-}, (iii) SO_3^{2-}.

22 (a) When aqueous solutions of ammonium chloride, NH_4Cl, and sodium hydroxide, $NaOH$, are mixed, ammonia gas is liberated. Using the Brönsted-Lowry theory, write the appropriate equation for the reaction. Label the conjugate acid-base pairs. (b) Smelling salts, $(NH_4)_2CO_3$, liberate ammonia when the crystals contact water. Use the Brönsted-Lowry theory to write the ionic equation for the reaction and label the conjugate acid-base pairs.

23 Which of the following can act as a Brönsted-Lowry acid, Brönsted-Lowry base, Lewis acid, Lewis base? (a) NH_2^-, (b) OH^-, (c) NH_4^+, (d) I^-, (e) I^+, (f) BF_3, (g) H_2O, (h) H_2O_2.

24 K_{acid} For nitrous acid, HNO_2, $K_a = 4.5 \times 10^{-4}$. For hydrocyanic acid, HCN, $K_a = 4.0 \times 10^{-10}$. Which is the stronger acid?

25 Keeping in mind that an acid can act as an acid only in the presence of a base, explain what is meant by the statement, "K_{acid} is not a true measure of the absolute acid strength, but rather only a measure of the relative acid strength in a given solvent."

26 In a 0.100 M aqueous solution, acetic acid, CH_3COOH, ionizes to the extent of 1.33 %. Calculate K_a for this acid.

27 **Preparation of acids** Each of the following acids may be prepared from an oxide in which As, S, and N have the same oxidation number as in the acid: (a)

H_3AsO_3, (b) H_2SO_3, (c) HNO_3, (d) H_2SO_4, (e) H_3AsO_4. Write the formula of each oxide.

28 List the oxyacids of iodine (hypoiodous, HIO, iodic, HIO_3, and periodic, HIO_4) in order of (a) increasing oxidation number of iodine, (b) increasing number of oxygen atoms, (c) decreasing electron density of the conjugate base, (d) decreasing proton attraction of the conjugate base, (e) decreasing basicity of the conjugate base, and (f) increasing acidity.

29 **Library** Read one of the following:

(a) "A Modern Approach to Acid-Base Chemistry," R. Drago, *Journal of Chemical Education,* volume 51, 1974, page 300.
(b) "Hard and Soft Acids and Bases," R. Pearson, *Chemistry in Britain,* volume 3, March 1967, page 103.
(c) "The Theory of Acids and Bases," F. Hall, *Education in Chemistry,* volume 1, 1964, page 91.
(d) "Properties of Antacids," S. Hem, *Journal of Chemical Education,* volume 52, June 1975, page 383.
(e) "Acid-Base Theory," W. Jensen, *Chemistry,* Part I, March 1974, page 11; Part II, April 1974, page 13; Part III, May 1974, page 14.
(f) "Acid Precipitation," G. Likens, *Chemistry and Engineering News,* 22 November 1976, page 29.

---

30 The K_{acid} of acetic acid is 1.8×10^{-5}. What is the value of K_{base} of the acetate ion, CH_3COO^-, the conjugate base of acetic acid?

31 Sodium hydroxide solution is carefully added to a solution of acetic acid until *only* sodium acetate remains in the aqueous solution. Is the solution neutral, acidic, or basic? Explain.

32 In $\left[CH_3-C\begin{smallmatrix}O\\ \\O\end{smallmatrix} \right]^-$ an electron is spread over the three COO atoms, while in $[CH_3-CH_2-O]^-$ the electron is mainly confined to the O atom. Pick the weaker base and the weaker acid. Explain.

33 $H_{13}O_6^+$ represents the largest protonated cluster of

water molecules yet characterized. Two of the H_2O molecules are bonded as shown:

Add to this diagram the remaining H_2O molecules.

34 Show that any acid for which K_a is 1 or larger is a strong acid, by calculating K_a for 0.10 M HX solution, 92 % dissociation.

35 Use Brönsted-Lowry theory to write the ionic equation and label the conjugate acid-base pairs for each of the following aqueous reactions: (a) $:C\equiv C:^{2-}$ (acetylide) + H_2O, acetylene is the main product; (b) $NaHCO_3$ (baking soda) + H_2SO_4, fire extin-

guisher in which CO_2 is the main product; (c) $NaHCO_3$ (baking soda) + $Al_2(SO_4)_3$, baking powder in which CO_2 is the main product; (d) $:H^-$ (hydride) + H_2O, hydrogen is the main product.

36 Write the formula of the oxide that in water forms (a) H_2CO_3, (b) H_3PO_4, (c) H_3PO_3, (d) HNO_3, (e) $HClO_4$.

ANSWERS

1 (a) (i) HCl, KOH
   (ii) HCl, KOH
   (b) (i) and (ii) $HCl + KOH \longrightarrow KCl + H_2O$

2 (a) (i) HNO_3, (ii) Br^-
   (b) $HClO_4 + NH_3 \rightleftharpoons NH_4^+ + ClO_4^-$
      $Acid_1 \quad Base_2 \qquad Acid_2 \quad Base_1$

3 *Strong Acid*   *Weak Base*
   HCl Cl^-
   HI I^-

   Weak Acid   *Strong Base*
   HCO_3^- CO_3^{2-}
   CH_3COOH CH_3COO^-

4 (a) $H_3O^+ + OH^- \longrightarrow 2H_2O$
      ($HNO_3 + KOH \longrightarrow KNO_3 + H_2O$)
   (b) $NH_4^+ + NH_2^- \longrightarrow 2NH_3$
      ($NH_4NO_3 + KNH_2 \longrightarrow 2NH_3 + KNO_3$)

5 basic solutions: HS^-, F^-

6 acidic solutions: B^{3+}, Fe^{3+}, Cu^{2+}, Cd^{2+}

7 acidic: ii, iv, v
   basic: vi, vii, ix, x
   neutral: i, iii, viii

8 HNO, HNO_2, HNO_3
   strongest acid HNO_3, weakest acid HNO
      +6   +4

9 H_2SO_4 H_2SO_3

10 (a) (i) NH_4^+, (ii) NH_3, (iii) HPO_4^{2-}, (iv) PH_4^+,
      (v) HS^-, (vi) HNO_3, (vii) HCO_3^-, (viii) HO^-
   (b) (i) Cl^-, (ii) SO_4^{2-}, (iii) HO_2^-, (iv) PO_4^{3-},
      (v) HCO_3^-, (vi) NH_3, (vii) NH_2^-, (viii) HPO_4^{2-}

12 (a) $HS^- + OH^- \longrightarrow H_2O + S^{2-}$
      $HS^- + H_3O^+ \longrightarrow H_2S + H_2O$
   (b) $HPO_4^{2-} + OH^- \longrightarrow H_2O + PO_4^{3-}$
      $HPO_4^{2-} + H_3O^+ \longrightarrow H_2PO_4^- + H_2O$

13 $HNO_3 + CH_3OH \rightleftharpoons NO_3^- + CH_3OH_2^+$
   $Acid_1 \quad Base_2 \qquad Base_1 \quad Acid_2$

14 acidic: a, c, i
   basic: b, e
   neutral: d, f, g, h

15 acidic: c, d, e, f, i
   basic: b, g, j
   neutral: a, h

17 (a) basic: ii
   (b) acidic: iii

18 (a) smaller

19 $NH_2^- + H_2O \longrightarrow NH_3 + OH^-$
   stronger base: NH_2^- (amide ion)

20 $HSO_4^- + HSO_4^- \rightleftharpoons SO_4^{2-} + H_2SO_4$
   $Acid_1 \quad Base_2 \qquad Base_1 \quad Acid_2$

21 (a) (i) $HNO_3 + H_2O \rightleftharpoons H_3O^+ + NO_3^-$
      (ii) $HPO_4^{2-} + H_2O \rightleftharpoons H_3O^+ + PO_4^{3-}$
      (iii) $H_2PO_4^- + H_2O \rightleftharpoons H_3O^+ + HPO_4^{2-}$
   (b) (i) $H_2PO_4^- + H_2O \rightleftharpoons H_3PO_4 + OH^-$
      (ii) $PO_4^{3-} + H_2O \rightleftharpoons HPO_4^{2-} + OH^-$
      (iii) $SO_3^{2-} + H_2O \rightleftharpoons HSO_3^- + OH^-$

22 (a) $NH_4^+ + OH^- \rightleftharpoons NH_3 + H_2O$
      $Acid_1 \quad Base_2 \qquad Base_1 \quad Acid_2$
   (b) $NH_4^+ + CO_3^{2-} \rightleftharpoons NH_3 + HCO_3^-$
      $Acid_1 \quad Base_2 \qquad Base_1 \quad Acid_2$

23 Brönsted-Lowry acid: c, g, h
   Brönsted-Lowry base: a, b, d, g
   Lewis acid: e, f
   Lewis base: a, b, d, g, h

24 Nitrous acid, HNO_2

26 1.7×10^{-5}

27 (a) As_2O_3, (b) SO_2, (c) N_2O_5, (d) SO_3, (e) As_2O_5

28 HIO, HIO_3, HIO_4

30 $K_b = 5.6 \times 10^{-10}$

31 Basic

32 Weaker base: CH_3COO^-
   Weaker acid: CH_3CH_2OH

34 $K_a = 1.06$

35 (a) $C_2^{2-} + 2H_2O \rightleftharpoons C_2H_2 + 2OH^-$
      $Base_2 \quad Acid_1 \qquad Acid_2 \quad Base_1$
   (b)(c) $HCO_3^- + H_3O^+$ (from H_2SO_4 or $Al_2(SO_4)_3$)
      $Base_2 \quad Acid_1$
      $\rightleftharpoons H_2CO_3 + H_2O$
      $\qquad\qquad Acid_2 \quad Base_1$
   (d) $:H^- + H_2O \rightleftharpoons OH^- + H_2$
      $Base_2 \quad Acid_1 \qquad Base_1 \quad Acid_2$

36 (a) CO_2, (b) P_2O_5, (c) P_2O_3, (d) N_2O_5, (e) Cl_2O_7

GLOSSARY

acidic solution An aqueous solution in which $[H^+]$ is higher than $[OH^-]$.

alkali Same as a base, but refers to a soluble strong base like NaOH or KOH.

alkaline solution Same as a basic solution; see **basic solution.**

amphoteric compound A substance capable of acting as an acid and a base.

basic solution An aqueous solution in which $[OH^-]$ is higher than $[H^+]$.

Brönsted-Lowry acid A substance capable of liberating protons.

Brönsted-Lowry base A substance capable of accepting protons.

conjugate acid The substance formed by addition of a proton to a Brönsted-Lowry base.

conjugate base The substance formed by removal of a proton from a Brönsted-Lowry acid.

conjugate acid-base pair (Brönsted-Lowry) Two particles—molecules or ions—related to each other by removal or addition of a proton; for example, CH_3COOH and CH_3COO^-, and $H_2PO_4^-$ and HPO_4^{2-}.

hydrolysis (Brönsted-Lowry) A reaction with an anion or cation that involves water, resulting in the production of H^+ or OH^- ions.

hydroxide ion The OH^- ion.

Lewis acid A substance which accepts an unshared electron pair.

Lewis base A substance which donates an unshared electron pair.

neutralization A reaction between an acid and a base, producing the solvent and a salt.

neutral solution A solution in which $[H^+] = [OH^-]$; it is neither acidic nor basic.

oxyacid An acid containing more than one OH group per molecule.

polyprotic acid A substance capable of liberating more than one proton per molecule.

salt See **neutralization**.

strong acid An acid with a strong tendency to liberate protons in water.

strong base A base with a strong tendency to accept protons in water.

weak acid An acid with a small tendency to liberate protons in water.

weak base A base with a small tendency to accept protons in water.

IONIC EQUILIBRIUM 14

INTRODUCTION_____14.1

In this chapter we shall apply the principles of chemical equilibrium (Chap. 12) to equilibria of ions and molecules in aqueous solutions. A knowledge of these equilibria is important because they form the basis of calculations used to determine the amount of substances in solution (analytical chemistry). They also lead to an understanding of many industrial and physiological processes. We shall also develop a measure of acid and base strengths (Chap. 13) and learn how differences in concentration affect the acidic or basic properties of solutions.

THE IONIZATION OF WATER_____14.2

In Chap. 13, we learned that water reacts with itself; it undergoes self-ionization

$$H_2O + H_2O \rightleftharpoons H_3O^+ + OH^-$$

for which the equilibrium condition is

$$K_w = [H_3O^+][OH^-] = 1.002 \times 10^{-14} \ (25 \ ^\circ C)$$

Recall page 380; pure solids or pure liquids are omitted from the equilibrium condition.

This expression means that water always contains a certain amount of H_3O^+ and OH^-. It also means that in pure water, the concentrations of hydrogen and hydroxyl ions are equal; one H_3O^+ forms for every OH^- formed.

The molar concentration, the concentration in moles per liter, of these ions in pure water at 25 °C may be obtained from the equilibrium condition by letting $x = [H_3O^+]$. Since the concentration of OH^- is equal to the concentration of H_3O^+, $[OH^-]$ must also equal x. Thus,

$$x = [H_3O^+] = [OH^-] \ in \ pure \ water$$

Substituting

$$[H_3O^+][OH^-] = K_w = 1.0 \times 10^{-14}$$
$$x \times x = 1.0 \times 10^{-14}$$
$$x^2 = 1.0 \times 10^{-14}$$
$$x = \sqrt{1.0 \times 10^{-14}} = 1.0 \times 10^{-7} \ \text{mole}/\ell$$

At temperatures other than 25 °C, the H$^+$ and OH$^-$ concentrations are, of course, still equal in pure water, but the values are different from that at 25 °C. For example, at 0 °C

$$[H_3O^+][OH^-] = K_w = 0.115 \times 10^{-14}$$

from which

$$x^2 = 0.115 \times 10^{-14}$$
$$x = [H_3O^+] = [OH^-] = 0.339 \times 10^{-7} \text{ mole}/\ell$$

Unless otherwise stated, equilibrium data in this chapter are at 25 °C.

PROBLEM 1   **At 35 °C, $K_w = 2.09 \times 10^{-14}$. Calculate [H$_3O^+$] and [OH$^-$] in pure water at 35 °C.**

The addition of an acid, such as hydrochloric acid, HCl, or ammonium chloride, NH$_4$Cl (page 415), or a base, such as sodium hydroxide, NaOH, or sodium carbonate, Na$_2$CO$_3$ (page 416), changes [H$_3$O$^+$] and [OH$^-$] so that they are not equal. These two concentrations are not equal, but their product, [H$_3$O$^+$] $\times$ [OH$^-$], must equal the equilibrium constant, K_w. Therefore, when an acid is added, the H$_3$O$^+$ concentration is increased and the OH$^-$ ion concentration must decrease. For example, in 0.010 M HCl, [H$_3$O$^+$] = 0.010 mole/ℓ. Recall (page 327) that HCl is a typical strong electrolyte; it completely dissociates in water:

$$HCl(aq) + H_2O \longrightarrow H_3O^+(aq) + Cl^-(aq)$$

Then

$$[H_3O^+][OH^-] = 1.0 \times 10^{-14}$$
$$0.010 \times [OH^-] = 1.0 \times 10^{-14}$$
$$[OH^-] = \frac{1.0 \times 10^{-14}}{1.0 \times 10^{-2}} = 1.0 \times 10^{-14} \times 10^2$$
$$= 1.0 \times 10^{-12} \text{ mole}/\ell$$

[H$_3$O$^+$] produced by ionization of water is negligible compared to [H$_3$O$^+$] produced by the HCl.

When a base is added to water, the OH$^-$ concentration increases and the H$_3$O$^+$ concentration decreases. For example, in 0.020 M NaOH, a strong electrolyte,

$$NaOH(aq) \longrightarrow Na^+(aq) + OH^-(aq)$$

[OH$^-$] = 0.020 mole/ℓ. Then

$$[H_3O^+][OH^-] = 1.0 \times 10^{-14}$$
$$[H_3O^+] \times 0.020 = 1.0 \times 10^{-14}$$
$$[H_3O^+] = \frac{1.0 \times 10^{-14}}{2.0 \times 10^{-2}} = 0.50 \times 10^{-14} \times 10^2 = 0.50 \times 10^{-12}$$
$$= 5.0 \times 10^{-13} \text{ mole}/\ell$$

PROBLEM 2   **Calculate [H$_3$O$^+$] and [OH$^-$] in (a) 0.0025 M HCl, and (b) 0.0050 M NaOH.**

14.3   EXPRESSING SMALL NUMBERS: pH

The hydrogen ion concentration is a significant quantity; every biological (biochemical) reaction and many industrial processes are controlled by [H$_3$O$^+$]. An increase in the concentration of H$_3$O$^+$ resulting from the dissociation of carbonic acid (CO$_2$ + H$_2$O) is involved in triggering the release of oxygen from the hemoglobin-oxygen carrier in blood (page 322). Frequently, the concentration of H_3O^+ is a very small number. Since it is sometimes inconvenient to use exponential numbers, a scheme has been invented to convert them to more common numbers. A symbol called **"pH"** is defined as the negative logarithm (base 10) of the H_3O^+ concentration in moles per liter:[*]

$$pH = -\text{logarithm } [H_3O^+] = -\log [H_3O^+]$$

Let us examine more closely how pH values are calculated. By definition, the logarithm (log) of a number is the power to which 10 must be raised to give that number. For example, the log of 100 is 2; this is another way of saying that 10 raised to the power of 2, 10^2, equals $10 \times 10 = 100$. The log of 1000 is 3, because $10^3 = 10 \times 10 \times 10 = 1000$. Other examples follow:

The Number	The Number Written as an Exponential Number	Log of the Number; the Power to which 10 Is Raised to Give the Number
10,000	10^4	$\log 10{,}000 = \log 10^4 = 4$
10	10^1	$\log 10 = \log 10^1 = 1$
1	10^0	$\log 1 = \log 10^0 = 0$
0.1	10^{-1}	$\log 0.1 = \log 10^{-1} = -1$
0.01	10^{-2}	$\log 0.01 = \log 10^{-2} = -2$
0.0001	10^{-4}	$\log 0.0001 = \log 10^{-4} = -4$

But what are the logarithms of numbers such as 1420, 142.0, or 0.0000001420? To determine these logarithms, *first* rewrite the number as an exponential number in powers of 10 so that *only one digit* remains before the decimal point. Thus

$$1420 \text{ is rewritten as } 1.420 \times 10^3$$
$$142.0 \text{ is rewritten as } 1.420 \times 10^2$$
$$0.0000001420 \text{ is rewritten as } 1.420 \times 10^{-7}$$

We have rewritten these numbers as two parts: 1.420 multiplied by an exponential number. In fact, the name logarithm is derived from *logos* and *arithmos,* the Greek words for part-number.

A law of logarithms states that adding the logs of two numbers—for example

$$\log 10^2 + \log 10^2 = 2 + 2 = 4$$

is the same as the log *after multiplying* the two numbers

$$\log (10^2 \times 10^2) = \log 10^4 = 4$$

Thus

$$\log (10^2 \times 10^2) = \log 10^2 + \log 10^2 = 2 + 2 = 4$$

In general

$$\log (x \times y) = \log x + \log y$$

---

[*] Since pH measurements involve an equilibrium, $H_2(g) \rightleftharpoons 2H^+(aq) + 2e^-$, this definition is valid only for dilute solutions (page 323). To emphasize the importance of hydrogen ion concentration, Sören Sörenson (1909) suggested that an acidity scale be based on $pH^+ = -\log [H_3O^+]$. The symbol pH^+, derived from *potenz,* the Danish word for power, is an abbreviation of "power of hydrogen ion." Later simplified to pH, the scheme was also generalized to express any small number; for example $pK = -\log K$, $pCl = -\log [Cl^-]$, $pOH = -\log [OH^-]$.

the log of the product of the numbers = sum of the log of each number. Hence

$$log\ (1.420 \times 10^3) = log\ 1.420 + log\ 10^3$$
$$log\ (1.420 \times 10^2) = log\ 1.420 + log\ 10^2$$
$$log\ (1.420 \times 10^{-7}) = log\ 1.420 + log\ 10^{-7}$$

Then, determine the log of each part (number). The log of the first number is found in the logarithm table (App. X), a small portion of which is reproduced in Table 14.1. To find 1.42 in the table, find 1.4 in the column labeled "Number," or *N*, and then go across the table, left to right, to the column marked "2." Here, we find the number 0.1523. The logarithm of 1.420 is therefore 0.1523. Notice that the log of the first part (which is always a number between 1 and 10, because we have rewritten it to have only one digit before the decimal point) is always a number between 0 and 1.

TABLE 14.1
A PORTION OF THE LOGARITHM TABLE*

NUMBER	0	1	2
1.0	0.0000	0.0043	0.0086
1.1	0.0414	0.0453	0.0492
1.2	0.0792	0.0828	0.0864
1.3	0.1139	0.1173	0.1206
1.4	0.1461	0.1492	0.1523
2.0	0.3010	0.3032	0.3054

*See App. X.

The log of the second part (number) is the power to which 10 is raised: $log\ 10^3 = 3$, $log\ 10^2 = 2$, $log\ 10^{-7} = -7$.

Finally, add the two logs:

$$log\ (1.420 \times 10^3) = log\ 1.420 + log\ 10^3 = 0.1523 + 3 = 3.1523$$
$$log\ (1.420 \times 10^2) = log\ 1.420 + log\ 10^2 = 0.1523 + 2 = 2.1523$$
$$log\ (1.420 \times 10^{-7}) = log\ 1.420 + log\ 10^{-7} = 0.1523 + (-7) = -6.8477$$

Thus, at 25 °C in a neutral solution (page 413), $[H_3O^+] = [OH^-] = 1.0 \times 10^{-7}$

$$pH = -log\ [H_3O^+] = -log\ (1.0 \times 10^{-7})$$

but

$$log\ (1.0 \times 10^{-7}) = 0 + (-7.00) = -7.00$$

so that

$$pH = -(-7.00) = 7.00$$

7.00 is easier to use than 1.0×10^{-7}.

Example 1

What is the pH of a solution in which $[H_3O^+] = 12.1 \times 10^{-6}$?

Answer

First, if necessary, rewrite the number as an exponential number so that one digit remains before the decimal point: 1.21×10^{-5}. Then, find the log of the number (Table 14.1):

$$\log (1.21 \times 10^{-5}) = \log 1.21 + \log 10^{-5} = 0.0828 + (-5) = -4.9172$$

Finally, convert this to the pH:

$$pH = -\log [H_3O^+] = -\log (1.21 \times 10^{-5}) = -(-4.9172) = 4.917$$

PROBLEM 3   What is the pH of a solution in which $[H_3O^+] = 4.67 \times 10^{-3}$?

Example 2

Find the pH of a 0.00278 M NaOH solution.

Answer

First calculate $[H_3O^+]$ as on page 430: 0.00278 M NaOH = 2.78×10^{-3} M NaOH, from which $[OH^-] = 2.78 \times 10^{-3}$. Then

$$[H_3O^+][OH^-] = 1.0 \times 10^{-14}$$
$$[H_3O^+] \times 2.78 \times 10^{-3} = 1.0 \times 10^{-14}$$
$$[H_3O^+] = \frac{1.0 \times 10^{-14}}{2.78 \times 10^{-3}} = 0.36 \times 10^{-11} = 3.6 \times 10^{-12}$$

Then, calculate pH as in Example 1:

$$\log (3.6 \times 10^{-12}) = \log 3.6 + \log 10^{-12} = 0.5563 + (-12) = -11.4437$$
$$pH = -\log [H_3O^+] = -(-11.44) = 11.44$$

PROBLEM 4   What is the pH of 0.0074 M KOH?

pH values are calculated in powers of 10. The hydrogen ion concentration of a solution with a pH of 1.0 is ten times greater than a solution with a pH of 2.0. The greater the hydrogen ion concentration, the smaller the pH; see Table 14.2. When the pH is above 7, the solution is basic (alkaline), and when the pH is below 7, the solution is acidic.

TABLE 14.2
pH and $[H_3O^+]$ VALUES, FOR NEUTRAL SOLUTIONS
AT 25 °C, pH = 7.00

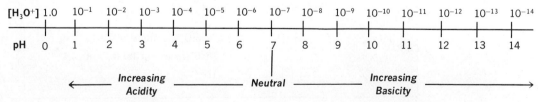

Conversion of pH to [H₃O⁺] Acidity measurements are made in pH units that are frequently converted to $[H_3O^+]$.

Example 3

The pH of a certain beer is 4.70. What is the $[H_3O^+]$?

Answer

By definition, $pH = -\log[H_3O^+] = 4.70$, from which $\log[H_3O^+] = -4.70$. We therefore must find the number whose log is -4.70, or the "antilog" of -4.70. But we have to work with a negative number. This log is made up of two parts, -4.0 and -0.70, which equals the -4.70 ($-4.00 - 0.70 = -4.70$). We can then write

$$\log[H_3O^+] = -4.70 = -4.00 - 0.70$$

then

$$[H_3O^+] = \text{antilog} -4.0 \times \text{antilog} - 0.70$$

The log table, however, contains only positive numbers. It is then necessary to convert -0.70 to a positive number. The simplest way to make this change is to add a $+1.0$ to -0.70 and a -1.0 to -4; thus

$$\log[H_3O^+] = -4.70 = -4.0 - 0.70 = (-4.0 - 1.0) \text{ and } (+1.0 - 0.70)$$
$$= -5.0 + 0.30 = -4.70$$

Observe that this operation does *not* change the value of $\log[H_3O^+]$:

$$\log[H_3O^+] = -4.70 = -4.0 - 0.70 = -5.0 + 0.30 = -4.70$$

Then

$$[H_3O^+] = \text{antilog} -5.0 \times \text{antilog} +0.30$$
$$= 10^{-5} \times \text{antilog} + 0.30$$

The antilogarithm of $+0.30$ is found in the log table, page 430. We look for the number whose logarithm is 0.30. This number is 2.0. The number 2.0 is the antilog of 0.30. Hence

$$[H_3O^+] = 10^{-5} \times 2.0 = 2.0 \times 10^{-5} \text{ mole}/\ell$$

Example 4

The pH of a soft-drink (soda) is 3.82. Find $[H_3O^+]$.

Answer

$$pH = -\log[H_3O^+] = 3.82, \text{ from which}$$
$$\log[H_3O^+] = -3.82 = -3.0 - 0.82 = (-3.0 - 1.0) \text{ and } (+1.0 - 0.82)$$
$$= -4.0 + 0.18 = -3.82$$

Then

$$[H_3O^+] = \text{antilog} -4.0 \times \text{antilog} +0.18$$
$$= 10^{-4} \times 1.5 \text{ (from log table, App. X)}$$
$$= 1.5 \times 10^{-4}$$

Known as the antilogarithm, abbreviated antilog. For example, $\log 100 = 10^2 = 2$; the antilog of 2 is 10^2 or 100. The $\log 1.41 = 0.1492$; the antilog of 0.1492 is 1.41.

PROBLEM 5   **What is the $[H_3O^+]$ of milk of magnesia in which pH = 10.50?**

As we have learned, strong acids like HCl are practically 100 % dissociated in water. This means that the number of moles of H_3O^+ in solution is the same as the number of moles of HCl present. A 0.010 M HCl solution contains 0.010 M H_3O^+ (page 428). The pH of this solution is 2.00. A 0.0010 M HCl solution contains 0.0010 M H_3O^+, and its pH is 3.00. The greater the acid concentration, the greater is the H_3O^+ concentration and the lower is the pH.

Similarly, a strong base like NaOH is practically 100 % dissociated in water, so that a 0.020 M NaOH solution contains 0.020 M OH^-. The pH of this solution is 12.30. A 0.0020 M NaOH solution contains 0.0020 M OH^-, and its pH is 11.30. The greater the base concentration, the smaller is the H_3O^+ concentration, and the higher is the pH. Thus, the higher the H_3O^+ concentration, the lower the pH; but the higher the OH^- concentration, the higher the pH.

WEAK ACIDS AND WEAK BASES _____ 14.4

Unlike strong acids and strong bases, solutions of weak acids and weak bases contain positive and negative ions in equilibrium with molecules of undissociated acid or base. Acetic acid, a typical weak acid, exists largely as molecules in dilute aqueous solution (page 327). Its tendency to form ions is very small, as seen from the small value of its equilibrium constant (very much smaller than 1.0):

$$CH_3COOH(aq) \rightleftharpoons H^+(aq) + CH_3COO^-(aq) \qquad K_a = 1.8 \times 10^{-5}$$

The equilibrium constant describes the relationship between the H_3O^+ concentration and the undissociated acid concentration. Some acid equilibrium constants are listed in Table 14.3; a few polyprotic acids (page 417) are included. In general, the H_3O^+ concentration of a polyprotic acid solution is determined mainly by the first equilibrium constant, K_1, since the second constant, K_2, is at least a thousand times smaller.

The larger the equilibrium constant, the stronger the acid, the higher the $[H_3O^+]$, and the lower the pH.

TABLE 14.3
EQUILIBRIUM CONSTANTS* OF ACIDS IN WATER AT 25 °C

NAME	FORMULA	K_1	K_2	K_3
Acetic acid	CH_3COOH	1.79×10^{-5}		
Ammonium ion	NH_4^+	5.73×10^{-10}		
Arsenic acid	H_3AsO_4	5.99×10^{-3}	1.05×10^{-7}	3.16×10^{-12}
Benzoic acid	C_6H_5COOH	6.5×10^{-5}		
Carbonic acid**	H_2CO_3	4.45×10^{-7}	4.69×10^{-11}	
Chlorous acid	$HClO_2$	1.1×10^{-2}		
Hydrocyanic acid	HCN	6.08×10^{-10}		
Hydrofluoric acid	HF	6.5×10^{-4}		
Hydrogen sulfide	H_2S	8.7×10^{-8}	1.2×10^{-14}	
Hydrogen sulfate	HSO_4^-	1.0×10^{-2}		
Hypobromous acid	HOBr	2.2×10^{-9}		
Hypochlorous acid	HOCl	2.9×10^{-8}		
Nitrous acid	HNO_2	5.13×10^{-4}		
Phosphoric acid	H_3PO_4	7.00×10^{-3}	6.21×10^{-8}	4.73×10^{-13}

*Source: *Pure and Applied Chemistry*, volume 20, No. 2, 1969, page 133.
**See footnote, Table 13.1, page 412.

Example 5

K_a of acetic acid is 1.79×10^{-5}. Calculate the $[H_3O^+]$ and pH in a 0.010 M CH_3COOH solution.

Answer

For the reaction

$$CH_3COOH(aq) + H_2O \rightleftharpoons H_3O^+(aq) + CH_3COO^-(aq)$$

$$K_a = \frac{[H_3O^+][CH_3COO^-]}{[CH_3COOH]} = 1.79 \times 10^{-5}$$

In a solution containing only acetic acid, the concentrations of H_3O^+ and CH_3COO^- are equal; one H_3O^+ ion is formed for every CH_3COO^- ion formed.* Let x = moles per liter of CH_3COOH ionized in reaching equilibrium. According to the chemical equation, for every mole of CH_3COOH ionized, 1 mole of H_3O^+ and 1 mole of CH_3COO^- must form. Then, x is also the number of moles/liter of H_3O^+ and CH_3COO^- formed. In summary

	CH_3COOH	+	H_2O	$\rightleftharpoons$	H_3O^+	+	CH_3COO^-
Initial concentration, mole/liter	0.010				0		0
Change in concentration, from chemical equation	$-x$				$+x$		$+x$
At equilibrium (sum of first two lines)	$0.010 - x$				x		x

$$K_a = \frac{[H_3O^+][CH_3COO^-]}{[CH_3COOH]} = \frac{x \times x}{0.010 - x} = \frac{x^2}{0.010 - x} = 1.8 \times 10^{-5} \quad (1)$$

We can avoid the labor of solving Equation 1 by assuming, just as we did in the equilibrium calculations in Chap. 12, that x is so small compared to 0.010 that it may be discarded without introducing a serious error into our calculations. For our purposes (page 387), *a quantity not larger than 0.1 of the initial quantity may be discarded*. Thus, to discard x in Equation 1, x should not be larger than 0.001 ($0.1 \times 0.010 = 0.001$). Equation 1 then becomes

$$\frac{x^2}{0.010} \approx 1.8 \times 10^{-5} \text{ (on the assumption that x is not larger than 0.001)} \quad (2)$$

Now, solving for x

$$x^2 \approx 1.8 \times 10^{-5} \times 1.0 \times 10^{-2} \approx 1.8 \times 10^{-7}$$
$$x \approx \sqrt{1.8 \times 10^{-7}} \approx \sqrt{18 \times 10^{-8}} \approx 4.2 \times 10^{-4}$$

Therefore

$$x = [H_3O^+] = 4.2 \times 10^{-4} \text{ mole/}\ell$$

---

*The H_3O^+ produced by the ionization of water ($K_w = 1.0 \times 10^{-14}$) is sufficiently small compared to the amount of H_3O^+ produced by acetic acid to be disregarded. It is *not* negligible for very dilute solutions (about 10^{-5} M) of very weak acids (K_a = about 10^{-10}).

Since 4.2×10^{-4} is less than 0.001, we are justified in changing $0.010 - x$ to 0.010 in Equation 2. Then

$$pH = -\log [H_3O^+] = -\log (4.2 \times 10^{-4})$$
$$\log (4.2 \times 10^{-4}) = \log 4.2 + \log 10^{-4} = 0.62 + (-4) = -3.38$$
$$pH = 3.38$$

PROBLEM 6 Calculate the $[H_3O^+]$ and pH of a 0.30 M solution of HCN. The chemical equation is

$$HCN(aq) + H_2O \rightleftharpoons H_3O^+(aq) + CN^-(aq) \qquad K_a = 6.08 \times 10^{-10}$$

The ionization of weak bases is similarly treated; the only difference is that the $[OH^-]$ rather than $[H_3O^+]$ is calculated from the chemical equation. Some basicity constants are given in Table 14.4.

TABLE 14.4
EQUILIBRIUM CONSTANTS OF SOME BASES IN
WATER AT 25 °C

NAME	FORMULA	K_b*	ILLUSTRATIVE REACTION
Acetate	CH_3COO^-	5.63×10^{-10}	$CH_3COO^- + H_2O \rightleftharpoons CH_3COOH + OH^-$
Ammonia	NH_3	1.76×10^{-5}	$NH_3 + H_2O \rightleftharpoons NH_4^+ + OH^-$
Carbonate	CO_3^{2-}	2.15×10^{-4}	$CO_3^{2-} + H_2O \rightleftharpoons HCO_3^- + OH^-$
Cyanide	CN^-	1.66×10^{-5}	$CN^- + H_2O \rightleftharpoons HCN + OH^-$
Fluoride	F^-	1.55×10^{-11}	$F^- + H_2O \rightleftharpoons HF + OH^-$
Nitrite	NO_2^-	1.96×10^{-11}	$NO_2^- + H_2O \rightleftharpoons HNO_2 + OH^-$
Phosphate	PO_4^{3-}	2.13×10^{-2}	$PO_4^{3-} + H_2O \rightleftharpoons HPO_4^{2-} + OH^-$
Sulfide	S^{2-}	0.84	$S^{2-} + H_2O \rightleftharpoons HS^- + OH^-$

*Recall page 414; K_b is usually calculated from K_w/K_a.

Example 6

K_b of ammonia, NH_3, is 1.76×10^{-5}. Calculate the $[OH^-]$, $[H_3O^+]$, and pH in a 0.10 M NH_3 solution.

Answer

For the reaction

$$NH_3(aq) + H_2O \rightleftharpoons NH_4^+(aq) + OH^-(aq)$$
$$K_b = \frac{[NH_4^+][OH^-]}{[NH_3]} = 1.76 \times 10^{-5}$$

In a solution containing only ammonia, the concentrations of OH^- and NH_4^+ are equal: one OH^- ion is formed for every NH_4^+ ion formed. Let x = mole per liter of NH_3 ionized in reaching equilibrium. According to the chemical equation, for every mole of NH_3 ionized, 1 mole of OH^- and 1 mole of NH_4^+ must form. Then, x is also the number of moles/liter of OH^- and NH_4^+ formed. In summary,

The OH^- produced by the ionization of water is sufficiently small compared to the amount of OH^- produced by ammonia to be disregarded.

	NH_3	$+$	H_2O	$\rightleftharpoons$	OH^-	$+$	NH_4^+
Initial concentration, mole/liter	0.10				0		0
Change in concentration, from chemical equation	$-x$				$+x$		$+x$
At equilibrium (sum of first two lines)	$0.10 - x$				x		x

$$K_b = \frac{[NH_4^+][OH^-]}{[NH_3]} = \frac{x \times x}{0.10 - x} = \frac{x^2}{0.10 - x} = 1.76 \times 10^{-5} \qquad (3)$$

We assume that x is not larger than 0.1 of the initial quantity of NH_3 (0.1×0.10) and so may be discarded. Equation 3 is then rewritten as

$$\frac{x^2}{0.10} \approx 1.8 \times 10^{-5} \text{ (on the assumption that x is not larger than 0.01)} \qquad (4)$$

Solving for x

$$x^2 \approx 1.8 \times 10^{-5} \times 0.10 = 1.8 \times 10^{-6}$$
$$x \approx \sqrt{1.8 \times 10^{-6}} \approx 1.3 \times 10^{-3}$$

Therefore
$$x = [OH^-] = 1.3 \times 10^{-3} \text{ mole}/\ell$$

Since 1.3×10^{-3} is less than 0.01 we are justified in rewriting Equation 3 as Equation 4. Then

$$[H_3O^+][OH^-] = 1.0 \times 10^{-14}$$
$$[H_3O^+] \times 1.3 \times 10^{-3} = 1.0 \times 10^{-14}$$
$$[H_3O^+] = \frac{1.0 \times 10^{-14}}{1.3 \times 10^{-3}} = 0.77 \times 10^{-11} = 7.7 \times 10^{-12}$$

and
$$pH = -\log [H_3O^+] = -\log (7.7 \times 10^{-12})$$
$$\log (7.7 \times 10^{-12}) = \log 7.7 + \log 10^{-12} = 0.89 + (-12) = -11.11$$
$$pH = 11.11$$

Example 7

Calculate the $[OH^-]$, $[H_3O^+]$, and pH of 0.10 M CO_3^{2-} solution (Na_2CO_3). The chemical equation is

$$CO_3^{2-}(aq) + H_2O \rightleftharpoons HCO_3^-(aq) + OH^-(aq) \qquad K_b = 2.15 \times 10^{-4}$$

Answer

Let x = mole per liter of CO_3^{2-} ionized in reaching equilibrium. Then, from the chemical equation, x is also the number of moles/liter of HCO_3^- and OH^- formed. In summary,

	CO_3^{2-}	+	H_2O	$\rightleftharpoons$	HCO_3^-	+	OH^-
Initial concentration, mole/liter	0.10				0		0
Change in concentration, from chemical equation	$-x$				$+x$		$+x$
At equilibrium	$0.10 - x$				x		x

$$K_b = \frac{[HCO_3^-][OH^-]}{[CO_3^{2-}]} = \frac{x \times x}{0.10 - x} = \frac{x^2}{0.10 - x} = 2.2 \times 10^{-4} \tag{5}$$

$$\frac{x^2}{0.10} \approx 2.2 \times 10^{-4} \text{ (on the assumption that } x \text{ is not larger than } 0.1 \times 0.10) \tag{6}$$

Solving for x:

$$x^2 \approx 2.2 \times 10^{-5}$$
$$x = \sqrt{2.2 \times 10^{-5}} = \sqrt{22 \times 10^{-6}} = 4.7 \times 10^{-3} = [OH^-]$$

Since x is less than 0.01, we are justified in writing Equation 6. Then

$$[H_3O^+][OH^-] = 1.0 \times 10^{-14}$$
$$[H_3O^+] \times 4.7 \times 10^{-3} = 1.0 \times 10^{-14}$$
$$[H_3O^+] = \frac{1.0 \times 10^{-14}}{4.7 \times 10^{-3}} = 0.21 \times 10^{-14} \times 10^{-3} = 2.1 \times 10^{-12}$$

and

$$pH = -\log [H_3O^+] = -\log (2.1 \times 10^{-12})$$
$$\log (2.1 \times 10^{-12}) = \log 2.1 + \log 10^{-12} = 0.32 + (-12) = -11.68$$
$$pH = 11.68$$

Example 8

Find the $[OH^-]$, $[H_3O^+]$, and pH in a 0.10 M solution of sodium acetate. The chemical equation is

$$CH_3COO^-(aq) + H_2O \rightleftharpoons OH^-(aq) + CH_3COOH(aq) \qquad K_b = 5.6 \times 10^{-10}$$

Answer

In a solution containing only sodium acetate, the concentrations of OH^- and CH_3COOH are equal; one OH^- ion is formed for every CH_3COOH molecule formed. Let x = mole per liter of acetate ion, CH_3COO^-, ionized in reaching equilibrium. Then x is also the number of moles/liter of OH^- and CH_3COOH formed. In summary,

	CH_3COO^-	+	H_2O	$\rightleftharpoons$	OH^-	+	CH_3COOH
Initial concentration, mole/liter	0.10				0		0
Change in concentration, from chemical equation	$-x$				$+x$		$+x$

At equilibrium $\qquad$ 0.10 − x $\qquad$ x $\qquad$ x

$$K_b = \frac{[CH_3COOH][OH^-]}{[CH_3COO^-]} = \frac{x \times x}{0.10 - x} = \frac{x^2}{0.10 - x} = 5.6 \times 10^{-10} \qquad (7)$$

$$\frac{x^2}{0.10} \approx 5.6 \times 10^{-10} \text{ (on the assumption that x is not larger than 0.1 × 0.10)} \qquad (8)$$

Solving for x

$$x^2 \approx 5.6 \times 10^{-11}$$
$$x \approx \sqrt{5.6 \times 10^{-11}} \approx \sqrt{56 \times 10^{-12}} = 7.5 \times 10^{-6} = [OH^-]$$

Since 7.5×10^{-6} is less than 0.01, we are justified in writing Equation 8. Then

$$[H_3O^+][OH^-] = 1.0 \times 10^{-14}$$
$$[H_3O^+] \times 7.5 \times 10^{-6} = 1.0 \times 10^{-14}$$
$$[H_3O^+] = \frac{1.0 \times 10^{-14}}{7.5 \times 10^{-6}} = 1.3 \times 10^{-9}$$

and

$$pH = -\log [H_3O^+] = -\log (1.3 \times 10^{-9})$$
$$\log (1.3 \times 10^{-9}) = \log 1.3 \times \log 10^{-9} = 0.11 + (-9) = -8.89$$
$$pH = 8.89$$

PROBLEM 7 (a) Calculate the $[OH^-]$, $[H_3O^+]$, and pH of a 0.0200 M solution of acetate ion (sodium acetate).

$$CH_3COO^-(aq) + H_2O \rightleftharpoons OH^-(aq) + CH_3COOH(aq) \qquad K_b = 5.6 \times 10^{-10}$$

(b) Calculate the $[OH^-]$, $[H_3O^+]$, and pH of a 0.200 M solution of methylamine, CH_3NH_2.

$$CH_3NH_2(aq) + H_2O \rightleftharpoons OH^-(aq) + CH_3NH_3^+(aq) \qquad K_b = 4.4 \times 10^{-5}$$

The larger the equilibrium constant, the stronger the base, the higher the $[OH^-]$, the smaller the $[H_3O^+]$, and the higher the pH.

14.5 THE PRINCIPLE OF LE CHATELIER REVISITED

Le Chatelier's principle (page 389) states that increasing the concentration of one substance in an equilibrium mixture causes the reaction to take place in the direction which consumes some of the substance added, and that decreasing the concentration of a substance causes the equilibrium to shift in the direction which produces more of that substance. This means that the H_3O^+ concentration in equilibrium with a weak acid may be changed. For example, the equilibrium $CH_3COOH(aq) + H_2O \rightleftharpoons H_3O^+(aq) + CH_3COO^-(aq)$ is shifted to the left, the equilibrium concentration of H_3O^+ is decreased by the addition of the acetate ion, CH_3COO^-. The addition of sodium acetate, a strong electrolyte, thus makes the solution less acidic.* In fact,

---

*Since acetic acid and sodium acetate have the acetate ion in common, this shift of the equilibrium is frequently named the common ion effect. However, there is nothing special about it; see page 396.

acetate ion is a (Brönsted) base (Table 14.4, page 435) and decreases the acidity of any acid solution.

Example 9

Calculate the hydrogen ion concentration in a solution containing 0.10 M acetic acid and 0.10 M sodium acetate.

$$CH_3COOH(aq) + H_2O \rightleftharpoons H_3O^+(aq) + CH_3COO^-(aq) \qquad K_a = 1.8 \times 10^{-5}$$

Answer

Unlike a solution containing only acetic acid (page 434), the concentration of acetate ion, CH_3COO^-, is not equal to the H_3O^+ concentration; in this solution the acetate ion comes from two sources: the strong electrolyte sodium acetate and the weak electrolyte acetic acid.

As in Example 5 (page 434), let x = mole/liter of CH_3COOH ionized in reaching equilibrium. Then x is also the number of moles/liter of H_3O^+ and CH_3COO^- *formed from the ionization of the acetic acid.* In summary,

	CH_3COOH	+	H_2O	$\rightleftharpoons$	H_3O^+	+	CH_3COO^-
Initial concentration, mole/liter	0.10				0		0.10
Change in concentration, from chemical equation	$-x$				$+x$		$+x$
At equilibrium	$0.10 - x$				x		$0.10 + x$

$$K_a = \frac{[H_3O^+][CH_3COO^-]}{[CH_3COOH]} = \frac{x(0.10 + x)}{0.10 - x} = 1.8 \times 10^{-5} \qquad (9)$$

$$\frac{x \times 0.10}{0.10} \approx 1.8 \times 10^{-5} \text{ (on the assumption that } x \text{ is not larger than } 0.1 \times 0.10)$$

$$(10)$$

from which
$$x = [H_3O^+] = 1.8 \times 10^{-5} \text{ mole/}\ell$$

Since x is less than 0.01, we are justified in writing Equation 10.

If sodium acetate were *not* added, $[H_3O^+]$ would be given by

$$\frac{x^2}{0.10} \approx 1.8 \times 10^{-5}$$

from which
$$x = [H_3O^+] = 1.3 \times 10^{-3} \text{ mole/}\ell$$

Note that, as predicted by Le Chatelier's principle, the hydrogen ion concentration is less in the acetic acid solution containing the sodium acetate.

PROBLEM 8 Calculate $[H_3O^+]$ in a solution containing 0.030 M HF and 0.030 M F⁻ (NaF).

$$HF(aq) + H_2O \rightleftharpoons H_3O^+(aq) + F^-(aq) \qquad K_a = 6.5 \times 10^{-4}$$

14.6 _____ BUFFER SOLUTIONS

Solutions of weak acids and their conjugate bases—for example, acetic acid and sodium acetate—have the ability to react with added acids and bases. The acid (acetic acid) reacts with an added base, while its conjugate base (acetate ion) reacts with an added acid. The addition of relatively small amounts of acids and bases thus has little effect on the pH of the initial solution. Since these solutions prevent comparatively large changes in pH, they are called **buffer solutions.** Such solutions are not particularly sensitive to the addition of *small* amounts of an acid or a base. Weak bases (NH_3) and their conjugate acids (NH_4Cl) are also buffer solutions.

Buffer solutions play a large part in our life processes. The pH of the gastric juices that aid food digestion is maintained around 0.85 by buffering action. Saliva is maintained at a pH of 6.4 to 6.9. Blood is maintained very closely between the normal pH limits of 7.3 and 7.5 by a complex system of buffer solutions consisting of serum proteins (Chap. 23) composed of amino acids containing acidic (—COOH) and basic (—NH_2) groups; carbonate, CO_3^{2-}, and hydrogen carbonate, HCO_3^-, ions; and dihydrogen phosphate ($H_2PO_4^-$) and hydrogen phosphate (HPO_4^{2-}) ions. The human body can tolerate only small pH changes between 7.0 and 7.8 in the blood. Pain is produced by a decrease in pH. Muscle pain, lumbago, for example, is produced by a metabolic change that results in tissue acidosis, a sharp decrease in pH.

When a strong acid, HCl, is added to a solution containing acetic acid and sodium acetate, the added hydrogen ion reacts with the base, the acetate ion:

$$CH_3COOH + H_2O \rightleftharpoons H_3O^+ + CH_3COO^-$$

The addition of H_3O^+ (HCl) shifts the equilibrium to the left, which means that the acetate ion, CH_3COO^-, concentration is decreased. It also means that the addition of a small amount of HCl to a large supply of acetate ion causes only a small change in pH. Practically all of the added H_3O^+ is *removed* by reaction with acetate ion, CH_3COO^-, forming molecular acetic acid, CH_3COOH. The addition of the HCl thus has only a slight effect on the pH of the solution.

On the other hand, if a strong base, NaOH, is added to the solution, the added OH^- reacts with acetic acid:

$$CH_3COOH + OH^- \rightleftharpoons H_2O + CH_3COO^-$$

The addition of a small amount of NaOH to a large supply of acetic acid causes only a small change in pH. Practically all of the added OH^- is *removed* as water, H_2O, by reaction with acetic acid. Hence, the effect on the pH of the solution is slight. This is like adding or subtracting two peanuts to or from 1000 peanuts.

The hydrogen ion concentration of a 0.010 M HCl solution is 1.0×10^{-2} M and its pH is 2.0. The addition of an equal volume of a 0.010 M NaOH solution results in a neutral solution: the pH undergoes a large change from 2.0 to 7.0. If, however, 0.010 mole NaOH is added per liter to a solution containing 0.10 mole acetic acid per liter and 0.10 mole sodium acetate per liter, the hydrogen ion concentration changes only slightly from 1.8×10^{-5} M to 1.5×10^{-5} M (see Example 10). This corresponds to a pH change from 4.74 to 4.82.

Example 10

The hydrogen ion concentration in a solution containing 0.100 M acetic acid and 0.100 M acetate ion (sodium acetate) is 1.8×10^{-5} M (Example 9, page 439) and the pH is 4.74. Calculate the pH of this solution after 0.010 mole NaOH is added per liter.

Answer

We assume that all of the added base, OH^- (NaOH), reacts with the acetic acid to form water and acetate ion

This is a very good assumption.

$$CH_3COOH(aq) + OH^-(aq) \rightleftharpoons H_2O + CH_3COO^-(aq)$$

For every mole of OH^- that reacts, 1 mole of CH_3COOH is consumed and 1 mole of CH_3COO^- is produced. Thus, adding 0.010 mole NaOH per liter decreases CH_3COOH by 0.010 mole per liter and increases CH_3COO^- by 0.010 mole per liter. The effect of adding the NaOH is to decrease the molarity of CH_3COOH from 0.100 M to 0.090 M and to increase the molarity of CH_3COO^- from 0.100 M to 0.110 M. In summary,

	CH_3COOH	$+$	H_2O	$\rightleftharpoons$	H_3O^+	$+$	CH_3COO^-
Initial concentration, mole/liter	0.100						0.100
Change in concentration, due to reaction with added NaOH	-0.010						$+0.010$
At equilibrium (sum of first two lines)	0.090				?		0.110

We now solve for $[H_3O^+]$

$$K_a = \frac{[H_3O^+][CH_3COO^-]}{[CH_3COOH]} = \frac{[H_3O^+] \times 0.110}{0.090} = 1.8 \times 10^{-5}$$

from which

$$[H_3O^+] = 1.8 \times 10^{-5}\frac{0.090}{0.110} = 1.5 \times 10^{-5}$$

and

$$pH = -\log[H_3O^+] = -\log(1.5 \times 10^{-5}) = 4.82$$

The pH thus changes from 4.74 to 4.82. However, if we add 0.010 mole NaOH to water to make 1.0 liter of solution, the pH changes from 7.00 to 12.00.

Example 11

A solution contains 0.100 M acetic acid and 0.100 M acetate ion (sodium acetate). Calculate the pH of the solution after 0.010 mole HCl is added per liter.

Answer

We assume that all of the added acid, H_3O^+ (HCl), reacts with the acetate ion to form acetic acid:

This is also a very good assumption.

$$CH_3COOH(aq) + H_2O \rightleftharpoons H_3O^+(aq) + CH_3COO^-(aq)$$

For every mole of H_3O^+ that reacts, 1 mole of CH_3COO^- is consumed and 1 mole of CH_3COOH is produced. Thus, adding 0.010 mole HCl per liter decreases CH_3COO^- by 0.010 mole per liter and increases CH_3COOH by 0.010 mole per liter. The effect of adding the HCl is to decrease the molarity of CH_3COO^- from 0.100 M to 0.090 M, and to increase the molarity of CH_3COOH from 0.100 M to 0.110 M. In summary,

	CH_3COOH	+ H_2O $\rightleftharpoons$	H_3O^+ +	CH_3COO^-
Initial concentration, mole/liter	0.100			0.100
Change in concentration, due to reaction with added HCl	+0.010			−0.010
At equilibrium (sum of first two lines)	0.110		?	0.090

We now solve for $[H_3O^+]$

$$K_a = \frac{[H_3O^+][CH_3COO^-]}{[CH_3COOH]} = \frac{[H_3O^+] \times 0.090}{0.110} = 1.8 \times 10^{-5}$$

from which

$$[H_3O^+] = 1.8 \times 10^{-5}\frac{0.110}{0.090} = 2.2 \times 10^{-5}$$

and

$$pH = -\log [H_3O^+] = -\log (2.20 \times 10^{-5}) = 4.66$$

The pH thus changes from 4.74 to 4.66. But if we add 0.010 mole HCl to water to make 1.0 liter of solution, the pH changes from 7.00 to 2.00.

Notice that the $[H_3O^+]$ is controlled by the ratio of the concentration of undissociated acid to the concentration of its conjugate base:

$$[H_3O^+] = 1.8 \times 10^{-5}\frac{[CH_3COOH]}{[CH_3COO^-]} \qquad (11)$$

The addition of a strong acid or a strong base changes this ratio as shown in Examples 10 and 11. The larger the ratio change, the greater is the change in $[H_3O^+]$, but the change in the buffer is not as large as in water.

PROBLEM 9 A solution contains 0.200 M acetic acid and 0.200 M acetate ion (sodium acetate) and the pH is 4.74. Calculate the pH of the solution after the addition of (a) 0.0050 mole HCl per liter; (b) 0.0050 mole NaOH per liter.

$$CH_3COOH(aq) + H_2O \rightleftharpoons H_3O^+(aq) + CH_3COO^-(aq) \qquad K_a = 1.8 \times 10^{-5}$$

14.7 _____ INDICATORS

Indicators are dyes (substances) which change color over a short pH range. Methyl orange (Table 14.5), for example, changes color in the pH range of 3.1 to 4.4. Since the colors of these dyes are sensitive to pH changes, the dyes are used as

TABLE 14.5
RANGE AND COLOR CHANGE OF SOME COMMON
ACID-BASE INDICATORS*

	pH SCALE												
INDICATORS	1	2	3	4	5	6	7	8	9	10	11	12	13

Methyl orange   ←— red —→3.1–4.4←————————— orange ————————→
Methyl red   ←——— red —→4.4 ——— 6.2←———— yellow ————————→
Bromthymol blue   ←——— yellow ———→6.2—7.6←———— blue ————————→
Neutral red   ←———— red ———→6.8—8.0←———— yellow ————————→
Phenolphthalein   ←——— colorless———————→8.0———10.0←——— red ——→colorless beyond 13.0

*Adapted from Roger Bates, *Determination of pH, Theory and Practice*, John Wiley & Sons, Inc., New York, 1964, pages 138–139.

indicators, as reagents to indicate the pH of a solution. More accurate measurements are made with an electrical device (voltmeter) known as a pH meter. The device measures the voltage of a galvanic cell (electric battery, Chap. 15) in which one of the electrodes is extremely sensitive to pH (H_3O^+) changes.

Indicators are extremely weak acids or bases. The color change occurs when protons are transferred to form a conjugate base or a conjugate acid of a different color:

Indicators as acids (or bases) are too weak to affect significantly the pH of a solution.

$$H \text{ Indicator} + H_2O \rightleftharpoons H_3O^+ + \text{Indicator}^-$$
acid, one color   *conjugate base,*
                                      another color

Indicators are used in **volumetric analysis,** a technique based on volume measurements to determine the quantity of a substance in solution. This technique involves the process of titration, the addition of a known volume of one solution to another solution.

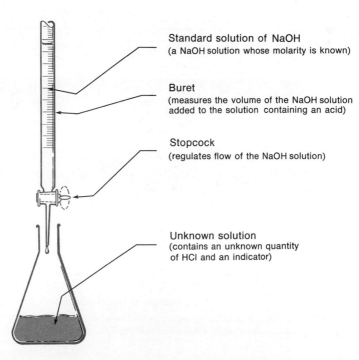

FIGURE 14.1 A typical titration setup.

Standard solution of NaOH
(a NaOH solution whose molarity is known)

Buret
(measures the volume of the NaOH solution added to the solution containing an acid)

Stopcock
(regulates flow of the NaOH solution)

Unknown solution
(contains an unknown quantity of HCl and an indicator)

A solution of known concentration, called a **standard solution,** is added to the solution containing the substance whose quantity is unknown. The addition is continued to the point, called the **equivalence point,** at which the unknown substance is completely consumed by reaction with the added standard solution. *Equivalence point* means that "chemically equal" amounts of reactants have been mixed and have reacted; "chemically equal" means that the amounts of reactants are in exact agreement with the balanced equation for the reaction.

The indicator is used to detect the equivalence point, the point at which all of the substance whose quantity is unknown has reacted with the added standard solution. See Fig. 14.1. Change in color of the indicator signals the point at which to stop the addition of the standard solution. The pH at which the indicator changes color is called the **end point.**

14.8 TITRATION CURVES

A titration curve, Fig. 14.2, shows how the pH of an acidic or basic solution changes with the addition of a standard solution of base or acid.

The meaning of a titration curve may be explained by reviewing the titration process in more detail. Suppose we wish to determine the amount of HCl in 100 ml of solution (containing only HCl). Two drops of phenolphthalein are added to the HCl solution, and the solution is titrated with 0.100 M NaOH (standard solution). As NaOH solution is added, the pH increases, slowly at first and then very sharply, and the curve becomes almost vertical (Fig. 14.2). With this very rapid increase in pH, the indicator suddenly and sharply changes color (in this case, from colorless to red). The color change indicates that the end point has been reached. The volume of NaOH corresponding to the end point is practically the same as the equivalence point, the point at which the molar quantities mixed exactly agree with the balanced equation

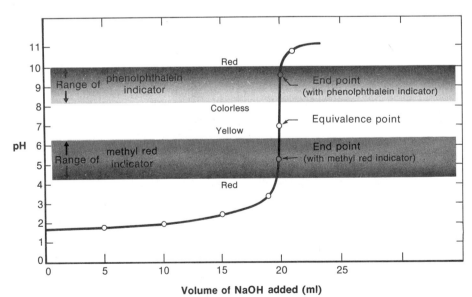

FIGURE 14.2 Typical titration curve: pH plotted against the volume of 0.100 M NaOH solution added from a buret to a dilute solution containing 2.00 mmol of HCl. (Solutions do not contain CO_2.)

for the reaction. The difference in volume of NaOH solution between the end point and the equivalence point in Fig. 14.2 is not significant for most titrations.

Example 12

20.00 ml of 0.1000 M NaOH is required to titrate an HCl solution. Calculate the number of mmol and the mass in mg of HCl (36.46 g/mole) in the solution. The chemical equation is

$$HCl(aq) + NaOH(aq) \longrightarrow NaCl(aq) + H_2O$$

Answer

From the given data first calculate (page 334) the number of mmol of NaOH added:

$$20.00 \text{ ml NaOH} \times 0.1000 \frac{\text{mmol NaOH}}{\text{ml NaOH}} = 2.000 \text{ mmol NaOH}$$

Then the number of mmol of HCl can be calculated from the chemical equation. The equation tells us that 1 mole (1 mmol) of NaOH reacts with exactly 1 mole (1 mmol) of HCl. The conversion factor (page 8) is therefore $\frac{1 \text{ mmol HCl}}{1 \text{ mmol NaOH}}$. The number of mmol of HCl is then given by

$$2.000 \text{ mmol NaOH} \times \frac{1 \text{ mmol HCl}}{1 \text{ mmol NaOH}} = 2.000 \text{ mmol HCl}$$

The mass of HCl is then given by

$$2.000 \text{ mmol HCl} \times \frac{36.46 \text{ g HCl}}{1 \text{ mmol HCl}} = 72.92 \text{ mg HCl}$$

If we had been asked to calculate only the mass of HCl, we would have used $\frac{36.46 \text{ mg HCl}}{1 \text{ mmol NaOH}}$ as the conversion factor:

$$2.000 \text{ mmol NaOH} \times \frac{36.46 \text{ mg HCl}}{1 \text{ mmol NaOH}} = 72.92 \text{ mg HCl}$$

Example 13

25.0 ml of 0.200 M NaOH is required to titrate an H_2SO_4 solution. Calculate the number of mmol and the mass in mg of H_2SO_4 (98.1 g/mole) in the solution. The chemical equation is

$$H_2SO_4(aq) + 2NaOH(aq) \longrightarrow Na_2SO_4(aq) + 2H_2O$$

Answer

The number of mmol of NaOH added is

$$25.0 \text{ ml NaOH} \times 0.200 \frac{\text{mmol NaOH}}{\text{ml NaOH}} = 5.00 \text{ mmol NaOH}$$

In this reaction, however, 2 mmol of NaOH reacts with exactly 1 mmol of H_2SO_4. The conversion factor is therefore $\dfrac{1 \text{ mmol } H_2SO_4}{2 \text{ mmol NaOH}}$; the number of mmol of H_2SO_4 is therefore given by

$$5.00 \text{ mmol NaOH} \times \frac{1 \text{ mmol } H_2SO_4}{2 \text{ mmol NaOH}} = 2.50 \text{ mmol } H_2SO_4$$

and the mass is given by

$$2.50 \text{ mmol } H_2SO_4 \times \frac{98.1 \text{ mg } H_2SO_4}{1 \text{ mmol } H_2SO_4} = 245 \text{ mg } H_2SO_4$$

If we had been asked to calculate only the mass of H_2SO_4, we would have used $\dfrac{98.1 \text{ mg } H_2SO_4}{2 \text{ mmol NaOH}}$ as the conversion factor:

$$5.00 \text{ mmol NaOH} \times \frac{98.1 \text{ mg } H_2SO_4}{2 \text{ mmol NaOH}} = 245 \text{ mg } H_2SO_4$$

Example 14

40.1 ml of 0.500 M $Na_2C_2O_4$ (sodium oxalate) is used to titrate 100.0 ml of $KMnO_4$ (potassium permanganate) solution. Calculate the number of mmol of $KMnO_4$ in the solution. The chemical equation is

$2KMnO_4(aq) + 5Na_2C_2O_4(aq) + 8H_2SO_4(aq) \longrightarrow$
$\qquad 2MnSO_4(aq) + 10CO_2(g) + K_2SO_4(aq) + 5Na_2SO_4(aq) + 8H_2O$

Answer

The number of mmol of $Na_2C_2O_4$ added is

$$40.1 \text{ ml } Na_2C_2O_4 \times 0.500 \frac{\text{mmol } Na_2C_2O_4}{\text{ml } Na_2C_2O_4} = 20.1 \text{ mmol } Na_2C_2O_4$$

In this reaction, 5 mmol of $Na_2C_2O_4$ reacts with exactly 2 mmol of $KMnO_4$. The conversion factor is therefore $\dfrac{2 \text{ mmol } KMnO_4}{5 \text{ mmol } Na_2C_2O_4}$; the number of mmol of $KMnO_4$ is therefore

$$20.1 \text{ mmol } Na_2C_2O_4 \times \frac{2 \text{ mmol } KMnO_4}{5 \text{ mmol } Na_2C_2O_4} = 8.04 \text{ mmol } KMnO_4$$

If we had been asked to calculate the mass of $KMnO_4$ (158 g/mole), we would have used $\dfrac{2 \times 158 \text{ mg } KMnO_4}{5 \text{ mmol } Na_2C_2O_4}$ as the conversion factor:

$$20.1 \text{ mmol } Na_2C_2O_4 \times \frac{2 \times 158 \text{ mg } KMnO_4}{5 \text{ mmol } Na_2C_2O_4} = 1.27 \times 10^3 \text{ mg } KMnO_4$$

PROBLEM 10 35.2 ml of 0.100 M NaOH is required to titrate (a) an HBr solution; (b) an H₂SO₄ solution. Calculate the number of mmol and the mass in mg of (a) HBr and (b) H₂SO₄ (see Example 13 for chemical equation).

For the titration of a strong acid (HCl) and a strong base (NaOH) (Fig. 14.2), the equivalence point occurs at a pH of 7.0, on the steeply rising part of the curve. The pH is 7.0 because the product of the reaction (NaCl) is neither acidic nor basic in water (page 416). However, the pH of a solution at the equivalence point is not always necessarily 7.0; it may be higher or lower, depending on the product of the reaction. For example, in titrating acetic acid with sodium hydroxide

$$CH_3COOH(aq) + NaOH(aq) \longrightarrow CH_3COONa(aq) + H_2O$$

the product of the reaction, sodium acetate, is a basic substance (Table 14.4, page 435), and the equivalence point occurs at a higher pH, about 8.9 (Fig. 14.3). On the other hand, the titration of sodium carbonate, Na_2CO_3, with HCl yields carbonic acid

$$Na_2CO_3(aq) + 2HCl(aq) \longrightarrow H_2CO_3(aq) + 2NaCl(aq)$$

and the equivalence point occurs at a lower pH, about 3.5. The *selection of an indicator* (Table 14.5) is therefore *determined by the pH of the solution at the equivalence point*. Hence, for the titration of Na_2CO_3 with HCl, methyl orange is selected; for acetic acid titration with NaOH (Fig. 14.3), phenolphthalein is chosen. For the titration of HCl with NaOH (Fig. 14.2), either phenolphthalein or methyl red may be used.

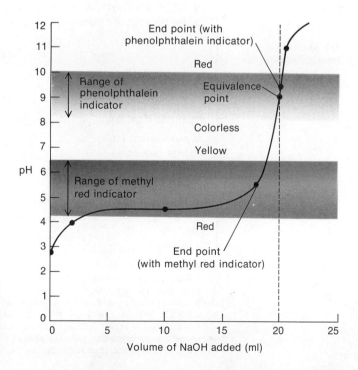

FIGURE 14.3 Typical titration curve of a weak acid titrated with a strong base. pH plotted against the volume of 0.100 M NaOH solution added from a buret to a dilute solution containing 2.00 mmol of acetic acid. Note the large negative error introduced by using methyl red as the indicator.

14.9_____EQUILIBRIA OF SLIGHTLY SOLUBLE SALTS

Reminder: Slightly soluble salts are commonly called "insoluble" and are generally 100 % dissociated in water.

Slightly soluble salts dissolve in water, establishing an equilibrium (pages 323 and 376) between the undissolved solid and its ions in solution. Typical is the solution of silver chloride, for which the equilibrium condition is

$$AgCl(c) \rightleftharpoons Ag^+(aq) + Cl^-(aq)$$
$$K_{sp}^* = [Ag^+][Cl^-]$$

Like any other equilibrium constant, the K for slightly soluble salts may be calculated from equilibrium concentrations expressed in molarity, moles/liter (page 332). However, equilibrium constants for slightly soluble salts are most frequently calculated from galvanic cells (electric batteries), page 460.

Since solubility data for slightly soluble salts are frequently tabulated as equilibrium constants, solubilities are sometimes calculated from them. However, more commonly, solubility data are obtained from tables of solubilities.

Example 15

The equilibrium constant for a saturated solution of silver bromide, AgBr, is 5.34×10^{-13}. Calculate the solubility of AgBr in mole/liter:

$$AgBr(c) \rightleftharpoons Ag^+(aq) + Br^-(aq)$$

Answer

In a solution containing only dissolved AgBr, the concentrations of Ag^+ and Br^- are equal; one Ag^+ ion is formed for every Br^- ion formed. Let x = mole per liter of AgBr dissolved in reaching equilibrium. Since 1 mole of Ag^+ and 1 mole of Br^- must form for every mole of AgBr dissolved, x is also the number of moles/liter of Ag^+ and Br^- in solution. In summary

The dissolved silver bromide, AgBr(aq), is 100 % dissociated.

	$AgBr(aq)$	$\longrightarrow$	$Ag^+(aq)$	+	$Br^-(aq)$
Initial concentration, mole/liter	x		0		0
Change in concentration, from chemical equation	$-x$		$+x$		$+x$
At equilibrium (sum of first two lines)	0		x		x

Then
$$K_{sp} = [Ag^+][Br^-] = x \times x = 5.34 \times 10^{-13}$$
$$x^2 = 5.34 \times 10^{-13} = 53.4 \times 10^{-14}$$
$$x = 7.31 \times 10^{-7} \text{ mole/} \ell \text{ of AgBr dissolved}$$

---

*Recall (page 380) that the concentration of a pure solid is fixed at a given temperature: AgCl(c) therefore does not appear in K_{sp}. Also recall (page 394) that the law of chemical equilibrium as used in this text is applicable only to dilute solutions and therefore cannot be used for soluble salts. Equilibrium constants (25 °C) are calculated from "Selected Values of Chemical Thermodynamic Properties," Technical Note 270 Series, National Bureau of Standards, Washington, D.C., 1968–1976. These equilibrium constants are commonly called **solubility products,** symbolized by K_{sp}, meaning the multiplication of concentrations obtained from solubility measurements.

Example 16

The equilibrium constant for the saturated solution of barium fluoride, BaF_2, is 1.81×10^{-7}. Calculate the solubility of BaF_2 in mole/liter:

$$BaF_2(c) \rightleftharpoons Ba^{2+}(aq) + 2F^-(aq)$$

Answer

In this solution, 2 F^- ions form for every Ba^{2+} ion formed. Let $x =$ mole per liter of BaF_2 dissolved in reaching equilibrium. According to the chemical equation, for every mole of BaF_2 dissolved, 1 mole of Ba^{2+} and 2 moles of F^- must form. Then x is also the number of moles/liter of Ba^{2+} and $2x$ is the number of moles/liter of F^- in solution. In summary,

	$BaF_2(aq)$	$\longrightarrow$	$Ba^{2+}(aq)$	+	$2F^-(aq)$
Initial concentration, mole/liter	x		0		0
Change in concentration, from chemical equation	$-x$		$+x$		$+2x$
At equilibrium (sum of first two lines)	0		x		$2x$

$$K_{sp} = [Ba^{2+}][F^-]^2 = x \times (2x)^2 = 1.81 \times 10^{-7}$$
$$x \times 4x^2 = 4x^3 = 1.81 \times 10^{-7}$$
$$x^3 = 0.453 \times 10^{-7} = 45.3 \times 10^{-9}$$

The cube of a number is the product obtained when the number is twice multiplied by itself (page 9) or when the number appears three times in a multiplication. Thus, "2 cubed" $= 2^3 = 2 \times 2 \times 2 = 8$. The cube root of a given number is the number that when twice multiplied by itself produces the given number. Thus, the cube root of 8, denoted as $\sqrt[3]{8}$, is 2 because $2 \times 2 \times 2 = 8$. The cube root of 27, $\sqrt[3]{27}$, is 3 because $3 \times 3 \times 3 = 27$. The cube root of 0.25, $\sqrt[3]{0.25}$, is 0.63 because $0.63 \times 0.63 \times 0.63 = 0.25$. The cube root of 10^{-6} is 10^{-2} because $10^{-2} \times 10^{-2} \times 10^{-2} = 10^{-6}$, and the cube root of 10^{-9} is 10^{-3} because $10^{-3} \times 10^{-3} \times 10^{-3} = 10^{-9}$. Then, the cube root of 45.3×10^{-9} is

$$x = \text{the cube root of } 45.3 \times 10^{-9} = 3.56 \times 10^{-3} \text{ mole/}\ell \text{ of } BaF_2 \text{ dissolved}$$

PROBLEM 11   **The equilibrium constant for the saturated solution of barium sulfate, $BaSO_4$, is 1.06×10^{-10}. Calculate the solubility of $BaSO_4$ in mole/liter.**

$$BaSO_4(c) \rightleftharpoons Ba^{2+}(aq) + SO_4^{2-}(aq)$$

Solubilities and Le Chatelier's Principle   Solubility is an equilibrium process subject to Le Chatelier's principle. The extent of the reaction, the solubility (undissolved solid $\rightleftharpoons$ dissolved solid), is determined by the composition of the equilibrium mixture. Thus, while the equilibrium constant remains constant at a given temperature, the solubility can be changed by changing the composition of the solution.

Example 17

For the reaction

$$AgCl(c) \rightleftharpoons Ag^+(aq) + Cl^-(aq)$$

the equilibrium constant is 1.77×10^{-10}

$$K_{sp} = [Ag^+][Cl^-] = 1.77 \times 10^{-10}$$

(a) A solution contains $[Ag^+] = 2.0 \times 10^{-6}$ and $[Cl^-] = 3.0 \times 10^{-7}$. Is the reaction at equilibrium? If not, in which direction will the reaction go? Will AgCl(c) form (precipitate) or dissolve? (b) A solution contains $[Ag^+] = 2.0 \times 10^{-6}$ and $[Cl^-] = 1.0 \times 10^{-2}$. Is the reaction at equilibrium? If not, in which direction will the reaction go? Will AgCl(c) precipitate or dissolve? (c) Chloride ion (sodium chloride) is added to water to make a 0.010 M solution. Is the solubility of AgCl(c) more or less in the NaCl solution than in pure water? Calculate the solubility of AgCl(c) in this solution.

Answer

(a) First, calculate the concentration term (pages 377 and 380):

concentration term $= [Ag^+][Cl^-] = (2.0 \times 10^{-6}) \times (3.0 \times 10^{-7}) = 6.0 \times 10^{-13}$

The concentration term does not equal K_{sp}; the reaction is therefore not at equilibrium. The concentration term is smaller than K_{sp}. The reaction goes from left to right—solid AgCl dissolves to increase the concentration of Ag^+ and Cl^- until K_{sp} is reached. Precipitation does not occur when the concentration term is less than K_{sp}; solid AgCl will not form (precipitate). Of course, if solid AgCl is not present, no reaction will occur.

(b) First, calculate the concentration term:

concentration term $= [Ag^+][Cl^-] = (2.0 \times 10^{-6}) \times (1.0 \times 10^{-2}) = 2.0 \times 10^{-8}$

The concentration term does not equal K_{sp}; the reaction therefore is not at equilibrium. The concentration term is greater than K_{sp}. The reaction goes from right to left, and solid AgCl will form (precipitate). Precipitation occurs when the concentration term is greater than K_{sp}, and continues until equilibrium is established.

(c) The solubility is less in the NaCl solution than in pure water. Addition of Cl^- or Ag^+ shifts the equilibrium to the left. But a definite amount of AgCl(c) does dissolve. Let x = mole per liter of AgCl dissolved in reaching equilibrium. Since 1 mole of Ag^+ and 1 mole of Cl^- form for every mole of AgCl dissolved, x is also the number of moles/liter of Ag^+ and $0.010 + x$ is the number of moles/liter of Cl^- at equilibrium. In summary,

	AgCl(aq)	$\longrightarrow$	Ag$^+$(aq)	+	Cl$^-$(aq)
Initial concentration, mole/liter	x		0		0.010
Change in concentration, from chemical equation	$-x$		$+x$		$+x$
At equilibrium (sum of first two lines)	0		x		$0.010 + x$

Then

$$[Ag^+][Cl^-] = x \times (0.010 + x) = 1.77 \times 10^{-10} \qquad (12)$$

We assume that x is not larger than 0.1 of 0.010, or 0.001, and then rewrite Equation 12 as

$$x \times 0.010 \approx 1.77 \times 10^{-10} \qquad (13)$$

from which

$$x \approx \frac{1.77 \times 10^{-10}}{1.0 \times 10^{-2}} \approx 1.8 \times 10^{-8} \text{ mole}/\ell = [Ag^+] = \text{solubility of AgCl}(c)$$

The solubility of AgCl(c) in the given NaCl solution is therefore 1.8×10^{-8} mole/ℓ, less than in pure water, 1.3×10^{-5} mole/ℓ. Since x is less than 0.001, Equation 13 is justified.

PROBLEM 12   (a) A solution contains $[Ag^+] = 3.0 \times 10^{-7}$ and $[Cl^-] = 1.0 \times 10^{-7}$. Does AgCl($c$) precipitate? (b) Calculate the solubility of AgCl in a 0.010 M solution of Ag$^+$ (silver nitrate). Is the solubility more or less in this solution than in pure water?

Solubilities of Slightly Soluble Sulfides   As predicted from Le Chatelier's principle, the solubility of a solid may be increased by shifting the reaction, undissolved solid $\rightleftharpoons$ dissolved solid, to the right. For example, the reaction

$$AgCl(c) \rightleftharpoons Ag^+(aq) + Cl^-(aq) \qquad K_{sp} = 1.77 \times 10^{-10}$$

can be shifted to the right by decreasing the concentration of Ag$^+$ or Cl$^-$. The addition of ammonia ties up Ag$^+$ as Ag(NH$_3$)$_2$$^+$ (Chap. 21), thus sharply decreasing the Ag$^+$ concentration. AgCl(c) may therefore be dissolved in ammonia solution. On the other hand, silver iodide, AgI(c)

$$AgI(c) \rightleftharpoons Ag^+(aq) + I^-(aq) \qquad K_{sp} = 8.53 \times 10^{-17}$$

is not dissolved by the addition of ammonia. The equilibrium constant for the solution of AgI(c) is so much smaller than the equilibrium constant for AgCl(c) that NH$_3$ cannot tie up a sufficient quantity of Ag$^+$ to cause the silver iodide to dissolve. This is typical of the many applications made of Le Chatelier's principle in separating components of mixtures to make identification easier (**qualitative analysis**).

Of particular interest is the separation of metal ions, such as Cu^{2+} and Fe^{2+}. Advantage is taken of the differences in solubilities of their sulfides in acid solutions.

In hydrogen sulfide, H_2S, solutions, the concentration of the sulfide ion, S^{2-}, is determined only by the H_2S and H_3O^+ concentrations. In a saturated solution of H_2S (0.10 M), the S^{2-} concentration is determined only by the H_3O^+ concentration; the larger the H_3O^+ concentration, the smaller the S^{2-} concentration.

Example 18

A saturated H_2S solution contains $[Fe^{2+}] = 0.010$ M, $[Cu^{2+}] = 0.010$ M, and the acidity is adjusted so that $[S^{2-}] = 8.1 \times 10^{-21}$ M. Will $FeS(c)$ and $CuS(c)$ precipitate?

$$FeS(c) \rightleftharpoons Fe^{2+}(aq) + S^{2-}(aq) \qquad K_{sp} = 1.58 \times 10^{-19}$$
$$CuS(c) \rightleftharpoons Cu^{2+}(aq) + S^{2-}(aq) \qquad K_{sp} = 1.30 \times 10^{-36}$$

Answer

This problem is similar to Example 17 (page 450). We calculate the concentration terms, and compare with K_{sp} in each case.

concentration term $= [Fe^{2+}][S^{2-}] = 0.010 \times 8.1 \times 10^{-21} = 8.1 \times 10^{-23}$

concentration term $= [Cu^{2+}][S^{2-}] = 0.010 \times 8.1 \times 10^{-21} = 8.1 \times 10^{-23}$

Compare with K_{sp}. For $FeS(c)$, the concentration term is smaller than K_{sp}; the reaction goes from left to right, and $FeS(c)$ will not precipitate. For $CuS(c)$, however, the concentration term is larger than K_{sp}; the reaction goes from right to left, and $CuS(c)$ will precipitate.

PROBLEM 13 A saturated H_2S solution contains nickel(II) ion, $[Ni^{2+}] = 0.020$ M, lead(II) ion, $[Pb^{2+}] = 0.020$ M, and mercury(II) ion, $[Hg^{2+}] = 0.020$ M. The acidity is adjusted so that $[S^{2-}] = 5.2 \times 10^{-21}$ M. Which metal ions, if any, precipitate?

$$NiS(c) \rightleftharpoons Ni^{2+}(aq) + S^{2-}(aq) \qquad K_{sp} = 1.09 \times 10^{-21}$$
$$PbS(c) \rightleftharpoons Pb^{2+}(aq) + S^{2-}(aq) \qquad K_{sp} = 8.89 \times 10^{-29}$$
$$HgS(c) \rightleftharpoons Hg^{2+}(aq) + S^{2-}(aq) \qquad K_{sp} = 6.49 \times 10^{-53}$$

PROBLEMS

14 Vocabulary Define or explain (a) pH, (b) common ion effect, (c) buffer solution, (d) indicator, (e) standard solution, (f) titration curve, (g) equivalence point.

15 K_w Calculate $[H_3O^+]$ and $[OH^-]$ in (a) 0.0010 M HI, (b) 0.00040 M HBr, (c) 0.00050 M KOH and (d) 0.0040 M KOH. $K_w = 1.0 \times 10^{-14}$.

16 pH Find the pH of each solution given in Problem 15.

17 At 40 °C, $K_w = 2.916 \times 10^{-14}$. (a) Calculate the $[H_3O^+]$ and pH of pure water at 40 °C. (b) If a patient has a fever of 104 °F (40 °C), do you think this would affect his blood pH readings?

18 At 60 °C, $K_w = 9.614 \times 10^{-14}$. (a) Calculate $[H_3O^+]$, $[OH^-]$, and pH. (b) See Problem 17. Is the dissociation of water an exothermic reaction? Explain.

19 What is the pH of a solution in which (a) $[H_3O^+] =$ (i) 1.4×10^{-5}, (ii) 1.36×10^{-10}, (iii)

1.45 × 10^{-4}, (iv) 1.90 × 10^{-4}; (b) [OH$^-$] = 6.35 × 10^{-6}, (ii) 4.60 × 10^{-11}, (iii) 3.56 × 10^{-10}, (iv) 1.70 × 10^{-4}; (c) the concentration of NaOH is 0.0022 M?

20 Calculate the pH of each of the following solutions: (a) 0.00010 M HNO$_3$, (b) 0.00050 M NaOH, (c) 0.0050 M KOH, (d) 0.0030 M HI.

21 Find [H$_3$O$^+$] in a solution whose pH is (a) 4.00, (b) 4.54, (c) 8.90, (d) 2.74, (e) 10.82, (f) 12.74.

22 (a) The optimum level of [H$_3$O$^+$] in blood is 4.0 × 10^{-8}. To what pH does this correspond? (b) The pH (i) of gastric juices is 0.85 and (ii) of saliva is 6.4 to 6.9. What are the corresponding [H$_3$O$^+$] concentrations?

23 The enzyme urease catalyzes the breakdown of urea to CO$_2$ and NH$_3$ most efficiently in the pH range between 6.0 and 7.0. What are the corresponding [H$_3$O$^+$] concentrations?

24 The [OH$^-$] concentration in a swimming pool is 5.0 × 10^{-7} M. What is the pH?

25 (a) The pH of orange juice is 2.8. What is the [H$_3$O$^+$]? (b) A solution of household ammonia has a pH of 11.9. What is the [OH$^-$]? (c) The pH of a lemonade drink is 2.1. What is the [OH$^-$]?

26 (a) The pH of an alcoholic drink (tomato juice and vodka) is 4.1. What is the [H$_3$O$^+$]? (b) The pH of vodka averages 7.2. Is tomato juice basic, neutral, or acidic? Explain.

27 Weak acid Calculate [H$_3$O$^+$] and pH of (a) 0.00400 M NH$_4^+$ for which $K_a = 5.73 × 10^{-10}$, NH$_4^+$(aq) + H$_2$O $\rightleftharpoons$ H$_3$O$^+$(aq) + NH$_3$(aq); (b) 0.060 M HCN for which $K_a = 6.08 × 10^{-10}$, HCN(aq) + H$_2$O $\rightleftharpoons$ H$_3$O$^+$(aq) + CN$^-$(aq).

28 Weak base Calculate the [OH$^-$], [H$_3$O$^+$], and pH of (a) 0.0050 M NH$_3$ for which $K_b = 1.76 × 10^{-5}$, (b) 0.070 M sodium acetate for which $K_b = 5.63 × 10^{-10}$, CH$_3$COO$^-$(aq) + H$_2$O $\rightleftharpoons$ CH$_3$COOH(aq) + OH$^-$(aq).

29 The K_a of ascorbic acid(aq), vitamin C, is 7.9 × 10^{-5}. What is the pH of a 0.050 M solution? Ascorbic acid dissociates one H$^+$ ion per molecule.

30 (a) Find the [H$_3$O$^+$] and pH of a solution prepared by dissolving 0.020 mole of CN$^-$ (sodium cyanide) in water to a volume of 1.00 liter? $K_b = 1.66 × 10^{-5}$ for CN$^-$(aq) + H$_2$O $\rightleftharpoons$ HCN(aq) + OH$^-$(aq). (b) Find the [H$_3$O$^+$] and pH of a solution prepared by dissolving 0.020 mole of benzoic acid in water to a volume of 1.00 liter. $K_a = 6.5 × 10^{-5}$ for C$_6$H$_5$COOH(aq) + H$_2$O $\rightleftharpoons$ H$_3$O$^+$(aq) + C$_6$H$_5$COO$^-$(aq).

31 Calculate [H$_3$O$^+$] in 0.10 M NH$_4$Cl. $K_a = 5.73 × 10^{-10}$ for NH$_4^+$(aq) + H$_2$O $\rightleftharpoons$ NH$_3$(aq) + H$_3$O$^+$(aq).

32 Calculate [H$_3$O$^+$] in 0.010 M Al(H$_2$O)$_6$$^{3+}$. $K_a = 1.5 × 10^{-5}$ for Al(H$_2$O)$_6$$^{3+}$(aq) + H$_2$O $\rightleftharpoons$ Al(H$_2$O)$_5$OH^{2+}(aq) + H$_3$O$^+$(aq).

33 Weak electrolyte and salt (a) Calculate [H$_3$O$^+$] in a solution containing 0.060 M acetic acid and 0.050 sodium acetate, CH$_3$COONa; $K_a = 1.8 × 10^{-5}$ for the ionization of CH$_3$COOH. (b) Calculate [OH$^-$] in a solution containing 0.0010 M ammonia, NH$_3$, and 0.0020 M ammonium chloride, NH$_4$Cl; $K_b = 1.8 × 10^{-5}$ for NH$_3$(aq) + H$_2$O $\rightleftharpoons$ NH$_4^+$(aq) + OH$^-$(aq). (c) Calculate [H$_3$O$^+$] in a solution containing 0.030 M formic acid, HCOOH, and 0.025 M sodium formate, HCOONa; $K_a = 1.8 × 10^{-4}$ for HCOOH(aq) + H$_2$O $\rightleftharpoons$ H$_3$O$^+$(aq) + HCOO$^-$(aq).

34 Buffer (a) A solution contains 0.080 M acetic acid and 0.070 M acetate ion (sodium acetate). (i) Calculate the pH of the solution. Calculate the pH after (ii) 0.020 mole of NaOH is added per liter, (iii) 0.010 mole of HCl is added per liter, $K_a = 1.8 × 10^{-5}$ for ionization of CH$_3$COOH. (b) A solution contains 0.050 M NH$_3$ and 0.080 M NH$_4^+$ (NH$_4$Cl). (i) Calculate the pH of the solution. Calculate the pH after (ii) 0.010 mole of KOH is added per liter, (iii) 0.010 mole of HCl is added per liter; $K_b = 1.8 × 10^{-5}$ for NH$_3$(aq) + H$_2$O $\rightleftharpoons$ NH$_4^+$(aq) + OH$^-$(aq). (c) A solution contains 0.060 M CO$_3^{2-}$ (Na$_2$CO$_3$) and 0.070 M HCO$_3^-$ (NaHCO$_3$). (i) Calculate the pH of the solution. Calculate the pH after (ii) 0.010 mole of HCl is added per liter; (iii) 0.010 mole of NaOH is added per liter; $K_b = 2.15 × 10^{-4}$ for CO$_3^{2-}$(aq) + H$_2$O $\rightleftharpoons$ OH$^-$(aq) + HCO$_3^-$(aq).

35 Arrange the following solutions of sodium acetate and acetic acid in the order of increasing pH (put the solution with the lowest pH first): (a) 0.10 M sodium acetate, 0.10 M acetic acid; (b) 0.20 M acetate, 0.10 M acid; (c) 0.10 M acetate, 0.20 M acid; (d) 0.01 M acetate, 0.01 M acid; (e) 0.050 M acetate, 0.10 M acid; (f) 0.10 M acetate, 0.050 M acid. $K_a = 1.8 × 10^{-5}$ for CH$_3$COOH.

36 A buffer solution is prepared using 0.0100 M formic acid, HCOOH, and 0.080 M sodium formate, HCOONa. (a) What is the pH of this solution? What is the pH (b) after 0.0010 mole of NaOH per liter is added; (c) after 0.0010 mole of HCl per liter is added? $K_a = 1.8 × 10^{-4}$ for HCOOH(aq) + H$_2$O $\rightleftharpoons$ H$_3$O$^+$(aq) + HCOO$^-$(aq).

37 Titration (a) 35.0 ml of 0.300 M HCl is required to titrate a solution of *Drano* (NaOH). Calculate the number of mmol and the mass in mg of NaOH in the solution. (b) 18.0 ml of 0.240 M H_2SO_4 is used to titrate a KOH solution. Calculate the number of mmol and the mass in mg of KOH; $H_2SO_4(aq) + 2KOH(aq) \longrightarrow K_2SO_4(aq) + 2H_2O$. (c) 32.4 ml of 0.0970 M NaOH is used to titrate a phosphoric acid solution; $H_3PO_4(aq) + NaOH(aq) \longrightarrow NaH_2PO_4(aq) + H_2O$. Calculate the number of mmol and the mass in mg of H_3PO_4 in the solution. (d) 23.2 ml of 0.189 M H_2SO_4 solution reacts with how many mg of Na_2CO_3? $Na_2CO_3(aq) + H_2SO_4(aq) \longrightarrow Na_2SO_4(aq) + CO_2(g) + H_2O$. (e) 39.5 ml of 0.100 M $KMnO_4$ is used to titrate sodium oxalate, $Na_2C_2O_4$; $2KMnO_4(aq) + 5Na_2C_2O_4(aq) + 8H_2SO_4(aq) \longrightarrow 2MnSO_4(aq) + 10CO_2(g) + K_2SO_4(aq) + 5Na_2SO_4(aq) + 8H_2O$. Calculate the number of mmol and the mass in g of $Na_2C_2O_4$. (f) 24.6 ml of 0.00500 M sodium thiosulfate, $Na_2S_2O_3$, is used to titrate I_2 solution; $2Na_2S_2O_3(aq) + I_2(aq) \longrightarrow Na_2S_4O_6(aq) + 2NaI(aq)$. Calculate the mass of I_2 in mg.

38 Cu^{2+} is titrated with 25.65 ml of 0.110 M I^-. Find the mass of Cu^{2+} in the solution. $2Cu^{2+}(aq) + SO_3^{2-}(aq) + 2I^-(aq) + H_2O \longrightarrow 2CuI(c) + SO_4^{2-}(aq) + 2H^+(aq)$.

39 How many mmol of HCl react with 25.4 ml of 0.832 M NaOH?

40 (a) Select from Table 14.5, page 443, an indicator suitable for the titration of H_3PO_4 with NaOH, $H_3PO_4(aq) + 2NaOH(aq) \longrightarrow Na_2HPO_4(aq) + 2H_2O$. The equivalence point occurs at a pH of about 9. (b) Which indicator is suitable for the titration of a base with H_2SO_4? The equivalence point occurs at a pH of about 5.

41 Insoluble salt Calculate the solubility in mole/liter of:
(a) $CaCO_3$, $CaCO_3(c) \rightleftharpoons Ca^{2+}(aq) + CO_3^{2-}(aq)$
$K_{sp} = 4.96 \times 10^{-9}$
(b) CoS, $CoS(c) \rightleftharpoons Co^{2+}(aq) + S^{2-}(aq)$
$K_{sp} = 9.77 \times 10^{-21}$
(c) PbS, $PbS(c) \rightleftharpoons Pb^{2+}(aq) + S^{2-}(aq)$
$K_{sp} = 8.89 \times 10^{-29}$
(d) $Ag_2C_2O_4$, $Ag_2C_2O_4(aq) \rightleftharpoons$
$2Ag^+(aq) + C_2O_4^{2-}(aq)$ $K_{sp} = 5.46 \times 10^{-12}$
(e) Ag_2CrO_4, $Ag_2CrO_4(c) \rightleftharpoons$
$2Ag^+(aq) + CrO_4^{2-}(aq)$ $K_{sp} = 1.12 \times 10^{-12}$

(f) $PbCl_2$, $PbCl_2(c) \rightleftharpoons Pb^{2+}(aq) + 2Cl^-(aq)$
$K_{sp} = 1.70 \times 10^{-5}$
(g) $PbSO_4$, $PbSO_4(c) \rightleftharpoons Pb^{2+}(aq) + SO_4^{2-}(aq)$
$K_{sp} = 1.88 \times 10^{-8}$

42 Write the equilibrium constant for the solution of each of the following insoluble salts:
(a) $Mg(OH)_2(c) \rightleftharpoons Mg^{2+}(aq) + 2OH^-(aq)$
(b) $Fe(OH)_3(c) \rightleftharpoons Fe^{3+}(aq) + 3OH^-(aq)$
(c) $Hg_2Cl_2(c) \rightleftharpoons Hg_2^{2+}(aq) + 2Cl^-(aq)$

43 (a) A saturated solution of H_2S contains $[Mn^{2+}] = [Cd^{2+}] = [Fe^{2+}] = [Pb^{2+}] = [Co^{2+}] = [Hg^{2+}] = 0.0010$ M, and $[S^{2-}] = 1.4 \times 10^{-20}$ M. Which metal ions precipitate? $MnS(c) \rightleftharpoons Mn^{2+}(aq) + S^{2-}(aq)$, $K_{sp} = 4.57 \times 10^{-14}$. Other K_{sp} values are CdS(c), $K_{sp} = 1.42 \times 10^{-29}$; FeS(c), $K_{sp} = 1.59 \times 10^{-19}$; PbS(c), $K_{sp} = 8.89 \times 10^{-29}$; CoS(c), $K_{sp} = 9.77 \times 10^{-21}$; HgS(c), $K_{sp} = 6.49 \times 10^{-53}$. (b) A solution contains $[CH_3COO^-] = [Br^-] = [Cl^-] = [I^-] = [SO_4^{2-}] = 0.0010$ M, and $[Ag^+] = 0.0010$ M. Which ions precipitate? $CH_3COOAg(c) \rightleftharpoons Ag^+(aq) + CH_3COO^-(aq)$, $K_{sp} = 1.93 \times 10^{-3}$. Other K_{sp} values are AgBr(c), $K_{sp} = 5.34 \times 10^{-13}$; AgCl(c), $K_{sp} = 1.77 \times 10^{-10}$; AgI(c), $K_{sp} = 8.53 \times 10^{-17}$; $Ag_2SO_4(c)$, $K_{sp} = 1.20 \times 10^{-5}$.

44 A solution contains $[S^{2-}] = 1.40 \times 10^{-20}$, and $[Pb^{2+}] = [Mn^{2+}] = 0.040$ M. Will these two metal ions be separated?

$MnS(c) \rightleftharpoons Mn^{2+}(aq) + S^{2-}(aq)$
$$K_{sp} = 4.57 \times 10^{-14}$$

$PbS(c) \rightleftharpoons Pb^{2+}(aq) + S^{2-}(aq)$
$$K_{sp} = 8.89 \times 10^{-29}$$

45 Library Read one of the following:
(a) "Development of the pH Concept," F. Szabadvary, translated by R. E. Oesper, *Journal of Chemical Education,* volume 41, 1964, page 105.
(b) "Is the Solubility Product Constant?" R. C. Goodman and R. H. Petrucci, *Journal of Chemical Education,* volume 42, 1965, page 104.
(c) "Heterogeneous Equilibrium in General Chemistry," L. C. Grotz, *Journal of Chemical Education,* volume 40, 1963, page 479.

ADDITIONAL PROBLEMS

46 (a) The pH meter (page 443) is an electrical instrument designed to measure pH. Should this instrument have a temperature control knob? Explain. (b) Clear rainwater has a pH of about 5.6. Estimate the $[H_3O^+]$. Account for the acidity of rain. (See Problem 29(f), page 423.)

47 What is the pH of a solution made (a) by dissolving 4.0 g of NaOH in 500 ml of solution(aq); (b) by dissolving 0.63 g of HNO_3 in 100 ml of solution(aq); (c) by dissolving 0.81 g of HBr in 100 ml of solution(aq)?

48 Calculate the pH of an aqueous solution which contains (a) 0.340 g of NaOH in 500 ml of solution; (b) 26.0 g of NH_3 in 250 ml of solution; (c) 40.0 g of acetate ion in 750 ml of solution; (d) 36.0 g of cyanide ion in 840 ml of solution. See Table 14.4, page 000, for K_b values.

49 K_a for lysergic acid, $C_{15}H_{15}N_2COOH$, starting material for the synthesis of LSD, is 6.3×10^{-4}. What are the $[H_3O^+]$ and pH of a 0.25 M solution of the acid?

50 The equilibrium constant for nitrous acid, HNO_2, is 5.13×10^{-4}. What concentration of HNO_2 is needed to make a solution of HNO_2 in which $[H_3O^+] = 2.30 \times 10^{-3}$ M? Make no approximations.

51 The equilibrium constant for hypobromous acid, HOBr, is 2.2×10^{-9}. Find the concentration of HOBr required to make a solution of HOBr in which $[H_3O^+] = 1.4 \times 10^{-5}$ M.

52 What is (a) the acetic acid concentration, (b) the pH of a solution made by adding water to 40.0 ml of a 0.10 M CH_3COOH solution to form 75.0 ml of solution?

53 The pH of a 0.10 M acetic acid solution is 2.87. Find its K_a.

54 What should be the molar ratio of CH_3COOH to CH_3COONa used to prepare a buffer solution having a pH of 5.00? For acetic acid, $K_a = 1.8 \times 10^{-5}$ (see Equation 11, page 442).

55 (a) A convenient remedy for so-called "acid indigestion" is $\frac{1}{2}$ teaspoon (1.40 g) of baking soda ($NaHCO_3$) in a glass (250 ml) of water. Assuming the volume of the solution equals the volume of the water, what is the pH of the solution? The only reaction to consider is

$$HCO_3^-(aq) + H_2O \rightleftharpoons H_2CO_3(aq)(CO_2 + H_2O)$$
$$+ OH^-(aq)$$
$$K_b = 2.27 \times 10^{-8}$$

(b) If, after you drink this solution, it mixes with 250 ml of 0.020 M HCl in your stomach, calculate the pH of the resulting solution. Consider only the reaction $HCO_3^-(aq) + HCl(aq) \longrightarrow CO_2(g) + H_2O + Cl^-(aq)$, and assume that the final volume is 500 ml.

56 Which of the given silver halides would you add to water containing $[Cl^-] = 1.00 \times 10^{-4}$ M, $[Br^-] =$

1.50×10^{-5} M, and $[I^-] = 4.27 \times 10^{-10}$ M in order to obtain $[Ag^+] = 2.0 \times 10^{-7}$ M, an amount of silver ion sufficient to contol bacterial growth?

$$AgCl(c) \rightleftharpoons Ag^+(aq) + Cl^-(aq)$$
$$K_{sp} = 1.77 \times 10^{-10}$$
$$AgBr(c) \rightleftharpoons Ag^+(aq) + Br^-(aq)$$
$$K_{sp} = 5.34 \times 10^{-13}$$
$$AgI(c) \rightleftharpoons Ag^+(aq) + I^-(aq)$$
$$K_{sp} = 8.53 \times 10^{-17}$$

57 Calculate the pH of the solution prepared by mixing 50 ml of 0.20 M HNO_2 and 50 ml of 0.20 M $NaNO_2$. $K_a = 5.13 \times 10^{-4}$ for $HNO_2(aq) + H_2O \rightleftharpoons H_3O^+(aq) + NO_2^-(aq)$.

58 What is the pH of a solution resulting from the addition of 40.0 ml of 0.10 M CH_3COOH to 20.0 ml of 0.10 M KOH, forming 60.0 ml of solution? The reaction is $CH_3COOH(aq) + OH^- \rightleftharpoons CH_3COO^-(aq) + H_2O$.

59 What is the pH of a solution made by adding 0.035 mole of solid NaOH to a liter of 0.020 M HCl, without a change in volume?

60 A solution contains 0.020 M NH_4^+ ion (NH_4Cl) and 0.0100 M HCl. What is the pH of the solution? $K_a = 5.73 \times 10^{-10}$ for $NH_4^+(aq) + H_2O \rightleftharpoons NH_3(aq) + H_3O^+(aq)$.

61 Find the solubility of $PbSO_4$ in mg/100 ml. $K_{sp} = 1.88 \times 10^{-8}$ for $PbSO_4(c) \rightleftharpoons Pb^{2+}(aq) + SO_4^{2-}(aq)$.

62 Does a precipitate form on mixing equal volumes of solutions of 0.020 M lead nitrate, $Pb(NO_3)_2$, and 0.020 M potassium iodide? $K_{sp} = 8.51 \times 10^{-9}$ for $PbI_2(c) \rightleftharpoons Pb^{2+}(aq) + 2I^-(aq)$.

63 0.010 mole of Ba^{2+} is added to a solution containing 0.050 mole of SO_4^{2-}, and the total volume is 1.0 liter. Does Ba^{2+} precipitate? $K_{sp} = 1.06 \times 10^{-10}$ for $BaSO_4(c) \rightleftharpoons Ba^{2+}(aq) + SO_4^{2-}(aq)$.

64 A saturated solution of H_2S contains $[S^{2-}] = 1.80 \times 10^{-18}$ M. K_{sp} for FeS is 1.59×10^{-19}. In which, if any, of the following Fe^{2+} solutions does FeS precipitate? (a) 5.0 M, (b) 1.0 M, (c) 0.10 M, (d) 0.0010 M, (e) 0.00010 M.

65 For calcium carbonate, $CaCO_3$, at 1.00 atm, $K_{sp} = 4.96 \times 10^{-9}$; at 750 atm, the ratio $K_{sp}(750\text{ atm})/K_{sp}(1\text{ atm}) = 2.36$. Calculate the solubility of $CaCO_3$ at 750 atm. Is the solution of $CaCO_3$ accompanied by an increase or decrease in volume?

66 A 2.000 M OH^- solution is passed through an ion exchange process (Chap. 20) during which 1.198×10^{23} OH^- ions are removed and replaced by Cl^- ions per liter of solution. Find the pH of the resulting solution.

67 A wine is tested for the quantity of SO_2 (used to sterilize grape juice in the manufacture of wine prior to fermentation) by titration with I_2 solution: $SO_2(aq) + I_2(aq) + 2H_2O \longrightarrow H_2SO_4(aq) + 2HI(aq)$. When 12.50 ml of 0.00500 M I_2 solution is used to titrate 100 ml of wine, find the mass in mg of SO_2 per liter of wine.

68 A solution of Na_2CO_3 is basic but a solution of $NaHCO_3$ is less basic. Explain.

69 (a) Compare the quantities of H^+ and OH^- present in pure water. How do these quantities change with temperature? $\Delta H = +13.35$ kcal for $H_2O \rightleftharpoons H^+(aq) + OH^-(aq)$. Is the pH of water, 7.0, independent of temperature? Explain. (b) At $-50\,°C$, for the self-ionization of NH_3, $NH_3 + NH_3 \rightleftharpoons NH_4^+ + NH_2^-$, $K = 1.0 \times 10^{-33}$. Find pNH_4^+ in neutral liquid ammonia at $-50\,°C$.

70 Find the number of mmol of HCl that reacts with 25.5 ml of 0.110 M NaOH. What volume of 0.20 M HCl is needed to furnish this quantity of HCl?

71 In medical practice, CO_2 and HCO_3^-, important inorganic components of blood, are related by the equation $CO_2(aq) + H_2O \rightleftharpoons H^+(aq) + HCO_3^-(aq)$, $K_a = 4.5 \times 10^{-7}$. The partial pressure of CO_2 in the atmosphere, p_{CO_2}, fixes its solubility in

blood (page 63), expressed at 37 °C (normal body temperature) by

$$\frac{0.51 \text{ ml(STP) } CO_2}{\text{ml blood}} \times \frac{p_{CO_2}}{760 \text{ torr}}$$

For a given patient, $p_{CO_2} = 23$ torr and blood $[HCO_3^-]$, quickly measured by instrumental analysis (Chap. 24), is 5.0×10^{-3} M.* Find the blood $[CO_2]$, $[H^+]$, and pH. Compare with the pH values on page 440.

72 (a) Check your answer for Problem 71 by using the formula for the pH of blood.

$$pH = pK + \log \frac{[HCO_3^-]}{3.0 \times 10^{-5} p_{CO_2}}.$$

(b) Use the information in Problem 71 to obtain the equation given in part (a) of this problem. Recall (footnote, page 429) that $pK = -\log K$, that the log of the product of two numbers is equal to the sum of the logs of the individual numbers (page 429), and that $-\log \frac{[CO_2]}{[HCO_3^-]}$ is the same as $+\log \frac{[HCO_3^-]}{[CO_2]}$.

73 A solution of a weak acid ($HA \rightleftharpoons H^+ + A^-$) is titrated with NaOH solution to a pH of 6.00. At this pH, exactly one half of the initial quantity of HA is converted to A^-. Find K_a.

---

*The normal range of $[HCO_3^-]$ is 24×10^{-3} to 30×10^{-3} M.

ANSWERS

1 $[H_3O^+] = [OH^-] = 1.45 \times 10^{-7}$
2 (a) $[H_3O^+] = 2.5 \times 10^{-3}$
$[OH^-] = 4.0 \times 10^{-12}$
(b) $[OH^-] = 5.0 \times 10^{-3}$
$[H_3O^+] = 2.0 \times 10^{-12}$
3 2.331
4 11.87
5 $[H_3O^+] = 3.2 \times 10^{-11}$
6 $[H_3O^+] = 1.4 \times 10^{-5}$
pH = 4.85
7 (a) $[OH^-] = 3.35 \times 10^{-6}$
$[H_3O^+] = 2.99 \times 10^{-9}$
pH = 8.52
(b) $[OH^-] = 2.97 \times 10^{-3}$
$[H_3O^+] = 3.4 \times 10^{-12}$
pH = 11.47
8 $[H_3O^+] = 6.5 \times 10^{-4}$
9 (a) 4.72
(b) 4.77
10 (a) 3.52 mmol HBr,
285 mg HBr
(b) 1.76 mmol H_2SO_4
173 mg H_2SO_4

11 1.03×10^{-5} mole/ℓ $BaSO_4$
12 (a) no
(b) 1.77×10^{-8} mole/ℓ, less than in pure water
13 Pb^{2+} and Hg^{2+} precipitate
15 (a) $[H_3O^+] = 1.0 \times 10^{-3}$
$[OH^-] = 1.0 \times 10^{-11}$
(b) $[H_3O^+] = 4.0 \times 10^{-4}$
$[OH^-] = 2.5 \times 10^{-11}$
(c) $[H_3O^+] = 2.0 \times 10^{-11}$
$[OH^-] = 5.0 \times 10^{-4}$
(d) $[H_3O^+] = 2.5 \times 10^{-12}$
$[OH^-] = 4.0 \times 10^{-3}$
16 (a) 3.00
(b) 3.40
(c) 10.70
(d) 11.60
17 (a) $[H_3O^+] = 1.708 \times 10^{-7}$
pH = 6.767 or 6.77
(b) blood pH readings taken at fever temperature would not be the same as pH at normal body temperature; equilibrium constants

change with temperature
18 (a) $[H_3O^+] = [OH^-] = 3.100 \times 10^{-7}$
pH = 6.509 or 6.51
(b) no, K_w increases with temperature
19 (a) (i) 4.85, (ii) 9.866 or 9.87, (iii) 3.839 or 3.84, (iv) 3.721 or 3.72; (b) (i) 8.80, (ii) 3.66, (iii) 4.55, (iv) 10.23; (c) 11.34
20 (a) 4.00
(b) 10.70
(c) 11.70
(d) 2.52
21 (a) 1.0×10^{-4}
(b) 2.9×10^{-5}
(c) 1.3×10^{-9}
(d) 1.8×10^{-3}
(e) 1.5×10^{-11}
(f) 1.8×10^{-13}
22 (a) 7.40
(b) (i) 1.4×10^{-1}
(ii) 4.0×10^{-7}, 1.3×10^{-7}
23 1×10^{-6}, 1×10^{-7}

24 7.70
25 (a) $[H_3O^+] = 1.6 \times 10^{-12}$
  (b) $[OH^-] = 7.9 \times 10^{-3}$
  (c) $[OH^-] = 1.3 \times 10^{-12}$
26 (a) $[H_3O^+] = 7.9 \times 10^{-5}$
  (b) the lower pH means the drink is more acidic than vodka; tomato juice is acidic
27 (a) $[H_3O^+] = 1.51 \times 10^{-6}$
    pH = 5.821 or 5.82
  (b) $[H_3O^+] = 6.04 \times 10^{-6}$
    pH = 5.22
28 (a) $[OH^-] = 2.97 \times 10^{-4}$
    $[H_3O^+] = 3.37 \times 10^{-11}$
    pH = 10.47
  (b) $[OH^-] = 6.28 \times 10^{-6}$
    $[H_3O^+] = 1.59 \times 10^{-9}$
    pH = 8.80
29 2.70
30 (a) $[H_3O^+] = 1.74 \times 10^{-11}$
    pH − 10.76
  (b) $[H_3O^+] = 1.14 \times 10^{-3}$
    pH = 2.94
31 7.6×10^{-6}
32 3.9×10^{-4}
33 (a) $[H_3O^+] = 2.16 \times 10^{-5}$
  (b) $[OH^-] = 9.0 \times 10^{-6}$
  (c) $[H_3O^+] = 2.2 \times 10^{-4}$
34 (a) (i) 4.69; (ii) 4.92
  (iii) 4.57; (b) (i) 9.05;
  (ii) 9.19; (iii) 8.90; (c) (i)
  10.27; (ii) 10.13; (iii) 10.40
35 (c),(e) 4.44 > (a),(d) 4.74
  > (b),(f) 5.05
36 (i) 4.65; (ii) 4.70; (iii) 4.60
37 (a) 10.5 mmol NaOH, 420 mg
  (b) 8.64 mmol KOH, 485 mg
  (c) 3.14 mmol H_3PO_4, 308 mg
  (d) 4.38 mmol Na_2CO_3, 464 mg

  (e) 9.88 mmol $Na_2C_2O_4$, 1.32 g
  (f) 0.0615 mmol I_2, 15.6 mg
38 179 mg Cu^{2+}
39 21.1 mmol HCl
40 (a) phenolphthalein
  (b) methyl red
41 (a) 7.04×10^{-5} mole/ℓ $CaCO_3$
  (b) 9.88×10^{-11} mole/ℓ CoS
  (c) 9.43×10^{-15} mole/ℓ PbS
  (d) 1.11×10^{-4} mole/ℓ $Ag_2C_2O_4$
  (e) 6.54×10^{-5} mole/ℓ Ag_2CrO_4
  (f) 1.62×10^{-2} mole/ℓ $PbCl_2$
  (g) 1.37×10^{-4} mole/ℓ $PbSO_4$
42 (a) $K_{sp} = [Mg^{2+}][OH^-]^2$
  (b) $K_{sp} = [Fe^{3+}][OH^-]^3$
  (c) $K_{sp} = [Hg_2^{2+}][Cl^-]^2$
43 (a) Mn^{2+} no precipitate
    Cd^{2+} precipitate
    Fe^{2+} no precipitate
    Pb^{2+} precipitate
    Co^{2+} no precipitate
    Hg^{2+} precipitate
  (b) CH_3COO^- no precipitate
    Br^- precipitate
    Cl^- precipitate
    I^- precipitate
    SO_4^{2-} no precipitate
44 yes, MnS does not precipitate, PbS precipitates
46 (a) equilibrium constants and pH voltage vary with temperature. Accurate pH readings require temperature calibration and a knob to adjust for temperature changes.
  (b) $[H_3O^+] = 2.5 \times 10^{-6}$, acidity due to dissolved CO_2 and impurities like SO_2
47 (a) 13.30

  (b) 1.00
  (c) 1.00
48 (a) 12.23
  (b) 12.02
  (c) 9.36
  (d) 11.72
49 $[H_3O^+] = 0.012$
    pH = 1.92
50 1.26×10^{-2} M
51 8.9×10^{-2}
52 (a) 5.33×10^{-2} M
  (b) 3.01
53 1.8×10^{-5}
54 5.6×10^{-1}
55 (a) 9.59
  (b) 9.36
56 AgI
57 3.29
58 4.74
59 12.17
60 2.00
61 4.15 mg
62 yes
63 yes
64 (a)(b)(c)
65 1.08×10^{-4} mole/ℓ; decrease in volume
66 14.25
67 40.0 mg/ℓ
68 HCO_3^- can donate a H^+ and accept a H^+; CO_3^{2-} can act only as an acceptor.
69 (b) 16.49
70 2.81 mmol HCl; 14 ml
71 $[CO_2] = 6.9 \times 10^{-4}$
    $[H^+] = 6.2 \times 10^{-8}$
    pH = 7.21
73 $K_a = [H^+] = 1.0 \times 10^{-6}$

GLOSSARY

buffer solution A solution which maintains a nearly constant pH upon the addition of small amounts of strong acid or strong base. The solution consists of a weak acid and its conjugate base, or a weak base and its conjugate acid.

end point The end point in a titration is reached when a distinct color change is observed in an indicator. See **equivalence point, indicator,** and **titration.**

equivalence point The equivalence point in a titration is reached when the molar quantities mixed exactly agree with the balanced equation for the reaction. The difference between the end point and the equivalence point is not significant for most titrations.

indicator A substance, usually a dye, that changes color suddenly over a narrow range of pH, used in acid-base titrations.

logarithm (log) The logarithm of a number is the power to which 10 must be raised to give that number. The log of 100 is 2.

pH A symbol defined as the negative logarithm (base 10) of the H_3O^+ concentration in moles per liter, pH = $-\log[H_3O^+]$. It measures the acidity or alkalinity of a solution.

standard solution A solution of known concentration.

titration The process of adding one reactant, for example, a standard solution, to a second reactant whose quantity is unknown, until the end point is reached. See **end point** and **standard solution.**

titration curve A graph showing how the pH of an acidic or basic solution changes with the addition of a standard solution. See **titration.**

volumetric analysis Involves a titration to determine the quantity of a substance. The analysis is based on the addition of a solution of known concentration until the substance being determined is completely consumed. See **titration.**

ELECTROCHEMISTRY 15

INTRODUCTION _____ 15.1

Electrolytes play a very important role in human physiology. Human cells contain the electrolyte potassium chloride, KCl. These cells are bathed by a solution containing the electrolyte sodium chloride, NaCl. When these electrolytes, especially the potassium ion, migrate across cell membranes—for example, the membranes of the muscle cells of the heart—the electrical balance of the membrane changes. Consequently, the heart acts like an electric generator and produces detectable electric currents which, in turn, give rise to a detectable magnetic field (page 201). Excessive electrical impulses transmitted to the brain from the inner ear signal "motion sickness" (seasickness). Our balance sensing mechanism is located in the inner ear. When the head is subjected to unusual rotations by the up-down, side-to-side movement of a boat, too many signals are transmitted. The brain interprets this as an alarm signal, triggering a feeling of nausea. An understanding of bio-electrical processes is also essential to the study of higher brain functions like memory and learning.

The human heart induces about 0.002 volt at the surface of the body. This is small, fortunately, compared to the electric eel, which can put out more than 500 volts.

From naus, Greek word for ship.

When a bone is broken, electric currents are generated that appear to control the healing process. Bone healing is therefore accelerated by application of low electric currents. In China, major surgery, including open heart surgery, is performed with electroacupuncture as the only anesthesia. The patient is anesthetized for 9 hours by connecting an electric source (5 volts, 0.005 ampere) for 20 minutes to two or three pairs of needles (electrodes) inserted in appropriate places in the body. The needle irritates a nerve, causing the release of endorphin, a pain-killing compound, composed of five linked amino acids, that behaves like morphine.

These are examples of the types of phenomena studied in electrochemistry. Electrochemistry also deals with electrolysis, chemical reactions caused by electricity, and with the reverse, the production of electricity from chemical reactions. This is the basis of batteries and dry cells, and of fuel cells, developed especially for space vehicles because of the high efficiency and convenience of such cells as portable sources of power. Electrochemistry is also involved in the commercial preparation of chemicals and metals (Chap. 20). It also forms the basis of the generally accepted theory of the corrosion of metals (page 489), and has helped provide a substantial experimental background for theoretical discussions of electron transfer.

Chemical reactions are under investigation as a source of electric power for vehicle propulsion in order to reduce the pollution from gasoline and to diminish the noise of internal combustion engines. In its quest for energy independence and fossil fuel substitutes, the U.S. program for energy research and development includes increasing emphasis on electrochemistry.

Electrochemistry has its origin in the discovery by Luigi Galvani (1786) of the effects of two different metals on the muscles of a dead frog. Galvani noticed a movement or contraction of the muscles of the legs when the frog, attached to copper hooks, touched an iron rack. He reasoned that a "vital fluid" passed from the nerves to the muscle. But Alessandro Volta (1796) concluded that the contact of unlike metals produces electricity from a chemical reaction.

15.2 _____ ELECTRICITY FROM CHEMICAL REACTIONS: GALVANIC CELLS

A set-up used to generate electricity from a chemical reaction is known as a **galvanic cell,** or more frequently, a **cell.** A typical example is the reaction between metallic zinc and aqueous solution of a copper(II) salt:

$$Zn(c) + CuSO_4(aq) \longrightarrow Cu(c) + ZnSO_4(aq)$$
$$Zn(c) + Cu^{2+}(aq) \longrightarrow Cu(c) + Zn^{2+}(aq) \quad \Delta H = -53 \text{ kcal}$$

The reaction is exothermic, so that the addition of Zn to a Cu^{2+} solution evolves heat, but electricity is not obtained. To obtain electricity, the Zn must *not* be placed in the Cu^{2+} solution. Rather, it must be separated from the Cu^{2+} solution, and then the two parts must be connected by a wire. A common arrangement is shown in Fig. 15.1. A zinc bar (electrode) is suspended in a solution of Zn^{2+} ions (or in water), and a copper bar (electrode) is suspended in a solution of Cu^{2+}. Connecting the two electrodes by a wire does *not* complete the electrical circuit; the two solutions must also be brought

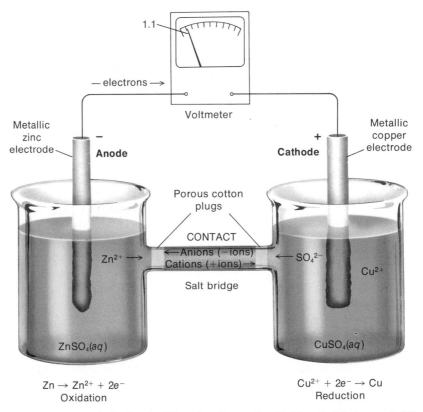

Zn → Zn²⁺ + 2e⁻
Oxidation

Cu²⁺ + 2e⁻ → Cu
Reduction

Also known as the Daniell cell. **FIGURE 15.1** A typical galvanic cell based on the reaction, $Zn(c) + Cu^{2+}(aq) \longrightarrow Zn^{2+}(aq) + Cu(c)$.

into *contact* as shown in Fig. 15.1. This permits the migration of negative and positive ions. The circuit is now complete ("closed"), and electrons flow from the Zn electrode through the wire to the Cu electrode. This flow of electrons constitutes electricity which can run a motor, operate a radio, or light a bulb.

From experimental studies, we conclude that the electric current is produced as follows: Zinc dissolves as Zn^{2+}; the mass of the Zn electrode decreases while the mass of Zn^{2+} in solution increases. The source of electrons is the oxidation of the zinc; it generates electrons:

$$Zn \longrightarrow Zn^{2+} + 2e^- \qquad oxidation \ (half\text{-}reaction)$$

The electrons flow through the wire, a motor, a bulb, or a radio to the Cu electrode. At this electrode, Cu^{2+} is reduced to Cu; the mass of the electrode increases while the mass of Cu^{2+} in solution decreases:

$$Cu^{2+} + 2e^- \longrightarrow Cu \qquad reduction \ (half\text{-}reaction)$$

The overall cell reaction is the addition of the two electrode reactions

$$Zn + Cu^{2+} \longrightarrow Cu + Zn^{2+}$$

This is a typical oxidation-reduction reaction, the basis of galvanic cells.

The electrode at which *oxidation takes place* is called the **anode;** the other electrode at which *reduction takes place* is called the **cathode.*** There are *no exceptions* to these definitions. The *negative sign* $(-)$ is *always used to indicate the source of electrons,* so that the zinc electrode is given a negative $(-)$ sign while the copper electrode takes a positive $(+)$ sign.** Similarly, the "hot end," the end from which electrons leave an electric generator, is labeled $(-)$:

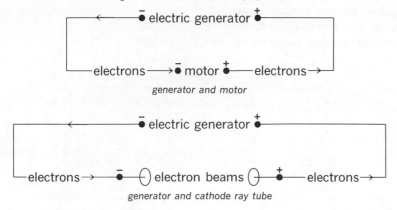

generator and motor

generator and cathode ray tube

Zn^{2+} ions are produced at the anode and Cu^{2+} ions are removed at the cathode. Yet, the solutions do *not* become charged because the two solutions are in contact, permitting migration of negative and positive ions. Negative ions are called **anions** because they *always* move toward the anode; positive ions are called **cations** because

---

*Anode is derived from the Greek words *ana* and *hodos,* meaning upward. Cathode is derived from *kata* and *hodos,* meaning downward. The word *croak* helps to recall these definitions: C (cathode), R (reduction), O (oxidation), A (anode), K (constant, no exceptions).

**The reader is *warned* that although these definitions are fixed, it does not follow that the anode is always negative and that the cathode is always positive. Since oxidation always occurs at the anode and so serves as the electron source, the anode in a galvanic cell is always negative. In the reverse process (page 472), in which electricity is used to induce a chemical change, these definitions make the anode take a positive sign.

they *always* move toward the cathode. The migration of SO_4^{2-} anions prevents accumulation of Zn^{2+} ions, and the migration of Zn^{2+} cations makes up for the loss of Cu^{2+} ions. The migration of these ions is just as important as the oxidation-reduction reaction. While the electric current is a flow of electrons in the metal parts of the circuit, it is the migration of ions that constitutes the electric current in the solution (page 461); no migration, no electricity. This discussion is summarized in Fig. 15.1.

Example 1

The reaction

$$Mg(c) + CdCl_2(aq) \longrightarrow MgCl_2(aq) + Cd(c)$$

or

$$Mg(c) + Cd^{2+}(aq) \longrightarrow Mg^{2+}(aq) + Cd(c)$$

is used in a cell to generate electricity. Identify the electrode reactions, the anode, the cathode, the negative and the positive electrode, the direction of migration of anions and cations, and the direction of flow of electrons.

Answer

$$Mg \longrightarrow Mg^{2+} + 2e^-$$ *oxidation*, therefore anode; *source of electrons*, therefore, negative electrode

$$Cd^{2+} + 2e^- \longrightarrow Cd$$ *reduction*, therefore cathode; positive electrode

Mg^{2+} cations migrate toward cathode.
Cl^- anions migrate toward anode.
Electrons flow from Mg electrode to Cd electrode.
The answer can also be given by use of a diagram:

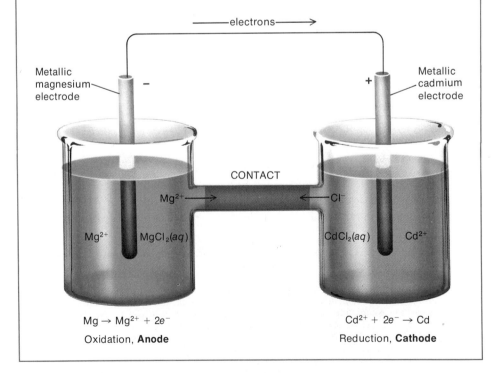

Metallic magnesium electrode

Metallic cadmium electrode

CONTACT

$Mg^{2+} \rightarrow$ $\leftarrow Cl^-$

Mg^{2+} $MgCl_2(aq)$ $CdCl_2(aq)$ Cd^{2+}

Mg → Mg²⁺ + 2e⁻
Oxidation, **Anode**

Cd²⁺ + 2e⁻ → Cd
Reduction, **Cathode**

Unequal flows of Na^+ ions into and K^+ ions out of a nerve cell, under the influence of acetylcholine,* trigger the passage of a nerve impulse. A deficiency of acetylcholine in the brain causes brain damage and lack of control of movement (Huntington's disease).

PROBLEM 1   **The reaction**

$$Ni(c) + CuCl_2(aq) \longrightarrow NiCl_2(aq) + Cu(c)$$
$$Ni(c) + Cu^{2+}(aq) \longrightarrow Ni^{2+}(aq) + Cu(c)$$

is used in a cell to generate electricity. Identify the electrode reactions, the anode, the cathode, the negative and the positive electrode, the direction of migration of anions and cations, and the direction of flow of electrons.

Gases, of course, may also participate in oxidation-reduction reactions. But, as you can well imagine, it is impossible to attach a wire to a gas. Hence, gases are bubbled over an inert electrode, a metal which holds gas molecules on its surface but does not react with the gas or the solution. A typical set-up is shown in Fig. 15.2. In summary, the operation of a galvanic cell requires an oxidation-reduction reaction, an anode where electrons are produced by oxidation, a cathode where reduction

----

*Acetylcholine, $\left[H_3C-\overset{\displaystyle O}{\overset{\displaystyle \|}{C}}-O-C_2H_4-\overset{\displaystyle CH_3}{\underset{\displaystyle CH_3}{\overset{\displaystyle |}{\underset{\displaystyle |}{N}}}}-CH_3 \right]^+$;   note its relation to NH_4^+. The role of acetyl-

choline in the transmission of a nerve impulse was discovered by David Nachmanson in 1938.

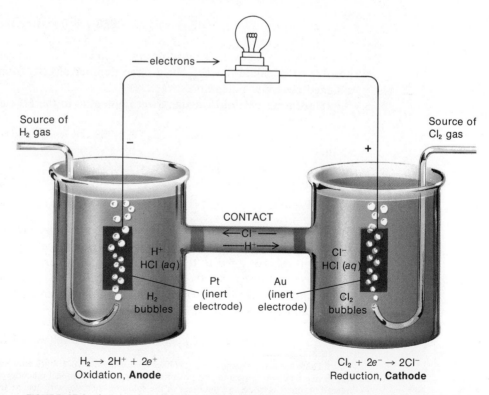

$$H_2 \rightarrow 2H^+ + 2e^+$$
Oxidation, **Anode**

$$Cl_2 + 2e^- \rightarrow 2Cl^-$$
Reduction, **Cathode**

FIGURE 15.2   A galvanic cell based on the reaction, $H_2(g) + Cl_2(g) \longrightarrow 2H^+(aq) + 2Cl^-(aq)$.

occurs by accepting electrons, an external circuit for the passage of electrons, a flow of cations (positive ions) toward the cathode, and a flow of anions (negative ions) toward the anode.

VOLTAGE OF A GALVANIC CELL: THE STANDARD ELECTRODE POTENTIAL

When a current flows between two points, a *difference of potential* is said to exist between them. The potential difference is measured in volts, V. The greater the potential difference, the greater the voltage.

The voltage, the potential difference of a cell, measured with a voltmeter as shown in Fig. 15.1, *always* measures the potential difference between *two* metal electrodes, *never* between one electrode and the solution in which it is suspended.*

Any galvanic cell must have two electrodes, and the potential difference between them is, by tradition, given a special name, **the electromotive force,** EMF, of the cell, designated as E_{cell}. Then, experimentally we measure E_{cell}, the difference between the potential of the cathode, the electrode at which reduction occurs, $E_{reduction}$, and the potential of the anode, the electrode where oxidation occurs, $E_{oxidation}$:

$$\text{measured } E_{cell} = E_{reduction} - E_{oxidation}$$

The student is cautioned always to write the difference as $E_{reduction} - E_{oxidation}$. For the cells in Figs. 15.1 and 15.2,

$$E_{cell} = E_{Cu} - E_{Zn} = 1.10 \text{ volt } (measured)$$

and

$$E_{cell} = E_{Cl_2} - E_{H_2} = 1.358 \text{ volt } (measured)$$

Nevertheless, it is advantageous to *assign* a potential to each electrode; this makes it possible to calculate the E_{cell} for a large number of cells from a small number of assigned electrode potentials.

Thus, if we *arbitrarily* assign a zero potential to the H_2 electrode, we can write

$$E_{cell} = E_{Cl_2} - E_{H_2} = 1.358 \text{ volt } (measured)$$

so that

$$E_{cell} = E_{Cl_2} - 0 = 1.358 \text{ volt}$$

from which

$$E_{Cl_2} = 1.358 \text{ volt } (assigned)$$

We thus assign a potential of $+1.358$ volt to the chlorine electrode. This is a familiar procedure. In the design of the Celsius temperature scale (page 22), a value of zero was arbitrarily assigned to the freezing point of water.

This procedure is strictly bookkeeping. Having assigned zero potential to the H_2 electrode and $+1.358$ volt to the Cl_2 electrode, the potential difference calculated for the cell must agree with the measured value:

$$E_{cell} = E_{Cl_2} - E_{H_2} = +1.358 \text{ volt} - 0 \text{ volt} = +1.358 \text{ volt}$$

---

*There are two wire ends to any voltage measuring device; if both ends are placed on one electrode, the device reads zero, meaning no potential difference, no chemical reaction, no electricity. If one end is placed on one electrode and the other in the solution, then the wire acts as an electrode giving rise to a galvanic cell. If the wire is inert, then no electrode reaction occurs, no chemical reaction, no electricity, no potential difference, and the device reads zero.

Similarly, we can assign a potential to the Zn electrode by setting up a cell composed of Zn and H_2 electrodes, based on the reaction

$$Zn(c) + 2HCl(aq) \longrightarrow ZnCl_2(aq) + H_2(g)$$
$$Zn(c) + 2H^+(aq) \longrightarrow Zn^{2+}(aq) + H_2(g)$$

as shown:

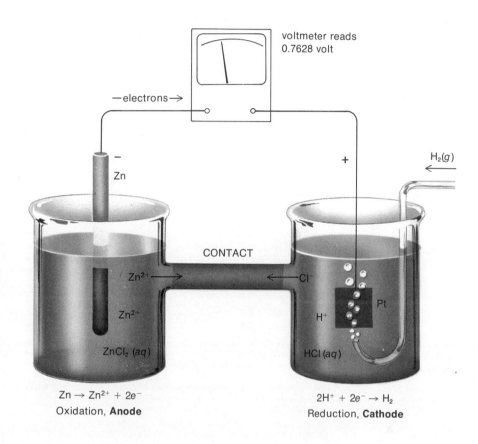

voltmeter reads
0.7628 volt

—electrons→

$H_2(g)$

Zn

CONTACT

$Zn^{2+} \longrightarrow$ $\longleftarrow Cl^-$

Pt

Zn^{2+} H^+

$ZnCl_2\ (aq)$ $HCl\ (aq)$

$Zn \rightarrow Zn^{2+} + 2e^-$ $2H^+ + 2e^- \rightarrow H_2$
Oxidation, **Anode**   Reduction, **Cathode**

Then

$$E_{cell} = E_{reduction} - E_{oxidation}$$
$$E_{cell} = E_{H_2} - E_{Zn} = +0.7628\ volt\ (measured)$$
$$E_{cell} = 0 - E_{Zn} = +0.7628\ volt$$

from which

$$E_{Zn} = -0.7628\ volt\ (assigned)$$

A potential of -0.7628 volt is thus assigned to the Zn electrode.

The potential difference of the cell, E_{cell}, depends on the temperature and concentration of the solutions surrounding the electrodes. Thus, for the above cell, increasing the H^+ concentration shifts the reaction to the right and so increases E_{cell}. Similarly, increasing the concentration of Zn^{2+} or increasing the pressure of H_2 decreases E_{cell}. However, recall (page 380) that at a given temperature the concentration of a solid substance is a constant and therefore E_{cell} *does not* depend on the size of the zinc (solid) electrode. We are therefore forced to fix only temperature, concentration, and pressure. Our measurements are restricted to 25 °C. But what we do with concentration and pressure is fairly complex and well beyond the scope of this book. We therefore satisfy ourselves with an *incorrect* but nevertheless generally acceptable

Le Chatelier's principle (page 388).

465

TABLE 15.1
STANDARD AQUEOUS ELECTRODE POTENTIALS
AT 25 °C*

ELEMENT	ELECTRODE	$E°$, VOLT
Li**	$Li^+(aq) + e^- \rightleftharpoons Li(c)$	-3.045
K	$K^+(aq) + e^- \rightleftharpoons K(c)$	-2.925
Ca	$Ca^{2+}(aq) + 2e^- \rightleftharpoons Ca(c)$	-2.87
Na	$Na^+(aq) + e^- \rightleftharpoons Na(c)$	-2.713
Mg	$Mg^{2+}(aq) + 2e^- \rightleftharpoons Mg(c)$	-2.37
Al	$Al^{3+}(aq) + 3e^- \rightleftharpoons Al(c)$	-1.66
H_2	$2H_2O + 2e^- \rightleftharpoons H_2(g) + 2OH^-(aq)$	-0.8277
Zn	$Zn^{2+}(aq) + 2e^- \rightleftharpoons Zn(c)$	-0.7628
Cr	$Cr^{3+}(aq) + 3e^- \rightleftharpoons Cr(c)$	-0.74
Fe	$Fe^{2+}(aq) + 2e^- \rightleftharpoons Fe(c)$	-0.44
Cd	$Cd^{2+}(aq) + 2e^- \rightleftharpoons Cd(c)$	-0.403
Ni	$Ni^{2+}(aq) + 2e^- \rightleftharpoons Ni(c)$	-0.25
Sn	$Sn^{2+}(aq) + 2e^- \rightleftharpoons Sn(c)$	-0.14
Pb	$Pb^{2+}(aq) + 2e^- \rightleftharpoons Pb(c)$	-0.126
H_2	$2H^+(aq) + 2e^- \rightleftharpoons H_2(g)$ (standard electrode)	0.000
Cu	$Cu^{2+}(aq) + 2e^- \rightleftharpoons Cu(c)$	$+0.34$
I_2	$I_2(c) + 2e^- \rightleftharpoons 2I^-(aq)$	$+0.535$
Fe	$Fe^{3+}(aq) + e^- \rightleftharpoons Fe^{2+}(aq)$	$+0.771$
Hg	$Hg^{2+}(aq) + 2e^- \rightleftharpoons Hg(l)$	$+0.792$
Ag	$Ag^+(aq) + e^- \rightleftharpoons Ag(c)$	$+0.7994$
Br_2	$Br_2(l) + 2e^- \rightleftharpoons 2Br^-(aq)$	$+1.08$
O_2	$\frac{1}{2} O_2(g) + 2H^+(aq) + 2e^- \rightleftharpoons H_2O$	$+1.229$
Cl_2	$Cl_2(g) + 2e^- \rightleftharpoons 2Cl^-(aq)$	$+1.358$
Au	$Au^{3+}(aq) + 3e^- \rightleftharpoons Au(c)$	$+1.42$
Mn	$MnO_4^-(aq) + 8H^+(aq) + 5e^- \rightleftharpoons Mn^{2+}(aq) + 4H_2O$	$+1.51$
F_2	$F_2(g) + 2e^- \rightleftharpoons 2F^-(aq)$	$+2.87$

* Defined in accord with Josiah Gibbs, one of the founders of chemical thermodynamics, and the International Union of Pure and Applied Chemistry, IUPAC-GIBBS STOCKHOLM Sign Convention. Source: "Selected Constants, Oxidation-Reduction Potentials in Aqueous Solution," Gaston Charlot, *IUPAC Supplement*, 1971.

** For pure metals that react violently with water, an amalgam saturated with metal is used as the electrode.

definition of the assigned electrode potential, called the **standard electrode potential.** It is the potential of an electrode when the concentration of each solute is 1 mole per liter and each gas pressure is 1 atm at 25 °C; it is assigned the symbol $E°$, read as "E zero." A list of standard potentials is given in Table 15.1. The potential difference of a cell calculated from standard electrode potentials is called the **standard EMF** of the cell, denoted as $E°_{cell}$.*

Before using Table 15.1, let us study its meaning. A positive value for an electrode potential means that the electrode has a relatively strong tendency to gain electrons. Thus,

$$F_2(g), F^- \text{ electrode, } E° = +2.87 \text{ volt}$$

has a stronger tendency to gain electrons than

---

*More correctly, the standard EMF of a cell is the measured potential difference when the electrodes are in contact with *ideal solutions* in which each solute and gas has an *activity* of exactly 1. The activity is the concentration multiplied by a correction term that corrects for deviation from ideality; the correction term changes mole/liter to activity. A real solution of unit activity has an actual concentration that is near but measurably different from 1 mole/liter.

$Cl_2(g)$, Cl^- electrode, $E° = +1.358$ volt

or

Cu, Cu^{2+} electrode, $E° = +0.34$ volt

or

Zn, Zn^{2+} electrode, $E° = -0.7628$ volt

The more positive the electrode potential, the greater the tendency to gain electrons. But a substance that gains electrons is an oxidizing agent. Therefore, the more positive the electrode potential, the greater is its tendency to act as an oxidizing agent. Thus, when the $F_2(g)$, F^- and $Cl_2(g)$, Cl^- electrodes are coupled (set up as a cell), the $F_2(g)$, F^- acts as the oxidizing agent; it must gain electrons and so be reduced. Then the $Cl_2(g)$, Cl^- has no choice other than to act as the reducing agent; it must lose electrons and so be oxidized. We can summarize this discussion as shown:

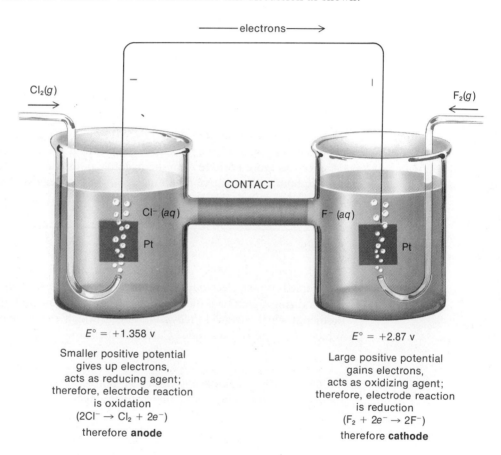

$E° = +1.358$ v

Smaller positive potential
gives up electrons,
acts as reducing agent;
therefore, electrode reaction
is oxidation
$(2Cl^- \rightarrow Cl_2 + 2e^-)$
therefore **anode**

$E° = +2.87$ v

Large positive potential
gains electrons,
acts as oxidizing agent;
therefore, electrode reaction
is reduction
$(F_2 + 2e^- \rightarrow 2F^-)$
therefore **cathode**

The cell reaction is therefore

$$2Cl^-(aq) + F_2(g) \longrightarrow Cl_2(g) + 2F^-(aq)$$

and the standard EMF of the cell is

$$E°_{cell} = E°_{reduction} - E°_{oxidation}$$
$$= 2.87 \text{ volt} - 1.358 \text{ volt} = 1.51 \text{ volt}$$

If the Cu, Cu^{2+} and $Cl_2(g)$, Cl^- electrodes are coupled, the $Cl_2(g)$, Cl^- electrode now acts as the oxidizing agent because its potential is more positive than that of the Cu, Cu^{2+} electrode:

Reactions of fluorine with water (page 624) are here ignored.

Never change the sign of the standard electrode potentials, shown in Table 15.1.

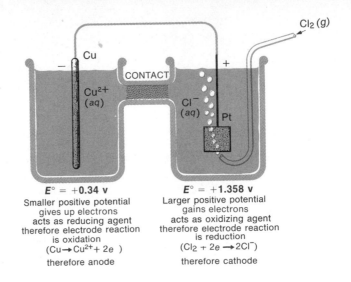

$E° = +0.34$ v
Smaller positive potential
gives up electrons
acts as reducing agent
therefore electrode reaction
is oxidation
$(Cu \rightarrow Cu^{2+} + 2e\ )$
therefore anode

$E° = +1.358$ v
Larger positive potential
gains electrons
acts as oxidizing agent
therefore electrode reaction
is reduction
$(Cl_2 + 2e \rightarrow 2Cl^-)$
therefore cathode

The cell reaction is therefore

$$Cu(c) + Cl_2(g) \longrightarrow Cu^{2+}(aq) + 2Cl^-(aq)$$

and

$$E°_{cell} = E°_{reduction} - E°_{oxidation}$$
$$= 1.36 \text{ volt} - 0.34 \text{ volt} \doteq 1.02 \text{ volt}$$

In coupling two electrodes with different potential signs, one negative potential and one positive potential, the positive potential electrode always acts as the oxidizing agent since it is more positive than the negative potential electrode. In coupling two electrodes, both with negative potential signs, the less negative electrode always acts as the oxidizing agent. For example, -1.87 volt is less negative and therefore is a more positive number than -2.54 volt.

Example 2

Two electrodes, Mg, Mg^{2+}, $E° = -2.37$ volt, and Al, Al^{3+}, $E° = -1.66$ volt, are coupled. Which electrode potential is more positive? Which electrode acts as the oxidizing agent? Predict each electrode reaction and the cell reaction. Predict at which electrode reduction and at which electrode oxidation occurs. Which electrode is the anode? Calculate the standard EMF of the cell, $E°_{cell}$.

Answer

-1.66 volt is less negative and therefore more positive than -2.37 volt. Hence, the Al, Al^{3+} electrode acts as the oxidizing agent:

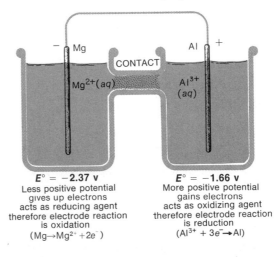

$E° = -2.37$ v
Less positive potential
gives up electrons
acts as reducing agent
therefore electrode reaction
is oxidation
$(Mg \rightarrow Mg^{2+} + 2e^-)$

$E° = -1.66$ v
More positive potential
gains electrons
acts as oxidizing agent
therefore electrode reaction
is reduction
$(Al^{3+} + 3e^- \rightarrow Al)$

The cell reaction is

$$Mg(c) + Al^{3+}(aq) \longrightarrow Mg^{2+}(aq) + Al(c) \ (unbalanced)$$
$$3Mg(c) + 2Al^{3+}(aq) \longrightarrow 3Mg^{2+}(aq) + 2Al(c) \ (balanced)$$

and

$$E°_{cell} = E°_{reduction} - E°_{oxidation}$$
$$= -1.66 \text{ volt} - (-2.37 \text{ volt})$$
$$= -1.66 \text{ volt} + 2.37 \text{ volt} = 0.71 \text{ volt}$$

Equally correct, we could say that the more negative the electrode potential, the greater the tendency to lose electrons, and the greater the tendency to act as a reducing agent. Thus, the Mg, Mg^{2+} electrode potential is more negative than the Al, Al^{3+} electrode potential and therefore acts as the reducing agent. The Al, Al^{3+} electrode then must act as the oxidizing agent.

PROBLEM 2   **(a) The two electrodes $Cl_2(g)$, Cl^-, $E° = +1.358$ volt, and $Br_2(l)$, Br^-, $E° = +1.08$ volt, are coupled. (b) The two electrodes Mg, Mg^{2+}, $E° = -2.37$ volt, and Zn, Zn^{2+}, $E° = -0.7628$ volt, are also coupled. For each cell, which electrode is more positive? Which electrode acts as the oxidizing agent? Predict each electrode reaction and cell reaction. Predict at which electrode reduction and at which electrode oxidation occurs. Which electrode is the anode? Calculate the standard EMF of the cell, $E°_{cell}$.**

Example 3

Calculate the standard EMF of the cell, $E°_{cell}$, in which the cell reaction is
(a) $Ca(c) + 2H^+(aq) \longrightarrow Ca^{2+}(aq) + H_2(g)$
(b) $BaI_2(aq) + Cl_2(g) \longrightarrow BaCl_2(aq) + I_2(c)$
(c) $CaF_2(aq) + Cl_2(g) \longrightarrow CaCl_2(aq) + F_2(g)$

Answer

(a) As written, H^+ is reduced to H_2, while Ca is oxidized to Ca^{2+}

$$2H^+ + 2e^- \longrightarrow H_2 \quad reduction$$
$$Ca \longrightarrow Ca^{2+} + 2e^- \quad oxidation$$
$$E°_{cell} = E°_{reduction} - E°_{oxidation}$$

From Table 15.1, $H_2(g)$, H^+, $E° = 0.00$ volt; and Ca, Ca^{2+}, $E° = -2.87$ volt.

$$E°_{cell} = 0.00 \text{ volt} - (-2.87 \text{ volt}) = 2.87 \text{ volt}$$

(b) As written, I^- is oxidized to I_2, while Cl_2 is reduced to Cl^-

$$2I^- \longrightarrow I_2 + 2e^- \quad oxidation$$
$$Cl_2 + 2e^- \longrightarrow 2Cl^- \quad reduction$$
$$E°_{cell} = E°_{reduction} - E°_{oxidation}$$

Taking electrode potential values from Table 15.1,

$$E°_{cell} = 1.358 \text{ volt} - 0.535 \text{ volt} = 0.823 \text{ volt}$$

(c) As written, F^- is oxidized to F_2, while Cl_2 is reduced to Cl^-

$$2F^- \longrightarrow F_2 + 2e^- \quad \text{oxidation}$$

$$Cl_2 + 2e^- \longrightarrow 2Cl^- \quad \text{reduction}$$

$$E°_{cell} = E°_{reduction} - E°_{oxidation}$$

Taking electrode potential values from Table 15.1,

$$E°_{cell} = 1.358 \text{ volt} - 2.87 \text{ volt} = -1.51 \text{ volt}$$

We have answered (c) correctly, but the negative sign for $E°_{cell}$ informs us that Equation (c) has a greater tendency to go from right to left rather than as written. More realistically, the equation should have been written as $CaCl_2(aq) + F_2(g) \longrightarrow CaF_2(aq) + Cl_2(g)$, for which we would have calculated $E°_{cell} = 1.51$ volt.

PROBLEM 3   **Find the standard EMF of the cell, $E°_{cell}$, in which the cell reaction is**
(a) $Ca(c) + Cl_2(g) \longrightarrow Ca^{2+}(aq) + 2Cl^-(aq)$
(b) $3K(c) + AlCl_3(aq) \longrightarrow 3KCl(aq) + Al(c)$ $(3K + Al^{3+} \longrightarrow 3K^+ + Al)$
(c) $Pb(c) + H_2SO_4(aq) \longrightarrow PbSO_4(aq) + H_2(g)$ $(Pb + 2H^+ \longrightarrow Pb^{2+} + H)$

15.4   EMF OF A CELL AND CONCENTRATION

The relationship between the EMF of a cell, E_{cell}, and solution concentrations, derived by Walther Nernst (1889), is

Known as the Nernst equation; units of 0.0592 are volt $\times$ moles of electron and n has the units of moles of electron transferred, so that the unit of $\frac{0.0592}{n}$ is volt.

$$E_{cell} = E°_{cell} - \frac{0.0592 \text{ volt}}{n} \log \text{ concentration term}$$

Here E_{cell} is the observed EMF of the cell and $E°_{cell}$ is the standard EMF of the cell. 0.0592 is a constant at 25 °C; n is the number of moles of electrons transferred in the cell reaction *as written;* and the concentration term for the cell reaction as written is the same term we used in our study of chemical equilibrium (page 377). This equation is only used for solutions sufficiently dilute to behave like ideal solutions (page 394).

Example 4

Calculate the EMF of the cell (page 460) in which the cell reaction is

$$Zn(c) + Cu^{2+}(aq) \longrightarrow Cu(c) + Zn^{2+}(aq)$$

when the concentration of Zn^{2+} is 0.100 M and the concentration of Cu^{2+} is 0.0100 M, written as

$$Zn\,|\,Zn^{2+}\,(0.100\text{ M})\|Cu^{2+}\,(0.0100\text{ M})\,|\,Cu$$

$$Zn \longrightarrow Zn^{2+} + 2e^- \qquad\qquad Cu^{2+} + 2e^- \longrightarrow Cu$$
$$\text{oxidation} \qquad\qquad\qquad \text{reduction}$$

The line | indicates the boundary between the electrode and the solution; the double lines ‖ represent a salt bridge joining the two solutions.

Answer

First use Table 15.1, page 466, to calculate $E°_{cell}$ as in Example 3:

$$E°_{cell} = E°_{reduction} - E°_{oxidation}$$
$$= 0.34 \text{ volt} - (-0.7628 \text{ volt}) = 1.10 \text{ volt}$$

Then, from the cell reaction as written, determine the value of n and write the concentration term for the reaction. Two moles of electrons are transferred; therefore, $n = 2$ and

$$\text{concentration term} = \frac{[Zn^{2+}]}{[Cu^{2+}]}$$

$$E_{cell} = E°_{cell} - \frac{0.0592 \text{ volt}}{n} \log \text{concentration term}$$

$$= 1.10 \text{ volt} - \frac{0.0592 \text{ volt}}{n} \log \frac{[Zn^{2+}]}{[Cu^{2+}]}$$

$$= 1.10 \text{ volt} - \frac{0.0592 \text{ volt}}{2} \log \frac{0.100}{0.0100}$$

Solving for the log term (App. X),

$$\log \frac{0.100}{0.0100} = \log 10.0 = 1.00$$

and

$$E_{cell} = 1.10 \text{ volt} - 0.0296 \times 1.00 \text{ volt} = 1.07 \text{ volt}$$

The decrease in voltage is predictable from Le Chatelier's principle (page 388). The smaller concentration of Cu^{2+} and the larger concentration of Zn^{2+} shift the reaction to the left and so decrease E_{cell}.

Example 5

Calculate the EMF of the cell in which the cell reaction is $Mg(c) + 2Ag^+(aq) \longrightarrow Mg^{2+}(aq) + 2Ag(c)$, when $[Mg^{2+}] = 0.130 \text{ M}$ and $[Ag^+] = 1.00 \times 10^{-4} \text{ M}$, written as

$$Mg \,|\, Mg^{2+} \,(0.130 \text{ M}) \,\|\, Ag^+ \,(1.00 \times 10^{-4} \text{ M}) \,|\, Ag$$

$$Mg \longrightarrow Mg^{2+} + 2e^- \qquad\qquad Ag^+ + 1e^- \longrightarrow Ag$$
$$\text{oxidation} \qquad\qquad\qquad\qquad \text{reduction}$$

Answer

From Table 15.1, page 466,

$$E°_{cell} = E°_{reduction} - E°_{oxidation}$$
$$= 0.7994 \text{ volt} - (-2.37 \text{ volt}) = 3.17 \text{ volt}$$

Two moles of electrons are transferred in the reaction *as written;* therefore, $n = 2$ and

$$\text{concentration term} = \frac{[Mg^{2+}]}{[Ag^+]^2}$$

$$E_{cell} = 3.17 \text{ volt} - \frac{0.0592 \text{ volt}}{2} \log \frac{0.130}{(1.00 \times 10^{-4})^2}$$

$$\log \frac{0.130}{(1.00 \times 10^{-4})^2} = \log \frac{1.30 \times 10^{-1}}{1.00 \times 10^{-8}} = \log (1.30 \times 10^7) = \log 1.30 + \log 10^7$$

$$= 0.114 + 7.00 = 7.114$$

$$E_{cell} = 3.17 \text{ volt} - 0.0296 \times 7.114 \text{ volt}$$

$$= 3.17 \text{ volt} - 0.21 \text{ volt} = 2.96 \text{ volt}$$

Again, the smaller concentration of Ag^+ and the larger concentration of Mg^{2+} shift the reaction to the left and so decrease E_{cell}.

PROBLEM 4   Calculate the EMF of the cell in which the cell reaction is $Ca(c) + Fe^{2+}(aq) \longrightarrow Ca^{2+}(aq) + Fe(c)$, when $[Fe^{2+}] = 0.160 \text{ M}$ and $[Ca^{2+}] = 1.00 \times 10^{-3} \text{ M}$, written as

$$Ca\,|\,Ca^{2+}\ (1.00 \times 10^{-3}\,M)\,\|\,Fe^{2+}\ (0.160\,M)\,|\,Fe$$

$$Ca \longrightarrow Ca^{2+} + 2e^- \qquad\qquad Fe^{2+} + 2e^- \longrightarrow Fe$$

oxidation   *reduction*

In this case, the smaller concentration of Ca^{2+} and the larger concentration of Fe^{2+} shift the reaction to the right and so increase E_{cell}.

15.5 ELECTROLYSIS

When an electric current is passed through a solution or a molten salt, the passage of the current is accompanied by a chemical reaction. A half-reaction occurs at each electrode. The current does *not* flow until some reaction occurs at each electrode. This process, the reverse of a galvanic cell, is called **electrolysis.** The electrode reactions depend on the nature of the electrolyte and of the electrodes and on the voltage applied.

Electrolysis of a Molten Salt   Molten ionic compounds conduct the electric current because ions migrate toward the electrodes. Typical is the electrolysis of molten sodium chloride, for which the electrode reactions are shown:

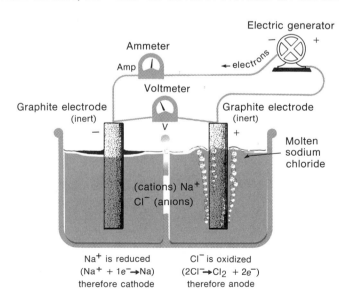

Sodium is produced at the cathode (negative electrode), and chlorine at the anode (positive electrode). The cell reaction is

$$2NaCl(l) \xrightarrow[\text{current}]{\text{electric}} 2Na(l) + Cl_2(g)$$

Notice that the cell reaction for the electrolysis of NaCl is the reverse of the cell reaction that produces electricity in the galvanic cell, for which the cell reaction is

$$2Na(l) + Cl_2(g) \longrightarrow 2NaCl(l)$$

Electrolysis of Aqueous Sodium Chloride   The presence of water introduces the possibility that it might be oxidized to oxygen

$$2H_2O \longrightarrow O_2(g) + 4H^+(aq) + 4e^- \tag{1}$$

in competition with

$$2Cl^-(aq) \longrightarrow Cl_2(g) + 2e^- \tag{2}$$

or reduced to hydrogen

$$2H_2O + 2e^- \longrightarrow H_2(g) + 2OH^-(aq)$$

in competition with

$$Na^+(aq) + 1e^- \longrightarrow Na(c) \tag{3}$$

Water is much more easily reduced than sodium ion, but water and chloride ion can be oxidized almost equally under the same concentration conditions. On the other hand, if the solution is saturated with sodium chloride, then the increased chloride ion concentration favors electrode reaction 2 over 1. The main electrode reactions are then

$$2NaCl(aq) \longrightarrow 2Na^+(aq) + 2Cl^-(aq)$$
$$\text{at cathode } (reduction)\ 2H_2O + 2e^- \longrightarrow H_2(g) + 2OH^-(aq) \tag{4}$$
$$\text{at anode } (oxidation)\ 2Cl^-(aq) \longrightarrow Cl_2(g) + 2e^- \tag{5}$$

The cell reaction for the electrolysis of aqueous sodium chloride is then

$$2NaCl(aq) + 2H_2O \longrightarrow 2Na^+(aq) + 2OH^-(aq) + H_2(g) + Cl_2(g) \tag{6}$$

This reaction is the basis of the commercial production of hydrogen, chlorine, and sodium hydroxide. The sodium hydroxide is obtained by evaporation of the solution.

The commercial conditions do not correspond to the concentrations under which $E°$ is determined. Nevertheless, Table 15.1, page 466, may be used to confirm that Reaction 6 is more likely than the reaction

$$2NaCl(aq) \longrightarrow 2Na(c) + Cl_2(g) \tag{7}$$

We do this by calculating the $E°_{cell}$ for Reactions 6 and 7 as written; the reaction with the *more positive* $E°_{cell}$ will be favored. For Reaction 6, the electrode reactions are (4) and (5) above, from which

$$E^\circ{}_{cell} = E^\circ{}_{reduction} - E^\circ{}_{oxidation}$$
$$= -0.89 \text{ volt} - (+1.36 \text{ volt}) = -2.19 \text{ volt}$$

For Reaction 7 the electrode reactions are (3) and (5) above, from which

$$E^\circ{}_{cell} = E^\circ{}_{reduction} - E^\circ{}_{oxidation}$$
$$= -2.71 \text{ volt} - (+1.36 \text{ volt}) = -4.07 \text{ volt}$$

The $E^\circ{}_{cell}$ for Reaction 7, -4.07 volt, is *more negative* than that for Reaction 6, -2.19 volt. Equally correct, we can say that the $E^\circ{}_{cell}$ for Reaction 6 is *more positive* than that for Reaction 7. Therefore, Reaction 6 occurs in preference to Reaction 7.

It is true that the negative sign for $E^\circ{}_{cell}$ means (page 470) that both reactions prefer to go from right to left instead of as written. Hence, energy (electricity) must be used to force the reactions to go as written. But less force (voltage) is required for Reaction 6, so it occurs in preference to Reaction 7.

15.6 _____ ELECTRICAL UNITS

Named in honor of Charles Coulomb, page 118.

Named in honor of Michael Faraday, page 118.

More exactly, 96,485 coulombs, which is commonly written to three significant figures as 96,500.

The ampere is the SI unit of electric current. Named in honor of André Marie Ampère.

The quantity of electricity, the electric charge, is measured in **coulombs**, C. Another unit of the quantity of electricity, useful for the chemist, is the **faraday.** One faraday equals one mole of electrons, 6.02×10^{23} electrons; one faraday also equals 96,500 coulombs. This is the quantity of electricity that will produce exactly one mole (107.868 g) of Ag from an aqueous solution of silver nitrate:

$$1 \text{ faraday} = 96,500 \text{ C} = 1 \text{ mole of electrons} = 6.02 \times 10^{23} \text{ electrons}$$
$$= 107.87 \text{ g Ag}$$

An electric *current* is measured in **amperes,** A or amp, defined as the passage of one coulomb in one second, so that $1 \text{ C} = 1$ amp second or

$$\text{electric charge, } quantity\ of\ electricity = \text{electric current} \times \text{seconds}$$
$$= \text{amperes} \times \text{seconds}$$
$$= \frac{C}{\cancel{s}} \times \cancel{s} = \text{coulombs}$$

The electric energy, or the work done by a current, the quantity that determines your electric bill, is the product of the quantity of electricity and the voltage:

$$\text{electric work} = \text{potential difference} \times \text{electric charge}$$
$$= \text{volts, V} \times \text{coulombs, C} = \text{joules*}$$

The measurement of the electric work also provides a direct method of calculating equilibrium constants (page 377), the most important property of chemical reactions, and therefore constitutes one of the most important parts of electrochemistry.

Matter—a wire, a solution, a column of gas—resists the flow of an electric current through it. The smaller the resistance, the faster the electrons travel, and the

---

*The unit of electric work is the joule (page 25). The unit of electric power is the watt, named in honor of James Watt, inventor of the practical steam engine; 1 watt = 1 volt × 1 amp.

greater is the current. Resistance is a measurable and characteristic property of matter.

Three factors are thus involved in the flow of electricity: the "pressure"—the potential difference that causes the current to flow, measured in volts; the rate of flow, measured in amperes; and the resistance of matter to the flow, measured in **ohms.***

Example 6

A current of 6.0 amperes flows for 10 minutes through a circuit, the matter through which the current flows. How many (a) coulombs, (b) electrons, (c) faradays pass through the circuit?

Answer

(a) The quantity of electricity is determined by the current and the time:

quantity of electricity, *coulombs* = electric current, *amperes* × *seconds*

From the data, converting minutes to seconds

$$\text{quantity of electricity} = 6.0 \text{ amp} \times 10 \text{ min} \times 60 \frac{s}{\text{min}} = 3600 \text{ amp s}$$

But the answer is desired in coulombs; we therefore convert ampere seconds to coulombs by using the conversion factor, $1 \text{ C} = 1 \text{ amp s}$, $\dfrac{\text{C}}{\text{amp s}}$:

$$3600 \text{ amp s} \times \frac{\text{C}}{\text{amp s}} = 3600 \text{ C} = 3.6 \times 10^3 \text{ C}$$

(b) To convert coulombs to the number of electrons, we need the conversion factor, the relationship between coulombs and number of electrons, $96{,}500 \text{ C} = 6.02 \times 10^{23}$ electrons:

$$3.6 \times 10^3 \text{ C} \times \frac{6.02 \times 10^{23} \text{ electrons}}{9.65 \times 10^4 \text{ C}} = 2.2 \times 10^{22} \text{ electrons}$$

(c) To convert coulombs to the quantity of electricity in faradays, we use the conversion factor, $1 \text{ faraday} = 96{,}500 \text{ C}$:

$$3.6 \times 10^3 \text{ C} \times \frac{1 \text{ faraday}}{9.65 \times 10^4 \text{ C}} = 3.7 \times 10^{-2} \text{ faraday}$$

Equally correct, the number of electrons can be converted to faradays with the conversion factor, $1 \text{ faraday} = 6.02 \times 10^{23}$ electrons:

$$2.2 \times 10^{22} \text{ electrons} \times \frac{1 \text{ faraday}}{6.02 \times 10^{23} \text{ electrons}} = 3.7 \times 10^{-2} \text{ faraday}$$

---

*The unit of resistance is the ohm, named in honor of George Ohm, who investigated (1827) the relationship, now known as *Ohm's law,* between voltage and current: electric current, ampere = $\dfrac{\text{potential difference, volt}}{\text{resistance, ohm}}$.

PROBLEM 5   A current of 3.0 amperes flows for 30 minutes through a solution. How many (a) coulombs, (b) electrons, and (c) faradays pass through the solution?

15.7 _____ QUANTITY OF ELECTRICITY AND QUANTITY OF SUBSTANCE

Michael Faraday studied the relation between the quantity of electricity and the mass of substances produced or consumed at the electrodes and found (1833) that _the mass of a substance produced or consumed at an electrode is proportional to the quantity of charge (electricity) passed through the cell._ This generalization is known as **Faraday's law.** The quantity of charge is measured in coulombs (page 474)

$$1 \text{ faraday} = 96{,}500 \text{ C} = 6.02 \times 10^{23} \text{ electrons} = 1 \text{ mole of electrons}$$

It is calculated from the current in amperes and the time in seconds (page 474). For example, 1 mole of electrons (96,500 C) produces 1 mole of silver atoms

$$Ag^+ + 1e^- \longrightarrow Ag$$

But 2 moles of electrons ($2 \times 96{,}500$ C) produces 1 mole of copper atoms or 1 mole of chlorine molecules or 2 moles of silver atoms

$$Cu^{2+} + 2e^- \longrightarrow Cu$$
$$2Cl^- \longrightarrow Cl_2 + 2e^-$$
$$2Ag^+ + 2e^- \longrightarrow 2Ag$$

and 3 moles of electrons ($3 \times 96{,}500$ C) produces 1 mole of aluminum atoms

$$Al^{3+} + 3e^- \longrightarrow Al$$

while 4 moles of electrons ($4 \times 96{,}500$ C) produces 1 mole of oxygen molecules

$$2H_2O \longrightarrow O_2 + 4H^+ + 4e^-$$
$$2O^{2-} \longrightarrow O_2 + 4e^-$$

Thus, from an electrode reaction and quantity of charge, the mass of substances produced or consumed may be calculated.

Example 7

Calculate the mass of gold deposited from a solution of gold(III) chloride, $AuCl_3$, by the passage of a current of 2.30 amperes for 2.00 hours. The electrode reaction is $Au^{3+} + 3e^- \longrightarrow Au$.

Answer

We are given a definite quantity of electricity (recall Example 6, page 475)

$$\text{quantity of electricity} = 2.30 \text{ amp} \times 2.00 \, \cancel{h} \times 60 \, \frac{\cancel{min}}{\cancel{h}} \times 60 \, \frac{s}{\cancel{min}}$$

$$= 16{,}600 \, \cancel{amps} \times \frac{C}{\cancel{amps}} = 1.66 \times 10^4 \text{ C}$$

To convert this quantity of electricity to a quantity of gold, we need the relationship between these two quantities, the conversion factor. This is obtained from the electrode reaction. Three moles of electrons ($3 \times 96,500$ C) produce 1 mole (197 g) of gold atoms. The conversion factor is therefore $\dfrac{197 \text{ g Au}}{3 \times 96,500 \text{ C}}$. The mass of gold deposited is then given by*

$$1.66 \times 10^4 \, \cancel{C} \times \frac{197 \text{ g Au}}{3 \times 9.65 \times 10^4 \, \cancel{C}} = 11.3 \text{ g Au}$$

PROBLEM 6   Calculate the mass of zinc deposited from a solution of $ZnSO_4$ by the passage of a current of 2.50 amperes for 2.00 hours. The electrode reaction is $Zn^{2+} + 2e^- \longrightarrow Zn$.

Example 8

Calculate the number of coulombs required to deposit 40.5 g of Al when the electrode reaction is $Al^{3+} + 3e^- \longrightarrow Al$.

Answer

We are given a quantity of Al and seek an answer in coulombs. From the electrode reaction, 1 mole (27.0 g) of Al requires 3 moles of electrons ($3 \times 96,500$ C). The conversion factor is therefore $\dfrac{3 \times 96,500 \text{ C}}{27.0 \text{ g Al}}$ and the required number of coulombs is then given by

$$40.5 \, \cancel{\text{g Al}} \times \frac{3 \times 9.65 \times 10^4 \text{ C}}{27.0 \, \cancel{\text{g Al}}} = 4.34 \times 10^5 \text{ C}$$

PROBLEM 7   Calculate the number of coulombs required to deposit 47.3 g of Pb when the electrode reaction is $Pb^{2+} + 2e^- \longrightarrow Pb$.

PRACTICAL CELLS, STORAGE CELLS, _____ 15.8
AND BATTERIES

Three kinds of galvanic cells, the **dry cell,** the **storage cell,** and the **fuel cell,** are commonly used as portable sources of electric power.

The dry cell, shown in Fig. 15.3, is used to operate appliances such as flashlights,

---

*In fact, the charge on ions is determined by this kind of calculation. For example, the mass of gold deposited, 11.3 g, is a measurable quantity, as is the quantity of charge, 1.66×10^4 C. The charge on the gold ion is the number of moles of electrons required to produce 1 mole of gold atoms:

$$Au^{n+} + n \text{ moles of electrons} \longrightarrow Au^0$$

Then n is given by

$$1.66 \times 10^4 \text{ C} \times \frac{197 \text{ g Au}}{n \times 9.65 \times 10^4 \text{ C}} = 11.3 \text{ g Au}$$

In a nomenclature *no longer accepted* by IUPAC, the number of moles of electrons would be called the number of *equivalents,* so that in this reaction 1 mole of Au or Au^{3+} would be said to be 3 equivalents (or 1 millimole = 3 milliequivalents, meq); 1 meq of Na^+ or K^+ would then have the same mass as 1 mmol of Na^+ or K^+.

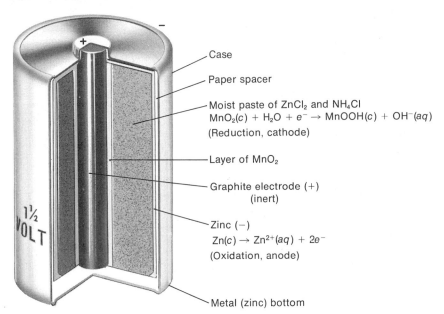

Case

Paper spacer

Moist paste of $ZnCl_2$ and NH_4Cl
$MnO_2(c) + H_2O + e^- \rightarrow MnOOH(c) + OH^-(aq)$
(Reduction, cathode)

Layer of MnO_2

Graphite electrode (+)
(inert)

Zinc (−)
$Zn(c) \rightarrow Zn^{2+}(aq) + 2e^-$
(Oxidation, anode)

Metal (zinc) bottom

FIGURE 15.3 A representation of a typical dry cell that generates a potential difference of about 1.5 volts.

Also known as the Leclanché cell, developed by Georges Leclanché (1867).

toys, and radios. The zinc container serves as the anode (negative electrode). Manganese dioxide serves as the cathode (positive electrode). A carbon (graphite) rod serves as an inert electrode for the cathode reaction. A moist paste—hence, the name "dry"—of ammonium chloride, NH_4Cl, and zinc chloride, $ZnCl_2$, serves as the electrolyte. The electrode reactions* are

$$Zn(c) \longrightarrow Zn^{2+}(aq) + 2e^- \ (oxidation,\ anode)$$
$$\underline{2MnO_2(c) + 2H_2O + 2e^- \longrightarrow 2MnOOH(c) + 2OH^-(aq)\ (reduction,\ cathode)}$$
$$Zn(c) + 2MnO_2(c) + 2H_2O \longrightarrow 2MnOOH(c) + Zn^{2+}(aq) + 2OH^-(aq)\ (cell\ reaction)$$

The **lead-acid storage cell** consists of a spongy lead electrode which serves as the anode (negative electrode) and a lead dioxide, PbO_2, electrode which serves as the cathode (positive electrode). Dilute sulfuric acid is the electrolyte. When the cell operates (discharges), the electrode reactions are

$$Pb(c) + HSO_4^-(aq) \longrightarrow PbSO_4(c) + H^+(aq) + 2e^-\ (oxidation,\ anode)$$
$$\underline{PbO_2(c) + HSO_4^-(aq) + 3H^+(aq) + 2e^- \longrightarrow PbSO_4(c) + 2H_2O\ (reduction,\ cathode)}$$
$$Pb(c) + PbO_2(c) + 2HSO_4^-(aq) + 2H^+(aq) \longrightarrow 2PbSO_4(c) + 2H_2O\ (cell\ reaction)$$

The lead sulfate formed at each electrode adheres to the electrodes. The electrode reactions may be reversed by imposing an electric current (charging of a cell), restoring the cell to its original condition. The ability to discharge and charge is the characteristic of a storage cell. During the discharge reaction, sulfuric acid is consumed and the density of the solution decreases. The extent to which the cell is

---

Journal of Chemical Education, volume 49, September 1972, page 587. The cathode reaction may be represented as Mn^{4+} in $MnO_2(c)$ gaining 1 electron and one O^{2-} in $MnO_2(c)$ gaining 1 proton:

$$Mn^{4+} + O^{2-} + O^{2-}\ in\ solid\ MnO_2 + HOH + e^- \longrightarrow$$
$$Mn^{3+} + O^{2-} + OH^-\ in\ same\ solid\ phase + OH^-(aq)$$

discharged is determined by measuring the density of the electrolyte. A **battery** consists of cells connected together so that 3 cells, each 2 volts, make a 6 volt battery, and 6 cells make a 12 volt battery. Grouping of cells is necessary because the output of individual cells seldom exceeds 2 or 3 volts. The cell voltage is fixed by the nature of the electrodes and electrolytes (and temperature). However, the amperage, the quantity of current or the number of coulombs per second available from the battery, is determined by the rate of the reaction, the number of moles of reactants consumed per second. While the voltage is the same for a one-inch square plate and for a one-foot square plate, the rate of the reaction is greater for the larger plate (Chap. 17), and the amperage is therefore greater for the larger plate. In short, the larger the electrodes, the larger the electric current; but the voltage remains constant (page 465).

The density of the acid solution in the charged cell, EMF about 2 volts, is about 1.3 g/ml.

The use of a gelled sulfuric acid electrolyte makes it possible to seal lead-acid batteries. This makes the battery spill-proof and has the added advantage of an increased lifetime.

The **Edison storage cell** is longer lasting than the lead-acid cell, but its higher initial cost has limited its use as an automobile battery. The cell reaction is the oxidation of iron by nickel dioxide; the electrolyte is an aqueous solution of potassium hydroxide:

$$Fe(c) + 2OH^-(aq) \longrightarrow Fe(OH)_2(c) + 2e^- \text{ (oxidation, anode)}$$
$$\underline{2NiO_2(c) + H_2O + 2e^- \longrightarrow Ni_2O_3(c) + 2OH^-(aq) \text{ (reduction, cathode)}}$$
$$Fe(c) + 2NiO_2(c) + H_2O \longrightarrow Fe(OH)_2(c) + Ni_2O_3(c) \text{ (cell reaction)}$$

The EMF of this cell is about 1.4 volts, smaller than the EMF of the lead-acid storage cell. Hence, more cells are required than in a lead-acid battery to supply the same voltage. But the Edison battery is rugged and finds use in lift-trucks.

Other electrode combinations, such as zinc-mercury(II) oxide, magnesium-silver chloride, cadmium-silver(I) oxide, cadmium-nickel(II) oxide, zinc-air, and sodium-sulfur, are used in batteries to supply electric power for space vehicles.

Amazingly, archeological evidence shows that batteries may have been used as early as 200 B.C. in Mesopotamia (now Iraq) and Persia (now Iran). It is believed that they may have been used for electroplating gold and silver and for magical rituals involved in the healing of disease by electricity.

The tiny mercury cell, about 1.3 volts, used in hearing aids, pacemakers, and cameras, consists of zinc (anode), potassium hydroxide (electrolyte), and mercury(II) oxide (cathode). The cell reaction is

$$Zn(c) + HgO(c) \longrightarrow ZnO(c) + Hg(l)$$

This cell has a large electric energy output per gram or per milliliter, and is characterized by a very stable voltage and a long storage life.

The rechargeable nickel-cadmium cell, about 1.2 volts, consists of cadmium (anode), potassium hydroxide (electrolyte), and nickel(III) oxide hydroxide (cathode). The cell reaction during discharge is

$$Cd(c) + 2OH^-(aq) \longrightarrow Cd(OH)_2(c) + 2e^- \text{ (oxidation)}$$
$$\underline{2NiOOH(c) + 2H_2O + 2e^- \longrightarrow 2Ni(OH)_2(c) + 2OH^-(aq) \text{ (reduction)}}$$
$$Cd(c) + 2NiOOH(c) + 2H_2O \longrightarrow Cd(OH)_2(c) + 2Ni(OH)_2(c) \text{ (cell reaction)}$$

In this cell the OH^- consumed in the oxidation half-reaction is regenerated in the reduction half-reaction, so that potassium hydroxide is not consumed. This eliminates the need for density measurements. Further, since gases are not produced while the battery is being charged, it is possible to manufacture a sealed, rechargeable cell or battery. Although more expensive, the nickel-cadmium storage cell has a longer life than the lead-acid storage cell. It can be discharged and charged many more times than the lead-acid cell and is widely used in photo-flashlights, in appliances such as portable power tools, and as an emergency power supply for operating elevators, fire pumps, and other essential services.

The major failing of these cells is their necessary replacement from time to time. When the electrodes are consumed, the cell is useless ("dead"). Fuel cells, however, operate *continuously* because gases, the reactants oxidized or reduced, can be continuously supplied and the products continuously removed.

Discovered by William Grove in 1839.

In a "fuel cell," electric energy is directly obtained *without* combustion from oxygen and a gas that can be oxidized.* That is, the operation of a fuel cell is *not* based on combustion. For example, in a typical fuel cell hydrogen and oxygen are fed to porous electrodes containing platinum catalyst (page 394). A water-soaked solid serves as the electrolyte; see Fig. 15.4. The electrode reactions are

$$2H_2(g) \longrightarrow 4H^+(aq) + 4e^- \text{ (oxidation, anode)}$$
$$O_2(g) + 4H^+(aq) + 4e^- \longrightarrow 2H_2O(l) \text{ (reduction, cathode)}$$
$$\overline{2H_2(g) + O_2(g) \longrightarrow 2H_2O(l) \text{ (cell reaction)}}$$

---

*While power plants operate at an efficiency of about 40 % (page 310), electrochemical conversion of the energy of a reaction can be as high as 90 %; lead-acid cells have an efficiency of 70 %.

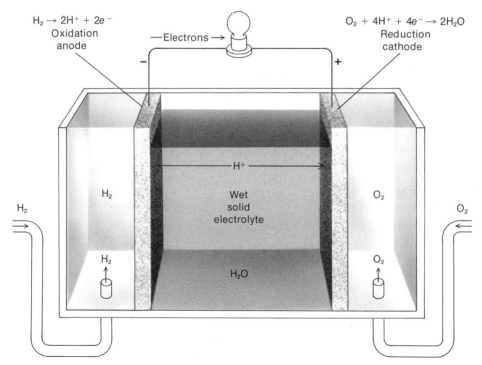

FIGURE 15.4 Representation of a fuel cell; oxygen and hydrogen are fed into the cell and water is removed. The hydrogen and oxygen are in the gas spaces behind the porous electrodes. The solid electrolyte is an H^+ ion-exchanger (Chap. 20). The EMF of the cell is about 1 volt. Fuel cells were first used in the Gemini spacecraft.

The product water is continuously removed and may be used as drinking water, especially useful in space vehicles as a source of fresh water.

The successful substitution of a cheaper gas such as methyl alcohol, CH_3OH, or natural gas for hydrogen could radically change our methods of generating electric power and driving engines. The detection of the EMF of a fuel cell set up by natural gases leaking to the surface from deep deposits under land or sea correctly predicts the location of oil. However, although fuel cells are useful and highly reliable in space ships, they are not yet economical for general use nor competitive with power plants.

The Electric Powered Vehicle A Congressional law supporting the development of electric vehicles within five years reflects the concern for pollution control and petroleum conservation. The design of a practical battery to yield the same energy as the same mass of gasoline within this time is an extremely difficult goal. For example, 826 ml (610 g) of gasoline fired in an engine (28 % efficiency) can quickly lift a 10^5 g (200 lb) load from sea level to the top of Mount Everest. Only the combustion of hydrogen, aluminum, or magnesium can match this feat. In more practical terms, this spells out a battery requirement of 432 kJ per pound delivered in one hour. While recent developments, involving lithium atoms interspersed between atomic layers of the disulfides of transition metals like TiS_2, have attained theoretical battery yields of over 600 kJ per pound delivered in one hour, a fantastic amount of work still remains to move successfully from the laboratory to the street to meet the economic competition from other fuels.

Public Law 94-413,
U.S. Congress, 1976.

EQUILIBRIUM CONSTANTS REVISITED _____ 15.9

Since voltage measurements can be made with extremely high accuracy, the standard EMF of cells is very frequently used to calculate equilibrium constants. The basis of this calculation is the fact that when equilibrium is established, for all practical purposes the chemical reaction stops (page 375). When the cell reaction stops, the EMF of the cell, E_{cell}, must equal zero. Also, at equilibrium the concentration term equals K, the equilibrium constant for the reaction (page 377). Equilibrium in this situation means no reaction, no EMF, and concentration term $= K$. Then, the equation (page 470)

$$E_{cell} = E^\circ_{cell} - \frac{0.0592 \text{ volt}}{n} \log \text{ concentration term}$$

becomes

$$0 = E^\circ_{cell} - \frac{0.0592 \text{ volt}}{n} \log K$$

from which

$$E^\circ_{cell} = \frac{0.0592 \text{ volt}}{n} \log K$$

and

$$\log K = \frac{n \times E^\circ_{cell}}{0.0592 \text{ volt}}$$

Thus, this equation can be used to calculate the equilibrium constant for any reaction for which the standard EMF can be calculated.

Example 9

Calculate the equilibrium constant (25 °C) for the reaction

$$Zn(c) + Cu^{2+}(aq) \longrightarrow Cu(c) + Zn^{2+}(aq)$$

$$Zn \longrightarrow Zn^{2+} + 2e^- \qquad\qquad Cu^{2+} + 2e^- \longrightarrow Cu$$

oxidation   reduction

Answer

First calculate $E°_{cell}$ and determine n as in Example 4, page 470. $E°_{cell} = 1.10$ volt and $n = 2$. Then

$$\log K = \frac{n \times E°_{cell}}{0.0592 \text{ volt}} = \frac{2 \times 1.10 \text{ volt}}{0.0592 \text{ volt}} = 37.2$$

and (page 432)

$$K = \text{antilog of } 37.2 = \text{antilog of } 0.2 \times \text{antilog of } 37$$

$$\text{antilog of } 0.2 = 2 \quad \text{and} \quad \text{antilog of } 37 = 10^{37}$$

$$K = 2 \times 10^{37} = \frac{[Zn^{2+}]}{[Cu^{2+}]}$$

This large value of K means that the reaction proceeds practically to completion.

The chemist often speaks of $E°_{cell}$ as "the driving force of a chemical reaction" because it determines the equilibrium constant.

PROBLEM 8 **Calculate the equilibrium constant (25 °C) for the reaction $Ca(c) + Fe^{2+}(aq) \longrightarrow Ca^{2+}(aq) + Fe(c)$. See the answer to Problem 4 for additional information.**

Example 10

Calculate the equilibrium constant (25 °C) for silver chromate, a slightly soluble salt (page 448), $Ag_2CrO_4(c) \longrightarrow 2Ag^+(aq) + CrO_4^{2-}(aq)$, for which $E°_{cell} = -0.3533$ volt and $n = 2$.

Answer

$$\log K_{sp} = \frac{n \times E°_{cell}}{0.0592 \text{ volt}} = \frac{2 \times -0.3533 \text{ volt}}{0.0592 \text{ volt}} = -11.94$$

$$K_{sp} = \text{antilog } -11.94$$

We now convert the negative logarithm to a positive logarithm (page 432) by adding $+1$ to -0.94 ($+1.00 - 0.94 = +0.06$) and subtracting 1 from -11 ($-1 - 11 = -12$). Then

$$K_{sp} = \text{antilog } (+0.06 - 12) = \text{antilog } 0.06 \times \text{antilog } -12$$

$$\text{antilog } 0.06 = 1.1 \quad \text{and} \quad \text{antilog } -12 = 10^{-12}$$

$$K_{sp} = 1.1 \times 10^{-12} = [Ag^+]^2[CrO_4^{2-}]$$

This small value of K_{sp}, like the negative sign for $E°_{cell}$, indicates that the reverse reaction is favored and that silver chromate is an insoluble salt.

The larger (more positive) the value of $E°_{cell}$, the greater is the K value, and the more complete is the reaction as written.

MAXIMUM ELECTRICAL WORK _____ 15.10

When a current flows, some of the electrical energy appears as heat, as in a toaster, electric light bulb, or electric heater, because of the resistance of matter (page 475). The maximum electrical work is thus never obtained when electricity is used. However, the use of a low resistance wire makes it possible to obtain nearly the maximum amount of electrical work obtainable from a galvanic cell. Nevertheless, it is possible to measure the maximum electrical work by measuring the EMF of the cell at *no current flow:* when no current flows, there is no change of electrical energy to heat.

An instrument has been designed to oppose the flow of current in a galvanic cell under study. The instrument is adjustable so that the cell current could be made to flow from anode to cathode, or from cathode to anode, or in neither direction. When the current flow is zero, the opposing currents are balanced and the EMF of the cell exactly equals the EMF of the instrument; this value corresponds to the maximum EMF obtainable from the cell. Electrical work (energy) is given (page 474) by

Known as a potentiometer, a meter that measures voltages accurately to 7 or 8 significant figures.

$$\text{electrical work} = \text{EMF of cell, in volts} \times \text{electric charge, in coulombs}$$

But the electric charge is given by

$$\text{electric charge} = n \text{ moles of electrons} \times 96{,}500 \frac{\text{coulomb}}{\text{mole of electrons}}$$

where n is the *number* of moles of electrons transferred in the cell reaction as written. Then

$$\text{electrical work} = n \times 96{,}500 \frac{\text{coulomb}}{\text{mole of electrons}} \times E_{cell}$$

Example 11

Calculate the maximum electrical work, in volt coulombs, in joules, J, and in calories, available from the cell reaction $Zn(c) + Cu^{2+}(aq) \longrightarrow Zn^{2+}(aq) + Cu(c)$ when the maximum EMF measured is 1.10 volt. 1 joule = 1 volt $\times$ 1 coulomb; 4.184 joules = 1 calorie.

Answer

Since the EMF of the cell is measured under conditions to obtain the maximum EMF, the electrical work is also a maximum:

$$\text{maximum electrical work} = n \times 96{,}500 \frac{\text{coulomb}}{\text{mole of electrons}} \times E_{cell}$$

$$n = 2 \text{ moles of electrons} \quad \text{and} \quad E_{cell} = 1.10 \text{ volt}$$

$$\text{maximum electrical work} = 2 \text{ mole of electrons} \times 9.65 \times 10^4 \frac{\text{coulomb}}{\text{mole of electrons}}$$
$$\times 1.10 \text{ volt} = 2.12 \times 10^5 \text{ volt coulomb} = 2.12 \times 10^5 \text{ J}$$

There are 4.184 J in 1 cal; the conversion factor is therefore $\frac{1 \text{ cal}}{4.184 \text{ J}}$ and

maximum electrical work $= 2.12 \times 10^5 \cancel{J} \times \frac{1 \text{ cal}}{4.184 \cancel{J}} = 5.07 \times 10^4$ cal.

PROBLEM 9 Calculate the maximum electrical work, in volt coulombs, in joules, and in calories, avilable from the cell reaction $Mg(c) + 2Ag^+(aq) \longrightarrow Mg^{2+}(aq) + 2Ag(c)$ under conditions at which the measured maximum EMF of the cell is 2.50 volts. 1 J = 1 volt $\times$ 1 coulomb; 1 cal = 4.184 J.

Significance of the Maximum Electrical Work. First, this quantity is very frequently used to determine in which direction a chemical reaction will go for a given set of concentration conditions—right to left, left to right, or in neither direction. This application of the maximum EMF of cells is named the Gibbs energy change.* It is named "Gibbs" after Josiah Gibbs, who established (1875) this principle. It is named "change" because, like the enthalpy change (page 288), the Gibbs energy of the products may be more or less than the Gibbs energy of the reactants. The Gibbs energy change is denoted by ΔG:

$$\Delta G = -n \times 96{,}500 \frac{\text{coulomb}}{\text{mole of electrons}} \times E_{cell}$$

The Gibbs energy change, ΔG, measures the maximum electrical work available from a cell. The *minus sign* means that *the Gibbs energy decreases* as electrical work is done, just as the minus sign for an enthalpy change means the enthalpy decreases as heat is evolved (page 288).

Example 12

(a) Calculate the Gibbs energy change, ΔG, in joules for each of the following cell reactions *as written,* when the maximum EMF of the cell is the given voltage:

(i) $Ca(c) + 2H^+(aq) \longrightarrow Ca^{2+}(aq) + H_2(g)$ $E_{cell} = $ 2.76 volt

(ii) $Fe^{3+}(aq) + Ag(c) \longrightarrow Fe^{2+}(aq) + Ag^+(aq)$ $E_{cell} = $ 0.00 volt

(iii) $CaF_2(aq) + Cl_2(g) \longrightarrow CaCl_2(aq) + F_2(g)$ $E_{cell} = -1.50$ volt

(b) In which direction will each reaction go?

Answer

(a) (i) $\Delta G = -n \times 9.65 \times 10^4 \frac{\text{coulomb}}{\text{mole of electrons}} \times E_{cell}$

2 moles of electrons are transferred; therefore $n = 2$ and

$$\Delta G = -2 \; \cancel{\text{mole of electrons}} \times 9.65 \times 10^4 \frac{\text{coulomb}}{\cancel{\text{mole of electrons}}} \times 2.76 \text{ volt}$$

---

*Formerly known as Gibbs "free energy" change, called "free energy" not in the sense of being without cost but because, once the cell is *properly* set up, electrical energy and not just heat is obtainable from the chemical reaction.

$\Delta G = -5.33 \times 10^5$ volt coulombs $= -5.33 \times 10^5$ joules

(b) (i) The minus sign of ΔG means that electrical work is obtained; the reaction therefore goes as written from left to right.

(a) (ii) 1 mole of electrons is transferred; therefore $n = 1$ and

$$\Delta G = -1 \text{ mole of electrons} \times 9.65 \times 10^4 \frac{\text{coulomb}}{\text{mole of electrons}} \times 0.00 \text{ volt}$$

$\Delta G = 0.00$ joule

(b) (ii) Zero voltage means no (net) reaction occurs; equilibrium has been established.

(a) (iii) Two moles of electrons are transferred; therefore $n = 2$ and

$$\Delta G = -2 \text{ moles of electrons} \times 9.65 \times 10^4 \frac{\text{coulomb}}{\text{mole of electrons}} \times (-1.50) \text{ volt}$$

$\Delta G = +2.90 \times 10^5$ volt coulombs $= +2.90 \times 10^5$ joules

(b) (iii) The plus sign of ΔG means that electrical work is *not* obtainable from the cell reaction *as written;* therefore, the reaction goes from right to left. ΔG predicts the direction of a chemical reaction but, like the EMF of a cell or an equilibrium constant, it tells us nothing about the speed of the reaction; recall page 393. These conclusions agree with the predictions based on the sign of the EMF of the cell (page 470).

PROBLEM 10   For each of the following, determine by inspection (calculations not necessary) (a) the sign of ΔG ($-$, 0, or $+$) and (b) the direction in which the reaction will go when the maximum E_{cell} is the given voltage.
(a) $2Ag(c) + Zn^{2+}(aq) + 2Cl^-(aq) \longrightarrow Zn(c) + 2AgCl(c)$ maximum $E_{cell} = 0.00$ volt
(b) $Zn^{2+}(aq) + H_2S(g) \longrightarrow ZnS(c) + 2H^+(aq)$ maximum $E_{cell} = -0.763$ volt
(c) $2Ag^+(aq) + H_2(g) \longrightarrow 2Ag(c) + 2H^+(aq)$ maximum $E_{cell} = 0.800$ volt
(d) $2Ag^+(aq) + Hg(l) \longrightarrow Hg^{2+}(aq) + 2Ag(c)$ maximum $E_{cell} = -0.50$ volt

PROBLEM 11   The foods we eat pass through a complicated series of oxidation-reduction reactions in which sugars and fatty molecules end up as carbon dioxide and water. Somewhere along this pathway, a molecule of nicotinamide adenine dinucleotide, symbolized as NADH, serves as a chemical agent in the metabolism of these food molecules:

$$NAD^+ + R{-}\overset{\displaystyle H}{\underset{\displaystyle OH}{C}}{-}R' \rightleftharpoons NADH + R{-}\overset{\displaystyle \parallel}{\underset{\displaystyle O}{C}}{-}R' + H^+$$

(a) Find the change in the oxidation number of carbon (the nature of R and R' in a sugar molecule, page 700, need not concern us here; assign oxidation number $+1$ to R and R' in both reactant and product). What is oxidized? What is reduced? What serves as the oxidizing agent?
    (b) The NADH then reacts with the oxygen we breathe, supplying the energy required for the synthesis of ATP from ADP, an endothermic reaction (page 293). In this way, energy is stored in ATP, the "biological energy storage tank":

$$\tfrac{1}{2}O_2 + NADH + H^+ \rightleftharpoons H_2O + NAD^+$$

Electrode potentials are given for biological cell conditions, pH $= 7.0$ at 25 °C:

$$\tfrac{1}{2}O_2 + 2H^+ + 2e^- \rightleftharpoons H_2O \qquad E = +0.82 \text{ volt}$$
$$NAD^+ + H^+ + 2e^- \rightleftharpoons NADH \qquad E = -0.32 \text{ volt}$$

For the reaction as written at these conditions, (i) calculate E_{cell} and ΔG in joules and in kcal. (ii) Does the reaction go as written? (iii) How many ATP molecules are synthesized for each $\frac{1}{2} O_2$ molecule reduced? One mole of ATP requires 9.0 kcal.

The larger the value of E_{cell}, the smaller is the value of ΔG (a more negative ΔG), the more complete is the reaction, and the greater is the value of K for the reaction as written. Thus, for the reaction at 25 °C

$$H_2(g) + \tfrac{1}{2} O_2(g) \rightleftharpoons H_2O(l) \qquad E°_{cell} = 1.229 \text{ volt}$$
$$\Delta G = 56.7 \text{ kcal}$$
$$K = 4.30 \times 10^{43}$$

The natural tendency favors the forward reaction. The reverse reaction is never seen in nature. However, water can be decomposed, but *only if energy is expended*. A ball released from an upper floor bounces down the stairs; it never naturally bounces up the stairs. But it can be thrown upstairs. Similarly, in photosynthesis (page 195) photons decompose water, and in electrolysis (page 472) electricity decomposes water into its elements.

15.11 ENTHALPY AND ENTROPY REVISITED

The temptation to conclude that a decrease in enthalpy alone determines the direction of a chemical reaction is indeed strong. Data such as

$$N_2(g) + 3H_2(g) \rightleftharpoons 2NH_3(g) \qquad K = 4.0 \times 10^8, \Delta H = -22.1 \text{ kcal}$$
$$2NO(g) \rightleftharpoons N_2(g) + O_2(g) \qquad K = 2.2 \times 10^{30}, \Delta H = -43.2 \text{ kcal}$$

appear to confirm this incorrect impression. This temptation is kept within proper limits when we recall (page 102) the natural tendency of substances to become more disordered. The entropy change cannot be ignored. A reaction is thus favored by a *decrease in enthalpy* **and** an *increase in entropy*.

It is therefore instructive to compare the heat evolved, when reactants are mixed together at constant temperature and constant pressure (ΔH) (page 288), with the maximum electrical work, ΔG, obtainable when the same reactants are separated in a galvanic cell. Rarely are these quantities equal. For example, when zinc and copper(II) sulfate react in solution in a beaker, 53 kcal/mole are evolved:

$$Zn(c) + Cu^{2+}(aq) \longrightarrow Zn^{2+}(aq) + Cu(c) \qquad \Delta H = -53 \text{ kcal}$$

But set up as a cell, the maximum electrical work obtainable is 51 kcal/mole, $\Delta G = -51$ kcal. The work obtainable under conditions of maximum efficiency does not equal the heat evolved when the reactants are mixed. How do we account for the difference of 2 kcal? The 2 kcal are *evolved as heat by the cell as it does its electrical work*, so that the cell gives out 51 kcal of electrical work plus 2 kcal of heat. This difference, the difference between the heat available and the maximum electrical work available from the same chemical reaction, is a measure of the *change in entropy* (order-disorder), denoted by ΔS, in going from reactants to products:

$$\text{entropy change, } \Delta S = \frac{\text{enthalpy change, } \Delta H - \text{Gibbs energy change, } \Delta G}{T}$$

The introduction of T, the absolute temperature, requires an explanation. Entropy is associated with the degree of disorder of matter. With the addition of heat, molecular motions (page 301) become more violent and disorder increases. This change in disorder is not the same at all temperatures. A bit of matter already at a high temperature and therefore already in a state of high disorder increases only slightly in disorder on further addition of heat. On the other hand, at low temperatures, order is fairly high and the addition of heat produces a noticeable increase in disorder. Hence, the entropy changes become smaller as temperature increases. Rearranging the above equation gives

$$T \, \Delta S = \Delta H - \Delta G \qquad (8)$$

the relationship among three important characteristic properties of chemical reactions. This relationship is summarized in the following diagram:

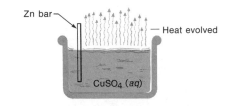

Zn bar — Heat evolved

CuSO$_4$ (aq)

heat evolved (constant T, constant P) is 53 kcal $\qquad \Delta H = -53$ kcal

Zn | Zn^{2+}(aq) ‖ Cu^{2+}(aq) | Cu

maximum electrical work obtainable is 51 kcal $\qquad \Delta G = -51$ kcal

heat evolved by cell during its operation → is 2 kcal, hence

$T \Delta S = \ -2$ kcal

We see that $T \, \Delta S$ is the heat evolved, -2 kcal, by the cell as it does its electrical work:

$$T \, \Delta S = \Delta H - \Delta G$$
$$T \, \Delta S = -53 \text{ kcal} - (-51) \text{ kcal} = -53 \text{ kcal} + 51 \text{ kcal} = -2 \text{ kcal}$$

Example 13

The relationship among ΔH, ΔG, and $T \, \Delta S$ for the reaction

$$\text{Pb}(c) + \text{Cu}(\text{CH}_3\text{COO})_2(aq) \longrightarrow \text{Pb}(\text{CH}_3\text{COO})_2(aq) + \text{Cu}(c)$$

is summarized in the following diagram (notice that the electrical work available in this case is *greater* than heat evolved when mixed):

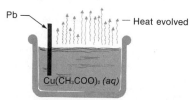

Pb — Heat evolved

Cu(CH$_3$COO)$_2$ (aq)

heat evolved (constant T, constant P) is 18 kcal

galvanic cell, maximum electrical work obtainable is 22 kcal

Data obtained at 0 °C; recall that data are given at 25 °C unless stated otherwise.

Find ΔH, ΔG, and $T \Delta S$.

Answer

ΔH is the heat evolved or absorbed at constant t, P; therefore, $\Delta H = -18$ kcal. ΔG is the maximum electrical work obtainable; therefore $\Delta G = -22$ kcal. $T \Delta S$ is the difference between ΔH and ΔG, 4 kcal. But in this case, 4 kcal is *absorbed* by the cell during its operation, making the electrical work obtainable *greater* than the heat evolved when merely mixed; therefore, $T \Delta S = +4$ kcal. This answer may be checked by the relationship

$$T \Delta S = \Delta H - \Delta G = -18 \text{ kcal} - (-22) \text{ kcal} = -18 \text{ kcal} + 22 \text{ kcal} = +4 \text{ kcal}$$

PROBLEM 12   **From the following diagram for the reaction**

$$\textbf{Zn}(c) + \textbf{2HCl}(aq) \longrightarrow \textbf{ZnCl}_2(aq) + \textbf{H}_2(g)$$

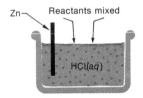

heat evolved (constant T, constant P) is 77 kcal

galvanic cell, maximum electrical work obtainable is 35 kcal

(a) Find ΔH, ΔG, and $T \Delta S$. (b) Is heat evolved or absorbed during cell operation?

If we rewrite Equation 8 as

$$\Delta G = \Delta H - T \Delta S$$

we see that ΔG is not determined by ΔH alone. It is determined by both ΔH and ΔS at a given temperature. The more negative the enthalpy of the reaction, ΔH, and the more positive the increase in disorder, ΔS, in going from reactants to products, the more negative is the ΔG for the reaction as written and the greater is the tendency for the reaction to occur as written. Thus, for the solution of sodium chloride (page 326),

$$Na^+Cl^-(c) + H_2O \longrightarrow Na^+(aq) + Cl^-(aq) \qquad \Delta H = +0.91 \text{ kcal}$$

the heat absorbed tends to favor the sodium chloride crystal, $NaCl(c)$. But the large increase in disorder in going from the highly organized crystal to the comparatively disorganized state of the Na^+ and Cl^- ions in solution tends to favor the solution of sodium chloride. The comparatively large increase in disorder overcomes the increase in enthalpy:

$$\Delta G = \Delta H - T \Delta S$$
$$= +0.91 \text{ kcal} - (+3.06 \text{ kcal})$$
$$= +0.91 \text{ kcal} - 3.06 \text{ kcal} = -2.15 \text{ kcal}$$

The reaction thus proceeds as written. This means that sodium chloride dissolves in water at 25 °C in spite of the heat absorption. The natural tendency of a reaction to occur is governed by the change in the Gibbs energy, ΔG, not by individual changes in enthalpy or entropy.

Example 14

ΔH and ΔS are given for the aqueous solution reaction at 25 °C:

$$NH_4Cl(c) \rightleftharpoons NH_4Cl(aq) \quad \Delta H = +3.53 \text{ kcal}$$
$$\Delta S = +18.0 \text{ cal/deg}$$

Is the reaction as written favored?

Answer

The direction that is favored is determined by ΔG. We therefore calculate ΔG:

$$\Delta G = \Delta H - T \Delta S$$

From the data, $\Delta H = +3.53$ kcal; being careful to convert cal to kcal,

$$T \Delta S = 298 \text{ deg} \times 18.0 \text{ cal/deg} \times 1 \text{ kcal}/10^3 \text{ cal}$$
$$= 5.36 \text{ kcal}$$

and

$$\Delta G = +3.53 \text{ kcal} - 5.36 \text{ kcal} = -1.83 \text{ kcal}$$

The reaction as written is therefore favored. In fact, because heat is absorbed, $NH_4Cl(c)$ rapidly dissolved in water lowers the temperature sufficiently to cool a "Coke."

PROBLEM 13 ΔH **and** ΔS **are given for the reaction at 25 °C:**

$$2Ag(c) + CdCl_2(aq) \rightleftharpoons 2AgCl(c) + Cd(c) \quad \Delta H = +40 \text{ kcal}$$
$$\Delta S = +30 \text{ cal/deg}$$

Find ΔG**; does the reaction go as written?**

CORROSION_____ 15.12

Corrosion is the destruction of a metal to an unwanted product by *chemical reaction with the environment*. Yearly losses from corrosion amount to billions of dollars. Applied to iron, the most common metal in use, corrosion is called *rusting*.

The conditions required for the rusting of iron are well known. Iron does not rust in water from which oxygen has been expelled, nor does it rust in oil, saturated with oxygen, from which water has been expelled. It easily rusts in water containing oxygen (air), but if such water is made alkaline, pH 9 to 10, the iron does not rust. On the other hand, acids and salts increase the speed of corrosion. Although the chemistry of rusting is still not completely understood in spite of much study, the most generally accepted theory is the electrochemical theory proposed (1903) by Willis Whitney. Iron is oxidized by H_2O or hydrogen ion:

Erosion means gradual wear due to physical forces such as wind or water flow.

Soluble organic bases are the main components of radiator antirust mixtures.

$$Fe(c) \longrightarrow Fe^{2+}(aq) + 2e^- \text{ (oxidation)} \qquad (9)$$

$$2H^+(aq) + 2e^- \longrightarrow 2H(aq) \text{ (reduction)} \qquad (10)$$

The H atoms may combine to form H_2 molecules or they may combine with oxygen to form water:

$$2H(aq) + \tfrac{1}{2} O_2(aq) \longrightarrow H_2O \qquad (11)$$

If the hydrogen ion concentration is high (pH is low), then, by the Le Chatelier principle (page 388), the reactions

$$Fe + 2H^+(aq) \longrightarrow 2H(aq) + Fe^{2+}(aq)$$

$$2H(aq) \longrightarrow H_2(g)$$

Basic salts such as sodium carbonate stop corrosion.

are favored and iron rusts very rapidly. On the other hand, an alkaline solution removes H^+ and stops this reaction. In ordinary air-saturated waters, the reaction is slower and H atoms are removed as H_2O (Reaction 11).

The Fe^{2+} ion also reacts with oxygen and water, forming the familiar reddish-brown rust and regenerating the H^+ ions consumed in the reduction reaction, Reaction 10:

$$4Fe^{2+}(aq) + O_2(aq) + 4H_2O + 2x\ H_2O \longrightarrow 2Fe_2O_3(H_2O)_x(c) + 8H^+(aq) \qquad (12)$$

The overall reaction is then the addition of Reactions 9, 10, 11, and 12:

$$4Fe(c) + 3O_2(aq) + 2x\ H_2O \longrightarrow 2Fe_2O_3(H_2O)_x(c)$$

It is interesting to note that while iron(III) oxide, rust, flakes from iron objects and thus leads to corrosion of the object, aluminum oxide "sticks" to the surface of the aluminum objects on which it forms, and so protects the remaining metal.

Metals with a more negative standard electrode potential (Table 15.1, page 466) than iron have a greater tendency to be oxidized. Zinc ($E° = -0.76$ volt), for example, which is more negative than Fe ($E° = -0.44$ volt), has a greater tendency to lose electrons and therefore can reduce Fe^{2+} to Fe:

$$
\begin{array}{ll}
Zn(c) \longrightarrow Zn^{2+}(aq) + 2e^- \text{ (oxidation)} & E°_{oxid} = -0.76\ V \\
Fe^{2+}(aq) + 2e^- \longrightarrow Fe(c) \text{ (reduction)} & E°_{red} = -0.44\ V \\
\hline
Zn(c) + Fe^{2+}(aq) \longrightarrow Zn^{2+}(aq) + Fe(c) \text{ (cell reaction)} & E°_{cell} = +0.32\ V
\end{array}
$$

Thus, metals like zinc and magnesium with more negative standard electrode potentials than iron are commonly used to "protect" iron from corrosion; they corrode instead of the iron. Underground pipes and the hulls and propellers of ships are protected by being connected to magnesium or zinc. **Galvanized iron** (zinc coating on iron) products find many applications.

Tin plate (tin coating on iron) is extensively used in the manufacture of "tin cans." Tin ($E° = -0.14$ volt) has a smaller negative standard electrode potential than iron, so that iron tends to protect the tin:

$$
\begin{array}{ll}
Fe(c) \longrightarrow Fe^{2+}(aq) + 2e^- \text{ (oxidation)} & E°_{oxid} = -0.44\ V \\
Sn^{2+}(aq) + 2e^- \longrightarrow Sn(c) \text{ (reduction)} & E°_{red} = -0.14\ V \\
\hline
Fe(c) + Sn^{2+}(aq) \longrightarrow Fe^{2+}(aq) + Sn(c) \text{ (cell reaction)} & E°_{cell} = +0.30\ V
\end{array}
$$

Hence, the tin plate normally protects the iron by excluding the oxygen and water necessary for rusting; but if the tin plate is broken, the iron corrodes and so protects the tin.

However, in the presence of certain food and fruit juices (very complex chemical mixtures) and in the absence of air, the concentrations of Sn^{2+} and Fe^{2+} are so changed that the tin now has the greater tendency to lose electrons (page 470) and so protects the iron. Tin cans are also lacquered to protect them against corrosion. The lacquer covers the tin surface, excluding oxygen and water. Paint and grease are also generally used to prevent corrosion by isolating the surface from its environment.

Food mixtures are too complex to determine the molarities of $Sn^{2+}(aq)$ and $Fe^{2+}(aq)$.

Electrochemical machining is a kind of desirable corrosion. Hard alloys difficult to cut with tools can be worked to a smooth finished shape in an electrolysis cell in which the hard alloy is the anode.

EPILOG "The Mole," R. M. Gunter, Buxton Girls School, Derbyshire, England, *A Modern Approach to Chemistry*, Makerere University, Kampala, Uganda, Issue No. 11, February 1976

"Once upon a time there was a merry little mole whose name was Avogadrosnumber, but his friends just called him '*N*.' His mother, who knew him best of all, called him 6.02×10^{23}, but then she was a rather fussy woman.

"Mole was often misunderstood by those who did not know him well, but that was only because he was so fond of dressing up, each time changing into new attire. Underneath he was always the same, always as his mother would say, he was just 6.02×10^{23}. Some days he dressed up as a mole of atoms, nothing very posh, just a mole of magnesium atoms or sodium atoms. On other days he might fancy himself as a more complicated mole, a mole of molecules. He might be anything from a mere mole of H_2 to some complicated mole like butane, C_4H_{10}. Occasionally he fancied stripping off a layer of electrons and prancing around as a mole of ions; he liked to call this his dance of the eight veils, and he always ended up very positive. For an encore he liked to start with seven veils of electrons and then put one on; that was very negative entertainment, though.

"Now *N* had a weight problem; whenever he dressed up as someone else he changed weight. This did not worry him because he knew deep down inside that he was 6.02×10^{23}, but it made him more difficult to recognize. Fortunately he soon found a list of atomic masses and then all his problems added up easily; when he was a mole of atoms he just looked at the list and muttered 'grams' to himself, when he was molecules or even ions he added up all his atoms and then muttered 'that's just grams.'

"He was very fond of swimming and when he plunged into a litre of water, whatever he was dressed up as, his friends said, 'There's a molar solution.'

"His favorite party trick was to turn into a gas, line up all the other guests' litre drinking vessels and see how many of them he could fill; early in the party while his pressure and temperature were normal he always filled 22.4 but by the end of a hot party he could fill more (unless the room had filled to a greater pressure of course, in which case he filled fewer).

"From time to time his Aunts An and Cath Ode came to visit him in their electrolyte and they often took him out for a picnic with current buns and battery eggs and played ring-a-ring-of-circuits. On these occasions he had to turn out in his smallest disguise as a mole of electrons.

"Naturally he would rush up to his Aunt An who would pick him up and toss him into the external circuit and down again to Aunt Cath. All sorts of gay things could happen when these three went picnicking in the electrolyte.

"But for An and Cath there was always a tinge

of sadness as they remembered past picnics when Uncle Faraday had been there with his friends gram-atom, gram-molecule and gram-ion, not to mention that horrible little brat gram-equivalent who used to upset Mole so much when he was young. Those were the good old days when everything was complicated and hardly anyone knew what was going on. 'Perhaps after all,' An would say to Cath, 'it's easier with only dear little Mole to worry about.'"

PROBLEMS

14 Vocabulary Define or explain the following terms: (a) anode, (b) cathode, (c) faraday, (d) coulomb, (e) galvanic cell, (f) electrolysis, (g) E_{cell}, (h) Faraday's law, (i) joule, (j) fuel cell.

15 Cell What is the difference between a galvanic cell and an electrolysis cell?

16 The following electrodes are coupled: (i) Zn(c), $Zn^{2+}(aq)$, $E° = -0.7628$ volt and Hg(c), $Hg_2^{2+}(aq)$, $E° = +0.792$ volt; (ii) Pt, $I_2(c)$, $I^-(aq)$, $E° = +0.535$, and $H_2(g)$, Pt, $H^+(aq)$, $E° = 0.000$ volt. For each cell (a) predict each electrode reaction and the cell reaction; (b) predict at which electrode oxidation and at which electrode reduction occurs. Which electrode is the anode? (c) Calculate the standard EMF of each cell, $E°_{cell}$.

17 (a) Refer to Table 15.1, page 466. Calculate the standard EMF of the cells in which the following reactions occur:
(i) $Cl_2(g) + 2Fe^{2+}(aq) \longrightarrow$
$$2Cl^-(aq) + 2Fe^{3+}(aq)$$
(ii) $2Fe^{3+}(aq) + Hg(l) \longrightarrow$
$$2Fe^{2+}(aq) + Hg_2^{2+}(aq)$$
(iii) $2Cr^{3+}(aq) + 3Pb(c) \longrightarrow 2Cr(c) + 3Pb^{2+}(aq)$
(iv) $2Ag(c) + Zn^{2+}(aq) \longrightarrow 2Ag^+(aq) + Zn(c)$
(b) Predict the direction, forward or reverse, of the reactions given above when $E_{cell} = E°_{cell}$. (c) Hydrogen peroxide may act as an oxidizing agent so that it is reduced, $H_2O_2(aq) + 2H^+(aq) + 2e^- \longrightarrow 2H_2O$ (cathode), or as a reducing agent so that it is oxidized, $H_2O_2(aq) \longrightarrow O_2(g) + 2H^+(aq) + 2e^-$ (anode). Write the cell reaction. To which electrode should a base be added to increase the EMF of the cell? Explain in terms of Le Chatelier's principle.

18 Refer to Table 15.1, page 466. Calculate the standard EMF of the cells in which the following reactions occur:
(a) $Cd(c) + Pb^{2+}(aq) \longrightarrow Pb(c) + Cd^{2+}(aq)$
(b) $Ni^{2+}(aq) + H_2(g) + 2OH^-(aq) \longrightarrow$
$$Ni(c) + 2H_2O$$
(c) $Cu(c) + 2Fe^{3+}(aq) \longrightarrow Cu^{2+}(aq) + 2Fe^{2+}(aq)$

19 $E°$ Within the halogen family, pick the element that is (a) the strongest oxidizing agent and (b) the strongest reducing agent. (Disregard astatine).

20 Direction of Reaction Calculate $E°_{cell}$ from standard electrode potentials, $E°$ (Table 15.1, page 466) and predict which of the following reactions go as written when $E_{cell} = E°_{cell}$.
(a) $Cu(c) + 2Ag^+(aq) \longrightarrow Cu^{2+}(aq) + 2Ag(c)$
(b) $3Cu(c) + 2Al^{3+}(aq) \longrightarrow 3Cu^{2+}(aq) + 2Al(c)$
(c) $Zn(c) + Fe^{2+}(aq) \longrightarrow Zn^{2+}(aq) + Fe(c)$
(d) $3Mg(c) + 2Al^{3+}(aq) \longrightarrow 3Mg^{2+}(aq) + 2Al(c)$
(e) $2Al(c) + 3Hg^{2+}(aq) \longrightarrow 2Al^{3+}(aq) + 3Hg(l)$
(f) $2Ag(c) + Ca^{2+}(aq) \longrightarrow 2Ag^+(aq) + Ca(c)$

21 EMF and ΔG See page 484; calculate (a) the EMF of the cell and (b) ΔG for the cell reaction: (i) $Ni(c) + Sn^{2+}(aq) \longrightarrow Ni^{2+}(aq) + Sn(c)$ when $[Ni^{2+}] = 0.00300$ M and $[Sn^{2+}] = 0.300$ M

$Ni|Ni^{2+}$ (3.00 × 10⁻³ M)$\|Sn^{2+}$ (0.300 M)$|Sn$
oxidation   *reduction*

(ii) $Pb(c) + Sn^{2+}(aq) \longrightarrow Pb^{2+}(aq) + Sn(c)$ when $[Pb^{2+}] = 0.00100$ M and $[Sn^{2+}] = 0.010$ M

$Pb|Pb^{2+}$ (1.00 × 10⁻³ M)$\|Sn^{2+}$ (0.010 M)$|Sn$
oxidation   *reduction*

22 For the formation of Al_2O_3 and Cr_2O_3, ΔG is a large negative change:

$2Al(c) + 1\frac{1}{2} O_2(g) \longrightarrow Al_2O_3(c)$
$$\Delta G = -378.2 \text{ kcal}$$

$2Cr(c) + 1\frac{1}{2} O_2(g) \longrightarrow Cr_2O_3(c)$
$$\Delta G = -252.9 \text{ kcal}$$

Yet aluminum and chromium are almost corrosion-resistant. Explain.

23 Given the ΔH and ΔS values at 25 °C for the reaction

$$Ca(OH)_2(c) \rightleftharpoons Ca(OH)_2(aq)$$
$$\Delta H = -4.00 \text{ kcal}, \quad \Delta S = -37.7 \text{ cal/deg}$$

calculate ΔG. Is the preference for the solution or the precipitation of calcium hydroxide?

24 Equilibrium constant (a) Calculate $E°_{cell}$, n, and K for each reaction as written:

(i) $Cd(c) + Ni^{2+}(aq) \longrightarrow Cd^{2+}(aq) + Ni(c)$
$$Cd, Cd^{2+}, E° = -0.403 \text{ volt}$$
$$Ni, Ni^{2+}, E° = -0.25 \text{ volt}$$

(ii) $Ag(c) + V^{3+}(aq) \longrightarrow Ag^+(aq) + V^{2+}(aq)$
$$Ag, Ag^{2+}, E° = 0.7994 \text{ volt}$$
$$Pt, V^{3+}, V^{2+}, E° = -0.2555 \text{ volt}$$

(b) Calculate K_w for the reaction $H_2O \longrightarrow H^+ + OH^-$, for which $E°_{cell} = -0.828$ volt and $n = 1$.

25 The zinc/silver oxide cell is used in hearing aids and electric watches:

$$Zn \longrightarrow Zn^{2+} + 2e^- \quad E° = -0.763 \text{ volt}$$
$$Ag_2O + H_2O + 2e^- \longrightarrow 2Ag + 2OH^-$$
$$E° = +0.344 \text{ volt}$$

(a) What is oxidized and reduced? (b) Find $E°_{cell}$ and ΔG in joules.

26 The electrolysis of an aqueous KBr solution is similar to that described for NaCl (page 472). Write the oxidation and reduction electrode reactions and the overall reaction.

27 Faraday's law (a) Calculate the number of grams of copper deposited when a 15.0 ampere current is passed through a solution of Cu^{2+} for 2.50 hours. The electrode reaction is $Cu^{2+} + 2e^- \longrightarrow Cu$. (b) Calculate the number of coulombs required to deposit 160 g of Al when the electrode reaction is $Al^{3+} + 3e^- \longrightarrow Al$.

28 Calculate the mass of lead, Pb, converted to lead sulfate in a battery when it requires 2.25 minutes to start the car in the winter. The battery current is 120 amperes and the electrode reaction may be considered to be $Pb(c) \longrightarrow Pb^{2+}(aq) + 2e^-$.

29 Storage cell (a) Explain how the measurement of the density of the electrolyte in an automobile lead-acid battery indicates the extent to which it is charged. (b) The lead-acid cell is a faithful, but too heavy, servant for electrical storage systems. The following lightweight cell (about 3 volts) has been developed:

$$Li(c) | LiCl(sol) | graphite (inert) | Cl_2(g)$$

Write the most likely reactions occurring at the anode and at the cathode, and the cell reaction. What substance serves as the electrolyte?

30 (a) A recently developed storage cell for electric auto power uses a lithium anode plate, a copper(II) chloride cathode, and an organic electrolyte. (b) The development of a lithium-water cell has recently been announced. (c) A sodium/zirconium phospho-silicate solid electrolyte/sulfur battery is being tested for commercial practicability. For each cell, write the most likely reactions occurring at the anode and cathode. (d) What by-products are obtained from the cell in part (b)?

31 From the following diagram for the reaction $3Ca(c) + 2AlCl_3(aq) \longrightarrow 3CaCl_2(aq) + 2Al(c)$:

when mixed, heat evolved (constant T, P) is 135 kcal

galvanic cell, maximum electric work available is 165 kcal

(a) Find ΔH, ΔG, and $T\Delta S$. (b) Is heat evolved or absorbed during cell operation?

32 Corrosion (a) CO_2 is always present in natural waters. Explain its effect (increases, stops, or no effect) on rusting of iron. Use Le Chatelier's principle to explain the effect of increasing the oxygen pressure on the rusting of iron. (b) Is it advisable to connect two different metals—for example, copper and iron pipes—in home plumbing? (c) Recalling that $E°_{cell}$ values are used to calculate equilibrium constants, explain the following statement. "In corrosion, the anode with the more negative potential has a greater tendency to corrode, but it may not have a higher rate of corrosion."

33 History James Maxwell (1873), in explaining Faraday's studies of electrolysis, assumed that "molecules of the ions within the electrolyte are actually charged with definite quantities of electricity," and suggested that "we call the constant value for the molecular charge, one molecule of electricity." What do we call the "molecules of the ions" and the "one molecule of electricity" today?

34 Library Read one of the following:
(a) "Corrosion," Henry Leidheiser, *Chemical and Engineering News,* 5 April 1965, page 78.
(b) "Alessandro Volta," Giorgio de Santillana, *Scientific American,* January 1965, page 82.
(c) "Electric Enhancement of Bone Healing," Morris Shamos, Robert A. Rinaldi, and Abraham R. Liboff, *Science,* volume 175, 10 March 1972, page 1118.
(d) "The Electric Citicar," *Consumer Reports,* October 1976, page 572.
(e) "Equivalents—A Winner or A Dead Horse," Frank Brescia, *Journal of Chemical Education,* volume 53, June 1976, page 362.
(f) "Advanced Storage Batteries: Progress But Not Electrifying," *Science,* volume 192, 7 May 1976, page 541.

ADDITIONAL PROBLEMS

35 The following reactions generate electricity in a cell:
(a) $Fe(c) + HgCl_2(aq) \longrightarrow FeCl_2(aq) + Hg(l)$
(b) $Zn(c) + 2HBr(aq) \longrightarrow H_2(g) + ZnBr_2(aq)$
(c) $Cd(c) + SnCl_2(aq) \longrightarrow Sn(c) + CdCl_2(aq)$
Identify the electrode reactions, the anode, the cathode, the negative and positive electrodes, the direction of migration of anions and cations, and the direction of flow of electrons.

36 Write the cell reaction and calculate $E°_{cell}$ for the following cells. Assume that the electrode on the left side is the anode.
(a) $Fe \,|\, Fe^{2+}(aq) \| Br_2(l), \ Br^-(aq) \,|\, Pt$
(b) $Pb \,|\, Pb^{2+}(aq) \| Ag^+(aq) \,|\, Ag$
(c) $Pt \,|\, H_2(g), \ H^+(aq) \| Ag^+(aq) \,|\, Ag$

37 Write the cell reaction and calculate the EMF of the following cells. Assume that the electrode on the left side is the anode.
(a) $Zn \,|\, Zn^{2+}$ (0.0010 M)$\| Cu^{2+}$ (0.000010 M)$\,|\, Cu$
(b) $Cr \,|\, Cr^{3+}$ (0.010 M)$\| Cu^{2+}$ (0.0010 M)$\,|\, Cu$
(c) $Ag \,|\, Ag^+$ (0.00010 M)$\| Cu^{2+}$ (0.00010 M)$\,|\, Cu$

38 (a) For the electrolysis of aqueous potassium bromide, use Table 15.1, page 466, to calculate $E°_{cell}$ for two possible reactions and determine which reaction is favored:

$$2KBr(aq) \rightleftharpoons 2K(c) \;|\; Br_2(l)$$

$$2KBr(aq) + 2H_2O \rightleftharpoons 2K^+(aq) + 2OH^-(aq) + H_2(g) + Br_2(l)$$

(b) Answer the same question for the electrolysis of $CuCl_2(aq)$, for which the two possible reactions are

$$CuCl_2(aq) \rightleftharpoons Cu(c) + Cl_2(g)$$

$$CuCl_2(aq) + 2H_2O \rightleftharpoons Cu^{2+}(aq) + 2OH^-(aq) + H_2(g) + Cl_2(g)$$

39 (a) Coating iron with a metal with a more negative standard electrode potential protects it from corrosion. Explain. (b) *Ignoring practical difficulties,* would you protect (plate) iron with (i) chromium, (ii) lithium, or (iii) silver? (c) Covering iron with a plastic film protects it from corrosion. Explain.

40 Cells also produce a voltage when two identical electrodes are placed in solutions of different concentrations. Find the voltage of a cell consisting of one zinc electrode in a 1.00 M $ZnSO_4$ solution and a second zinc electrode in a 0.000100 M solution of the same electrolyte:

$$Zn \,|\, Zn^{2+} \ (1.00 \times 10^{-4} \ M) \| Zn^{2+} \ (1.00 \ M) \,|\, Zn$$
oxidation   *reduction*

Hint: $E°_{cell} = 0$; show that the overall reaction is

$$Zn^{2+} \ (1.00 \ M) \longrightarrow Zn^{2+} \ (1.00 \times 10^{-4} \ M).$$ Such cells are known as "concentration cells."

41 Does the equation $\Delta G = \Delta H - T\Delta S$ contradict the statement that a decrease in enthalpy and an increase in entropy favor a reaction as written?

42 What is the change in the oxidation number of iron in the corrosion reaction, $4Fe(c) + 3O_2(aq) + 2x\,H_2O \longrightarrow 2Fe_2O_3(H_2O)_x(c)$? Find the number of grams of iron so corroded during the generation of 1 mole of electrons.

43 Use Table 15.1, page 466, to show that for the cell reaction $\frac{1}{2} O_2(g) + H_2(g) \longrightarrow H_2O(l)$ the standard EMF is $E°_{cell} = +1.229$ volt.

44 What is the advantage, if any, of inert electrodes that very rapidly oxidize oxygen to water in a fuel cell?

45 Like enthalpy changes (page 288), Gibbs energy changes, ΔG, can be obtained by addition of chemical equations and their accompanying Gibbs energy changes. It is highly desirable to decrease NO emission in automobile engine exhaust. Would you recommend a research project hoping to eliminate NO by reducing it to N_2 by the following reactions?

$$CH_4(g) + NO(g) \longrightarrow CH_3OH(g) + N(g)$$
$$\Delta G = +61.60 \text{ kcal}$$

$$NO(g) + N(g) \longrightarrow N_2(g) + O(g)$$
$$\Delta G = -74.18 \text{ kcal}$$

Justify your answer.

46 In principle, a cell may be set up based on the overall reaction of glucose with oxygen and ADP:

$$C_6H_{12}O_6(aq) + x \text{ ADP} + x \text{ phosphate} + 6O_2(aq) \longrightarrow 6CO_2(aq) + x \text{ ATP} + 6H_2O$$

The energy available from this exothermic reaction is stored in ATP (page 293). (a) Find the oxidation number of C in glucose and in carbon dioxide. (b) What is oxidized and what is reduced? (c) How many electrons are transferred per glucose molecule? (d) The rules and regulations of ordinary electrochemical cells apply to biochemical electric currents produced over extremely short distances (a few angstroms). An individual consumes 1.0 mole of glucose as shown above over a period of 24 hours. If the electrons were passed through a wire, find the number of amperes that would be produced.

47 A watt-hour is a measure of electric power, one watt delivered in one hour. Show that 1 watt-hour = 3600 joules.

48 The reaction x Li(c) + TiS$_2$(c) (titanium disulfide) $\longrightarrow$ Li$_x$TiS$_2$(c) (lithium titanium disulfide) is the basis of a reversible, high-energy, lightweight, inexpensive cell, EMF = 2.5 volt. Assume $x = 2$. Find the oxidation number of Li and Ti in the reactants and in the product. What is the anode, and what is the cathode?

49 Like the enthalpy change of a reaction (page 288), the Gibbs energy change of a reaction may also be calculated by subtracting the sum of Gibbs energies of formation (App. VI) for each reactant from the sum of the Gibbs energies of formation for each product:

$$\Delta G_{reaction} = \Delta G_{f\,products} - \Delta G_{f\,reactants}$$

All living organisms that breathe use the oxidation of glucose (sugar) as a main source of energy:

$$C_6H_{12}O_6(aq) + 6O_2(g) \longrightarrow 6CO_2(g) + 6H_2O(l)$$

Calculate ΔG for the reaction from the given Gibbs energies of formation: C$_6$H$_{12}$O$_6$(aq) = −219.22 kcal; O$_2$(g) = 0; CO$_2$(g) = −94.254 kcal; H$_2$O(l) = −56.687 kcal. Is the reaction favored as written?

50 Cytochrome, a complex molecule represented as CyFe^{2+}, reacts with the oxygen we breathe to supply energy required to synthesize ATP (page 293). From the given electrode potential data (pH = 7.00, 25 °C)

$$\tfrac{1}{2}\,O_2 + 2H^+ + 2e^- \rightleftharpoons H_2O \qquad E = +0.82 \text{ volt}$$
$$CyFe^{3+} + e^- \rightleftharpoons CyFe^{2+} \qquad E = +0.22 \text{ volt}$$

determine (a) what is oxidized and reduced, and (b) which molecule is the oxidizing agent. (c) Write the equation for the cell reaction and find E_{cell} and ΔG in kcal for the reaction as written. (d) How many moles of ATP are synthesized from ADP per mole of O$_2$? One mole of ATP requires 9.0 kcal.

51 Gasoline has an energy output of 3.22×10^4 kcal/gal. A car travels 200 miles averaging 18.0 miles/gal. The engine efficiency is 30 %. (a) Calculate the energy in kcal that moved the car (the remainder is lost as heat). (b) The engine is replaced by a battery of fuel cells based on the reaction, H$_2$(g) + $\tfrac{1}{2}$ O$_2$(g) $\rightleftharpoons$ H$_2$O(l), E_{cell} = 1.50 volt. (i) Calculate the maximum electrical work available in kcal per mole H$_2$. (ii) Assuming 90.0 % efficiency, find the number of moles, grams, and pounds of H$_2$ required to move over the same distance. (c) Compare the H$_2$ weight with that of the gasoline consumed; density of gasoline is 0.15 lb/gal. (d) If lead storage cells producing the same voltage as the fuel cells (Pb $\longrightarrow$ Pb^{2+} + 2e^-, E_{cell} = 1.50 volt) are substituted for the fuel cells, calculate the weight of lead in pounds that would be consumed, assuming 90.0 % efficiency. (e) Arrange these fuels on the basis of *weight efficiency*, placing the least efficient fuel first.

52 In one cell, zinc reacts (Zn $\longrightarrow$ Zn^{2+} + 2e^-) at the rate of 0.500 mole/hour, while in a second cell of the same composition, the surface area is increased so that zinc reacts at the rate of 5.00 mole/hour. (a) If the voltage in the first cell is 1.01 volt, what is the voltage in the second cell? (b) Find the amperage in each cell.

ANSWERS

1

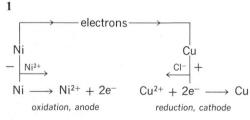

2 (a) 2Br$^-$ + Cl$_2$ $\longrightarrow$ 2Cl$^-$ + Br$_2$
　　0.278 volt
　(b) Mg + Zn^{2+} $\longrightarrow$ Mg^{2+} + Zn
　　1.61 volt

3 (a) 4.23 volt; (b) 1.27 volt;
　(c) 0.126 volt
4 2.50 volt
5 (a) 5.4×10^3 C
　(b) 3.4×10^{22} electrons
　(c) 5.6×10^{-2} faraday
6 6.10 g Zn
7 4.41×10^4 C
8 1×10^{82}
9 4.83×10^5 volt C, 4.83×10^5 J,
　1.16×10^5 cal
10 (a) zero, equilibrium; (b)(d) negative E,

right to left; (c) positive E, left to right

11 (a) -2 to 0, sugar is oxidized, NAD^+ is reduced and is oxidizing agent; (b)(i) 1.14 volt, -2.20×10^5 J, -5.26×10^1 kcal; (ii) $-\Delta G$ and $+E_{cell}$, goes from left to right; (iii) $5.8 \approx 6$ molecules

12 (a) $\Delta H = -77$ kcal, $\Delta G = -35$ kcal, $T\Delta S = -42$ kcal; (b) evolved

13 31 kcal; no

16 (i) (a)(b) $Zn \longrightarrow Zn^{2+} + 2e^-$ (oxidation), anode; $Hg^{2+} + 2e^- \longrightarrow Hg$ (reduction), cathode; (c) 1.55 volt; (ii) (a)(b) $H_2 \longrightarrow 2H^+ + 2e^-$ (oxidation), anode; $I_2 + 2e^- \longrightarrow 2I^-$ (reduction), cathode; (c) 0.535 volt

17 (a)(i) 0.587 volt, (ii) -0.021 volt, (iii) -0.61 volt, (iv) -1.5622 volt; (b)(i) forward, (ii)(iii)(iv) reverse; (c) $2H_2O_2 \longrightarrow 2H_2O + O_2$, anode

18 (a) 0.277 volt; (b) 0.58 volt; (c) 0.43 volt

19 (a) fluorine, strongest oxidizing agent; (b) iodine, strongest reducing agent

20 (a) 0.46 volt (forward); (b) -2.00 volt (reverse); (c) $+0.32$ volt (forward); (d) 0.71 volt (forward); (e) 2.45 volt (forward); (f) -3.67 volt (reverse)

21 (i)(a) 0.17 volt, (b) -3.3×10^4 volt C; (ii)(a) 0.016 volt, (b) -3.1×10^3 volt C

23 7.23 kcal, precipitation

24 (a)(i) 0.15 volt, 2, 1×10^5, (ii) -1.0549 volt, 1, 1.5×10^{-18}; (b) 1×10^{-14}

25 (a) Zn oxidized, Ag_2O reduced; (b) 1.11 volt, -2.14×10^5 J

27 (a) 44.4 g Cu; (b) 1.72×10^6 C

28 17.4 g Pb

29 (b) $Li \longrightarrow Li^+ + e^-$, oxidation, anode; $Cl_2 + 2e^- \longrightarrow 2Cl^-$, reduction, cathode; $2Li + Cl_2 \longrightarrow 2LiCl$, cell reaction; $LiCl(sol)$, electrolyte

30 (a) anode, oxidation, $Li \longrightarrow Li^+ + e^-$; cathode, reduction, $Cu^{2+} + 2e^- \longrightarrow Cu$; (b) anode, oxidation, $Li \longrightarrow Li^+ + e^-$; cathode, reduction, $2H_2O + 2e^- \longrightarrow H_2 + 2OH^-$; (c) anode, oxidation, $Na \longrightarrow Na^+ + e^-$; cathode, reduction, $S + 2e^- \longrightarrow S^{2-}$; (d) H_2, LiOH

31 $\Delta H = -135$ kcal; $\Delta G = -165$ kcal; $T\Delta S = +30$ kcal; absorbed

33 anions and cations, electrons

35 (a)

electrons

$(-)$ anode   cathode $(+)$

$Fe \longrightarrow Fe^{2+} + 2e^-$ (cations) $Hg^{2+} + 2e^- \longrightarrow Hg$ (anions)

(b)

electrons

$(-)$ anode   cathode $(+)$

$Zn \longrightarrow Zn^{2+} + e^-$ (cations) $2H^+ + 2e^- \longrightarrow H_2$ (anions)

(c)

electrons

$(-)$ anode   cathode $(+)$

$Cd \longrightarrow Cd^{2+} + 2e^-$ (cations) $Sn^{2+} + 2e^- \longrightarrow Sn$ (anions)

36 (a) $Fe + Br_2 \longrightarrow Fe^{2+} + 2Br^-$, 1.52 volt; (b) $Pb + 2Ag^+ \longrightarrow Pb^{2+} + 2Ag$, 0.925 volt; (c) $H_2 + 2Ag^+ \longrightarrow 2H^+ + 2Ag$, 0.7994 volt

37 (a) $Zn + Cu^{2+} \longrightarrow Zn^{2+} + Cu$, 1.04 volt; (b) $2Cr + 3Cu^{2+} \longrightarrow 2Cr^{3+} + 3Cu$, 1.03 volt; (c) $2Ag + Cu^{2+} \longrightarrow 2Ag^+ + Cu$, -0.34 volt

38 (a) $2KBr + 2H_2O$ favored; (b) $CuCl_2 \longrightarrow Cu + Cl_2$ favored

39 (b) Li or Cr

40 0.118 volt

41 no

42 $Fe^0 \longrightarrow Fe^{3+}$, 18.6 g

43 1.229 volt

45 yes, reduction to N_2 goes as written

46 (a) $C_6H_{12}O_6 = 0$, $CO_2 = +4$; (b) $C_6H_{12}O_6$ oxidized, O_2 reduced; (c) 24; (d) 27 amp

48 $Li = 0$, $Ti = +4$ goes to $Li = +1$, $Ti = +2$; Li anode, TiS_2 cathode

49 -686.43 kcal, yes

50 (a) $CyFe^{2+}$ oxidized; O_2 reduced; (b) O_2; (c) $2CyFe^{2+} + \frac{1}{2}O_2 + 2H^+ \longrightarrow H_2O + 2CyFe^{3+}$, 0.60 volt, -28 kcal; (d) $6.2 \approx 6$ moles

51 (a) 1.07×10^5 kcal; (b)(i) -69.3 kcal/mole; (ii) 1.72×10^3 moles, 3.44×10^3 g, 7.58 lb H_2; (c) 68.3 lb gasoline; (d) 784 lb lead; (e) lead, gasoline, H_2

52 (a) 1.01 volt; (b) 26.8 amp, 268 amp

ampere (A) The SI unit of electric current; it is the passage of one coulomb (C) in one second, $A = C/s$.

anion A negative ion, it always moves toward the anode.

anode Always the electrode at which oxidation occurs.

battery Consists of cells connected together. See **galvanic cell.**

cation A positive ion; it always moves toward the cathode.

cathode Always the electrode at which reduction occurs.

corrosion The destruction of a metal to an unwanted product by chemical reaction with the environment.

coulomb (C) Measures the electric charge, the quantity of electricity. It is related to the electric current measured in amperes and to the time the current is allowed to flow: $C = A \times s$

dry cell A galvanic cell having a moist electrolyte paste. The cell is sealed to prevent evaporation of water. Water must be present in the paste to allow movement of ions. See **galvanic cell.**

E_{cell} The potential difference between two electrodes in a galvanic cell. $E_{cell} = E_{reduction} - E_{oxidation}$

$E_{oxidation}$ The potential of the anode, the electrode where oxidation occurs.

$E_{reduction}$ The potential of the cathode, the electrode where reduction occurs.

electrical work The product of the quantity of electricity and the voltage; electrical work in joules (J) =

coulomb (C) $\times$ volts (V) = n moles of electrons $\times$

$96,500 \dfrac{C}{\text{mole of electrons}} \times E_{cell}$

electrochemistry The study of the relations between chemical changes and electricity.

electrode As used in this chapter, that part of a cell (galvanic or electrolysis) in which the oxidation or the reduction half-reaction occurs. A Cu bar suspended in a solution of Cu^{2+}, and $Cl_2(g)$ passed over a Pt bar suspended in a solution of Cl^-, are typical examples.

electrolysis The passage of an electric current through a solution or a molten salt to carry out a chemical reaction.

EMF of a cell Same as E_{cell}. See E_{cell}.

faraday A unit of electric charge (quantity of electricity), equal to one mole of electrons or approximately 96,500 coulombs.

Faraday's law The mass of a substance produced or consumed at an electrode is proportional to the quantity of charge (electricity) passed through a cell.

fuel cell A cell which converts oxygen and an oxidizable gas directly to energy (without burning the gas as in a furnace).

ΔG The maximum electrical work available from a cell. $\Delta G = 0$ shows that the chemical reaction is at equilibrium; the reaction goes as written when ΔG has a negative value. See **maximum electrical work.**

galvanic cell A cell, an arrangement which when properly set up generates electricity from a chemical reaction.

galvanized iron A zinc coating on iron used to prevent corrosion of the iron.

Gibbs energy change (ΔG) $\Delta G = \Delta H - T \Delta S$. See ΔG and ΔS.

joule The product of volts $\times$ coulombs. See **electrical work.**

lead-acid storage cell A galvanic cell having a spongy lead anode and a lead dioxide cathode. See **storage cell.**

maximum electrical work The electrical work at no current flow. See **electrical work.**

potential difference A potential difference exists between two electrodes whenever an electric current is produced by a cell. The potential difference of a cell is measured with a voltmeter. The measured voltage is the voltage of the cell, E_{cell}. See E_{cell}.

rusting The corrosion of iron. See **corrosion.**

ΔS The change in entropy, a measure of the change in the disorder in going from reactants to products. A positive value for ΔS, corresponding to an increase in disorder, tends to favor a reaction as written. It also measures the quantity of heat evolved or absorbed during the operation of a galvanic cell.

standard electrode potential, $E°$ The potential of an electrode when the concentration of each solute is 1 mole per liter and each gas pressure is 1 atm at 25 °C. Standard electrode potentials are measured by combining the electrode with the standard electrode, $2H^+(aq)(1\ M) + 2e^- \rightleftharpoons H_2(1\ atm)$, to which a standard potential of zero is arbitrarily assigned.

standard EMF, $E°_{cell}$ The potential difference of a cell calculated from standard electrode potentials, $E°_{cell} = E°_{reduction} - E°_{oxidation}$

storage cell A galvanic cell that operates reversibly; after serving as a source of electricity it can be charged, restoring the cell to its original condition. See **lead-acid storage cell.**

tin plate The tin coating on iron used to protect iron from corrosion. See **corrosion.**

Courtesy of Sam Andre

CHEMICAL KINETICS 16

INTRODUCTION _____ 16.1

Graphite, compared to diamond, is thermodynamically the more stable (page 379) form of carbon at room conditions. This means that diamond is unstable and should change to the cheaper graphite. However, we know that diamonds are very durable and possess great value. How can this be?

In the presence of an electrical spark, hydrogen and oxygen gases react to form water, $K = 4.30 \times 10^{43}$ (25 °C). However, in the absence of a spark these gases do not react. Why is another agent necessary for the reaction to occur?

In both cases, we know in which direction the reaction should go. At room conditions, graphite will not change into diamond nor will water, of its own accord without outside help, decompose into hydrogen and oxygen gas. We know that water forms from hydrogen and oxygen gases and that diamond may be changed into graphite. However, thermodynamic instability tells us nothing about how long it takes for these reactions to occur. The speed with which these reactions occur is known as the **rate of reaction.** The rate of reaction is the change in concentration or amount of a given substance over a given period of time. Graphite should burn very rapidly to carbon dioxide

$$C(graphite) + O_2(g) \longrightarrow CO_2(g) \qquad \Delta H = -94.1 \text{ kcal}$$
$$K = 1.2 \times 10^{69} \text{ (25 °C)}$$

−94.1 kcal = −394 kJ

The number of moles of graphite should decrease while the number of moles of CO_2 should increase. But, under ordinary conditions graphite does not burn and hence serves a very useful purpose in our pencils. The ability to slow down or speed up chemical reactions is, therefore, a powerful tool.

The study of the rate of chemical reactions is called **chemical kinetics.** Kinetic studies tell us that although diamond is unstable, the rate of conversion into graphite is so extremely slow that it has no practical effect on the life of the gem. Likewise, the rate of the reaction of hydrogen and oxygen, in the absence of an electric spark, is so slow that no measurable formation of water occurs. On the other hand, many reactions, explosions for example, appear to be immeasurably fast; see Color Plate X.

From the Greek word kinetik, meaning moving.

The rate at which molecules are changed in chemical reactions is of major practical and theoretical importance. Chemical kinetics gives us information about the way molecules change and about the role played by the solvent and other conditions in these changes. We also learn about energy requirements and how to change these requirements to obtain faster reactions. And what we learn from experiments, theory tries to explain. In turn, theory suggests kinds of experimentation so that in the hands of a specialist, chemical kinetics becomes a blend of experiment and theory.

CONDITIONS AFFECTING REACTION RATES

Experimentally, we find that the rate of a chemical reaction depends upon a number of factors. These are (1) the nature of the reactants, (2) the concentration of the reactants, (3) the particle size of a solid or liquid reacting with gases, (4) the temperature of the reaction mixture, and (5) the presence or absence of a catalyst.

Chemical Composition of the Reactants   The reaction of magnesium with oxygen in the presence of a flame proceeds very rapidly to form magnesium oxide. However, under identical conditions, copper reacts extremely slowly to form copper oxide. The oxidation of aqueous hydrogen iodide requires several hours under ordinary conditions. The rate of oxidation depends, then, on the nature of the reactant.

Other reactions also show this characteristic. When a silver nitrate solution is added to a sodium chloride solution, insoluble silver chloride precipitates immediately:

$$Ag^+(aq) + Cl^-(aq) \xrightarrow{\text{fast}} AgCl(c)$$

On the other hand, mixing a solution of magnesium nitrate with a solution of sodium oxalate produces insoluble magnesium oxalate very slowly:

$$Mg^{2+}(aq) + C_2O_4{}^{2-}(aq) \xrightarrow{\text{slow}} MgC_2O_4(c)$$

Concentration of the Reactants   The effect of the concentration of the reactants, at constant temperature, upon the reaction rate is given by the **law of mass action** generally expressed as a so-called **rate equation.** This generalization, announced (1864) by Cato Guldberg and Peter Waage, states that *the rate of a chemical reaction is proportional to the product of the molar concentrations of the reaction substances raised to appropriate powers.*

For the general hypothetical reaction

$$aA + bB \longrightarrow cC + dD$$

the rate at which A and B react to form C and D is proportional to the concentration of A multiplied by the concentration of B, each raised to a particular power. The rate equation is then written as

Recall that [ ] indicates concentration in mole/liter.

$$rate = k[A]^x[B]^y$$

The k in the rate equation, a proportionality constant characteristic of a particular reaction at a specific temperature, is known as the **rate constant.**

The numerical value of the exponents x and y must be *determined experimentally. They cannot be deduced* from the balanced equation and *they need not necessarily be the same as a and b.* For many reactions, the exponents in the rate equation, x and y, do *not* equal the coefficients a and b in the balanced equation.

If experimentally the rate is given by

$$rate = k[A]^x[B]^y$$

then *the sum of the powers of the concentration terms appearing in such rate equations is known as the order of the reaction.* For example, the overall reaction for the decomposition of *laughing gas,* dinitrogen oxide, a colorless gas used as an anesthesia in dentistry, is

$$2N_2O(g) \longrightarrow 2N_2(g) + O_2(g)$$

An overall reaction is a chemical reaction in which the initial reactants and the final products are experimentally determined and summarized in a balanced equation (page 153). But it does not tell us how the reactants changed to products. The reaction follows the rate equation

$$rate = k[N_2O]$$

This reaction is said to be a first order reaction since the concentration of the only reactant, N_2O, is raised to the first power. This means that the rate of decomposition of N_2O is directly proportional to the concentration of N_2O. If the concentration of N_2O is doubled, the rate of decomposition will double; tripling the concentration triples the rate. Notice that even though the coefficient in the balanced equation is 2 for N_2O, this reaction is first order. The exponent of the molar concentration of N_2O has been found by experiment to be 1, not 2.

The reaction of carbon monoxide gas with chlorine gas to form phosgene

$$CO(g) + Cl_2(g) \longrightarrow COCl_2(g)$$

follows the rate equation

$$rate = k[CO][Cl_2]$$

This reaction is a second order reaction; the sum of the exponents for the concentration terms is two. The reaction is also said to be first order with respect to CO and first order with respect to Cl_2. Doubling the concentration of CO while keeping the concentration of Cl_2 constant doubles the rate. Doubling the concentrations of CO and Cl_2 quadruples the rate.

For the reaction

$$2NO(g) + O_2(g) \longrightarrow 2NO_2(g)$$

the rate equation is given by

$$rate = k[NO]^2[O_2]$$

This reaction is second order with respect to NO and first order with respect to O_2. Thus, it is a third order reaction. Doubling the concentration of NO while keeping the concentration of O_2 constant quadruples the rate, but doubling the concentration of O_2 while keeping the concentration of NO constant doubles the rate.

Experimental data consist of reaction concentrations as a function of time, illustrated in Fig. 16.1 for the decomposition of dinitrogen pentoxide to nitrogen

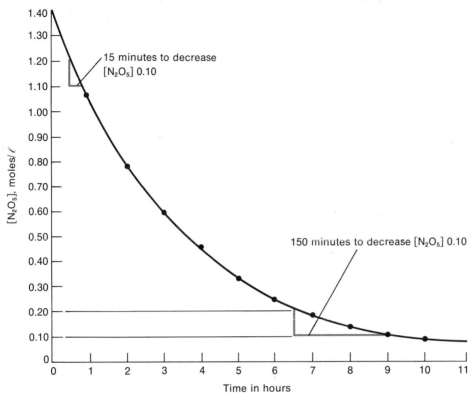

FIGURE 16.1 Plot of concentration against time showing that the rate of reaction decreases as the concentration decreases. It takes 15 minutes to decrease the concentration from 1.2 to 1.1 mole/ℓ, while it takes 150 minutes to decrease the concentration by the same amount from 0.2 to 0.1 mole/ℓ.

dioxide and oxygen, $2N_2O_5(g) \longrightarrow 4NO_2(g) + O_2(g)$, at 30 °C. We see that the concentration of N_2O_5 decreases as time increases. Notice also that as the concentration decreases, it takes longer to change the concentration by the same amount. This is another way of saying that the rate of the reaction decreases as the concentration decreases.

Example 1

For the decomposition of dinitrogen pentoxide, N_2O_5, dissolved in carbon tetrachloride

$$2N_2O_5 \longrightarrow 4NO_2(g) + O_2(g)$$

the following data were obtained at 30 °C. The rate given in column 2 is the rate measured at the instant of time when the concentration is that given in column 1:

Concentration of N_2O_5, mole/liter	Rate of decomposition of N_2O_5, mole/(liter hour), at the given concentrations
0.170	0.050
0.340	0.10
0.680	0.20

(a) Write the rate equation for the reaction. What is the order of the reaction? (b) Calculate the rate constant for the reaction at 30 °C. (c) Calculate the decomposition rate at 30 °C at the instant when $[N_2O_5] = 0.600$.

Answer

(a) The data show that doubling the concentration of N_2O_5 from 0.170 to 0.340 mole/ℓ, or from 0.340 to 0.680 mole/ℓ, doubles the rate from 0.05 to 0.10 mole/ℓ per hour, or from 0.10 to 0.20 mole/ℓ per hour. Therefore, the rate of this reaction is directly proportional to the N_2O_5 concentration, or

$$rate = k[N_2O_5]$$

Since the rate is proportional to the first power of one reactant, the reaction is first order. (b) To calculate the rate constant, we first solve the rate equation for k:

$$k = \frac{rate}{[N_2O_5]}$$

Then substitute any of the three sets of data

$$k = \frac{0.050 \; \frac{mole}{liter \; hour}}{0.170 \; \frac{mole}{liter}} = \frac{0.29}{hour}$$

or

$$k = \frac{0.10 \; \frac{mole}{liter \; hour}}{0.340 \; \frac{mole}{liter}} = \frac{0.29}{hour}$$

or

$$k = \frac{0.20 \; \frac{mole}{liter \; hour}}{0.680 \; \frac{mole}{liter}} = \frac{0.29}{hour}$$

Notice that in a first order reaction the rate constant has only the unit of time. (c) From the previous calculation, we can now write

$$rate = \frac{0.29}{hour}[N_2O_5]$$

so that when $[N_2O_5] = 0.600$

$$rate = \frac{0.29}{hour} \times 0.600 \; \frac{mole}{liter}$$

$$rate = 0.17 \frac{mole}{liter\ hour}$$

This means that when the concentration of N_2O_5 is 0.600 mole/ℓ, it reacts at the rate of 0.17 mole/ℓ per hour.

Example 2

The data in the following table were obtained at 25 °C for the oxidation of iodide ion by peroxydisulfate ion to iodine:

$$S_2O_8{}^{2-}(aq) + 2I^-(aq) \longrightarrow 2SO_4{}^{2-}(aq) + I_2(aq)$$

Reactant concentrations, mole/liter		Rate of formation of I_2, mole/(liter minute), at the given concentrations
$[S_2O_8{}^{2-}]$	$[I^-]$	
1.0×10^{-4}	1.0×10^{-2}	0.65×10^{-6}
2.0×10^{-4}	1.0×10^{-2}	1.30×10^{-6}
2.0×10^{-4}	2.0×10^{-2}	2.60×10^{-6}

(a) What is the rate equation for the reaction? What is the order of the reaction? (b) Calculate the rate constant for the reaction at 25 °C. (c) Calculate the rate of formation of I_2 at 25 °C at the instant when $[S_2O_8{}^{2-}] = 1.0 \times 10^{-4}$ and $[I^-] = 2.0 \times 10^{-2}$.

Answer

(a) It can be seen that the rate is doubled from 0.65×10^{-6} to 1.30×10^{-6} when the concentration of $S_2O_8{}^{2-}$ is doubled from 1.0×10^{-4} to 2.0×10^{-4} while the concentration of I^- remains constant. We see that doubling the concentration of I^- from 1.0×10^{-2} to 2.0×10^{-2} also doubles the reaction rate from 1.30×10^{-6} to 2.60×10^{-6}. Therefore, the reaction is first order with respect to $S_2O_8{}^{2-}$ and first order with respect to I^- and, hence, a second order reaction:

$$rate = k[S_2O_8{}^{2-}][I^-]$$

Note that the chemical equation for the reaction might incorrectly lead one to expect a third order rate. (b) Solving for k, as in Example 1,

$$k = \frac{rate}{[S_2O_8{}^{2-}][I^-]}$$

$$k = \frac{0.65 \times 10^{-6} \frac{mole}{liter\ minute}}{\left(1.0 \times 10^{-4} \frac{mole}{liter}\right) \times \left(1.0 \times 10^{-2} \frac{mole}{liter}\right)}$$

$$k = 0.65 \frac{liter}{mole\ minute}$$

or

$$k = \frac{1.30 \times 10^{-6} \frac{mole}{liter\ minute}}{\left(2.0 \times 10^{-4} \frac{mole}{liter}\right) \times \left(1.0 \times 10^{-2} \frac{mole}{liter}\right)}$$

$$k = 0.65 \frac{liter}{mole\ minute}$$

or

$$k = \frac{2.60 \times 10^{-6} \frac{mole}{liter\ minute}}{\left(2.0 \times 10^{-4} \frac{mole}{liter}\right) \times \left(2.0 \times 10^{-2} \frac{mole}{liter}\right)}$$

$$k = 0.65 \frac{liter}{mole\ minute}$$

(c) Since the rate constant equals 0.65 liter/(mole minute), the rate of formation of I_2 is given by

$$rate = k[S_2O_8{}^{2-}][I^-] = 0.65 \frac{liter}{mole\ min} [S_2O_8{}^{2-}][I^-]$$

so that when $[S_2O_8{}^{2-}] = 1.0 \times 10^{-4}$ and $[I^-] = 2.0 \times 10^{-2}$, the rate of formation of I_2 is

$$rate = 0.65 \frac{liter}{mole\ min} \times 1.0 \times 10^{-4} \frac{mole}{liter} \times 2.0 \times 10^{-2} \frac{mole}{liter}$$

$$rate = 1.3 \times 10^{-6} \frac{mole}{liter\ min}$$

This means that when the concentration of $S_2O_8{}^{2-}$ is 1.0×10^{-4} mole/ℓ and the I^- concentration is 2.0×10^{-2} mole/ℓ, the rate of formation of iodine is 1.3×10^{-6} mole/ℓ per minute.

Example 3

For the decomposition of hydrogen iodide at 600 K

$$2HI(g) \longrightarrow H_2(g) + I_2(g)$$

the following data were obtained:

Reactant concentrations, mole/liter	Rate of decomposition of HI, mole/(liter second), at the given concentrations
[HI]	
0.10	2.75×10^{-8}
0.20	11.00×10^{-8}
0.30	24.75×10^{-8}

(a) Write the rate equation for the reaction. What is the order of the reaction? (b) Calculate the rate constant for the reaction at 600 K. (c) Calculate the decomposition rate at 600 K at the instant when [HI] = 0.25.

Answer

(a) The data show that multiplying the concentration of HI by 2, from 0.10 to 0.20 mole/ℓ, multiplies the rate by 4, from 2.75×10^{-8} to 11.00×10^{-8}. Multiplying the concentration of HI by 3, from 0.10 to 0.30 mole/ℓ, multiplies the rate by 9, from 2.75×10^{-8} to 24.75×10^{-8}. But 4 is the square of 2, 2^2, and 9 is the square of 3, 3^2. Therefore, the rate of this reaction is directly proportional to the HI concentration raised to the second power, or

$$rate = k[HI]^2$$

Since the rate is proportional to the second power of one reactant, the reaction is second order. (b) Solving for k as in the previous examples,

$$k = \frac{rate}{[HI]^2}$$

and substituting any one of the three sets of data

$$k = \frac{2.75 \times 10^{-8} \dfrac{\text{mole}}{\text{liter second}}}{\left(0.10 \dfrac{\text{mole}}{\text{liter}}\right)^2} = 2.8 \times 10^{-6} \dfrac{\text{liter}}{\text{mole second}}$$

or

$$k = \frac{11.00 \times 10^{-8} \dfrac{\text{mole}}{\text{liter second}}}{\left(0.20 \dfrac{\text{mole}}{\text{liter}}\right)^2} = 2.8 \times 10^{-6} \dfrac{\text{liter}}{\text{mole second}}$$

or

$$k = \frac{24.75 \times 10^{-8} \dfrac{\text{mole}}{\text{liter second}}}{\left(0.30 \dfrac{\text{mole}}{\text{liter}}\right)^2} = 2.8 \times 10^{-6} \dfrac{\text{liter}}{\text{mole second}}$$

(c) From the previous calculations, we can now write

$$rate = \frac{2.8 \times 10^{-6} \text{ liter}}{\text{mole second}} [HI]^2$$

and

$$rate = \frac{2.8 \times 10^{-6} \text{ liter}}{\text{mole second}} \times \left(0.25 \dfrac{\text{mole}}{\text{liter}}\right)^2$$

$$rate = 1.8 \times 10^{-7} \dfrac{\text{mole}}{\text{liter second}}$$

PROBLEM 1   The following data were obtained at 700 K for the formation of hydrogen iodide from hydrogen and iodine:

Reactant concentration, mole/liter		Rate of formation HI, mole/(liter second), at the given concentrations
[H_2]	[I_2]	
0.10	0.10	3.02×10^{-4}
0.10	0.20	6.04×10^{-4}
0.20	0.10	6.04×10^{-4}

(a) Write the rate equation for the reaction. What is the order of the reaction? (b) Calculate the rate constant for the reaction at 700 K. (c) Calculate the rate of formation of HI at the instant when [H_2] = 0.20 and [I_2] = 0.30.

Determination of Concentration Changes with Time   The concentration of a substance undergoing reaction can be determined by a variety of methods. The concentration of a given substance is related to such measurable quantities as pressure (for a gas), "color" (intensity of visible or invisible spectra), acidity, alkalinity, conductivity, and volume. Any change in concentration of a reactant leads to a corresponding change in one or more of these quantities. Thus, a rate equation can be derived from these changes.

An example is the reaction of potassium with liquid ammonia:

$$2K(NH_3) + 2NH_3 \longrightarrow 2K^+(NH_3) + 2NH_2^-(NH_3) + H_2(g)$$

Since very little potassium (about 1×10^{-3} mole/ℓ) is dissolved in the liquid ammonia, the ammonia concentration remains, for all purposes, constant and the rate of the reaction depends only on the potassium concentration. The solution at the beginning of the reaction has an intense blue color (page 607). This color slowly fades with time until, by the end of the reaction, the solution is practically colorless. The amount of unreacted potassium remaining in solution at any time is related to the intensity of the blue color of the solution. By a spectral method (Chap. 6), color intensity is measured in an instrument that is calibrated against solutions of known potassium concentration. Typical experimental data are given:

Instrument is a spectrophotometer (Chap. 24).

| Time | | Color | Concentration, |
hr	min	intensity	mole/liter
0	0	1.702	1.13×10^{-3}
1	0	1.588	1.05×10^{-3}
2	33	1.476	9.80×10^{-4}
4	34	1.322	8.77×10^{-4}
6	36	1.196	7.94×10^{-4}
9	38	0.996	6.62×10^{-4}
12	55	0.851	5.65×10^{-4}
21	26	0.506	3.36×10^{-4}

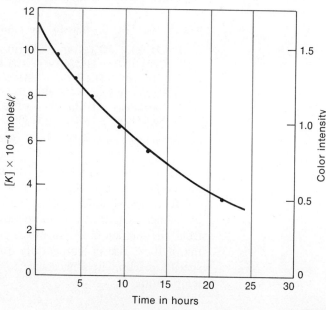

FIGURE 16.2 Plot of concentration and color intensity against time yields the same graph. Notice from the data that the change in concentration is proportional to the color intensity change. Thus, as shown, plotting color intensity or concentration against time yields the same graph.

Plotting the concentration of potassium against time, Fig. 16.2, yields the same kind of graph as in Fig. 16.1. The graph is typical for first order reactions.

Particle Size in Heterogeneous Reactions   Reactions are frequently classified as **homogeneous** or **heterogeneous.** A homogeneous reaction occurs in a single phase (page 28)—for example, in the gaseous state or in solution:

$$2NO(g) + O_2(g) \longrightarrow 2NO_2(g)$$
$$H^+(aq) + OH^-(aq) \longrightarrow H_2O$$

Heterogeneous reactions usually involving solids or liquids and gases, take place at a surface; for example

$$Zn(c) + 2H^+(aq) \longrightarrow Zn^{2+}(aq) + H_2(g)$$
$$2Mg(c) + O_2(g) \longrightarrow 2MgO(c)$$
$$C_{10}H_{24}(l) + 16O_2(g) \longrightarrow 10CO_2(g) + 12H_2O(g)$$
(petroleum oil)

Since heterogeneous reactions occur only at a surface, the rate of such reactions is proportional to the surface area. For this reason, the rate of many reactions is influenced by the shapes of containers, an important consideration in moving from laboratory to plant production. When a given mass is subdivided into smaller particles, the surface area is increased and, consequently, the rate of reaction increases. For example, a bar of steel heated to dull redness and then plunged into pure oxygen gas glows with a bright red color (900 °C). However, steel wool heated to dull redness and then plunged into pure oxygen gas burns with a bright white flame (1550 °C), showing a faster reaction rate. Thus, by increasing the surface area, the rate of reaction between iron and oxygen is increased. Lumps of soft coal, which do not burn readily in air, burn with explosive force when ground to powder. "Coal dust" suspended in air, rather than methane gas, is responsible for most disastrous coal mine explosions. Concrete grain elevators (wheat storage bins) have been ripped apart by explosions due to ignition of grain dust. *In general, combustible dusts suspended in air are explosive hazards.*

PROBLEM 2   **(a) Classify the following reactions as homogeneous or heterogeneous:**

(i) $CH_4(g) + 2O_2(g) \longrightarrow CO_2(g) + 2H_2O(g)$
(ii) $CH_3OH(l) + HCl(g) \longrightarrow CH_3Cl(l) + H_2O(l)$
(iii) $SOCl_2(g) + H_2O(l) \longrightarrow 2HCl(g) + SO_2(g)$
(iv) $P_4(c) + 6Cl_2(g) \longrightarrow 4PCl_3(l)$
(v) $NaOH(aq) + HCl(aq) \longrightarrow NaCl(aq) + H_2O$
(vi) $Na_2CO_3(c) + CO_2(g) + H_2O(l) \longrightarrow 2NaHCO_3(c)$

(b) Iron filings rust (oxidize) faster than an iron bar of equal weight. Explain.

Effect of Temperature   The rate of a chemical reaction usually increases when the temperature is raised. This effect is observed for endothermic as well as exothermic reactions. Similarly, a decrease in temperature decreases the rate. The magnitude of the increase in rate with temperature varies from one reaction to another and also from one temperature range to another. A very rough but useful approximation is that a 10 °C rise in temperature doubles or triples the reaction rate. But for each specific reaction it is necessary to determine experimentally the actual effect of temperature.

Catalysis   The production of goods valued at more than 100 billion dollars per year in the United States is dependent on the use of catalysts. A catalyst is a substance that increases the rate of a reaction and is recovered chemically unchanged at the end of the reaction. Although the catalyst is not used up, it is generally agreed that the catalyst enters into the reaction but is subsequently regenerated.

From the Greek word katalysis, meaning to loosen or set free, coined by J. Berzelius (1836).

Dinitrogen oxide, N_2O, is an unreactive gas at room temperature; at elevated temperatures, however, it slowly decomposes to nitrogen and oxygen:

$$2N_2O(g) \xrightarrow{\text{slow}} 2N_2(g) + O_2(g) \tag{1}$$

However, the rate of this reaction can be increased by trace (extremely small) amounts of chlorine gas. A possible explanation for this catalytic effect is the substitution of the following fast reactions for the direct, slow Reaction 1. First, rapid dissociation of Cl_2 occurs:

$$Cl_2(g) \xrightarrow{\text{fast}} 2Cl(g)$$

This is followed by a rapid reaction of N_2O with Cl atoms

$$2N_2O(g) + 2Cl(g) \xrightarrow{\text{fast}} 2N_2(g) + 2ClO(g)$$

and a rapid decomposition of ClO with the regeneration of Cl_2

$$2ClO(g) \xrightarrow{\text{fast}} Cl_2(g) + O_2(g)$$

Adding these three equations leads to the same observed overall reaction as for the uncatalyzed reaction:

$$2N_2O(g) \xrightarrow{\text{fast}} 2N_2(g) + O_2(g)$$

It is evident that we have merely substituted three fast reactions for a slow one to yield the same overall reaction. In a similar way the mass production of many new chemicals has been made possible. Another typical catalytic reaction is the action of NO in accelerating the conversion of ozone to oxygen (page 386).

Recall that a catalyst speeds up the forward and reverse reactions equally so that K is not changed (page 394).

Generalizing, a catalyst increases the rate by changing the "mechanism" or "the path" of the reaction. A **mechanism** is the series of individual steps by which a reaction proceeds in going from reactants to products. It is not common for reactants to change to products in one step as shown by a balanced equation. The balanced equation summarizes an experimental fact; it tells us what substances react to form the products. The mechanism is an attempt to explain how the reaction occurs step-by-step.

The study of the sequence of steps that leads to the observed overall reaction is of practical, as well as theoretical, interest. Interferon,* for example, can lead to successful treatment of various viral diseases and, perhaps, cancer only after the mechanism of its action is determined.

---

*Discovered in 1957, interferon is a natural antiviral protein that stops the growth of a number of viruses, including viral hepatitis and viral encephalitis. See "Interferon: Chemical Application of Molecular Biology," *Science,* volume 170, 4 December 1970, page 1068.

Example 4

The proposed mechanism for a gaseous reaction is given:

$$Step\ (1)\quad NO + O_2 \longrightarrow NO_3$$
$$Step\ (2)\quad NO_3 + NO \longrightarrow 2NO_2$$

What is the observed overall reaction being studied?

Answer

The observed overall reaction is the sum of the steps summarizing the mechanism for the reaction. Thus, adding steps 1 and 2 gives the observed overall reaction:

$$NO + O_2 \longrightarrow \cancel{NO_3}$$
$$\cancel{NO_3} + NO \longrightarrow 2NO_2$$
$$\overline{2NO + O_2 \longrightarrow 2NO_2}$$

PROBLEM 3   **The proposed mechanism for a gaseous reaction is given:**

$$Step\ (1)\quad ClNO_2 \longrightarrow Cl + NO_2$$
$$Step\ (2)\quad ClNO_2 + Cl \longrightarrow NO_2 + Cl_2$$

What is the observed overall reaction being studied?

Enzymes (Chap. 23) are complex substances which act as catalysts for biochemical reactions occuring in all living matter. For example, *ptyalin,* an enzyme found in saliva, accelerates the conversion of starch to sugar. Although starch will react with water to form sugar, several weeks are required for the conversion to occur in the absence of the enzyme. A trace of ptyalin suffices to make the reaction proceed in minutes at body temperature. Such a rate is necessary for proper biological functioning. Likewise, *zymase,* an enzyme of the yeast plant, speeds up the conversion of sugar to ethyl alcohol and carbon dioxide (page 697), a process called **fermentation.** Enzymes are used for tenderizing beefsteaks.

Substances that retard chemical reactions are known as **inhibitors** or **poisons.** Physiological poisons like mercury (Hg^{2+}) and snake venom react with enzymes in the body, rendering them useless for the catalysis of essential biochemical reactions. The Hg^{2+} ion combines with sulfur atoms in enzyme molecules, forming very stable bonds so that the body retains practically all ingested Hg^{2+}.

16.3 THEORIES OF REACTION RATES

Collision Theory   Many of the observed facts of chemical kinetics have been interpreted in terms of the so-called collision theory. This theory makes the basic assumption that, for a chemical reaction to occur, particles must collide. In the resulting collision, atoms are rearranged. Bonds are broken and formed, leading to the production of new substances.

Consider a general gas reaction between two diatomic molecules, A_2 and B_2, which proceeds as shown:

$$A_2(g) + B_2(g) \longrightarrow 2AB(g)$$

However, *not* every collision between molecules A_2 and B_2 results in a reaction. A collision may not be effective in producing a chemical change for two reasons. First, the molecules may be improperly aligned. Second, the impact of the collision may not produce sufficient energy to cause a reaction to occur.

In more familiar terms, the damage resulting from the collision of two cars depends on the strength of the car bodies, their speeds (energies), and their relative positions upon impact; see Figures 16.3 and 16.4. Experiments are performed in which individual molecules in definite orientations may be selected and studied. For example, in the gaseous reaction $Cl^- + CH_3I \longrightarrow CH_3Cl + I^-$, a Cl atom replaces

the I atom in the molecule CH_3I. The orientation $Cl^- + H\!-\!\underset{\overset{|}{H}}{\overset{\overset{H}{|}}{C}}\!-\!I$ leads to *reaction,* *Problem 25, page 522.*

while *no reaction* occurs when the orientation is $Cl^- + I\!-\!\underset{\overset{|}{H}}{\overset{\overset{H}{|}}{C}}\!-\!H$.

According to collision theory, the rate of a reaction is directly proportional to *the number of molecules that collide per second and the fraction of these collisions which are effective and lead to chemical change.* The first postulate tells us that if you increase the number of molecules present in a given volume, the number of collisions increases and, consequently, the rate of reaction increases. This explains the dependence of the rate of reaction on the concentration of reactants.

However, if no other factor influenced the rate of the reaction, all reactions would proceed at extremely fast rates. The number of molecules in one liter of any

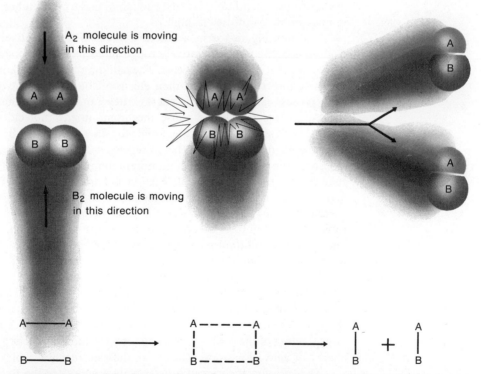

FIGURE 16.3 Collision between A_2 and B_2 molecules resulting in a reaction. Molecules possess sufficient energy and proper orientation.

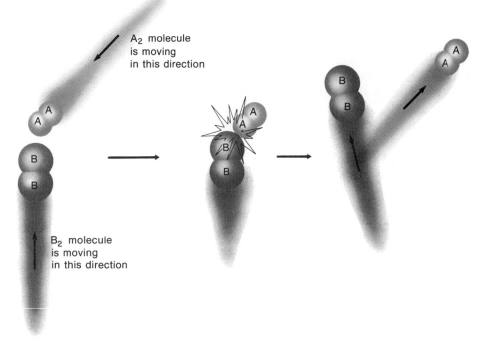

FIGURE 16.4 Collision between A_2 and B_2 molecules resulting in no reaction. Molecules possess sufficient energy but orientation is poor.

gas at ordinary conditions is large enough to make the number of molecules colliding in one second fantastically high.

The limiting factor in a reaction, then, is the effectiveness of the collisions. Collisions between comparatively tough molecules (high bond energies) may be so ineffective that no reaction occurs. The colliding particles are merely repelled by the repulsive forces generated by their electron clouds. If, however, the colliding molecules possess sufficient kinetic energy, they can easily use that energy to overcome these repulsive forces and cause the atoms in the molecules to vibrate violently (page 299). Thus, bonds holding atoms together are broken by this violent vibration, and new bonds are formed. Therefore, we assume that molecules react only if upon collision they possess a certain minimum amount of energy. This amount of energy required to produce chemical reaction is known as the **energy of activation.** The activation energy depends upon the nature of the reactants (bond energies) and is, therefore, a characteristic value for each reaction. If the energy of the colliding molecule is equal to or greater than the energy of activation, reaction occurs; if the energy of the colliding molecules is less than the energy of activation, no reaction occurs. Hence, *the larger the activation energy, the slower is the reaction rate.*

The fraction of the colliding molecules that reacts is very sensitive to the activation energy. If the energy of activation is high—say, 50 kcal/mole—then only a very small fraction of the colliding molecules reacts and the reaction rate is slow. On the other hand, if the energy of activation is low—say, 10 kcal/mole—then a very large fraction of the colliding molecules reacts and the reaction rate is fast. When the energy of activation approaches zero, the rate reaches explosive proportions.

The collision theory can satisfactorily account for the four major factors which influence reaction rates: (1) The rate depends on the concentration of reactants because the number of collisions depends on the concentration of molecules; the

50 kcal = 209 J

greater the concentration, the greater the number of molecules per liter, and the greater the number of collisions. (2) Since the activation energy differs from one reactant to another, the rate depends on the nature of the chemical reactants. (3) The rate increases with temperature. However, the average kinetic energy of molecules also increases with temperature and more of the molecules have a greater kinetic energy (page 70). Hence, the higher the temperature, the larger is the average kinetic energy of the molecules, and the larger is the fraction of molecules having the required energy of activation. (4) A catalyst increases the reaction rate by changing the mechanism of the reaction to a pathway that requires a lower energy of activation. The lower the energy of activation, the faster is the reaction rate.

In his explanation of the effect of temperature on reaction rates, Svante Arrhenius (1889) evolved the concept of activation energy.

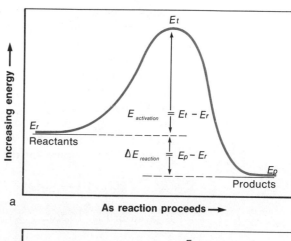

FIGURE 16.5 Representation (not to scale) of (a) a typical exothermic reaction (energy of the products is less than the energy of the reactants), and (b) a typical endothermic reaction (energy of the products is greater than the energy of the reactants). (c) A representation of the reaction $2CN(g) \longrightarrow C_2(g) + N_2(g)$.

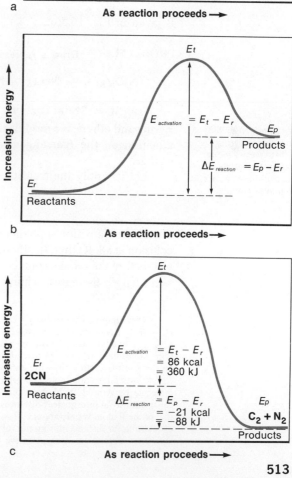

PROBLEM 4   From the given energies of activation, at the same conditions of temperature and concentration, pick the fastest and slowest reactions.

(a) Formation of ethane: $C_2H_4(g) + H_2(g) \longrightarrow C_2H_6(g)$, 43.2 kcal/mole
(b) Decompostion of acetaldehyde: $CH_3CHO(g) \longrightarrow CH_4(g) + CO(g)$, 45 kcal/mole
(c) Formation of ethylene: $C_2H_5Cl(g) \longrightarrow C_2H_4(g) + HCl(g)$, 56.9 kcal/mole
(d) Decomposition of nitrogen dioxide: $2NO_2(g) \longrightarrow N_2(g) + 2O_2(g)$, 25 kcal/mole

Reaction-Energy Diagrams   A representation of the energy changes accompanying the breaking and formation of bonds in going from reactants to products is useful in giving us a more detailed picture of a chemical change. See Fig. 16.5. E_r represents the energy of the initial reactants. Reactants that acquire the necessary energy to reach E_t, the top of the curve, change to products. The difference, $E_t - E_r$, corresponds to the energy of activation,* $E_{activation}$. In passing over the top to products, energy is evolved. The difference, $E_p - E_r$, corresponds to ΔE, the heat of reaction (page 283). If E_p, the energy of the products, is less than E_r, the energy of the reactants, the reaction is exothermic; if E_p is larger than E_r, the reaction is endothermic. Notice that the ΔE for the reaction depends only on the difference between E_p and E_r, and not on E_t. $\Delta E_{reaction}$ does *not* depend on $E_{activation}$. Equally well, we can say that $E_{activation}$ does not depend on $\Delta E_{reaction}$. A highly exothermic reaction need not be fast; it is slow when a large $E_{activation}$ stands between the reactants and the products. The diagram for the reaction

$$2CN(g) \longrightarrow C_2(g) + N_2(g) \qquad \Delta E = -21 \text{ kcal}, E_{activation} = 86 \text{ kcal}$$

is given in Fig. 16.5(c).

PROBLEM 5   Draw a representation of the energy changes for the gaseous reaction

$$N_2O_5(g) \longrightarrow NO_2(g) + NO_3(g) \qquad \Delta E = +22.2 \text{ kcal}, E_{activation} = 26 \text{ kcal}$$

Fritz London (1928) and Henry Eyring (1931) were among the first to apply quantum mechanics to chemical kinetics.

Transition State Theory   The transition state theory, developed by Henry Eyring and others, is a modification of the collision theory. This theory focuses greater attention on the rearrangement of the atoms in molecules undergoing chemical change.

Let us apply the transition state theory to the reaction

$$2CN(g) \longrightarrow C_2(g) + N_2(g)$$

In the transition state theory, the "collision" of the collision theory is not really a collision at all. Rather, the theory assumes that changes in the reacting molecules start well before they make contact.** During these changes, some bonds weaken and the bond length increases, while other bonds may start to form. Finally, the reacting

---

*Very frequently, the energy is expressed in terms of enthalpy, H_r, $H_{activation}$, H_p, in which case $H_p - H_r = \Delta H$ of the reaction (page 288), and $H_{activation}$, the enthalpy of activation, is assumed to equal $E_{activation}$. In either case, the **entropy of activation,** associated with the relative positions or orientations that some molecules must have to react, is ignored. In most reactions, $E_{activation}$ has a much greater influence on the rate of reaction than the entropy of activation.

**Very interesting molecular orbital calculations (Chap. 18) on the formation of the lithium fluoride molecule by Arnold Wahl show that the electron cloud densities of Li and F atoms start to change conspicuously at internuclear distances of 10 Å, while the radius of the Li atom is only about 1.33 Å and that of the F atom is only about 0.71 Å. A film loop showing the changes in electron density as a function of internuclear distance during the formation of the LiF molecule is available from McGraw-Hill Book Co., New York, New York. Also see Problem 24, page 522.

molecules form some kind of hypothetical structure, known as the **transition state:**

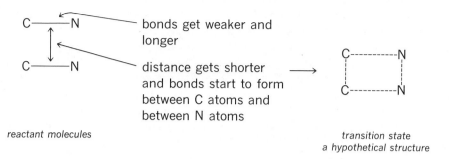

reactant molecules

transition state
a hypothetical structure

The transition state does *not* represent a real molecule; it is impossible experimentally to detect the transition state. Once formed, it splits apart to form the product molecules. The C—N bond length increases further while the C—C and N—N bond lengths decrease:

bonds get weaker and longer

bonds get shorter and stronger
transition state

C—C and N—N

product molecules

The energy changes accompanying this reaction are shown in Fig. 16.6. As the interatomic distance increases in C—N, energy is absorbed, while the tendency of C atoms to form C_2 molecules and the tendency of N atoms to form N_2 evolve energy. However, in forming the transition state, more energy is absorbed than evolved. E_t is, therefore, always greater than E_r.

As the transition state splits into product molecules, the C—C atoms and the N—N atoms attract each other very strongly. Hence, considerable energy is evolved.

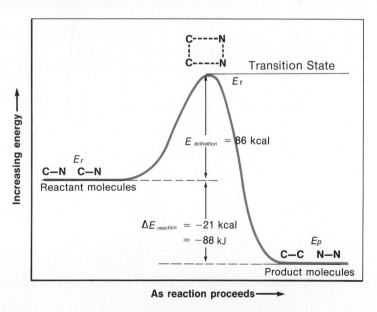

FIGURE 16.6 Representation of the energy changes accompanying the decomposition of CN, a compound recently discovered in outer space.

E_p is, therefore, always lower than E_t. The transition state therefore always sits at the highest point of the reaction-energy diagram.

This theory explains the observed facts for the rate of a reaction as follows: (1) The nature of the reactants determines the transition state and, therefore, the energy of activation. (2) The concentration of the reactants and the energy of activation determine the concentration of the transition state. The concentration of the transition state determines the rate of the reaction. The greater the reactant concentration and the smaller the energy of activation, the greater the concentration of the transition state and the faster the rate of the reaction. (3) The concentration of the transition state is sensitive to temperature changes. The higher the temperature, the greater the concentration of the transition state and the faster the reaction rate. (4) The addition of a catalyst lowers the energy of activation by changing the reaction pathway so that less energy is required to form the transition state, illustrated in Fig. 16.7.

The main advantage of transition state theory over collision theory rests on its ability to make predictions, a basic aim of science.

A catalyst conserves energy by reducing activation energies, and conserves resources by promoting the desired reaction over undesired reactions.

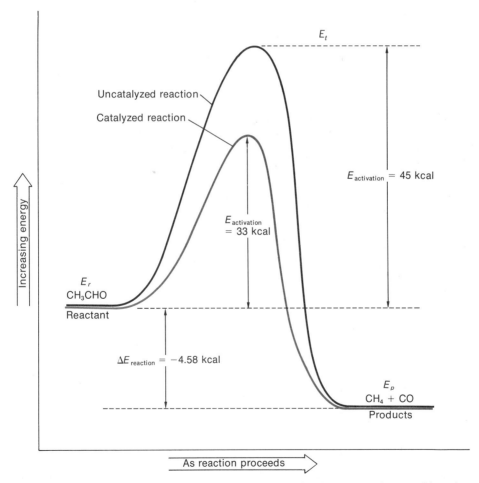

FIGURE 16.7 Illustrating the effect of a catalyst on $E_{activation}$ for the gaseous decomposition of acetaldehyde.

When a chemical reaction proceeds by a mechanism in which an atom or a molecule consumed in one step is regenerated in another step, the mechanism is called a **chain mechanism.** For example, the formation of HBr occurs in the presence of light (photons, *hf*):

$$H_2(g) + Br_2(g) \xrightarrow{hf} 2HBr(g)$$

Since the bond energy of H_2 is 104 kcal/mole while that of Br_2 is 46.1 kcal/mole (page 295), a plausible mechanism involves the following steps:

Step (1) $Br_2 + hf \longrightarrow$:$\overset{..}{\underset{..}{Br}}\cdot$ + :$\overset{..}{\underset{..}{Br}}\cdot$

Step (2)   :$\overset{..}{\underset{..}{Br}}\cdot$ + $H_2 \longrightarrow$ HBr + H$\cdot$

:$\overset{..}{\underset{..}{Br}}\cdot$ is a typical **free radical.** A free radical is an atom or molecule containing one or more unpaired electrons. In the next step, H$\cdot$, formed in Step 2, regenerates :$\overset{..}{\underset{..}{Br}}\cdot$

Step (3)   H$\cdot$ + $Br_2 \longrightarrow$ HBr + :$\overset{..}{\underset{..}{Br}}\cdot$

Steps 2 and 3 are called **chain-propagating** steps, since each one forms a product (H$\cdot$ or :$\overset{..}{\underset{..}{Br}}\cdot$) that is used as a reactant in another step. These chain-propagating steps frequently continue until all reactant molecules are consumed. However, the reaction may be terminated by any one of a number of so-called **termination steps;** for example

Addition of chain-propagating steps yields the overall reaction.

:$\overset{..}{\underset{..}{Br}}\cdot$ + :$\overset{..}{\underset{..}{Br}}\cdot \longrightarrow Br_2$

H$\cdot$ + H$\cdot \longrightarrow H_2$

H$\cdot$ + :$\overset{..}{\underset{..}{Br}}\cdot \longrightarrow$ HBr

These are called termination steps because two free radicals combine to form a molecule that is not a free radical and is incapable of continuing the reaction.

PROBLEM 6   **For the heat-induced decomposition of ethane, C_2H_6, the main reaction is**

$$3C_2H_6 \longrightarrow 2CH_4 + C_4H_{10}$$

(Very small amounts of C_2H_4 also form.) This type of reaction, known as *cracking*, is very important in the production of gasoline from crude petroleum. The following mechanism has been proposed:

$$CH_3CH_3 + heat \longrightarrow 2CH_3\cdot$$
$$CH_3\cdot + CH_3CH_3 \longrightarrow CH_4 + CH_3CH_2\cdot$$
$$2CH_3CH_2\cdot \longrightarrow CH_3CH_2CH_2CH_3$$
$$CH_3\cdot + H\cdot \longrightarrow CH_4$$
$$CH_3CH_2\cdot \longrightarrow H\cdot + CH_2CH_2$$

(a) List all the free radicals involved in the mechanism. (b) Write (i) the chain-propagating step(s) and (ii) the chain-terminating step(s).

Ethyl free radicals, easily formed from lead tetraethyl, $Pb(C_2H_5)_4 \longrightarrow Pb + 4C_2H_5\cdot$, inhibit undesirable chain reactions in the combustion of gasoline and thus greatly improve the performance of low grade gasolines.

Free radical reactions not only are involved in normal biochemical reactions in all living organisms but are also believed to be a major cause of aging. Oxygen, a free radical (with two unpaired electrons, page 203), is necessary for life processes, but it is also suspected of initiating undesirable reactions. According to this theory, chemicals which decrease the concentration of free radicals in an organism should delay the aging process. Most of the plastic and synthetic rubber and fiber industry rests on reactions involving free radical* chain mechanisms.

"Free Radicals in Biological Systems," Scientific American, August 1970, page 70.

Free Radicals and Spray Cans   A free radical chain mechanism is involved in the possible destruction of the Earth's ozone layer. *Chlorofluoromethanes,* such as $CFCl_3$ and CF_2Cl_2, discovered in 1930 and in common use as aerosol propellants ("spray cans") and in refrigerators, have now diffused into the ozone layer in the upper atmosphere (page 523). How nature disposes of these compounds is an important environmental problem. Like nitrogen oxide, they can destroy large amounts of ozone, thereby destroying the natural ozone balance (page 386). A photon (sunlight) breaks one Cl atom from one molecule of a chlorofluoromethane:

$$(\textit{Freon 12})\; CF_2Cl_2(g) + hf \longrightarrow \cdot CF_2Cl(g) + Cl\cdot(g)$$

Postulated by F. Sherwood Rowland and Mario Molina (1974).

It is then postulated that $Cl\cdot$ starts a catalytic chain reaction through the formation of chlorine monoxide

$$Cl\cdot(g) + O_3(g) \longrightarrow ClO\cdot + O_2(g) \tag{2}$$

followed by the reaction

$$ClO\cdot(g) + O(g) \longrightarrow Cl\cdot + O_2(g) \tag{3}$$

The net reaction of Reactions 2 and 3 is the catalytic destruction of one ozone molecule and one oxygen atom:

$$O_3(g) + O(g) \longrightarrow 2O_2(g) \tag{4}$$

It is further postulated that through the chain of Reactions 2 and 3, one Cl atom can destroy many ozone molecules before diffusing out of the ozone layer. However, it is recognized that some other hydrogen compounds in the upper atmosphere may compete for $Cl\cdot$, for example

At least 60 reactions are involved.

$$Cl\cdot + H_2 \longrightarrow HCl + H\cdot$$
$$Cl\cdot + CH_4 \longrightarrow HCl + \cdot CH_3$$

But these reactions are not as fast as Reaction 2, so that ozone appears to be the more important scavenger for $Cl\cdot$ free radicals.

PROBLEM 7   **Show how the action of UV photons on carbon tetrachloride, CCl_4, may lead to the catalytic decomposition of ozone.**

---

* Moses Gomberg isolated (1900) what was believed to be the first stable organic free radical. Recent investigations indicate that he did not actually isolate a free radical. Readers interested in this subject are referred to "The Hexaphenylethane Landmark Falls," *Journal of Chemical Education,* volume 147, July 1970, page 535.

The National Academy of Sciences agrees that the release of chlorofluorocarbon compounds to the atmosphere presents a danger that cannot be ignored. Cause for serious concern is justifiable. But more studies are necessary before the controversy over the destruction of the ozone layer is settled. Meanwhile, a partial ban on the use of chlorofluorocarbons is in effect.*

"Halocarbons: Environmental Effects of Chlorofluoro-methane," National Academy of Sciences, Washington, D.C., 1976.

STABILITY REVISITED _____ 16.5

Stability is a term much used and abused. Further clarification of the term is worthy of a few moments of our time. *Thermal stability* (page 297) refers to the resistance to change under heating in a vacuum. *Thermodynamic stability* (pages 297, 379) refers to resistance to chemical change with respect to certain products at certain conditions and is governed by the equilibrium constant for the reaction; the smaller the equilibrium constant, the greater is the thermodynamic stability. **Kinetic stability** refers to the rate of chemical reaction (**"reactivity"**) and is governed by the energy of activation; the greater the $E_{activation}$, the smaller the rate constant and the greater the kinetic stability.

These stabilities do not, however, necessarily parallel one another. The following reactions (25 °C) illustrate this point.

(a) In the formation of water from hydrogen and oxygen

$$H_2(g) + \tfrac{1}{2} O_2(g) \longrightarrow H_2O(l) \qquad K = 4.30 \times 10^{43}$$

the reactants are both thermodynamically and kinetically unstable. These reactants possess such great kinetic instability that, in the presence of a spark, they react with explosive force. On the other hand, the product of the reaction is thermodynamically stable. Thus, in order to decompose water

$$H_2O(l) + energy \longrightarrow H_2(g) + \tfrac{1}{2} O_2(g)$$

a large amount of electrical energy has to be expended (electrolysis, pages 472, 600).

(b) In the rapid reaction of silicon(IV) chloride with water to form silicon dioxide and hydrogen chloride

$$SiCl_4(l) + 2H_2O(l) \longrightarrow SiO_2(c) + 4HCl(g) \qquad K = 1.3 \times 10^{49}$$

the reactants exhibit both thermodynamic and kinetic instability. However, in a similar reaction between carbon tetrachloride and water, leading to carbon dioxide and hydrogen chloride

$$CCl_4(l) + 2H_2O(l) \longrightarrow CO_2(g) + 4HCl(g) \qquad K = 9.7 \times 10^{65}$$

the reactants are thermodynamically unstable but kinetically stable. Thus, *no reaction* occurs.

(c) The removal of nitrogen oxides from motor vehicle exhausts is a more difficult problem to solve than the removal of hydrocarbons and carbon monoxide. It should be possible to decompose the nitrogen oxides, which are thermodynamically unstable:

---

*Dichloromethane, CH_2Cl_2, is under investigation as a substitute in aerosol products for chlorofluorocarbons. It decomposes in the lower atmosphere without effect on the O_3 layer.

$$2NO(g) \longrightarrow N_2(g) + O_2(g) \qquad K = 2.2 \times 10^{30}$$
$$2NO_2(g) \longrightarrow N_2(g) + 2O_2(g) \qquad K = 6.7 \times 10^{16}$$

However, the oxides are kinetically stable and no catalyst has yet been found to accelerate their decomposition. More promising is the attempt to catalyze the reduction of nitrogen oxides by the carbon monoxide already present in the exhaust gas

Catalytic control of automobile pollutants also catalyzes the oxidation of SO_2 to SO_3, page 621, but the sulfate emission is not serious.

$$NO(g) + CO(g) \longrightarrow \tfrac{1}{2} N_2(g) + CO_2(g) \qquad K = 2.9 \times 10^{60}$$

(d) In the reaction with itself

$$C_2H_2(g) \longrightarrow 2C(graphite) + H_2(g) \qquad K = 4.45 \times 10^{36}$$

acetylene is thermodynamically and kinetically unstable. Therefore, acetylene (compressed gas, liquid, or solid) may violently explode. For commercial use, it is safely stored as a solution in acetone.

The human body, like ordinary organic matter (Chap. 22)—for example, methane—is thermodynamically very unstable with respect to CO_2 and H_2O

$$CH_4(g) + 2O_2(g) \longrightarrow CO_2(g) + 2H_2O(l)$$

but fortunately the body is kinetically stable. Beware of your catalyst!

PROBLEM 8 **Pick the reactions that occur (25 °C):**

(a) **$2H_2O_2(l) \longrightarrow 2H_2O(l) + O_2(g)$**
Thermodynamically unstable
Kinetically unstable

(b) **$H_2(g) + Cl_2(g) \longrightarrow 2HCl(g)$**
Thermodynamically unstable
Kinetically stable

(c) **$C_2H_5OH(l) + HCl(aq) \longrightarrow C_2H_5Cl(l) + H_2O$**
Thermodynamically unstable
Kinetically unstable

(d) **$CH_3Cl(l) + H_2O \longrightarrow CH_3OH(l) + HCl(aq)$**
Thermodynamically stable
Kinetically stable

PROBLEMS

9 Vocabulary Define and/or illustrate (a) order of a reaction, (b) rate constant, (c) transition state, (d) mechanism, (e) chain mechanism, (f) free radical, (g) energy of activation, (h) thermodynamic stability, (i) kinetic stability, (j) thermal stability.

10 Rate The reaction

$(C_2H_5)_3N(l) + CH_3I(l) \longrightarrow (C_2H_5)_3CH_3NI(c)$
triethyl amine   methyl   triethyl methyl
         iodide   ammonium iodide*

---

*Analogous to NH_4I, ammonium halides of the general formula $[NR_4]^+Br^-$, used in industrial sterilization processes, possess great germicidal properties.

has been studied at 25 °C:

Reactant concentrations, mole/liter		Rate of formation of $(C_2H_5)_3CH_3NI$ at given concentrations, mole/(liter second)
$[(C_2H_5)_3N]$	$[CH_3I]$	
0.020	0.020	1.0×10^{-2}
0.020	0.040	2.0×10^{-2}
0.010	0.040	1.0×10^{-2}

(a) Write the rate equation for the reaction. What is the order of the reaction? Calculate the rate constant for the reaction. (b) Calculate the rate of formation of $(C_2H_5)_3CH_3NI$ at the instant when $[(C_2H_5)_3N] = 0.050$ and $[CH_3I] = 0.010$.

11 The reaction

$$C_2H_5Cl(g) \longrightarrow C_2H_4(g) + HCl(g)$$

has been studied at 300 K:

Reactant concentrations, mole/liter	Rate of formation of C_2H_4 at the given concentrations, mole/(liter second)
$[C_2H_5Cl]$	
0.250	1.80×10^{-30}
0.500	3.60×10^{-30}
1.00	7.20×10^{-30}

(a) Write the rate equation for the reaction. What is the order of the reaction? Calculate the rate constant for the reaction. (b) Calculate the rate of formation of C_2H_4 at the instant when $[C_2H_5Cl] = 5.00$.

12 The reaction

$$2NOCl(g) \longrightarrow 2NO(g) + Cl_2(g)$$

has been studied at 400 K:

Reactant concentrations, mole/liter	Rate of formation of NO at the given concentrations, mole/(liter second)
$[NOCl]$	
1.00×10^{-2}	2.80×10^{-9}
2.00×10^{-2}	1.12×10^{-8}
3.00×10^{-2}	2.52×10^{-8}

(a) Write the rate equation for the reaction. What is the order of the reaction? Calculate the rate constant for the reaction. (b) Calculate the rate of formation of NO_2 at the instant when $[NOCl] = 5.00 \times 10^{-2}$.

13 The reaction

$$2NO(g) + Cl_2(g) \longrightarrow 2NOCl(g)$$

has been studied at 50 °C:

Reactant concentrations, mole/liter		Rate of formation of NOCl at the given concentrations, mole/(liter second)
$[NO]$	$[Cl_2]$	
0.500	0.500	1.14×10^{-5}
1.00	0.500	4.56×10^{-5}
1.00	1.00	9.12×10^{-5}

(a) Write the rate equation for the reaction. What is the order of the reaction? (b) Calculate the rate of

formation of NOCl at the instant when $[NO] = 0.250$ and $[Cl_2] = 0.250$.

14 Homogeneous and heterogeneous reactions Classify the following as homogeneous or heterogeneous.

(i) $C_6H_6(l) + Cl_2(g) \longrightarrow C_6H_5Cl(l) + HCl(g)$
(ii) $Ca(OH)_2(aq) + H_2SO_4(aq) \longrightarrow$
      $CaSO_4(aq) + 2H_2O$
(iii) $2H_2O_2(l) \longrightarrow 2H_2O(l) + O_2(g)$
(iv) $CO(g) + 2LiO(c) \longrightarrow Li_2CO_3(c)$
(v) $2HgO(c) \longrightarrow 2Hg(l) + O_2(g)$

15 Mechanism The proposed mechanism for a reaction is given:

Step (1) $CH_3OH + HCl \longrightarrow CH_3{}^+ + H_2O + Cl^-$
Step (2) $CH_3{}^+ + Cl^- \longrightarrow CH_3Cl$

What is the overall reaction being studied?

16 Chemical reactions in electric power plant stack emissions produce ozone. The reactions are believed to be

$$SO_2 + \cdot OH \longrightarrow HSO_3\cdot$$

$$HSO_3\cdot + NO_2 \longrightarrow NO + HSO_4\cdot$$

$$NO + O_2(excited) \longrightarrow NO_2 + O$$

$$O_2(excited) + O \longrightarrow O_3$$

Add up these equations to determine what is actually consumed and produced. Is your final equation balanced?

17 The reaction

$$C_2H_6(g) + Cl_2(g) + hf \longrightarrow C_2H_5Cl(l) + HCl(g)$$

proceeds by a chain mechanism. The initial step is

$$Cl_2 + hf \longrightarrow :\overset{..}{\underset{..}{Cl}}\cdot + :\overset{..}{\underset{..}{Cl}}\cdot$$

(a) Show the formation of $\cdot C_2H_5$ as the next step. (b) A propagation step involves the chlorine molecule and the ethyl free radical ($\cdot C_2H_5$). Write the equation showing the formation of $:\overset{..}{\underset{..}{Cl}}\cdot$. (c) Write three equations showing how the reaction can be terminated.

18 Reaction-energy diagrams Draw a reaction-energy diagram for (a) an endothermic reaction, and (b) an exothermic reaction. Indicate on the diagrams the following: (i) $\Delta E_{reaction}$, (ii) $E_{activation}$, (iii) E_t, (iv) $E_{reactants}$, (v) $E_{products}$.

19 (a) Draw a reaction-energy diagram for each of the following sets of conditions:

(i) $E_{activation} = 50$ kcal, $\Delta E_{reaction} = -20$ kcal
(ii) $E_{activation} = 25$ kcal, $\Delta E_{reaction} = 10$ kcal

(b) Classify the reactions as exothermic or endothermic. (c) At the same conditions of temperature and concentration, which reaction is faster?

20 Stability Pick the reaction(s) that occur (25 °C):

(i) $C(diamond) \longrightarrow C(graphite)$
Thermodynamically unstable
Kinetically stable

(ii) $C(graphite) + 2H_2(g) \longrightarrow CH_4(g)$
Thermodynamically unstable
Kinetically stable

(iii) $CH_3CH{=}CH_2(g) + H_2(g) \longrightarrow C_3H_8(g)$
Thermodynamically unstable
Kinetically stable

(iv) $Cl_2(g) + H_2O \longrightarrow HOCl(aq) + HCl(aq)$
Thermodynamically unstable
Kinetically unstable

(v) $SO_2(g) + 3S(c) \longrightarrow 2S_2O(g)$
Thermodynamically stable
Kinetically stable

(vi) $SiO(c) \longrightarrow Si(c) + \frac{1}{2}O_2(g)$
Thermodynamically unstable
Kinetically stable

21 (a) With respect to Reactions 2 and 3, page 518, is the reaction $ClO\cdot + ClO\cdot \longrightarrow Cl_2 + O_2$ chain-propagating or chain-terminating; and should this reaction increase or decrease the rate of destruction of the ozone layer? (b) Would you study the substitution of pressurized (i) carbon dioxide, (ii) carbon monoxide, (iii) oxygen, (iv) nitrogen, (v) nonflammable water–natural gases, for chlorofluoromethane in spray cans?

22 Library Read one of the following:

(a) "Free Radical Pathology," *Chemical and Engineering News,* 7 June 1971, page 34.

(b) "Catalysis," V. Haenzel and R. Burwell Jr., *Scientific American,* December 1971, pages 46–58.

(c) "Vitamin E and Aging. Free Radicals," *The Sciences,* volume 14, November 1974, page 6.

(d) "The Formation of Interstellar Molecules," *Physics Today,* June 1976, page 32.

(e) "Speculation of Possible Health Effects Related to Reactive Intermediates Formed in Urban Atmospheres," Proceedings of the Conference on Health Effects of Air Pollutants, National Academy of Sciences. U.S. Government Printing Office, Washington, D.C., November 1973, pages 76–81.

(f) "Fluorocarbons and Ozone—A Classical Dilemma," *What's Happening in Chemistry?,* American Chemical Society, Washington, D.C., 1975, page 40.

ADDITIONAL PROBLEMS

23 Data (room temperature) for the overall reaction, $2H_2O_2(aq) \longrightarrow 2H_2O + O_2(g)$, are given:

$[H_2O_2]$	$[I^-]$	$[H^+]$	Rate of formation of O_2, mole/(liter minute)
0.500	0.0125	0.0125	8.31×10^{-3}
0.250	0.0125	0.0125	4.16×10^{-3}
0.250	0.0250	0.0125	8.31×10^{-3}
0.250	0.0125	0.0250	4.16×10^{-3}

(a) Write the rate equation. (b) Pick out the catalyst(s), if any.

24 Like a spear thrown at a shark, at about 0.8 nm a potassium atom transfers one electron (the "spear") to Br_2, forming K^+ and Br_2^-. Then K^+ and Br_2^- strongly attract one another. Finally, the "spear" is drawn in, forming an ionic molecule and leaving Br behind. Write the equation for each step. Write the overall reaction.

25 For each of the gaseous reactions

(a) $Cl^- + CH_3I \longrightarrow CH_3Cl + I^-$
(b) $K + CH_3I \longrightarrow KI + \cdot CH_3$

two orientations leading to the transition state have been experimentally studied:

(a) (i) $Cl^- + H{-}\underset{\underset{H}{|}}{\overset{\overset{H}{|}}{C}}{-}I \longrightarrow Cl\text{---}\underset{\underset{H}{|}}{\overset{\overset{H\ \ H}{}}{C}}\text{---}I$

(ii) $Cl^- + I{-}CH_3 \longrightarrow Cl\text{---}I{-}CH_3$

(b) (i) $K + I{-}\underset{\underset{H}{|}}{\overset{\overset{H}{|}}{C}}{-}H \longrightarrow K\text{---}I\text{---}\underset{\underset{H}{|}}{\overset{\overset{H}{}}{C}}{-}H$

(ii) $K + H{-}\underset{\underset{H}{|}}{\overset{\overset{H}{}}{C}}{-}I \longrightarrow K\text{---}H{-}\underset{\underset{H}{|}}{\overset{\overset{H}{}}{C}}{-}I$

For each reaction, pick the orientation leading to reaction.

26 The $\cdot OH$ radical may be important in converting NO in photochemical smogs to NO_2. First, $\cdot OH$ generates the $\cdot H$ radical:

$$\cdot OH + CO \longrightarrow \cdot H + CO_2$$

The $\cdot H$ radical then initiates a chain reaction:

$$H + O_2 + M \longrightarrow HO_2 + M \text{ (page 301)}$$
$$HO_2 + NO \longrightarrow NO_2 + OH$$
$$OH + CO \longrightarrow H + CO_2$$

(a) Write the overall reaction resulting from the chain reaction. (b) Show how the chain reaction continues.

27 The formation of nitrous acid in the atmosphere, $NO(g) + NO_2(g) + H_2O(g) \longrightarrow 2HNO_2(g)$, has been studied; it was found that $rate = \dfrac{2.2 \times 10^3}{atm^2\,min}$ $[NO][NO_2][H_2O]$, in which concentrations are expressed in units of atm. (a) Calculate the rate in atm/min when $[NO] = 0.430$ Pa, $[NO_2] = 0.881$ Pa, and $[H_2O] = 300$ Pa. (b) Express the rate in mole/(liter minute) when the atmospheric temperature is 22 °C. See App. III.

28 Cyclohexene, C_6H_{10}, is used in the manufacture of adipic acid (page 719). Cyclohexene may be made from ethylene and butadiene, $C_2H_4 + C_4H_6 \longrightarrow C_6H_{10}$, for which the reaction-energy diagram is given:

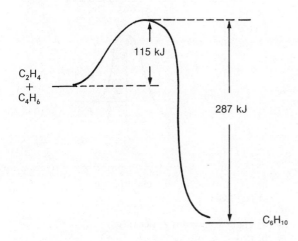

(a) Find $\Delta E_{reaction}$ in kcal. See App. III. (b) Should the forward reaction be fast? (c) What are the chances of the reverse reaction occurring?

29 The rate constant for the hydrogen-bonding reaction of pyridol, a colorless solid,

$$2HOC_5H_4N \longrightarrow (HOC_5H_4N)_2$$

in carbon tetrachloride has been measured at 13 °C:

$$rate_1 = k_1[HOC_5H_4N]^2$$
$$k_1 = 17 \times 10^8 \text{ liter/(mole second)}$$

The rate constant for the reverse reaction has also been measured in the same solvent at 13 °C:

$$rate_2 = k_2[HOC_5H_4N\text{---}HOC_5H_4N]$$
$$k_2 = 0.90 \times 10^8 \text{ s}^{-1}$$

(a) Write the equilibrium condition for the reaction

$$2HOC_5H_4N \underset{k_2}{\overset{k_1}{\rightleftarrows}} (HOC_5H_4N)_2$$

(b) Keeping in mind that at equilibrium $rate_1 = rate_2$, calculate K for the reaction in CCl_4 at 13 °C. (c) At 40 °C, $K = 14$. Is this reaction exothermic or endothermic? Explain.

30 The number of atoms of a radioactive element (N) (Chap. 17) disintegrating per unit of time is given by $N = k \times$ number of atoms present. Calculate the number of ^{222}Rn atoms disintegrating per minute at the instant when a cancer patient is treated with 100 mg of a gas containing 0.25 % ^{222}Rn, radon, a radioactive gas for which $k = 2.1 \times 10^{-6} \text{ s}^{-1}$.

31 Hydroxyl free radical, $\cdot OH$, present in the upper atmosphere (page 399), takes part in a key reaction which may destroy chlorofluoromethanes and so protect the ozone layer:

$$\cdot OH + CF_3Cl \longrightarrow HClO + \cdot CF_3$$
$$K = 3.9 \times 10^{-15}$$

(a) The reaction is believed to have a very high energy of activation. Can hydroxyl protect the O_3 layer against destruction by CF_3Cl? Explain. (b) If studies show that E_{act} is not high and that high-energy photons can raise $\cdot OH$ molecules to excited states, would this alter your answer? Explain. (c) Hydroxyl removes Cl from HCl, $\cdot OH + HCl \longrightarrow H_2O + \cdot Cl$, $K = 6.7 \times 10^{10}$. HCl is released from space shuttle engines. HCl and $\cdot OH$ are kinetically unstable with respect to H_2O and $\cdot Cl$. Can hydroxyl molecules participate in the destruction of the O_3 layer?

32 The rate constants for the reactions

$$F + CH_4 \longrightarrow HF + CH_3$$
$$F + H_2 \longrightarrow HF + H$$

are very much greater than the rate constant for

$$F + O_3 \longrightarrow FO + O_2$$

Show that the photochemical reaction, $CF_2Cl_2 + hf \longrightarrow F + CFCl_2$, is not a threat to the ozone layer.

33 Show how chloromethane, CH_3Cl, could destroy the ozone layer.

34 A scientist warned that "bromides could be used as a war weapon to destroy food crops and disable people." Explain.

523

1 (a) *rate* = $k[H_2][I_2]$; second order
  (b) $k = 3.0 \times 10^{-2}$ liter/(mole second)
  (c) *rate* = 1.8×10^{-3} mole/(liter second)
2 homogeneous; i, v; heterogeneous: ii, iii, iv, vi
3 $2ClNO_2 \longrightarrow 2NO_2 + Cl_2$
4 fastest: d; slowest: c
5

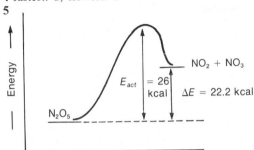

6 (a) $CH_3\cdot$, $CH_3CH_2\cdot$, $H\cdot$
  (b) (i) $CH_3\cdot + CH_3CH_3 \longrightarrow CH_4 + CH_3CH_2\cdot$
$$CH_3CH_2\cdot \longrightarrow H\cdot + CH_2CH_2$$
  (ii) $CH_3\cdot + H\cdot \longrightarrow CH_4$
$$2CH_3CH_2\cdot \longrightarrow CH_3CH_2CH_2CH_3$$
7 $CCl_4(g) + hf \longrightarrow \cdot CCl_3(g) + \cdot Cl(g)$
  $\cdot Cl(g) + O_3(g) \longrightarrow \cdot ClO(g) + O_2(g)$
8 a and c occur
10 (a) *rate* = $k[(C_2H_5)_3N][CH_3I]$; second order
      $k = 25$ liter/(mole second)
  (b) *rate* = 1.3×10^{-2} mole/(liter second)

11 (a) *rate* = $k[C_2H_5Cl]$; first order
      $k = 7.20 \times 10^{-30}$ s^{-1}
  (b) *rate* = 3.60×10^{-29} mole/(liter second)
12 (a) *rate* = $k[NOCl]^2$; second order
      $k = 2.80 \times 10^{-5}$ liter/(mole second)
  (b) *rate* = 7.00×10^{-8} mole/(liter second)
13 (a) *rate* = $k[NO]^2[Cl_2]$; third order
      $k = 9.12 \times 10^{-5}$ liter^2/(mole^2 second)
  (b) *rate* = 1.43×10^{-6} mole/(liter second)
14 homogeneous: ii, iii, v; heterogeneous: i, iv
15 $CH_3OH + HCl \longrightarrow CH_3Cl + H_2O$
16 $SO_2 + \cdot OH + 2O_2 \longrightarrow HSO_4 \cdot + O_3$
17 (a) $:\ddot{C}l\cdot + C_2H_6 \longrightarrow H:Cl + C_2H_5\cdot$

  (b) $C_2H_5\cdot + :\ddot{C}l:\ddot{C}l: \longrightarrow C_2H_5:Cl + :\ddot{C}l\cdot$

  (c) $2:\ddot{C}l\cdot \longrightarrow Cl_2$

$$C_2H_5\cdot + \cdot\ddot{C}l: \longrightarrow C_2H_5:Cl$$
$$2C_2H_5\cdot \longrightarrow C_4H_{10}$$
18 (a)

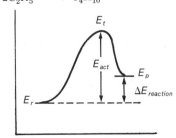

19 (a) (i)

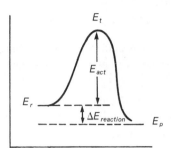

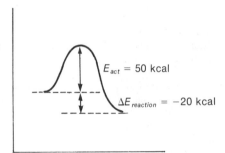

  (ii)

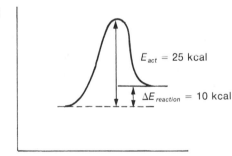

  (b) (i) exothermic; (ii) endothermic
  (c) (ii) faster
20 iv
21 (a) chain terminating, decrease
  (b) no—i, ii, iii, iv; yes—v
23 (a) *rate* = $k[H_2O_2][I_2]$
  (b) I^- is catalyst
24 $K + Br_2 \longrightarrow K^+ + Br_2^-$
  $\underline{K^+ + Br_2^- \longrightarrow KBr + Br}$
  $K + Br_2 \longrightarrow KBr + Br$
25 (a) i; (b) i
26 (a) $O_2 + NO + CO \longrightarrow NO_2 + CO_2$
  (b) $H\cdot + O_2 + M \longrightarrow HO_2 + M$
27 (a) *rate* = 2.4×10^{-10} atm/min
  (b) *rate* = 9.9×10^{-12} mole/(liter min)
28 (a) $\Delta E_{reaction} = -41.1$ kcal
  (b) yes, $E_{act} = 27.5$ kcal
  (c) small

29 (a) $K = \dfrac{[(HOC_5H_4N)_2]}{[HOC_5H_4N]^2}$
  (b) $K = 19$
  (c) exothermic
30 8.5×10^{13} atoms/min

catalyst A substance which increases the rate of a reaction without apparently being consumed; its consumption in one step of the reaction is offset by its regeneration in another step.

chain mechanism A mechanism in which a free radical consumed in one step is regenerated in another step, allowing a reaction to continue.

chemical kinetics A study of the rates and mechanisms of chemical reactions.

chlorofluorocarbon A compound containing chlorine, fluorine, and carbon derived from methane, such as CCl_2F_2.

energy of activation The minimum amount of energy necessary for the reactants to change to products. It is the difference between the energy of the transition state and the energy of the reactants. See **transition state.**

free radical An atom, molecule, or ion containing an unpaired electron.

heterogeneous reaction A reaction involving more than one phase.

homogeneous reaction A reaction occurring in one phase.

inhibitor A substance that retards or decreases the rate of a reaction.

kinetic stability Refers to reactivity, the rate constant of a reaction; it is determined by the energy of activation.

mechanism A series of steps showing how the reactants change to products.

order of a reaction The sum of the powers of the concentration terms appearing in rate equations; for example, if $rate = k[A]^2[B]^1$, the reaction is third order.

poison An inhibitor. See **inhibitor.**

rate constant A proportionality constant relating the reaction rate to the molar concentrations of reactants that appear in the rate equation. See **rate equation.**

rate-determining step The slowest step in a series of steps showing how the reactants are changed to products. See **mechanism.**

rate equation An equation relating the rate of a reaction to the molar concentration of the reactants, raised to appropriate experimentally determined powers.

rate of reaction The change in concentration of a given substance per unit time.

thermal stability Refers to the resistance to change when a substance is heated in a vacuum.

thermodynamic stability Refers to resistance to change as measured by the equilibrium constant for the reaction.

transition state A hypothetical arrangement of atoms that is less stable or has more energy than either the reactant(s) or product(s). It corresponds to the highest point between the reactant and product molecules in the reaction-energy diagram for the rate-determining step.

NUCLEAR CHEMISTRY   17

On July 16, 1945, at Trinity Flat, New Mexico, the largest, and most intensive and costly research and development project* in the history of scientific investigation to that time was brought to a successful conclusion. The spectacular result of this project, the detonation of the first atomic bomb, as well as the events that followed, have provoked the most complex and searching questions into the social and moral implications of scientific research.

Yet, these years of research have provided significant knowledge about the nature of the atom, explained the primary source of energy in our universe, and made possible the conversion of one element into another and the synthesis of new elements. With resolution of associated environmental problems, these conversions may provide the only possibility of satisfying unlimited demands for electric power. They provide new techniques in medicine, chemical analysis, kinetic studies, and industrial processes. They also make possible the calculation of the age of archaeological artifacts and rocks of geological interest.

NATURE OF RADIOACTIVITY _____ 17.1

Radioactivity was accidentally discovered in 1896 by Henri Becquerel while studying phosphorescence (page 214). Many minerals, called phosphors, glow for some time after exposure to sunlight or ultraviolet light. This glow, like light, darkens a photographic plate. Since the newly discovered X-rays (page 120) also produced a glow in phosphors, Becquerel probed for a possible connection between phosphors and X-rays. One such phosphor in his collection was a uranium salt. In his experiments, he exposed the uranium salt to sunlight and then placed the salt on a photographic plate *wrapped in black paper* to prevent exposure of the plate to sunlight. He found that the glow emitted by the uranium salt darkened the plate. Unlike sunlight, the radiation emitted by the uranium salt *penetrated the black paper*. This indicated to him the presence of an X-ray in the uranium radiation. It was assumed that the X-ray resulted from exposing the uranium salt to sunlight. However, Becquerel made the startling discovery that the uranium salt darkened the photographic plate even without previous exposure to sunlight. He concluded that

Potassium uranyl sulfate, $K_2(UO_2)(SO_4)_2(H_2O)_2$.

---

*Code name: Manhattan Engineering District. On August 6, 1945, the day the atomic bomb was dropped on Hiroshima, President Harry Truman said of the Manhattan Project, ". . . the greatest marvel is not the size of the enterprise, its secrecy or its cost, but the achievement of scientific brains in putting together infinitely complex pieces of knowledge, held by many men in different fields of science, into a workable plan . . ."

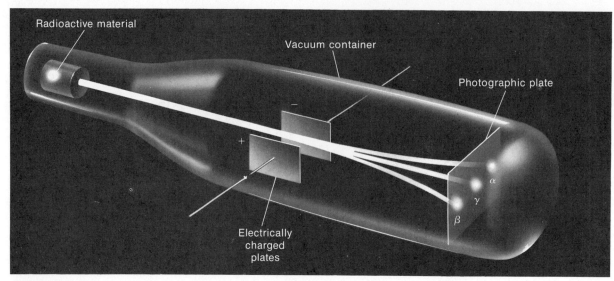

FIGURE 17.1 Behavior of α, β, and γ emissions in an electric field.

Named by Marie and Pierre Curie (1898).

Impure U_3O_8.

With G. Bémont, they isolated milligram quantities of radium from tons of pitchblende.

Polonium, named in honor of Poland, Marie Curie's homeland.

The relative penetrating power of α, β, and γ emissions in air is 1, 100, and 10,000, respectively.

uranium naturally emits X-rays without the absorption of sunlight. This phenomenon was named **radioactivity.** *Elements that naturally emit energy without the absorption of energy are said to be naturally radioactive.*

The mineral *pitchblende* exhibited a greater activity than other uranium salts. Since this observation indicated the presence of a substance more radioactive than uranium, Pierre and Marie Curie carried out a complete analysis of the mineral. They isolated (1898) two new chemical elements: polonium, Po, 400 times more radioactive than uranium, and radium, Ra, a million times more radioactive than uranium.

Ernest Rutherford (1899) and Paul Villard (1898), using the type of apparatus shown in Fig. 17.1, identified three different beams emitted by radioactive substances. These are labeled **alpha,** α, **beta,** β, and **gamma,** γ. The alpha beam, attracted toward the negatively charged plate, must be composed of positively charged particles. Further studies have proven that α particles (page 126) are *helium nuclei,* $^4_2\text{He}^{2+}$, ejected at high speeds from certain radioactive isotopes. Rutherford isolated alpha particles in the apparatus shown in Fig. 17.2.

The β beam, attracted to the positive plate, must be composed of negatively charged particles. The electric charge and mass of a β particle equal those of an electron. Thus, beta particles are electrons ejected at high speeds from certain radioactive isotopes. The γ-ray is unaffected by the electric field. The properties of γ-rays are similar to those of X-rays, except that they have higher energies (photons with shorter wavelengths, page 191).

Alpha particles have limited penetrating power (they can be stopped by several sheets of ordinary paper) but present a great internal health hazard. Beta particles are somewhat more penetrating than α particles (they can be stopped by a one-eighth inch aluminum plate) and cause serious damage to body tissue. Gamma radiation is most penetrating (thick layers of lead and concrete are required to minimize penetration) and produces severe body damage. The characteristics of the three beams are summarized in Table 17.1. Large doses of any of these radiations disrupt normal cellular reactions in living organisms, causing illness or even death. The main radiation hazard to miners in uranium mines is the α particle emission from radon,

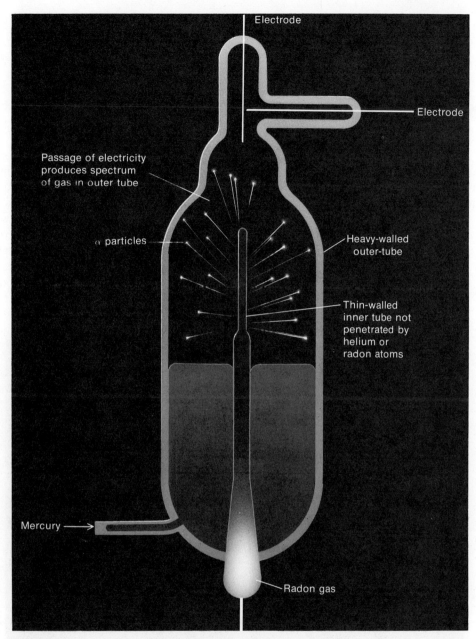

FIGURE 17.2 The Rutherford and Royd apparatus for isolating α particles ejected from radon. The α particles penetrate the thin-walled innertube containing the radon gas. The spectrum of the gas collected in the heavy-walled tube is the same as the helium spectrum. (The apparatus is the same as that shown in Fig. 4.10, page 138, but more detail is included.)

TABLE 17.1
CHARACTERISTICS OF α, β, AND γ EMISSIONS

NAME	SYMBOL	CHARGE	MASS, g/PARTICLE	VELOCITY IN VACUUM, km/s	RELATIVE ABILITY TO IONIZE AIR
Alpha	$_2^4He^{2+}$, $_2^4\alpha$	+2	6.65×10^{-24}	1.6–2.1×10^4	10,000
Beta	$_{-1}\beta^0$, $_{-1}^0e$	−1	9.11×10^{-28}	2.7×10^5	100
Gamma	$_0^0\gamma$, γ	0		3.0×10^5	1

Rn, a radioactive noble gas present in the mine air (Fig. 17.5). However, radon is oxidized by the ionic solid $ClF_2^+ SbF_6^-$ to a solid product:

$$ClF_3(l) + SbF_5(l) \longrightarrow ClF_2^+SbF_6^-(c)$$

Lewis base   Lewis acid   complex

$$Rn(g) + ClF_2^+SbF_6^-(c) \longrightarrow RnF^+SbF_6^-(c) + ClF(g)$$

These reactions are 100 % complete, making them efficient for the removal of radon. Dioxygenyl hexafluoroantimony(V), O_2SbF_6, is also useful in removing radioactive xenon and krypton gases from nuclear power plant emissions.

Invented by Charles Wilson (1911).

Particles and their interactions are detectable in a Wilson cloud chamber. The chamber, shown in Fig. 17.3, is filled with clean air saturated with water vapor. When the piston is pulled down, the expansion cools the air but *no* condensation occurs; the air is now supersaturated (page 323) with respect to water vapor. The passage of any particle, capable of ionizing air, through the chamber produces ions on which water droplets condense. When photographed, these droplets appear as faint lines, illustrated in Fig. 17.4. The bubble chamber, which uses a superheated liquid under

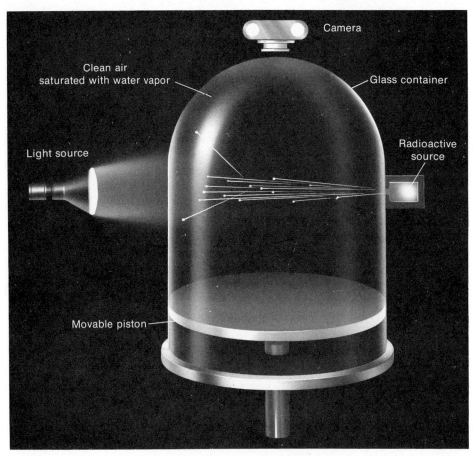

FIGURE 17.3 The principle of the Wilson cloud chamber. Moving the piston downward causes the air in the chamber to become supersaturated with respect to water vapor. The chamber allows the detection of ionizing particles.

FIGURE 17.4 Wilson cloud chamber photograph of α particles. (Courtesy of Lise Meitner.)

pressure, is superior to the cloud chamber for the detection of particles. The path of the particles is defined by a line of vapor bubbles in a liquid rather than condensed water droplets in a gas. Various types of Geiger counters (page 137) are also used as particle detectors.

Invented by Donald Glaser (1953); liquid hydrogen is most frequently used.

Rutherford found that radium not only emits α particles, but also produces radon. It was then discovered that many radioisotopes (radioactive isotopes) produce other radioisotopes.

These observations led Rutherford and Frederick Soddy, in 1902, to propose the theory that radioactivity is the result of a natural change (transformation, disintegration) of the isotope of one element into an isotope of a different element. This theory contradicted the idea, developed over a century of work, that atoms are unalterable and could not be changed into other atoms. "Soddy, according to his biographer, turned to his colleague and blurted: 'Rutherford, this is transmutation!' Rutherford rejoined: 'For Mike's sake, Soddy, don't call it transmutation. They'll have our heads off as alchemists.' Rutherford and Soddy were careful to use the term 'transformation' rather than 'transmutation'." Lord Kelvin rejected the formation of helium from radium, and Mendeleev rejected the discovery of the electron and Rutherford's explanation of radioactivity in the fear that so many additional elements could not be accommodated by his periodic table. But the concept of isotopes ("same place," page 122) preserved the basic structure of the periodic table.

Scientific American, August 1966, page 91.

These changes, called **nuclear reactions,** generally involve a change in the atomic number and the mass number of the radioisotope. The emission of an alpha particle by radium may be represented by the equation

$$^{226}_{88}\text{Ra} \longrightarrow {}^{4}_{2}\text{He} + {}^{222}_{86}\text{Rn}$$

in which the subscripts represent the atomic numbers and the superscripts represent the mass numbers, the number of nucleons (page 180) in a nucleus. Additional examples of α emission are given:

$$^{210}_{84}\text{Po} \longrightarrow {}^{206}_{82}\text{Pb} + {}^{4}_{2}\text{He}$$
$$^{234}_{92}\text{U} \longrightarrow {}^{230}_{90}\text{Th} + {}^{4}_{2}\text{He}$$

In chemical changes, atoms are rearranged in molecules or ions; they are not created or destroyed. The number of atoms remains the same. In nuclear reactions, nucleons are rearranged; they are not created or destroyed. It is possible for one nucleon to change into a different nucleon; a proton can change to a neutron or a neutron can change to a proton, but the total number of nucleons remains the same. Therefore, in nuclear reactions, mass numbers are conserved. *The sum of the mass numbers of reacting nuclei must equal the sum of the mass numbers of nuclei produced.* To maintain electrical balance, *the sum of the atomic numbers of the products must equal the sum of the atomic numbers of the reactants.* These principles are verified by the experimentally determined equations written for α emission:

$$Ra \longrightarrow He + Rn$$
$$mass\ number\ 226 \longrightarrow 4 + 222 = 226$$
$$atomic\ number\ \ 88 \longrightarrow 2 + 86 = 88$$

and

$$Po \longrightarrow Pb + He$$
$$mass\ number\ 210 \longrightarrow 206 + 4 = 210$$
$$atomic\ number\ \ 84 \longrightarrow 82 + 2 = 84$$

PROBLEM 1   **Write the equation showing the emission of an alpha particle by neptunium, $^{227}_{93}Np$, producing protactinium.**

PROBLEM 2   **Consult the table of atomic weights on the back inside cover. Predict the product formed when each of the following radioisotopes emits an alpha particle: (a) $^{221}_{88}Ra$, (b) $^{257}_{103}Lr$, (c) $^{220}_{86}Rn$, indicating mass and atomic number of the product.**

The emission of a beta particle from $^{235}_{92}U$ may be represented as

$$^{235}_{92}U \longrightarrow {_{-1}}\beta^0 + {^{235}_{93}}Np$$

Another typical beta emission reaction is

$$^{32}_{15}P \longrightarrow {_{-1}}\beta^0 + {^{32}_{16}}S$$

Since a beta particle carries a charge of -1, electrical balance makes the atomic number of the product greater than that of the reacting nucleus by one:

$$P \longrightarrow \quad \beta + S$$
$$mass\ number\ 32 \longrightarrow \quad 0 + 32 = 32$$
$$atomic\ number\ 15 \longrightarrow -1 + 16 = 15$$

How does a nucleus, composed only of protons and neutrons, eject an electron it does not have? The accepted explanation involves a series of reactions in which, essentially, a neutron in the nucleus is transformed into a proton with the creation of an electron.*

Due to Enrico Fermi (1931) and Hideki Yukawa (1935).

PROBLEM 3   **Write the equation showing the emission of a beta particle by sulfur, $^{35}_{16}S$, producing chlorine.**

PROBLEM 4   **Consult the table of atomic weights (inside back cover). Predict the product formed when each of the following radioisotopes emits a beta particle: (a) $^{3}_{1}H$, (b) $^{131}_{53}I$, (c) $^{210}_{83}Bi$.**

---

*Experimental results suggest that a neutron consists of a neutral core surrounded by a negatively and positively charged cloud; the two clouds electrically cancel each other, so that ordinary instruments "see" a neutral particle.

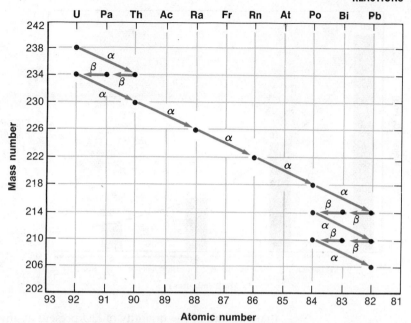

FIGURE 17.5 $^{238}_{92}$U radioactive series. The radioisotopes emit either α or $_{-1}\beta^0$ particles. $^{206}_{82}$Pb is the "end product." (A few elements may emit both α and $_{-1}\beta^0$ particles, but these are not shown for simplicity.)

In many cases, the emission of an alpha or beta particle results in the formation of an isotope which is also radioactive.* The new radioactive isotope may thus undergo a number of successive transmutations until a stable (nonradioactive) isotope is finally produced. This series of transformations is called a **radioactive series.** The $^{238}_{92}$U series, in which $^{206}_{82}$Pb appears as the stable (end) product, is shown in Fig. 17.5.

PROBLEM 5   The radioactive series, known as the actinium series, that begins with $^{235}_{92}$U and ends with $^{207}_{82}$Pb undergoes a sequence of emissions, the start of which is: α, β, α, α, β. Identify the radioactive isotope produced in each of these steps starting with $^{235}_{92}$U.

RATES OF DISINTEGRATION REACTIONS _____ 17.2

Radioactive nuclei have different stabilities and thus disintegrate at different rates. The lower the stability, the faster is the disintegration rate. The rate is proportional to the quantity of radioactive element present, independent of temperature. The quantity may be expressed in moles, grams, or number of atoms, $rate = k \times$ quantity; k, of course, is expressed in the unit of $1/\text{time}$. The time required for one-half of a given sample to react is referred to as its **half-life,** given the symbol $t_{1/2}$. The larger the rate constant, the faster the rate of reaction, the shorter is the half-life. For disintegration reactions, the half-life, like the rate constant, is a constant, independent of temperature and of the amount of reactant or of the number of nuclei present.** Hence, the half-life is commonly used as a measure of the speed of these reactions. For example, $^{15}_{8}$O disintegrates with the emission of a **positron,** $_{+1}\beta^0$ (page 211). The half-life of $^{15}_{8}$O is 2.0 minutes ($^{15}_{8}$O $\longrightarrow$ $^{15}_{7}$N + $_{+1}\beta^0$). This means

---

* A nucleus formed as the result of an alpha or beta particle emission is generally in an excited state and so emits a γ-ray (photon). Photon emission by an excited state of the nucleus is exactly analogous to the emission of a photon by an excited hydrogen atom (page 186).

** The half-life and the rate constant are constants, independent of quantity or concentration, only for first order reactions. All disintegration reactions are first order. It is impossible to predict when a single atom or molecule will react. Rate calculations may be made only for a collection of particles.

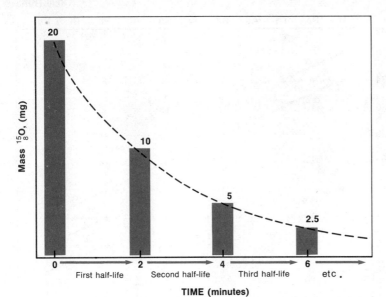

FIGURE 17.6 Decay of 20 mg of $^{15}_{8}O$. For each half-life, the quantity is reduced by one-half.

that one-half of the quantity of $^{15}_{8}O$ present at any given time will disintegrate every 2.0 minutes. Thus, if we start with 20 mg of $^{15}_{8}O$, 10 mg of $^{15}_{8}O$ remains after 2.0 minutes, 5.0 mg remains after 4.0 minutes (two half-lives), 2.5 mg remains after 6.0 minutes (three half-lives), and so on. Fig. 17.6 and Table 17.2 illustrate the decay of $^{15}_{8}O$.

Example 1

Starting with 10 g of $^{15}_{8}O$, how much will remain after 8.0 min? $t_{1/2} = 2.0$ min.

Answer

First, find the number of half-lives in the given time period of 8.0 min. Since the half-life is 2.0 min, the number of half-lives is

$$\frac{8.0 \text{ min}}{2.0 \frac{\text{min}}{\text{half-life}}} = 4.0 \text{ half-lives}$$

TABLE 17.2
EFFECT OF THE NUMBER OF HALF-LIVES ON INITIAL QUANTITY OF A SAMPLE

NUMBER OF HALF-LIVES	FRACTION OF INITIAL QUANTITY REMAINING	QUANTITY REMAINING, mg
0	1	20.0 (*initial*)
1	$\frac{1}{2}$	10.0
2	$\frac{1}{4}$	5.00
3	$\frac{1}{8}$	2.50
4	$\frac{1}{16}$	1.25
5	$\frac{1}{32}$	0.625

This means, then, that the initial quantity, 10 g, is reduced four times by $\frac{1}{2}$

$$10\,g \times \tfrac{1}{2} \times \tfrac{1}{2} \times \tfrac{1}{2} \times \tfrac{1}{2} = 10\,g \times \tfrac{1}{16} = 0.63\,g$$

The rate of decay (disintegration) is also expressed in terms of activity, the number of disintegrations per unit of time. We can then say that the number of disintegrations per unit of time is proportional to the number of atoms present. The number of disintegrations per unit of time is conveniently measured with a Geiger counter (page 137).

PROBLEM 6   **Strontium-90, $^{90}_{38}Sr$, is a radioisotope, $t_{1/2} = 29$ years ($^{90}_{38}Sr \longrightarrow {}^{90}_{39}Y + {}_{-1}\beta^0$), produced in atomic bomb explosions. Its long life and its tendency to concentrate in bone marrow make it particularly dangerous. A sample of $^{90}_{38}Sr$ emits 2000 beta particles per minute. How many half-lives and how many years are necessary to reduce the emission to 125 beta particles per minute?**

The half-lives of some common radioisotopes are given in Table 17.3.

Dating   For each half-life period, the quantity of $^{15}_{8}O$ is reduced by one-half or

20 mg (*initial quantity*) $\times$ 0.5 (*first half-life*) $\times$ 0.5 (*second half-life*)
$\times$ 0.5 (*third half-life*) = 2.5 mg (*quantity after three half-lives; 6 minutes later*)

This expression is the same as

$$20\,mg \times (0.5)^{3.0} = 2.5\,mg$$

in which the number 3.0 corresponds to the number of half-lives:

$$\frac{\text{the time period, 6.0 } \cancel{\text{minutes}}}{\text{the half-life, 2.0 } \cancel{\text{minutes}}}$$

We can generalize this relation as follows

$$\frac{initial}{quantity} \times 0.5^{\frac{time\ period}{half\text{-}life}} = \frac{quantity\ at}{end\ of\ time\ period}$$

and express it in the form of logarithms* (page 429):

---

*The log of a number raised to some power equals the power multiplied by the log of the number: log (number)^{power} = power $\times$ log (number) so that $\log 3^{10} = 10 \times \log 3 = 10 \times 0.477 = 4.77$.

TABLE 17.3
HALF-LIVES OF SOME COMMON RADIOACTIVE ISOTOPES

ISOTOPE	DECAY PROCESS	HALF-LIFE ($t_{1/2}$)
$^{238}_{92}U$	$^{238}_{92}U \longrightarrow {}^{234}_{90}Th + {}^{4}_{2}He$	4.47×10^9 years
$^{3}_{1}H$	$^{3}_{1}H \longrightarrow {}^{3}_{2}He + {}_{-1}\beta^0$	12.3 years
$^{14}_{6}C$	$^{14}_{6}C \longrightarrow {}^{14}_{7}N + {}_{-1}\beta^0$	5.73×10^3 years
$^{32}_{15}P$	$^{32}_{15}P \longrightarrow {}^{32}_{16}S + {}_{-1}\beta^0$	14.3 days
$^{60}_{27}Co$	$^{60}_{27}Co \longrightarrow {}^{60}_{28}Ni + {}_{-1}\beta^0$	5.27 years
$^{131}_{53}I$	$^{131}_{53}I \longrightarrow {}^{131}_{54}Xe + {}_{-1}\beta^0$	8.04 days
$^{239}_{94}Pu$	$^{239}_{94}Pu \longrightarrow {}^{235}_{92}U + {}^{4}_{2}He$	2.44×10^4 years

log *quantity at end of time period*

$$= \log \text{ } initial \text{ } quantity + \frac{time \text{ } period}{half\text{-}life} \times \log(5 \times 10^{-1}) \quad (1)$$

Equation 1 can be used in terms of measured activities. This relationship finds its greatest use in determining the time necessary to decrease a known amount of a radioisotope.

Example 2

High-level radioactive waste (page 548), $t_{1/2} = 200$ years, is stored in underground tanks. What time period is required to reduce an activity of 6.50×10^{12} disintegrations per minute (dpm) to a fairly harmless activity of 3.00×10^{-3} dpm?

Answer

From the given data, the initial quantity is 6.50×10^{12} dpm, the quantity at the end of the time period is 3.00×10^{-3} dpm, and $t_{1/2} = 200$ yr. Then, using Equation 1,

$$\log(3.00 \times 10^{-3}) = \log(6.50 \times 10^{12}) + \frac{time \text{ } period}{200 \text{ } yr} \times \log(5 \times 10^{-1})$$

we solve for the *time period*:

$$\log 3.00 + \log 10^{-3} = \log 6.50 + \log 10^{12} + \frac{time \text{ } period}{200 \text{ } yr} \times (\log 5 + \log 10^{-1})$$

From the log tables (App. X)

$$+0.477 - 3.000 = +0.813 + 12.000 + \frac{time \text{ } period}{200 \text{ } yr} \times (0.699 - 1.000)$$

$$-2.523 = +12.813 + \frac{time \text{ } period}{200 \text{ } yr} \times -0.301$$

$$-2.523 - 12.813 = \frac{time \text{ } period}{200 \text{ } yr} \times -0.301$$

$$-15.336 = \frac{time \text{ } period}{200 \text{ } yr} \times -0.301$$

$$time \text{ } period = \frac{-15.336 \times 200 \text{ } yr}{-0.301} = 10190 \text{ } yr = 1.02 \times 10^4 \text{ } yr$$

Example 3

A sample of radon, $t_{1/2} = 3.825$ days, initially emitted 7.0×10^4 α particles (disintegrations) per second; it now emits 2.1×10^4 α particles. What is the age of the sample? The age is the time period the sample has been decaying.

Answer

To find the age of the sample, we find the time period using the given data and Equation 1. From the data, the quantity at the end of the time period = 2.1×10^4 particles, the initial quantity = 7.0×10^4 particles, and $t_{1/2} = 3.8$ days. Substituting the data into Equation 1

$$\log (2.1 \times 10^4) = (\log 7.0 \times 10^4) + \frac{time\ period}{3.8\ days} \times \log (5 \times 10^{-1})$$

and solving

$$\log 2.1 + \log 10^4 = \log 7.0 + \log 10^4 + \frac{time\ period}{3.8\ days} \times (\log 5 + \log 10^{-1})$$

$$+0.322 + 4.000 = 0.845 + 4.000 + \frac{time\ period}{3.8\ days} \times (0.699 - 1.000)$$

$$4.322 = 4.845 + \frac{time\ period}{3.8\ days} \times -0.301$$

$$4.322 - 4.845 = -0.523 = \frac{time\ period}{3.8\ days} \times -0.301$$

$$time\ period = \frac{-0.523 \times 3.8\ days}{-0.301} = 6.6\ days$$

The sample is, therefore, 6.6 days old.

An interesting application of the use of radioactivity, known as **radiochemical dating,** is the determination of the age of rocks and fossils that date back to the origin and development of Man and life of the very remote past. The age of rocks gives us information about the age of the Earth. The significance of fossils and tools of very remote ancestors of Man, discovered at Olduvai Gorge (Tanzania), Olorgesailie Site (Kenya), Lake Turkana (Kenya), and several sites in Peru, could not be realized until the age of those objects was determined (Fig. 17.7). Ages, however, are *not directly* measured; we measure the activity, the number of disintegrations (particles emitted) per minute per gram of the object under study or of material, like rock layers, associated with the object.

Age determinations with $^{14}_6C$, developed by Willard Libby (1950), illustrate how radioisotopes are used for dating objects. Natural carbon contains small amounts of $^{14}_6C$. The interesting feature about $^{14}_6C$ is that its activity in living plants and animals and in the air is approximately constant at about 14 disintegrations per minute per gram (d/(min g)) of carbon. We *assume* that this activity was about the same in ancient times as it is now. The activity remains fairly constant because the activity lost through disintegration, $^{14}_6C \longrightarrow _{-1}\beta^0 + {}^{14}_7N$, $t_{1/2} = 5.73 \times 10^3$ years, is balanced by the production of ^{14}C through the action of neutrons with $^{14}_7N$ in the atmosphere, $^{14}_7N + {}_0n^1 \longrightarrow {}^{14}_6C + {}^1_1H$. Plants absorb carbon dioxide from the atmosphere, converting it to foodstuffs (page 195), and so incorporate $^{14}_6C$ into living tissues. As long as the plant or animal is alive, the $^{14}_6C$ activity remains constant. But with death, $^{14}_6C$ disintegration continues *without being replaced* and, consequently, the activity decreases with the passage of time. The smaller the activity, the greater the age; that is, the longer the time period between death and now.*

---

*The Earth is showered with particles, including neutrons from outer space. The concentration of these particles varies but the atmospheric ^{14}C activity has been calibrated against tree-rings of known ages so that ^{14}C dating may be used with confidence.

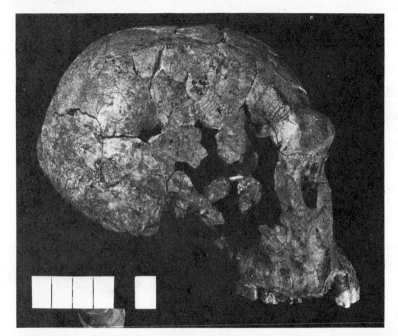

FIGURE 17.7 Three views (side, top, and front) of the skull of *Australopithecus africanus*, a small-brained, small-toothed hominid (remote ancestor of Man) discovered by Richard Leakey in the Koobi Fora Formation near Lake Turkana in Kenya's Rift Valley, radiodated 2–3 million years old. Top view shows cm scale. (Courtesy of Richard Leakey and National Museums of Kenya.)

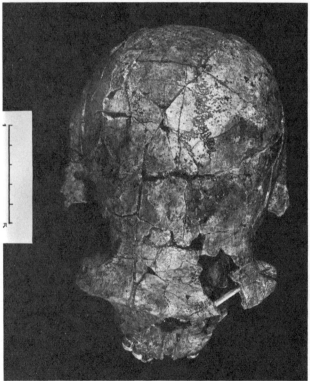

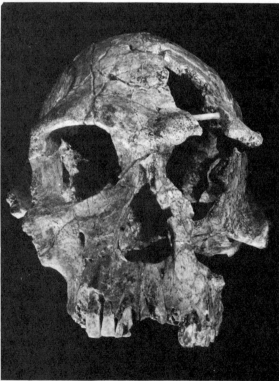

Hebrew manuscripts of the Books of the Old Testament found in Palestine in 1947.

Example 4

The activity of $^{14}_{6}C$ in the linen wrappings of the Book of Isaiah of the so-called Dead Sea Scrolls is about 11 d/(min g). Calculate the approximate age of the Scrolls.

Answer

Substituting the information into Equation 1 (page 536), quantity at end of time period = 11 d/(min g), initial quantity = 14 d/(min g), and $t_{1/2} = 5.73 \times 10^3$ years:

$$\log 11 = \log 14 + \frac{time\ period}{5.73 \times 10^3\ years} \times \log (5 \times 10^{-1})$$

$$1.0414 = 1.1461 + \frac{time\ period}{5.73 \times 10^3\ years} \times -0.301$$

$$time\ period = \frac{-0.1047 \times 5.73 \times 10^3\ years}{-0.301} = 1993\ years$$

Therefore, the age of the Scrolls is about 2000 years.

PROBLEM 7   A Japanese wooden temple guardian statue of the Kamakura period (AD 1185-1334) has a $^{14}_{6}C$ activity of 12.9 d/(min g). What is the age of the statue? In what year was the statue made? Initial quantity of $^{14}_{6}C$ = 14 d/(min g) and $t_{1/2} = 5.73 \times 10^3$ years.

Other Decay Processes   Some nuclei decay by the emission of a positron,* $^{207}_{84}Po \longrightarrow {}_{+1}\beta^0 + {}^{207}_{83}Bi$, while other nuclei may transmute by the emission of a proton, ^1_1H

$$^{43}_{21}Sc \longrightarrow {}^{42}_{20}Ca + {}^1_1H$$

Nuclei also reduce the atomic number by electron capture. The capture of an electron, usually from the lowest atomic orbital energy level (*K* shell), by the nucleus, decreases the atomic number by one:

$$^7_4Be + e^- \text{ (orbital electron)} \longrightarrow {}^7_3Li$$
$$^{15}_8O + e^- \text{ (orbital electron)} \longrightarrow {}^{15}_7N$$
$$^{40}_{19}K + e^- \text{ (orbital electron)} \longrightarrow {}^{40}_{18}Ar$$

It is interesting to note that the use of $^{40}_{19}K + e^- \longrightarrow {}^{40}_{18}Ar$ in dating shows that the age of moon rocks is about 4.4 billion years, while the oldest rock discovered on the Earth is about 3.8 billion years old. However, this does not prove that the moon is older than the Earth. While volcanic activity ceased on the moon, the Earth continued to be geologically active, remelting old rocks and recrystallizing them as new rocks.

$^{40}_{19}K$ *also changes to* $^{40}_{20}Ca + e^-$.

PROBLEM 8   Balance the following nuclear reactions (indicate element symbol where possible, mass number, and atomic number for ?):
(a) $^{13}_7N \longrightarrow {}^{13}_6C + ?$
(b) $^{41}_{20}Ca + e^- \text{ (orbital electron)} \longrightarrow ?$
(c) $^{21}_{12}Mg \longrightarrow ? + {}_{+1}\beta^0$
(d) $^{11}_6C \longrightarrow {}^{11}_5B + ?$

*Discovered in 1932 by Carl Anderson, the positron is an "anti-electron," one of a group of particles that have become known as "anti-matter." "Matter" and "anti-matter" have identical masses but opposite charge signs. Contact between a particle and its anti-particle always results in mutual annihilation of both particles with the production of high energy photons (γ-rays). Fig. 9.4 b, page 303. There is speculation that somewhere an anti-universe exists, that is, a universe made of anti-matter.

17.3 —————————— STABILITY OF ATOMIC NUCLEI

The fact that some nuclei are stable (nonradioactive) while others are unstable (radioactive) leads us to consider the factors that impart stability to the nucleus. The bond energy of a molecule (page 295) is the energy required to separate a gaseous molecule into gaseous atoms, or the energy evolved when these atoms combine to form the molecule. Similarly, the energy required to separate a nucleus into its individual nucleons, or the energy evolved when these nucleons combine to form the nucleus, is known as the **bond** (binding) **energy** of a nucleus. The greater the bond energy of a nucleus, the greater is its stability.

Our view that the nucleus contains protons—similarly charged particles—separated by only about 10^{-13} cm, would compel us to conclude that stable nuclei should not exist because of the repulsive force between the protons. These tremendous repulsive forces must, therefore, be moderated by the presence of neutrons. Examination of the composition of stable nuclei provides the following information:

The stable isotopes $^2_1$H, $^4_2$He, $^{12}_6$C, $^{16}_8$O, $^{14}_7$N, $^{20}_{10}$Ne, and $^{40}_{20}$Ca each contain *equal numbers* of protons and neutrons. For example, the $^4_2$He nucleus, containing 2 protons and 2 neutrons, is particularly stable. Apparently, the presence of neutrons has a strong stabilizing effect, strong enough to prevent the repulsive forces between the protons from tearing the nucleus apart. Very striking is the stability of $^3_2$He, in which the strong repulsive force between 2 protons is overcome by the presence of only 1 neutron. As the atomic number approaches the region of about 30, the number of neutrons increases over the number of protons; there is an especially stable ratio of neutrons to protons for each element. Radioactive nuclei emit particles so as to achieve a stable neutron-to-proton ratio.

It is found that highly stable nuclei contain a so-called **magic number** of either protons or neutrons, the magic numbers being 2, 8, 20, 28, 50, 82, and 126. The stability is further enhanced when the nuclei possess magic numbers of both protons and neutrons. Of the isotopes of oxygen, $^{15}_8$O, $^{16}_8$O, $^{17}_8$O, and $^{18}_8$O, $^{16}_8$O is the most stable; it contains an equal magic number of both protons and neutrons. $^{208}_{82}$Pb is another example of an extremely stable nucleus. Although it does not contain an equal number of protons and neutrons, it does have a magic number of both protons (82) and neutrons (126). Even a nucleus with only one magic number has an enhanced stability; for example, $^{120}_{50}$Sn is more stable than its neighbor, $^{120}_{49}$In.

Just as we noted that certain electronic structures—for example, He, $1s^2$, and Ne, $1s^2\,2s^2\,2p^6$—possess great chemical stability (page 246), so we can visualize nuclear energy shells occupied by magic numbers of protons and neutrons that give great stability to certain nuclei (page 203). Current theories, for example, suggest that the nuclei in the range from about $^{298}_{114}$X to about $^{310}_{126}$X may be stable.

PROBLEM 9   **From each given set, pick the most stable nucleus: (a) $^{60}_{27}$Co, $^{60}_{28}$Ni, $^{60}_{29}$Cu; (b) $^{22}_{12}$Mg, $^{23}_{12}$Mg, $^{24}_{12}$Mg.**

A measure of nuclear stability is the energy evolved when nucleons combine to form a nucleus. The energy is calculated (page 302) from the difference between the mass of the nucleus and the sum of the masses of the individual nucleons. As an example, consider the formation of deuterium from hydrogen and a neutron, $^1_1$H + $_0$n^1 ⟶ $^2_1$H. The masses are

$$\begin{array}{ll} ^1_1\text{H} = 1.007825 \text{ g/mole} & ^2_1\text{H} = 2.01410 \text{ g/mole} \\ \underline{_0\text{n}^1 = 1.008665 \text{ g/mole}} & \\ 2.016490 \text{ g/mole} & \end{array}$$

The difference in mass, Δm, is

$$\Delta m = \text{mass of product} - \text{mass of reactant}$$
$$= 2.01410\ \text{g/mole} - 2.01649\ \text{g/mole}$$
$$= -0.00239\ \text{g/mole}$$

The energy liberated in forming 1 mole of $^2_1$H, 2.15×10^8 kJ/mole (5.15×10^7 kcal/mole), is calculated (page 304) as follows:

$$\Delta E = \Delta m\ c^2$$

$$= -2.39 \times 10^{-3} \frac{\text{g}}{\text{mole}} \times 9.00 \times 10^{20} \frac{\text{cm}^2}{\text{s}^2}$$

$$= -2.15 \times 10^{18} \frac{\text{g cm}^2}{\text{mole s}^2}$$

But $1\ \dfrac{\text{g cm}^2}{\text{s}^2} = 1$ erg, and there are 10^{10} ergs in 1 kJ; therefore,

$$\Delta E = -2.15 \times 10^{18} \frac{\text{erg}}{\text{mole}}$$

and

$$\Delta E = -2.15 \times 10^{18} \frac{\text{erg}}{\text{mole}} \times \frac{1\ \text{kJ}}{10^{10}\ \text{erg}} = -2.15 \times 10^8 \frac{\text{kJ}}{\text{mole}}$$

For comparison, ΔE is only -435 kJ/mole (-104 kcal/mole) for H + H $\longrightarrow$ H$_2$.

In the same way, the bond (binding) energy of other nuclei may be calculated. The greater the energy released per nucleon, the greater the stability of the nucleus. If we plot the relative stability as a function of the mass number, Fig. 17.8 is obtained. The point of maximum stability occurs in the vicinity of $^{56}_{26}$Fe. All other nuclei are unstable compared to the nuclei near this maximum point. This means that very heavy nuclei may split (fission), with the production of tremendous quantities of

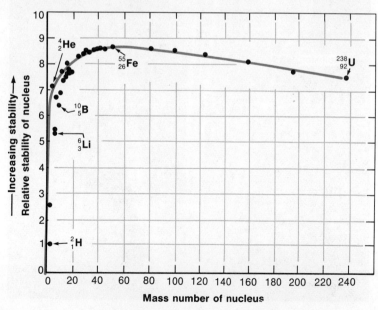

FIGURE 17.8 The relative stability of nuclei. (Based on the energy evolved in the formation of the nucleus divided by the number of nucleons.)

energy. Also, one may expect very light nuclei to fuse (fusion) exothermically into heavier nuclei. Very heavy or very light nuclei may be said to be thermodynamically unstable (page 519) with respect to nuclei in the neighborhood of $_{26}^{56}$Fe.

PROBLEM 10 Calculate the bond (binding) energy, in kJ/mole and kcal/mole, for the formation of $_{3}^{6}$Li, 3_{1}^{1}H $+ 3_{0}$n^{1} $\longrightarrow$ $_{3}^{6}$Li. The masses are $_{1}^{1}$H $= 1.00783$ g/mole, $_{0}$n$^{1} =$ 1.00867 g/mole, and $_{3}^{6}$Li $= 6.01690$ g/mole; $c = 3.00 \times 10^{10}$ cm/s; 10^{10} ergs $= 1$ kJ, and 4.184 kJ $= 1$ kcal.

17.4 _____ ARTIFICIAL TRANSMUTATIONS

In the course of his experiments, Rutherford found (1919) that α particles interact with (ionize) hydrogen gas, knocking off an electron. The proton so produced could be detected on a scintillation screen.* With nitrogen gas, however, he observed that bombardment with α particles *also produced protons*. He concluded, quite correctly, that α particles had knocked protons out of nitrogen nuclei:

$$_{2}^{4}\text{He} + _{7}^{14}\text{N} \longrightarrow _{8}^{17}\text{O} + _{1}^{1}\text{H}$$

Cloud chamber (page 530) tracks show that the α particle suddenly disappears, but a branched pair of new tracks appears (Fig. 17.9). The branch shows the collision of the α particle with the nitrogen nucleus. The thin track is produced by the proton. The other track, short and heavy, is produced by the $_{8}^{17}$O particle.

_____

* A screen coated with zinc sulfide, ZnS (pages 177, 216 ftn). Each alpha particle that hits the screen produces a flash (scintillation) of light. Modern scintillation counters convert the flashes into electric signals which are automatically counted.

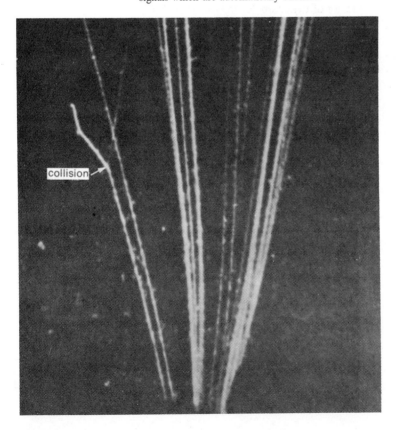

collision →

FIGURE 17.9 Cloud chamber photograph of the first artificial nuclear transformation, (adapted from an actual photograph taken by Patrick Blackett), shows an α particle striking a nitrogen nucleus. The α particle entering from the bottom collides with a nitrogen nucleus producing a proton, $_{1}^{1}$H, and $_{8}^{17}$O. The point of disintegration is clearly visible. 20,000 pictures taken by Blackett show only eight such transformations.

Subsequent experiments with α particles showed that high-speed protons are obtained from nearly all the elements up to potassium, atomic number 19, on exposure to α particles. Of particular significance is the experiment that led to the discovery of the neutron. Rutherford had proposed that protons and neutrons are the fundamental building blocks of nuclei (page 180). But his search for the neutron was not fruitful. In an experiment, beryllium, bombarded with α particles, produced a radiation originally believed to be a very high frequency gamma radiation. However, James Chadwick (1932) correctly interpreted the experimental results in terms of an uncharged particle, named the neutron:

$$\ce{^{9}_{4}Be} + \ce{^{4}_{2}He} \longrightarrow \ce{^{12}_{6}C} + \ce{_{0}n^{1}}$$

Neutrons, particularly damaging to the eyes, destroy the process by which white blood cells are produced in the body. Such damage promotes a high susceptibility to infection.

Almost every element can be transmuted by neutrons. Before a charged particle—for example, an α particle—is captured by a nucleus, it must have sufficient kinetic energy (high velocity) to overcome the repulsive force developed as a positive particle approaches a positive nucleus. But the neutron is electrically neutral. Enrico Fermi (1934) reasoned, therefore, that a nucleus would not oppose its entry. Practically all elements have since been transmuted. In addition, a number of transuranium elements have been synthesized. For example,

$$\ce{^{238}_{92}U} + \ce{_{0}n^{1}} \longrightarrow \ce{^{239}_{92}U} \longrightarrow \ce{^{239}_{93}Np} + \ce{_{-1}\beta^{0}}$$

Elements following uranium in the periodic table, neptunium and plutonium isotopes, identified by mass spectrometry, are naturally found in extremely small quantities.

which then decays as follows:

$$\ce{^{239}_{93}Np} \longrightarrow \ce{^{239}_{94}Pu} + \ce{_{-1}\beta^{0}}$$

Particle accelerators are used to impart high velocities to charged particles. The accelerators propel charged particles at speeds approaching the speed of light toward fixed targets composed of the element to be transmuted. Illustrative examples of transmutations achieved through the use of particle accelerators follow:

$$\ce{^{238}_{92}U} + \ce{^{12}_{6}C} \longrightarrow \ce{^{246}_{98}Cf} + \ce{4_{0}n^{1}}$$
$$\ce{^{253}_{99}Es} + \ce{^{4}_{2}He} \longrightarrow \ce{^{256}_{101}Md} + \ce{_{0}n^{1}}$$

In spite of their great instabilities, elements 104 through 107[*] have been identified:

$$\ce{^{249}_{98}Cf} + \ce{^{12}_{6}C} \longrightarrow \ce{^{257}_{104}X} + \ce{4_{0}n^{1}}$$
$$\ce{^{249}_{98}Cf} + \ce{^{15}_{7}N} \longrightarrow \ce{^{260}_{105}X} + \ce{4_{0}n^{1}}$$
$$\ce{^{249}_{98}Cf} + \ce{^{18}_{8}O} \longrightarrow \ce{^{263}_{106}X} + \ce{4_{0}n^{1}}$$
$$\ce{^{208}_{82}Pb} + \ce{^{55}_{25}Mn} \longrightarrow \ce{^{261}_{107}X} + \ce{2_{0}n^{1}}$$

PROBLEM 11 **Balance the following nuclear reactions (indicate element symbol where possible, mass number, and atomic number for ?):**
(a) $\ce{^{13}_{6}C} + \ce{_{0}n^{1}} \longrightarrow \ce{^{4}_{2}He} + ?$
(b) $\ce{^{14}_{7}N} + \ce{^{4}_{2}He} \longrightarrow \ce{_{0}n^{1}} + ?$
(c) $\ce{^{25}_{12}Mg} + \ce{^{4}_{2}He} \longrightarrow \ce{^{28}_{13}Al} + ?$
(d) $\ce{^{65}_{29}Cu} + \ce{_{0}n^{1}} \longrightarrow \ce{^{65}_{28}Ni} + ?$

[*]Elements 104 through 107 have not yet been officially named by the International Commission on Atomic Weights (page 126). G. Flevov, Dubna Laboratories (U.S.S.R.), has proposed that 104 be named Kurchatovium in honor of Ivan Kurchatov and that element 105 be named in honor of Neils Bohr. Albert Ghiorso, Radiation Laboratory (U.S.A.), has proposed that elements 104 and 105 be named in honor of Ernest Rutherford and Otto Hahn.

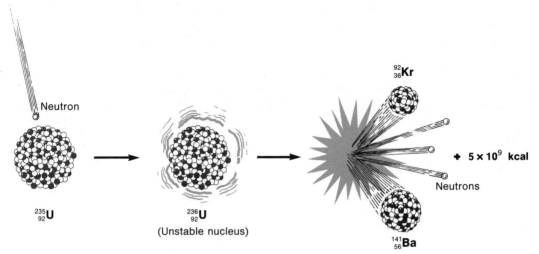

FIGURE 17.10 The fission of a $^{236}_{92}$U nucleus; the electrical repulsion between protons rips the nucleus apart.

17.5 _____ NUCLEAR FISSION

The attempt by Enrico Fermi (1934) to synthesize element 93 by bombarding uranium with neutrons unexpectedly led to the discovery of a new type of nuclear reaction: called **fission,** the splitting of a nucleus into two nuclei. Ida Noddack (1934) suggested that rather than a synthesis of a new element, Fermi had caused the uranium nucleus to split into two nuclei. Experimental work and interpretation by Otto Hahn, Fritz Strassman, Lise Meitner, and Otto Frisch confirmed that the capture of a neutron causes the uranium nucleus to undergo fission, illustrated in Fig. 17.10:

−5 × 10⁹ kcal

$$^{235}_{92}U + _0n^1 \longrightarrow {}^{236}_{92}U \longrightarrow {}^{141}_{56}Ba + {}^{92}_{36}Kr + 3_0n^1 \qquad \Delta E^* = -2 \times 10^{10} \text{ kJ}$$

The fact that each fission process emits more than one neutron is important. Since the fission of a uranium nucleus is induced by a single neutron, the neutrons so produced induce other nuclei to split. Thus, 3 neutrons released in one fission reaction induce 3 fission reactions, which release 9 neutrons subsequently followed by 27 fissions, and so on. Since the ^{236}U fission reaction is extremely rapid, this sequence sets up an explosively fast chain reaction, illustrated in Fig. 17.11. If the amount of ^{235}U is small, so many neutrons escape (are not captured by other ^{235}U nuclei) that the explosive chain reaction is not continued. In an atomic bomb, two small pieces of uranium, each incapable of sustaining a chain reaction, are brought together to form one piece capable of sustaining a chain reaction. A comparatively small atomic bomb (*neutron bomb*) produces excessive neutron damage while minimizing blast and fire damage.

^{236}U nucleus undergoes fission in about 10^{-9} second.

Known as the critical *mass.*

17.6 _____ CONTROLLED NUCLEAR REACTIONS

The fission rate may be decreased by limiting the number of neutrons available. In a **nuclear** (atomic) **reactor,** the rate of fission is slowed down by removing some of

*It has realized that a tremendous amount of energy would accompany fission; a conclusion verified by calorimetric measurements (page 284). At the time, physicists, using electronic equipment, dismissed occasional bursts produced by this energy as "electronic noises." Nuclear fission was thus discovered by chemists who identified barium as a reaction product.

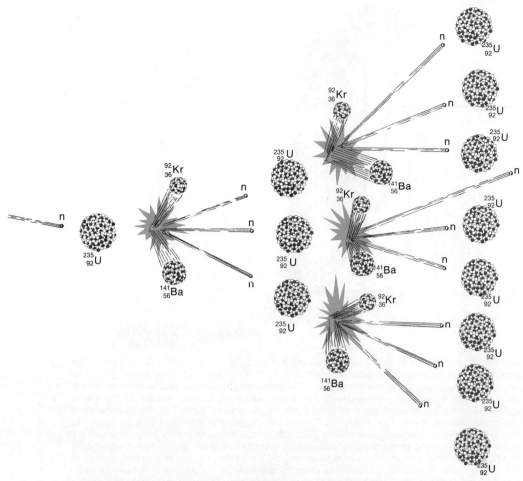

FIGURE 17.11 Illustration of a chain reaction initiated by capture of a stray neutron. (Many pairs of different isotopes are produced but only one kind of pair is shown.)

the neutrons available for fission. This is accomplished by inserting cadmium rods or other "neutron absorbers" into the reactor. These rods absorb neutrons and, by inserting or withdrawing the rods, the rate of the reaction can be decreased or increased. The rods are adjusted to yield about one neutron for each fission. If the number increases above one, the reaction rate dangerously increases; if it decreases below one, the reaction stops, for all practical purposes. A nuclear reactor is the heat source of a nuclear power plant (Fig. 17.12).

The more abundant ^{235}U requires a high energy of activation for fission. It is therefore not a good reactor "fuel." However, it can be transformed into plutonium, Pu, an excellent fuel, by the absorption of neutrons:

$$^{238}_{92}U + (fast)\ _0n^1 \longrightarrow\ ^{239}_{94}Pu + 2_{-1}\beta^0$$

The so-called **breeder reactor** manufactures *more fuel* (Pu) from ^{238}U than it consumes, and is, therefore, more efficient in producing electric power. For example, one fissionable ^{235}U atom consumed may yield two fissionable ^{239}Pu atoms:

$$^{235}U + {}_0n^1 \longrightarrow \text{fission products} + 3_0n^1$$
$$2^{238}_{92}U + 2_0n^1 \longrightarrow 2^{239}_{94}Pu + 4_{-1}\beta^0$$

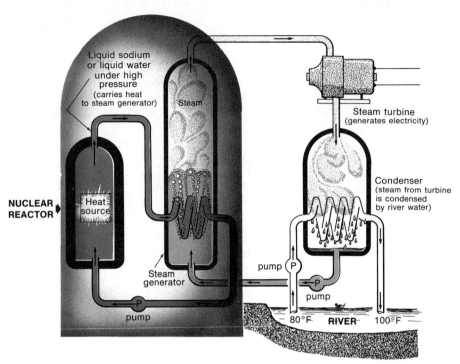

FIGURE 17.12 Essential parts of a nuclear power plant. Liquid water (or liquid sodium) is circulated through the reactor, where it is heated to about 325 °C. This hot water (or liquid sodium) converts other water into steam in the steam generator. The steam so produced is used to drive an electric generator. The steam is condensed back into liquid water, which then returns to the steam generator, where the water is again converted into steam, and so forth. The High Temperature Gas-cooled Reactor, operating at above 890 °C, uses helium gas to transfer heat from the reactor to the steam generator. Tremendous quantities (page 309) of outside cooling water (rivers or lakes) are needed to condense the steam; these outside sources are returned to the lake or river at appreciably higher temperatures than when they were taken into the condenser. The increase in temperature of the cooling water may cause a disturbance (thermal pollution) in the ecology of the lake or river. However, a nuclear power (Swiss) plant that uses a gas instead of steam to operate the electric generator is air-cooled and requires *no* cooling water. Although sodium explosively reacts with water and becomes intensely radioactive, it is, nevertheless, an excellent heat transfer agent.

Further, the neutrons produced in reactors are used to prepare many useful radio-isotopes. The uses of these radioisotopes will be discussed in Section 17.8.

The world faces a ^{235}U shortage before the year 2000. Breeder reactors provide a way of using most of the natural uranium (99.3 % ^{238}U) that is not fissionable. The breeder thus represents an almost unlimited source of energy. Breeder power stations are in operation in France, Great Britain, West Germany, and the U.S.S.R.

See Problem 38.

This projected shortage has initiated the search for more efficient methods of separating isotopes. Laser isotope separation promises a very efficient, comparatively low-cost method for preparing pure isotopes. The gas diffusion uranium isotope separation method (page 63) depends on very small differences in the diffusion rates of molecules, and this movement of molecules consumes large amounts of energy. On the other hand, the precise control of laser frequency makes it possible to excite only those molecules containing the desired isotope, for example,

U spectrum consists of 3×10^5 visible lines, making it easy to tune a laser to one of its transitions. Difference in size of ^{235}U and ^{238}U nuclei produces a difference in spectral lines easily seen by a laser.

$$^{235}UF_6 + {}^{238}UF_6 + hf \longrightarrow {}^{235}UF_6(excited) + {}^{238}UF_6(ground\ state)$$

The excited molecule is then removed by some chemical reaction:

$^{235}UF_6(excited) + {}^{238}UF_6(ground\ state) + $ chemical reagent $\longrightarrow$
$$^{235}UF_6(combined) + {}^{238}UF_6(ground\ state)$$

Plutonium, however, is the stuff of atomic weapons. President James Carter has therefore announced, "We will defer indefinitely the reprocessing of plutonium produced in U.S. nuclear power plants ... and ... we will defer the date when breeder reactors would be put into commercial use."

At this point, we may well consider the controversy surrounding the use of nuclear power plants. Its proponents regard nuclear power as an essential part of an advancing, technologically dependent society, independent of foreign energy sources. The economic health of our society and its standard of living are energy-dependent. The production of electric power barely keeps pace with increasing demands, and nuclear power appears to be the answer. Nuclear power plants are not only capable of satisfying these demands, they are also a "clean source" of power in the sense that they do not pollute the atmosphere with ash, smoke, or oxides of nitrogen, sulfur, and carbon. In addition, the supply of fossil fuels will not be depleted.

Although most critics recognize the need for electric power, they justly pinpoint the dangers of a nuclear power plant. Radioactive isotopes may be released to the atmosphere in an accident, and radioactive tritium (^3_1H) is formed in the cooling water taken from and discharged back to lakes and rivers. Also, some radioactive gas is emitted by the plant. However, these activity levels are below the levels to which we are naturally exposed, and the United States Environmental Protection Agency (E.P.A.) claims that they are acceptable. We are always exposed to radiation originating outside the body (such as cosmic radiation and natural radioactivity in rocks) as well as within the body. The critics, however, believe that any level of additional radiation is unsafe and that it is therefore impossible to accept the E.P.A. recommendations. They are even more concerned about the possibility of a major accident which might spread radioactive material into the environment.

See App. IX for units of radioactivity and standard units of biological effect on Man.

The crucial problem centers around cancer and genetic damage resulting from injury to *one* or a few cells of the body. This practically means that there is *no* dosage level* below which these effects cannot be induced in a cell; a single particle, an alpha particle or an X-ray photon may injure a cell. Exposure to natural background radiation then represents the major source of radiation-induced body damage in the general population, while for an individual the major source of radiation is exposure to medical and dental X-rays. The present guides (App. IX) attempt to balance these risks against the needs of society, but it appears that these needs can be met with lower exposures. Readers interested in this very important subject are referred to "The Effects on Populations of Exposure to Low Levels of Ionizing Radiation," National Academy of Sciences, Washington, D.C., November 1972. A discussion of the photochemistry involved in these effects can be found in "Proceedings of the International Meeting on Primary Radiation Effects in Chemistry and Biology," Argentina National Atomic Energy Commission, Buenos Aires, May 1971.

"One can scarce be in the most humanized society without risking one's life," Richard Steele (1709).

Another problem is also presented by the reactor fission products. Highly radioactive, they are not suitable as a nuclear fuel and must be discarded. The safe disposal of this very lethal radioactive waste is a major environmental problem. Most of the nuclear waste now in storage resulted from old weapons programs, not from nuclear

---

*Known as the *threshold level;* some scientists conclude that the no-dosage (no-threshold) level concept has no sensible biological basis. See, for example, *Science,* volume 175, 1972, page 495. Readers interested in the study of risk appraisal are referred to the book review by Malcolm Renfrew of "Of Acceptable Risk," *Journal of Chemical Education,* volume 54, Aug. 1977, page A345.

The American Physical Society reports (1977) that high-level nuclear reactor waste can be handled and disposed of safely.

power plants.* Radioactive waste can be converted to glassy material having a volume of about 2 m³ per reactor per year and stored deep underground in geological formations like rock salt deposits, known to be stable for hundreds of millions of years. It is concluded that the burden of nuclear waste to future generations is negligible.**

At the present time, nuclear plants supply only about 9 % of the electricity generated in the United States. It is, however, estimated that by the year 2000, more than 50 % of electric power will be produced by nuclear plants. Our situation is not novel; the political institution that separates science and technology from society has not been invented. The benefits derived from any technological advance must be considered and balanced against the disadvantages before a final decision is made. However, it is generally agreed that radioisotopes and nuclear reactions, particularly fusion, will play an increasingly important role in future industrial, medical, agricultural, and scientific developments. "The Reactor Safety Study, An Assessment of Accident Risks in U.S. Commercial Nuclear Power Plants," carried out by Norman Rasmussen, concluded that "the risk attached to the operation of nuclear power plants is very low compared to other natural and man-made risks." As a matter of record, the rest of the world is not so concerned with disadvantages as we are. No technology at any time, anywhere, has been subjected to safety scrutiny comparable to that of the American nuclear power plant. Plutonium is indeed one of the most dangerous poisons and explosives known, and the fear of its accessibility to terrorists is real. The development of technologies involved in the conversion of solar energy to electricity may displace nuclear energy sources *in the distant future*. Presently, the only practical

Report WASH-1400 (NUREG-75/104), October 1975, Nuclear Regulatory Commission, Washington, D.C. 20555.

Pu is a very powerful carcinogen.

---

*About 70 million gallons of radioactive waste are stored underground in large storage tanks at AEC installations. This waste from old programs will remain lethal for at least another 500 years.

**Robert Seamans, Administrator of Energy Research and Development Administration; "Environmental Hazards in Radioactive Waste Disposal," Bernard Cohen, *Physics Today,* January 1976, page 9.

FIGURE 17.13 Bronze Horse dated by thermoluminescence and proven to be about 2000 years old. Such studies have exposed archaeological forgeries that were less than 12 years old. (Courtesy Metropolitan Museum of Art, New York City.)

alternative to nuclear power is coal. And here, the fear is excessive carbon dioxide atmospheric pollution (page 308).

A *measurement* of radiation dosage is based on an application of thermoluminescence. When certain solids are exposed to high-energy (ionizing) radiation, electrons are removed from ions or atoms and occupy a higher energy level. When the electron returns to its ground state, light is emitted. But, frequently, the electron finds this higher energy level very comfortable and does not return to its ground state. In these cases, light emission can be made to occur by heating the crystal. This technique is called thermoluminescence (see Color Plate XI). Since the light emitted upon heating is proportional to the intensity of the radiation to which the solid is exposed, such solids are used in radiation detection badges and other devices (radiation dosimeters) to measure radiation dosages. Age determinations (*dating*) are also made from ancient fired clays, pottery, bricks, and metal castings. Impurities, such as natural radioactive potassium, lead, and uranium, in these objects raise electrons to higher energy levels. Upon heating, the electrons return to ground state; the amount of light given off is related to the length of time since the object was made (Fig. 17.13).

FUSION: THE SUN'S ENERGY —————————— 17.7

Tremendous amounts of energy are emitted when comparatively light nuclei combine to form heavier nuclei. Such a reaction is known as nuclear **fusion.** A typical fusion reaction is

$$_1^2H + _1^2H \longrightarrow _2^3He + _0n^1 \qquad \Delta E = -2.9 \times 10^8 \text{ kJ}$$

—6.9 × 10⁷ kcal

PROBLEM 12 **From the following, indicate which one is not a fusion reaction.**
(a) $_1^1H + _1^1H \longrightarrow _1^2H + _{+1}\beta^0$
(b) $_2^3He + _2^3He \longrightarrow _2^4He + 2_1^1H$
(c) $_{94}^{240}Pu \longrightarrow _{51}^{135}Sb + _{43}^{103}Tc + 2_0n^1$
(d) $_3^7Li + _1^1H \longrightarrow 2_2^4He$

The sun is our primary source of energy. The source of the sun's energy is not yet completely understood, but a portion of the energy comes from the fusion of four protons into one helium nucleus*

$$4_1^1H \longrightarrow _2^4He + 2_{+1}\beta^0 \qquad \Delta E = -2.5 \times 10^9 \text{ kJ}$$

—6 × 10⁸ kcal

A temperature of 10^6 to 10^7 °C, the estimated average temperature of the sun, is necessary for this fusion reaction to occur. The high temperature is required to bring the positively charged nuclei together with enough force to overcome the repelling electrical force. Nuclear fusion• is the basis of the hydrogen bomb. An atomic (fission) bomb provides the high temperatures necessary for the fusion of hydrogen or other light nuclei. Both fusion and fission bombs cause incredible devastation, difficult for most people to imagine. Unfortunately, most people tend to underestimate the destructiveness of nuclear weapons. In addition to intense shock waves, the tremendous heat generated by the blast produces complete destruction over a wide range, estimated at over 50 miles (Color Plate XIIA). The radiation produced is extremely dangerous even beyond this range.

•*Thermonuclear reaction.*

---

*The fusion reaction does not occur in one step as shown; rather, it involves a number of steps in which ^{12}C is first synthesized and then serves as a catalyst for the reaction.

Hopefully, present international research and peace efforts will harness and use nuclear power only as a practical and safe energy source. Since the signing of a protocol (1975), hundreds of American and Soviet scientists have exchanged visits in fusion laboratories of both countries. Progress in fusion research aimed at controlling fusion makes it possible at this time only to *visualize* the design of a practical fusion power plant. *In principle,* fusion plants are safer than fission plants. Nuclear waste problems are eliminated, radiation hazards are reduced, and the fuel supply, ^{2}H and ^{3}H in water, is practically unlimited. The fusion and fission reaction, $^{11}_{5}B + ^{1}_{1}H \longrightarrow ^{12}_{6}C \longrightarrow 3^{4}_{2}He$, has been proposed as an absolutely clean source of nuclear energy. A Soviet fission-fusion experiment, the "T-20 Tokamak," is being designed at an estimated cost of over $1 billion (although it has many of the disadvantages of a fission reactor).

Tokamak (fusion reactor), from the Russian words to (toroidal, shape), ka (chamber), mak (magnetic, page 200).

17.8 _____ USES OF RADIOISOTOPES

Although radiation may induce cancer in living organisms, radiation has also been successfully used in the treatment of cancer. Cancerous cells are more sensitive to radiation than normal cells. The idea is to select a dosage that destroys the malignant cells but not the normal cells. Gamma radiation is applied to a cancerous growth in three ways: (a) from an external source of radiation, usually ^{60}Co (cobalt-60), directed into the body so that it passes through the growth; (b) by inserting a radioisotope directly into the cancerous tissue; or (c) by inserting the radiation source into an accessible body cavity near the cancerous growth. However, cells at the center of a tumor may be deprived of oxygen; such cells become more resistant to gamma ray photons. Unfortunately, the increased resistance of tumor cells requires a dosage that also damages healthy cells. A small but significant percentage of patients develop radiation-caused cancers five or more years later. However, the oxygen-deprived cancerous cells remain sensitive to neutrons and to heavy ions like nitrogen nuclei; these kinds of radiation may prove useful in selectively destroying cancer tissue.

The most intriguing application of radioisotopes is their use as tracers. Since the chemical properties of the isotopes of an element are identical,† a radioisotope may be used to "tag" an element without changing its chemical properties. Since the radio-isotope is easily detected with a Geiger counter, the element may be followed, "traced," through a series of reactions. For example, ammonia prepared from nitrogen containing a small amount of radioactive nitrogen is said to be tagged and is written as NH_3^*. The NH_3^* may now be traced through any number of chemical and physical changes. A few specific examples of the use of tagged isotopes follow: Hemoglobin (page 665) contains iron. The rate at which injected radioactive ^{59}Fe (iron-59) appears in the blood provides a measurement of the red blood cell production. After a small amount of blood serum labeled with ^{131}I* is injected into the body, the amount of blood pumped by the heart per minute can be determined by measuring blood activity with a detector placed over the heart. The volume of blood in the body is determined by measuring the dilution of ^{14}C activity after injecting a ^{14}C tagged compound into the blood stream. The search for bacterial life in Martian soil centered about experiments involving ^{14}C (Problem 31, page 554).

Radioactive iodine-131 is used in the diagnosis and treatment of thyroid gland disorders. The thyroid gland, located in the neck, affects the rate of growth and

---

†Significant differences, resulting from mass differences, are found in the physical properties and reaction rates of the lighter elements, particularly the isotopes of hydrogen.

metabolism. Disorders in the gland are associated with the rate at which iodine-131 appears in the gland. Thus, a patient is given a solution of tagged NaI*. A detector placed near the thyroid gland measures the uptake of iodine in the gland.

Obstruction of a blood vessel by a clot or a bubble (embolism) is detected with *fibrinogen,* a soluble protein, tagged with ^{125}I*; the tagged fibrinogen piles up at the obstruction and signals an above-average blood activity.

Brain tumors can be located with great accuracy because of their greater tendency to absorb certain radioisotopes, such as ^{111}In and ^{64}Cu, from the bloodstream. Gallium-67 has been proved 95 % accurate in locating lesions due to Hodgkin's disease that are located deep within the body.

The reactions of many biochemicals of metabolic interest, such as sugars, fats, amino acids, hormones, and drugs, can be followed in the body by tagging these compounds with carbon-14 or tritium, ^3H. Recent studies in which tagged tetrahydrocannabinol (the major active component in marijuana, page 133) was administered intravenously show that this compound persists in the blood stream for more than 3 days, and that the products of metabolism of the compound are excreted in the urine for more than 8 days.

The application of radioisotope tracers in agriculture has given us a better understanding of the mechanism of plant growth. This, in turn, has led to an increase in crop production. Also, more efficient use of fertilizers has resulted from studies with fertilizers tagged with radioactive phosphorus, potassium, and copper. The direct application of radiation to the seeds or the plants themselves has given rise to new varieties of better plant products.

The ban on the use of synthetic pesticides such as DDT† has accelerated the search for other methods of controlling destructive insects. An ingenious application utilizes the fact that somewhat less than lethal doses of radiation cause sterility in male insects. Gamma irradiation of the screwworm fly has practically eliminated the fly from the island of Curacao (Caribbean Sea) and has effectively controlled the fly in the United States. The screwworm fly lays its eggs in the wounds of farm animals. The resulting larvae feed on living flesh and eventually kill the animal. The release of male flies, sterilized by radiation, along with the fact that female flies mate only once in their lifetime, causes the majority of eggs not to hatch and thus greatly reduces the fly population. The *sterile male release* technique is now under study to control other insect pests. It has been successfully used to eliminate the wild Mediterranean fruit-fly population that recently invaded Southern California. However, the attempt to eradicate the mosquito in El Salvador by use of a chemical sterilizing agent has not been successful.

Since the decrease in the intensity of radiation is dependent on the quantity of matter it passes through, radiation is used as a gauge in the thickness control of industrial products ranging from metal plates and plastic films to cigarettes. The wear-resistant properties of the moving parts of an engine are easily measured by using radioactive parts and determining the transfer of radioactivity to the lubricating oil. Similarly, the wear-resistant properties of tools, automobile tires, and floor waxes may be determined.

Extremely sensitive methods of analysis are based on the formation of radioiso-

---

† Because of its tendency to concentrate in certain tissue in fish (page 325) and its effect on the bird population, DDT, a persistent pesticide, has been banned. Many insect pests, such as the housefly and the mosquito, have built up an immunity to DDT. Chromatographic studies with DDT tagged with carbon-14 show that the fly changes the DDT to a harmless compound known as "DDE" by an enzymatic reaction. The use of DDT in the control of yellow fever, encephalitis, dengue, and elephantiasis disease-carrying mosquitoes is an absolute necessity for many countries. A vaccine that immunizes monkeys against human malaria has been developed by Wasim Siddiqui at the University of Hawaii.

topes by neutron capture. When a sample is exposed to neutrons, each constituent element forms a specific radioisotope, identified from its characteristic half-life. Then, from the activity of the radioisotope, the mass of the element from which it was formed is obtained; the greater the activity, the greater the quantity of the element present. The method, known as **neutron activation analysis,** makes it possible to analyze elements in complex biological systems, in archaeological samples, and in meteorites, *without destruction* of the original sample. More recently, the method has found application in the investigation of crime. For example, it is possible to determine whether a suspect has recently fired a gun; the detonation of the primer leaves extremely small quantities of antimony, barium, and copper on the hand. A wax cast made of the hand picks up these elements; the cast is then subjected to neutron activation analysis.

The future of radiosiotope applications appears to be limited only by our imagination.

EPILOG From "Our Point of View." Copyright © 1921 by Scientific American, Inc. All rights reserved.

"The subject of atomic energy was well to the fore in the recent convention of chemists in New York, where some of the best papers were devoted to the study of the ever-recurring question these days as to how and whence the coming generations will secure the needed energy for light, heat, transportation and the thousand-and-one other requirements of human life. In this search we have at one time or another considered (with more or less doubt as to their filling the huge demand) coal and oil, natural gas, the energy of the earth's rotation and that of the wind, the tides and the waves. Water power, of course, is included, and we are told that the solar heat that beats on the Sahara desert represents in energy the daily equivalent of some six billion tons of coal. But none of these possibilities is so attractive as that of atomic energy. It was Rutherford who said, 'The race may date its development from the day of the discovery of a method of utilizing atomic energy. So enormous is this energy that it will confer on the man or the nation that learns to release and control it a power only less than that of the Omnipotent. Before that day arrives let us hope that a way will have been found to put more of the human into what we are pleased to call human nature.'"

PROBLEMS

13 Vocabulary Define or illustrate (a) α particle, (b) β particle, (c) γ ray, (d) positron, (e) binding energy, (f) radioactive series, (g) half-life, (h) fission, (i) fusion, (j) radioactive tracer.

14 Balance the following nuclear reactions (write element symbols where possible, mass number, and atomic number for ?):

(a) $^{54}_{26}Fe + ^{4}_{2}He \longrightarrow 2^{1}_{1}H + ?$

(b) $^{27}_{13}Al + ^{4}_{2}He \longrightarrow ^{30}_{15}P + ?$

(c) $^{32}_{16}S + _{0}n^{1} \longrightarrow ^{1}_{1}H + ?$

(d) $^{96}_{42}Mo + ^{2}_{1}H \longrightarrow _{0}n^{1} + ?$

(e) $^{98}_{42}Mo + _{0}n^{1} \longrightarrow ^{99}_{43}Tc + ?$

(f) $^{13}_{6}C + ? \longrightarrow ^{14}_{6}C$

(g) $^{40}_{18}Ar + ? \longrightarrow ^{43}_{19}K + ^{1}_{1}H$

(h) $? + _{0}n^{1} \longrightarrow ^{24}_{11}Na + ^{4}_{2}He$

(i) $^{40}_{20}Ca + ? \longrightarrow ^{40}_{19}K + ^{1}_{1}H$

(j) $^{241}_{95}Am + ^{4}_{2}He \longrightarrow ^{243}_{97}Bk + ?$

(k) $^{246}_{96}Cm + ^{12}_{6}C \longrightarrow 4_{0}n^{1} + ?$

(l) $^{238}_{92}U + ? \longrightarrow ^{249}_{100}Fm + 5_{0}n^{1}$

(m) $^{27}_{13}Al + ? \longrightarrow ^{25}_{12}Mg + ^{4}_{2}He$

(n) $^{250}_{98}Cf + ^{11}_{5}B \longrightarrow 4_{0}n^{1} + ?$

(o) $^{9}_{4}Be + ? \longrightarrow ^{6}_{3}Li + ^{4}_{2}He$

(p) $^{53}_{24}Cr + ^{4}_{2}He \longrightarrow ? + ^{56}_{26}Fe$

(q) $^{37}_{17}Cl + _{0}\nu^{0}$ (neutrino*) $\longrightarrow ^{37}_{18}Ar + ?$

*The neutrino is a massless, chargeless particle predicted by Wolfgang Pauli and Enrico Fermi in 1931 to maintain conservation principles in particle disintegrations.

(r) $_{82}Pb + _{82}Pb \longrightarrow ?$

(s) $^{205}_{81}Tl + ^{58}_{26}Fe \longrightarrow ? + 2_0n^1$

15 Balance the following nuclear reactions (write element symbols where possible, mass number, and atomic number for ?):

(a) $^{104}_{47}Ag \longrightarrow ^{104}_{48}Cd + ?$

(b) $^{87}_{36}Kr \longrightarrow _{-1}\beta^0 + ?$

(c) $^{231}_{91}Pa \longrightarrow ^{227}_{89}Ac + ?$

(d) $^{230}_{90}Th \longrightarrow ^{4}_{2}He + ?$

(e) $^{82}_{35}Br \longrightarrow ^{82}_{36}Kr + ?$

(f) $? \longrightarrow ^{24}_{12}Mg + _{-1}\beta^0$

(g) $^{212}_{84}Po \longrightarrow ^{208}_{82}Pb + ?$

(h) $^{122}_{53}I \longrightarrow ^{122}_{54}Xe + ?$

(i) $? \longrightarrow ^{23}_{11}Na + _{+1}\beta^0$

(j) $^{19}_{10}Ne \longrightarrow _{+1}\beta^0 + ?$

(k) $^{59}_{26}Fe \longrightarrow _{-1}\beta^0 + ?$

(l) $^{40}_{19}K \longrightarrow ? + _{-1}\beta^0$

(m) $^{37}_{18}Ar + e^- \, (orbital \, electron) \longrightarrow ?$

(n) $^{56}_{26}Fe + e^- \, (orbital \, electron) \longrightarrow ?$

(o) $^{26}_{13}Al \longrightarrow ^{25}_{12}Mg + ?$

(p) $^{137}_{53}I \longrightarrow _0n^1 + ?$

(q) $^{22}_{11}Na \longrightarrow ^1_1H + ?$

16 Series (a) The radioactive series that begins with $^{235}_{92}U$ and ends with $^{207}_{82}Pb$ undergoes the following sequence of emissions: $\alpha, \beta, \alpha, \beta, \alpha, \alpha, \alpha, \alpha, \beta, \beta, \alpha$. Identify the radioisotope produced in each step. (b) Marie Curie and others isolated polonium from uranium ores. Yet its half-life of 138.3 days indicates that the polonium should have disappeared from the Earth many years ago. How can you explain this apparent inconsistency?

17 Half-life (a) The half-life of $^{60}_{37}Co$ is 5.3 yr. Starting with 10.0 mg of ^{60}Co, how much will remain after 21.2 yr? (b) How much will be left after approximately 1100 days, starting with 20.0 g of sample? 365 days = 1 yr.

18 The carcinogen nitrosamine (nitroso dimethylamine, Chap. 19) has a half-life of 30 minutes in direct sunlight. Starting with 1.00 mg in the morning (sunny day), find the quantity remaining after 6 hours.

19 (a) A radioisotope disintegrates at the rate of 6400 counts per minute. 6.00 hours later, the disintegration rate is 1600 counts per minute. What is the half-life of the radioisotope? (b) The quantity of "bomb-test ^{90}Sr" in the bones of an individual in 1959 was about 80 disintegrations per second, dps. How many half-lives and how many years are necessary to reduce the activity to the natural back-

ground level of 2.5 dps? In what year will the activity be 2.5 dps? See page 535.

20 The activity of a sample of ^{90}Sr is 6000 dps. After 87 years the activity is 750 dps. Calculate the half-life of ^{90}Sr.

21 (a) Use Equation 1, page 536. A sample of an axhead found in Non Nok Tha, Thailand, has a ^{14}C activity of 8.7 d/(min g). Estimate the age of the ax. (b) A sample of wood from a Thracian chariot found in an excavation in Karanovo, Bulgaria, yields an activity of 11.2 d/(min g). Estimate the age of the chariot and the year it was made.

22 The concentration of $^{85}_{36}Kr$, $t_{1/2} = 10.73$ yr, at 15 km altitude is 10.0 picocuries, pc, per m^3 (see App. IX). How many years will pass before the concentration of $^{85}_{36}Kr$ is reduced to 0.625 pc/m^3?

23 Mass-energy Calculate the bond (binding) energy, in kJ/mole and kcal/mole of P, for the formation of (a) $^{30}_{15}P$ ($15^1_1H + 15_0n^1 \longrightarrow ^{30}_{15}P$) and (b) $^{31}_{15}P$ ($15^1_1H + 16_0n^1 \longrightarrow ^{30}_{15}P$). Which is the more stable isotope? $^1_1H = 1.00783$; $_0n^1 = 1.00867$; $^{30}_{15}P = 29.9880$; $^{31}_{15}P = 30.97376$.

24 Calculate the energy released or absorbed, in (a) erg/mole, (b) kJ/mole, and (c) kcal/mole, for the following reactions:

(i) $^{230}_{90}Th \longrightarrow ^4_2He + ^{226}_{88}Ra$

(ii) $^{59}_{27}Co + ^2_1H \longrightarrow ^{60}_{27}Co + ^1_1H$

(iii) $^{26}_{13}Al \longrightarrow ^1_1H + ^{25}_{12}Mg$

Atomic masses: $^{230}_{90}Th = 230.0332$; $^{226}_{88}Ra = 226.02544$; $^4_2He = 4.00260$; $^{59}_{27}Co = 58.9332$; $^{60}_{27}Co = 59.9529$; $^2_1H = 2.01410$; $^1_1H = 1.00783$; $^{26}_{13}Al = 25.9941$; $^{25}_{12}Mg = 24.98584$. 10^{10} erg = 1 kJ.

25 Given:

$$_{82}Pb + _{24}Cr \longrightarrow W$$
$$_{98}Cf + _8O \longrightarrow W$$
$$W \longrightarrow \alpha + X$$
$$X \longrightarrow \alpha + Y$$
$$Y \longrightarrow \alpha + Z$$

State (a) the atomic numbers of W, X, Y, and Z, and (b) the element symbols of W, X, Y, and Z.

26 One method of estimating the minimum age of the Earth is based on an analysis of natural uranium minerals from various parts of the world, all of which contain $^{206}_{82}Pb$ (Fig. 17.5, page 533). From the quantity of $^{206}_{82}Pb$ found in a mineral, the amount of $^{238}_{92}U$ that disintegrated can be calculated. For example, a mineral contains 100 mg of $^{238}_{92}U$ and 15.0 mg of $^{206}_{82}Pb$. One mole of ^{238}U produces one mole of ^{206}Pb; then the initial quantity of ^{238}U is given by

100 mg ^{238}U

$$+ \left(15.0 \text{ mg } ^{206}Pb \times \frac{238 \text{ mg } ^{238}U}{206 \text{ mg } ^{206}Pb}\right)$$

$$= 117 \text{ mg } ^{238}U$$

The $t_{1/2}$ for $^{238}U \longrightarrow {}^{206}Pb$ is 4.47×10^9 yr. Calculate the age of the mineral, taken as the minimum age of the Earth.

27 The lifetime of a proton is 10^{35} seconds. How does this span of time compare with the age of the universe, estimated at 10^{10} years? (a) Is it longer or shorter? (b) By how many years?

28 Radioisotopes are used to measure the normal or abnormal action of the thyroid gland. Explain.

29 See Fig. 17.6, page 534. Plot the log of the mass of $^{15}_{8}O$ (y-axis) versus the time (x-axis). Describe the graph, which is typical of first order reactions.

30 A laser selectively excites ^{202}Hg but not ^{200}Hg nor ^{201}Hg. The mercury gas is then subjected to an oxidation process that produces a solid. Which isotope is most likely to separate out? Explain.

31 **Tracers** (a) A soil is bathed with ^{14}C-labeled nutrients and incubated. The gaseous products emitted contain ^{14}C. Draw a conclusion and justify it. (b) A soil is exposed to ^{14}CO and $^{14}CO_2$ and incubated. After some time, all gases are removed and the soil is baked at 625 °C; the products contain ^{14}C. Draw a conclusion and justify it.

32 The ion H^{2-} (existence predicted in 1936 [Chap. 18], detected in a mass spectrometer in 1975) decomposes to $H^- + e^-$. Its activity is decreased by $1/8$ in 6.9×10^{-8} s. Find its half-life.

33 **Pollution** In studies near Boulder, Colorado, 6.4×10^{17} atoms of radioactive ^{210}Po have been detected per gram of pine needles. Find the number of atoms, moles, and grams of ^{210}Po deposited on 1.0 kg of pine needles.

34 Biological half-lives include both radioactive decay rates and excretion rates. The biological half-life of ^{14}C for fatty tissue is 12 days. Its radioactive decay half-life is 5.73×10^3 yr. What is the significance of these data?

35 $^{20}_{10}Ne$, $^{23}_{11}Na$, $^{25}_{12}Mg$, and $^{27}_{13}Al$ are stable isotopes. What is the most likely path of decay for unstable $^{25}_{11}Na$?

36 A laser beam is "tuned" to the frequency corresponding to the vibrational frequency of the ^{37}Cl isotope:

$$^{35}Cl + {}^{37}Cl + hf \longrightarrow$$
$$^{35}Cl(ground\ state) + {}^{37}Cl\ (excited)$$

The gases are then treated with ethylene:

^{35}Cl (*ground state*) + ^{37}Cl (*excited*) +

One photon separates one atom of isotope ^{37}Cl. Find the minimum number of photons needed to obtain 3.50 mg of H_2IC—$CH_2{}^{37}Cl$.

37 Library Read one of the following:
(a) "The Nature of the α Particle from Radioactive Substances," E. Rutherford and T. Royds, *Philosophical Magazine,* volume 17, 1909, page 281.
(b) "Superheavy Elements," *Science,* volume 178, 8 December 1972, page 1047.
(c) "Oil Spills," Philip Abelson, *Science,* volume 195, 14 January 1977, page 138.
(d) "A National Plan for Energy Research, Development and Demonstration: Creating Energy Choices for the Future," Report ERDA 76-1, Volume 1: The Plan, U.S. Energy Research and Development Administration, Washington, D.C., 20545.
(e) "Nuclear Power Compared to What?" David Rose, Patrick Walsh, and Larry Leskovjan, *American Scientist,* volume 64, 1976, page 291.
(f) "Energy: Use, Conservation, and Supply," A Special *Science* Compendium, Philip Abelson, Editor, American Association for the Advancement of Science, 1974.
(g) "Scientists with a Secret," Spencer Weart, *Physics Today,* February 1976, page 23.
(h) "Meteorological Consequences of Atmospheric Krypton-85," William Boeck, *Science,* volume 193, 16 July 1976, page 195 (skip the math).
(i) "European Breeders," *Science,* volume 191, 13 February 1976, page 551.
(j) "The Maturity and Future of Nuclear Energy," Alvin Weinberg, *American Scientist,* volume 64, January/February 1976, page 16.
(k) "Atomic Bomb Radiation Studies in Japan," Stuart Finch and Howard Hamilton, *Science,* volume 192, 28 May 1976, page 845.
(l) "Nuclear Energy, A Policy Proposal," President-Elect James Carter, *Chemical Technology,* November 1976, page 668.
(m) "Reprocessing of Nuclear Fuels," William Bebbington, *Scientific American,* December 1976, page 30.
(n) "The Technology Behind Nuclear Proliferation", *Chemical and Engineering News,* 25 July 1977, page 17.

38 France is the leader in developing new (nuclear breeder) energy technology. An experimental breeder power station, expected to be ready for operation in the United States about 1983, may be further delayed. In what way, if any, does this affect you? Explain.

39 Calculate the bond (binding) energy in (a) erg/mole, (b) kJ/mole, and (c) kcal/mole of ^{12}C for the formation of $^{12}_6C$: $6^1_1H + 6_0n^1 \longrightarrow {}^{12}_6C$. Masses are: $^1_1H = 1.00783$ g/mole, $_0n^1 = 1.00867$ g/mole.

40 Assume that a nuclear fuel reprocessing plant releases 10 megacuries of ^{85}Kr, a $_{-1}\beta^0$ emitter with $t_{1/2} = 10.73$ yr. Find the number of years required to reduce this quantity to 3 nanocuries. See App. II and App. IX.

41 A laser beam is tuned to ionize $^{32}SF_6(g)$ but not $^{33}SF_6(g)$ nor $^{34}SF_6(g)$. After the ionization, what kind of instrument would you use to effect an isotopic separation?

42 Absorption of $^{99}_{43}Tc$ by cells in brain tumors is greater than in normal cells. Sodium technetate(VII), $Na^{99}TcO_4$, is therefore used in brain scanning to obtain information about the size and location of tumors. Plot the following data and find the ^{99}Tc half-life:

Disintegrations per minute, d/min	Time, h
200	0
144	2.5
116	5.0
86	7.5
65	10.0
51	12.5
38	15.0
27	17.5

43 (a) A good grade of coal averages an output of 6.1×10^6 kcal/ton. Fission of one mole of ^{235}U releases 5×10^9 kcal. Find the coal tonnage needed to produce the same energy as one pound of ^{235}U. (b) Power plants supplying New York City require the equivalent of about 2×10^5 tons of coal per day. Calculate the number of days that 1 lb of ^{235}U could supply New York City. See App. III for conversion factors.

44 A piece of charred bone found in the ruins of an American Indian village has a ^{14}C to ^{12}C ratio 0.72 times that found in living organisms. Calculate the age of the bone fragment.

45 On December 2, 1942, the first man-made self-sustaining nuclear fission chain reactor was operated by Enrico Fermi under the University of Chicago stadium. In June, 1972, natural fission reactors, operating billions of years ago, were discovered by the French Atomic Energy Laboratories in Oklo, Gabon. At present, natural uranium contains 0.720 % ^{235}U. How many years ago did natural uranium contain 3.00 % ^{235}U, sufficient to sustain a natural reactor? What would you search for in natural uranium to find evidence of fission? $t_{1/2}$ for ^{235}U is 7.04×10^8 yr.

46 The oldest known fossil cells form a biological cluster found in Swaziland, South Africa. The fossil has been dated by the reaction $^{87}Rb \longrightarrow {}^{87}Sr + {}_{-1}\beta^0$, $t_{1/2} = 4.7 \times 10^{10}$ yr. The ratio of the present quantity to the original quantity of ^{87}Rb is 0.951. Calculate the age of the fossil cells.

47 Over the past 28 years, 20,000 oil wells were drilled, resulting in only three major spills (including one at Santa Barbara, California; see Problem 37c). A National Academy of Business study concludes that production accounts for 1.3 % of ocean petroleum pollution, while tankers account for 34.9 %. The U.S. General Accounting Office suggests "that importing more oil may be better national policy than financing high cost privately-owned synthetic fuel projects." What, in your opinion, should be the national priority among the following energy sources? (a) oil importation, (b) drilling off the Atlantic shore, (c) nuclear energy, or (d) synthetic fuels. Before answering, look at "High Price Tag on Energy Program," *Chemical & Engineering News,* 30 August 1976, page 17.

48 Radiation biological damage starts with the production of highly reactive substances like H, OH, HO_2, H_2O_2, and $e^-(H_2O)_x$. Write balanced equations showing how these could be formed from water.

49 A 1.0 cm thickness of lead and a 5.0 cm thickness of concrete reduce γ-radiation by 1/2. Find the wall thickness of (a) lead and (b) concrete required (i) to reduce 1280 roentgen, r (see App. IX), to 5 r; (ii) to reduce 2000 r to 1 r.

50 Acetic acid, $CH_3-\overset{\overset{O}{\|}}{C}-OH$, reacts with methyl alcohol, CH_3OH, by eliminating a molecule of H_2O to form methyl acetate, $CH_3-\overset{\overset{O}{\|}}{C}-O-CH_3$. How would you use ^{18}O to show whether the oxygen atom in the water product comes from the $-OH$ in the acid or from the $-OH$ in the alcohol?

51 See page 541. Calculate the energy released, in kJ/mole and in kcal/mole of ^1H, for the fusion-fission reaction $^{11}_{5}B + ^{1}_{1}H \longrightarrow ^{12}_{6}C \longrightarrow 3^{4}_{2}He$. Atomic masses: $^{11}_{5}B = 11.0093$, $^{4}_{2}He = 4.00260$, $^{1}_{1}H = 1.00783$.

52 Comment on the statement (Richard Falk, Professor of International Law): "Even if we develop a nearly flawless nuclear energy technology, we cannot visualize a flawless cadre of human overseers of this technology so as to provide protection for tens of centuries. We are the wrong species for this technology."

ANSWERS

1 $^{227}_{93}Np \longrightarrow ^{4}_{2}He + ^{223}_{91}Pa$

2 (a) $^{217}_{86}Rn$; (b) $^{253}_{101}Md$; (c) $^{216}_{84}Po$

3 $^{35}_{16}S \longrightarrow _{-1}\beta^{0} + ^{35}_{17}Cl$

4 (a) $^{3}_{2}He$; (b) $^{131}_{54}Xe$; (c) $^{210}_{84}Po$

5 $^{231}_{90}Th$, $^{231}_{91}Pa$, $^{227}_{89}Ac$, $^{223}_{87}Fr$, $^{223}_{88}Ra$

6 4 half-lives, 116 yr

7 about 6.76×10^{2} yr old, about 1300

8 (a) $_{+1}\beta^{0}$; (b) $^{41}_{19}K$; (c) $^{21}_{11}Na$; (d) $_{+1}\beta^{0}$

9 (a) $^{60}_{28}Ni$; (b) $^{24}_{12}Mg$

10 2.93×10^{9} kJ/mole, 7.02×10^{8} kcal/mole

11 (a) $^{10}_{4}Be$; (b) $^{17}_{9}F$; (c) $^{1}_{1}H$; (d) $^{1}_{1}H$

12 (c) fission

14 (a) $^{56}_{26}Fe$; (b) $_{0}n^{1}$; (c) $^{32}_{15}P$; (d) $^{97}_{43}Tc$; (e) $_{-1}\beta^{0}$; (f) $_{0}n^{1}$; (g) $^{4}_{2}He$; (h) $^{27}_{13}Al$; (i) $_{0}n^{1}$; (j) $2_{0}n^{1}$; (k) $^{254}_{102}No$; (l) $^{16}_{8}O$; (m) $^{2}_{1}H$; (n) $^{257}_{103}Lr$; (o) $^{1}_{1}H$; (p) $_{0}n^{1}$; (q) $_{-1}\beta^{0}$; (r) $_{164}X$; (s) $_{107}^{261}X$

15 (a) $_{-1}\beta^{0}$; (b) $^{87}_{37}Rb$; (c) $^{4}_{2}He$; (d) $^{226}_{88}Ra$; (e) $_{-1}\beta^{0}$; (f) $^{24}_{12}Na$; (g) $^{4}_{2}He$; (h) $_{-1}\beta^{0}$; (i) $^{23}_{12}Mg$; (j) $^{19}_{9}F$; (k) $^{59}_{27}Co$; (l) $^{40}_{20}Ca$; (m) $^{37}_{17}Cl$; (n) $^{56}_{25}Mn$; (o) $^{1}_{1}H$; (p) $^{136}_{53}I$; (q) $^{21}_{10}Ne$

16 $^{235}_{92}U \longrightarrow ^{231}_{90}Th \longrightarrow ^{231}_{91}Pa$

$^{223}_{88}Ra \longleftarrow ^{227}_{90}Th \longleftarrow ^{227}_{89}Ac$

$^{219}_{86}Rn \longrightarrow ^{215}_{84}Po \longrightarrow ^{211}_{82}Pb$

$^{207}_{82}Pb \longleftarrow ^{211}_{84}Po \longleftarrow ^{211}_{83}Bi$

17 (a) 0.625 mg; (b) 13.5 g

18 2.44×10^{-4} mg

19 (a) 3.0 h; (b) 5 half-lives, 2104

20 29 yr

21 (a) about 3930 yr old;
(b) about 1844 yr old, about 133 AD

22 42.9 yr

23 (a) 2.34×10^{10} kJ/mole, 5.59×10^{9} kcal/mole
(b) 2.54×10^{10} kJ/mole, 6.07×10^{9} kcal/mole, more stable

24 (i)(a) -4.64×10^{18} erg/mole
(b) -4.64×10^{8} kJ/mole
(c) -1.11×10^{8} kcal/mole
(ii)(a) $+1.21 \times 10^{19}$ erg/mole
(b) $+1.21 \times 10^{9}$ kJ/mole
(c) $+2.89 \times 10^{8}$ kcal/mole
(iii)(a) -3.6×10^{17} erg/mole
(b) -3.6×10^{7} kJ/mole
(c) -8.6×10^{6} kcal/mole

25 $_{106}W$, $_{104}X$, $_{102}No$, $_{100}Fm$

26 1.01×10^{9} yr

27 (a) proton longer; (b) 10^{27} yr

30 ^{202}Hg

32 2.3×10^{-8} s

33 6.4×10^{20} atoms, 1.1×10^{-3} mole, 2.2×10^{-1} g

35 $^{25}_{11}Na \longrightarrow _{-1}\beta^{0} + ^{25}_{12}Mg$

36 1.10×10^{19} photons

39 (a) -8.91×10^{19} erg/mole
(b) -8.91×10^{9} kJ/mole
(c) -2.13×10^{9} kcal/mole

40 555 yr

42 6.1 h

43 (a) 1.6×10^{3} tons; (b) 0.008 day

44 2717 yr

45 1.4×10^{9} yr

46 3.4×10^{9} yr

49 (i)(a) 8.0 cm lead; (b) 40 cm concrete
(ii)(a) 11 cm lead; (b) 55 cm concrete

51 8.39×10^{8} kJ/mole, 2.01×10^{8} kcal/mole

GLOSSARY

alpha particle The nucleus of a helium atom, $^{4}_{2}He$, consisting of two neutrons and two protons, emitted by radioactive nuclei.

beta particle A high speed electron, $_{-1}\beta^{0}$, emitted by radioactive nuclei.

binding energy The energy required to separate a nucleus into its individual nucleons.

breeder reactor A nuclear reactor that produces more fissionable atoms than it consumes.

fission The splitting of one nucleus into two nuclei.

fusion The combination of small nuclei to form larger nuclei.

gamma radiation A radiation similar to X-rays, but of higher energy, emitted by radioactive nuclei.

half-life The time required for one half of a given quantity of sample to react.

nuclear reaction The conversion of an isotope of one element into an isotope of another element.

nuclear reactor A device in which a nuclear fission chain reaction is controlled and serves as a heat source.

positron A particle identical to an electron except that its charge is $+1$, $_{+1}\beta^0$.

radioactive series A number of successive nuclear reactions starting with an unstable isotope and stopping with the formation of a stable isotope.

radioactivity Nuclear changes that occur naturally with the emission of highly energetic beams, usually consisting of one or more of three separate beams, $_2^4\alpha$, $_{-1}\beta^0$, or γ.

radiodating The use of half-lives of nuclear reactions to determine the age of rocks, fossils, and other objects.

radioisotope A radioactive isotope.

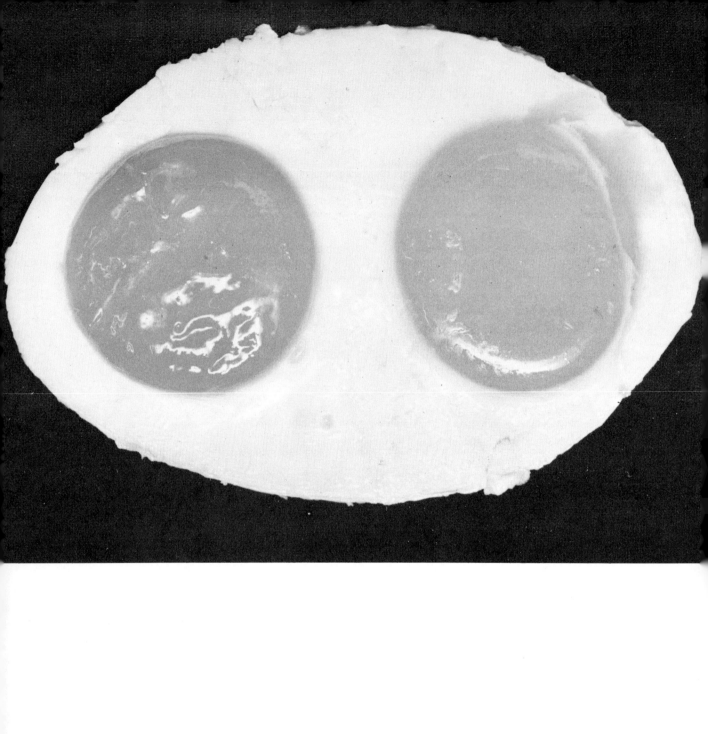

THE COVALENT BOND: THE SHAPE OF MOLECULES

18

THE COVALENT BOND AND ATOMIC ORBITALS REVISITED————————18.1

In a previous chapter (Chap. 8) we attempted to explain how atoms are held together by electrical attraction. In ionic solids, the electronic charges practically sit on the atoms: Na^+Cl^-, $Mg^{2+}O^{2-}$. Intermolecular attractive forces arise from the partial electronic charges sitting at the ends of molecules; $\overset{\delta^+ \ \ \delta^-}{H—F}$. But in representing a bond between atoms with a "dash" or "two dots" and calling it a "covalent bond," we have really labeled our ignorance. This is useful scientific procedure—explanation by use of a label. We think we understand the nature of the ionic bond, but we also recognize what appears to be a different kind of bond, even more widespread in nature than the ionic bond. However, the Lewis theory of bonding cannot locate the charges responsible for holding one hydrogen atom to another, $H:H$, or to a fluorine atom, $H:F$. We will now attempt to locate the charges that give rise to the strong electric attraction (104 kcal/mole) in the $H:H$ molecule.* This compels us to revisit our theory of atomic orbitals.

Atoms are no longer regarded as hard spheres. An atom is viewed as a collection of electrons and a nucleus, the electrons occupying atomic orbitals of definite energy and shape (pages 180 and 197). The orbitals are electron clouds (regions of definite shape) in which the chance of finding an electron is high (page 180).

Properties of Atomic Orbitals: Conservation of Atomic Orbitals   Modern theory assumes that when atoms combine, the action is between the atomic orbitals (electron clouds). For example, in the reaction $H\cdot + H\cdot \longrightarrow H:H$, the $1s$ orbital on one H atom interacts with the $1s$ orbital on a second H atom. These *interactions*—electron-electron repulsion between electrons housed in atomic orbitals, proton-proton repulsion between nuclei, and nuclei-electron attractions—*change the shapes of the orbitals*. The *electron distribution is changed*. However, the *number of orbitals* involved in any chemical change, like the number of atoms, is *conserved*. The interaction of two atomic orbitals results in the formation of two orbitals of different

---

*Partial charges or London forces (page 259) are too small to account for these strong attractive forces, and it is impossible to regard H_2 and HF, gases at room temperatures, as ionic, H^+H^-, H^+F^- (pages 247, 264).

shapes (two different electron distributions). When three atomic orbitals interact, three orbitals of different shapes are formed, and so on.

An atomic orbital corresponds to a definite energy state; the energy of a $2s$ or $2p$ orbital differs from the energy of a $1s$ orbital. Similarly, when atomic orbitals interact, the energy states of the resulting orbitals differ from those of the original atomic orbitals.

These atomic orbital interactions produce new electron distributions with different energies, called **molecular orbitals, MO's.** These molecular orbitals play an important role in holding atoms together in molecules (page 562).

PROBLEM 1   **Six atoms, each with one atomic orbital, are combined so that the six atomic orbitals interact. How many molecular orbitals (MO's) of different shapes and energies are formed?**

The Movement for Electron Freedom   Electrons housed in atomic orbitals are largely confined to the region of space near the nucleus of the atom. However, it is possible to widen the region of space available to an electron by the interaction of atomic orbitals. For example, the electron clouds of two atoms may fuse (overlap), so that the new electron cloud embraces the two nuclei:

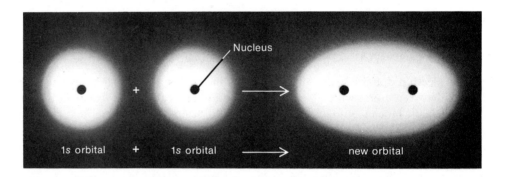

The electrons are no longer restricted to the region of space around one nucleus. They can now wander over the region of two nuclei; the confining volume is increased. To describe this situation, the scientist says that "the electron is *delocalized*." **Delocalization** of an electron means that the region in which it is confined *increases*—electrons can now spread out over a greater portion of space.

With this greater freedom of motion comes a greater stability. More energy is required to remove the electron from the new orbital as compared to the original atomic orbital. Invariably, *the delocalized electron is more stable than the localized electron*. The delocalized electron occupies a lower energy level than the localized electron. Also, more energy is now required to decompose the molecule embraced by the new orbital into isolated atoms.

PROBLEM 2   **Imagine a chain of six carbon atoms and one electron localized in an atomic orbital of one of the six carbon atoms. Now imagine that this electron is delocalized, so that it is free to move throughout the region of the six carbon atoms. (a) Which electron, the localized or the delocalized one, is more stable? (b) The removal to infinity of which electron requires more energy? (c) The separation of which six carbon atoms (C_6 localized or C_6 delocalized) would require more energy?**

This concept of delocalization is used to explain the forces that hold atoms together in molecules and in metals (Chap. 20).

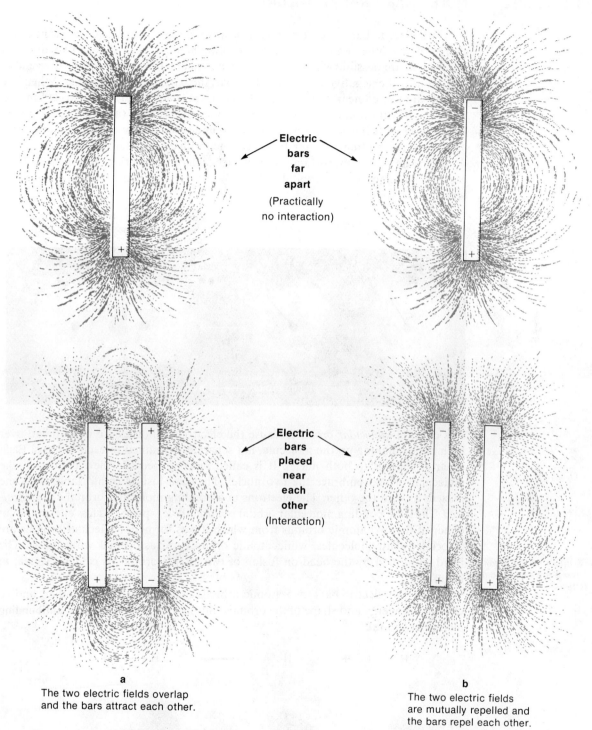

a

The two electric fields overlap
and the bars attract each other.

b

The two electric fields
are mutually repelled and
the bars repel each other.

FIGURE 18.1 The interaction of two electric bars. The two possible changes in the electric fields surrounding the two bars upon approaching each other result in (a) attraction and (b) repulsion without the disappearance of a bar.

18.2—————————**MOLECULAR ORBITAL THEORY**

Two electric bars, each carrying a positive charge at one end and a negative charge at the other end (Fig. 18.1), are brought near each other. Two different interactions are possible without losing one of the bars. If we place the positive end of one bar near the negative end of the other bar, the bars *attract* each other. When like charges are placed near one another, the bars *repel* each other, as illustrated in Fig. 18.1. The distribution of the electric fields in each position, (a) and (b), is altered. These observable interactions may help us to understand atomic orbital interactions.

When two hydrogen atoms approach, each with a $1s$ orbital, two interactions are possible. The two atomic orbitals may attract each other, overlap, and so change the energy and shape of the orbitals; this new orbital is called a **bonding molecular orbital:**

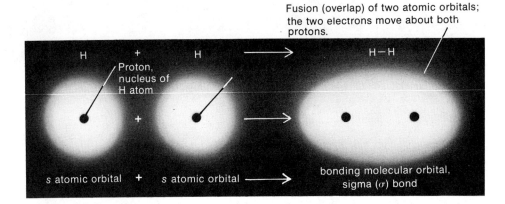

It is called a *molecular orbital* because the electrons it houses are now spread over both nuclei making up the molecule, not separately confined to each nucleus. Each electron belongs to both nuclei. It is called *bonding* because the electrons in the molecular orbital embrace the two nuclei. They are just as comfortable with one nucleus as with the other. The electrons in a bonding molecular orbital are *delocalized*. Thus, the bonding molecular orbital is *more stable*—possesses less energy—than either of the two atomic orbitals from which it was formed. Molecular orbitals are associated with molecules, while atomic orbitals are associated with atoms. The bond so formed by the head-on fusion of two atomic orbitals is called a **sigma, σ, bond.**

Sigma, σ, is the Greek letter equivalent to our letter s.

Like two electric bars, two atomic orbitals may also repel each other, and so change the energy and shape of the orbitals; this new orbital is called an **antibonding molecular orbital:**

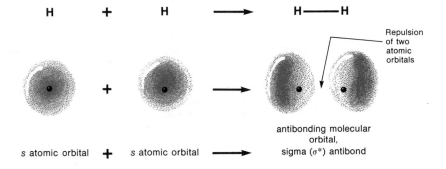

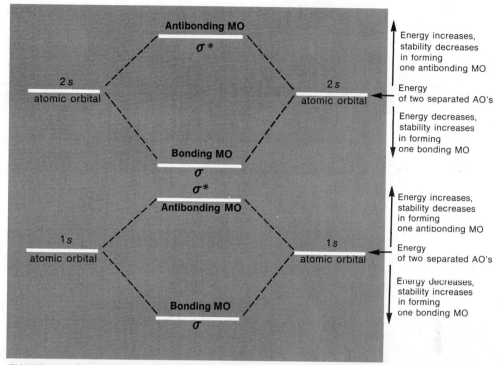

FIGURE 18.2 Energy level diagram showing energies of molecular orbitals resulting from interactions of atomic orbitals.

It is called a *molecular orbital* because the electrons it houses are now associated with the nuclei making up the molecule. It is called *antibonding* because each electron now strongly prefers to stay near the nucleus to which it was originally bound. There is *no overlap,* no fusion of the atomic orbitals. Rather, the repulsion of the atomic orbitals exposes the positively charged nuclei; the *nuclei* thus *repel each other.* Therefore, the antibonding molecular orbital is *less stable,* possesses more energy, than either of the two atomic orbitals from which it was formed. The antibond so formed by the head-on approach of two atomic orbitals is called a **sigma antibond,** denoted by "sigma star," σ^*.

In general, the interaction of any two s orbitals will result in the formation of one bonding molecular orbital, the sigma bond, σ, and one antibonding molecular orbital, the sigma antibond, σ^*.

This discussion may be summarized by an energy level diagram (Fig. 18.2) showing the energy of the molecular orbitals (MO's) that arise from the interaction of s atomic orbitals (AO's).

The shape of an orbital, represented by an electron cloud diagram (pages 181 and 562), tells us the chances of finding electrons in the region of the nucleus of an atom (AO), and in the region of the nuclei of a molecule (MO). In the bonding MO, the electron cloud density is greatest in the region on the line *between* the positive nuclei. It is this high electron density region that attracts and holds nuclei together in molecules. This explains the electrical character of the sigma bond, the covalent bond. The covalent bond results from the flow of electron density from each atom to the region between the nuclei. The positive charges sitting on the two nuclei are attracted

The energies of MO's are not the same for all molecules. They depend upon the energies of the AO's from which they are formed.

to the dense electron region sitting between the two nuclei. This can be visualized as follows:

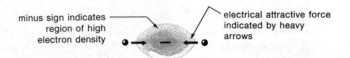

minus sign indicates region of high electron density

electrical attractive force indicated by heavy arrows

The sigma bond in a diatomic molecule

The bonding in diamond, a typical network covalent solid (page 261), may be visualized* as

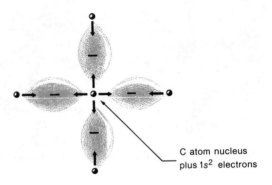

C atom nucleus plus $1s^2$ electrons

These representations are analogous to the arrangement of Na^+ and Cl^- ions in the ionic solid NaCl (page 262):

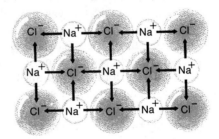

Two electrons in a bonding MO correspond to one bond in electronic formulas (Chap. 8).

In the antibonding MO, the electron density is zero in the region between the positive nuclei. The chance of finding an electron between the nuclei is zero. Rather, the electron density is concentrated at the ends of the molecule *away* from the region between the nuclei, so that the nuclei are exposed to each other. Thus, unlike the bonding MO, the antibonding MO provides no electrical attractive force. The two

---

*The two $1s$ electrons in carbon, not involved in bonding, make no contribution to the bonding and, therefore, are said to be in a *nonbonding molecular orbital*. The energy of nonbonding molecular orbitals is the same as the energy of the atomic orbitals from which they are formed and it has no influence on bonding.

nuclei repel each other. This makes it impossible for the nuclei to approach each other closely.

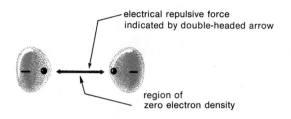

No electrical attractive force

The sigma antibond in a diatomic molecule

Our necks, it seems, have been placed in a theoretical noose: Two hydrogen atoms (two AO's) interact to form a molecule with a bonding MO and an antibonding MO. One causes attraction of the nuclei, and the other causes repulsion of the nuclei. Which one wins the race? The race is described in the next section.

MO ENERGY LEVEL DIAGRAM: ELECTRONIC _____ 18.3
STRUCTURE OF MOLECULES

Recall page 197, where atomic orbital energy levels were set up and successfully used to predict the electronic structures of most atoms. Similarly, the MO energy level diagram on page 563 makes it possible to determine the electronic structure of molecules. The electronic structure of atoms is described by atomic orbitals, while the electronic structure of molecules is described by molecular orbitals.

The existence of molecules may be predicted from these molecular electronic structures.† *If the number of electrons in bonding MO's is greater than the number in antibonding MO's, then the molecule can exist.* However, if the number of bonding and antibonding electrons is equal, or if the antibonding electrons outnumber the bonding electrons, the molecule cannot exist. Like AO's (page 198), MO's are filled in order of decreasing stability, each holding a maximum of two paired electrons; if two or more MO's have the same energy, then (page 205) electrons stay unpaired until each MO has at least one electron in it.

To illustrate this principle, we restrict ourselves to the four MO's generated from two $1s$ and two $2s$ AO's (page 563), identifying them for convenience by the symbols σ_1, σ_1^*, σ_2, σ_2^*. Four MO's, each taking two electrons, make it possible to discuss diatomic (gaseous) molecules having a maximum of eight electrons.

H_2 Does H_2 exist? This molecule has two electrons; these enter the σ_1 MO as shown in Fig. 18.3. The bonding electrons outnumber the antibonding electrons; we therefore predict that H_2 should exist. And, of course, as everyone knows, hydrogen does exist. In fact, liquid hydrogen is shipped (in tank-trucks larger than milk-trucks) through southern states housing space exploration facilities.

---

† The application is here restricted to simple diatomic molecules, but MO's may embrace more than two nuclei. The application of MO theory to more complex molecules becomes more complicated. In the hands of Erich Hückel (1931), the theory has successfully predicted the existence of many previously unknown compounds, typical of which is the ionic compound tropylium bromide, $C_7H_7^+Br^-$, synthesized by William von E. Doering (1954).

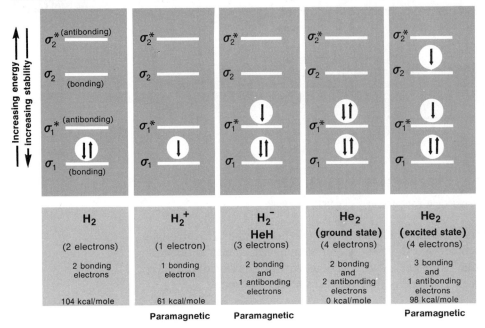

FIGURE 18.3 MO energy level diagrams.† Electronic structures of molecules and ions. Bond energies are given for H_2, H_2^+, and He_2. As in atoms, paramagnetism (page 203) in molecules and ions is associated with unpaired electrons.

†For simplicity, the same diagram is used for the different molecules and ions. Actually, the difference between energy levels depends on the atomic number and the number of electrons in the MO's.

H_2^+ Does H_2^+ exist? This ion has one electron, which enters the σ_1 MO (Fig. 18.3). Since the ion has only one bonding electron, H_2^+ should be easier to decompose (less stable) than H_2, but it should exist. It has been experimentally observed and it is less stable than H_2.

H_2^- Does H_2^- exist? This ion has three electrons (one from each H atom plus the added charge). These fill the σ_1 MO and the third electron enters the σ_1^* MO (Fig. 18.3). Since one electron is in an antibonding MO, H_2^- should be less stable than H_2, but it should exist. It has been experimentally observed. Does helium hydride, HeH, exist? Yes, since like H_2^-, it has three electrons (two from the He atom and one from the H atom).

He_2 Does He_2 exist? This molecule has four electrons, which fill both the σ_1 and σ_1^* MO's (Fig. 18.3). The numbers of bonding and antibonding electrons are now equal; the bonding tendency is canceled by the antibonding tendency. We therefore predict that He_2 should not exist. He_2 has not been experimentally detected. But photon excitation that would "kick" an electron to the next available MO should produce an electron structure (Fig. 18.3) in which the bonding electrons exceed the antibonding electrons. $He_2(excited)$ should exist. It has been experimentally detected and studied.

PROBLEM 3   **See the table of atomic weights (inside back cover) for atomic numbers. (a) How many electrons are in each of the following molecules or ions: (i) $H_3^+(g)$, (ii) $Be_2(g)$, (iii) $BeH(g)$, (iv) $Li_2^+(g)$? (b) Give the MO electronic structure, as in Fig. 18.3, for each particle in (a). (c) Predict which of these should exist. (d) Predict which of these should be paramagnetic.**

Sigma Bonds   Sigma (σ) bonds may also be formed from head-on fusion of an *s* and a *p* AO, or from two *p* AO's, as shown:

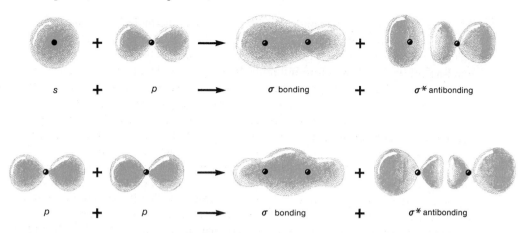

Notice that in each case the bonding MO has a high electron density *between* the nuclei.†

MOLECULAR ORBITAL PI BONDS _____ 18.4

As shown above, two *p* orbitals may approach "head-on" to form sigma bonds. However, another approach is possible. Two *p* orbitals, parallel like railroad tracks, may approach sideways. They fuse together into a bonding MO, called a **pi, π, bond,** and repel each other to form an antibonding MO called a **pi antibond,** denoted by "pi star", π^*:

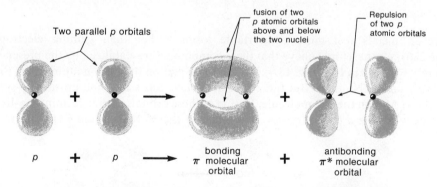

Notice that in the pi (π) bond, fusion of the electron clouds occurs *above* and *below* the two nuclei. The electron density is high in these regions but *zero* between the nuclei. For this reason, π bonds are mainly found in molecules in which σ bonds also form. In the pi star (π^*) bond, repulsion between the lobes of the *p* AO's makes the electron density between them zero.

PROBLEM 4   **Identify as σ, σ^*, π, or π^* and *roughly* sketch the two MO's formed from the following pairs of AO's. (a) s, p head-on; (b) p, p head-on; (c) p, p parallel, side-by-side.**

_____

†These are simplified diagrams. Reproductions (not artist's conceptions) of accurately calculated electron density diagrams of molecular orbitals have been published by Arnold Wahl, *Science,* 25 February 1966, page 961; *Scientific American,* April 1970, page 54.

18.5 _____ MO DECLARES A DIVIDEND:
THE ANTIBONDING MOLECULAR ORBITAL

The occupancy of antibonding orbitals weakens the molecular bond, while the removal of electrons from such orbitals strengthens the bond. This statement emphasizes the view that antibonding orbitals are just as much a part of the molecule as bonding orbitals and therefore influence its properties. The interpretation of many chemical reactions, and the photochemistry (page 195) and ultraviolet (UV) spectra of molecules, involve antibonding orbitals. Three examples will suffice for us.

Electronic transitions in atoms, giving rise to characteristic atomic spectra, involve differences in the energy of AO's (pages 186 and 193). Similarly, electronic transitions in molecules giving rise to characteristic molecular spectra involve differences in the energy of MO's. As with the energy difference between AO's in atoms, the energy difference between MO's is experimentally obtained from spectral studies. These transitions occur in the visible and UV range (Color Plate V(A)) and almost invariably the photon absorbed excites an electron to an antibonding MO. A π to π^* transition in formaldehyde (page 131) produces its characteristic UV absorption.

Carbon monoxide ($:C\equiv O:$) directly combines with many transition metals, forming *carbonyl* compounds such as chromium hexacarbonyl, $Cr(CO)_6$, a colorless solid decomposing at about 190 °C; iron pentacarbonyl, $Fe(CO)_5$, a yellow liquid, b.p. 103 °C; and nickel tetracarbonyl, $Ni(CO)_4$, a colorless liquid, b.p. 43 °C. The electron pair at the carbon end of the molecule is used for bond formation, as in the combination of NH_3 with H^+ or BF_3 (page 250), as shown:

Dangerous: in general, carbonyl compounds are very toxic and flammable, and their vapors form explosive mixtures with air.

However, metals feel more comfortable losing rather than gaining electrons (page 226). We therefore believe that these compounds are stabilized by the presence of empty π^* MO's in CO (Fig. 18.4). The electron pair on the carbon atom enters the *d* orbitals on the Ni atom. But these *d* orbitals have lobes that line up side-by-side with the π^* MO on the CO molecule. Fusion of these orbitals occurs, forming a π-like bond between the *d* orbital on the Ni atom and the π^* MO on the CO molecule:

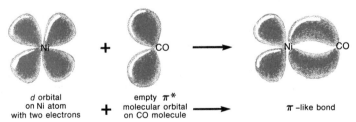

d orbital
on Ni atom
with two electrons

+

empty π^*
molecular orbital
on CO molecule

π –like bond

This type of bonding, important in the chemistry of transition metals, stabilizes the metal—CO bond, but since the electrons enter an antibonding orbital in CO, the $C\equiv O$ bond is weakened, although the bonding electrons still outnumber the antibonding electrons (Fig. 18.4).

The electron transition, π to π^*, makes many atmospheric (photochemical smog, page 196) and biochemical reactions possible. Vision requires the turning around of a double-bonded carbon atom, as shown:

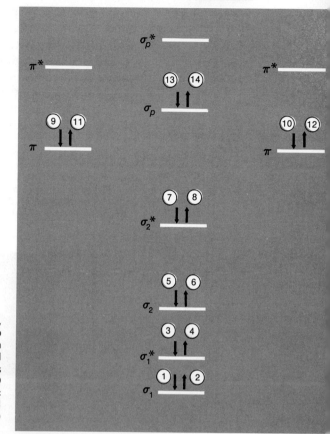

FIGURE 18.4 Electronic structure of CO. Five AO's from C (one 1s, one 2s, three 2p) and five AO's from O (one 1s, one 2s, three 2p) interact to generate 10 MO's. σ_p and $\sigma_p{}^*$ denote MO's formed from the head-on approach of two p AO's (page 567). The 14 electrons in CO, six from $_6$C and eight from $_8$O, are placed in the MO's in the order given by the numbers over the arrows. (The reader should not attempt to memorize this MO energy level diagram; the energy of these orbitals is affected by atomic numbers.) Cancelling bonding and antibonding electrons leaves one σ and two π bonds to hold the C and O atoms together. The electronic (Lewis) formula is :C≡O:.

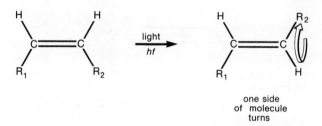

R$_1$ and R$_2$ represent two complicated structures of C, H, and O atoms that need not concern us.

No turn, no vision. How does this reaction occur? The electronic structure of the double bond (four electrons) is

$$
\begin{array}{ll}
\sigma^* & \text{———} \\
\pi^* & \text{———} \\
\pi & \text{↓↑} \\
\sigma & \text{↓↑}
\end{array}
$$

Upon absorption of a photon, one electron is excited from the π (bonding) to the π^* (antibonding) MO. This weakens the bond, making it possible for one end to turn (rotate) with respect to the other end.

THE SHAPE (GEOMETRY) OF MOLECULES _____ 18.6

We remind ourselves that the existence of atoms and molecules is an essential assumption of all theories of matter. Nevertheless, today we talk about the shape (geometry) of molecules—the position of atoms in molecules with respect to each other*—with justifiable confidence that we may falsely conclude that their existence is proven. Rather, the shape, like bond lengths (page 234), is obtained from an *interpretation* of diffraction patterns (page 188) generated by the reflection of photons or electrons by matter (Fig. 18.5). Max von Laue predicted and verified (1912) that the atoms of matter are so closely packed that they can produce diffraction patterns. The geometry of molecules is an indispensable crutch in understanding the properties and reactions of elements and compounds. *Molecular biology,** for

---

*The establishment of the foundation for writing structural formulas with the understanding that definite bonds exist between atoms arranged in a particular manner is credited to Friedrich Kekulé (1858), Archibald Couper (1858), Alexander Butlerov (1861), and Alexander (Crum) Brown (1861).

**The branch of biology that recognizes that biological structures are molecular structures and interprets the chemistry—the functioning—of living organisms at the molecular level in terms of these structures. William Astbury (page 265) is generally recognized as the father of molecular biology.

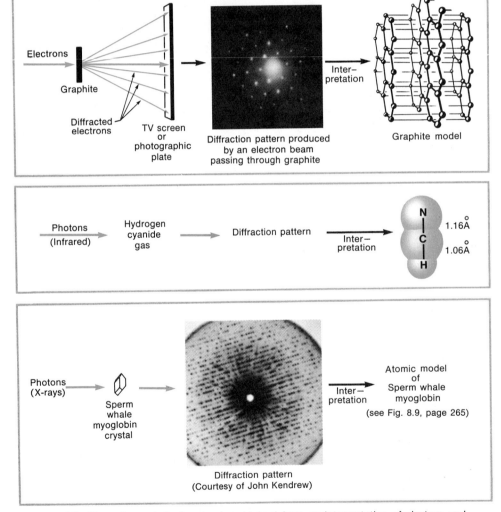

FIGURE 18.5 Shape (geometry) of molecules obtained from an interpretation of electron and photon diffraction patterns. Graphite (Chap. 20) consists of carbon atoms bonded together in layers; the layers are stacked. The distance between C atoms is 1.42 Å, while the distance between layers is 3.35 Å. This hexagonal structure was first proposed in 1924 by John Bernal. HCN is a linear molecule—all three atoms are on a straight line. The distance between atoms is given.

example, would be impossible without the development of the methods that gave us the three-dimensional structures of biological molecules (page 265). The messages that make up our senses of smell, taste, seeing, hearing, and touch are carried by specific molecules. An astonishing example is the fact that the amino acid leucine, a water-soluble, colorless solid found in living matter, has a *sweet taste* when its —NH₂ group "looks to the right," and a *bitter taste* when it "looks to the left":

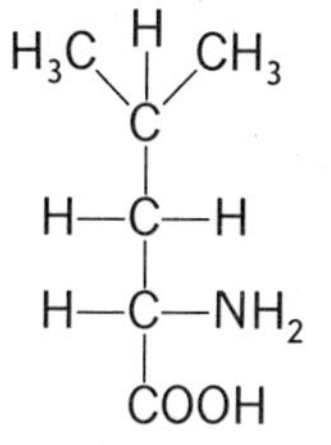

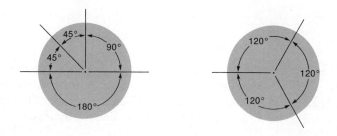

"right-handed" leucine*   "left-handed" leucine*
      sweet taste   bitter taste

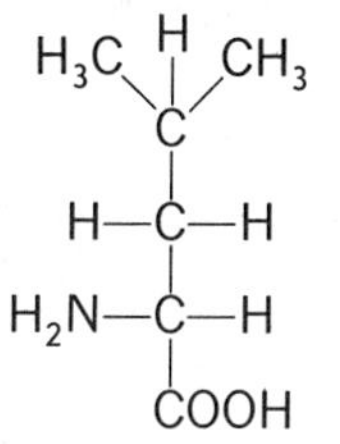

The smell of an orange and a lemon is caused by the same compound, limonene ($C_{10}H_{16}$). But as in leucine, the difference is due to the difference in the "handedness" of the molecule. It smells like an orange when it "looks to the right," but like lemon when it "looks to the left." These differences in taste and smell mean that biological reactions are generally determined by the geometry of molecules.

Construction of Models   The construction of models from Styrofoam balls and tooth-picks or pipe cleaners (2-inch or 5-cm lengths) is helpful to our discussion:

Hook one ball to a second ball as shown: (A)——(B) ⟶ A—B. This repre-

sents a *linear* diatomic *molecule* (two atoms on a straight line); examples are H—H (H_2), and C≡O (CO).

Hook a third ball to ball A so that it is on the same straight line with A—B. The

result is (C)——(A)——(B) ⟶ C—A—B, where three atoms lie on a straight line.

This arrangement is called a *linear* triatomic molecule. Examples are O=C=O (CO_2) and H—C≡N (HCN). The angle between any two bonds is called the **bond angle.** All diatomic molecules are linear. But when the same atom combines with more than one atom and so forms more than one bond, the molecule may not be linear.

The degree symbol, °, is also the unit for measuring angles. A circle corresponds to 360 degrees (360°), ½ circle corresponds to 180°, ¼ circle to 90°, ⅓ circle to 120°, ⅛ circle to 45°, and so forth:

Styrofoam spheres, ¾ inch and 1½ inch in diameter, and many other sizes are obtainable from Star Band Co., Broad & Commerce Sts., Portsmouth, VA 23707.

*Also known as dextroleucine and levoleucine; dextro from *dexter,* the Latin word for right, and *levo* from *loevus,* the Latin word for left. The relationship of odor to shapes of molecules was proposed by John Amoore in 1952.

Divide a circle into three parts as shown above. Hook together four balls in the positions shown:

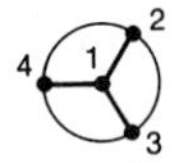

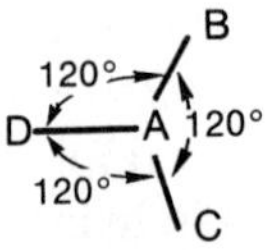

The four atoms lie in a plane, in a flat surface without an atom above or below the others. This arrangement is called **triangular plane.** An example is BF_3

Called triangular plane because the three atoms, DBC, form a triangle lying in a plane (flat surface). Also known as "planar trigonal."

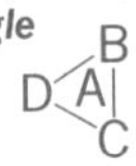

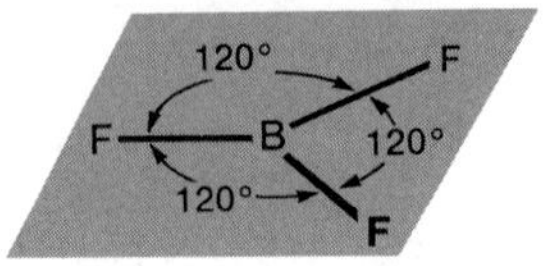

in which the bond angle is 120°.

Hook two balls to a third one to look like "rabbit-ears," like this

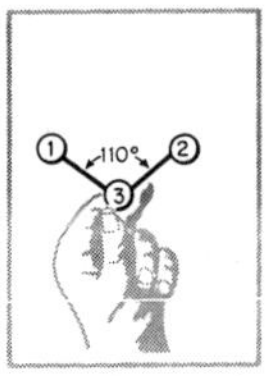

Next, rotate the center ball (3) so as to turn down the "rabbit-ears," as shown:

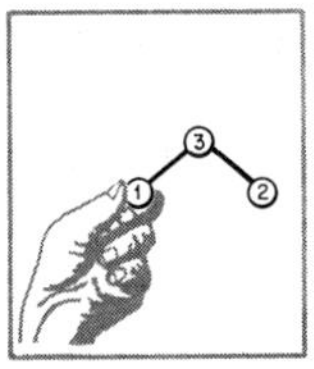

Now, rotate the center ball to the right or left so that the three balls line up with you in a north-south position: Ball 3 stands above the other two. Hook

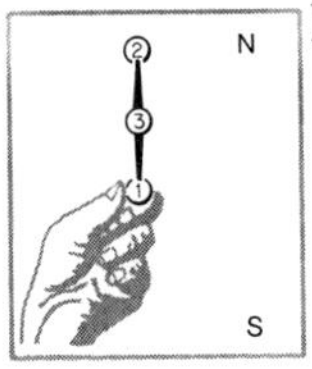

another two balls to ball 3 to look like "rabbit-ears," . You now have two

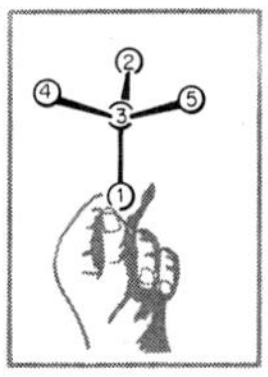

sets of "rabbit-ears" hooked to one ball, one set pointing up, the other pointing down; one set points in the east-west direction, the other in the north-south direction. If the model is rotated so as to place three of the "ears" on the surface of the table, it looks like . If balls 1, 2, and 5 are joined by lines, a triangle, 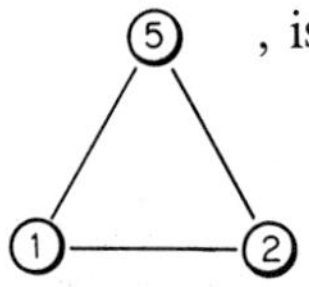 , is

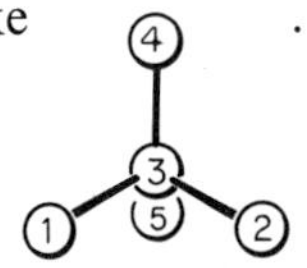

formed. If we join these three balls to the number 4 ball, a pyramid is obtained,

, a figure with four faces known as a *tetrahedron*. This tetrahedral structure is

*From the Greek words
tettares and hedra,
meaning four bases.
Each face of the
tetrahedron is an
equilateral triangle, a
triangle having three
equal sides (edges).*

very common in carbon compounds, of which methane, CH_4, a **tetrahedral molecule,** is typical:

The angle between any two bonds in a tetrahedral molecule is about 110°.

Remove ball number 4 from your model; balls 1, 2, and 5 form a triangle. Joining these three balls by lines with ball 3 forms a **triangular pyramid,** .

A typical example is ammonia, $\ddot{N}H_3$; the three H atoms form the triangular base of the pyramid with the N atom at the apex (tip). The bond angle in $\ddot{N}H_3$ is 107°,

Remove another ball, say number 5, from the model, leaving 1, 3, and 2 *bent* as shown: . Water, bond angle 105°, is a typical **bent molecule,**

It is advisable to keep these models before you in discussions of the shape of molecules.

Self-Interaction of Atomic Orbitals: Shape of Molecules   Theory holds that the shape of molecules is determined by the shape of the atomic orbitals used in the bonding. However, as early as 1931 Linus Pauling recognized that in bonding, atoms rarely use the AO's, *s, p, d,* and so forth, associated with the isolated atom. Rather, an atom, a C atom for example, prefers to *interact with* ("mix up") *its own orbitals* before combining with other atoms. The *significance* of this self-interaction **(hybridization)** of atomic orbitals lies in the change that occurs in the energy and shape of the orbitals—the shape of the electron clouds is changed. Typical are the self-interactions of the AO's of carbon, boron, and beryllium. Invented and named by Pauling, hybridization is a purely mathematical device, not a real process. No one has yet invented an instrument capable of detecting such a process.

The chemistry of carbon essentially involves its *one 2s* orbital and its *three 2p* orbitals. The interaction of these four AO's produces *four* new AO's of equal energy.

2p ↓ ↓ __

⟶ 2sp³ ↓ ↓ ↓ ↓

2s ↓↑

1s ↓↑   1s ↓↑

ground state of C   *imaginary sp³ state of C*

Since these are generated from one s and three p orbitals, they are called sp^3 atomic orbitals. One s AO + three p AO's $\longrightarrow$ four sp^3 AO's.

By analogy to biological processes, Linus Pauling called these imaginary states *hybrid atomic orbitals*. Again, they are theoretical. A mule, the offspring of a horse and an ass, is an example of a hybrid. But there is a significant difference. If you are kicked by a mule, blame the hybrid mule. If you are knocked down by a coal dust explosion, blame the coal dust in the air, not the hybrid orbitals. Further, hybrid AO's unlike s, p, d AO's and bonding, antibonding, and nonbonding MO's, cannot be identified by or associated with atomic and molecular spectra.

Each sp^3 AO has the same shape, roughly like a teardrop, or one-half of a p orbital, ◊, and each spreads to a corner of a tetrahedron (page 573):

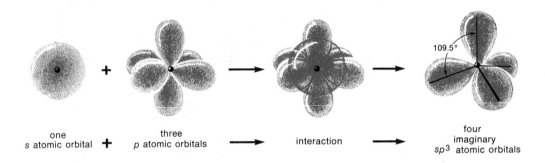

| one s atomic orbital | **+** | three p atomic orbitals | $\longrightarrow$ | interaction | $\longrightarrow$ | four imaginary sp^3 atomic orbitals |

For clarity, details are omitted from figures.

The tetrahedral arrangement of the four sp^3 AO's is reasonable. Imagine each of these orbitals as a weightless bar, all with equal electric charges. Arrange the four bars around a frictionless sphere. What positions will the bars take relative to one another? The geometry of the bars around the sphere is determined only by the repulsive interactions between like charges (page 117). Repulsion pushes the bars into positions in which they are equally distant from one another. Each bar then experiences the *same repulsive force*. A tetrahedral arrangement satisfies this requirement:

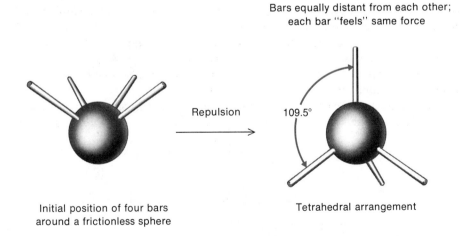

Bars equally distant from each other; each bar "feels" same force

Initial position of four bars around a frictionless sphere

Tetrahedral arrangement

Push one bar closer to another: the distances between the bars now differ. Consequently, the bars do not "feel" the same force. The longer the distance, the weaker the force; the shorter the distance, the stronger the force (page 118). The stronger force then pushes the bar against the weaker force, restoring the tetrahedral arrangement:

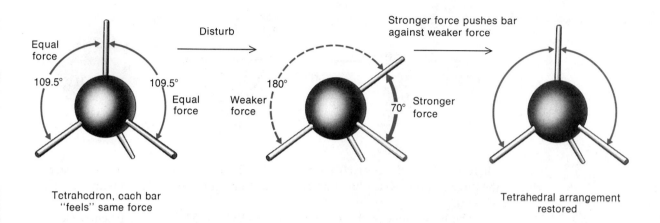

Tetrahedron, each bar "feels" same force

Tetrahedral arrangement restored

Any other arrangement brings two bars closer, and repulsion again pushes them apart.

A model of sp^3 AO's may be constructed from the model for a tetrahedral molecule, page 572, by removing balls 1, 2, 4, and 5, but leaving the pipe-cleaner connectors as the sp^3 AO's. This model is useful in following the discussion on the geometry of CH_4, $\ddot{N}H_3$, and $H_2\ddot{O}$.

In a methane molecule, CH_4, the four C—H bonds are identical, each pointing toward a corner of a tetrahedron (page 573). Therefore, we conclude that the C atom uses sp^3 AO's in forming CH_4. Each sp^3 AO interacts with the $1s$ AO of an H atom to form a σ and σ^* MO bond. For clarity, only bonding orbitals will be shown:

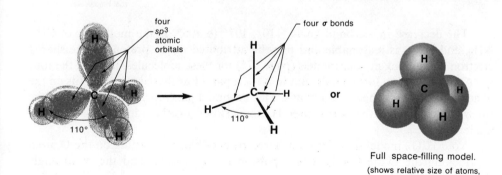

Full space-filling model.

(shows relative size of atoms, tetrahedral molecular arrangement)

The shape is determined only by the positions of the atoms.

There are eight valence electrons in CH_4, four from the C atom and one from each H atom. Each σ bond takes two electrons for a total of eight.

The bond angle in the ammonia molecule, $\ddot{N}H_3$, 107°, is sufficiently close to 109.5° so that, like the C atom in CH_4, the N atom in $\ddot{N}H_3$ also uses sp^3 AO's. Three of these fuse with H atoms, forming σ bonds; the unshared pair of electrons is housed in the fourth sp^3 AO:

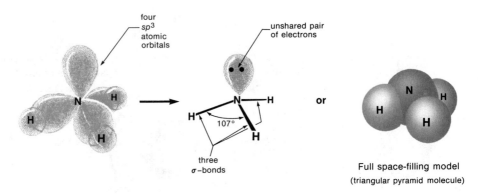

four sp^3 atomic orbitals

unshared pair of electrons

three σ–bonds

107°

or

Full space-filling model
(triangular pyramid molecule)

There are eight valence electrons in $\ddot{N}H_3$, five from the N atom and one from each of the three H atoms. Each bond takes two electrons, plus the unshared pair, for a total of eight.

The bond angle in the water molecule, $H_2\ddot{O}:$, 105°, is also sufficiently close to 109.5° so that the O atom uses sp^3 AO's. Two of these fuse with H atoms forming σ bonds, while the remaining two house the two unshared pairs of electrons:

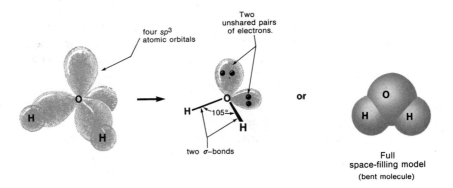

four sp^3 atomic orbitals

Two unshared pairs of electrons.

105°

two σ–bonds

or

Full space-filling model
(bent molecule)

The decrease in the bond angle, 110°, 107° to 105°, in the molecules of CH_4, $\dot{N}H_3$, and $H_2\ddot{O}:$ is reasonable and may be attributed to the presence of unshared electron pairs. Look at your models (page 575) for these molecules. In CH_4, the four sp^3 AO's are used to form bonds. But in NH_3, a pair of unshared electrons sits on the N atom overlooking the three σ bonds. This unshared pair repels the electrons in the three σ bonds and so forces the three H atoms closer together, decreasing the bond angle.

Your $H_2\ddot{O}:$ model shows *two* unshared pairs of electrons sitting on the O atom overlooking the two σ bonds. The repulsion is now greater and the bond angle decreases to 105°.

We now generalize: An atom without unshared pairs of electrons and bonded to four atoms forms a tetrahedral molecule or ion; the atom uses sp^3 AO's. Examples include CH_4, $SiCl_4$, $BeCl_4^{2-}$, SO_4^{2-}, and ethane, $H_3C—CH_3$. In an ethane molecule, *each* C atom, bonded to four atoms (three H and one C), uses sp^3 AO's (page 581).

An atom with one unshared pair of electrons and bonded to three atoms forms a triangular pyramid molecule or ion; the atom uses sp^3 AO's. Examples include $\ddot{N}H_3$, $\ddot{P}Cl_3$, $H_3\ddot{O}^+$, and the bromate ion $\ddot{B}rO_3^-$.

A few exceptions exist, such as $\dot{P}H_3$ (bond angle 93°), $\dot{A}sH_3$ (92°), and $\dot{S}bH_3$ (91°).

An atom with two unshared pairs of electrons and bonded to two atoms forms a bent molecule or ion; the atom uses sp^3 AO's. Examples include $H_2\ddot{O}:$, $Cl_2\ddot{O}:$, and $:\ddot{N}H_2^-$.

A few exceptions are $H_2\ddot{S}:$ (93°), $H_2\ddot{S}e:$ (91°), and $H_2\ddot{T}e:$ (90°).

PROBLEM 5 **For each of the following molecules or ions, give (a) its shape, (b) its *approximate* bond angle (about 90°, 110°, 120°, or 180°), and (c) the AO's used: (i) $:\ddot{C}lO_2^-$, (ii) NF_4^+, (iii) $AlCl_4^-$, (iv) $\ddot{X}eO_3$, (v) $:\ddot{O}F_2$, (vi) SnF_4. (d) Sketch the shapes of (ii), (iii), and (iv), showing the positions of unshared pairs of electrons.**

PROBLEM 6 **The bond angle is given for each of the following molecules:**

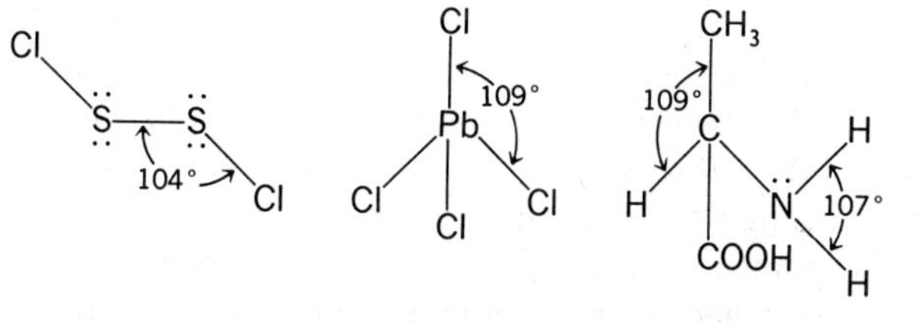

amino acid

Give the type of AO's used by the C, N, Pb, and S atoms.

In the triangular plane (flat) molecule BF_3 (page 572), the three B—F bonds are identical, separated by 120°. To account for this shape, we assume that *one s* orbital interacts with *two p* orbitals to produce *three* new AO's of equal energy. Since these are generated from one *s* and two *p* orbitals, they are called sp^2 AO's. The third *p* orbital remains unchanged in energy and shape:

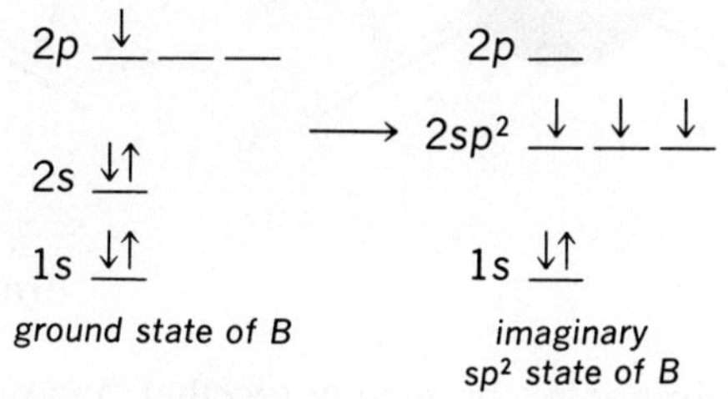

ground state of B

imaginary
sp^2 state of B

Each sp^2 AO has the same shape, similar to an sp^3 AO. Each sp^2 AO, separated by 120° from the others, lies in the same plane:

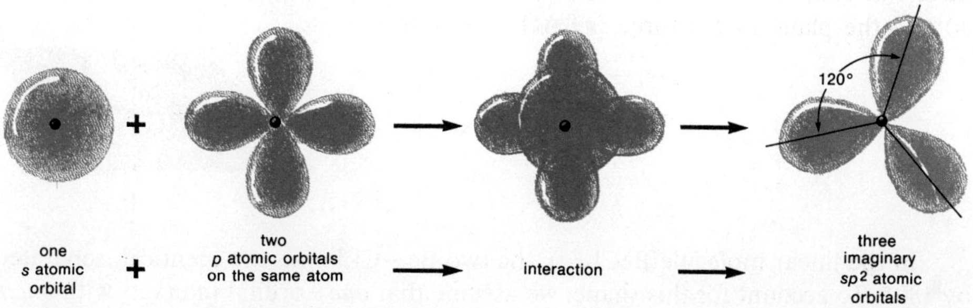

one
s atomic
orbital

+

two
p atomic orbitals
on the same atom

interaction

three
imaginary
sp^2 atomic
orbitals

577

Each sp^2 AO fuses with one F atom to form a σ bond:

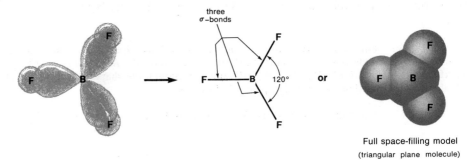

Full space-filling model
(triangular plane molecule)

*Six of the 7 valence
electrons of F, not
involved in bonding,
are not shown here.*

There are six valence electrons in BF_3, three from the B atom and one from each F atom. Each σ bond takes two electrons, for a total of six. The unused p orbital on the B atom remains empty but available. The unused p orbital, not shown, lies on the z-axis (page 183) through the B atom.

The triangular plane arrangement of the three sp^2 AO's is reasonable: Removal of one bar from the tetrahedral arrangement, page 575, causes the repulsive forces to push the remaining three bars into positions in which they are again equally distant. A triangular plane geometry satisfies this requirement:

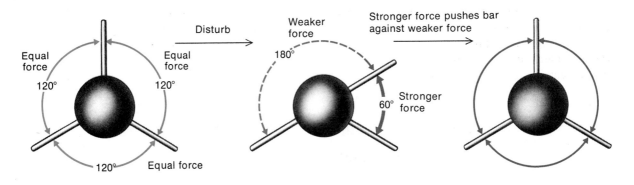

Triangular plane, each bar
"feels" same force

Triangular plane restored

Any other arrangement brings two bars closer together, and repulsion again restores the triangular plane arrangement.

A model of an atom in the imaginary sp^2 state may be constructed from the model for a triangular plane molecule (page 572) by removing balls 2, 3, and 4 but leaving the pipe-cleaner connectors as the sp^2 AO's. Next, pin one pipe-cleaner connector at the top and pin a second connector at the bottom of ball 1, and visualize these two connectors as the lobes of a p_z orbital (page 183), perpendicular (upright, 90°) to the plane of the three sp^2 AO's, as shown:

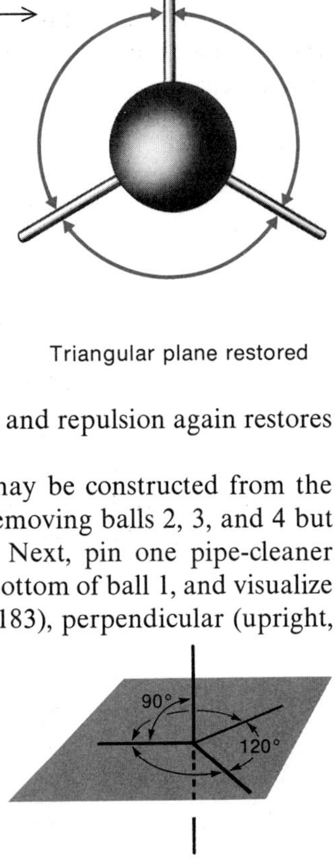

In the linear molecule $BeCl_2(g)$, the two Be—Cl bonds are identical, separated by 180°. To account for this shape, we assume that *one s* orbital interacts with *one p* orbital to produce *two* new AO's of equal energy. Since they are generated from one *s* and one *p* orbital, they are called *sp* AO's. The remaining two *p* orbitals remain unchanged in energy and shape:

$$2p \underline{\ \ } \underline{\ \ } \underline{\ \ } \qquad 2p \underline{\ \ } \underline{\ \ }$$

$$2s \underline{\downarrow\uparrow} \qquad \longrightarrow \quad 2sp \underline{\downarrow} \ \underline{\downarrow}$$

$$1s \underline{\downarrow\uparrow} \qquad \qquad 1s \underline{\downarrow\uparrow}$$

ground state   imaginary
of Be   sp state of Be

Each *sp* orbital has the same shape, similar to an *sp*^{3} or *sp*^{2} AO, but pointing in exactly opposite directions, separated by 180°:

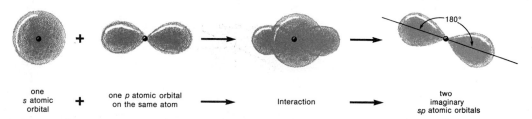

one   +   one p atomic orbital   two
s atomic   on the same atom   Interaction   imaginary
orbital   sp atomic orbitals

Each *sp* AO fuses with one Cl atom to form a σ bond:

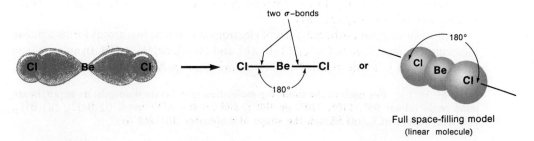

Full space-filling model
(linear molecule)

There are four valence electrons in BeCl$_2$, two from the Be atom and one from each Cl atom. Each σ bond takes two electrons, for a total of four. The two unused *p* orbitals on the Be atom remain empty but available. The unused *p* orbitals, not shown, lie on the *y*- and *z*-axes (page 183) through the Be atom. The linear arrangement for the two *sp* AO's is reasonable: Removal of one bar from the triangular plane geometry, page 578, causes the repulsive forces to push the remaining two bars into a linear arrangement where they are again equally distant:

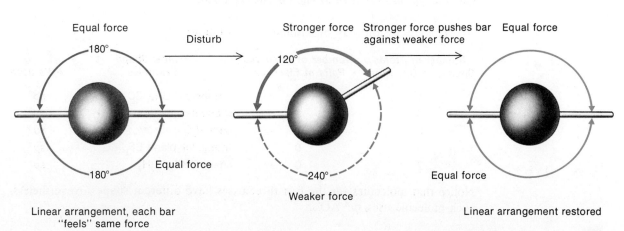

Any other arrangement brings the two bars closer, and repulsion again restores the linear arrangement.

A model of an atom in the imaginary sp state may be constructed from the model for a linear molecule (page 571) by removing balls C and B but leaving the pipe-cleaner connectors as the sp AO's. Add one p orbital by pinning a connector at the top and another at the bottom of ball A. Rotate the ball so that this p orbital points in the north-south direction. Now, add the second p orbital by pinning a connector at the top and another at the bottom of ball A. The two sp AO's are in a straight line; the two unused p orbitals are perpendicular (90°) to the straight line and to each other, as shown:

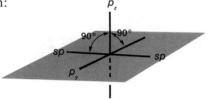

Generalizing, an atom without unshared pairs of electrons bonded to three atoms forms a triangular plane molecule or ion. Examples include BF_3, GaI_3, CO_3^{2-}, and ethylene, $H_2C=CH_2$. In an ethylene molecule, *each* C atom, bonded to three atoms, uses sp^2 AO's (page 581).

An atom without unshared pairs of electrons bonded to two atoms forms a linear molecule. Examples are $BeCl_2(g)$, $MgBr_2(g)$, and acetylene, $HC≡CH$. In an acetylene molecule, *each* C atom, bonded to two atoms, uses sp AO's (page 582).

A few exceptions exist. Gaseous MgF_2 (158°) is not linear.

PROBLEM 7 **For each of the following molecules, give (a) its shape, (b) its approximate bond angle (about 90°, 110°, 120°, or 180°), and (c) the AO's used: (i) BeH_2, (ii) BH_3, (iii) CH_3^+, (iv) $ZnCl_2$. (d) Sketch the shape of molecules (iii) and (iv).**

PROBLEM 8 **The bond angle is given for each of the following molecules and ions:**

$$H_5C_2 \overset{180°}{\longleftrightarrow} Hg \longleftrightarrow C_2H_5$$

$$\begin{bmatrix} & & CH_3 \\ 120° \rightarrow & & \\ H_3C \longrightarrow & Pb & 120° \\ 120° \rightarrow & & \\ & & CH_3 \end{bmatrix}^+$$

$$Cl \longrightarrow Ga \overset{Cl}{\underset{Cl}{\diagdown}} 120°$$

Give the type of AO's used by Hg, Pb, and Ga atoms.

This discussion may be summarized as follows:

Number of Atoms Bonded to One Atom	Number of Unshared Pairs of Electrons	Typical Shape Examples	AO's used
4	0	tetrahedral CH_4, SO_4^{2-}	sp^3
3	1	triangular pyramid $\ddot{N}H_3$, $H_3\ddot{O}^+$	sp^3
2	2	bent $H_2\ddot{O}:$	sp^3
3	0	triangular plane BF_3, CO_3^{2-}	sp^2
2	0	linear $BeCl_2$, C_2H_2	sp

Notice that molecules for the first three cases have different shapes. Nevertheless, each molecule uses sp^3 AO's.

MO DESCRIPTION OF DOUBLE AND_____18.7
TRIPLE BONDED MOLECULES

Over 95 % of the known chemical compounds contain carbon. Carbon compounds are therefore of special interest to chemists. The bonding in ethane, C_2H_6,
ethylene, C_2H_4, acetylene, C_2H_2, and benzene, C_6H_6 (Chap. 22), is typical of the kind
found in carbon compounds. The geometry and bonding in these compounds, simple
or complex, of which over a million are known, may be explained in terms of sp^3, sp^2,
and sp AO's. Students are advised to follow this discussion with their sp^3, sp^2, and sp
models (pages 575, 578, and 580).

Ethane, a component of natural gas, is a tetrahedral molecule with bond angles
of 109°; all C—H bonds are identical. Therefore, the C atoms use sp^3 AO's. One sp^3
AO from each C atom fuses to form a σ bond as shown (simplified diagrams are used
for clarity):

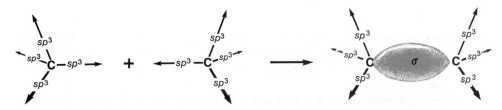

The remaining six sp^3 AO's fuse with hydrogen s AO's to form six σ bonds:

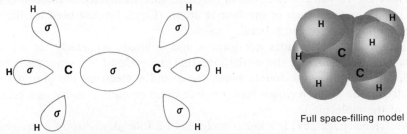

Full space-filling model

There are 14 valence electrons in ethane; four from each of the two C atoms (eight)
and one from each of the six H atoms (six). Since each σ bond takes two electrons, the
14 electrons are used in the seven σ bonds in ethane.

Ethylene (page 268) is a plane (flat) molecule with bond angles of about 120°.
The four C—H bonds are identical and the C=C bond is a double bond. Therefore,
the C atoms use sp^2 AO's. One sp^2 AO from each C atom fuses to form a σ bond as
shown:

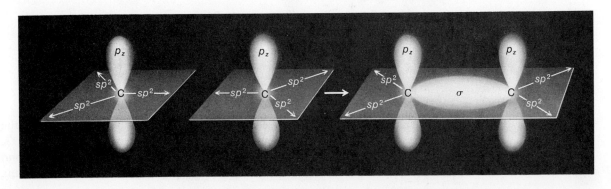

The remaining four sp^2 AO's fuse with hydrogen to form four σ bonds, while the two parallel p_z orbitals, upright and side-by-side, fuse to form a π bond (page 567) as shown:

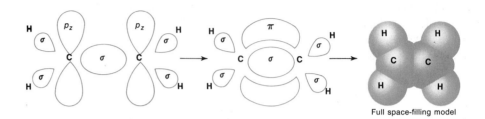

Full space-filling model

Reminder: σ^* and π^* bonds are not shown for clarity.

The two C atoms, the four H atoms, and the σ bonds are in the same plane; they lie in a flat surface. But the electron clouds of the π bond (page 567) are above and below the σ bond joining the two C atoms; that is, above and below the plane of the molecule.

The single bonds are σ bonds. *The double bond consists of one σ and one π bond.* This MO description also agrees with the fact that the energy required to break a double bond (C=C) is *not* double that of the single (σ) bond (C—C, page 270).

There are 12 valence electrons in ethylene, four from each of the two C atoms (eight) and one from each of the four H atoms (four). Ten are used for the five σ bonds, leaving two for the π bond.

Charles Coulson and co-workers, Proceedings of the National Academy of Sciences, *volume 38, April 1952, page 372.*

(Nature, of course, does not form σ and π bonds separately, as we do *for convenience.* We therefore dispel the idea that the π cloud lies separate from and outside the σ cloud. In a double bond, the σ and π electrons are almost equally delocalized. The π and σ clouds fuse into one cloud extending above and below the plane of the molecule.)

Acetylene (page 269) is a linear molecule; all four atoms sit on a straight line. The two C—H bonds are identical, and the C≡C bond is a triple bond. Therefore, the C atoms use sp AO's; each C atom uses one sp to form a σ bond between them:

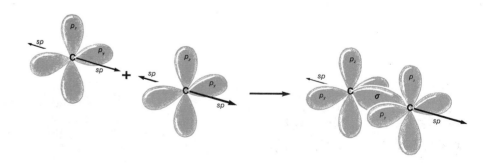

The remaining two sp AO's fuse with hydrogen, forming two σ bonds, while the four p orbitals fuse in the following manner: as in ethylene, the two parallel p_z AO's, upright and side-by-side, fuse to form a π bond with its electron clouds above and below the C—C σ bond. The two p_y orbitals, also parallel to each other and lying side-by-side in the plane of the paper, also fuse to form a π bond with its electron clouds alongside the C atoms, like a tugboat carrying a barge on each of its sides:

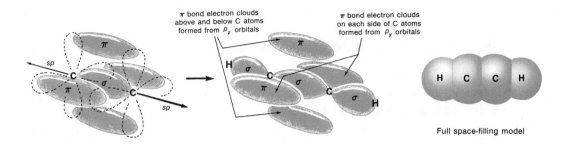

π bond electron clouds above and below C atoms formed from P_z orbitals

π bond electron clouds on each side of C atoms formed from P_y orbitals

Full space-filling model

The single bonds are σ bonds. *The triple bond consists of one σ and two π bonds.**

There are 10 valence electrons in acetylene; four from each of the two C atoms (eight) and one from each of the two H atoms (two). Six are used for the three σ bonds, leaving four for the two π bonds.

PROBLEM 9 **(a) Carbonyl chloride (*phosgene*), $Cl_2C{=}O:$, a colorless, poisonous gas, is a triangular plane molecule in which the bond angles are 120°. The O atom uses sp^2 AO's. (b) Chlorine cyanide, $Cl{-}C{\equiv}N:$, is a linear molecule (bond angle 180°). The N atom uses sp AO's. For each molecule, (i) what kind of AO's does the C atom use? (ii) Explain the geometry and bonding in terms of σ and π bonds. (iii) Roughly sketch the molecule, showing the location of σ and π bonds.**

Where necessary, the student is told the type of AO's used by atoms attached to a C atom.

THE DILEMMA OF THE CARBONATE ION————————————18.8

Carbon dioxide dissolves in water, about 90 ml CO_2 at room conditions in 100 ml water, forming a solution of carbonic acid:

$$H_2O + CO_2(g) \longrightarrow H_2CO_3(aq)$$

This is the basis of carbonated beverages. At higher pressures, more CO_2 may be dissolved, but when the pressure is reduced by opening the container, CO_2 is liberated, producing a bubbling drink. *Limestone* ($CaCO_3$) and *dolomite* ($CaCO_3MgCO_3$) mountains are very common. Calcium carbonate is also the main constituent of marble, chalk, pearls,* coral reefs, and marine shells such as those of clams and oysters. Although insoluble in water, calcium carbonate dissolves in water containing carbon dioxide. It is converted to the more soluble calcium hydrogen carbonate, $Ca(HCO_3)_2$

$$CaCO_3(c) + H_2O + CO_2(aq) \longrightarrow Ca^{2+}(aq) + 2HCO_3^-(aq)$$

Composed of $CaCO_3$ deposited as a series of thin shells on a grain of sand which has entered (or, more frequently, which has been placed in) an oyster.

This chemical reaction is responsible for the formation of caves and tremendous underground hollow spaces (Mammoth Cave, Kentucky, and Carlsbad Caverns, New Mexico). The rock ($CaCO_3$) formations found in these caves also result from this reaction. Ground waters—rivers, creeks—containing calcium hydrogen carbonate,

——————————

*As in ethylene, the separation is for convenience. Actually, these three bonds fuse to form a cylindrically symmetrical electron cloud around the two C atoms. This means that the electron cloud looks the same no matter how the molecule is turned around the line joining the two H atoms.

$Ca(HCO_3)_2$, seep through cracks in the rock, finally reaching the cave ceiling. CO_2 escapes and water evaporates, depositing calcium carbonate on the ceiling:

$$Ca^{2+}(aq) + 2HCO_3^-(aq) \longrightarrow CO_2(g) + H_2O(g) + CaCO_3(c)$$

Ground waters may also drip to the cave floor where they deposit calcium carbonate.* Although calcium carbonate is a white solid, these formations may be colored by dissolved salts, usually iron salts.

These chemical reactions are also responsible for the erosion of marble and limestone monuments of historical and cultural importance, such as the Taj Mahal in India, the Mayan temples in Mexico and Guatemala, and the Rock Churches in Ethiopia. Also, atmospheric sulfur dioxide, SO_2, in the presence of moisture forms sulfurous, H_2SO_3, and sulfuric, H_2SO_4, acids which attack limestone and marble monuments. The carbonate stone is damaged by conversion of the relatively insoluble carbonate to the relatively soluble sulfate. The soluble sulfate is then washed away by rain water. The Ancient Greek-Sicilian-Roman cities in the Mediterranean Basin are particularly susceptible to such erosion.

The life of these monuments is now being extended by treatment with barium hydroxide, $Ba(OH)_2$, and urea, $(NH_2)_2CO$, to form the more resistant barium carbonate:

$$H_2N-\overset{\overset{\textstyle O}{\|}}{C}-NH_2(aq) + H_2O \longrightarrow 2NH_3(aq) + CO_2(aq)$$
$$Ba(OH)_2(aq) + CO_2(aq) \longrightarrow BaCO_3(c) + H_2O$$

Further, in the presence of atmospheric sulfur dioxide, barium carbonate changes to highly insoluble barium sulfate,

$$2BaCO_3(c) + 2SO_2(aq) + O_2(aq) \longrightarrow 2BaSO_4(c) + 2CO_2(aq)$$

which forms a very strongly adhering layer on the stone. This layer should protect the stone in the same way that the layer of oxide, formed on exposure to air, prevents rusting of metals such as aluminum, chromium, and nickel.

Difficulty strikes when we attempt to write an electronic formula for the carbonate ion. The formula

satisfies the octet rule. The formula, however, predicts that one C to O bond (the double bond, C=O) should be *shorter* than the single bonds (page 270). But experimentally, all three C to O bonds are identical, corresponding to neither a single bond, C—O, nor a double bond, C=O. Shifting the position of the double bond on paper

---

*The formations hanging from the ceiling are called **stalactites** (from the Greek word *stalaktos,* for oozing out in drops, a trickle), while those found on the floor are called **stalagmites** (from the Greek word *stalagmos,* for a dripping).

does not improve the situation. The electronic formula of a carbonate ion *cannot* be satisfactorily represented by any one of these formulas. *All three are incorrect:* each incorrectly predicts that the bonds are not identical.

We are now faced with a situation that must appear irrational. You might, with justice, conclude that since we cannot write a correct electronic formula for the ion, we should confess our ignorance and move on to the MO description of this ion. Theorists, however, decided to hide our ignorance under a label and so *preserve* the concept of electronic formulas, still deeply entrenched in chemical explanations.

First, this inability to write a correct electronic formula is hidden under the label *resonance*. According to the principle of resonance, *a molecule or ion that cannot be described by one electronic formula is correctly described by two or more electronic formulas.* It certainly sounds like nonsense: two or more incorrect electronic formulas combined together, or put on top of one another, make a correct electronic formula. Each particular incorrect electronic formula is called a **contributing** or **resonance structure**. A contributing (resonance) structure *does not represent reality and does not have a physical existence.* But in principle, each contributing (fictitious) structure makes a contribution to the actual and real electronic structure of the molecule or ion. Thus, according to the resonance concept, the carbonate ion is considered to be a combination of the three incorrect electronic formulas given above; each one of these formulas is a contributing (fictitious) structure. The idea of resonance here implies that each O atom is somehow bonded to the C atom in a way that cannot be described with electronic formulas. But we can say that the bonds in CO_3^{2-} are something between a single and a double bond.*

Example 1

The electronic formula of the nitrate ion is $\left[\begin{array}{c} :\ddot{O}: \\ | \\ N \\ :\dot{O}.\quad .\dot{O}: \end{array}\right]^{-1}$. Experimentally, *all bonds are identical.* (a) Is the electronic formula correct? (b) Write the contributing structures consistent with the octet rule for the ion.

Answer

(a) No, although it satisfies the octet rule, the electronic formula is incorrect because it predicts that one bond length should differ from the other two. (b) In writing contributing structures, the relative positions of the atoms remain the same.** The position of electrons—most usually an electron pair—is changed, as shown:

---

*The $>C=O$ bond length is 1.22 Å, while the $>C-O-$ bond length is 1.43 Å, but the CO bond length in CO_3^{2-} is between the two: namely, 1.31 Å.

**Also, the number of unpaired electrons cannot be changed since this determines the magnetic properties of molecules and ions. Thus, $\dot{N}\equiv\dot{N}$ and $\cdot\ddot{N}=\ddot{N}\cdot$ are not contributing structures of N_2, $:\ddot{O}=\ddot{O}:$ and $:\ddot{O}-\ddot{O}:$ are not contributing structures of O_2.

PROBLEM 10   The electronic formula of SO_2 is ːSː   . The two bonds are identical. (a) Is
                                                      O̤   O̤
this electronic formula correct? If not, why not? (b) Write two contributing structures
consistent with the octet rule for SO_2.

The concept of resonance* was introduced by Werner Heisenberg (1926) and
largely developed by Linus Pauling. While the MO description of such molecules
(next section) robbed the chemist of his familiar and convenient electronic formula,
the resonance concept neatly meshed into traditional thinking habits. The resonance
concept is still very widely used in the correlation and explanation of almost countless
reactions involving compounds of C, N, O, and S (organic chemistry).

18.9 _____ MO DESCRIPTION OF THE CARBONATE ION: DELOCALIZED PI BOND

Models of four atoms, each in the imaginary sp^2 state (page 578), are very helpful in following this discussion.

CO_3^{2-} is a triangular plane ion. The C atom, therefore, uses sp^2 AO's; the O
atoms also use sp^2 AO's. Each of the C sp^2 AO's fuses with one sp^2 AO of an O atom
to form three σ bonds:

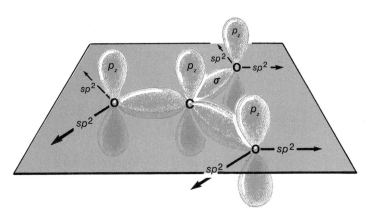

The four p_z AO's, now all parallel, upright and side-by-side, fuse to form a π bond. As
in ethylene, the electron clouds are above and below the plane of the ion, but the
clouds *now extend over* and embrace *all four atoms,* not just two as in ethylene. The pi

---

*The choice of this word is indeed unfortunate, having led to much confusion because "resonance" is
also used to describe observable (real) events, such as the action of a musical tuning fork on an air column.
If a tuning fork is held over a hollow tube in air and the height of the tube is changed, at some position an
appreciable increase in the loudness of the sound occurs. The increase in sound is due to the fact that the
air column (the mass of air) in the tube now vibrates with the same frequency as the tuning fork; the
physicists would say that "the air column and the tuning fork are in resonance." The term was borrowed to
mean that a contributing (fictitious) structure has some features of the real molecule and that the
combination of these contributing structures resembles the real molecule and makes the real molecule
more stable than any one of the contributing structures.
    The use of a double-headed arrow, ⟷, between contributing structures is also very misleading
because it may be incorrectly interpreted to mean that a compound is a mixture of different molecules
switching back and forth ("oscillating," "resonating") among one another. A non-existent contributing
structure is incapable of any action.
    Equally unfortunate and misleading is the use of the term "*resonance hybrid*" for the structure of the
molecule resulting from the combination of contributing structures. A mule, a real animal, is the offspring
(hybrid) of two other real animals, a horse and an ass. While it is true that a mule is neither "half-horse"
nor "half-ass," how do you mate non-existent structures? And don't borrow a unicorn (a fictitious horse) to
pull your "surrey with the fringe on top."

bond now bonds more than two atoms. Such a bond is known as a **delocalized pi bond**:

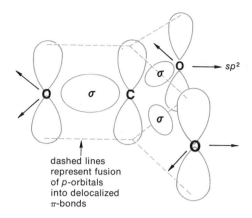

dashed lines
represent fusion
of *p*-orbitals
into delocalized
π-bonds

There are 24 valence electrons in the ion: four from one C atom (four), six from each of the three O atoms (18), and two to acquire the 2^- charge. These are placed as follows: each remaining sp^2 AO on the O atoms takes two electrons; the three O atoms therefore require 12 electrons. The three σ bonds take six electrons. This accounts for 18 electrons $(12 + 6)$, leaving six electrons $(24 - 18)$ for the delocalized pi bond:

Reminder: Four MO's form, three of which take 6 electrons, but only one is shown for clarity; also, σ^* MO's are not shown.

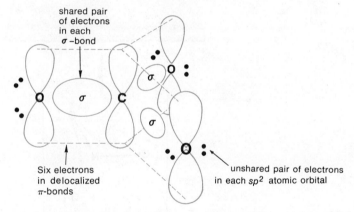

shared pair
of electrons
in each
σ–bond

Six electrons
in delocalized
π-bonds

unshared pair of electrons
in each sp^2 atomic orbital

This MO description is in agreement with the known properties of the ion; a triangular plane ion in which all bonds are identical, separated by about 120°. The ion is more stable—more energy is required to decompose it to one C and three O atoms—than it would be in the absence of the delocalized π bond (page 560). This conclusion agrees with experiment.

Dotted lines are commonly used to represent delocalized π bonds, as illustrated:

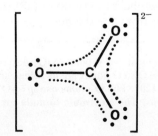

Example 2

Write the delocalized π bond (MO) description for the nitrate ion, NO_3^-, a triangular plane ion in which all bonds are identical. The O atoms use sp^2 AO's. Indicate σ and π bonds. Account for the valence electrons; how many in unused sp^2 AO's, and in the σ and π bonds?

Answer

Since NO_3^- is triangular plane ion, the N uses sp^2 AO's to form σ bonds with each of the three O atoms. The N and each O atom have a p_z AO located side-by-side, and these fuse to form a delocalized π bond:

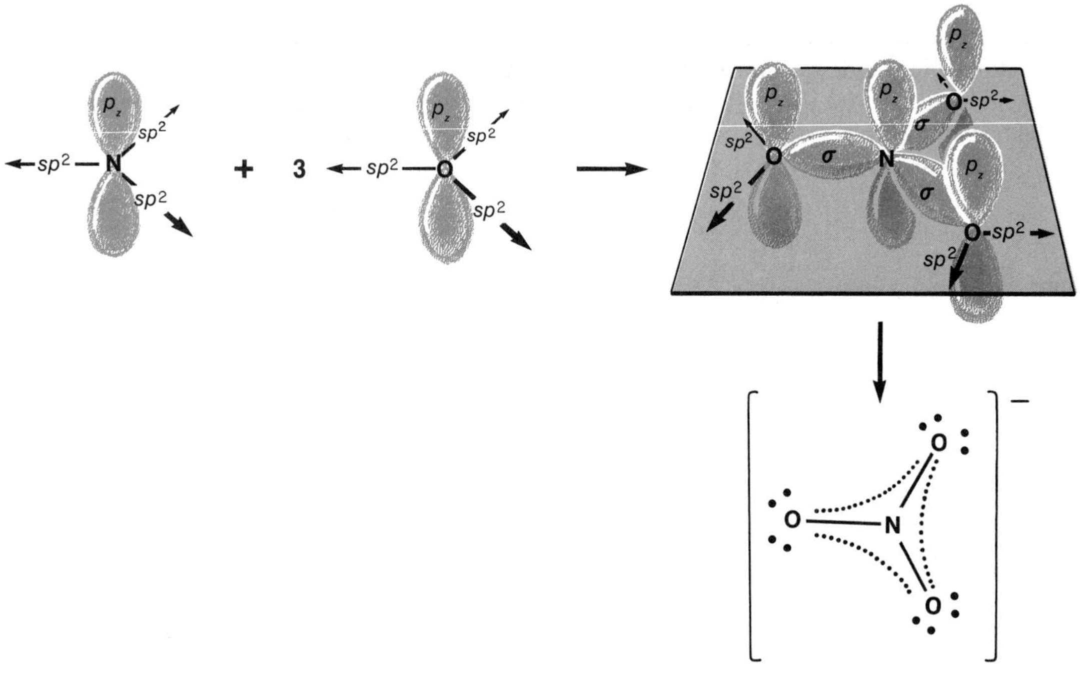

The unused sp^2 AO's on the O atoms each take two electrons for a total of twelve electrons; each σ bond takes two electrons for a total of six electrons. This accounts for 18 electrons. But the ion has 24 valence electrons, five from one N atom (five), six from each of the three O atoms (18), and one to acquire the 1^- charge. This leaves six electrons for the delocalized π bond.

PROBLEM 11   Write the delocalized π bond (MO) description for the O_3 molecule, a plane (flat) molecule in which the O to O bonds are identical, separated by 120°. Which AO's, sp, sp^2, or sp^3, are separated by 120°. The O atoms use sp^2 AO's. Indicate σ and π bonds and account for the valence electrons. The electronic formula for O_3 is

Quantum mechanics is the most widely used and most successful description of nature (page 211), and as in our treatment of atoms (Chap. 6), our explanations in this chapter have been given in the language of quantum mechanics.

The application of quantum mechanics to even the simplest molecules, H_2 or H_2^+, is so extremely complicated that predictions about the properties of these molecules cannot be made without simplifying assumptions. The complexity arises from our inability to deal with more than one interaction (force). Thus, one proton and one electron—a "two-body system"—essentially involve one interaction, one electrical attractive force, and exact predictions may be made about the H atom.

Add a second proton with another electron to build up a molecule, and the interactions increase to a number that no one yet knows how to handle mathematically. In H_2, each proton repels the other one, each electron repels the other one; but each proton attracts the two electrons. We feel certain that these kinds of interactions produce the glue that binds atoms together in all substances. But all the computers in the world cannot tell us who will win this tug-of-war: if the attractive forces exceed the repulsive forces, H_2 will form; if not, two H atoms will form. The computers cannot give us an answer because no one knows how to give the mathematical instructions to the computer. Nevertheless, theoretical chemists, theoretical physicists, and theoretical mathematicians are confident that quantum mechanics is correct in principle even though its exact applications to complex nuclei, atoms, and molecules yield impossibly difficult equations.*

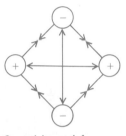

2 repulsive and 4 attractive forces in an H_2 molecule

PROBLEM 12   **How many interactions among charged particles are involved in H_2^+?**

Under these circumstances, two approaches to the quantum mechanical description of electronic bonding in molecules have been evolved. One practical method of approach, evolved by Walter Heitler and Fritz London (1927), and further developed and applied by John Slater and Linus Pauling, uses quantum mechanical formulations that may be verbalized as follows: Start with separated atoms; allow them to approach; electron-pair bonds form between the nuclei as the atoms approach, but *imagine* different reasonable positions for the electron-pair. For example, let atoms A· and ·B: approach each other. A bond forms between them as they approach, and now we *imagine* three plausible—*imaginary but reasonable*—positions for the bond:

A:B̈: (*purely covalent, nonpolar structure*),

A⁻̈ B̈:⁺ (*ionic, polar structure; A more electronegative than B*),

A⁺ :B̈:⁻ (*ionic, polar structure, B more electronegative than A*)

These three imagined structures are called contributing (resonance) structures. Hence, this method is referred to as the **resonance method** or the **valence-bond (VB) method.**

---

*This problem is *not* peculiar to quantum mechanics; it also exists in our treatment of planetary systems. But in our planetary system, the sun is so much larger than any of the planets, and thus the gravitational attractive force it exerts so exceeds the forces with which the planets attract one another, that the motion of each planet can be calculated as if it were attracted *only* by the sun. It is not yet mathematically possible to calculate *exactly* the motion of a planet. The situation is greatly aggravated in atoms and molecules containing more than two charged particles, because none of the participating forces can be considered insignificant. In mathematics, this is known as the "many-body problem."

It is called VB because the method permits writing a bond as a dash or two dots. The real molecule is calculated to be a composite of these three imaginary structures, but the contribution that each one makes may vary from substance to substance. In actual practice, reasonable structures are selected on the basis of experience. For example, applied to two H atoms in forming H_2, imaginary $H\!:\!H$ makes the major contribution; it accounts for 95 % of the energy (104 kcal/mole) needed to separate the H atoms in the molecule. However, imaginary H^-H^+ and H^+H^- each make equally small contributions (each 2.5 %). Applied to $H\cdot$ and $\cdot\ddot{F}\!:$ atoms in forming HF, imaginary $H\!:\!F$ makes a significant contribution; it accounts for 65 % of the bond energy (135 kcal/mole). But because of the large electronegativity of the F atom, imaginary H^+F^- also makes an important contribution (35 %), while the contribution of imaginary H^-F^+ is insignificant.

PROBLEM 13   When the valence-bond approach is used to calculate the bond energy of HI—electronegativities, H (2.1) and I (2.2)—which of the following imaginary (contributing) structures should make (a) the major, and (b) the least contribution: (i) $H\!:\!I$, (ii) H^-I^+, (iii) H^+I^-?

The influence of Linus Pauling in the application and propagation of this approach is so great that VB and "LP" are literally synonymous.

The second practical method, invented in 1932 by Friedrich Hund, Robert Mulliken, Erich Hückel, and John Lennard-Jones, uses quantum mechanical formulations that parallel the method used to predict electronic structures of atoms (Chap. 6). It may be verbalized as follows: nuclei are assembled in position in a molecule; atomic orbitals (atomic energy levels) interact to form an equal number of molecular orbitals (molecular energy levels); the necessary number of electrons are added to the molecular orbitals in the same manner as the build-up process for free atoms. The bond energy is determined by the electron occupancy of the molecular orbitals, just as in atoms the ionization energies are determined by electron occupancy of atomic orbitals. Hence, this method is known as the **molecular orbital (MO) method.** For example, applied to He_2, place two helium nuclei as in a molecule; interact two $1s$ AO's to form two MO's; add four electrons to the two MO's. Addition of the energy of the four electrons, determined by the energy of the MO each occupies, gives a bond energy of zero. No energy is needed to separate He_2 to 2He, which is merely another way of saying He_2 will not form.

In recognition of his influence in the development and application of this method, Robert Mulliken is known as "Mr. Molecule."

At the practical level of application, each method has serious defects. It's like the story of the two partially blind men who decided to paint an elephant on canvas. One sat at one end while the other made himself comfortable at the opposite end. Each painted what he saw at his end. At the exhibition, it was impossible to make only one award, to decide that one painting truly represented an elephant while the other did not. Each painting, surely incomplete, nevertheless contained essential features of a real elephant. Of course, if the eyesight had improved as the men painted, the paintings would probably have looked more and more alike. Similarly, the results of VB and MO methods become more and more alike as simplifying assumptions are eliminated.

Another analogy with respect to the H_2 molecule is also useful. We order "two eggs sunnyside-up." The VB chef cracks two eggs into a frying pan and discards the egg shells. The MO chef carefully opens two eggs, separates and adds the yolks in proper position to the frying pan, and then adds the "white" of the eggs without disturbing the yolks. The result is the same in both kitchens: two yolks (two protons) surrounded by the "white" of the eggs (the electron cloud composed of two electrons). But there is a difference. The VB chef is empty-handed while the MO chef has two empty egg shells, corresponding to the excited states of a molecule, and so provides an understanding of the spectra of molecules and their photochemical reactions. The MO theory is more extensively used, particularly for explaining our experimental knowledge of aromatic compounds (Chap. 22) and metallic bonding (Chap. 20), and in making verifiable predictions about the stability and properties of unknown substances. Currently, Robert Woodward and Roald Hoffmann are applying MO theory to predict some remarkably specific chemical reactions, a major breakthrough in the field of chemical kinetics. Recent applications of quantum mechanics to organic chemistry are bringing chemistry closer to being a branch of applied mathematics. Computations are now made for large molecules like $C_{25}N_4O_7H_{14}$. Highly improved MO calculations by Paul von R. Schleyer and John Pople (1976) predict that the geometry of the molecules like CF_2Li_2 or $CF_3(BH_2)$ are planar, *not* tetrahedral. Such compounds do exist. But their shapes have not been studied because no one thought they could have a geometry other than tetrahedral.

Recipients of the first Arthur C. Cope Award (1973) of the American Chemical Society for this basic theoretical contribution.

We do not, however, wish to leave you with the false impression that scientists eagerly rush to test new theories. The energy of activation required for a change in point of view is frequently large. Unexplored gold veins still exist in the writings of the original fathers of quantum mechanics. All the computer output of the theoretical physicist and chemist is valueless without experimental output.

EPILOG David Craig, University College, London. From *Chemical Technology,* September, 1971, page 573.

"At the beginning of the study of quantum chemistry hopes were entertained that calculations could be made which would give, even for complex molecules, exact values of quantities such as bond lengths and bonding energies. Such quantities would then not need to be measured experimentally and, figuratively speaking, calculating machines would have replaced test tubes in a large field of chemical enquiry. Experience has shown that such complete a priori calculations are not feasible in any but the simplest molecules, and perhaps not even worthwhile. Emphasis in theoretical chemistry has thus come to be placed much more on calculations of an empirical kind which can supplement the information gained by experiment, and on the elaboration of models or simplified pictures of systems which can be used for interpreting their properties. A fruitful interplay has developed between theoretical and experimental methods of research which very often leads to better insight and quicker solutions of chemical problems."

PROBLEMS

14 **Vocabulary** Define and illustrate (a) atomic and molecular orbital, (b) bonding and antibonding MO, (c) σ and σ^* bond, (d) π and π^* bond, (e) bond angle, (f) linear molecule, (g) triangular plane (planar) molecule, (h) tetrahedral molecule, (i) triangular pyramid (pyramidal) molecule, (j) bent molecule, (k) sp^3, sp^2, and sp AO's, (l) double and triple bonds in terms of σ and π bonds, (m) delocalized π bond, (n) contributing (resonance) structure.

15 Pick the two sets of words that when put together make sense in terms of MO theory: (a) overlap, (b) no overlap, (c) no fusion of AO's, (d) high electron density between nuclei, (e) σ, (f) repulsive force, (g) σ^*, (h) antibonding MO, (i) bonding MO, (j) fusion of AO's, (k) attractive force, (l) zero electron density between nuclei.

16 (a) Use the MO energy level diagram (page 566) to

write the electronic structure of the following gaseous particles: (i) BH, (ii) BH^+, (iii) BH^-, (iv) Li_2, (v) LiH^-, (vi) LiH^+, (vii) HeH_2, (viii) CH. (b) Which of these should exist? (c) Which should be paramagnetic?

17 The MO energy level diagram generated by the AO's of two atoms of each of the first 10 elements is similar to Fig. 18.4, page 569, since each atom contains five AO's (one 1s, and 2s, and three 2p). (a) Use this figure to write the electronic structure of the following gaseous particles: (i) O_2, (ii) O_2^-, (iii) C_2, (iv) B_2, (v) N_2, (vi) F_2, (vii) F_2^-, (viii) F_2^{2-}, (ix) F_2^+, (x) Ne_2. (b) Which of these should exist? (c) Which should be paramagnetic?* (d) Of the three particles, O_2, O_2^-, and O_2^+, which one should be the most stable? Explain. (e) Upon canceling bonding and antibonding electrons, what type of bonding, σ or π or both, binds C_2 and N_2?

18 Use Fig. 18.4, page 569. (a) How many electrons are in BeH_2, BN, CO^+, BO, CO, NO, NO^+, BeO, CN, CN^+, CN^-? Write the electronic structure of (i) BO, (ii) NO, (iii) CN^-. (b) Upon canceling bonding and antibonding electrons, what type of bonding, σ or π or both, binds (i) BO and (ii) NO? (c) Which should have a higher bond stability, C_2 or CH?

19 sp^3, sp^2, and sp (a) Use three apples and one peach ground together to bake a pie. Divide the pie into four equal pieces; how many apples and peaches are in each piece? (b) Use two apples and one peach ground together to bake a pie. Divide the pie into three equal pieces; how many apples and peaches are in each piece? (c) Use one apple and one peach ground together to bake a pie. Divide the pie into two equal pieces; how many apples and peaches are in each piece?

20 Predict (a) the shape and (b) the type of AO's of the following ions and gaseous molecules: (i) GaH_3, (ii) AlI_3, (iii) $BeBr_2$, (iv) BBr_3, (v) $GaCl_3$, (vi) SbH_3, (vii) CH_4, (viii) CH_3^-, (ix) CH_3^+, (x) $POCl_3$, (xi) BeF_4^{2-}, (xii) PO_4^{3-}, (xiii) $Ag(CN)_2^-$, (xiv) $:N≡C—C≡N:$, (xv) NF_3, (xvi) $AsCl_3$, (xvii) CaF_2, (xviii) SiH_4, (xix) $HOCl$, (xx) H_2CO, (xxi) CS_2, (xxii) XeO_4, (xxiii) SO_3, (xxiv) SO_3^{2-},

(xxv) $:GeCl_2$, (xxvi) BO_3^{3-}, (xxvii) $Hg(CH_3)_2$, (xxviii) BrO_3^-, (xxix) Cl_2SO, (xxx) $:SeF_2$, (xxxi) $:SCl_2$, (xxxii) ZnI_2, (xxxiii) $Cd(CH_3)_2$, (xxxiv) CBr_2I_2, (xxxv) $FCHCl_2$, (xxxvi) $Zn(CN)_4^{2-}$, (xxxvii) $H—C≡P:$ (c) Predict the shape of methylene, $:CH_2$, the molecule obtained by removing H^+ from CH_3^+; see (ix) in part (b).

21 (a) Predict the shape of the following ions from the AO's used by the Br atom: perbromate, BrO_4^- (sp^3); bromate, BrO_3^- (sp^3); bromite, BrO_2^- (existence not yet firmly established) (sp^3); hypobromite, BrO^-. (b) From the bond angles given for a portion of a protein molecule

predict the AO's used by N, C, C, N, C atoms in the order in which they appear.

22 In general, the geometry of molecules with an unpaired electron is the same as though the unpaired electron were not present in the molecule. Predict the shape of methyl, $·CH_3$, with one unpaired electron.

23 (You may use your models.) Sketch the MO description for the following molecules, clearly showing the shape and indicating the approximate bond angles (110°, 120°, or 180°): (a) methyleneimine, $H_2C=NH$ (N in sp^2 state); (b) formaldehyde, $H_2C=Ö:$ (O in sp^2 state); (c) hydrogen cyanide, $H—C≡N:$ (N in sp state); (d) butadiene, $H_2C=CH—CH=CH_2$; (e) diacetylene, $H—C≡C—C≡C—H$; (f) methyl cyanide, $H_3C—C≡N:$ (N in sp state); (g) cyanogen, $:N≡C—C≡N:$ (N in sp state); (h) $H_2C=CH—Ö—C≡N:$ (O is sp^3, N is sp); (i) acetylide ion, $:C≡C:^{2-}$; (j) urea, $H_2N—\overset{\overset{\textstyle O}{\|}}{C}—NH_2$ (N and O are sp^2); (k) silaethylene, H_2CSiH_2.

24 Write the indicated number of contributing structures consistent with the octet rule for each of the following molecules: (a) SO_2 (two); (b) SO_3 (three; each O atom is attached to the S atom). (c) Given one contributing structure for (i) NO_2, $\overset{\displaystyle N}{\underset{:\ddot{O}\qquad \ddot{O}:}{\diagup \diagdown}}$,

---

write two more; (ii) formate ion, $\left[\begin{array}{c} :\ddot{O}: \\ \| \\ H-C-\ddot{O}: \end{array}\right]^{-}$,

write one more; (iii) methyl nitrate, $H_3C-\ddot{\underset{..}{O}}-N\overset{\overset{\ddot{O}:}{\|}}{\underset{O}{\diagdown}}$, write one more. (d) Does any *one* of these contributing structures correctly represent the structure of the molecule?

sp^2 state; account for valence electrons: (a) SO_2; (b) SO_3; (c) NO_2^-; (d) formate ion (see Problem 24). (e) Answer the same question for dinitrogen oxide, N_2O or NNO, in which the N atoms are in the *sp* state and O is in the sp^2 state.

27 History Pick out the one entirely incorrect representation of the ethylene molecule:*

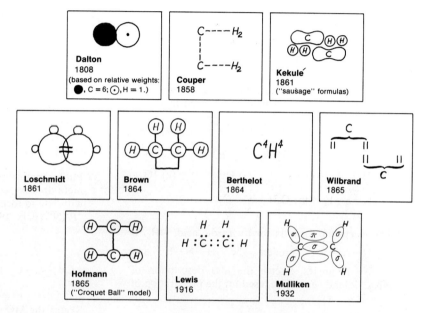

25 Two contributing structures are written for cyanogen, C_2N_2, with calculated bond lengths in Å units:

$:N\!\equiv\!\!\equiv\!C\!-\!C\!\equiv\!\!\equiv\!N:$ $:N\!=\!\!=\!C\!=\!\!=\!C\!=\!\!=\!\ddot{N}:$
1.15 1.54 1.15   1.27   1.33   1.27

The observed bond lengths are N——C——C——N
1.16   1.37   1.16

(a) Is either one of the contributing structures a correct representation of the structure of C_2N_2? If not, why not? (b) In terms of these contributing structures, what can you say about the nature of the C—C and the N—C bonds? (c) Sketch the MO description of C_2N_2; the end atoms are in the *sp* state (use *sp* models).

26 (You may use your sp^2 models.) Sketch the MO description for each of the following planar (plane) molecules, in which all atoms (except H) are in the

28 Library Read one of the following:

(a) "Spectroscopy, Molecular Orbitals and Chemical Bonding," Nobel Prize Lecture, Robert Mulliken, *Science,* 7 July 1967, pages 13–24. Skip the few parts with heavy mathematical language but look for the historical nuggets.

(b) *The Development of Modern Chemistry,* Aaron Ihde, pages 304–311, Harper and Row, New York, 1964.

(c) "The Three-Dimensional Structure of a Protein Molecule," John Kendrew, *Scientific American,* December 1961, pages 96–110.

(d) "The Valence-Shell Electron-Pair Repulsion Theory," Ronald Gillespie, *Journal of Chemical Education,* June 1963, page 295.

(e) "Science is Honest," Robert Mulliken, *Chemistry in Britain,* March 1976, page 96.

(f) "Malodor Counteractants: The Nose No Longer Knows," *Science,* volume 190, 28 November 1975, page 870.

_____

*Adapted from *The Development of Modern Chemistry,* Aaron Ihde, Harper and Row, New York, 1964 and *A History of Chemistry,* volume 3, James Partington, Macmillan and Company Ltd., London, 1962.

29 (a) Write the electronic formula consistent with the octet rule and common valences for hydrazine, N_2H_4. Predict the type of AO's used by the N atoms in N_2H_4. Predict the H—N—H angle. (The measured angle is 108°.) (b) Answer the same question for dinitrogen difluoride, N_2F_2. Predict the N—N—F angle. (The measured angle is 115°.) (c) Liquid aluminum bromide consists of Al_2Br_6 molecules,

$$Br\diagdown_{Br}\diagup^{Al}\diagdown_{Br}\diagup^{Br}\diagup^{Al}\diagdown_{Br}\diagup^{Br}$$. Predict the type of AO's used

by Al atoms and the Br—Al—Br and Al—Br—Al angles.

30 Predict the shape of the following molecules and ions (unshared electron pairs are housed in imaginary AO's): (a) $\ddot{S}nCl_2$, (b) $ZnCl_4{}^{2-}$, (c) $:\!\ddot{S}Cl_2$, (d) $Cu(CN)_4{}^{3-}$ (e) $\ddot{P}bCl_2$, (f) $\dot{N}H_2{}^+$, (g) $HgCl_2$, (h) $\ddot{P}F_3$, (i) $\ddot{C}Cl_2$, (j) $HgI_3{}^-$, (k) $\dot{I}O_3{}^-$, (l) $:\!N\!\!=\!\!\overset{..}{S}\!\!-\!\!F$, (m) $C_2H_5\!-\!\ddot{O}\!-\!C_2H_5$.

31 The electronic formula for hydrazoic acid, NH_3, is $H\!-\!\ddot{N}\!-\!N\!\!\equiv\!\!N:$; predict the H—N—N and N—N—N angles. Sketch the MO description of HN_3, violently explosive, used for the preparation of amides, $R\!-\!\overset{O}{\underset{\|}{C}}\!-\!NH_2$; azides, salts of hydrazoic acid, resemble the halides in solubilities.

32 One contributing structure (a) for N_2O is $:\!N\!\!=\!\!N\!\!=\!\!\ddot{O}:$, and (b) for CO is $:\!C\!\!=\!\!\ddot{O}:$. For each molecule, write one more contributing structure, each consistent with the octet rule.

33 In the reaction $BF_3 + \ddot{N}H_3 \longrightarrow F_3B\!-\!NH_3$, which molecule suffers a large change in geometry? Explain.

34 Sketch the MO description of the following molecules and ions (unshared electron pairs are housed in imaginary AO's): (a) trifluoromethyl trioxide, $F_3C\!-\!\ddot{O}\!-\!\ddot{O}\!-\!\ddot{O}\!-\!CF_3$; (b) thiosulfate, $S_2O_3{}^{2-}$, in which one S atom replaces one O atom in $SO_4{}^{2-}$; (c) tetracyanoethylene,

$$\begin{matrix}:N\!\!\equiv\!\!C & & C\!\!\equiv\!\!N:\\ & \diagdown C\!\!=\!\!C\diagup & \\ :N\!\!\equiv\!\!C & & C\!\!\equiv\!\!N:\end{matrix}\ ;$$

(d) nitrosyl chloride, $:\!\ddot{O}\!\!=\!\!N\!\!-\!\!Cl$; (e) nitronium ion, $NO_2{}^+$, $\left[:\!\ddot{O}\!\!=\!\!N\!\!=\!\!\ddot{O}:\right]^+$; (f) cyanate ion, NCO^-,

$\left[:\!N\!\!=\!\!C\!\!=\!\!\ddot{O}:\right]^-$; (g) fulminate ion, CNO^-, $\left[:\!\ddot{C}\!\!=\!\!N\!\!=\!\!\ddot{O}:\right]^-$; (h) azide ion, $N_3{}^-$, $\left[:\!\ddot{N}\!\!=\!\!N\!\!=\!\!\ddot{N}:\right]^-$; (i) dimethyl sulfoxide, $CH_3\!-\!\overset{O}{\underset{\cdot\cdot}{S}}\!-\!CH_3$, an interesting but controversial drug.

35 Write the electronic formulas consistent with the octet rule and common valences and draw sketches of the oxides of hydrogen, H_2O, H_2O_2, H_2O_3 (decomposes at -100 °C) and H_2O_4 (decomposes at -55 °C). Indicate approximate bond angles.

36 An *angle* represents the amount of space between its sides. (a) A pie is divided into four equal slices. Express the amount of each slice in degrees. (b) Answer the same question for a pie divided into six equal slices.

37 Photochemical reactions in smog ultimately form the methylperoxy compound, CH_3COO_2, which reacts with NO to form peroxyacetyl nitrate, the notorious "PAN" (page 196):

$$CH_3\!-\!\overset{O}{\underset{\|}{C}}\!-\!O_2 + NO_2 \longrightarrow CH_3\!-\!\overset{O}{\underset{\|}{C}}\!-\!O\!-\!O\!-\!NO_2$$

Sketch the MO description of PAN (O and N atoms in sp^2 state).

38 Show by diagram how the π^*, the antibonding MO in ethylene, C_2H_4, may be used to bond with a d orbital with two electrons on a metal atom. As a result of this fusion, should the C—C bond length in ethylene increase, decrease, or remain the same? Explain.

39 Sketch the MO description for BF_3 and $BF_4{}^-$. Assume that the F atom is in the same imaginary state as the B atom. Explain the observation that the B—F distance is shorter in BF_3.

40 The energy difference between bonding π and antibonding π^* MO orbitals in ethylene (page 569) is 1.225×10^{-11} erg/molecule. Find the wavelength of the photon in Å needed to excite one electron to the π^* MO.

41 Write the electronic formula for HF. Its MO energy level diagram (not scale) is given on page 595. See the footnote on page 564 for an explanation of the term nonbonding MO, *nb*.
(a) How many electrons are in HF? (b) Use the diagram to write the electronic structure of HF.

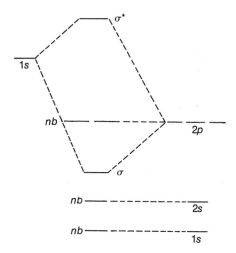

nb ———————— ————————
                         2s

nb ———————— ————————
                         1s

(c) What type of bonding binds HF? (d) What kind of orbital houses the unshared pairs shown in its electronic formula?

42 The upper MO energy levels of the azide ion, N_3^-, are given:

π_2 —— 92.4 kcal/mole

σ_3 ↓↑ 185

σ_2 ↓↑ 219

π_1 ↓↑ 296

σ_1 ↓↑ 559

Find (a) the energy required to remove an electron from the σ_3 MO; (b) the energy of the transition between σ_3 and π_2.

43 Each of the following particles containing 16 valence electrons is linear: N_3^-, CO_2, N_2O, CS_2, CN_2^{2-}. Each of the following, also containing 16 valence electrons, is nonlinear: H_2CCO, H_2NCN, H_2CNN. From the following, pick the linear and nonlinear molecules: OCS, H_2CCCH_2. Check your answer by writing electron formulas consistent with the octet rule and common valences and predicting the type of AO's used by the C and N atoms.

44 The 12 AO's of formaldehyde, H_2CO (2H $\longrightarrow$ two 1s; C and O each $\longrightarrow$ one 1s, one 2s, three 2p) form 12 MO's (crudely) represented as

σ^* —— —— ——
π^* ——
π ——
nb —— ——
σ ——
σ —— ——
nb —— ——

(See the footnote on page 564 for an explanation of nonbonding MO, nb.) (a) Write the electronic structure of formaldehyde. (b) What type of bonding is involved? (c) How many sigma and pi bonds are there? (d) Sketch the MO description of H_2CO.

_____ **ANSWERS**

1 six MO's
2 (a) delocalized more stable;
(b) delocalized electron;
(c) C_6 delocalized
3 (a)(i) 2; (ii) 8; (iii) 5;
(iv) 5; (b)(i) $\sigma_1(2)$; (ii)
$\sigma_1(2)\ \sigma_1^*(2)\ \sigma_2(2)\ \sigma_2^*(2)$;
(iii) (iv) $\sigma_1(2)\ \sigma_1^*(2)\ \sigma_2(1)$;
(c) Be_2 does not exist, others
do; (d) BeH, Li_2^+
4 (a)(b) σ, σ^*; (c) π, π^*
5 (a) tetrahedral, (ii)(iii)(vi);
bent, (i)(v); triangular pyramid,
(iv); (b) all about 110°; (c) sp^3
6 sp^3
7 (a) linear, (i)(iv); triangular
planar (plane), (ii)(iii); (b)
180° (i)(iv); 120° (ii)(iii)
(c) sp (i)(iv); sp^2 (ii)(iii)
8 Hg sp, Pb sp^2, Ga sp^2
9 (a)(i) sp^2, (ii) C—Cl σ, C=O
σ and π; (b)(i) sp, (ii) C—Cl σ,
C≡N σ and 2π

10 (a) incorrect; (b)
11 sp^2, , five unshared
electron pairs (10), two σ (4),
delocalized π (4)
12 three interactions: attraction
between electron and each of two
protons, repulsion between two
protons
13 (a) H:I, (b) H⁻I⁺
15 (a)(d)(e)(i)(j)(k); (b)
(c)(f)(g)(h)(l)
16 (b) all except HeH_2; (c) BH^+, BH^-,
LiH^-, LiH^+, CH
17 (b) O_2, O_2^-, C_2, B_2, N_2, F_2,
F_2^-, F_2^+; (c) O_2, O_2^-, B_2,
F_2^-, F_2^+; (d) O_2^+; (e) $C_2\pi$,
N_2 σ and π
18 (a) 6, 12, 13, 13, 14, 15,
14, 12, 13, 12, 14; (b)(i)
(ii) σ and π; (c) C_2

19 (a) ¾ apple, ¼ peach; (b) ⅔ apple, ⅓ peach; (c) ½ apple, ½ peach

20 (a)(b) triangular plane, sp^2, (i)(ii)(iv)(v)(ix)(xx) (xxiii)(xxvi); linear, sp, (iii)(xiii)(xiv)(xvii) (xxi)(xxvii)(xxxii)(xxxiii) (xxxvii); triangular pyramid, sp^3, (vi)(viii)(xv)(xvi) (xxiv)(xxviii)(xxix); tetrahedral, sp^3, (vii)(x)(xi) (xii)(xviii)(xxii)(xxxiv) (xxxv)(xxxvi); bent, sp^3, (xix)(xxv)(xxx)(xxxi); (c) bent

21 (a) tetrahedral, triangular pyramid, bent, linear; (b) sp^3, sp^3, sp^2, sp^3, sp^3

22 triangular plane

27 C^4H^4

29 (a)(b) 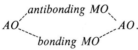, sp^2, 120°; (c) sp^3, 110°

30 bent (a)(c)(e)(f)(i) (l)(m); tetrahedral (b) (d); linear (g); triangular pyramid (h)(k); triangular plane (j)

31 110°, 180°

32 :N≡N—O̤:, :C≡O:

33 BF_3

35 H—O̤—H, H—O̤—O̤—H, H—O̤—O̤—O̤—H,

   H—O̤—O̤—O̤—O̤—H, 110°

36 (a) 90°, (b) 60°

38 increase

40 1622 Å

41 (a) 10; (b) nb (4) σ (2) nb (4); (c) σ; (d) nb

42 (a) 185 kcal/mole; (b) 93 kcal/mole

43 linear OCS

44 (b) σ and π; (c) three σ, one π

GLOSSARY

antibonding molecular orbital See **bonding molecular orbital.**

bent molecule A triatomic molecule in which the three atoms are not on a straight line. Examples: H_2O, Br_2O.

bond angle The angle between two bonds.

bonding and antibonding molecular orbitals When two atoms combine, each pair of interacting atomic orbitals forms a pair of molecular orbitals. One, the bonding MO, is more stable (has less energy) than the other MO, known as an antibonding MO; for example,

$$AO \underset{bonding\ MO}{\overset{antibonding\ MO}{\diamond}} AO.$$

The bonding orbitals are designated as sigma, σ, or pi, π, while antibonding orbitals are designated as sigma star, σ*, or pi star, π*.

delocalization of an electron When an electron goes from an atomic orbital to a molecular orbital, the region of space available to it is increased and the electron is said to be delocalized. See **molecular orbital.** Electrons in H—H are more delocalized than in an H atom; electrons in molecular orbitals spread over four atoms are even more delocalized than in H_2. The greater the delocalization for a given molecule, the lower the energy of the electrons, and the more stable the molecule.

double bond Consists of a sigma and a pi bond.

electronic structure of molecules The number of electrons in a molecule is the sum of the number of electrons in the atoms from which it is formed. The electronic structure of molecules shows how these electrons are distributed in molecular orbitals in the order of decreasing stability. See **molecular orbital.**

geometry of molecules The shape of molecules determined by the positions of their atoms.

linear molecule All the atoms of the molecule lie on a straight line. Example: H—C≡N.

molecular orbital The region of space about a molecule in which an electron has a comparatively high chance of being found. Molecular orbitals result from the interaction of atomic orbitals. The shape and energy of MO's differ from those of the AO's from which they are formed. MO's have the letter designations sigma, σ, sigma star, σ*, pi, π, and pi star, π*. Like an AO, an MO can house only two electrons.

molecular orbital theory Analogous to atomic orbital theory (electronic structure of atoms); the properties of molecules, such as stability, depend on the distribution of electrons in molecular orbitals. The theory predicts that a molecule will exist only when the number of electrons in bonding MO's is greater than the number in antibonding MO's. H_2, with two electrons in bonding MO's, does exist; He_2, with two electrons in bonding MO's and two electrons in antibonding MO's, does not exist. See **bonding and antibonding MO's.**

pi bond and pi antibond Bonds formed by the interaction of p AO's in a side-to-side approach. In a pi bond, π, the regions of high electron density are above and below the line joining the two atoms. A pi antibond, π*, has a region of zero electron density between the atoms.

resonance method See **valence-bond theory.**

resonance structures See **valence-bond theory.**

sigma bond and sigma antibond Bonds formed by the interaction of two s AO's, one s and one p AO, or two p AO's in a head-to-head approach. A sigma bond, σ, has a high electron density between the bonded atoms. A sigma antibond, σ*, has a region of zero electron density between the atoms.

single bond A sigma bond.

sp^3, sp^2, sp atomic orbitals A purely mathematical device in which it is imagined that the atomic orbitals of an atom interact with one another before the atom interacts with other atoms. This device has been termed *hybridization* even though it is not in any sense related to the biological process in which an offspring is produced from plants or animals of different species; for example, a mule is a hybrid between a horse and an ass while a loganberry is a hybrid between a blackberry and raspberry. Four sp^3 AO's are generated from the interaction of one s with three p AO's. Each sp^3 AO points to the corner of a tetrahedron. Three sp^2 AO's are generated from the interaction of one s with two p AO's. All sp^2 AO's lie in the same plane, separated by 120°. Two sp AO's are generated from the interaction of one s with one p AO. These two sp orbitals are linear, separated by 180°.

tetrahedral molecule A molecule shaped like a tetrahedron, in which the angle between any two bonds is nearly 110°; for example, CH_4. A tetrahedron is a pyramid with four faces, each face being an equilateral triangle, a triangle having three equal edges. Each of four H atoms is located at a corner of the tetrahedron, while the fifth atom, C, is located in the center of the tetrahedron.

triangular plane (planar trigonal) molecule The atoms of the molecule lie in a plane, with three atoms attached to a fourth atom, forming bond angles of 120°. Examples: BF_3, $GaCl_3$.

triangular pyramid molecule A molecule shaped like a pyramid with three faces. The angle between any two bonds is about 110°. Example: NH_3. Each of the four atoms is located at a corner of the pyramid.

triple bond Consists of a sigma and two pi bonds.

valence-bond theory This theory retains the dash or two dots method of representing chemical bonds and explains properties of real molecules as the results of contributions made by imaginary structures, called *contributing structures*. For example, the properties of HF are determined by the contributions made by three imaginary structures, H:F (purely covalent), H^+F^- (purely ionic), and H^-F^+ (purely ionic). (Contributing structures are also known as *resonance structures;* VB theory is therefore also known as the *resonance method.*)

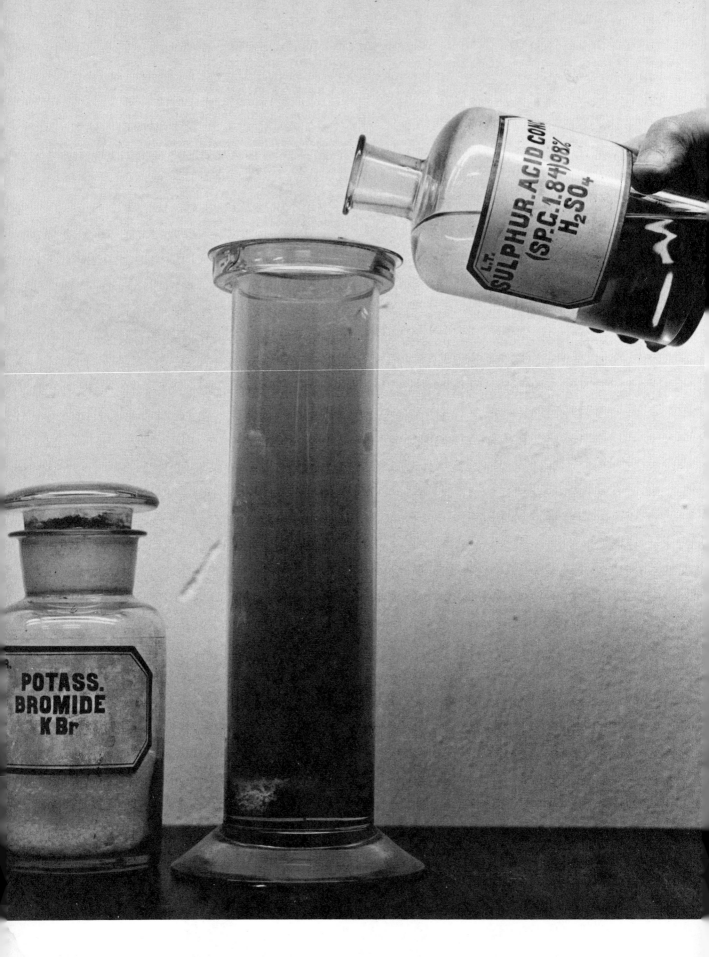

THE CHEMISTRY OF SEVERAL COMMON NONMETALLIC ELEMENTS

19

INTRODUCTION_____ 19.1

All elements are classified as either metals, semiconductors (page 633), or nonmetals. The elements that are poor conductors of heat and electricity are classified as nonmetals, found at the upper right side of the periodic table (page 226).

Nonmetals, more electronegative than metals, are generally good oxidizing agents (Table 15.1, page 466) and their oxides produce acidic aqueous solutions (page 583). Ordinarily, the molecules of nonmetallic elements—H_2, Cl_2, N_2, O_2—are bonded by covalent bonding (page 247) and most of the properties exhibited by these elements are characteristic of this type of bonding.

In this chapter we shall limit our discussion to the nonmetallic elements that are relatively abundant, oxygen, nitrogen, phosphorus, sulfur, and the halogens.

OXYGEN_____ 19.2

Oxygen was first prepared by Joseph Priestley* (1774) by heating red mercury(II) oxide in a closed tube, as shown in Fig. 19.1:

$$HgO(c) \longrightarrow Hg(l) + \tfrac{1}{2} O_2(g) \qquad \Delta H = +90.8 \text{ kJ}; \ K = 1.10 \times 10^{-11}$$

Reminder: ΔH and K values are at 25 °C.

Priestley observed that the gas generated in this manner caused a burning candle to burn more brightly. However, it remained for Antoine Lavoisier (1775 to 1777) to show the important role that oxygen plays in combustion and respiration.

_____

* Actually, oxygen was prepared in 1771 by Carl Scheele, who, however, did not publish his results until 1774, after Priestley's results were already published. Thus, Priestley is generally acknowledged as the discoverer.

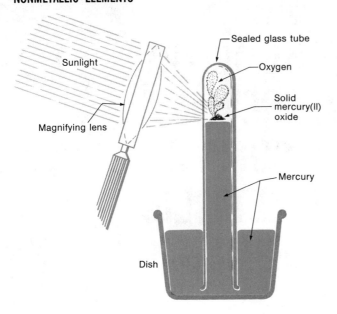

FIGURE 19.1 Priestley's apparatus for preparation of oxygen. The mercury(II) oxide was prepared by heating mercury in ordinary air.

Oxygen is the most abundant element: about 21 % of our atmosphere, nearly 90 % of water, and nearly 50 % of the rocks of the Earth's crust are oxygen. In combination with carbon, hydrogen, and nitrogen, oxygen constitutes a large percentage of the mass of plants and animals.

Commercially, oxygen is prepared from the two cheapest sources available, air and water; approximately 97 % is obtained from air and 3 % by the electrolysis of water.

The preparation of pure oxygen from air involves a distillation (page 30). Air is liquefied by cooling to below its critical temperature, to approximately -200 °C. The liquid air is then slowly warmed, and at -196 °C, nitrogen distills from the mixture. Further warming removes other gases (mainly argon), leaving relatively pure liquid oxygen. The resulting oxygen can be vaporized and stored as a gas in high-pressure steel cylinders, or it can be stored and shipped in the liquid state (called *LOX*) in large Dewar flasks. Dewar flasks are essentially high quality thermos (heat-insulated) bottles.

Very pure oxygen, made by the electrolysis of water, shown in Fig. 19.2, is more costly, but hydrogen is also produced:

$$H_2O(l) \xrightarrow{\text{electricity}} H_2(g) + \tfrac{1}{2}\,O_2(g) \qquad K = 2.33 \times 10^{-44}$$
$$\Delta G = +56.7 \text{ kcal}$$

Hydrogen is a major industrial chemical used in the production of substances such as ammonia (page 374) and methyl alcohol (page 381). Most of the hydrogen is produced by the reaction of steam with natural gas

$$CH_4(g) + H_2O(g) \longrightarrow CO(g) + 3H_2(g) \qquad \Delta H = +206 \text{ kJ}$$

or by partial oxidation of petroleum hydrocarbons (oil) in controlled quantities of oxygen. A typical reaction is

$$C_4H_{10}(g) + 2O_2(g) \longrightarrow 4CO(g) + 5H_2(g) \qquad \Delta H = -317 \text{ kJ}$$

Hydrogen, however, is receiving much attention as the ideal ecological fuel; its main source and combustion product is *water*. But the cost and decreasing reserves of natural gas and petroleum present a barrier to new uses. Research, therefore, concentrates on the thermochemical decomposition of water in the hope that the process can compete with electrolysis in cost. A typical series of reactions in which all substances consumed, except water, are regenerated is given in Problem 39, page 629. The possible biological production of hydrogen by various photosynthetic systems is also under investigation. An example is the study of a water fern as a source of hydrogen generated from water.

The acceptance of hydrogen as a "clean nonpolluting fuel" is based on the assumption that water is the only product when hydrogen is ignited in an engine. Trace amounts of hydrogen peroxide, however, have been detected in the exhaust of an engine using hydrogen as a fuel (Problem 40, page 629).

The preparation of oxygen in general chemistry laboratories involves the thermal

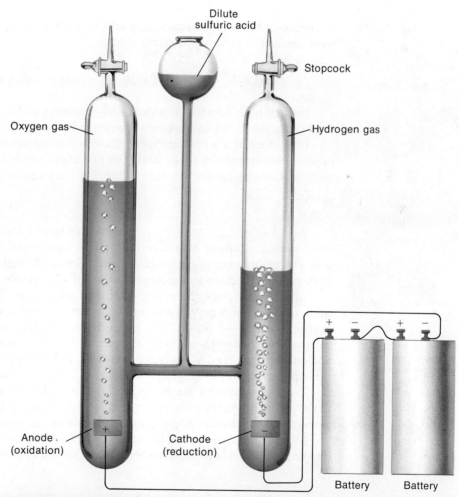

FIGURE 19.2 Apparatus for small-scale electrolysis of water. Note that the volume of hydrogen obtained is twice that of oxygen. Dilute sulfuric acid is generally used as the electrolyte.

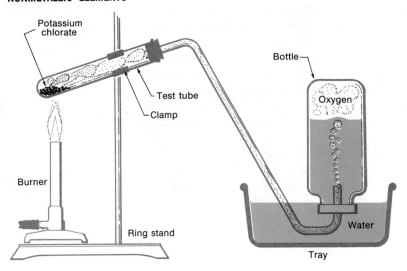

FIGURE 19.3 Apparatus for the laboratory preparation of oxygen. The oxygen is collected by the displacement of water, in which oxygen is only slightly soluble (about 3 ml/100 ml solution at room temperature).

decomposition of oxygen-containing salts (page 378), shown in Fig. 19.3. The salt most commonly used is potassium chlorate:*

$$2KClO_3(c) \xrightarrow{370\ °C} 2KCl(c) + 3O_2(g) \qquad \Delta H = -89.5\ \text{kJ}\quad K = 2.6 \times 10^{40}$$

Oxygen is an odorless, colorless, and tasteless gas. Liquid (b.p. $-183\ °C$) and solid (m.p. $-218\ °C$) oxygen are, however, pale blue.

Oxygen exists as a diatomic molecule with two unpaired electrons and, therefore, exhibits paramagnetism (page 203). The two unpaired electrons are in antibonding molecular orbitals (pages 567, 568) and for our purposes, oxygen may be represented as $:\overset{..}{\underset{.}{O}}—\overset{..}{\underset{.}{O}}:$

Reactions and Compounds of Oxygen   Oxygen combines with almost every other element, forming *oxides, peroxides,* and *superoxides.* Only fluorine combines with a larger number of elements. Oxygen, Group VI, highly electronegative (page 254), gains two electrons in most reactions and is, therefore, a good oxidizing agent.

In all compounds of oxygen, with the exception of the superoxides and the compounds in which oxygen is bound to fluorine, the oxidation number exhibited by oxygen is either -1 or -2. The peroxides are characterized by a direct oxygen-oxygen bond ($—\overset{..}{\underset{..}{O}}—\overset{..}{\underset{..}{O}}—$), giving oxygen an oxidation number of -1 (page 364). Sodium peroxide, Na_2O_2, is a typical peroxide, widely used as an oxidizing agent and in the preparation of hydrogen peroxide, H_2O_2. The compounds in which oxygen has a -2 oxidation number are the oxides, such as K_2O, and oxy compounds, such as K_2CO_3. In these compounds, the oxygen atom shares (or transfers) electrons with an atom of another element. Oxygen-oxygen bonds are not present in these compounds.

Superoxides are ionic solids containing the O_2^- ion; potassium superoxide, KO_2, is typical. It is used as an oxygen source in rescue-work masks. Moisture in the breath

Peroxides are known for the Group I and II elements, except Be and Au.

---

*The preparation of oxygen from potassium chlorate, generally with MnO_2 as catalyst, must be carefully performed (note the high K value). The presence of any organic or readily combustible material, such as dust, rubber, cork, paper, sulfur, and so forth, can lead to disastrous explosions.

reacts with the superoxide, producing oxygen and potassium oxide, which removes carbon dioxide:

Superoxides form with the larger and less electronegative metals, Na ⟶ Cs, Ca ⟶ Ra.

$$2KO_2(c) + H_2O \longrightarrow H_2O_2(l) + K_2O(c) + O_2(g)$$
$$2H_2O_2(l) \longrightarrow 2H_2O(g) + O_2(g)$$
$$K_2O(c) + CO_2(g) \longrightarrow K_2CO_3(c)$$

The oxidation number of oxygen in the superoxide is $-\frac{1}{2}$.

At room temperature all metals with standard electrode potentials of less than $+0.35$ volt (copper), Table 15.1, page 466, react with dilute oxygen (air). Thus, iron forms a red-brown oxide, the familiar rust, while aluminum forms aluminum oxide, Al_2O_3, the white coating found on aluminum storm windows and doors that protects the remaining metal (page 490). A new iron construction material (*Cor-Ten*), like aluminum, resists corrosion by forming an adhering oxide film.

Metal oxides that dissolve in water form basic solutions and are thus called **basic oxides.** Calcium oxide is typical:

$$CaO(c) + H_2O \longrightarrow Ca(OH)_2(aq)$$

Sulfur, typical of the nonmetals that react with oxygen, forms sulfur monoxide, $SO(g)$, sulfur dioxide, $SO_2(g)$, and sulfur trioxide, $SO_3(g)$, depending upon temperature and quantity of oxygen. Oxides of sulfur in the $+1$, $+3$, $+7$, and $+8$ oxidation states are also known.

Similarly, the combustion of carbon forms carbon monoxide, CO, or carbon dioxide, CO_2, if sufficient oxygen is available.

Most oxides of the nonmetals dissolve in water, forming acidic solutions (page 413) and thus are called **acidic oxides.** These acidic oxides are responsible for serious pollution problems (pages 307, 421, and 584).

The metal oxides are mainly ionic solids, while the nonmetal oxides are largely covalent. The reactions of these oxides with water may be regarded as a Lewis acid-base type of reaction (page 417):

There is no change in oxidation numbers of the elements involved, page 364.

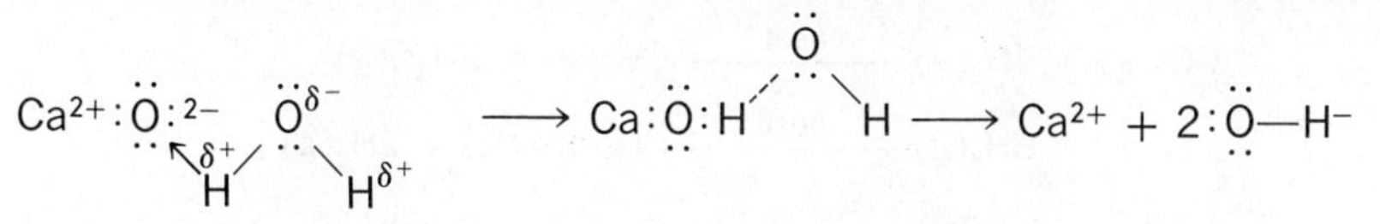

Lewis base Lewis acid

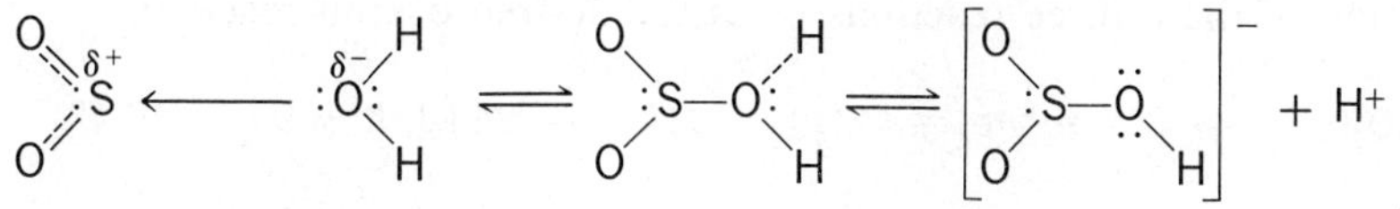

Lewis acid   Lewis base

S, sp^2 in SO_2 but sp^3 in HSO_3^- (Chap. 18). H_2SO_3 has never been isolated, page 620.

$$K = 1.71 \times 10^{-2}$$

Compounds that are composed of elements which are oxidized by oxygen will themselves react with oxygen. The products are the oxides of the component elements. Thus, all hydrocarbon fuels, such as methane (natural) gas, CH_4, are oxidized to carbon dioxide and water:

$$CH_4(g) + 2O_2(g) \longrightarrow CO_2(g) + 2H_2O(l) \quad \Delta H = -890.4 \text{ kJ}$$

Similarly, hydrogen sulfide gas, H_2S, is oxidized to water and sulfur dioxide. Compounds already containing oxygen may be further oxidized:

$$HCOOH(g) + \tfrac{1}{2} O_2(g) \longrightarrow CO_2(g) + H_2O(l) \qquad \Delta H = -301 \text{ kJ}$$

PROBLEM 1 (a) Propane, C_3H_8, and silicon hydride, SiH_4, are oxidized by O_2 in a manner similar to methane. Write balanced chemical equations for these reactions. (b) Write the formula for magnesium oxide and magnesium peroxide. (c) What is the product formed when magnesium oxide dissolves in water?

See page 154.

Three Russian Cosmonauts died (1971) of anoxia when their spacecraft developed a leak in outer space, practically a vacuum.

Uses of Oxygen Oxygen is necessary for respiration in all animals. The average adult inhales approximately 10,000 liters of air per day, from which only about 500 liters of oxygen is used. Without oxygen, a condition called *anoxia* develops and death results almost instantaneously. Man cannot survive for more than eight minutes in air that contains less than 6 % oxygen; permanent brain damage occurs in seconds.

Oxygen, then, is man's most precious possession, but it is not inexhaustible. Replenished by photosynthesis (page 195), the total oxygen in the atmosphere still remains constant, although the amount available in highly industrial areas may be subjected to considerable variations. Under certain conditions, pockets of oxygen-deficient air may form.

Oxygen is carried in spacecraft as a gas at a pressure greater than its critical pressure (49.7 atm). As oxygen is discharged, addition of heat maintains constant pressure. Carbon dioxide, a major waste product of man, is removed from the cabin atmosphere by reaction with lithium hydroxide:

$$2LiOH(c) + CO_2(g) \longrightarrow Li_2CO_3(c) + H_2O(g)$$

However, methods of regenerating oxygen from carbon dioxide are under examination. A promising scheme is the decomposition of the products of the reaction of carbon dioxide with hydrogen:

$$CO_2(g) + 4H_2(g) \xrightarrow{\text{heat}} CH_4(g) + 2H_2O(g)$$

$$CH_4(g) \xrightarrow{\text{heat}} C(graphite) + 2H_2(g)$$

$$2H_2O(l) \xrightarrow{\text{electrolysis}} 2H_2(g) + O_2(g)$$

The addition of these three reactions gives the desired overall reaction:

$$CO_2(g) \longrightarrow C(graphite) + O_2(g) \qquad \Delta H = +394 \text{ kJ}; K = 9.8 \times 10^{-70}$$

The Saturn 5B booster rocket, used to place a man on the moon, consumed liquid oxygen at the rate of 375,000 gallons per minute of burning.

Pure oxygen is used extensively in the manufacture of steel to remove impurities as oxides, and in oxyhydrogen and oxyacetylene torches. Large quantities of liquid oxygen are now used as the oxidizing agent in booster rockets used by NASA for manned spaceflights. However, almost 50 % of all oxygen used in industry is employed in producing other chemicals, such as acetylene, carbon monoxide, and hydrogen from natural gas:

$$6CH_4(g) + O_2(g) \longrightarrow 2C_2H_2(g) + 2CO(g) + 10H_2(g)$$

Oxygen is among the chemicals manufactured in the largest quantities by weight.

PROBLEM 2 **(a) Write a balanced chemical equation for each of three ways to prepare oxygen. (b) What is the largest commercial source of oxygen?**

NITROGEN _____ 19.3

Nitrogen was discovered in 1772 by the biologist Daniel Rutherford. He observed that when an animal is placed in a sealed chamber containing air, after a given period of time the animal dies. The gas remaining in the chamber is no longer air; it does not support life or combustion.

The same gas was found by Carl Scheele in his investigations of oxygen compounds. It remained, however, for Antoine Lavoisier to determine that nitrogen is an element.

Nitrogen comprises 78 % of the atmosphere by volume and 75 % by mass. Large quantities of nitrogen are found in South America as deposits of *saltpeter,* KNO_3, and *Chile saltpeter,* $NaNO_3$.

Nitrogen was recently discovered in diamonds by paramagnetic detection techniques. The nitrogen atom (mononitrogen), with five valence electrons, is bonded to four neighboring carbon atoms, C:N:C, leaving the nitrogen atom with one unpaired electron (paramagnetic). A pure diamond, very rare, is colorless; it does not absorb visible light (page 190). When nitrogen is present, however, the diamond has a greenish-yellow color because nitrogen atoms absorb a large portion of blue from the light passing through the diamond. The various colors of diamonds, "blue-white," "ice-white," and so forth, are due to differences in the state of the nitrogen atoms in the diamond.

First mentioned in the writing of Abd Allah, about 1200, who called it "Chinese snow," confirming the earlier use (10th century) in China of saltpeter mixtures in fireworks.

Industrially, nitrogen is prepared by the distillation of liquid air (page 600). Nitrogen so prepared is always contaminated with small amounts of oxygen and noble gases, particularly argon.

N_2 U.S. annual production 3.3 × 10^{11} cu. ft.

Small amounts of pure nitrogen can be prepared by heating a solution of ammonium nitrite:

$$NH_4NO_2(aq) \longrightarrow 2H_2O + N_2(g)$$

Nitrogen is a colorless, odorless, and tasteless gas; it boils at -195.8 °C and freezes at -210.0 °C.

The nitrogen molecule, :N≡N:, is an extremely kinetically stable molecule which does not exhibit paramagnetism. The triple bond, consisting of two π (pi) bonds and one σ (sigma) bond (page 268), is responsible for the stability of the nitrogen molecule. Unlike other compounds containing triple bonds, such as carbon monoxide, C≡O, and acetylene (page 583), HC≡CH, nitrogen generally reacts by a mechanism which requires dissociation into atomic nitrogen, $N_2 \longrightarrow 2N$. This highly endothermic step ($\Delta H = +945.6$ kJ) makes the energy of activation exceptionally large. Like a narrow street, this dissociation step is the bottleneck that determines the measured rate of the overall reaction. The step that is the bottleneck in the step by step outline of an overall reaction is called the **slow step,** Fig. 19.4. Therefore, any scheme that catalyzes the slow step, the rate of dissociation of nitrogen, automatically increases the rate of the overall reaction. The challenge is therefore the development of a catalyst that lowers the very high activation energies generally encountered in the reactions of nitrogen.

Thermodynamically, thermally, and kinetically unstable, $NH_4NO_2(aq)$ is prepared just before reaction by mixing solutions of sodium nitrite and ammonium chloride.

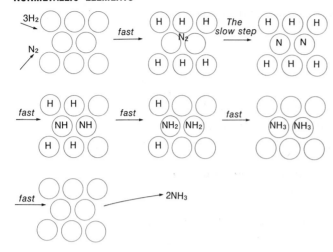

FIGURE 19.4 Representation of the catalytic preparation of NH_3. The circles represent a catalytic surface. N_2 and H_2 dissociate but N_2 does not dissociate until the temperature is about 450 °C, while H_2 easily dissociates even at -200 °C in the presence of the catalyst. The dissociation of N_2 is therefore the bottleneck. Dissociation is followed by the successive rapid addition of three H atoms to one N atom. Finally, NH_3 escapes.

At high temperatures, reaction rates become fast and nitrogen reacts to form ionic *nitrides,* N^{3-}, mainly with lithium and Group II metals, and covalent nitrides with many elements. $Li_3N(c)$, $Ca_3N_2(c)$, $Si_3N_4(c)$, and $P_3N_5(c)$ are typical nitrides. With oxygen, nitrogen forms nitrogen oxide (page 115). Generally, other nitrogen compounds are then prepared from these compounds rather than directly from nitrogen.

Although nitrogen is a highly electronegative element (page 254), it exhibits every oxidation state from -3 to $+6$, illustrated in Table 19.1.

Compounds of Nitrogen   Ammonia, $\overset{..}{N}H_3$, is a toxic colorless gas with a characteristic, irritating odor. It liquefies at -33.43 °C and freezes at -77.76 °C. Since its heat of vaporization is higher than that of all liquids except water, it is used as a refrigerant in large industrial plants.

Ammonia is highly polar and, therefore, is a good solvent for other polar compounds. The use of aqueous ammonia solutions as a household cleansing agent is

TABLE 19.1
OXIDATION STATES OF NITROGEN

OXIDATION NUMBER	TYPICAL COMPOUND (COMMON NAME)
$+6$	NO_3,* nitrogen trioxide
$+5$	N_2O_5, dinitrogen pentoxide
$+4$	N_2O_4, dinitrogen tetraoxide
$+3$	$NaNO_2$, sodium nitrite
$+3$	HNO_2, nitrous acid
$+2$	NO, nitrogen oxide (nitric oxide)
$+1$	N_2O, dinitrogen oxide (nitrous oxide)
0	N_2, nitrogen
-1	NH_2OH, hydroxylamine
-2	N_2H_4, hydrazine
-3	Na_3N, sodium nitride
-3	NH_3, ammonia

*Thermodynamically and kinetically unstable, NO_3 rapidly decomposes to $NO + O_2$.

based on its alkaline reaction. A high pH favors emulsification of greasy dirt (pages 345 and 346).

Ammonia may be prepared in the general chemistry laboratory by heating an aqueous solution of an ammonium salt and sodium hydroxide,

$$NH_4Cl(aq) + NaOH(aq) \longrightarrow NH_3(g) + H_2O + NaCl(aq)$$

or by the hydrolysis of ionic nitrides:

$$Mg_3N_2(c) + 6H_2O \longrightarrow 3Mg(OH)_2(c) + 2NH_3(g)$$

These reactions may be regarded as acid-base reactions:

$$\begin{array}{cc} acid & + \ base \\ NH_4^+ \ + \ OH^- & \longrightarrow \ NH_3 + H_2O \\ 3HOH + N^{3-} & \longrightarrow \ NH_3 + 3OH^- \end{array}$$

Commercially, however, ammonia is prepared by the *Haber process,* in which nitrogen and hydrogen are directly combined (page 374).

Liquid ammonia dissolves many of the alkali and alkaline earth metals. But because of their strong tendency to give up electrons, these metals exist as positive ions in solution (page 634):

Discovered by W. Weyl in 1864.

$$Na \xrightarrow[NH_3]{liquid} Na^+ + e^- \ (NH_3)$$

The solvated electron is called the "ammoniated electron" and is responsible for the characteristic blue color of these solutions. These metal-ammonia solutions are strong reducing agents, widely used for the reduction of many compounds, but if they are allowed to stand, hydrogen is slowly evolved and the *amide ion,* NH_2^-, results:

The electron is stabilized by delocalization in a molecular orbital (page 560) extending over a number of solvent molecules, as in ammonia or in water (e^- (aq)).

$$2Na_{(NH_3)} + 2NH_3 \longrightarrow 2Na^+_{(NH_3)} + 2NH_2^-_{(NH_3)} + H_2(g)$$

Rapid evaporation of metal-liquid ammonia solutions yields the metal.

Almost 75 % of all ammonia produced in the United States is used either as a fertilizer or in the manufacture of the solid fertilizers, ammonium nitrate, and ammonium sulfate. The remaining ammonia is used principally as an industrial refrigerant, in household cleaners, and in the chemical industry, particularly in the production of nitric acid.

Hydrazine is a colorless, poisonous liquid. Like liquid ammonia, it is a good solvent for polar compounds and for the alkali metals. Structurally, hydrazine is comparable to hydrogen peroxide (H—Ö—Ö—H) H—N̈—N̈—H.
$$\qquad\qquad\qquad\qquad\qquad\quad | \ \ |$$
$$\qquad\qquad\qquad\qquad\qquad\ \ H \ H$$

It is prepared by the oxidation of ammonia with sodium hypochlorite in aqueous solution:*

$$2NH_3(aq) + NaOCl(aq) \longrightarrow N_2H_4(l) + NaCl(aq) + H_2O$$

---

*The reaction proceeds in two steps:

Step (1) $\qquad\qquad NH_3 + NaOCl \longrightarrow NaOH + NH_2Cl$ (*fast*)

Step (2) $\qquad NH_3 + NaOH + NH_2Cl \longrightarrow N_2H_4 + NaCl + H_2O$ (*slow, the bottleneck*)

Anhydrous hydrazine is thermally stable but thermodynamically and kinetically unstable and, thus, is generally very reactive. It burns explosively in air or in the presence of other oxidizing agents and reacts extremely vigorously with the halogen acids:

$$2N_2H_4(l) \longrightarrow N_2(g) + 2NH_3(g) + H_2(g) \qquad \Delta H = -143 \text{ kJ}$$

$$N_2H_4(l) + O_2(g) \longrightarrow N_2(g) + 2H_2O(l) \qquad \Delta H = -623 \text{ kJ}$$

$$N_2H_4(l) + 2H_2O_2(l) \longrightarrow N_2(g) + 4H_2O(l) \qquad \Delta H = -820 \text{ kJ}$$

$$N_2H_4 + HCl(g) \xrightarrow[\text{N}_2\text{H}_4]{\text{in liquid}} N_2H_5{}^+ + Cl^-$$

Hydrazine and its related compounds are oxidized with tremendous evolution of heat. They are therefore used as rocket fuels (page 270). The rocket engine that lifted astronauts from the moon used dimethyl hydrazine, $(CH_3)_2N_2H_2$; it burns immediately when mixed with oxygen so that no ignition system is required.

Urea, NH_2CONH_2, and potassium cyanate, KNCO, are two important compounds used for the treatment of sickle-cell anemia (page 321). In solution, an equilibrium is established:

K at 37 °C and
pH = 7.4

$$H_2NCONH_2(aq) \rightleftharpoons NH_4{}^+(aq) + NCO^-(aq) \qquad K = 2.5 \times 10^{-5}$$

The use of urea as a treatment led to the investigation of cyanate as a preventative agent for sickling, Fig. 19.5. The reactive particle is cyanic acid, $H\!-\!\ddot{N}\!=\!C\!=\!\ddot{O}\!:$; it binds to hemoglobin (page 665) strongly enough so that it cannot be washed out or removed. This combination suffices to prevent sickling.

Nitric acid has been known for centuries. As early as the 9th century, nitric acid was used by alchemists to separate gold from silver. Silver dissolves in nitric acid (page 290) but gold does not.

Nitric acid is a colorless, corrosive liquid which boils at 86 °C and freezes at −42 °C to a white solid. It fumes in moist air, forming a cloud (droplets) of aqueous nitric acid.

Commercially, nitric acid is produced exclusively by the *Ostwald process.** Ammonia is oxidized to nitrogen oxide, which is then further oxidized to the dioxide. Finally, the nitrogen dioxide is hydrolyzed to nitric acid:

$$4NH_3(g) + 5O_2(g) \xrightarrow[\text{Pt catalyst}]{1000 \text{ °C}} 4NO(g) + 6H_2O(g) \qquad (1)$$

$$2NO(g) + O_2(g) \longrightarrow 2NO_2(g) \text{ (slowest reaction in the}$$
$$\text{process, the bottleneck} \qquad (2)$$

$$3NO_2(g) + H_2O \longrightarrow 2HNO_3(aq) + NO(g) \qquad (3)$$

The nitrogen oxide, NO, formed in Reaction 3 is oxidized to nitrogen dioxide for further reaction with water. The overall chemical equation for this three-stage process is

$$NH_3(g) + 2O_2(g) \longrightarrow HNO_3(aq) + H_2O(g)$$

Pure nitric acid is thermally unstable and decomposes to nitrogen dioxide:

$$4HNO_3(l) \xrightarrow{150 \text{ °C}} 4NO_2(g) + 2H_2O(g) + O_2(g)$$

---

*Developed (1902) by Wilhelm Ostwald on the basis of kinetic and equilibria studies. Readers interested in the significance of this process in World War I are referred to "Strong Water," Thomas Chilton, MIT Press Paperback, Cambridge, Mass., 1970, Chap. 3.

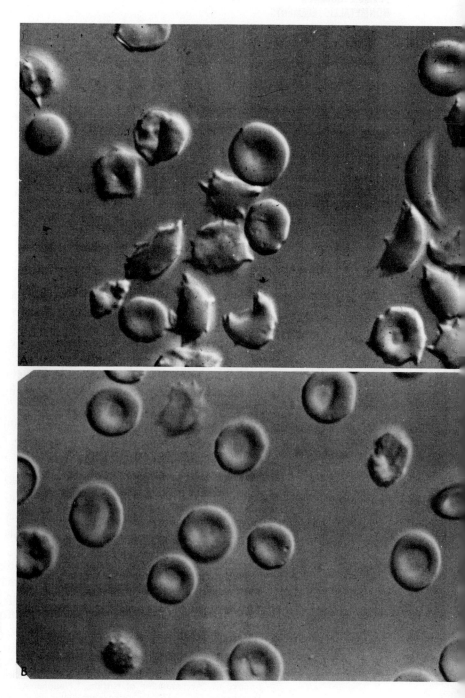

FIGURE 19.5 The effects of cyanate on sickled red blood cells. (a) Sickled red blood cells; (b) red blood cells after treatment with 0.03 M KNCO for 1 hour at 37 °C. (*Courtesy of Anthony Cerami, Rockefeller University, Proceedings of National Academy of Sciences, volume 68, June 1971, page 1180.*)

In aqueous solutions, it is a strong acid and a strong oxidizing agent. A few electrode reactions and their standard electrode potentials (page 466) illustrate the oxidizing strength of nitric acid:

$$2NO_3^-(aq) + 12H^+(aq) + 10e^- \longrightarrow N_2(g) + 6H_2O \qquad E° = +1.25 \text{ volt}$$

$$NO_3^-(aq) + 4H^+(aq) + 3e^- \longrightarrow NO(g) + 2H_2O \qquad E° = +0.96 \text{ volt}$$

$$NO_3^-(aq) + 10H^+(aq) + 8e^- \longrightarrow NH_4^+(aq) + 3H_2O \qquad E° = +0.88 \text{ volt}$$

$$NO_3^-(aq) + 2H^+(aq) + e^- \longrightarrow NO_2(g) + H_2O \qquad E° = +0.79 \text{ volt}$$

609

The product obtained depends upon the concentrations and the nature of the reducing agent used.

Commercially, nitric acid is used in the manufacture of explosives, plastics (Chap. 23), drugs (page 679), and nitrate fertilizers.

Nitric acid may be formed in photochemical smog. Ozone (page 386) may react with NO_2 to form NO_3

$$O_3(g) + NO_2(g) \longrightarrow NO_3(g) + O_2(g)$$

which forms N_2O_5 by reaction with another NO_2 molecule:

$$NO_3(g) + NO_2(g) \longrightarrow N_2O_5(g)$$

Finally, nitric acid forms from its anhydride:

$$N_2O_5(g) + H_2O(g) \longrightarrow 2HNO_3(sol)$$

Nitrates and nitrites have been in use for centuries to preserve foods. However, U.S. Food and Drug Administration chemists recently reported that the use of these preservatives in fish and meat processing has apparently increased the amount of a carcinogenic substance* in these foods. The Department of Agriculture has therefore decreased the allowable concentration of these compounds in processed foods.

Nitrogen Fixation and the Nitrogen Cycle in Nature   Nitrogen, a constituent of all proteins (page 726), is essential to all living organisms, but all animals and most plants cannot use (assimilate) the nitrogen of the air.** The conversion of nitrogen to compounds that can be assimilated by plants for protein synthesis is known as *nitrogen-fixation*. Nitrogen present in air is fixed as nitrates by lightning during thunderstorms:

$$N_2(g) + O_2(g) \longrightarrow 2NO(g)$$
$$NO(g) + \tfrac{1}{2} O_2(g) \longrightarrow NO_2(g)$$
$$NO_2(g) + rain \longrightarrow HNO_3(aq)$$
$$HNO_3(aq) + soil\ minerals \longrightarrow nitrates$$

Plants use these nitrates to synthesize plant proteins. In turn, these proteins, ingested as food by animals, are converted into animal protein or excreted as nitrogenous waste into the soil. Then, naturally occurring bacteria in the soil convert nitrogen compounds back to nitrogen and, thus, return it to the atmosphere, completing a

---

*The cancer-inducing substance is nitrosamine, H_2NNO, formed from nitrates and naturally occurring amines in foods, 26 nanograms per gram of fish, the same as 26 grams per billion grams of fish. This amount is significant only if large amounts of such fish are eaten. Readers interested in the subject are referred to "Accumulation of Nitrates," National Academy of Sciences, National Research Council, Washington, D.C., 1972. An amine (page 704) is a compound in which an H in NH_3 is replaced by a group of atoms. Nitrosamines are contained in cigarette and cigar smoke.

**Bacteria on the roots of some plants, particularly the legumes—plants such as beans, peas, and alfalfa, having seeds in a pod—convert atmospheric nitrogen into compounds that are assimilated by the plant and incorporated into proteins. The bacteria contain the enzyme nitrogenase, which catalyzes the conversion of nitrogen to ammonia. The quantity of nitrogen compounds generated by the bacteria is more than the plant requires but insufficient to meet the world's demand for food. Current research on the mechanism of nitrogenase systems may find ways for extending natural nitrogen fixation to major food crops. It appears that the bacteria are capable of converting atmospheric nitrogen to nitrogen compounds *without* the assistance of the legume roots. The legumes provide simple compounds and an oxygen-free atmosphere for the bacteria. The search thus concentrates on creating the same conditions for the bacteria in the roots of other plants.

cycle. This cycle, the nitrogen cycle, has been so severely unbalanced by increasing human population that massive starvation is prevented only by the widespread use of synthesized fertilizers and the development of new seeds.* Food specialists nevertheless feel that the world is at the beginning of a long period of chronic food shortages, in spite of improved farm technology.

PROBLEM 3 Write a balanced chemical equation for each of the following reactions: (a) $Li(c) + N_2(g)$; (b) $N_2(g) + O_2(g)$; (c) heating $NH_4NO_2(aq)$; (d) $Li(c) + NH_3(l)$.

Dinitrogen oxide, N_2O, is released from the soil by bacterial decomposition of nitrogen fertilizers and from the combustion of coal. Increased use of coal and continued use of nitrogen fertilizers might cause an increase in the quantity of dinitrogen oxide in the upper atmosphere. Here, it can be oxidized to nitrogen oxide, a compound capable of destroying ozone (page 386). In addition, N_2O strongly absorbs photons in the infrared (heat) region and so, like CO_2, contributes to the atmospheric greenhouse effect (page 308).

PHOSPHORUS _____ 19.4

Phosphorus was discovered in 1669 by Hennig Brand when he heated the solid residue obtained from evaporating urine with sand. He hoped that this experiment would yield the "Philosopher's Stone," believed to be the material which would transform other metals into gold. Instead, he discovered a substance which glowed in the dark, in reality, white phosphorus. It burns on exposure to air.

Phosphorus is found in nature as "phosphate rock," composed principally of calcium phosphate, $Ca_3(PO_4)_2$. It is also a major component of all vegetable and animal matter. The inorganic component of bone and dental enamel consists of $[Ca_3(PO_4)_2]_3Ca(OH)_2$ and $Ca_3(PO_4)_2$.** Many important biochemical compounds (page 725) are derived from phosphates. Plants need soluble phosphates to grow properly. It is therefore necessary to replenish the soil with synthetic phosphate fertilizers.

Phosphorus is obtained from the reduction of calcium phosphate by a mixture of carbon (coke) and silicon dioxide (sand) at very high temperatures:

$$Ca_3(PO_4)_2(c) + 3SiO_2(c) + 5C(c) \longrightarrow 3CaSiO_3(c) + 5CO(g) + P_2(g)$$

The $P_2(g)$ is then cooled under water:

$$2P_2(g) \longrightarrow P_4(g) \longrightarrow P_4(c) \text{ (white)}$$

Phosphorus is derived from phos and pherein, Greek words for light bearer. White phosphorus should never be touched with bare fingers.

Annual U.S. production of P is over 10^6 tons, with detergent, food, and beverage industries as major consumers.

---

*"Miracle rice," for example, a new strain of rice recently developed at the International Rice Institute, Los Banos, the Philippines, yields two to three harvests a year and doubles the tonnage of rice per acre; old strains permit only one crop per year. India is introducing new strains of wheat developed at the International Maize and Wheat Improvement Center, Texococo, Mexico, and success is predicted for the development of "high-lysine" corn, a more nutritional corn because of a higher content of lysine, an essential amino acid (page 705). Readers interested in this subject are referred to "High-Lysine Corn," *Scientific American,* August 1971, page 34. Population growth and poor technology in underdeveloped countries, however, tend to wipe out these gains; see *Science,* volume 181, 17 August 1973, page 634.

**The purpose of fluoridation (addition of a fluoride to water supplies) is to convert $[Ca_3(PO_4)_2]_3Ca(OH)_2$ to the harder, less soluble, and more acid-resistant $[Ca_3(PO_4)_2]_3CaF_2$, known as *phosphate rock* or *fluorapatite* (page 396).

Phosphorus exists as three different substances, white, red, and black, of which the white and red are important. When an element exists as two or more different substances, it is said to be **allotropic.** Many elements exhibit *allotropy:* carbon exists as graphite and diamond, and oxygen exists as (diatomic) oxygen, O_2, and trioxygen, ozone, O_3. In the periodic table the allotropic region roughly embraces the elements about the line that separates the nonmetallic from the metallic elements.

White phosphorus exists as a soft, white, translucent, waxlike solid melting at 44.2 °C and boiling at 280 °C. Its molecules are composed of 4 phosphorus atoms located at the corners of a tetrahedron, corresponding to the position of 4 hydrogen atoms in methane (page 575). Above 800 °C, P_4 dissociates into P_2, whose electronic structure is believed to be similar to that of nitrogen, $:P{\equiv}P:$

Red phosphorus is a mixture of at least six different allotropic forms.

Red phosphorus is prepared by heating white phosphorus to about 400 °C in the absence of air. The structure of red phosphorus is still unknown.

Although the chemical reactions of white and red phosphorus are similar, white phosphorus is kinetically more unstable than the red. Thus, white phosphorus is a violent flammable poison; burns caused by contact with it are extremely serious. Red phosphorus, however, is not a poison. While white phosphorus ignites at room conditions, the red must be heated to about 250 °C before it ignites. White phosphorus is therefore stored under water.

Compounds of Phosphorus Phosphorus in oxygen or air forms a series of oxides, of which two are important: phosphorus(III) oxide, P_4O_6, and phosphorus(V) oxide, P_4O_{10}. The simplest formulas, P_2O_3 and P_2O_5, account for the common names, *phosphorus trioxide* and *phosphorus pentoxide.*

Both oxides hydrolyze, forming phosphorous acid, H_3PO_3, and phosphoric acid, H_3PO_4, respectively. These acids can also be prepared from the hydrolysis of the chlorides PCl_3 and PCl_5 (page 421).

IUPAC approved name is phosphonic acid.

Phosphonic (phosphorous) acid, a diprotic acid,

$$\text{H}-\overset{\cdot\cdot}{\underset{\cdot\cdot}{\text{O}}}-\overset{\displaystyle \text{H}}{\underset{\displaystyle :\overset{\cdot\cdot}{\underset{\cdot\cdot}{\text{O}}}:}{\text{P}}}-\overset{\cdot\cdot}{\underset{\cdot\cdot}{\text{O}}}-\text{H}$$

dissociates in two steps as shown:

$$H_3PO_3(aq) + H_2O \rightleftharpoons H_3O^+(aq) + H_2PO_3^-(aq) \qquad K_1 = 1.6 \times 10^{-2}$$
$$H_2PO_3^-(aq) + H_2O \rightleftharpoons H_3O^+(aq) + HPO_3^{2-}(aq) \qquad K_2 = 7.0 \times 10^{-7}$$

It is preferable to write the formula of phosphonic (phosphorous) acid as H_2PHO_3. The traditional formula H_3PO_3 does *not* tell us that only *two* of the hydrogen atoms dissociate, while the formula H_2PHO_3, recommended by IUPAC, informs us that only the two hydrogen atoms written before the P atom dissociate. Hydrogen atom(s) written after the P atom do not dissociate. Thus, in the acid, $H_2P_2H_2O_5$ ($H_4P_2O_5$), only two hydrogen atoms dissociate.

Typical salts of phosphonic (phosphorous) acid are sodium hydrogen phosphonate (phosphite), $NaHPHO_3$, and disodium phosphonate, Na_2PHO_3.

The method of naming oxyacids (page 152) has limitations. For example, there may be more than one acid in the same oxidation state. Phosphoric acid is typical of oxyacids *in the same oxidation state that differ in water content*. The acids are named *ortho, pyro,* and *meta* as the degree of hydration decreases:

From ortho, the Greek word for regular, and pyro, the Greek word for heat-action.

$$2H_3\overset{+5}{P}O_4 \xrightarrow{250\ ^\circ C} H_4\overset{+5}{P_2}O_7 + H_2O$$

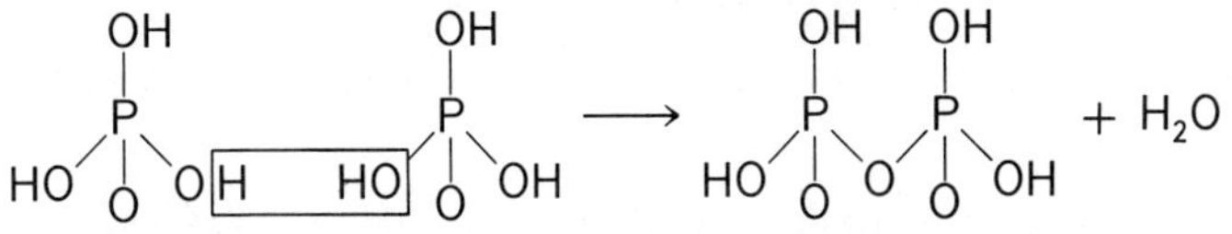

orthophosphoric acid
or
phosphoric acid

pyrophosphoric acid
or
diphosphoric acid

While phosphoric and diphosphoric acid exist as simple molecules, metaphosphoric acid is an extended type of molecule in which oxygen atoms sit between phosphorus atoms, so that the molecular formula of metaphosphoric acid is $(HPO_3)_n$:

An oxygen atom serves as a "bridge" between two phosphorus atoms.

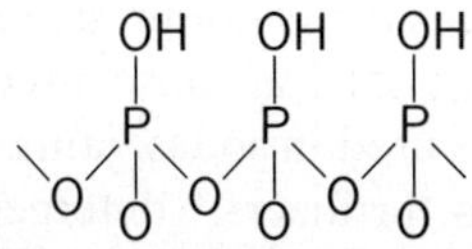

metaphosphoric acid

This type of linkage is found in many substances of great biological importance (page 732).

Typical salts of these acids are tetrasodium diphosphate, $Na_4P_2O_7$, disodium dihydrogen diphosphate, $Na_2H_2P_2O_7$, and sodium metaphosphate, $NaPO_3$, or $(NaPO_3)_n$. *Calgon,* used in detergents to soften water, is a complex mixture of sodium metaphosphates in which n takes values of 3 to at least 8. Chromatographic techniques (page 31) have been successfully used to separate and identify the components of such mixtures.

The electronic structure of phosphoric acid, a triprotic acid (page 417), is

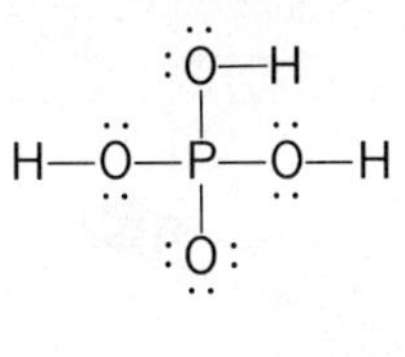

Typical salts of phosphoric acid are sodium dihydrogen phosphate, NaH_2PO_4, disodium hydrogen phosphate, Na_2HPO_4, and trisodium phosphate, Na_3PO_4. The aqueous solution of sodium dihydrogen phosphate is slightly acidic, while that of disodium hydrogen phosphate is slightly basic. Solutions of trisodium phosphate are strongly basic; HPO_4^{2-} is such a weak acid that PO_4^{3-}, its conjugate base, strongly reacts with water (page 410):

$$HPO_4^{2-}(aq) + H_2O \rightleftharpoons H_3O^+(aq) + PO_4^{3-}(aq) \qquad K_3 = 4.8 \times 10^{-13}$$
$$PO_4^{3-}(aq) + H_2O \rightleftharpoons HPO_4^{2-}(aq) + OH^-(aq) \qquad K = 2.1 \times 10^{-2}$$

PROBLEM 4   Is phosphinic (hypophosphorous) acid, HPH_2O_2 (H_3PO_2),

$$\begin{array}{c} O\!-\!H \\ | \\ P \\ \diagup\ \ \backslash \\ H\ \ \ H \\ O \end{array}$$

*IUPAC approved name
is phosphinic acid.*

a mono-, di-, or triprotic acid?

Phosphorus reacts with halogens, forming trihalides, PX_3, and pentahalides, PX_5. Typical reactions are

$$P_4(c) + 6Cl_2(g) \longrightarrow 4PCl_3(g) \qquad \Delta H = -1146\ kJ$$
$$P_4(c) + 10Cl_2(g) \longrightarrow 4PCl_5(g) \qquad \Delta H = -1498\ kJ$$

Uses of Phosphorus   Phosphorus was formerly used in the heads of "strike anywhere" matches. However, since it is a deadly poison, it is no longer used. Today, "strike anywhere" matches use a tetraphosphorus trisulfide head, while safety matches use a potassium chlorate-antimony(III) sulfide-red phosphorus combination (see Fig. 19.6).

Solid phosphorus(V) oxide is used extensively as a drying agent because its combination with water vapor reduces the vapor pressure of water to practically zero.

Large quantities of phosphorus salts are also used to produce fireworks and explosives; dilute phosphoric acid is used in sodas, jams, and jellies. Phosphate salts, however, find their greatest uses in fertilizers,* detergents, and water softeners.

Most laundry detergents contain about 35 to 75 % sodium triphosphate,**

---

*John Lawes (1834) discovered that treating bone with sulfuric acid produced a more effective phosphorus fertilizer, the basis of the *superphosphate* industry, which treats phosphate rock with sulfuric or phosphoric acids. The effect of synthetic nitrogen, phosphorus, and potassium fertilizers on crop yields was first studied by John Lawes and Henry Gilbert (1843).

**Also known as sodium tri*poly*phosphate (*polys,* the Greek word for many) because it is derived from the combination of 3 phosphoric acid molecules:

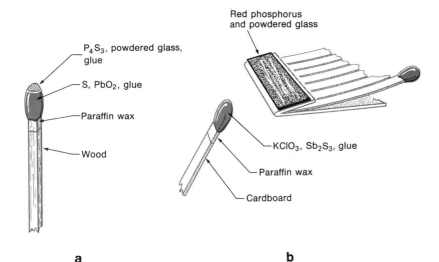

Two billion pounds per year are used in household detergents.

Red phosphorus
and powdered glass

P_4S_3, powdered glass, glue

S, PbO_2, glue

Paraffin wax

Wood

KClO$_3$, Sb$_2$S$_3$, glue

Paraffin wax

Cardboard

a

b

FIGURE 19.6 (a) "Strike anywhere" matches ignite when struck against any rough surface. (b) Safety matches ignite only when struck against the surface (red phosphorus and powdered glass) on the match-box.

$Na_5P_3O_{10}$, to serve two purposes: to provide an alkaline solution (pH 9.0 to 10.5), necessary for effective cleansing (page 345); to tie up calcium and magnesium ions found in natural waters and prevent them from interfering with the cleansing role of the detergent (page 346). Only alkali metal soaps are water soluble; all other metal soaps are insoluble and, therefore, useless as detergents. Thus, Ca^{2+} and Mg^{2+} ions react with soluble alkali soaps and many synthetic detergents, forming insoluble soaps, the "scum" that clings to cloth, glassware, tableware, and bathtubs; for example

$$2Na^+(aq) + 2C_{17}H_{35}COO^-(aq) + Ca^{2+}(aq) \longrightarrow Ca(C_{17}H_{35}COO)_2(c) + 2Na^+(aq)$$
soluble alkali soap   insoluble soap

A nuisance in washing, insoluble soaps are nevertheless used in the manufacture of greases and waterproofing materials.

Unfortunately, phosphates appear to be an ecological Jekyll and Hyde. It is a fact that *overfertilization* of natural bodies of water such as Lake Erie is causing very massive growths of undesirable blue-green algae,* a microscopic plant. It is a fact that the availability of inorganic nitrogen and phosphorus largely limits the growth of algae in water. It is also a fact that many scientists accept excess phosphates as the major factor in overfertilization. However, recent studies show that *nitrogen* is the critical limiting factor for algae growth in coastal waters of the New York City harbor. Removal of phosphates from detergents is, therefore, not likely to slow algae growth in the *New York City area*. The replacement of phosphates with nitrogen-containing substances may actually prove disastrous, and their replacement with *borax* (disodium tetraborate, $Na_2B_4O_7(H_2O)_{10}$) will definitely be disastrous. The role of boron in plant growth is a puzzling mystery. It is not required by algae and other microplants, but it is essential to higher plants. However, in excessive quantities, about 5 micrograms (5×10^{-6} g) of boron per gram of water, boron severely damages plant life (*boron injury*). Highly alkaline substances (sodium carbonate and silicates, SiO_3^{2-}, pH 11 and higher) can gel proteins and, like sodium hydroxide (lye), are hazardous substances. Each year thousands of children, particularly under 5 years old, swallow detergents, resulting in serious injuries or death. However, an acceptable substitute for phosphates has not yet been found. Washing only with synthetic detergents would require so much more detergent that the cost per wash would increase significantly, about 5 to 10 times. A promising alternative is substitution of synthetic *nonionic detergents* for the ionic detergents in use; nonionic detergents are not precipitated by Ca^{2+} or Mg^{2+} ions.

While nitrogen may be the limiting factor in waters dominated by the New York City area, in other regions of the country, the Great Lakes** and Florida, where waters receive agricultural runoff from fertilized fields and livestock feedlots, phosphates *are* the limiting factor. But, in most regions, information on water composition

Also known as eutrophication, derived from eu and trephein, the Greek words for well nourishing.

For example, "Nitrogen, Phosphorus and Eutrophication in the Coastal Marine Environment," Science, volume 171, 12 March 1971, page 1008.

Not enough natural fats are available in the United States to manufacture the required amount of laundry soap without interfering with our food supply.

---

*Algae in limited amounts are essential to marine life, but in uncontrolled growth they become offensive, choke waterways, and provide oxygen for excessive bacterial growth. In addition, the decay of massive quantities of dead algae produces smells, exhausts the oxygen supply needed for fish, and makes even treated water distasteful. Further, overfertilization causes depletion of silica required by diatoms (a microscopic plant) for growth, which in turn causes displacement of diatoms by blue-green algae.

**The United States and Canada have joined in a drive against phosphate pollution of border waters, such as the Great Lakes and the St. Lawrence River. Phosphate pollution of water is a criminal offense in Canada; all phosphate detergents have been banned in Canada and in the eight states, Minnesota to New York, bordering the Great Lakes. Similar actions have been taken by a number of other states, counties, and cities in the United States.

is meager. Pollution can be solved only after it is studied, analyzed, understood, and interpreted with a sense of responsibility.

Phosphates are easily removed from waste waters by the addition of positive ions, such as Al^{3+}, that form insoluble phosphates:

$$Al^{3+}(aq) + PO_4{}^{3-}(aq) \longrightarrow AlPO_4(c)$$

Nitrogen (agricultural) pollution can be greatly reduced by addition of sodium azide, NaN_3 ($:\ddot{N}{=}N{=}\ddot{N}:^-$), to ammonia fertilizer. The azide kills the soil bacteria that oxidize ammonia to nitrates which are more easily washed away (leached) from plant roots.

PROBLEM 5   **Is it necessary for our clothes to be "whiter than white"?**

Industrial waste, however, still constitutes the major portion of water pollution. Since arsenic is in the same Group (VA) as phosphorus, commercial phosphates are most likely contaminated with trace amounts of arsenates and may be a major source of arsenic in river waters. Sewage treatment plants are required to minimize pollution from these sources as well as from significant amounts of phosphates generated from human wastes. Sludge, the residue from sewage plants, harms marine life and pollutes beach areas when it is dumped into the oceans and waterways. It cannot be used as fertile topsoil because it contains dangerous bacteria and viruses. However, experiments at a sewage plant in Boston show that the sludge can be disinfected by bombardment with an intense electron beam.

Traditional methods of disposal of urban garbage and sewage, and animal manures, significant sources of overfertilization, are no longer adequate. Natural cycles, turned into corkscrews by increasing affluence and population, require technological assistance if they are to be replaced on circular tracks. Newsprint, organic waste, and cattle manure have been converted* to a heavy low-sulfur oil by heating (375 °C) in the presence of carbon monoxide and steam under pressure (25 atm).

University of California at Berkeley.

Another group of investigators has developed a process in which chicken waste is converted to useful products. Flushed into a tank, the liquid portion is piped to an algae pond, while the solids, treated with steam under pressure, are converted into a nutritious liquid and a gas. The gas is combustible and serves as a fuel, while the liquid is piped to the algae pond. Algae grow rapidly and are harvested, dried, and fed to the chickens as the protein portion of their diet. Cattle manure has been successfully recycled into cattle feed. Garbage recycling plants in which metals and glass are separated and the remainder burned for the generation of electricity are in use or under construction in many towns.

A novel process for purification of industrial and agricultural waste water is based on the use of membranes. Osmosis (page 342) is subject to the laws of equilibrium: water passes through the membrane from pure water to solution at a faster rate than in the opposite direction. However, *application of pressure on the solution increases the rate of flow of water from solution to pure water.* The extra pressure required to make the flow rates equal is the osmotic pressure of the solution;

---

*The United States generates about 3 billion tons of solid organic waste per year, of which 2.5 billion tons is agricultural waste that includes 2 billion tons of manure. About 90 % conversion was obtained in laboratory-scale experiments at the U.S. Bureau of Mines (Report of Investigations #7650, 1971). Readers interested in solid waste recovery are referred to "Mineral Resources and the Environment, Supplementary Report: Resource Recovery from Municipal Solid Wastes," National Academy of Sciences, Washington, D.C. 20005, 1975.

for all practical purposes, the flow of water stops. If the pressure on the solution is less than osmotic pressure, water flows from pure water to solution. If, on the other hand, the pressure on the solution is greater than the osmotic pressure, then water flows *from solution to pure water,* referred to as *reverse osmosis:*

OSMOSIS
(pressure on solution less than osmotic pressure)

EQUILIBRIUM
(no net flow of water across membrane—pressure on solution equals osmotic pressure)

REVERSE OSMOSIS
(pressure on solution greater than osmotic pressure)

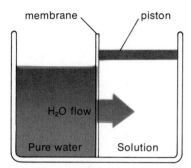

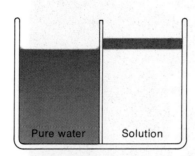

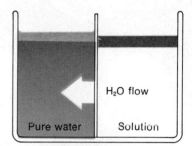

Membranes capable of withstanding pressures as high as 250 atmospheres have been developed for commercial water purification* by reverse osmosis. Pure water is thus pushed out of the polluted water. When sodium chloride is the major impurity, the process is called *desalinization.* Reverse osmosis finds many applications in concentrating prepared foods.

Also, highly magnetized filters have been developed for cleaning waste waters. Very finely suspended paramagnetic particles that absorb other nonparamagnetic particles are attracted to the magnetic field and trapped.

SULFUR _____ 19.5

Sulfur, known since ancient times, occurs in the elemental state in nature. Sulfur deposits, usually located several hundred feet underground, probably resulted from the bacterial decomposition of calcium sulfate, $CaSO_4$.

The world's largest sulfur deposits, found in the southern United States, are "mined" by the *Frasch process,* in which hot liquid water (170 °C and 7 atm) is used to melt the sulfur, which is then forced up to the surface with compressed air. Cooling yields sulfur 99.5 to 99.9 % pure.

Annual U.S. production of S is over 11×10^6 tons, with fertilizers and chemicals as major uses.

Sulfides of metals such as *zinc-blende,* ZnS, *pyrite,* FeS_2, *galena,* PbS, and *chalcocite,* Cu_2S, are widely distributed in nature. Sulfates such as *gypsum,* $CaSO_4(H_2O)_2$, *barite,* $BaSO_4$, and *epsom salt,* $MgSO_4(H_2O)_7$, are also abundant. Sulfur is also found in all animal and vegetable matter.

Of the several known allotropic forms of sulfur, the most important are the *rhombic* and *monoclinic.* Rhombic sulfur is the stable form at room conditions. It

See Problem 40, page 105.

---

*At room conditions, the osmotic pressure of a molar solution of particles (ions or molecules) is roughly 25 atmospheres. The first experiments on osmosis through artificial membranes were reported in 1855 by Adolf Fick.

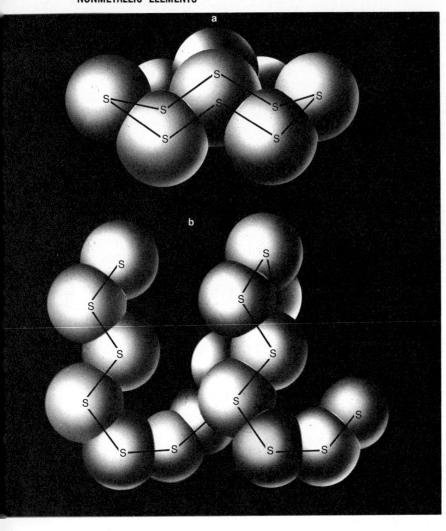

FIGURE 19.7 (a) Model of S_8 ring found in rhombic sulfur. (b) Model of plastic sulfur.

consists of molecules in which 8 sulfur atoms are bonded in a puckered ring, shown in Fig. 19.7 a. Heating rhombic sulfur above 96 °C leads to the formation of monoclinic sulfur, also composed of S_8 ring molecules but with the rings differently arranged.

The electronic formula of the S_8 ring is

It has been suggested that the double bond consists of a p—p sigma (σ) bond (page 567) and p—d pi (π) bond (page 568), leaving the s electrons as the unshared electrons.

Heated above the melting point (112.8 °C), sulfur undergoes a variety of changes: Originally, it is a mobile, freely flowing, pale yellow liquid, but above 160 °C it "thickens" and becomes viscous and flows extremely slowly like "thick" molasses; it again becomes mobile as the temperature approaches the boiling point (444.6 °C). If molten sulfur is rapidly cooled by pouring into water, *plastic sulfur* is produced. Plastic sulfur consists of long chains of sulfur atoms (Fig. 19.7 b). Thus, the change in viscosity of molten sulfur corresponds to a change in the arrangement of

618

the sulfur atoms. The mobile liquid consists of S_8 molecules while the viscous liquid consists of chains of different lengths. The intertwining of these long chains interferes with the free flow of the liquid. With further heating, these chains are broken into smaller fragments, probably S_4 and S_6 molecules, restoring mobility to the liquid. Sulfur vapor contains various molecules, S_8, S_6, S_4, and S_2, in equilibrium mixtures; at higher temperatures, S_2 is favored. S_2, like O_2, is paramagnetic.

Sulfur combines with all elements except the noble gases and iodine.

Sulfur acts as a reducing agent toward more electronegative elements, such as oxygen and the halogens

$$2S(c) + Cl_2(g) \longrightarrow S_2Cl_2(l) \ (disulfur \ dichloride) \qquad \Delta H = -50 \ kJ$$

and as an oxidizing agent toward less electronegative elements such as hydrogen, carbon, and iron:

$$H_2(g) + S(c) \longrightarrow H_2S(g) \qquad \Delta H = -20.6 \ kJ, \ K = 7.85 \times 10^5$$
$$C(graphite) + 2S(c) \longrightarrow CS_2(l) \qquad \Delta H = +89.5 \ kJ, \ K = 3.66 \times 10^{-12}$$
$$Fe(c) + S(c) \longrightarrow FeS(c) \qquad \Delta H = -95.0 \ kJ$$

Compounds of Sulfur *Hydrogen sulfide,* H_2S, can be produced by the reaction of iron(II) sulfide, FeS, with dilute sulfuric acid:

$$FeS(c) + H_2SO_4(aq) \longrightarrow FeSO_4(aq) + H_2S(g) \qquad \Delta H = -11.8 \ kJ$$
$$K = 1.6 \times 10^3$$

However, for laboratory purposes it is usually prepared at room temperature by the hydrolysis of thioacetamide in acid solutions:

thioacetamide   acetamide

Hydrogen sulfide burns in air:

$$2H_2S(g) + 3O_2(g) \longrightarrow 2H_2O(g) + 2SO_2(g) \qquad \Delta H = -1038 \ kJ, \ K = 7.97 \times 10^{174}$$

See footnote, page 249, for toxicity of H_2S.

but in a limited supply of oxygen, or with SO_2, sulfur is produced,

$$2H_2S(g) + O_2(g) \longrightarrow 2H_2O(g) + 2S(c) \qquad \Delta H = -444 \ kJ, \ K = 5.45 \times 10^{69}$$
$$2H_2S(g) + SO_2(g) \longrightarrow 2H_2O(g) + 3S(c) \qquad \Delta H = -233 \ kJ, \ K \approx \infty$$

accounting for sulfur deposits in the vicinity of volcanoes that emit hydrogen sulfide and sulfur dioxide.

Hydrogen sulfide reacts with metals:

$$Zn(c) + H_2S(g) \longrightarrow ZnS(c) + H_2(g) \qquad \Delta H = -185 \ kJ,$$
$$K = 2.5 \times 10^{29}$$
$$4Ag(c) + 2H_2S(g) + O_2(g) \longrightarrow 2Ag_2S(c) + 2H_2O(g) \qquad \Delta H = -506 \ kJ,$$
$$K = 6.97 \times 10^{83}$$

Silver sulfide, Ag_2S, is the black coating, known as tarnish, which forms on sterling silver.

619

As a diprotic acid it forms two series of salts, the hydrogen sulfides, of which sodium hydrogen sulfide, NaHS, is typical, and the sulfides, of which sodium sulfide, Na_2S, is typical.

Sulfur forms two common oxides, sulfur dioxide, SO_2, and sulfur trioxide, SO_3. Sulfur dioxide is commercially prepared by burning sulfur or by "roasting" (heating in air) sulfide ores (page 635).

In the general chemistry laboratory, sulfur dioxide is prepared by the action of hydrochloric acid upon a sulfite:

$$Na_2SO_3(c) + 2HCl(aq) \longrightarrow 2NaCl(c) + H_2SO_3(aq) \qquad \Delta H = -173.2 \text{ kJ},$$
$$K = 1.5 \times 10^{30}$$

$$H_2SO_3(aq) \longrightarrow H_2O + SO_2(g) \qquad \Delta H = +26.2 \text{ kJ},$$
$$K = 0.8$$

Sulfurous acid has not yet been isolated (obtained in a pure form), although the hydrate $SO_2(H_2O)_7$ has been crystallized from concentrated $SO_2(aq)$ solutions at low temperature. Aqueous solutions of SO_2 are best represented as

$$SO_2(g) + xH_2O \rightleftharpoons SO_2(H_2O)_x \qquad \text{(hydrated } SO_2\text{)}$$

But for practical calculations, the solution may be represented as

$$SO_2 + H_2O \rightleftharpoons HSO_3^- + H_3O^+ \qquad K_1 = 1.4 \times 10^{-2}$$
$$HSO_3^- + H_2O \rightleftharpoons SO_3^{2-} + H_3O^+ \qquad K_2 = 6.24 \times 10^{-8}$$

Although sulfurous acid does not exist, the hydrogen sulfite, HSO_3^-, and sulfite, SO_3^{2-}, salts are well known. In fact, as predicted (page 576), SO_3^{2-} is a triangular pyramid, like NH_3, while HSO_3^- is tetrahedral, like NH_4^+.

Combustion of coal is the largest single source of SO_2 pollution. The inorganic sulfur content of coal in the eastern United States is mainly *pyrite,* FeS_2. Iron(III) easily oxidizes *pyrite* to sulfur, as shown by electrochemical data:

$$2Fe^{3+}(aq) + 2e^- \longrightarrow 2Fe^{2+}(aq) \qquad E^\circ_{reduction} = +0.770 \text{ volt}$$
$$\underline{FeS_2(c) \longrightarrow Fe^{2+}(aq) + 2S(c) + 2e^- \qquad E^\circ_{oxidation} = -1.31 \text{ volt}}$$
$$2Fe^{3+}(aq) + FeS_2(c) \longrightarrow 3Fe^{2+}(aq) + 2S(c) \qquad E^\circ_{cell} = +2.08 \text{ volt},$$
$$K = 2 \times 10^{70}$$

Developed and designed by General Public Utilities Corp., New York City.

The economic feasibility of this process for the removal of "sulfur" from coal is currently being evaluated by the U.S. Environmental Protection Agency.

The nation's first coal-cleaning plant is in operation in Pennsylvania to test the practicality of the "deep-cleaning" method of removing pyrite sulfur. The pyrite sulfur is not chemically combined with the coal. Its separation from coal can therefore be based on the difference between the density of coal, about 1.3 g/ml, and that of FeS_2, 5.00 g/ml. The coal is crushed and stirred in a slurry of water and finely powdered magnetite (page 200). The magnetite is used to adjust the slurry density to about 1.8 g/ml. Clean coal floats to the top, while denser coal pieces containing FeS_2 sink. The product will be tested in a full-sized coal-fired plant. Its success will unlock billions of tons of high sulfur coal found in the Appalachian region.

Removal of more than 90% of the pyritic sulfur and at least 40% of the organic sulfur from coal by air oxidation at 60 atm and 175 °C is based on the following reactions:

$$2FeS_2(c) + 7\tfrac{1}{2}O_2(aq) + H_2O \longrightarrow Fe_2O_3(c) + 4H_2SO_4(aq)$$

$$R\!-\!S(c) + O_2(aq) \longrightarrow H_2SO_4(aq) \ (incomplete\ equation)$$

R—S(c) represents the largely unknown C—S—H compounds present in coal. Actual chemical equation is therefore not known.

This process, developed by the Pittsburgh Energy Research Center (U.S.E.R.D.A.), and one of the most economic proposals, is expected to add $10 per ton to the cost of coal.

Sulfur dioxide reacts with oxygen to produce sulfur trioxide, a liquid which boils at 44.6 °C. Sulfur trioxide is the anhydride of sulfuric acid.

Like the carbonate, CO_3^{2-}, and nitrate, NO_3^-, ions, SO_3 is represented by three contributing structures

and its delocalized π bond (MO) description is

similar to those of CO_3^{2-} and NO_3^- (pages 583–586), with six electrons in the delocalized π bond.

Pure sulfuric acid, hydrogen sulfate, is a colorless, oily liquid. Heating decomposes hydrogen sulfate, but more sulfur trioxide than water escapes and so dilutes the acid. When a concentration of 98.33 % H_2SO_4 is reached, no further decomposition occurs. This is referred to as concentrated sulfuric acid.

Sulfuric acid is produced (page 421) commercially by the *Cat-Ox* (contact) process, in which sulfur dioxide is oxidized by air to sulfur trioxide in a chamber containing divanadium pentoxide, $V_2O_5(c)$, a catalyst. Since sulfur trioxide is more soluble in sulfuric acid than in water, it is bubbled through concentrated H_2SO_4, forming *disulfuric acid,* $H_2S_2O_7$, which is then diluted to produce sulfuric acid:

Common name, pyrosulfuric acid.

$$H_2SO_4(l) + SO_3(g) \longrightarrow H_2S_2O_7(l)$$

$$H_2S_2O_7(l) + H_2O(l) \longrightarrow 2H_2SO_4(l)$$

Forming disulfuric acid from SO_3 and H_2SO_4 is the same, in principle, as combining two molecules of H_2SO_4 with the elimination of one molecule of water.

Sulfuric acid, , is a diprotic acid in which hydrogen bonding

(page 264) is so extensive that instruments "see" SO_4^{2-} ions held together by hydrogen bonds, accounting for its high boiling point, 338 °C. Sulfuric acid forms *sulfate* salts, for example Na_2SO_4, and *hydrogen sulfate* salts, of which $NaHSO_4$ is typical.

Concentrated sulfuric acid combines with water, reducing its vapor pressure to almost zero. Therefore, it is used as a dehydrating agent. In water, it is a strong acid and a good oxidizing agent; its standard electrode potential is given:

$$SO_4^{2-}(aq) + 4H^+(aq) + 2e^- \longrightarrow H_2SO_3(aq) + H_2O \qquad E^\circ = +0.17 \text{ volt}$$

Uses of Sulfur   Largely used in the manufacture of sulfuric acid, sulfur is also employed in the manufacture of explosives, fertilizers, medicines, and disulfur dichloride, a toxic, irritating liquid used to vulcanize rubber and to manufacture carbon tetrachloride (page 619):

$$2S_2Cl_2(l) + C(coke) \longrightarrow CCl_4(l) + 4S(c) \qquad \Delta H = -33.5 \text{ kJ}$$

Although it was once its most important use, carbon tetrachloride is no longer used in fire extinguishers. Upon heating in air, it is oxidized to phosgene, $COCl_2$, a poisonous gas (page 583).

In the manufacture of wine, sulfur dioxide is added to grape juice to kill bacteria, molds, and undesirable yeasts, after which a pure yeast is added. Sulfur dioxide is also used for the preservation of dried fruits.

19.6 THE HALOGENS

The halogens are relatively abundant in the combined state; they are not found uncombined because of their great reactivity. Fluorine occurs principally as *fluorspar*, CaF_2, *cryolite*, Na_3AlF_6, and *fluorapatite*, $[Ca_3(PO_4)_2]_3CaF_2$.

Chlorine, bromine, and iodine occur as sodium halides in sea-water and salt deposits. Iodine, as sodium iodate, $NaIO_3$, is also found as an impurity in *Chile saltpeter*, $NaNO_3$.

The halogens are prepared by oxidizing the corresponding halides (oxidation state -1) by various methods,

$$2X^- \longrightarrow X_2 + 2e^-$$

The ease of oxidation of the halide ions follows the order fluoride, F^- (most difficult), chloride, Cl^-, bromide, Br^-, and iodide, I^- (least difficult). This order may be predicted from the standard electrode potentials (Table 15.1, page 466) for the electrode reactions:

$$\begin{aligned} & & E^\circ \\ F_2(g) + 2e^- &\longrightarrow 2F^-(aq) & +2.87 \text{ volt} \\ Cl_2(g) + 2e^- &\longrightarrow 2Cl^-(aq) & +1.36 \\ Br_2(l) + 2e^- &\longrightarrow 2Br^-(aq) & +1.08 \\ I_2(c) + 2e^- &\longrightarrow 2I^-(aq) & +0.535 \end{aligned}$$

Fluorine is thus the strongest oxidizing agent of the halogens and, therefore, the fluoride ion $F^-(aq)$ is the most difficult to oxidize (page 359). Iodine, on the other hand, is the weakest oxidizing agent of the group and, therefore, the iodide ion, $I^-(aq)$, offers the least opposition to being oxidized.

The strong resistance of F^- to oxidation by other chemicals makes it necessary to employ an electrolytic oxidation. An electric current passed through a liquid mixture of potassium hydrogen fluoride, KHF_2, and anhydrous hydrogen fluoride, HF, produces hydrogen and fluorine gases:

$$2HF(sol) \xrightarrow{\text{electrolysis}} H_2(g) + F_2(g)$$

Chlorine is commercially prepared by the electrolytic oxidation of molten sodium chloride and aqueous sodium chloride solutions (page 473). Chlorine is also produced as a by-product in the electrolytic production of metallic sodium (page 472), calcium, and magnesium from chlorides. The *Kel-Chlor* process converts waste HCl to Cl_2 by a series of gaseous reactions represented as

$$2NOCl + O_2 + 4HCl \longrightarrow 2NO + 3Cl_2 + 2H_2O$$

Bromine is prepared from bromides in sea-water and salt wells by oxidation with chlorine:

$$2Br^-(aq) + Cl_2(g) \longrightarrow Br_2(l) + 2Cl^-(aq) \qquad E°_{cell} = +0.29 \text{ volt}$$

Iodine is prepared from iodides found in salt wells

$$2I^-(aq) + Cl_2(g) \longrightarrow I_2(c) + 2Cl^-(aq) \qquad E°_{cell} = +0.82 \text{ volt}$$

and from sodium iodate, by reduction with sodium hydrogen sulfite:

$$2IO_3^-(aq) + 5HSO_3^-(aq) \longrightarrow 5SO_4^{2-}(aq) + 3H^+(aq) + H_2O + I_2(c)$$

$$E°_{cell} = 1.00 \text{ volt}$$

Fluorine reacts extremely rapidly with most substances, including krypton, xenon, and radon (page 273). Even kinetically stable substances, such as wood and asbestos, ignite when held in a stream of fluorine gas. It displaces other halogens in the solid state and reacts explosively with hydrogen:

$$H_2(g) + F_2(g) \longrightarrow 2HF(g) \qquad \Delta H = -544 \text{ kJ}, K = 5.6 \times 10^{95}$$

Chlorine reacts with hydrogen in a light-catalyzed chain reaction (page 517)

$$H_2(g) + Cl_2(g) + hf \longrightarrow 2HCl(g) \qquad \Delta H = -184 \text{ kJ}, K = 2.5 \times 10^{33}$$

and oxidizes all metals, forming largely ionic chlorides; for example

$$2Au(c) + 3Cl_2(g) \xrightarrow{200 °C} 2AuCl_3(c)$$

Chlorine also reacts with all nonmetals, except the noble gases,* forming mainly covalent halides. Chlorine removes hydrogen, as HCl, from many organic compounds. For example, the reaction of methane with chlorine in the presence of sunlight leads to various products, CH_3Cl, CH_2Cl_2, $CHCl_3$, and CCl_4, depending on the amount of chlorine present (page 683).

---

*The compounds $XeCl_2$, $XeCl_4$, and $XeBr_2$ have been detected at 4 K in the beta emission reactions of radioactive $^{129}_{53}I$ in ICl_2^-, ICl_4^-, and IBr_2^-; for example, $^{129}_{53}ICl_4^- \longrightarrow {}^{129}_{54}XeCl_4 + {}_{-1}\beta^0 + e^-$.

Dissolved in water, chlorine is reduced to hydrochloric acid and oxidized to hypochlorous acid:

$$\text{oxidation number} \quad \underset{Cl_2(g)}{0} + H_2O(l) \longrightarrow \underset{HCl(aq)}{-1} + \underset{HOCl(aq)}{+1}$$

Chemically, *bromine* and *iodine* behave largely like chlorine. However, solid iodine has a slightly metallic luster and exhibits a positive oxidation state in compounds such as iodine triacetate, $I(C_2H_3O_2)_3$, and iodine trinitrate, $I(NO_3)_3$, in which it has a +3 oxidation number.

From astatos, the Greek word for unstable.

The chemistry of *astatine,* a radioactive element synthesized in 1940, is known only from tracer studies, which show that it mainly behaves like the other halogens, especially iodine. Astatine was recently found in nature but in extremely small amounts.

Compounds of the Halogens   Although the hydrogen halides may be prepared by the direct union of the elements, they are generally made by the reaction of metal halides with a strong acid (page 421). While hydrogen chloride and hydrogen fluoride can be made with concentrated sulfuric acid, hydrogen bromide and hydrogen iodide cannot, because the sulfuric acid oxidizes these halides, producing bromine and iodine:

$$NaBr(c) + H_2SO_4(l) \longrightarrow NaHSO_4(c) + HBr(g)$$
$$H_2SO_4(l) + 2HBr(g) \longrightarrow 2H_2O(l) + SO_2(g) + Br_2(g) \qquad K = 1.2 \times 10^{-4}$$

For the same reaction with HCl(g), $K = 2.5 \times 10^{-19}$, practically zero, and so the reaction does not occur.

Therefore, phosphoric acid is used to prepare hydrogen bromide and hydrogen iodide.

The hydrogen halides may also be prepared by the reaction of nonmetal halides with water (page 421). This method is particularly used for the preparation of hydrogen bromide and hydrogen iodide.

Hypohalous acids, such as hypochlorous acid, HOCl, are thermally unstable and decompose to the hydrohalide and oxygen: $2HOCl(aq) \longrightarrow 2HCl(aq) + O_2(g)$. These acids are prepared by reacting the halogen with water. The equilibrium can be shifted to the right by the addition of cold dilute base, producing the salts of the corresponding acids:

$$Cl_2(g) + 2NaOH(aq) \longrightarrow NaCl(aq) + NaOCl(aq) + H_2O$$

In this reaction, sodium hypochlorite, the active ingredient in many liquid household bleaches, such as *Clorox,* is obtained. Bleaching powder, made by passing chlorine into a lime suspension in water, is a mixture of calcium hypochlorite, $Ca(OCl)_2$, calcium chloride, and calcium hydroxide.

Readers interested in the chemistry of HOF are referred to the Journal of the American Chemical Society, volume 54, 1932, page 832, and volume 93, 1971, page 2350.

Fluorine rapidly oxidizes water to oxygen, mixed with some oxygen difluoride, OF_2, but if *only some* of the fluorine is allowed to react, then hypofluorous acid, HOF, forms. The acid reacts with water to produce HF, O_2, and H_2O_2.

Uses of Halogens and Their Compounds   Cobalt(III) fluoride and fluorine are used in the preparation of fluorocarbon compounds, hydrocarbons in which fluorine atoms are substituted for hydrogen atoms.

The preparation of fluoroheptane is typical:

$$C_7H_{16}(l) + 32CoF_3(c) \longrightarrow C_7F_{16}(l) + 16HF(g) + 32CoF_2(c)$$
$$2CoF_2(c) + F_2(g) \longrightarrow 2CoF_3(c)$$

Fluorocarbons, thermally and thermodynamically very stable (page 519), are used as lubricants, refrigerants, and high-temperature hydraulic fluids.

Fluorine emissions from industrial operations are converted into inert carbon tetrafluoride by reaction with charcoal. Uranium hexafluoride, UF_6, is used for the separation of uranium isotopes by diffusion (page 63). In fact, many industrialists now accept the consumption of fluorine rather than the consumption of sulfuric acid as a measure of a nation's industrialization.

Hydrofluoric acid dissolves glass and is therefore used to etch glass, primarily calcium silicate:

$$CaSiO_3(c) + 8HF(aq) \longrightarrow 2H^+(aq) + SiF_6^{2-}(aq) + CaF_2(c) + 3H_2O$$

Sodium fluoride is used as an insecticide and a fungicide; it is also added to drinking water (see footnote on page 611). Tin(II) fluoride is used as a toothpaste additive (page 396). Sodium fluoracetate, a rodenticide, is excellent for rat control.

Chlorine, used principally as a bleach in the papermaking and textile industries, is also employed extensively in the manufacture of chlorocarbon compounds that are used as dry cleaning fluids, anesthetics, mothproofing agents, insecticides, and solvents. Chlorine is also used in municipal systems to purify water and to disinfect raw sewage, the main defense against water-borne diseases such as typhoid fever. The sewage treatment, however, results in the formation of chloroamines

$$C_2H_5NH_2 \ (produced \ from \ sewage) + HOCl(aq) \ (produced \ from \ Cl_2) \longrightarrow C_2H_5NHCl(aq) + H_2O$$
ethylamine   *chloroethylamine*

that are toxic to fish and other aquatic life around the sewage treatment plant. Ozone is the most practical (but more costly) substitute for chlorine; it kills bacteria but releases oxygen as the by-product. The tendency of water chlorination to generate toxic substances like chloroamines and chloroform (page 18) is producing increased interest in the ozonation of municipal water supplies.

Hydrochloric acid is used for cleaning metals and in the manufacture of metal chlorides, glue, dyes, and various chlorocarbon compounds. Hydrochloric acid is one of the most important components of the gastric juices of the stomach.

Bromine is used in the production of photographic film (page 196), sedatives, dyes, and dibromoethane, $C_2H_4Br_2$, for addition to gasoline containing lead tetra-ethyl (page 269).

Iodine is used as an antiseptic in "tincture of iodine" and iodoform, CHI_3. Iodine is essential in the human diet for proper functioning of the thyroid glands and, hence, table salt containing very small amounts of sodium iodide is sold. The iodine lamp consists of a tungsten filament whose life is extended by the presence of iodine vapor. Near the comparatively cool wall of the lamp (600 K), I_2 combines with W atoms evaporated off the hot filament (6000 K), forming tungsten tetraiodide, WI_4. The WI_4 vapor diffuses back to the filament where its decomposition, $WI_4 \longrightarrow W + 2I_2$, redeposits the W atoms.

EPILOG from *Scientific American,* July, 1877

"Bones, though at first the main source, now furnish but little of the phosphoric acid of fertilizers, so great has been the demand for phosphatic manures. To supply the deficiency, the vast beds of mineral phosphates, so called, prove to be deposits of great aggregate value. The chief of them are located in Central Russia, Western Germany, Southern France, Canada, South Carolina, and in the Navassa, Sombrero, Jarvis and Baker Islands. The Navassa and South Carolina deposits are now the main sources of supply."

PROBLEMS

6 Define and illustrate allotropy.

7 Oxygen Write a balanced equation for each of the following: (a) preparation of oxygen by electrolytic decomposition of water, (b) burning of sulfur in excess air, (c) burning sulfur in a limited amount of air, (d) preparation of carbon monoxide, (e) laboratory preparation of oxygen from potassium chlorate.

8 (a) Describe the preparation of oxygen from air. (b) Explain oxygen's paramagnetism. (c) Soluble metal oxides dissolve in water to yield basic solutions, while nonmetal oxides yield acidic solutions. Explain. (d) At constant temperature, the addition of manganese dioxide speeds up the generation of oxygen from potassium chlorate. Explain.

9 Write a balanced equation for the reaction of oxygen with (a) C, (b) C_2H_2, (c) Li, (d) Ba, (e) S, (f) P, (g) C_2H_6, (h) CO, (i) SO, (j) HNO_2.

10 Nitrogen (a) Explain the following cycle:

$$\text{animal protein} \leftarrow \text{plant protein} \leftarrow \text{nitrates, nitrites} \quad \text{soil} \quad \text{atmosphere}$$

(b) Explain how this cycle can be disrupted. (c) Describe at least two methods by which atmospheric nitrogen is "fixed." (d) Write balanced equations for the laboratory preparation of ammonia and the industrial preparation of nitric acid.

11 Phosphorus Write a balanced equation for each of the following: (a) phosphorus(III) oxide added to water, (b) white phosphorus burned in excess oxygen, (c) the product of (b) dissolved in water, (d) phosphorus burned in excess bromine, (e) phosphorus burned in a limited supply of bromine.

12 Sulfur Write a balanced equation for the preparation of (a) hydrogen sulfide, (b) carbon disulfide, (c) zinc sulfide, (d) sodium sulfide.

13 Draw (a) the contributing structures and (b) the delocalized bond (MO) description of sulfur dioxide.

14 Halogens Write a balanced equation for the preparation of (a) fluorine, (b) chlorine, (c) bromine, and (d) iodine from the corresponding halides.

15 Write a balanced equation for (a) the reaction of chlorine with water, (b) the reaction of phosphorus pentachloride with water, (c) the preparation of hydrogen fluoride from a fluoride.

16 Fluorine is prepared by an electrolytic method in the absence of water. Explain.

17 Write a balanced equation for the reaction of chlorine with (a) magnesium, (b) water, (c) carbon, and (d) sodium.

18 (a) Write a balanced equation for the preparation of hydrogen bromide from PBr_5. (b) Pure hydrogen bromide cannot be prepared by reaction of concentrated sulfuric acid with sodium bromide. Explain.

19 Given the electrode reactions and the standard electrode potentials (as in Table 15.1, page 466):

$$\text{reduction } XeF_2 + 2e^- \longrightarrow Xe(g) + 2F^-(aq)$$
$$E^\circ = 2.2 \text{ volt}$$

$$\text{oxidation } ClO_3^-(aq) + H_2O \longrightarrow$$
$$ClO_4^-(aq) + 2H^+(aq) + 2e^- \quad E^\circ = 1.71 \text{ volt}$$

What is the cell reaction? Calculate the standard EMF of the cell, E°_{cell}. Predict the direction of the reaction, forward or reverse.

20 Fertilizer How many grams of phosphorus are in 2.00 moles of *phosphate rock*, $[Ca_3(PO_4)_2]_3CaF_2$? How many grams of phosphate rock must be processed to yield 1.50 g of phosphorus, the quantity in 10,000 g of wheat germ?* (The actual quantity of phosphate rock processed is much greater because, due to equilibrium conditions, a plant takes up only a small fraction of the phosphate in the soil.)

21 Nitrogen cycle The gaseous reaction $NO + NO_2 + H_2O \longrightarrow 2HNO_2$, $K = 42$, occurs immediately after a lightning bolt. Calculate the concentration of nitrous acid in air when the equilibrium concentrations are $[NO] = 2.0 \times 10^{-4}$, $[NO_2] = 3.0 \times 10^{-5}$, and $[H_2O] = 4.0 \times 10^{-3}$ mole/ℓ.

22 NO_3^-, NO_2^-, NO The following standard electrode potentials, E° (as in Table 15.1, page 466), are involved in this problem:

$$NO_3^-(aq) + 3H^+(aq) + 2e^- \longrightarrow$$
$$HNO_2(aq) + H_2O \quad E^\circ = +0.94 \text{ volt}$$

$$NO_3^-(aq) + 4H^+(aq) + 3e^- \longrightarrow$$
$$NO(g) + 2H_2O \quad E^\circ = +0.96$$

$$HNO_2(aq) + H^+(aq) + e^- \longrightarrow$$
$$NO(g) + H_2O \quad E^\circ = +1.00$$

The electrode reactions are given for two galvanic cells (1) and (2):

---

*Wheat germ, the embryo of the wheat seed, a rich source of vitamin E, is used as a "natural organic" food supplement.

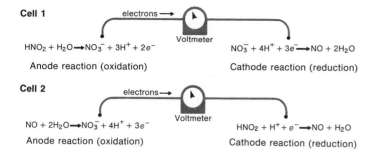

Cell 1

electrons →

Voltmeter

$HNO_2 + H_2O \longrightarrow NO_3^- + 3H^+ + 2e^-$

Anode reaction (oxidation)

$NO_3^- + 4H^+ + 3e^- \longrightarrow NO + 2H_2O$

Cathode reaction (reduction)

Cell 2

electrons →

Voltmeter

$NO + 2H_2O \longrightarrow NO_3^- + 4H^+ + 3e^-$

Anode reaction (oxidation)

$HNO_2 + H^+ + e^- \longrightarrow NO + H_2O$

Cathode reaction (reduction)

For each cell: (a) Are the electrode reactions the same? (b) Calculate the standard EMF of the cell, $E°_{cell}$. (c) Write the cell reaction; is the cell reaction the same? (d) Calculate n, the number of moles of electrons passing through the circuit for the cell reaction as written in (c) from the electrode reaction; is n the same for both cells? (e) Is the equilibrium constant the same for both cells?

23 People and food Plot the following data:

World's Population		Year
9×10^7	6000 BC	(Stone Age)
18×10^7	3000 BC	(Bronze Age)
36×10^7	0	(Christian Era begins)
38×10^7	1000 AD	(Middle Ages)
1×10^9	1800 AD	(Modern Times)
2×10^9	1900 AD	
3×10^9	1950 AD	

(a) What is the predicted population for 1980? (b) Discuss this plot in terms of food supply, synthetic fertilizers, the right to life, and restraining population growth in underdeveloped parts of the world.

24 A common fertilizer is *5-10-5*. These numbers refer to the percentage of nitrogen expressed as percent NH_4NO_3, of phosphorus as percent P_2O_5, and of potassium as percent K_2O. If the application rate is 10 pounds of *5-10-5* per 1000 square feet, calculate (a) the grams of nitrogen, (b) the grams of phosphorus, and (c) the grams of potassium available for plant growth per square foot of lawn.

25 Organic fertilizers The production of the world's food supply essentially comes from crops nourished by synthetic fertilizers. The 1970 consumption of such fertilizers in the United States follows: ammonia, nitrates, expressed as mononitrogen, N, 7.5×10^6 tons N; phosphates, expressed as P_2O_5, 4.6×10^6 tons P_2O_5; potassium salts, expressed as K_2O, 4.0×10^6 tons K_2O. Farm manure data are summarized in Table 19.2. (a) Estimate the number of horses needed to replace synthetic (i) nitrogen, (ii) phosphate, and (iii) potassium fertilizers. (iv) What is the average number of horses needed? Taking 2×10^8 persons as the population of the United States, what is the average number of horses needed per person to replace synthetic fertilizers? For comparison, the United States livestock (1965) population is given: 1.1×10^8 cattle, 3×10^6 horses, 3.8×10^6 hens. (b) Make the same calculation for cattle and (c) for hens. (d) Discuss the practicality of substituting farm manures for synthetic fertilizers. (Units: 2×10^3 lbs = 1 ton.)

26 Library Read one of the following:

(a) "Phosphate Replacement: Problems with the Washday Miracle," *Science,* volume 172, 1972, page 361.

(b) "Nitrogen Fixation Research: A Key to World Food?," *Science,* volume 188, 1975, page 133.

(c) "The Nitrogen Cycle," *Scientific American,* September 1970, page 137.

(d) "Environmental Disruption, From Lake Erie to

TABLE 19.2

APPROXIMATE ANNUAL MANURE PRODUCTION FOR ONE ANIMAL IN TONS, AND MANURE COMPOSITION IN POUND PER TON OF MANURE

ANIMAL	MANURE, TONS/YEAR	POUND PER TON OF MANURE*		
		N	P_2O_5	K_2O
Horse	11	14	4.6	14
Cattle	9	13	6.9	11
Hen	0.018	31	18	8.4

*Improper manure storage significantly reduces these quantities: N by 33%, P_2O_5 by 25%, K_2O by 50%. Data do not include micronutrients such as copper, zinc, iron, manganese, and molybdenum salts.

Lake Baekal, Los Angeles to Tbilisi," *Science,* volume 170, 1970, page 37.

(e) "Clean Water: What Is It? How Will We Achieve It?" *Chemical Technology,* June 1973, page 337.

(f) "The Sulfur Cycle," *Science,* volume 175, 1972, page 587.

(g) "The Hydrogen Economy, A Universal Fuel," *Scientific American,* January 1973, page 13.

(h) "Address of Acceptance," The Founding of the Sulfur Industry in U.S., Herman Frasch, *Journal of Industrial and Engineering Chemistry,* February 1912, reprinted *Chemical Technology,* February 1976, page 99.

(i) "Nitrosamines: Scientist on Trail of Prime Suspect in Urban Cancer," *Science,* volume 191, 23 January 1976, page 268.

(j) "Food: Politics, Economics, Nutrition, and Research," A Special *Science* Compendium, American Association for the Advancement of Science, Washington, D.C. 20005, 1975.

(k) "Fuel and Feedstock from Refuse," James Kuester and Loren Lutes, *Environmental Science and Technology,* volume 10, April 1976, page 339.

(l) "Salt Water Agriculture," Hugo Boyko, *Scientific American,* August 1967, page 440.

(m) "Short Term Effects of Ozone on the Human Lung," Proceedings of Conference on Health Effects of Air Pollutants, National Academy of Sciences, U.S. Government Printing Office, Washington, D.C. 20402, November 1973, pages 507–518.

(n) "Food and Agriculture," Sterling Wortman, *Scientific American,* September 1976, page 30.

ADDITIONAL PROBLEMS

27 Write the formula for the acidic oxide that in water forms (a) H_3VO_4, (b) H_3PO_4, (c) H_2CO_3, (d) H_2SO_3, (e) H_2SO_4.

28 What is the oxidation number of P in (a) H_3PO_4, (b) $H_2P_2O_7$, (c) HPO_3, (d) H_2PHO_3 or H_3PO_3, (e) HPH_2O_2 or H_3PO_2, (f) $H_5P_3O_{10}$?

29 Pick the oxides which in water give (a) a basic solution, and (b) an acid solution: (i) MgO, (ii) P_2O_3, (iii) K_2O, (iv) CaO, (v) NO_2, (vi) SO_3, (vii) BaO, (viii) As_2O_3, (ix) CO_2, (x) Cl_2O.

30 The osmotic pressure of a dilute salt solution is 0.10 atm per 150 ppm of salt. A brackish water contains 7500 ppm of salt. What is its osmotic pressure? Reverse osmosis units operate at 25 to 75 atm. Is reverse osmosis suitable for desalting brackish waters?

31 For the reactions

$$H_2(g) + N_2(g) + 3O_2(g) \longrightarrow 2HNO_3(l)$$
$$2H_2(g) + O_2(g) \longrightarrow 2H_2O(l)$$

H_2, N_2, and O_2 are thermodynamically unstable but kinetically stable with respect to HNO_3, while H_2 and O_2 are thermodynamically and kinetically unstable with respect to water at room conditions. (a) At room conditions, a mixture of H_2, N_2, and O_2 is sparked; reaction occurs. What is the product? (b) What properties should you try to develop in a catalyst to obtain nitric acid directly from air (N_2 and O_2) and H_2, a very desirable reaction?

32 At a concentration of about 10^{-2} M, HSO_3^- ion is in equilibrium with the disulfite ion, $S_2O_5^{2-}$

$$2HSO_3^-(aq) \rightleftharpoons H_2O + S_2O_5^{2-}(aq)$$

When the concentration of HSO_3^- is 0.012 M, equilibrium is established after 0.084 % of it reacts as shown. Calculate K for the reaction.

33 Osmotic pressure, like the freezing point depression, depends only on the *number* of solute particles in a given volume of solution. Ions have the same effect as molecules. At 25 °C, $OP = 24.5 \frac{\text{atm liter}}{\text{mole}} \times M \frac{\text{mole}}{\text{liter}}$. The main components of sea water are $NaCl$, 0.46 M; $MgCl_2$, 0.041 M; and $MgSO_4$, 0.032 M. What pressure must be exceeded in order to obtain pure water by reverse osmosis? Assume that these electrolytes are completely dissociated.

34 At room temperature, 4.5 picograms (App. II) of radon reacts with fluorine, forming radon difluoride. Write the equation and calculate the mass in picograms and in grams of the compound formed.

35 Photosynthesis converts solar energy to combustible organic material. A bushel of corn, for example, stores 3.97×10^5 kJ. It takes 24 lb of NH_3 per acre to increase the corn yield by 83 bushels/acre. But to manufacture, deliver, and apply 24 lb NH_3/acre requires 5.44×10^6 kJ. What is the ratio of energy harvested to fertilizer energy expended? Does the fertilizer energy generate even more energy in the form of food and livestock feed?

36 Decomposition of nitrogen fertilizer adds about 2.0×10^6 (metric) tons of N_2O to the 1.4×10^9 (metric) tons already present in the atmosphere. Find the percentage increase in atmospheric N_2O that is due to fertilizer.

37 A desalting (reverse osmosis) plant, capacity 1×10^8 gal water per day, is under construction near Yuma, Ariz. Distillation costs \$2.50 per 10^3 gal, while reverse osmosis costs 55 cents per 10^3 gal. What are the savings and percentage savings per year?

38 Plot the following data, in reference to improved dwarf varieties of rice developed jointly by the International Center of Tropical Agriculture and the Colombian National Rice Growers Federation, on the same graph:

Year	Area planted (hectares*)	Production (metric tons)
1961	220,000	460,000
1963	240,000	540,000
1965	380,000	660,000
1967	280,000	650,000
1969	220,000	680,000
1971	220,000	880,000
1973	300,000	1,160,000
1975	360,000	1,600,000

Plot the following data, also in reference to the Colombian rice program:

Year	Cost of research (10^6 dollars)	Value of additional crops harvested (10^6 dollars)
1957	0.00	0.00
1960	0.05	−0.05
1963	0.15	−0.15
1966	0.20	−0.25
1969	0.40	0.75
1972	0.45	50.0
1974	0.40	225.0

Draw conclusions.

---

*Hectare (metric system) = 100 acres; all data in this problem from *Scientific American*, September 1976, pages 190, 192.

39 (a) By the addition of the following reactions, find the net reaction:

$$MgO(c) + H_2O(g) + SO_2(g) + S(l) \xrightarrow{500\ K} MgSO_4(c) + H_2S(g) \quad \Delta H_{500} = -168.2\ kJ$$

$$H_2S(g) \xrightarrow{1400\ K} H_2(g) + \tfrac{1}{2} S_2(g) \quad \Delta H_{1400} = +90.67\ kJ$$

$$MgSO_4(c) \xrightarrow{1400\ K} MgO(c) + SO_2(g) + \tfrac{1}{2} O_2(g) \quad \Delta H_{1400} = +361.0\ kJ$$

$$\tfrac{1}{2} S_2(g) \xrightarrow{717\ K} S(l) \quad \Delta H_{717} = -54.02\ kJ$$

(b) List the minimum number of substances needed to start this process to generate H_2. (c) Is the heat required, as calculated from the given enthalpies, the same as or greater or smaller than the heat evolved ($\Delta H = -286\ kJ$) when 1 mole of H_2 is burned at 25 °C?

40 The condensed exhaust of an engine fueled with H_2 was analyzed for H_2O_2 by the reaction

$$2KMnO_4(aq) + 4H_2SO_4(aq) + 5H_2O_2(aq) \longrightarrow 2KHSO_4(aq) + 2MnSO_4(aq) + 8H_2O + 5O_2(g)$$

For 1.00×10^3 mg of exhaust, 12.40 ml of 1.10×10^{-3} M $KMnO_4$ was used to titrate the H_2O_2. Calculate (a) the mass of H_2O_2 and (b) the concentration of H_2O_2 in ppm by mass in the exhaust.

41 Although N_2O is a relatively unreactive molecule, it is attacked by O atoms in the upper atmosphere (stratosphere), forming nitrogen oxide. How many nitrogen oxide molecules are formed for each N_2O molecule reacting? Show how this reaction may affect the ozone layer.

ANSWERS

1 (a) $C_3H_8 + 5O_2 \longrightarrow 3CO_2 + 4H_2O$
$SiH_4 + 2O_2 \longrightarrow SiO_2 + 2H_2O$
(b) MgO; MgO_2
(c) $Mg(OH)_2$

2 (a) $2H_2O \xrightarrow{electricity} 2H_2 + O_2$
$2KClO_3 \xrightarrow{heat} 2KCl + 3O_2$
$2HgO \xrightarrow{heat} 2Hg + O_2$
(b) air

3 (a) $6Li + N_2 \longrightarrow 2Li_3N$
(b) $N_2 + 2O_2 \longrightarrow 2NO_2$
(c) $NH_4NO_2 \longrightarrow 2H_2O + N_2$
(d) $2Li + 2NH_3 \longrightarrow 2LiNH_2 + H_2$

4 monoprotic

7 (a) $2H_2O \xrightarrow{electricity} 2H_2 + O_2$
(b) $S + O_2 \longrightarrow SO_2$
(c) $2S + O_2 \longrightarrow 2SO$
(d) $2C + O_2 \longrightarrow 2CO$
(e) $2KClO_3 \xrightarrow{heat} 2KCl + 3O_2$

9 (a) $C + O_2 \longrightarrow CO_2$
(b) $C_2H_2 + 2O_2 \longrightarrow 2CO_2 + H_2O$
(c) $4Li + O_2 \longrightarrow 2Li_2O$
(d) $2Ba + O_2 \longrightarrow 2BaO$
(e) $S + O_2 \longrightarrow SO_2$
(f) $P_4 + 3O_2 \longrightarrow P_4O_6$
or
$4P + 3O_2 \longrightarrow 2P_2O_3$
or

$4P + 5O_2 \longrightarrow 2P_2O_5$

(g) $2C_2H_6 + 7O_2 \longrightarrow 4CO_2 + 6H_2O$

(h) $2CO + O_2 \longrightarrow 2CO_2$

(i) $2SO + O_2 \longrightarrow 2SO_2$

(j) $2HNO_2 + O_2 \longrightarrow 2HNO_3$

11 (a) $P_4O_6 + 6H_2O \longrightarrow 4H_3PO_3$

(b) $P_4 + 5O_2 \longrightarrow P_4O_{10}$
or
$4P + 5O_2 \longrightarrow 2P_2O_5$

(c) $P_4O_{10} + 6H_2O \longrightarrow 4H_3PO_4$
or
$P_2O_5 + 3H_2O \longrightarrow 2H_3PO_4$

(d) $P_4 + 10Br_2 \longrightarrow 4PBr_5$

(e) $P_4 + 6Br_2 \longrightarrow 4PBr_3$

12 (a) $S + H_2 \longrightarrow H_2S$

(b) $2S + C \longrightarrow CS_2$

(c) $S + Zn \longrightarrow ZnS$

(d) $S + 2Na \longrightarrow Na_2S$

13

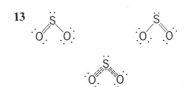

14 (a) $2HF \xrightarrow{\text{electrolysis}} H_2 + F_2$

(b) $MgCl_2 \xrightarrow{\text{electrolysis}} Mg + Cl_2$

(c) $2NaBr + Cl_2 \longrightarrow 2NaCl + Br_2$

(d) $2NaI + Cl_2 \longrightarrow 2NaCl + I_2$

15 (a) $Cl_2 + H_2O \longrightarrow HOCl + HCl$

(b) $PCl_5 + 4H_2O \longrightarrow H_3PO_4 + 5HCl$

(c) $CaF_2 + H_2SO_4 \longrightarrow CaSO_4 + 2HF$

17 (a) $Cl_2 + Mg \longrightarrow MgCl_2$

(b) $Cl_2 + H_2O \longrightarrow HOCl + HCl$

(c) $2Cl_2 + C \longrightarrow CCl_4$

(d) $Cl_2 + 2Na \longrightarrow 2NaCl$

18 (a) $PBr_5 + 4H_2O \longrightarrow H_3PO_4 + 5HBr$

19 $XeF_2 + ClO_3^- + H_2O \longrightarrow Xe + ClO_4^- + 2H^+ + 2F^-$,
$E°_{cell} = 0.5$ V, forward

20 372 g, 8.14 g

21 3.2×10^{-5} mole/ℓ

22 (a) no

(b) $E°_{cell(1)} = 0.02$ V;
$E°_{cell(2)} = 0.04$ V

(c) yes, $3HNO_2 \longrightarrow NO_3^- + H^+ + 2NO + H_2O$

(d) no; cell (1), $n = 6$ moles; cell (2), $n = 3$ moles

(e) yes; cell (1), $n \times E°_{cell} = +0.12$ V;
cell (2), $n \times E°_{cell} = +0.12$ V

24 (a) 0.08 g; (b) 0.2 g; (c) 0.2 g

25 (a) (i) 0.97×10^8, (ii) 1.8×10^8, (iii) 0.52×10^8,
(iv) 1.1×10^8 horses, (v) 0.6 horse/person

(b) (i) 1.3×10^8, (ii) 1.5×10^8, (iii) 0.80×10^8,
(iv) 1.2×10^8 cattle, (v) 0.6 cattle/person

(c) (i) 2.7×10^{10}, (ii) 2.9×10^{10}, (iii) 5.3×10^{10},
(iv) 3.6×10^{10} hens, (v) 2×10^2 hens/person

27 (a) V_2O_5, (b) P_2O_5, (c) CO_2, (d) SO_2, (e) SO_3

28 (a) $+5$, (b) $+6$, (c) $+5$, (d) $+3$, (e) $+1$, (f) $+5$

29 (a) i, iii, iv, vii

(b) ii, v, vi, viii, ix, x

30 (a) 5.0 atm, (b) yes

31 (a) H_2O, (b) lower activation energy

32 3.5×10^{-2}

33 27 atm

34 $Rn + F_2 \longrightarrow RnF_2$
5.3 pg, 5.3×10^{-12} g

35 6.1, yes

36 0.14%

37 7.1×10^7 dollars/year, 78%

39 (a) $H_2O(g) \longrightarrow H_2(g) + \frac{1}{2} O_2(g)$

(b) 4; (c) smaller

40 (a) 1.16 mg, (b) 1.16×10^3 ppm

41 2

GLOSSARY

acidic oxide A nonmetal oxide that dissolves in water forming an acidic solution.

allotropy The ability of an element to exist in more than one form; for example, diamond and graphite are allotropes of carbon.

basic oxide A metal oxide that dissolves in water forming a basic solution.

desalinization Refers to methods for the purification of salt waters.

eutrophication The early aging of lakes due to excessive plant growth resulting from the introduction of excess plant fertilizers, particularly phosphates and nitrates.

fluorocarbons Hydrocarbons in which fluorine atoms are substituted for all hydrogen atoms.

halogen An element in Group VIIA of the periodic table.

nitrogen cycle A complex series of reactions by which the natural balance (use and formation) of nitrogen in the atmosphere, in the soil, and in living organisms is maintained.

nitrogen fixation The conversion of nitrogen to nitrogen-containing compounds that can be assimilated by plants.

nonmetals The elements that are poor conductors of heat and electricity; they have higher ionization potentials and electron affinities and, therefore, higher electronegativities than metals.

Ostwald process   Used to make nitric acid from ammonia.

oxide   An oxygen compound in which oxygen exhibits a −2 oxidation state.

peroxide   An oxygen compound in which oxygen exhibits a −1 oxidation state.

reverse osmosis   A method for the purification of waste and salt waters by application of pressure greater than the osmotic pressure to force the passage of water—but not solutes—through a semipermeable membrane.

superoxide   An oxygen compound in which oxygen exhibits a −½ oxidation state.

THE CHEMISTRY OF SOME TYPICAL METALS

20

INTRODUCTION _____ 20.1

Solid nonmetallic elements are composed of loosely packed individual molecules. Metallic elements, on the other hand, are generally composed of tightly packed atoms, resulting in comparatively high boiling points (Table 8.2, page 264) and high densities. The densest elements, for example, tungsten, 19 g/ml, osmium, 23 g/ml, mercury, 14 g/ml, are metals. All metals, except mercury, are solids at 25 °C but a few metals, particularly Groups IA and IIA, are "light and soft metals" (page 228); for example, lithium, 0.53 g/ml, is actually less dense than nonmetallic sulfur, 2.1 g/ml. Copper, silver, and gold are also fairly soft (page 229). Metals are commonly characterized by a silvery white luster when polished; they absorb and emit light of all frequencies in the visible range. Copper and gold are noteworthy exceptions (page 649). Also unlike nonmetallic elements, metals generally may be stretched (rolled) or hammered into sheets and foils (malleable) or drawn into wire (ductile).

Most characteristic, however, are the unusually high electrical and heat conductivities of solid and molten metals. Cooking utensils are generally made of metals, but their handles are usually insulators made of wood or plastic. The electrical conductivities of metals are over a million times greater than that of a strong electrolyte. Also very significant is the difference in the behavior of solutions of molten salts and metals as conductors. A metal undergoes no change in properties when it carries a current. A copper wire may be used nearly endlessly to carry current. On the other hand, when a current is passed through a solution or molten salt, chemical reactions occur at the electrodes (page 472); materials are consumed and changes in chemical composition occur. Further, the effect of temperature is noteworthy. The conductivity of metals *decreases* with increasing temperature. At about 20 K or lower, certain metals become **superconductors;** the electrical resistance drops to zero. In fact, a metal may be defined as a substance whose conductivity decreases with increasing temperature.

Certain elements, of which silicon and germanium are typical, have conductivities that, unlike the metals, increase with increasing temperature. These are called **semiconductors** (page 647).

Mica, porcelain, diamond, sulfur, and wood are typical **insulators;** the conductivity of an insulator is about 10^{21} times smaller than that of a metal.

Metals exhibit low ionization energies (page 236), low electronegativities (page 254), low electron affinities (page 238), and mostly negative standard electrode

Most of the common metals crystallize with either the body-centered cubic or the face-centered cubic arrangement (page 263).

From malleare, *the Latin word meaning to beat with a hammer. From* ductilis, *the Latin word meaning to yield easily.*

Electrical conductivities (20 °C) relative to copper: Cu (1.0); Ag (1.1); KCl, 0.1 M (2.0×10^{-8}).

Discovered by Herke Onnes (1911).

Conductivities relative to copper: mica (2×10^{-22}); mahogany wood (4×10^{-20}); diamond (3×10^{-21}).

potentials (Table 15.1, page 466), all of which mean that metals have a strong tendency to lose electrons and so easily form positive ions. For the same reason, most metals are generally good reducing agents and generally emit electrons when exposed to high frequency photons (*photoelectric effect,* page 638) or when heated to high temperatures (*thermionic emission*).

20.2 _____ OCCURRENCE

As a general rule, metals with negative standard electrode potentials (Table 15.1, page 466) are almost always found in the combined state in nature, while metals with positive standard electrode potentials may also be found uncombined.

Insoluble solids found in the Earth's crust, from which metals are extracted, are called **ores.** Ores generally consist of a **mineral,** a comparatively pure substance, surrounded by large quantities of sand and rocks, commonly called the **gangue.** Some typical minerals are *hematite,* Fe_2O_3; *bauxite,* $Al_2O_3(H_2O)_2$; *cassiterite,* SnO_2; *cinnabar,* HgS; *horn silver,* $AgCl$; *chalcocite,* Cu_2S; and *pitchblend,* U_3O_8. Metals found uncombined include copper, gold, silver, and platinum.

Pronounced "gang," from the German word for a mining vein.

The oceans of the world contain an enormous amount of metal ions. For example, one ton of sea-water contains approximately 0.5 kg of sodium, 0.4 kg of calcium, 0.3 kg of potassium, and smaller amounts of many other metals such as iron, copper, lead, zinc, uranium, silver, and gold. Although the oceans contain approximately 8.5 million tons of gold, the content per liter is too small for economic recovery. At present, sodium, chlorine, magnesium, and bromine are extracted from sea-water.

20.3 _____ METALLURGY

Most metals are extracted from ores by a process called **smelting,** in which metal ions in a molten mixture (at high temperature) are reduced to the molten metal. In most smelting processes, a **flux** is added to the mixture of ore and reducing agent in order to carry off impurities (*gangue*). The flux, usually lime, CaO, obtained from limestone, $CaCO_3$, forms a **slag** with the silica (sand) and silicate impurities:

Over 20×10^6 tons of CaO are produced annually in the U.S., with steel and water treatment as the major consumers.

$$CaCO_3(c) \xrightarrow[\text{temperature}]{\text{high}} CaO(c) + CO_2(g)$$

$$\underset{\text{flux}}{CaO(c)} + \underset{\text{gangue}}{SiO_2(l)} \xrightarrow[\text{temperature}]{\text{high}} \underset{\text{liquid slag}}{CaSiO_3(l)}$$

The liquid slag, less dense than the molten metal, floats to the surface, where it is removed. The slag also protects the metal from attack by air.

Whether a reducing agent is needed and, if so, what should be the choice of reducing agent depends on the ore being processed. For example, mercury is extracted from HgS merely by roasting (page 390) in air:

$$HgS(c) + O_2(g) \longrightarrow Hg(g) + SO_2(g)$$

The mercury vapor formed is condensed to liquid mercury. Mercury may be so prepared because its oxide, HgO, is thermally unstable. However, more typically, oxides of metals are thermally stable and do not decompose at the temperature of roasting. Hence, roasting is frequently followed by a second reaction, namely, reduction by coke (page 692). The metallurgy of zinc

$$2ZnS(c) + 3O_2(g) \xrightarrow{roasting} 2ZnO(c) + 2SO_2(g)$$

$$2ZnO(c) + C(coke) \xrightarrow{reduction} 2Zn(g) + CO_2(g)$$

is typical of that used in the preparation of iron, tin, cadmium, nickel, lead, and many other metals. The direct reduction of sulfides

$$2ZnS(c) + C(coke) \longrightarrow 2Zn(g) + CS_2(g)$$

is not employed because the equilibrium constant is more favorable (34 times larger) for the oxide reduction.

PROBLEM 1 **Illustrate the roasting and reduction reactions with *pyrite*, FeS_2.**

As a general rule, the sulfides or oxides of metals with *positive* standard electrode potentials (page 466), such as Hg^{2+}, Hg ($E° = +0.79$ volt) and Cu^{2+}, Cu ($E° = +0.34$ volt), may be reduced to the metal by roasting. The sulfides of metals with *negative* standard electrode potentials between zero and about -0.77 volt, such as Zn^{2+}, Zn ($E° = -0.76$ volt), Cr^{3+}, Cr ($E° = -0.74$ volt), Fe^{2+}, Fe ($E° = -0.44$ volt), and Ni^{2+}, Ni ($E° = -0.25$ volt), are roasted to the oxide which is then reduced by coke, carbon monoxide, or hydrogen. The oxides of metals with *negative* standard electrode potentials between about -0.77 and about -1.5 volt require stronger reducing agents such as aluminum (Al^{3+}, Al, $E° = -1.7$ volt). Manganese dioxide is typical (Mn^{2+}, Mn, $E° = -1.2$ volt):

$$3MnO_2(c) + 4Al(c) \longrightarrow 2Al_2O_3(c) + 3Mn(l) \qquad \Delta H = -1770 \text{ kJ}$$

This reaction, the reduction of oxides by aluminum, is known as the **Goldschmidt reaction.** For metals with standard electrode potentials more negative than about -1.5 volt, electrolytic reduction, usually in nonaqueous media, is most practical. Typical is the production of aluminum by the **Hall-Héroult electrolytic reduction** of the oxide Al_2O_3; see Fig. 20.1. The oxide is electrolyzed in a solution of molten *cryolite,** Na_3AlF_6, with graphite electrodes. The electrode reactions are primarily $Al^{3+} + 3e^- \longrightarrow Al(l)$ (reduction) and $2O^{2-} \longrightarrow O_2 + 4e^-$ (oxidation), but the oxygen reacts with the graphite anode, forming carbon dioxide and carbon monoxide. A summary is given in Fig. 20.2.

Iron, the metal produced in the largest tonnage, is manufactured in a reaction vessel called a *blast furnace*. It is called a blast furnace because a blast of oxygen-

Also known as the thermite reaction, discovered by Hans Goldschmidt in 1905.

Invented independently by Charles Hall and Paul Héroult in 1886.

---

*Found in nature in commercial quantities only in Greenland, cryolite is manufactured from hydrofluoric acid, aluminum oxide, and sodium carbonate. When aluminum was first prepared by Henri Deville in 1856 ($6K + Al_2O_3 \longrightarrow 2Al + 3K_2O$), it was sufficiently expensive to be considered as a material for "the manufacture of jewelry and other articles of luxury."

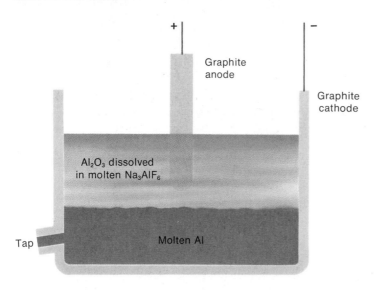

FIGURE 20.1 Representation of the reduction of aluminum.

enriched air (about 35 % oxygen) is forced through the furnace to increase the temperature, so as to increase the rate of the reactions involved:

$$C(coke) + O_2(g) \longrightarrow CO_2(g) \qquad \Delta H = -394 \text{ kJ}, \quad \Delta G = -393 \text{ kJ}$$

$$CO_2(g) + C(coke) \longrightarrow 2CO(g) \qquad \Delta H = +172 \text{ kJ}, \quad \Delta G = +120 \text{ kJ}$$

$$3CO(g) + Fe_2O_3(c) \longrightarrow 3CO_2(g) + 2Fe(l)^* \qquad \Delta H = -25.5 \text{ kJ}, \quad \Delta G = -29.2 \text{ kJ}$$

---

*This reaction does not occur in one step:

$$3Fe_2O_3 + CO \longrightarrow 2FeFe_2O_4 \ (Fe_3O_4) + CO_2$$
$$Fe_3O_4 + CO \longrightarrow 3FeO + CO_2$$
$$FeO + CO \longrightarrow Fe + CO_2$$

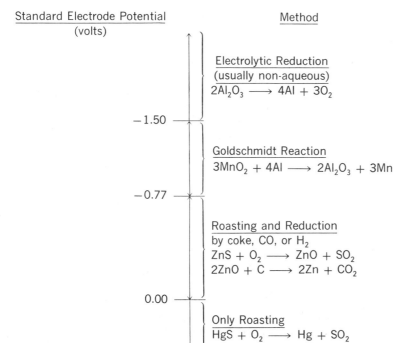

Standard Electrode Potential (volts)

Method

Electrolytic Reduction (usually non-aqueous)
$$2Al_2O_3 \longrightarrow 4Al + 3O_2$$

−1.50

Goldschmidt Reaction
$$3MnO_2 + 4Al \longrightarrow 2Al_2O_3 + 3Mn$$

−0.77

Roasting and Reduction by coke, CO, or H_2
$$ZnS + O_2 \longrightarrow ZnO + SO_2$$
$$2ZnO + C \longrightarrow 2Zn + CO_2$$

0.00

Only Roasting
$$HgS + O_2 \longrightarrow Hg + SO_2$$

FIGURE 20.2 A *general guide* to the metallurgy of common metals, with typical examples. Switchovers do, of course, occur; zinc is also prepared by electrolytic reduction, and chromium is also prepared by the Goldschmidt reaction.

The high temperature also suffices to melt the iron so that it can be drained from the furnace. Iron ores contain silicate impurities that form viscous, glassy solids. Limestone (flux) is therefore added to the coke and iron ore, forming a liquid slag ($CaSiO_3$) which also protects the molten iron from oxidation by the oxygen; see Fig. 20.3.

PROBLEM 2 Use Table 15.1, page 466, and Fig. 20.2 to predict the best method of preparation of tin from tin(II) oxide.

High-energy electrons directed into aqueous salt solutions become solvated (page 607). These solvated electrons and the H atoms produced are powerful reducing agents and are used to prepare small amounts of highly purified (99.999 %) metals; for example

$$Zn^{2+}(aq) + 2e^-(aq) \longrightarrow Zn(c)$$

and

$$Zn^{2+}(aq) + 2H(aq) \longrightarrow Zn(c) + 2H^+(aq)*$$

---

*OH molecules (radicals) are also formed by the high-energy electrons. The reaction, $Zn(c) + 2H^+(aq) \longrightarrow Zn^{2+}(aq) + H_2(g)$, does not occur because pure zinc does not catalyze the $2H(aq) \longrightarrow H_2(g)$ reaction.

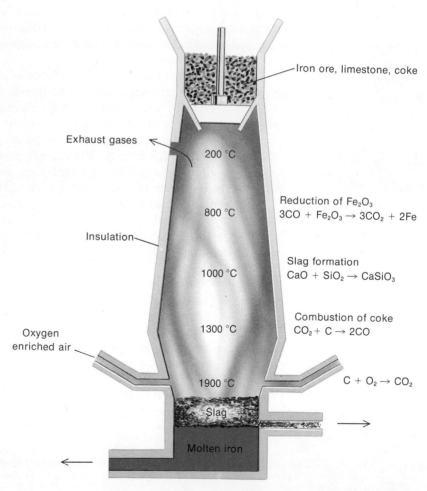

Iron ore, limestone, coke

Exhaust gases

200 °C

800 °C

Reduction of Fe_2O_3
$3CO + Fe_2O_3 \rightarrow 3CO_2 + 2Fe$

Insulation

1000 °C

Slag formation
$CaO + SiO_2 \rightarrow CaSiO_3$

1300 °C

Combustion of coke
$CO_2 + C \rightarrow 2CO$

Oxygen enriched air

1900 °C

$C + O_2 \rightarrow CO_2$

Slag

Molten iron

FIGURE 20.3 Representation of a blast furnace and the reduction of iron by coke.

20.4 _____ SOME REPRESENTATIVE METALS

Representative metals have their valence electrons in one shell, whereas transition metals have their valence electrons in more than one shell (page 661).

The Group IA or **alkali metals**, Li $\longrightarrow$ Fr (page 228), have one valence electron, s^1, and thus form $+1$ ions. They are rapidly oxidized by oxygen. Lithium forms an oxide, while sodium forms a peroxide and other alkali metals form superoxides (page 602):

$$2Na(c) + O_2(g) \longrightarrow Na_2O_2(c) \qquad \Delta H = -506 \text{ kJ}, \ K = 5.5 \times 10^{76}$$
$$K(c) + O_2(g) \longrightarrow KO_2(c)$$

They react very rapidly with cold water, producing hydrogen and hydroxide solutions (page 228), and they also react with hydrogen, forming hydrides:

$$2Li(c) + H_2(g) \longrightarrow 2LiH(c) \qquad \Delta H = -90.4 \text{ kJ}, \ K = 4.4 \times 10^{13}$$

Most of the alkali metal compounds are water-soluble and thus are naturally found mainly in sea-water, salt wells, and dry sea beds (Searles Lake, California; Stassfurt, Germany; and Chile). All animals and plants contain combined sodium and potassium. Plants extract a tremendous amount of potassium from the soil; therefore, fertilizers must contain potassium, mainly as potassium carbonate (*potash*).

The alkali metals (Fig. 20.2) are prepared by electrolytic reduction of the corresponding salts. The commercial preparation of sodium by the electrolysis of molten sodium chloride (page 473) is typical. Calcium chloride is usually added to lower the melting point of the mixture.

The alkali hydroxides are usually prepared by electrolysis of aqueous solutions. The commercial preparation of sodium hydroxide (page 473) is typical.

Because of their high reactivity—high thermodynamic instability and high kinetic instability—the alkali metals have limited application. However, tons of sodium are used in nuclear power plants to transfer heat from the nuclear reactor to the steam boiler (page 546). Sodium dissolved in liquid ammonia (page 607) is extensively used for the reduction of carbon compounds, and a sodium-lead alloy is used in the manufacture of lead tetraethyl, $Pb(C_2H_5)_4$.

When photons (light) strike the surface of a metal, electrons are ejected from the metal, leaving the metal positively charged. For every one photon absorbed, one electron is ejected.* This emission is called the **photoelectric effect,** first noticed as a chance observation by H. Hertz (1867) during experiments on the detection of radiation generated by (AC) electricity. Electrons are easily emitted by the alkali metals, particularly cesium, and thus the alkali metals are used in photocells, a device employed in "electric eye" burglar alarm systems, automatic door openers, and counters. Lithium compounds are used in fireworks to produce brilliant red colors, and in nuclear weapons. Lithium aluminum hydride, $LiAlH_4$, and lithium hydride, LiH, are extensively used as strong reducing agents. Lithium carbonate appears to be effective in the treatment of certain mental disorders. Admissions to mental hospitals appear to be lowest in regions where lithium levels in water supplies are high.

The Group IIA or the **alkaline earth metals**, Be $\longrightarrow$ Ra (page 230), have two valence electrons, s^2, and thus form compounds in which these metals exhibit the $+2$ oxidation state.

---

*The energy of the ejected electron equals the energy of the photon (hf) minus the energy required to remove the electron from the surface, verified by the experiments of Robert Millikan (1916).

The standard electrode potentials of these metals are highly negative (Table 15.1, page 466). They therefore act as good reducing agents; for example, magnesium reduces hot water to hydrogen:

$$Mg(c) + 2H_2O \longrightarrow Mg(OH)_2(c) + H_2(g)$$

Heated with hydrogen, alkaline earth metals form hydrides—for example, calcium hydride, $CaH_2(c)$—which decompose in water and thus serve as good sources of small amounts of hydrogen.

$$CaH_2(c) + 2H_2O \longrightarrow Ca(OH)_2(c) + 2H_2(g)$$

Although alkaline earth metals form oxides in oxygen or air, these oxides are generally prepared by thermal decomposition of abundant alkaline earth carbonates:

$$CaCO_3(c) \longrightarrow CaO(c) + CO_2(g)$$

Alkaline earth oxides react with water, forming hydroxides:

$$CaO(c) + H_2O \longrightarrow Ca(OH)_2(c)$$

This process is referred to as slaking.

The highly negative standard electrode potentials also dictate (page 634) that the alkaline earth metals exist in nature only in the combined state. These compounds generally exist as insoluble silicates, carbonates, sulfates, and phosphates. Beryllium is found only in small amounts as the mineral *beryl,* $Be_3Al_2Si_6O_{18}$.* Nevertheless, it is being used in increasing amounts in alloys as a hardening agent. Because of its high thermal stability, beryllium oxide is used in the manufacture of ceramics. Non-sparking tools are manufactured from beryllium-copper alloys for use in such places as oil refineries and explosives plants. A very toxic metal, beryllium causes respiratory diseases and damages the lungs (*berylliosis*). Therefore, the U.S. Environmental Protection Agency has placed beryllium and its compounds on the list of hazardous air pollutants.

Magnesium is widely distributed, principally as *magnesite,* $MgCO_3$, and *dolo-mite,* $CaCO_3MgCO_3$. Calcium, the most abundant alkaline earth metal, occurs as *limestone,* $CaCO_3$, as *gypsum,* $CaSO_4(H_2O)_2$, as *fluorspar,* CaF_2, and as *phosphate rock,* $[Ca_3(PO_4)_2]_3CaF_2$. Strontium and barium occur principally as carbonates, *strontianite,* $SrCO_3$, and *witherite,* $BaCO_3$; and as sulfates, *celestite,* $SrSO_4$, and *barite,* $BaSO_4$. Radium, which is radioactive, is extremely rare (page 528).

Alloys are mixtures or compounds, composed of two or more metals, that have metallic properties. Stainless steels, used for surgical instruments, food processing equipment, and cutlery, and beryllium-nickel steels, extremely hard and corrosion-resistant, are typical alloys. Magnesium has the advantage of lightness—density = 1.74 g/ml, compared with 7.86 g/ml for iron—and ease of forming alloys with other metals. The great tensile strengths of these alloys permit their use in the construction of balance beams, airplanes, railroad cars, truck and bus bodies, structural walls of buildings, auto pistons, and printing presses.

Tensile strength measures the stress (lb/in^2) required to stretch a rod to the breaking point.

When heated, magnesium burns rapidly in oxygen, forming magnesium oxide and raising the temperature to "white heat" (above 1200 °C). It is therefore used in photoflash bulbs.

---

*The gem stones emerald (pale green) and aquamarine (pale blue) are beryl, colored by trace amounts of chromium and iron oxides. These gems may be synthesized from highly purified BeO, Al_2O_3, SiO_2, Cr_2O_3, and Fe_2O_3.

Heating strontium salts produces brilliant red colors, while barium salts emit greenish-yellow colors. These compounds are therefore used in fireworks displays and "emergency" flares.

Partially dehydrated gypsum, known as *"plaster of paris,"*

$$2CaSO_4(H_2O)_2(c) \rightleftharpoons (CaSO_4)_2H_2O(c) + 3H_2O(l)$$

| gypsum | plaster of paris |

is used in medicine for casts, in sculpture to prepare molds, and in the building industry for stucco, plaster walls, and wallboards. Mixed with water, it sets to a solid mass of gypsum, with an increase in volume, tightly fitting any space into which it is poured.

Insoluble barium sulfate, because of its high electron density, is used to make the intestinal tract visible by means of X-rays. The barium ion so scatters the X-ray photons that they are not transmitted through the barium sulfate, while they are transmitted through the surrounding tissues. With new techniques, a "live" image of internal organs, including the brain, can be reproduced on a television screen.

20.5 _____ HARD WATER

Limestone and other calcium minerals are among the most abundant minerals in the Earth's crust. Consequently, natural waters invariably contain Ca^{2+} ions and, frequently, hydrogen carbonate ions, HCO_3^- (page 583). Other ions often found in natural waters include Mg^{2+} and Fe^{2+}. Natural waters containing objectionable concentrations of Ca^{2+}, Mg^{2+}, and Fe^{2+} ions are called **"hard."**

Hard water is an expensive annoyance in washing because the positive ions present form insoluble compounds with soaps (page 704). Soap, wasted in combining with these ions, appears as a "bathtub ring" or a yellowish scum on cloth. In addition, heating hard water that also contains hydrogen carbonate ions forms "boiler scum," principally calcium carbonate:

$$Ca^{2+}(aq) + 2HCO_3^-(aq) \longrightarrow CaCO_3(c) + CO_2(g) + H_2O$$

Formerly known as permanent hard water.

Formerly known as temporary hard water.

Two types of hardness are recognized: **Noncarbonate hard water** contains Ca^{2+}, Mg^{2+}, or Fe^{2+} ions as chlorides and sulfates. Water containing these metal ions and hydrogen carbonate ion is called **carbonate hard water.**

If more carbonate is needed, sodium carbonate is added.

Removal of these objectionable ions is known as **water softening.** Carbonate hard water may be softened by boiling; as shown above, the hardness ions are removed as carbonates. But this kind of treatment is satisfactory only for small quantities of water and assumes that sufficient hydrogen carbonate ions are present to precipitate all undesirable ions. More commonly, carbonate hard water is softened by the addition of a base, ammonia, NH_3, or lime, CaO. The purpose of the base is to remove a proton from HCO_3^-, forming CO_3^{2-}. The sequence of reactions is

$$NH_3(aq) + HCO_3^-(aq) \longrightarrow NH_4^+(aq) + CO_3^{2-}(aq)$$
$$Ca^{2+} + CO_3^{2-} \longrightarrow CaCO_3(c)$$

or

$$CaO(c) + 2HCO_3^-(aq) \longrightarrow Ca^{2+}(aq) + 2CO_3^{2-}(aq) + H_2O$$
$$Ca^{2+}(aq) + Ca^{2+}(aq) + 2CO_3^{2-}(aq) \longrightarrow 2CaCO_3(c)$$

Notice that while 1 mole of NH_3 yields 1 mole of $CaCO_3$, 1 mole of CaO yields 2 moles of $CaCO_3$. The carbonate precipitates the hardness ions as fine hard crystals that have no tendency to adhere to surfaces and that settle to the bottom of the container (washing machine).

Another common method of softening water is the addition of *washing soda,* $Na_2CO_3(H_2O)_{10}$, to precipitate hardness ions as carbonates.

A third common method of softening water is the addition of sodium triphosphate (page 615), which combines with the offending ions to form soluble compounds.

The soluble compound may be $Na_3CaP_3O_{10}$ $(3Na^+(aq) + CaP_3O_{10}{}^{3-}(aq))$.

Large quantities of hard water are softened by **ion-exchange,** a kind of chromatography (page 31) in which one ion displaces another ion in a solid which is held in a column. In this method, offending ions are exchanged for a non-offending ion, generally Na^+. The ion-exchange solid is usually a "plastic-like" material. Chemically, these solid ion-exchangers may be regarded as salts of complex organic acids in which Na^+ ions are very loosely bound. These Na^+ ions can be replaced with Ca^{2+} or other offending ions without changing the structure of the solid. Thus, when water containing Ca^{2+} ions flows through a column of solid ion-exchanger, exchange occurs; Na^+ ions in the exchanger are replaced by Ca^{2+} ions and the Ca^{2+} ions in the water are replaced by Na^+ ions:

$$2R—Na^+(c) \quad + Ca^{2+}(aq) \rightleftharpoons \quad (R)_2Ca^{2+}(c) \quad + 2Na^+(aq)$$

solid Na^+-exchanger   *hard water*   *solid ion-exchanger*   *soft water*

From time to time, the column is flushed with sodium chloride solution to reverse the reaction and so regenerate the Na^+-exchanger.

Hydrogen ion-exchangers as well as hydroxyl ion-exchangers have been synthesized:

$$R—H^+(c) \quad + Na^+(aq) \longrightarrow \quad R—Na^+(c) \quad + H^+(aq)$$

solid H^+-exchanger   *solution*   *solid ion-exchanger*   *solution*

$$R—OH^-(c) \quad + Cl^-(aq) \longrightarrow \quad R—Cl^-(c) \quad + OH^-(aq)$$

solid OH^--exchanger   *solution*   *solid ion-exchanger*   *solution*

$$H^+(aq) + OH^-(aq) \longrightarrow H_2O$$

It is evident that the use of these two exchangers will remove all ions from solution, as in a distillation. Since salts are replaced by water, the water is said to be **demineralized.**

Also known as "deionized water."

GROUP IIB ELEMENTS_____20.6

The Group IIB metals, Zn, Cd, and Hg, have two valence electrons, $d^{10}s^2$, and thus resemble the alkaline earth metals in forming compounds in the +2 oxidation state. Mercury, however, also has a +1 state. These elements also show properties common to the transition elements (Chap. 21).

Zinc occurs in nature principally as *sphalerite* (*zinc blende*), ZnS, and *smithsonite,* $ZnCO_3$.

Cadmium, a comparatively rare element, is found as an impurity in zinc ores. Cadmium is therefore obtained as a by-product during the preparation of zinc. It is more volatile and distills before zinc. The principal source of mercury is *cinnabar,* HgS.

On exposure to air, zinc forms a fairly strong adhering coating of zinc hydroxide carbonate, $Zn_2(OH)_2CO_3$, which protects it from corrosion. In addition, zinc has a greater tendency to lose electrons than iron and thus it is used as a protective coating on iron (page 490).

Granulated or mossy zinc, used with dilute acids to produce hydrogen for the reduction of carbon compounds, is manufactured by pouring molten zinc into cold water.

While the Zn^{2+} ion is acidic (page 415),

$$Zn(H_2O)_4{}^{2+}(aq) \longrightarrow H^+(aq) + Zn(H_2O)_3OH^+(aq)$$

insoluble zinc hydroxide, like insoluble aluminum hydroxide, is an amphoteric substance; in the presence of sodium hydroxide it behaves like an acid:

$$\underset{acid}{Zn(OH)_2(H_2O)_2(c)} + \underset{base}{2OH^-(aq)} \longrightarrow Zn(OH)_4{}^{2-}(aq) + 2H_2O$$

and in the presence of hydrochloric acid it behaves like a base:

$$\underset{base}{Zn(OH)_2(H_2O)_2(c)} + \underset{acid}{2H^+(aq)} \longrightarrow Zn(H_2O)_4{}^{2+}(aq)$$

For this reason, zinc hydroxide dissolves in strongly acid and strongly basic solutions. Also, like aluminum, it liberates hydrogen from strongly basic aqueous solutions because the hydroxides or oxides are soluble in these solutions (page 231):

$$Zn(c) + 2H_2O \longrightarrow Zn(OH)_2(c) + H_2(g)$$
$$Zn(OH)_2(c) + 2OH^-(aq) \longrightarrow Zn(OH)_4{}^{2-}(aq)$$
$$\overline{Zn(c) + 2OH^-(aq) + 2H_2O \longrightarrow Zn(OH)_4{}^{2-}(aq) + H_2(g)} \quad K = 1.7 \times 10^{12}$$

Zinc, cadmium, and mercury salts react with hydrogen sulfide, H_2S, yielding the corresponding sulfides, for example,

$$CdCl_2(aq) + H_2S(aq) \longrightarrow CdS(c)\ (yellow) + 2HCl(aq)$$

Mercury(I) sulfide is thermodynamically and kinetically unstable and immediately decomposes into mercury and mercury(II) sulfide:

$$Hg_2S(c) \longrightarrow Hg(l) + HgS(c)$$

Zinc is used in the manufacture of dry cells (page 478); in brass, an alloy of copper and zinc; and for galvanized iron (page 490). Zinc oxide is used in medicinal ointments, as a white paint pigment, and in tires to dissipate heat and so increase the life of the tire. Zinc chloride is the active ingredient in styptic pencils, used to stop bleeding from minor shaving cuts.

Cadmium is used as a protective coating on electronic parts, and in the manufacture of batteries and low-temperature melting alloys—for example, *Woods' metal* (melting point, 65.5 °C), used in automatic sprinkler systems and fire door controls. Cadmium rods are used in nuclear reactors as neutron absorbers (page 545). Cadmium sulfide is used as a paint pigment (*cadmium yellow*).

Owing to its high density, mobility, electrical conductivity, resistance to oxidation by air, and a liquid temperature range that covers all climatic conditions, liquid mercury (mp −38.9 °C, bp 356.6 °C) is used as the indicating liquid in thermometers and barometers, and for contacts in silent electrical switches. Mercury arc lamps are good sources of photons in the ultraviolet range. A fluorescent lamp is essentially a mercury-vapor discharge tube (page 118) with a coating of a fluorescent material on the inside surface. High-pressure mercury arc lamps are efficient sources of white light for street lighting.

Addition of argon gas makes it easier to light the lamp.

Mercury(II) fulminate, $Hg(ONC)_2$, thermodynamically very unstable and very sensitive to shock, is a high explosive, used in blasting caps to set off (detonate) larger charges of other explosives.

Amalgams (page 322) of tin, silver, and gold which rapidly solidify are used in dentistry for filling cavities. Alkali metals also dissolve in liquid mercury; these amalgams behave like a dilute alkali metal in the sense that the equilibrium, for example, $Na(c) \rightleftharpoons Na^+(aq) + e^-$, is shifted to the left, $Na(Hg) \rightleftharpoons Na^+(aq) + e^-$. The significance of this dilution effect is that it makes possible the electrolytic deposition of sodium from an aqueous sodium chloride solution when mercury is used as the cathode:

$$NaCl(aq) \longrightarrow Na^+(aq) + Cl^-(aq)$$
$$Hg(l)\ (cathode) + Na^+(aq) + e^- \longrightarrow Na(Hg)$$
$$Cl^-(aq)\ (anode) \longrightarrow \tfrac{1}{2} Cl_2(g) + e^-$$
$$\overline{NaCl(aq)\ |\ Hg(l)\ (cathode) \longrightarrow Na(Hg) + \tfrac{1}{2} Cl_2(g)}$$

The sodium amalgam is then pumped into water, forming hydrogen and a high-purity sodium hydroxide solution:

$$Na(Hg) + H_2O \longrightarrow Hg(l) + NaOH(aq) + \tfrac{1}{2} H_2(g)$$

The liquid mercury is then pumped back to the electrolysis cell. This is the principle of the **mercury cell** method of commercially producing sodium hydroxide; it constitutes the main source of mercury pollution in streams and lakes. Mercury is oxidized to mercury methyl ion, $HgCH_3^+$, which concentrates in fish, particularly in tuna and swordfish. For this reason, sale of swordfish has been banned and sale of tuna is restricted.

Readers interested in this subject are referred to "General and Analytical Aspects of Mercury Contamination," Journal of Chemical Education, volume 49, 1972, page 7.

THE COMPLETELY DELOCALIZED PI BOND: 20.7
THE METALLIC BOND

An electric current in a metal is a flow of electrons (page 118). Thus, electrons are not tightly bound to atoms in metals. Rather, they are free to move while the nuclei are anchored in fixed relative positions. For every electron entering at one end of a wire, an electron leaves at the other end. The larger the number of electrons so transported, the higher the current. This transportation of electrons through a metal wire without a change in the nature of the wire, called **metallic conduction,** forced the conclusion that the bond in metals could not be ionic or covalent. The metallic bond, the bond holding atoms together in metals, must be associated with free, mobile electrons. The electrons *cannot be localized* or permanently bound to atoms. The theory, then, must find a reasonable way of delocalizing electrons, freeing them from their oppositely charged mates. Molecular orbital (MO) theory provides a theoretical solution by the delocalization of electrons through the interaction of atomic orbitals (AO) (pages 560 and 567). Electrons housed in molecular orbitals are *not* confined to any one atom. Rather, molecular orbitals embrace a number of atoms.

Earlier theories assumed that a metal was composed of positive ions surrounded by a perfect gas of electrons. These theories, however, have been further developed by Felix Block (1928) and Alan Wilson (1931) into the **MO band theory of metals.** We illustrate this MO theory with lithium, a typical metal.

The number of MO's produced equals the number of AO's that interact. A lithium atom has two AO's, 1s and 2s, so that two interacting lithium atoms generate four MO's:

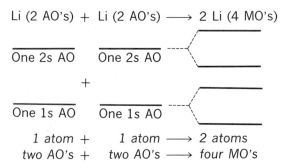

Li (2 AO's) + Li (2 AO's) ⟶ 2 Li (4 MO's)

One 2s AO   One 2s AO

+

One 1s AO   One 1s AO

1 atom +   1 atom ⟶ 2 atoms
two AO's +   two AO's ⟶ four MO's

Each MO embraces the two lithium atoms.

The interaction of 200 lithium atoms, each with two atomic orbitals, yields 400 molecular orbitals:

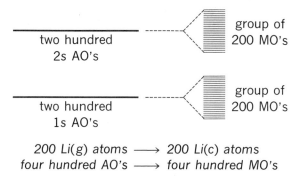

two hundred 2s AO's   group of 200 MO's

two hundred 1s AO's   group of 200 MO's

200 Li(g) atoms ⟶ 200 Li(c) atoms
four hundred AO's ⟶ four hundred MO's

Each molecular orbital (MO) now embraces 200 lithium atoms and the extent of delocalization is greater than it is for two lithium atoms.

As the number of interacting AO's increases, the number of MO's increases, delocalization becomes more extended, and the MO energy levels get closer and closer together. The interaction of 2×10^{20} Li atoms, corresponding to a small crystal of lithium, yields 4×10^{20} MO's, each embracing all the Li atoms in the crystal:

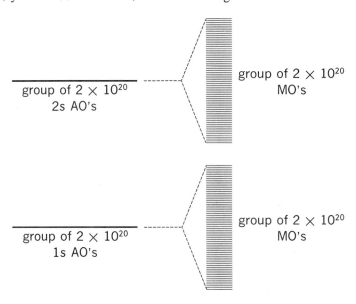

group of 2×10^{20} 2s AO's   group of 2×10^{20} MO's

group of 2×10^{20} 1s AO's   group of 2×10^{20} MO's

$$2 \times 10^{20} \; Li(g) \; atoms \longrightarrow 2 \times 10^{20} \; Li(c) \; atoms$$
$$4 \times 10^{20} \; AO's \longrightarrow 4 \times 10^{20} \; MO's$$

The energy difference between energy levels* is now so extremely small that this group of levels, for all practical purposes, forms a continuous energy series—no "jumps" are necessary to move from one energy level to another. This means that an electron is no longer confined, as in an isolated atom, in a definite AO corresponding to a definite energy. An electron in a metal can wander without much effort from a lower to a higher MO within a group of energy levels. The electrons have been completely liberated; they can move freely and independently from one part of a lithium crystal to another without being arrested.

A group of closely spaced MO's (molecular orbital energy levels), originating from a set of identical AO's (atomic orbital energy levels), is called an **energy band,** or simply a *band,* denoted as ▢. Thus, for lithium

2s AO's ⟶ ▢   2s band

} energy gap

1s AO's ⟶ ▢   1s band

Notice that an energy difference, an *energy gap,* remains between the bands. An electron is not free to jump across this gap from the 1s to the 2s band. Considerable energy is usually required to excite electrons from a lower to a higher band.

For metals with higher atomic numbers, the lower AO's do not participate in

---

*The decrease in the spacing, the energy difference between MO's accompanying electron delocalization, may be demonstrated as follows. Electrons in a molecule containing carbon atoms in the sp^2 state are more delocalized (page 586) than electrons in the *same molecule* containing carbon atoms in the sp^3 state. An atom in the sp^3 state, unlike the sp^2 state, does not have a p orbital that may be engaged in delocalizing electrons. Also, a molecule in which carbon atoms change from an sp^3 to an sp^2 state will also change its geometry (page 575). The molecule of the common indicator phenolphthalein in an acid solution (pH less than 9) contains sp^3 C atoms. The energy difference between the ground state and the next available orbital corresponds to photons in the UV range, and phenolphthalein is therefore colorless. Upon the addition of sodium hydroxide, the geometry of phenolphthalein changes, a number of sp^3 C atoms change to sp^2, delocalization occurs, the energy difference between the ground state and the next available orbital decreases so that the difference now corresponds to photons in the visible range, and a color develops. Upon the continued addition of sodium hydroxide, the sp^2 C atoms change back to sp^3 and the phenolphthalein again becomes colorless:

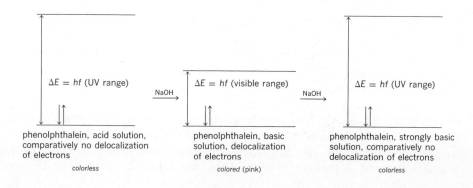

| $\Delta E = hf$ (UV range) | | $\Delta E = hf$ (visible range) | | $\Delta E = hf$ (UV range) |

phenolphthalein, acid solution, comparatively no delocalization of electrons

colorless

phenolphthalein, basic solution, delocalization of electrons

colored (pink)

phenolphthalein, strongly basic solution, comparatively no delocalization of electrons

colorless

the formation of MO's. Thus, the MO band theory description of sodium, $Na(1s^2\, 2s^2\, 2p^6\, 3s^1)$ is

☐ 3s band

____ $2p^6$

____ $2s^2$ or simply   ☐ 3s band

____ $1s^2$

Number of Electrons in One Band   We choose to follow the simplest scheme in answering this question, and we will illustrate the scheme with lithium. A $_3Li$ atom has 2 AO's and 3 electrons. 200 Li atoms have 400 AO's and 600 electrons. These 400 AO's form 400 MO's; 200 make up the $1s$ band and 200 make up the $2s$ band. Each MO can take 2 paired electrons, and the $1s$ band is filled before the $2s$ band. Therefore, the $1s$ band takes 400 electrons and is filled. This leaves only 200 electrons (600 − 400) for the $2s$ band, which then becomes only half-filled:

200 $_3Li(1s^2\, 2s^1)$ atoms = 400 AO's with 600 electrons

$\xrightarrow{interaction}$ 200 MO's with 400   200 MO's with 200
electrons   electrons

1s band filled $+$ 2s band half-filled

PROBLEM 3   Show, in a cluster of 10 $_3Li$ atoms, that the $1s$ band is filled and that the $2s$ band is half-filled.

We generalize and *simplify* this procedure by saying that an s band can take 2 electrons, indicated as ↑↓ for a filled band and as ↑ for a half-filled band. Then, the number of electrons in a band corresponds exactly to the number of electrons in the AO's of one isolated atom, and the MO band theory descriptions of $_3Li(1s^2\, 2s^1)$ and $_{11}Na(1s^2\, 2s^2\, 2p^6\, 3s^1)$ become

↑ 2s band, *half-filled*   ↑ 3s band, *half-filled*

} energy gap

↑↓ 1s band, *filled*

$_3Li$ $_{11}Na$

The p orbitals interact to form a p band capable of taking a maximum of 6 electrons, and a d band arising from d orbitals takes a maximum of 10 electrons.

In terms of this theory, *metals are characterized by incompletely filled bands.* An empty or incompletely filled band is called a **conducting band;** a completely filled band is called a **nonconducting band.**

A voltage is supplied by attaching two ends of a wire to the electrodes of a battery. When the voltage is applied to a solid (an **insulator**) with *completely filled bands, equal numbers of electrons flow in opposite directions* so that the *net number of electrons transported* from one end to the other end of the solid is *zero.* No electric current is obtained. A parking lot will not gain any cars if 25 arrive while 25 leave.

However, in an incompletely filled band, the electrons essentially *flow in one direction,** electrons are transported through the solid, and an electric current flow is obtained.

Since the metals with the highest electrical conductivities are also among the best heat (thermal) conductors, it is generally assumed that these two properties are related and that the conductance mechanism is the same for heat as for electricity. The fast motion of the free electrons (far above supersonic speeds) transfers heat rapidly throughout the metal. Atoms, molecules, and ions are "turtle-slow" compared to "jack-rabbit" free electrons.

On this basis, sodium, with a conducting band, is correctly predicted to be metallic while magnesium, $_{12}Mg(1s^2\,2s^2\,2p^6\,3s^2)$, with a filled $3s$ band, would appear to be nonmetallic. However, in magnesium, the upper MO's of the $3s$ band overlap the lower MO's of the $3p$ band, so that electrons may easily leak into the empty $3p$ band. This excitation of electrons from the $3s$ to the $3p$ band leaves the two bands only partly filled:

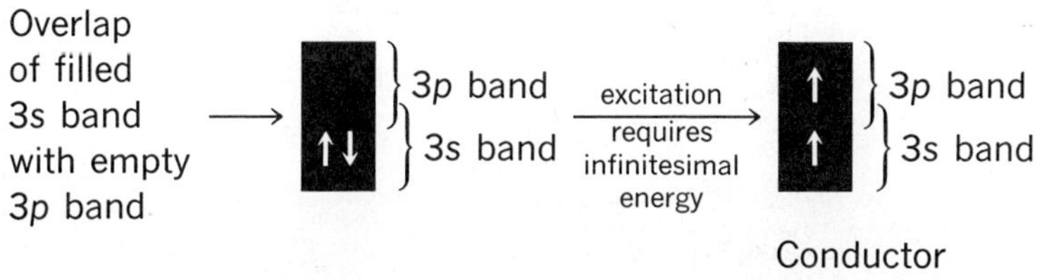

Overlap
of filled
3s band ⟶
with empty
3p band

⎱ 3p band
⎰ 3s band

excitation
requires
infinitesimal
energy

⟶

} 3p band
} 3s band

Conductor

An insulator also has filled conducting bands, but unlike magnesium, the energy gap between the filled and unfilled bands is so large that the energy required to excite an electron generally causes the substance to fly apart or decompose before excitation can be effected. In a **semiconductor,** the energy gap is sufficiently small to permit the excitation of electrons with increasing temperature. See Fig. 20.4.

The theoretical difference among metals, insulators, and semiconductors is associated with the extent of the energy gap between a filled and an empty band. The larger the gap, the poorer the conductivity (Fig. 20.4). Hence, in going across the periodic table from left to right, the change from metals to semiconductors to nonmetals occurs.

---

*This is a simplified view. It is only the electrons in the upper MO's of a partly filled band that are excited into unfilled MO's within the band and move in one direction. The electrons in the lower MO's remain paired. A more realistic figure would be

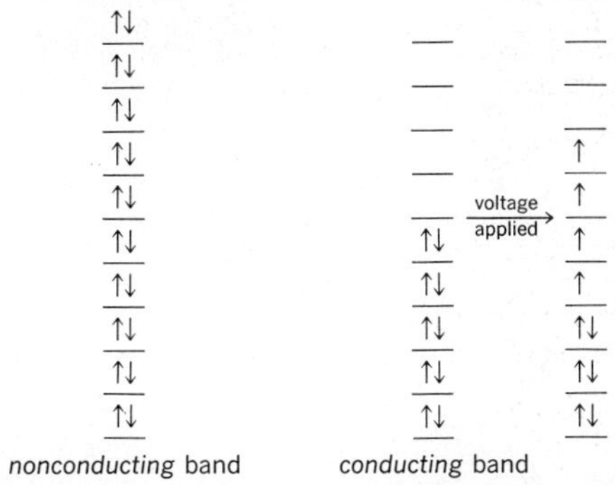

nonconducting band   *conducting* band

In a filled band, all electrons are paired, ↑↓. Consequently, paramagnetism (page 201) and conductivity do not exist. The paramagnetism and conductivity of one electron, ↑, are canceled by the paramagnetism and conductivity of the second electron, ↓.

METALS

Metallic
conductor

Metallic
conductor

↑ Partly
filled
band
(conducting band)

↑↓ Filled
band
(nonconducting band)

↑↓ Filled
and
empty
bands
overlap

NONMETALS

Insulator

Empty band
(conducting band)

↕ Large energy gap
(523 kJ/mole and higher)

↑↓ Filled band
(nonconducting band)

Semiconductor

Empty band
(conducting band)

↕ Reasonably small energy gap
(105 kJ/mole or less)

↑↓ Filled band
(nonconducting band)

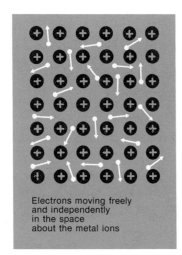

Electrons moving freely
and independently
in the space
about the metal ions

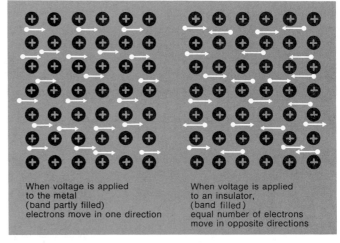

When voltage is applied
to the metal
(band partly filled)
electrons move in one direction

When voltage is applied
to an insulator,
(band filled)
equal number of electrons
move in opposite directions

FIGURE 20.4 Summary of the MO band theory of solids. The energy gap is frequently called a *forbidden zone,* because no electron can have an energy that does not correspond to one of the energy levels within a band. This is not a new idea because, as we already know, no electron in any atom or any molecule can have an energy that does not correspond to an atomic orbital or a molecular orbital. The existence of semiconductors was predicted from band theory by Alan Wilson (1931), but experimental techniques and the purity of metals at that time were not sufficiently advanced to permit their discovery. IUPAC approved name for semiconductors is **semimetal.**

The MO band theory nicely accounts for the difference in the effect of increasing temperature on conductivity of metals* (decreases) and semiconductors (increases). Atoms or ions in solids are not frozen stiff. They move—vibrate—about a fixed point. Electrical resistance is produced when vibrating metal ions scatter electrons. These vibrations interfere with the free flow of electrons by increasing the chances of collision. However, in the region of absolute zero, metal ions are frozen stiff and therefore do not collide with electrons. The electrical resistance is zero. But a rise in temperature increases the vibrations and so increases the number of collisions. The greater the number of collisions, the longer the time required for electrons to move across a solid, and the higher the resistance. The situation is analogous to the movement of cars on an expressway. The greater the number of collisions, the slower the movement of traffic. However, in a semiconductor, an additional temperature effect overcomes this tendency to decrease the conductivity. With a rise in temperature, the increasing number of collisions "kick" (excite) some electrons across the energy gap into the empty conducting band:

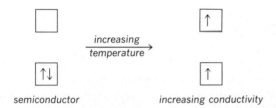

The conductivity of a semiconductor, therefore, increases with increasing temperature.

PROBLEM 4   Pick and name a solid—metal, semiconductor, or insulator—that fits each of the following descriptions: (a) The conducting band is empty at all temperatures. (b) The conducting band is partly filled at all temperatures. (c) The conducting band is practically empty at low temperatures but becomes partly filled at higher temperatures.

The liquid-helium refrigeration of underground transmission lines to zero resistance (superconducting) is under study for possible use by about 1990.

The silver-white "metallic luster" appearance, characteristic of polished metals, results from the fact that photons in the visible range are almost completely reflected; they bounce off the electrons unchanged in frequency. However, some metals, gold and copper in particular, have energy levels (AO's) available for the absorption of photons in the visible range (blue) and, hence, exhibit a color (yellow or red).

Our MO concept of the metallic bond is consistent with the general ability of metals to be rolled, hammered, and drawn without breakage. Like silicon carbide (page 261) or sodium chloride (page 262), a metal crystal may be regarded as a giant molecule. It consists of positive metal ions imbedded in an electron cloud that extends throughout the whole crystal. The electron cloud, consisting of the completely delocalized electrons, decreases the repulsive force between the positive ions and binds them in the same manner that the electron cloud decreases the repulsive force

*The effect of temperature on metallic conductance was first satisfactorily explained by John Bardeen, Leon Cooper, and J. Robert Schrieffer (1957) and their theory continues to stimulate a good deal of experimental work in the region of absolute zero. One of the most difficult theoretical problems of this century, the theory of superconductivity predicts that it should be possible to synthesize a large organic molecule that should behave as a superconductor at room temperature. Organic chemists are dreaming about this, but no one has yet made the dream come true. Nevertheless, an organic salt prepared in 1973 is a superconductor at 60 K, three times as high as the temperature at which metallic compounds become superconductors.

between two protons and binds them in a hydrogen molecule. In fact, according to our MO theory, the fundamental nature of chemical bonding is identical in all substances. The major difference lies only in the extent of electron delocalization. In so-called covalent substances, the delocalization is limited, usually confined to a comparatively small number of atoms—2 as in $H_2(g)$, $SiC(c)$, $CH_4(g)$, 3 as in SO_2, 4 as in NO_3^- and CO_3^{2-}, sometimes 6, as the 6 C atoms in benzene, C_6H_6, or 12, as the 12 C atoms in biphenylene, $C_{12}H_{10}$. In an ionic solid, delocalization is at a minimum; the electron practically sits on the negative ion. On the other hand, no one positive ion in a metal has any claim on any of the bonding electrons. Each electron belongs collectively to all other ions in the metallic crystal. The completely delocalized electrons act as the glue that holds the ions together. This makes it possible to squeeze the electron cloud without breakage. Rows of metal ions can slip by or glide over one another without change in internal structure and without breaking a significant number of bonds. The metal under stress thus "flows"; see Fig. 20.5 a. The situation is analogous to pumping a clay suspension through a series of pipes of different diameters; the water represents the electron cloud and the clay particles represent the positive ions. On the other hand, ionic crystals are generally brittle and shatter when hammered because deformation tends to line up ions of like charge, replacing attractive forces with repulsion forces,* illustrated in Fig. 20.5 b. The hardness of a substance depends on the ability of its atoms or ions to resist movement relative to one another. This resistance to movement is related to bond energy in an ionic (comparatively soft) or network covalent (very hard) substance. For example, on the Mohr-Woodhall hardness scale (page 259), CaF_2 (ionic) has a hardness of 4, SiO_2 (network covalent) has a hardness of 7, and diamond (network covalent) has a hardness of 42 (Problem 32, page 658).

---

*Hardnesses and melting and boiling points of metals which generally increase in going across the periodic table from Group I to VI and then decrease (illustrative boiling points: Cs (IA) 690 °C, W (VIB) 5930 °C, Bi (VA) 1560 °C) are probably dependent on the number of delocalized electrons per atom.

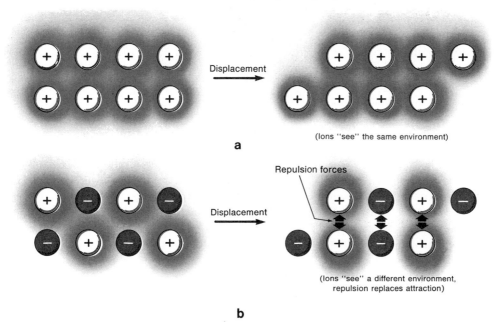

FIGURE 20.5 Displacement of ions (a) in a metallic crystal, and (b) in an ionic crystal. In the metallic crystal, positive metal ions are imbedded in an electron cloud. In the ionic crystal, the electron is firmly bound to the negative ion.

The hardest materials are invariably brittle; they resist distortion strongly but yield to a sharp blow by breaking. The brittleness of some transition metals, such as chromium, vanadium, and iron, is explained by some covalent (limited delocalization) bonding between metal ions in addition to metallic (highly delocalized) bonding. A diamond cutter does not "cut" a diamond. Diamond, in which bonding electrons are delocalized over only two atoms, is brittle.

PROBLEM 5   **How does a diamond cutter "cut" a diamond? Explain your answer.**

Prolonged heavy (fast) neutron dosages cause the stainless steel used as structural material in the core of a nuclear (breeder) reactor to swell and become brittle. This condition results from the formation of helium within the body of the steel:

$$_{26}^{56}\text{Fe} + {_0}\text{n}^1 \longrightarrow {_2^4}\text{He} + {_{24}^{53}}\text{Cr}$$
$$_{28}^{58}\text{Ni} + {_0}\text{n}^1 \longrightarrow {_2^4}\text{He} + {_{26}^{55}}\text{Fe}$$

While these problems do not affect the safety of the reactor, they do have a serious financial impact. The effects of changes in the heat treatment and composition of the steel in minimizing these problems are under investigation.

CHANGING NONMETALS TO METALS _____ 20.8

Graphite,* like diamond, is an elementary form of carbon. But unlike diamond, it is somewhat metallic in appearance, is sufficiently soft to be used in the manufacture of pencil "leads" and dry lubricants, and conducts electricity sufficiently for use as an electrode. Diamond is a network covalent solid (page 261) in which bonding electrons are delocalized over only two atoms. It is therefore an electrical insulator. Graphite also has a network covalent structure, but it is composed of widely separated layers of carbon atoms. In each layer the carbon atoms are bonded together by delocalized pi bonds, illustrated in Fig. 20.6. The pi bonds in each layer are completely delocalized; they embrace all the carbon atoms in that layer and so correspond to a conducting band. Hence, graphite is a good electrical conductor. Its softness is due partly to the ease with which the loosely bound layers can slide over one another. The use of graphite as a lubricant also depends on the presence of absorbed gases; completely degassed graphite is a poor lubricant. This is further proof of the metallic-like character of graphite. If, for example, a clean degassed lead block is placed on another such block, the two blocks bind and become one solid complete block; a gas layer suffices to prevent fusion of the electron clouds.

With confidence in our MO band theory, we now take a bold step forward. Our theory characterizes a metallic substance by a conducting band formed by the interaction of at least as many AO's as there are atoms in the metallic crystal. At least one electron per atom no longer moves about an individual atom but instead moves through the entire crystal. The main idea here is to engage a very large number of AO's to produce an equally large number of MO's, a band of energy levels spaced so closely that they may be regarded as a continuous series. Then, theoretically, nonmetallic substances may be made metallic by fusing together all available AO's. Ask a chemist, "Is hydrogen metallic or nonmetallic?" The answer "nonmetallic" is a

Natural blue diamonds are semiconductors; aluminum, identified by neutron analysis, is responsible for this property.

John Bernal was the first to predict that under very high pressures substances go into the metallic state.

_____

* *Graphit,* from the Greek word *graphein,* meaning "to write." Also known as "black lead," pencil lead is a mixture of clay and graphite. Graphite replaced metallic lead in pencils in the 16th century. However, the paint on pencils may contain lead compounds (yellow lead chromate; white lead, $Pb(OH)_2(PbCO_3)_2$), so that "chewing pencils" may be a source of lead poisoning.

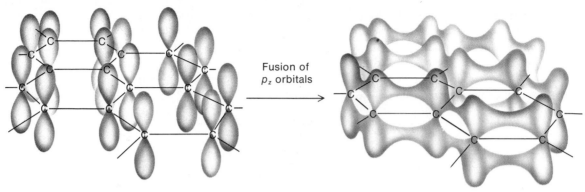

C atoms in imaginary sp^2 state

Fusion of p_z orbitals
binds all the C atoms in a layer

FIGURE 20.6 The graphite structure. The carbon atoms are arranged in hexagons bonded together in layers. Only a portion of one layer extending throughout the crystal is illustrated. The layers are stacked as shown in Fig. 18.5 (page 570). The distance between C atoms in any one layer is 0.142 nm, but the distance between layers is 0.335 nm. Bonding in the layer is strong sigma-pi delocalized bonding, while the weak bonding between layers, provided by van der Waals forces, offers little resistance to the movement of layers slipping past one another. Since the pi bonds do not tie the layers together, the electrons in the pi bonds do not move between layers. Therefore, graphite is a good conductor only in the direction of the layers. Conductivities relative to copper; diamond (3×10^{-21}) and graphite (0.0012). As in magnesium, full and empty bands overlap in graphite.

Pressure required is about a million atmospheres at 0 K. Techniques required for very high pressure research were developed during the 1930's by Percy Bridgman.

reflex reaction, not a reflective reaction. If, by the application of pressure, all the s orbitals in hydrogen can be sufficiently squeezed to interact and fuse as in lithium, metallic hydrogen should form. Attempts to prepare this hypothetical metallic form of hydrogen, first predicted by Eugene Wigner and Hillard Huntington (1935), are in progress. Astronomers believe the deep interiors of the largest planets, Jupiter and Saturn, consist of metallic hydrogen.

Metallic modifications of typical nonmetallic substances have been prepared at pressures of about 200,000 atmospheres; illustrative are silicon, phosphorus, zinc sulfide, and naphthalene (mothballs, $C_{10}H_8$). Thus, it is possible for a single substance to be an insulator, a semiconductor, or a metal, depending on the interatomic distance. This decreases with pressure and determines orbital interactions, the extent of electron delocalization, and gives rise to new atomic and electronic arrangements. Very interestingly, at high pressures, the graphite layers tend to buckle, so that the p_z orbitals (Fig. 20.6) are not completely parallel, electron delocalization is thus decreased, and the conductivity decreases; graphite becomes more nonmetallic. On the other hand, a third form of carbon, recently discovered (1968) in graphite layers in the Ries Crater, Germany, produced by natural shock waves, is more metallic in character than graphite.

About 10^6 atmospheres applied for about 10^{-6} second.

20.9 JUNK, SOLID WASTE, METAL POLLUTION

The United States, with 6 % of the world's population, uses one-third of the world's minerals. With increasing global industrialization, it is predicted that the world's mineral requirements over the next 20 years will equal all the minerals used since the Bronze Age. Formerly an exporter, the United States is now an importer of copper, zinc, and iron ore. Mineral utilization is definitely related to the vital needs of a nation: transportation, housing, health, food supply, and economic development. The Iron Age started about 5000 years ago and may continue for many more years with better methods of searching the earth for new resources. The ocean floor is now definitely recognized as a vast source of manganese, copper, nickel, and cobalt. But we are now at the start of a "New Materials Age": the synthesis of solid materials from readily available sources; air (oxygen and nitrogen), water (hydrogen and oxygen), and carbon. Plastics (Chap. 23), which are corrosion-proof, can be fabricated into materials superior to many metals in strength. Aluminum, beryllium, boron, and titanium will assume more important roles in materials fabrication. The principle involved is the addition of comparatively small amounts of *perfect* crystals of substances—for example, graphite, silicon carbide, or fiberglass—to traditional metals, plastics, and ceramics, the same basic principle used by the Chinese to strengthen lacquer with horsehair. Highly oriented graphite is used in the manufacture of heat shields in reentry space vehicles and in artificial heart valves.• Fiber-reinforced composites are used in the manufacture of tennis rackets, golf clubs, and truck springs.

•*Readers interested in this subject are referred to* Chemical Technology, *Jan. 1977, page 40.*

Atoms and molecules in real crystals of elements and compounds are not perfectly arranged as shown in textbook diagrams. More realistically, atoms and molecules are imperfectly arranged; the greater the number of such imperfections in a crystal, the weaker the solid. Crystal strength is thus related to the degree of disorder (entropy, page 486) of the solid; the greater the degree of disorder (entropy), the weaker the solid, and the smaller the stress• needed to pull the solid apart. A perfect crystal of a metal, on the other hand, has the highest degree of order (least entropy) and the greatest strength. Extremely purified perfect crystals have been prepared and are known as **whiskers,** so called because when first discovered they appeared as a whisker growth on another metal. An iron whisker (99.9999 % pure), for example, has 500 times the strength of an ordinarily purified iron crystal, while a graphite whisker is about 100 times stronger than usually accepted "pure" graphite. A silver whisker can be bent like a rubber rod without breakage. Silicon carbide whiskers, available in commercial quantities, have a strength 1500 times that of ordinary purified iron. Imperfections in metals increase the chances of collisions with conducting electrons or decrease the number of electrons in a conducting band, and so increase electrical resistance. Perfect crystals are therefore better electrical conductors; an aluminum whisker, for example, is 45,000 times better as a conductor than ordinarily purified aluminum.

•lb/in^2

More than $30 per ounce

PROBLEM 6   Arrange the following in the order of (a) increasing order, and (b) increasing entropy: (i) tin whisker, (ii) tin vapor, (iii) ordinary solid tin, (iv) tin liquid.

Glassy metals, noncrystalline (amorphous) mixtures of atoms such as Cr and Al, are prepared by rapid cooling, so fast that the liquid state is frozen stiff before the atoms can move to their proper sites (page 156). These glassy metals tend to be corrosion-resistant.

The creation of these new products has only added to the already serious problem of the struggle to maintain the beauty and resources of nature for future generations. The ecological battle rages; litter, junk, and solid waste materials accumulate. The United States throws out over a billion tons of inorganic waste materials per year; the manufacture of 1 ton of steel requires 65,000 gallons of water, and steel mills on Lake Michigan discharge polluted waters at the rate of 70,000 gallons per minute. A cadmium metallurgy plant in Japan discharged its metal wastes into a river that eventually deposited the cadmium (Cd^{2+}) in rice and soybean fields,

However, lead
exposure is still not
controlled in small-
scale industries.

Conclusion of the U.S.
Environmental
Protection Agency.

Natural isotopic
composition of lead is
not constant; see the
table of atomic
weights, inside back
cover.

Airborne Lead in
Perspective, National
Academy of Sciences,
Washington, D.C.,
1971

A combustion plant in
Newark, N.J., will
handle a minimum of
700 tons/day of solid
waste, producing fuel
gas and recovering
glass products and
metals. See footnote,
page 514.

resulting in heart and respiratory (lung) diseases from cadmium intake. Cadmium-plated food containers are now banned in the United States, but cadmium is still an industrial hazard to welders and metallurgists. Inhalation of tobacco smoke is a major source of cadmium and silver accumulation in man. Although stringent requirements have removed lead poisoning (plumbism) as an industrial hazard, it is still prevalent in city areas. Lead poisoning, for example, is a major problem in New York City, particularly among two and three year old children in older dwellings with lead-painted walls. In New Jersey, 22 children died from lead poisoning in the period from 1967 to 1971. New York City (1959) and New Jersey (1971) banned the use of high-content lead paint on indoor walls. An instrument that detects photons emitted by lead atoms when they are excited has been developed to detect lead in a paint coating under many layers of lead-free paint.

Inhalation of lead-polluted air, largely resulting from the combustion of gasolines containing "antiknock agent," lead tetraethyl, $Pb(C_2H_5)_4$, constitutes a public health hazard. Studies of lead poisoning of zoo animals (Staten Island, New York) conclude that air (lead aerosols) is the major source of lead pollution. Natural sources of lead discharged into rivers and oceans have been with us since man made his first appearance, but mass spectroscopic studies (page 121) in San Diego, California, show that natural sources are being overwhelmed by our addition of lead to the atmosphere. The isotopic composition of lead in lead aerosols and the lead in gasoline is identical, but it is different from that of lead resulting from natural weathering.

Lead (Pb^{2+}) tends to accumulate in the body and damage the central nervous system and the brain. It can replace Ca^{2+} in bone and it reacts with —SH— groups in enzymes, forming insoluble lead sulfide complexes which interfere with the catalytic life-function of the enzyme (page 728). Control of lead emissions into the environment therefore appears to be an unavoidable requirement. On the other hand, a report of the National Research Council concludes that the high lead concentration in the air of central cities is a potential health hazard to young children and certain workers (for example, police) but currently is no threat to the general population outside the cities.

Waste technologists are studying methods for reclaiming the mountains of trash, from beer and soda cans to junked automobiles, largely disposed as litter and in land dumps; at present, 52 % of the United States' consumption of lead is produced from scrap, compared with only 10 % of glass consumption. But as recycling practices increase, "waste" will become a major source of raw materials. Processes have been developed which produce bricks that are suitable for construction and that are economically competitive with traditional brickmaking. Solid inorganic material, from any source, is molded in a high-pressure press with a small amount of water, cement, and a catalyst. The traditional brick, made from clay and sand, requires firing in a furnace at high temperatures where complex (largely unknown) reactions occur, resulting in the formation of a variety of calcium silicates and aluminates.

Most important is a conservation policy that demands elimination of waste and more efficient use of materials through the cycle of extraction, manufacture, use, reuse, and ultimate discard. The comfortable state in which the materials, from which consumer articles are made, appear limitless is ended.

EPILOG

As mineral sources become exhausted, new technologies are being studied to separate desira-

ble metals from ores, ore wastes, and slags that cannot be economically used with present methods. One such novel scheme takes advantage of the differences in the (thermodynamic) stabilities of the metal chlorides relative to the corresponding oxides at a temperature at which reaction rates are rapid. For example, treatment of a mixture of oxides of zinc, iron, and aluminum with coke and chlorine results in the separation of these metals as the chlorides. Gaseous $ZnCl_2$ is first formed and collected, followed by the formation of gaseous $FeCl_3$, and finally gaseous $AlCl_3$ is collected (note the *decreasing order* of the equilibrium constants at 500 °C)

$$ZnO(c) + C(coke) + Cl_2(g) \longrightarrow$$
$$ZnCl_2(g) + CO(g) \qquad K = 4 \times 10^{12}$$
$$\tfrac{1}{2} Fe_2O_3(c) + \tfrac{3}{2} C(coke) + \tfrac{3}{2} Cl_2(g) \longrightarrow$$
$$FeCl_3(g) + \tfrac{3}{2} CO(g) \qquad K = 5 \times 10^{11}$$

$$\tfrac{1}{2} Al_2O_3(c) + \tfrac{3}{2} C(coke) + \tfrac{3}{2} Cl_2(g) \longrightarrow$$
$$AlCl_3(g) + \tfrac{3}{2} CO(g) \qquad K = 9 \times 10^{8}$$

Another process (*Electroslag Remelting, "ESR"*), already well established in the steel industry of the USSR and in use in Western Europe, is based on electrochemical processes in molten salts and therefore can electrolytically deposit the metals from the chlorides. In the temperature ranges of 100 °C–200 °C, sodium chloride is a typical ionic (polar) solvent that dissolves (polar) metal halides such as $ZnCl_2$, $FeCl_3$, and $AlCl_3$. Thus, highly reactive metals are electrodeposited from molten salt mixtures. The chlorine produced is recycled. These new technologies, referred to as "*chlorine metallurgy*," may make present metallurgy methods, such as blast furnaces and the Hall-Héroult process, obsolete within the next 10 years.

PROBLEMS

7 Vocabulary Define and illustrate (a) roasting; (b) gangue, flux, and slag; (c) carbonate and noncarbonate hard water; (d) amalgam; (e) ion-exchanger and demineralized water; (f) Goldschmidt reaction; (g) water softener; (h) galvanized iron; (i) ore; (j) mineral.

8 From an experimental point of view, distinguish (a) metal from nonmetal; (b) metal from semiconductor.

9 Roasting The roasting of some sulfide ores forms the oxide in some cases, while in other cases, such as Cu_2S, the metal is formed. Explain using equations.

10 Goldschmidt reaction (a) Write balanced equations for the preparation of iron and chromium from their metal(III) oxides by the Goldschmidt reaction. (b) $\Delta H = -536.0$ kJ for the reaction $2Al(c) + Cr_2O_3(c) \longrightarrow 2Cr(c) + Al_2O_3(c)$. Show that the heat evolved by the formation of 5.2 kg of chromium suffices to raise the temperature of a mixture (mass of mixture is 10.6 kg and its specific heat is 0.84 J/(g °C)) from 25 °C to the melting point of chromium (1890 °C) and to melt the chromium (heat of fusion = 318 J/g).

11 Alkali (a) The alkali metals are not found uncombined in nature. Explain. (b) By analogy to the reaction of sodium with water, HOH, write a balanced equation for the reaction of sodium with methyl alcohol, CH_3OH.

12 Write balanced equations for the electrolysis (a) of molten potassium bromide, and (b) of aqueous po-

tassium bromide using (i) graphite electrodes and (ii) a mercury cathode.

13 Alkaline earth (a) What is the difference in the electronic structure of the atoms of Group IA (alkali metals) and Group IIA (alkaline earth metals)? (b) By analogy to the formation of calcium ions in hard water, explain (i) how limestone caves form, and (ii) how "boiler scum" forms. (c) Explain with equations the preparation of plaster of Paris from gypsum. (d) Which is more likely to be an ionic solid crystal: a metal-halide or a nonmetal-halide? Explain.

14 Explain how hard water containing Ca^{2+} and Mg^{2+} can be softened by addition of (a) washing soda, $Na_2CO_3(H_2O)_{10}$, and (b) sodium triphosphate. Write a balanced equation for (a).

15 Hard water Explain the difference between (a) softening and "demineralizing" water; (b) noncarbonate and carbonate hard water.

16 How would you soften a hard water that contains (a) Ca^{2+} and Mg^{2+} as chlorides or sulfates; (b) Ca^{2+}, Mg^{2+}, and HCO_3^-? Write balanced equations.

17 Steel bonds Addition of other elements, such as Li, Be, C, Mg, Al, Si, V, Ca, Mn, Co, Ni, Cu, Mo, and La, to iron produces *steel*. Invariably, however, carbon is added (about 0.05 to 3.5 %); for example, Mo steels containing 3.5 % C are very hard and thus are used in cutting tools. The hardness (resistance to scratching) results from the formation of iron carbide, Fe_3C. But carbide formation *localizes bonds*.

655

Should this bond localization increase or decrease the brittleness (resistance to sudden sharp blows) of the metal?

18 Lead pollution In 1975 there were approximately 105 million motor vehicles registered in the United States. (a) If the average gasoline consumption is 15 miles per gallon and each car is driven approximately 12,000 miles per year, how many gallons of gasoline are consumed in one year? (b) Each gallon of "leaded gas" contains $6.0\,g$ of $Pb(C_2H_5)_4$, of which 70 % is expelled into the air as $PbCl_2$, 50 % of which remains suspended in the air. Calculate the number of pounds (i) of $PbCl_2$ and (ii) of Pb in lead aerosols produced from motor vehicles in one year, assuming that 92 % of them use "leaded gasoline" (page 654).

19 Metallic bond (a) As a chemical bond becomes more ionic, the bonding electrons tend to become more localized. Which is more likely to be a semiconductor, suitable for the preparation of transistors: AlN (ionic) or AlSb (covalent)? (b) Pure silicon, a very poor conductor, is converted into a good conductor ("doped semiconductor") at room temperature by the addition of certain impurities. Pick the appropriate part of Fig. 20.4, page 648, and show where you would introduce an empty conducting band to convert a poor conductor into a good conductor. (c) The MO description for the semiconductor germanium is

$67\,kJ/mole$. Show how (i) an impurity that

introduces an empty conducting band and (ii) an impurity that introduces a filled conducting bond into the highly purified Ge convert it into a very good conductor.* (d) (i) How is the conductivity of a metal with a half-filled s band changed by an impurity that adds electrons to this band? (ii) Can you offer a general explanation for the fact that traces of arsenic "poison" greatly reduce the conductivity of copper? (e) Metals feel cold to the touch; wood at the same temperature does not. Explain.

20 Explain how a nonmetallic substance like tetracyanoethylene,

$$N \equiv C \quad C \equiv N$$
$$\diagdown C \diagup$$
$$\| C \|$$
$$\diagup C \diagdown$$
$$N \equiv C \quad C \equiv N$$

, can be made into a metallic substance.

21 Plot the data shown in the table at the bottom of this page (*Science,* volume 161, 1968, page 118). What general statement may you make about the strength of the metallic bond as you go across the periodic table from left to right?

22 (a) Assume any three different numbers of lithium atoms, such as 6, 10, and 13, to show that in any piece of lithium, half of the MO's in the conducting band are filled. (b) The band in $Be(1s^2, 2s^2)$, generated by the overlap of the $2s$ and $2p$ bands, is $\frac{1}{4}$ filled. Explain.

23 In very pure Si, the gap between a filled band and an empty conducting band is 58.6 kJ/mole (14 kcal/mole). Is Si a conductor, a semiconductor, or an insulator? Explain how its conductivity changes with increasing temperature.

24 Materials cycle Rearrange the following blocks to portray an interlocking materials cycle:

*This is the principle used in manufacturing solar batteries for converting sunlight directly into electricity, in manufacturing transistors used to amplify electric currents in electric circuits, and in the development of electrodes sensitive to sunlight; using only sunlight, photoelectrolysis of water has been achieved, a possible economic source of hydrogen (page 600).

	Cs	Ba	La	Hf	Ta	W	Re	Os	Fr	Pt	Au	Hg	Tl	Pb
Number of delocalized electrons per atom	1	2	3	4	5	6	7	6	5	4	3	2	3	4
Heat of atomization $M(c) \longrightarrow M(g)$ kcal/mole	18.7	42.5	103	148	187	203	187	188	160	135	88	15.3	44	47

DATA FOR PROBLEM 21

25 Graphite (a) Some scientists like to refer to graphite as a "two-dimensional metal." Agree or disagree with this proposition. (b) Pick the substance most likely to be used as a dry lubricant: (i) magnesium oxide, MgO (ionic); (ii) aluminum arsenite, AlAs (network covalent); (iii) magnesium (metallic); (iv) molybdenum disulfide, MoS_2 (layer network covalent); (v) carbon tetrafluoride, CF_4 (covalent). (c) Graphite is not a reactive substance, but with molten potassium or cesium it forms compounds, such as C_8K or $C_{24}K$, in which electrons are transferred from K or Cs to *empty* conducting bands in graphite. The K^+ or Cs^+ ions lie in the space between the carbon layers in the graphite. Are these compounds metallic in character? Are they superconductors at low temperatures?

26 (a) Boron nitride, BN, a white solid prepared by heating boron in the presence of nitrogen, is known as *"inorganic graphite"* because, resembling graphite, it has a hexagonal layer structure consisting of alternating B and N atoms. What kind of imaginary AO's (sp, sp^2, sp^3) are used by B and N atoms in BN? Sketch one layer, containing at least three hexagons, showing σ and π bonding. However, *unlike* graphite, the energy gap between empty and full bands is very large.* Would "inorganic graphite" be a metallic conductor or an insulator? Explain. Would it have a high melting point? (b) The diamond-like form of boron nitride, known as *borazon*, BN, is obtained from "inorganic graphite" by heating it to a high temperature under high pressure in the presence of a catalyst—the same process used to synthesize diamond from graphite. Borazon, second to diamond in hardness, is used for rock drilling. What imaginary AO's are used by B and N atoms in borazon? Sketch a portion of the borazon structure using at least 4 B and 4 N atoms.

27 Al metallurgy (a) Balance each of the following equations:

$$Al_2O_3 + C + Cl_2 \longrightarrow AlCl_3 + CO$$
$$AlCl_3 + Mn \longrightarrow Al + MnCl_2$$
$$MnCl_2 + O_2 \longrightarrow MnO + Cl_2$$
$$MnO + C \longrightarrow Mn + CO$$

(b) What substances are (i) consumed and (ii) produced in the overall reaction?

---

*Energy gap is about 460 kJ/mole.

28 Cd poisoning From Table 15.1, page 466:

$$Zn(c) \longrightarrow Zn^{2+}(aq) + 2e^-$$
$$E° = -0.76 \text{ volt}$$
$$Cd^{2+}(aq) + 2e^- \longrightarrow Cd(c)$$
$$E° = -0.40 \text{ volt}$$
$$\overline{Zn(c) + Cd^{2+}(aq) \longrightarrow Zn^{2+}(aq) + Cd(c)}$$
$$E°_{cell} = ?$$

(a) Calculate the standard EMF of the cell, $E°_{cell}$. Should the reaction occur as written when $E_{cell} = E°_{cell}$? (b) Zn^{2+}, essential for the breakdown of fats and necessary to maintain normal concentrations of vitamin A in plasma, is present in the body in trace (very small) amounts. Cadmium, a nonessential element, is not present in a newborn healthy baby. (i) Can the forward or reverse reaction occur in the newborn baby? (ii) What reaction must occur as cadmium accumulates in the body?

29 Library Read one of the following:
  (a) "The Nature of Metals," *Scientific American*, September 1967, page 90.
  (b) "Our Children's Daily Lead," Morris Wessel and Anthony Dominski, *American Scientist*, volume 65, 1977, page 294.
  (c) "Aluminum from Bauxite: Are There Alternatives?" *American Scientist*, volume 65, 1977, page 345.
  (d) "The Disposal of Waste in the Ocean," *Scientific American*, August 1974, page 16.
  (e) "Salt Solution," *Chemistry in Britain*, volume 11, 1975, page 12.
  (f) "New Materials and Composites," William Hillig, *Science*, volume 191, 20 February 1976, page 733.
  (g) "Glassy Metals," R. M. J. Cotterill, *American Scientist*, July/August 1976, page 430.
  (h) "Chemistry of Fossilization," Laurence Huestis, *Journal of Chemical Education*, volume 53, May 1976, page 270.
  (i) "Relationship of Diet to Lead Poisoning in Children," Joyce Mooty and coworkers, *Pediatrics*, volume 55, May 1975, page 636.
  (j) "Energy Recovery from Waste," U.S. Environmental Protection Agency, U.S. Government Printing Office, Washington, D.C., 1973.
  (k) "The Recycling Index," T. W. F. Russell and M. W. Swartzlander, *Chemical Technology*, January 1976, page 32.
  (l) "Photovoltaic Generation of Electricity Through Use of Semiconductors," Bruce Chalmers, *Scientific American*, October 1976, page 34.

30 Show that the $3s$ band is half-full in a cluster of ten $^{23}_{11}Na$ atoms.

31 In the electrolytic reduction of aluminum, 80 % of the current is used for the reduction, the remainder being used to maintain the required temperature (1000 °C). A battery of cells produces 215 tons Al/day. (a) Write the partial equation for the reduction of Al^{3+}. Find the number of coulombs consumed per day and the current in amperes. (b) Only 8.3 % of this current is needed to produce Al from aluminum scrap. What would be the electricity saved per day, in coulombs, for the same Al production? (c) At 1000 °C, the density of molten aluminum is 2.29 g/ml, while the density of cryolite is 2.10 g/ml. From what part of the cell, top or bottom, would you draw the molten aluminum?

32 Given the following data:*

Substance	Lattice Energy MJ/mole	Molar Volume ml/mole	Hardness
NaCl (rock salt)	0.770	26.3	2
CaF$_2$ (calcite)	2.770	24.1	4
SiO$_2$ (quartz)	12.93	26.6	7
Al$_2$O$_3$ (corundum)	13.47	24.5	9
Diamond (C—C)	39.33	6.96	42.5

(a) **Lattice energy** is the heat absorbed when one mole of a crystal is separated into its individual ions or atoms, for example

$$NaCl(c) \rightleftharpoons Na^+(g) + Cl^-(g) \quad \Delta H = 0.770 \text{ MJ}$$

$$SiO_2(c) \rightleftharpoons Si(g) + 2O(g) \quad \Delta H = 12.93 \text{ MJ}$$

Calculate the lattice energy per unit volume in MJ/ml and plot these values (y-axis) against the given hardness values (x-axis). (b) Predict the hardness of (cubic) boron nitride, lattice energy 22.59 MJ, molar volume 10.8 ml/mole. (c) What single physical property must a substance possess to be harder than diamond? (d) Another important factor in determining hardness is the arrangement of atoms in the crystals. Illustrate this statement, using diamond and graphite as examples.

33 What ions form when Al$_2$O$_3$ dissolves in KOH solution?

34 Balance by inspection: $CuFeS_2(c) + O_2(g) \longrightarrow Cu(c) + FeO(c) + SO_2(g)$.

35 Sulfur and nitrogen, two nonmetals, have been combined to form metallic crystals of (SN)$_x$, lustrous golden color, from S$_2$N$_2$(g). The crystal consists of long chains of alternating S and N atoms, —N—S—N—S—. (a) Does much orbital overlapping occur in going from S$_2$N$_2$ to (SN)$_x$? Explain. (b) What is the band structure of (SN)$_x$? (c) Should the —S—N—S— angle be close to 180° or bent? (Recall Chap. 18.) (d) Which is the better representation of (SN)$_x$: —S—N—S—N—S—N— or ⩵S⩵N⩵S⩵N⩵?

36 According to the semiconductor theory of surface catalysis, a molecule, H$_2$ for example, is adsorbed on the surface of the solid catalyst. Then the molecule donates one electron to an unoccupied conducting band in the catalyst. (a) Is the molecule now more reactive, less reactive, or unchanged? Explain. (b) To improve the catalyst activity, should it be "doped" with atoms that accept electrons or donate electrons?

37 Over 6×10^6 tons of iron, known as **sponge iron,** are now produced annually by direct reduction (without melting) of iron ore (Fe$_2$O$_3$) with a mixture of CO and H$_2$. Assuming that equal volumes of CO and H$_2$ are consumed, find the volume of each gas consumed at STP in producing 6×10^6 metric tons of Fe. See App. III.

38 Write the Lewis symbols for Si and P. Traces of (nonmetallic) P atoms substituted for Si atoms in pure (semiconductor) Si make it a better electrical conductor. Explain.

39 Are the low density of Jupiter (1.33 g/ml compared to 5.52 g/ml for Earth) and its strong magnetic field consistent with the view that it is composed of at least 65 % hydrogen, much of it liquid and metallic H? Explain.

40 A highly oriented form of graphite has a conductivity about 20 times greater than that of ordinary graphite. Explain. Which form has a higher entropy?

41 The semiconductor germanium, Ge (Problem 19, page 656), is doped with indium, In, an element that accepts an electron from the Ge filled conducting band. Explain: "As the density of impurity states (In) is increased, metallic conductivity increases in the semiconductor (Ge)."

42 A **photoconductor** is a semiconductor whose energy gap is in the range of visible light. From the following set, in which the energy gap is expressed in erg/photon, pick the semiconductor that conducts in visible light (sunlight) but not in the dark: (a) 4.44×10^{-8} erg/photon; (b) 4.44×10^{-5} erg/photon; (c) 4.44×10^{-12} erg/photon.

---

*Johannes Plendl and Peter Gielesse, *Physical Reviews,* volume 125, February 1962, page 828, in which lattice energies are determined from vibrational spectra (pages 300, 749). 1 MJ = 10^6 joules.

ANSWERS

1 $2FeS_2 + 5\frac{1}{2}O_2 \longrightarrow Fe_2O_3 + 4SO_2$
$2Fe_2O_3 + 3C \longrightarrow 4Fe + 3CO_2$
2 Goldschmidt reaction

3 10 $_3$Li atoms, 30 electrons $\longrightarrow$ 1s band, 10 MO's, 20 electrons + 2s band, 10 MO's, 10 electrons
4 (a) insulator, (b) metal, (c) semiconductor

5 by sharp blows
6 (a) vapor, liquid, solid, whisker
    (b) whisker, solid, liquid, vapor
10 (a) $Fe_2O_3 + 2Al \longrightarrow Al_2O_3 + 2Fe$
    $Cr_2O_3 + 2Al \longrightarrow Al_2O_3 + 2Cr$
    (b) 1.8×10^4 kJ needed, 2.7×10^4 kJ liberated
11 (b) $Na + CH_3OH \longrightarrow CH_3ONa + \frac{1}{2}H_2$
12 (a) (i) $2KBr \longrightarrow 2K + Br_2$
      (ii) $2KBr + Hg \longrightarrow 2K(Hg) + Br_2$
    (b) (i) $2KBr + 2H_2O \longrightarrow H_2 + Br_2 + 2KOH$
      (ii) $2KBr + Hg \longrightarrow 2K(Hg) + Br_2$
14 $Ca^{2+} + Na_2CO_3(H_2O)_{10} \longrightarrow CaCO_3 + 2Na^+ + 10H_2O$
    $Mg^{2+} + Na_2CO_3(H_2O)_{10} \longrightarrow MgCO_3 + 2Na^+ + 10H_2O$
16 (a) addition of washing soda; (b) boiling
    $Ca^{2+} + Na_2CO_3(H_2O)_{10} \longrightarrow CaCO_3 + 2Na^+ + 10H_2O$
    $Ca^{2+} + 2HCO_3^- \longrightarrow CaCO_3 + CO_2 + H_2O$
17 increase brittleness
18 (a) 8.4×10^{10} gal; (b)(i) 3.1×10^8 lb; (ii) 2.3×10^8 lb
19 (a) AlSb
20 application of pressure
22 (b) $2s$ and $2p$ bands take a total of 8 electrons
23 semiconductor
24 1, 6, 4, 9, 3, 2, 5, 7, 8
25 (b) MoS_2, (c) yes, yes
26 (a) sp^2, insulator, high melting point
    (b) sp^3

27 (a) $Al_2O_3 + 3C + 3Cl_2 \longrightarrow 2AlCl_3 + 3CO$
    $2AlCl_3 + 3Mn \longrightarrow 2Al + 3MnCl_2$
    $2MnCl_2 + O_2 \longrightarrow 2MnO + 2Cl_2$
    $MnO + C \longrightarrow Mn + CO$
    (b) $Al_2O_3 + 6C + \frac{3}{2}O_2 \longrightarrow 2Al + 6CO$
28 (a) $+0.36$ volt, yes; (b) (i) no, (ii) reverse
30 10 $^{23}_{11}Na$ atoms, 110 electrons $\longrightarrow$ $1s$ band,
    10 MO's, 20 electrons + $2s$ band, 10 MO's,
    20 electrons + $2p$ bands, 30 MO's, 60 electrons +
    $3s$ band, 10 MO's, 10 electrons
31 (a) $Al^{3+} + 3e^- \longrightarrow Al^0$; 2.6×10^{12} C, 3.0×10^7
    amperes;
    (b) 2.4×10^{12} C; (c) bottom
32 (a) NaCl, 2.93×10^{-2}; CaF_2, 1.15×10^{-2}; SiO_2, 0.486;
    Al_2O_3, 0.550; diamond, 5.65 MJ/ml; (b) 18.5;
    (c) high lattice energy per unit volume
33 $K^+ + Al(OH)_4^- (Al(OH)_4(H_2O)_2^-)$
34 $2CuFeS_2 + 5O_2 \longrightarrow 2Cu + 2FeO + 4SO_2$
35 (a) extensive overlap; (c) bent
36 (a) more reactive, (b) electron acceptor
37 1.8×10^{12} liters (STP)
38 $\cdot \ddot{P} \cdot$, $\cdot \ddot{Si} \cdot$
39 yes
40 ordinary graphite
42 (c)

---

alloy A material containing more than one element and possessing characteristic properties of metals.

alkali metal An element in Group IA of the periodic table.

alkaline earth metal An element in Group IIA of the periodic table.

amalgam A liquid or solid solution of a metal in mercury.

carbonate hard water Water containing HCO_3^- ions as well as Ca^{2+}, Mg^{2+}, and Fe^{2+} ions.

demineralized water Water softened by ion-exchange methods in which all positive ions are exchanged for hydrogen ions and all negative ions are exchanged for hydroxide ions.

flux A substance added during the smelting process to remove impurities (gangue). See **smelting** and **gangue.**

gangue The unwanted portion of an ore. See **ore.**

Goldschmidt reaction A reaction in which metallic oxides are reduced by aluminum.

hard water Water containing Ca^{2+}, Mg^{2+}, and Fe^{2+} ions. See **carbonate** and **noncarbonate hard water.**

insulator A material with a very high electrical resistance.

ion-exchanger A solid material capable of exchanging one ion in solution for another ion.

metallic bond The complete delocalization of valence electrons among all the atoms of a metal crystal so that the electrons are free to move throughout the metal.

metallic conduction Electrical and heat conductivity in metals resulting from the movement of electrons through the metal.

metallurgy The extraction of metals from ores and the fabrication of metals into alloys.

mineral A naturally occurring solid compound or solid element (a rock is a heterogeneous mixture of different minerals).

noncarbonate hard water Water containing Ca^{2+}, Mg^{2+}, and Fe^{2+} ions and anions other than HCO_3^-.

ore A natural and economic source of an element.

photoelectric effect The emission of electrons when light shines on a metal surface.

roasting Heating an ore in air to convert sulfides and carbonates to oxides.

semiconductor A material whose electrical conductivity increases with temperature.

semimetal Same as semiconductor. See **semiconductor.**

slag The compound formed between the flux and the gangue during the smelting process.

smelting High temperature reduction processes for obtaining metals in the liquid state.

superconductor A metallic substance whose electrical resistance is zero, usually at a very low temperature.

water softener A compound which when added to water containing Ca^{2+}, Mg^{2+}, or Fe^{2+} precipitates these ions as water-insoluble compounds.

water softening The process of removing Ca^{2+}, Mg^{2+}, or Fe^{2+} ions from water.

whisker An extremely purified perfect crystal.

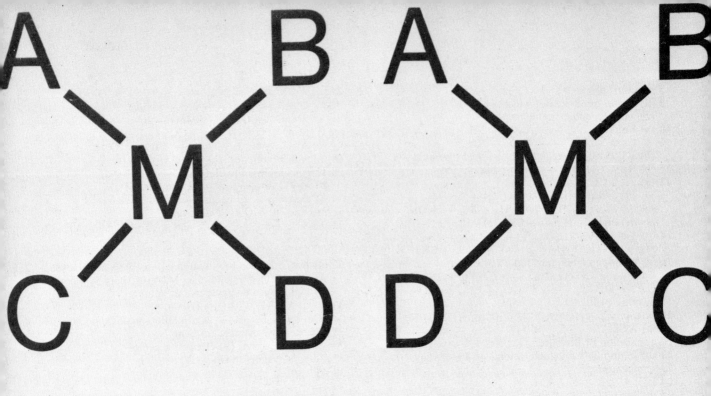

Try matching these without breaking them apart.

THE TRANSITION METALS

21

The elements that exist in the 10 subgroups between Groups IIA and IIIA in the periodic table (page 225) are called the **transition elements** or **transition metals**. These elements are associated with the addition of electrons to a d or an f subshell of the atom, so that practically all of these metals have valence electrons (page 227) in more than one shell. This leads to the distinctive chemistry and the different oxidation states associated with these elements. For example, aluminum, $_{13}Al$ $1s^2\,2s^2\,2p^6$ $3s^2\,3p^1$, a typical representative element, has its valence electrons, $3s^2\,3p^1$, in one shell, while manganese, $_{25}Mn\,KL\,3s^2\,3p^6\,3d^5\,4s^2$, a typical transition element, has its valence electrons, $3d^5$ and $4s^2$, in two shells. Loss of these electrons may lead to oxidation states of $1+$, $2+$, $3+$, $4+$, $6+$, and $7+$.

GENERAL PROPERTIES OF TRANSITION METALS_____21.2

All the transition elements are metals. Many transition metals are resistant to corrosion and are used to produce steels and as plating materials. Most compounds of the transition metals are colored. See Color Plates I and XIB. In fact, the intensity of color is used to determine the concentration of transition metal ions by spectroscopic means (page 746). The color of these ions is associated with incompletely filled d or f orbitals; when no d electrons are present, d^0, or when the five d subshells are filled, d^{10}, the ions are colorless. For example

Tungsten, chromium, and nickel are especially used in manufacturing special steels that are used in everything from spacecraft to razor blades.

Substance	Electronic Structure of Metal and Metal Ion		Color
$CuCl(c)$	$_{29}Cu\,KL\,3s^2\,3p^6\,3d^{10}\,4s^1$;	$Cu(I)\ d^{10},\,s^0$	colorless (white)
$CuCl_2(c)$		$Cu(II)\ d^9,\,s^0$	brownish yellow
$ScCl_3(c)$	$_{21}Sc\,KL\,3s^2\,3p^6\,3d^1\,4s^2$;	$Sc(III)\ d^0,\,s^0$	colorless (white)
$Cr^{2+}(aq)$	$_{24}Cr\,KL\,3s^2\,3p^6\,3d^5\,4s^1$;	$Cr(II)\ d^4,\,s^0$	blue
$Mn^{2+}(aq)$	$_{25}Mn\,KL\,3s^2\,3p^6\,3d^5\,4s^2$;	$Mn(II)\ d^5,\,s^0$	pink

Similarly, the color of the ions of the lanthanide and actinide metals (page 226) is associated with incompletely filled f orbitals. On the other hand, ions of the representative elements are colorless; d and f orbitals are either all filled or all empty in these ions.

Lanthoids is the recommended name for elements 57–71, and actinoids for elements 89–103.

PROBLEM 1 From the following, pick (a) the metal ions that have incompletely filled d orbitals, and (b) the ions most likely to have color: (i) $Cr^{3+}(aq)$; (ii) $Ca^{2+}(aq)$; (iii) $Ni^{2+}(aq)$; (iv) $Cd^{2+}(aq)$; (v) $Fe^{3+}(aq)$. Refer to App. IV for electronic structures.

Since many of the transition metal ions have incompletely filled d or f orbitals, the ions have unpaired electrons, and their compounds are therefore paramagnetic (page 201).

Also characteristic of transition metal ions is their ability to form complex ions, chemical combinations of a metal ion with negative ions or molecules, that are more or less thermodynamically stable. Some typical examples are:

Transition Metal Ion		Anion and/or Molecule	Complex Ion	K
Fe^{3+}	+	$6 \; :C\equiv N:^-$	$\longrightarrow Fe(CN)_6{}^{3-}$	10^{42}
			hexacyanoferrate(III)	
Zn^{2+}	+	$4 \; :\ddot{O}H^-$	$\longrightarrow Zn(OH)_4{}^{2-}$	10^{15}
Cd^{2+}	+	$4 \; \ddot{N}H_3$	$\longrightarrow Cd(NH_3)_4{}^{2+}$	10^7
Cr^{3+}	+	$5\ddot{N}H_3 + 1 \; :\ddot{C}l:^-$	$\longrightarrow [Cr(NH_3)_5Cl]^{2+}$	10^{34}
Pt^{2+}	+	$4 \; :\ddot{C}l:^-$	$\longrightarrow PtCl_4{}^{2-}$	10^{16}

Commonly called the ferricyanide ion (margin note, aligned with the Fe^{3+} row)

Typical compounds of these complex ions include $[Cd(NH_3)_4]Cl_2$ and $Na_3Fe(CN)_6$, known as **coordination compounds.***

Coordination compounds are also known as complexes. (margin note)

Notice that the anions or molecules combining with the metal ion have at least one pair of *unshared electrons*. The formation of a complex is therefore regarded as a Lewis acid-base reaction (page 417):

$$Lewis \; acid + Lewis \; base \longrightarrow complex$$
$$metal \; ion + anion \; or \; molecule \longrightarrow complex \; ion$$
$$Cu^{2+} + 4 \; \ddot{N}H_3 \longrightarrow Cu(NH_3)_4{}^{2+}$$
$$Sn^{4+} + 6 \; :\ddot{C}l:^- \longrightarrow SnCl_6{}^{2-}$$

Notice also that the charge of the complex ion is the sum of the charges of the components from which it is formed (conservation of charge).

PROBLEM 2   **Give the composition and charge of the complex ion formed in each case:**

(a) $Pt^{2+} + 4\ddot{N}H_3 \longrightarrow$?   (c) $Ag^+ + 2:\ddot{C}l:^- \longrightarrow$?

(b) $Cu^{2+} + 4:\ddot{O}H^- \longrightarrow$?   (d) $Fe^{3+} + 6:\ddot{C}\equiv N:^- \longrightarrow$?

Oxidation numbers: CO = 0, compound = 0, Ni = 0. (margin note)

Coordination compounds, such as tetracarbonyl nickel, $Ni(CO)_4$, may form from a metal atom and molecules so that the metal atom has a zero oxidation number.

21.3 _____ STRUCTURE OF COMPLEX IONS

The anions or molecules (the ligands) surround the metal cation (the central ion) of a complex in a regular geometric manner. The number of atoms bonded to the central metal ion is called the **coordination number** of the central ion. For example, in the complex $Ag(NH_3)_2{}^+$, $[H_3N—Ag—NH_3]^+$, the coordination number is 2 for Ag^+. The coordination number of Pt^{2+} is 4 in $[Pt(NH_3)_4]^{2+}$. Structurally, the four NH_3 molecules are located at the corners of a square; the Pt^{2+} cation is located at the center of the square. The four N atoms of the four NH_3 molecules are bonded to Pt^{2+}

4 and 6 are the most common coordination numbers. (margin note)

---

*The metal ion is called the **"central ion"** or **"central atom,"** while the anions and molecules with which it combines are called **ligands,** from *ligare,* Latin meaning to bind.

Since the Pt^{2+} ion and the four NH_3 molecules are in the same plane (page 569), this arrangement is known as *square planar*. The square planar arrangement is especially characteristic of Cu^{2+}, Ni^{2+}, Pd^{2+}, and Pt^{2+}. However, most of the complexes with a coordination number of 4 have a tetrahedral structure like that of CH_4 (page 573), with the metal ion in the center of the tetrahedron.

In the cobalt-ammonia complex, $[Co(NH_3)_6]^{3+}$ (coordination number 6), four of the six NH_3 molecules are at the corners of a square, with one NH_3 above and another NH_3 below the square; the Co^{3+} ion is located at the center of the square:

Accepted name: hexa-amine-cobalt(III).

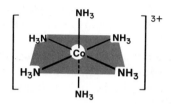

If the corners of the square are connected by lines to the NH_3 molecules below and above the square, a figure with eight equal faces is obtained. Corresponding to the four sides of the square, four faces look up to one NH_3, while the other four faces look down to the other NH_3 molecule. This arrangement is therefore called octahedral, from *octa* and *hedra,* meaning eight bases. Complexes in which the metal ion has a coordination number of 6 are always octahedral in shape.

These observations were first made by Alfred Werner (1893), a pioneer in coordination compound chemistry.

Complex ions with coordination number 2 are linear (page 579) in shape; for example, $[Cl—Cu—Cl]^-$ and $[H_3N—Ag—NH_3]^+$.

PROBLEM 3   **(a) Sketch the shape of each of the following complex ions: (i) $Cu(NH_3)_4^{2+}$, planar; (ii) $Zn(CN)_4^{2-}$, not planar; (iii) $Fe(CN)_6^{3-}$; (iv) $PdCl_4^{2-}$, not tetrahedral. (b) Give the coordination number of the central ion in each complex ion.**

EXPERIMENTAL STUDY OF COORDINATION COMPOUNDS_____21.4

Alfred Werner studied the chemistry of coordination compounds in aqueous solution and concluded (1893) that these compounds consist of a complex ion—molecules or negative ions attached to a central atom—and other necessary ions to make the compound electrically neutral.

Werner showed that the ligands in coordination compounds do not have their characteristic chemical properties. For example, the chloride ion, Cl^-, is precipitated by silver ion, Ag^+, forming $AgCl(c)$, while ammonia neutralizes sulfuric acid. However, he found that $Pt(NH_3)_2Cl_4$ does not neutralize sulfuric acid, and, like carbon tetrachloride (page 358), it does not form a precipitate of AgCl with silver nitrate. Thus, both the ammonia molecules and chloride ions must be tightly bound to the platinum cation. This conclusion is in agreement with the fact that the aqueous solution of $Pt(NH_3)_2Cl_4$ does not conduct electricity, indicating that platinum and chloride ions are not present—no ions, no electrical conductance (page 356). Werner wrote the complex within brackets, $[Pt(NH_3)_2Cl_4]$, to show that the four chloride ions and the two ammonia molecules are tightly bound to the Pt ion. On the other hand, when Werner tested $Pt(NH_3)_6Cl_4$ with silver nitrate and sulfuric acid, he found that one mole of $Pt(NH_3)_6Cl_4$ forms four moles of $AgCl(c)$, while the ammonia *does not* neutralize the sulfuric acid. Thus, he concluded that $Pt(NH_3)_6Cl_4$ consists of one $Pt(NH_3)_6^{4+}$ ion and four Cl^- ions, written as $[Pt(NH_3)_6]Cl_4$. Indeed, conductivity studies show that five ions per molecule are present in aqueous solution.

Werner also concluded that a relationship exists between the coordination number of the central atom and the shape of the complex it forms.

PROBLEM 4 The molecular formula of a compound is $Zn(NH_3)_4Cl_2$. With silver nitrate, 1 mole of the compound gives 2 moles of AgCl(*c*), but NH_4Cl is not produced with hydrochloric acid. Write the formula of the complex ion. Identify the number and kinds of ions in an aqueous solution of the compound.

21.5 SAME FORMULA, DIFFERENT COMPOUND: ISOMERISM

Compounds exist that have the same molecular formula (page 131) and yet are different compounds. These compounds have the same number of atoms of the same elements, but these atoms are not arranged in the same way. Merely arranging differently the same number of the same kinds of atoms so changes the chemical and physical properties that the different arrangements are recognized as different compounds, called **isomers.** Because they have different properties, isomers can be separated. For example, the atoms in the molecular formula C_2H_6O may be arranged to form different molecules as shown:

$$H-\overset{\overset{\displaystyle H}{|}}{\underset{\underset{\displaystyle H}{|}}{C}}-\overset{\overset{\displaystyle H}{|}}{\underset{\underset{\displaystyle H}{|}}{C}}-\overset{\cdot\cdot}{\underset{\cdot\cdot}{O}}-H \qquad H-\overset{\overset{\displaystyle H}{|}}{\underset{\underset{\displaystyle H}{|}}{C}}-\overset{\cdot\cdot}{\underset{\cdot\cdot}{O}}-\overset{\overset{\displaystyle H}{|}}{\underset{\underset{\displaystyle H}{|}}{C}}-H$$

structural formula   *structural formula*
ethyl alcohol   *dimethyl ether*
(b.p. 78.5 °C)   *(b.p. −23.7 °C)*

Both arrangements satisfy the octet rule and the common valences of the atoms involved. The sequence is C—C—O in one structural formula but C—O—C in the other. However, it is important to observe that *no matter how one structural formula is moved—turned, rotated, spun, flopped over—it cannot be made to fit or look like the other structural formula. They can be matched only if chemical bonds are broken.* This is the characteristic feature of all isomers, regardless of other terms used to describe them. Thus, ethyl alcohol and dimethyl ether are called **structural isomers;** an atom, O or C in this case, is not attached to the same kind of atoms in the isomers. These two isomers are easily separated by distillation (page 29). The two compounds $[Co(NH_3)_5(SO_4)]Br$ and $[Co(NH_3)_5Br]SO_4$ are also typical structural isomers. In one isomer, five NH_3 molecules and one SO_4^{2-} group are attached to Co, the central atom, while in the other isomer, five NH_3 molecules and one Br^- ion are attached to Co.

From isos and meros, the Greek words for equal parts.

Let us now examine molecules in which *the same kinds of atoms are attached to a given atom,* as in square planar $[Pt(NH_3)_2Cl_2]$. Two arrangements are possible:

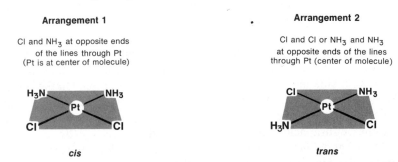

Arrangement 1

Cl and NH_3 at opposite ends
of the lines through Pt
(Pt is at center of molecule)

cis

Arrangement 2

Cl and Cl or NH_3 and NH_3
at opposite ends of the lines
through Pt (center of molecule)

trans

However, in spite of the fact that the same kinds of atoms are attached to Pt, the two arrangements are isomers. No matter how they are manipulated, one arrangement cannot be made to fit (superimpose) on the other. Similar to ethyl alcohol and dimethyl ether, the two arrangements can be matched *only if chemical bonds are broken*. The arrangements therefore correspond to two different compounds with entirely different chemical and physical properties. The two platinum compounds are typical **geometric isomers.** Arrangement (1) is named the **cis-isomer** while arrangement (2) is named the **trans-isomer.***

Also known as stereoisomers.

PROBLEM 5   **(a) Do two square planar isomers exist with the formula [Ni(CN)$_3$Br]$^{2-}$? (b) How many square planar isomers exist with the formula** [Ni(CN)$_2$Br$_2$]$^{2-}$, two, three, or four? (c) Classify the isomers in part (b) as structural or geometric isomers.**

Differences in properties of isomers are often very striking. One isomer may be sweet while the other may be bitter (page 571); one isomer may be an important food (nutrient) while the other may be a poison. A male insect—for example, the codling moth—is sexually stimulated by one isomer (*sex attractant*) but finds the other isomer unattractive.

GENERAL USES OF COORDINATION COMPOUNDS_____21.6

Coordination compounds serve many important uses in a variety of chemical processes ranging from securing oxygen from air to dry copying (Xerox process). Hemoglobin, the oxygen carrier in blood, is a combination of a protein (page 726) and an iron complex, as shown in Fig. 21.1.

Carbon monoxide and cyanide ion act as poisons because the complexes they

From haima *and* globus, *the Greek and Latin words for blood and ball, roughly the shape of hemoglobin, about 65 Å in diameter.*

_____
*From *cis,* the Latin word for "on this side," used here to mean that the 2Cl (or 2NH$_3$) are not diagonally opposite each other but are on the two upper or the two lower corners of the square molecule; they are *adjacent. Trans* is the Latin word for "across," used here to mean that 2Cl and 2NH$_3$ are on *diagonally* opposite sides of the molecule.

**Models are very useful in the study of isomers. To construct a square planar molecule, hook four balls to one ball so that each of the four is at a corner of a square. Simpler, cut a piece of paper into 1½ inch squares. Label the corners of the square with the appropriate chemical symbols.

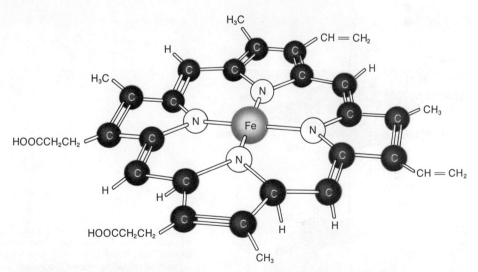

FIGURE 21.1 A hemoglobin molecule, a square planar complex consisting of Fe(II) surrounded by a porphyrin molecule (page 215). Actually, a hemoglobin molecule has four such complexes, each attached to a protein. One ml of blood contains about 5 × 10^9 red cells, each of which contains about 3 × 10^8 hemoglobin molecules.

form with iron, Fe(II), in hemoglobin are thermodynamically more stable (bound more tightly) than the oxygen complex.

Oxygen forms a bond sufficiently weak that it is released to the tissues where the oxygen pressure is low. In fact, the bond is so weak that iron remains in the Fe(II) state even when oxygenated. Nitrite ion acts as a poison by oxidizing hemoglobin.

Many medicinals are coordination compounds that make it easier for the body to incorporate an essential compound in its cells. For example, vitamin B_{12}, a complex of cobalt and a large organic portion, shown in Fig. 21.2, is a specific cure for pernicious anemia because of its ability to increase the number of hemoglobin molecules in the blood.*

An important method of water softening involves the use of phosphates (page 641) or other chemicals to tie up offending ions (Ca^{2+}, Mg^{2+}, and Fe^{2+}) as soluble complex ions.

The role of transition metal complexes as catalysts for nitrogen fixation (page 610) has become important. The reduction of N_2 to NH_3 is thermodynamically very attractive ($N_2(g) + 3H_2(g) \longrightarrow 2NH_3(g)$, $K = 4.0 \times 10^8$) but kinetically very unattractive (*rate* = zero mole/year) at ordinary conditions (page 605). In fact, nitrogen is so kinetically stable (page 605) that helium in uranium minerals was originally mistaken for nitrogen. Nevertheless, *titanocene,* $Ti(C_5H_5)_2$, in which one Ti atom is sandwiched between two C_5H_5 flat rings, fixes nitrogen very rapidly under ordinary conditions (page 394). The mechanism of the reaction is complicated but a very simplified view may be represented:

$$\diamond = C_5H_5 \qquad 2\left[\overline{Ti} \right] + N_2 \longrightarrow \overline{Ti}\text{----}N_2\text{----}\overline{Ti} \xrightarrow{H_2O} 2NH_3 + 2\left[\overline{Ti} \right]$$

---

*Readers interested in coordination compounds in biochemistry are referred to "Role of Metal Ions in Life Processes," John Bailar, *American Scientist,* volume 59, September 1971, pages 586–592.

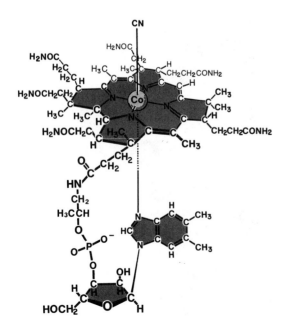

FIGURE 21.2 Structure of vitamin B_{12} (cyanocobalamin), a complex of cobalt. The largest and most complicated vitamin molecule known, first isolated in 1948, it was finally synthesized (1973) by a team effort led by Robert Woodward and Albert Eschenmoser and involving 99 scientists from 19 countries. Notice that four N atoms form a square plane around the Co atom while the CN group above and the group below the plane give the molecule an octahedral arrangement.

Many metals form a more uniform plate which adheres more strongly and has a better appearance when the metal is deposited (electroplated) from a solution in which it exists as a complex ion. Thus, in silver plating, the $Ag(CN)_2^-$ complex is employed as the electrolyte instead of Ag^+ ion:

$$Ag(CN)_2^-(aq) + e^- \longrightarrow Ag(c) + 2CN^-(aq) \ \textit{(reduction at cathode)}$$

The formation of complex ions is important in photography. When an exposed film is developed, only the excited silver bromide, AgBr (page 196), is reduced to silver. The unexposed silver bromide remains the same. The reduced silver appears black, while the remaining silver bromide appears clear and must be removed. When the unexposed silver bromide is removed, the photographed image is said to be **"fixed."** *"Hypo,"* sodium thiosulfate, is used to dissolve the insoluble silver bromide:

In forming the thiosulfate ion, $S_2O_3^{2-}$, a sulfur atom displaces an oxygen atom in SO_4^{2-}.

$$AgBr(c) + 2S_2O_3^{2-}(aq) \longrightarrow Ag(S_2O_3)_2^{3-}(aq) + Br^-(aq)$$

Silver is the life-blood of photography, a billion-dollar industry and the largest consumer of the metal. As a disinfectant, silver nitrate is more effective than chlorine; 1 ppm $AgNO_3$ by volume suffices to sterilize water, and a 1% solution by mass prevents infection in newborn babies' eyes. Silver, an excellent electrical conductor that resists corrosion, is used in many electrical systems from tiny hearing aids and computers to massive power plant switches. Silver-zinc batteries powered the Lunar Roving Vehicle and the Lunar Broadcasting Systems.

The formation of complex ions makes the metallurgy of silver and gold possible. Although copper and silver naturally occur in the combined and uncombined states, gold is found principally uncombined. Unlike copper and silver, gold is thermodynamically stable in natural waters containing oxygen and (CO_2) acid (note the large difference in equilibrium constants):

$$2Cu(c) + O_2(aq) + 4H^+(aq) \longrightarrow 2Cu^{2+}(aq) + 2H_2O \quad K = 10^{60}$$
$$4Au(c) + O_2(aq) + 4H^+(aq) \longrightarrow 4Au^+(aq) + 2H_2O \quad K = 10^{-34}$$

However, in the presence of cyanide ion, gold becomes thermodynamically unstable and dissolves as a cyanide complex:

$$4Au(c) + 8CN^-(aq) + O_2(aq) + 2H_2O \longrightarrow 4Au(CN)_2^-(aq) + 4OH^-(aq) \quad K = 10^{68}$$

This reaction is the basis of extracting **(leaching)** gold and silver from ores. The metals are then recovered from the cyanide solution by electrolysis.

Removal of dissolved mercury as Hg^{2+} or $HgCH_3^+$ (mercury methyl ion) from aqueous solutions by formation of a complex with a solid synthetic resin has been achieved and so provides a promising tool for the treatment of mercury-polluted waste waters.

BONDING IN COMPLEXES:———————21.7
ORIGIN OF COLOR AND PARAMAGNETIC PROPERTIES

The color and paramagnetic properties of matter are explained by photon absorption in the frequency range of visible light and by the presence of unpaired

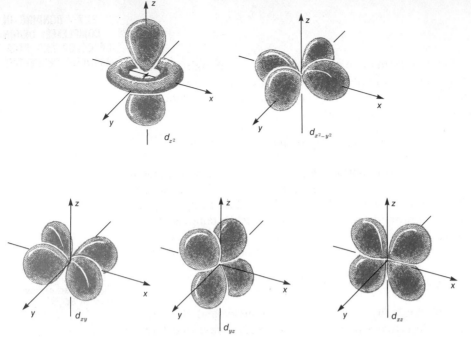

FIGURE 21.3 Representation of the five d orbitals. The designations for the d orbitals, d_{z^2}, $d_{x^2-y^2}$, d_{xy}, d_{yz}, and d_{xz}, give their positions relative to the axes, the same as in Fig. 6.9, page 183.

FIGURE 21.4 Crystal field theory. Illustrating the approach of six ligands to an octahedral complex. They approach along the x, y, and z axes. The d_{z^2} and $d_{x^2-y^2}$ orbitals of the central metal ion are *directly* in the path of the ligands and are therefore strongly repelled. The other three d orbitals, not shown, occupy spaces between the axes and are therefore not so strongly repelled.

electrons (Chap. 6). The frequency of the photon absorbed is determined by the difference of the energy states between which an electron undergoes a transition from a lower energy state (orbital) to a higher energy state (orbital) (page 191). Paramagnetism is determined by the order of electron occupancy of orbitals and the preference of electrons to stay unpaired (page 205). These principles are applicable to transition metal complexes. Also, the type of bonding, mainly covalent, between the central ion and the ligands may be described by molecular orbital theory (Chap. 18). However, the number of orbitals is more than we care to handle. Therefore, we shall content ourselves with a study of the nature of the bonding in terms of the crystal field theory, developed by Hans Bethe (1929) and John Van Vleck (1932). This theory does not conflict with the more detailed results of the molecular orbital theory.

The theory *limits* itself to the five d orbitals of the central metal ion, shown in Fig. 21.3. Further, the theory *assumes* that the force, the nature of the bond, between the central positive ion and the unshared electron pair on a ligand (ion or molecule) is purely ionic. By this assumption, it *disregards* the covalent character (the overlap or fusion of orbitals, page 560) of the bond. The theory concerns itself *only* with the electrical interaction between the electrons in the d orbitals and the ligand's unshared electron pair. This theory is a *useful* model that does *not* represent reality.

As a ligand with its unshared electron pair approaches the central ion, the electron pair repels electrons in the d orbitals. We illustrate the effect of this repulsive force on an octahedral complex in Fig. 21.4. The five d orbitals do not all feel the same repulsive force. The repulsive force experienced by electrons in d_{z^2} and $d_{x^2-y^2}$ is greater than that experienced by d_{xy}, d_{yz}, or d_{xz} electrons. This is so because d_{z^2} and $d_{x^2-y^2}$ orbitals stand directly along the path by which the six ligands approach the central ion. On the other hand, the d_{xy}, d_{yz}, and d_{xz} orbitals occupy spaces between these pathways and are not as strongly repelled. So, the five d orbitals are separated—"split"—into two sets of orbitals of different energies, as shown in the energy level diagram:

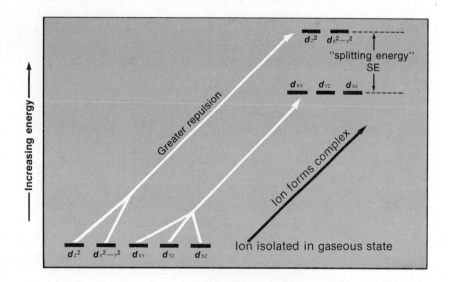

The energy difference between the two sets of d orbitals, the so-called "splitting energy," SE, is, of course, the energy required to excite an electron from a lower to an upper orbital. In fact, the main objective of this theory is to split the five d orbitals into sets of different energies. The energy differences (SE) then explain the color and paramagnetic properties of complexes. It is common to draw the energy level diagram for an octrahedral complex simply as

$$\underline{d_{z^2}} \qquad \underline{d_{x^2-y^2}}$$

$$\uparrow \text{SE} \downarrow$$

$$\underline{d_{xy}} \qquad \underline{d_{yz}} \qquad \underline{d_{xz}}$$

PROBLEM 6   Crystal field theory treats an inorganic complex as a purely (a) covalent, (b) ionic, (c) ionic-covalent compound. Pick the correct word.

A very important conclusion is that the separation, the energy difference, SE, between the two sets for a given central metal ion is determined by the nature of the ligand. Some ligands induce a comparatively large separation (large SE), while others induce a very small separation (small SE). Cyanide ion, $:C\equiv N:^-$, and ammonia, $\ddot{N}H_3$, generally induce large separations, while $H\ddot{O}H$ and the halides $(:\ddot{F}:^- \longrightarrow :\ddot{I}:^-)$ generally induce small separations, summarized as

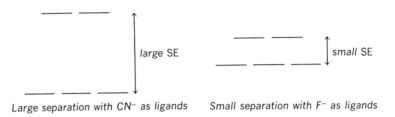

Large separation with CN^- as ligands   Small separation with F^- as ligands

Explanation of Color   Nearly all transition metal complexes possess color. If a substance absorbs all visible light, it appears black to the brain because no photons reach the eye; if no light is absorbed, the substance appears white (or colorless) because all photons reach the eye. A substance appears colored to the human eye when the substance absorbs photons in some part of the visible range, 4000 to 7000 Å:

Color and typical wavelength absorbed by substance	Color observed by eye
Violet, 4100 Å	Yellow
Blue, 4700	Orange
Green, 5200	Red
Yellow, 5750	Blue-violet
Red, 6500	Blue-green

Seeing color is a matter of personal taste. Only the absorption spectrum (Chap. 24) of a substance objectively records its color.

The energy of the photon absorbed is determined by the separation, the splitting energy, SE, induced by the ligands: $SE = hf$. The larger the SE, the larger the energy, the greater the frequency, and the shorter the wavelength of the absorbed photon. The energy separation between the d orbitals usually falls in the visible range. For a given central ion, each kind of ligand induces a characteristic separation and, therefore, each complex possesses a characteristic color (spectrum). For example, H_2O induces a small SE in Cu^{2+} and low energy photons are absorbed; thus, $Cu(H_2O)_4{}^{2+}$ appears bluish-green. Ammonia induces a larger SE, and higher energy

Splitting energies are experimentally obtained from a study of the energy of absorbed photons. Additional splitting of the upper and lower sets of orbitals is not uncommon.

photons are absorbed; thus, $Cu(NH_3)_4{}^{2+}$ appears blue-violet. Cyanide ion induces the largest SE, and highest energy photons are absorbed; thus, $Cu(CN)_2(c)$ appears yellow. The deep blue color of $Cu(NH_3)_4{}^{2+}$ ion is used as a test to confirm the presence of $Cu(H_2O)_4{}^{2+}$.

These ions may be written with two more H_2O molecules, but these two molecules are further from Cu^{2+} than the other four.

PROBLEM 7 $[Co(NH_3)_5SO_4]^+$ **appears red while** $[Co(NH_3)_5Br]^{2+}$ **appears violet. In which complex ion are the** *d* **orbitals of** Co^{3+} **more widely separated?**

Explanation of Paramagnetic Properties   When the separation of *d* orbitals is large (large SE), the lower set takes 6 electrons before electrons are housed in the upper set. However, when the separation is small (small SE), electrons in the five *d* orbitals stay unpaired until each *d* orbital has at least one electron in it. The separation is sufficiently small so that the five *d* orbitals behave as if they all had the same energy. Thus, a large difference in the paramagnetic properties of complexes may result from differences in the separation. For example,

Complex ion	$Fe(CN)_6{}^{4-}$	$Fe(H_2O)_6{}^{2+}$
Same central ion	Fe^{2+}	Fe^{2+}
	$_{26}Fe^{2+}$ *KL* $3s^2\ 3p^6\ 3d^6\ 4s^0$	$_{26}Fe^{2+}$ *KL* $3s^2\ 3p^6\ 3d^6\ 4s^0$
Number of *d* electrons	6	6
SE	large	small

The order of occupancy for the six electrons is shown, starting with 1 and ending with 6. Experimentally, the magnetic properties of $Fe(H_2O)_6{}^{2+}$ correspond to four unpaired electrons, while the magnetic properties of $Fe(CN)_6{}^{4-}$ correspond to zero unpaired electrons. Hence, $Fe(H_2O)_6{}^{2+}$ is paramagnetic while $Fe(CN)_6{}^{4-}$ is not, even though both contain iron in the same oxidation state.

PROBLEM 8 Fe^{3+} *KL* $3s^2\ 3p^6\ 3d^5\ 4s^0$ **has the same electronic structure both in** $[Fe(CN)_5NO_2]^{3-}$ **(large SE) and in** $FeCl_6{}^{3-}$ **(small SE). How many unpaired electrons are there in each complex ion?**

TRANSITION METAL COMPOUNDS_____21.8

Many transition metals form compounds that do not follow the law of definite composition (page 110). Atoms in these compounds are not present in whole number ratios like 1 to 1 or 2 to 3. For example, iron(II) sulfide is typical of a class of compounds in which some of the atoms may be missing—there is a vacant spot instead of an atom—so that the ratio of atoms does *not* conform to the ideal empirical composition, FeS; iron(II) sulfide, in fact, covers the range $Fe_{0.858}S$ to FeS. These small deviations are essential, however, for the preparation of semiconductors (page 647) by doping highly purified nonconductors.

Such compounds are referred to as nonstoichiometric.

Titanium absorbs hydrogen to form a hydride, TiH_x, where *x* is a variable number. A palladium cathode can absorb 1000 times its volume of hydrogen. The

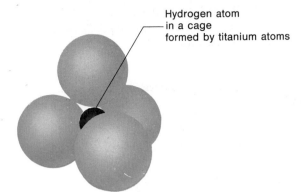

Hydrogen atom in a cage formed by titanium atoms

FIGURE 21.5 Titanium hydride, TiH_x, consists of titanium atoms with absorbed hydrogen atoms located in some of the holes between titanium atoms.

efficiency of solid metals like platinum, palladium, and nickel in catalyzing reactions involving hydrogen is due largely to their ability to absorb hydrogen. In reality, the hydrogen gas is adsorbed on the surface of the metal, where it dissociates into atoms. The hydrogen atoms then diffuse into the solid and occupy the empty spaces*—the holes—in the structure of the metal, as shown in Fig. 21.5. Another example is the gaseous reaction $CO + H_2O \longrightarrow CO_2 + H_2$, catalyzed by a solid with oxygen vacancies. A water molecule is reduced by filling an oxygen vacancy, while a carbon monoxide molecule is oxidized by picking up an oxygen atom and so creating a vacancy in the solid. This is crudely represented as

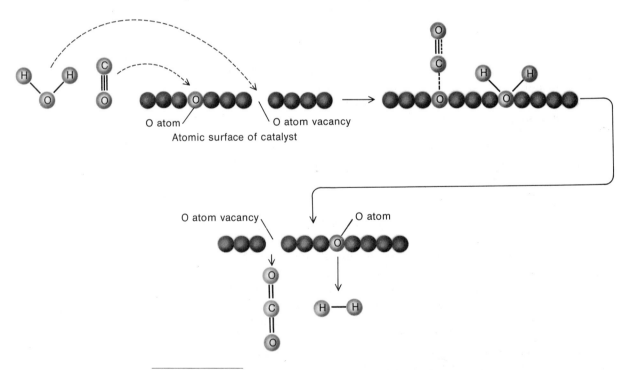

---

*These holes are called *interstices* and the hydrides are known as **interstitial compounds;** they are also called "cage compounds," since the hydrogen may be visualized as being trapped in a "cage" formed by the atoms of the metal.

Other small atoms whose size permits them to occupy empty spaces between the atoms of transition metals include nitrogen (forming nitrides), boron (forming borides), and carbon (forming carbides). Since the arrangement of the metal atoms in these compounds is not much disturbed, the compounds possess characteristic metallic properties, conductivity and luster. Generally speaking, they are very hard and have very high melting points. They are also generally chemically inert (thermodynamically and kinetically stable).

Some compounds of the lanthanides (L) and $3d$ transition metals (T) of composition LT_5, such as $SmCo_5$ and $LaNi_5$, are the most powerful but also most expensive magnets made. As magnetism becomes more important in industry, these substances will find significant applications. These magnets are presently used as "magnetic inspectors" to accept or reject paramagnetic materials and to lift out defective circuits on small wafers containing hundreds of circuits for use in electronic watches, computers, and communication devices. Red blood cells containing paramagnetic hemoglobin (page 665) may be separated from other blood components by magnetically attracting the hemoglobin to an appropriate filter. Also, the U.S. Department of Transportation has contracted for a passenger train to run without wheels on a magnetic (air) cushion. Magnetohydrodynamic (MHD) generators (page 308), successfully operating in the U.S.S.R., and the generation of power through nuclear fusion (page 544) require powerful magnetic materials. No material exists that can resist the high temperatures required for fusion without vaporization. Hence, magnetic fields, "magnetic bottles," will be used to confine the nuclei and electrons away from the walls of the container. Magnetic purification of polluted waters (pages 201, 617) and magnetic concentration of metal ores utilize very powerful magnets to attract paramagnetic components.

Removal of 98 % of the pyritic sulfur in coal by magnetic separation is based on the conversion of FeS_2 to highly paramagnetic pyrrhotite, Fe_7S_8.

EPILOG

Metallic sodium, a characteristic member of the alkali family, is strongly electropositive; it tends to give up its $3s^1$ electron with great ease, forming the familiar Na^+ cation. It reacts violently with the halogens, forming ionic halides; and it easily reduces water, forming H_2 and OH^-. Its standard electrode potential is a respectable -2.71 volts. In fact, sodium exists in nature only as its cation. The drive for the reaction $Na^+(g) + Na^-(g) \longrightarrow 2Na(c)$ is so strong ($\Delta G \ll 0$) that the possibility of the synthesis of sodium in the -1 oxidation state, like the synthesis of compounds of the noble gases (page 273), was never seriously considered—until recently.

It has been known for many years that the alkali metals exist as cations in the presence of solvated electrons in liquid ammonia:

$$Na(c) + NH_3 \longrightarrow Na^+(NH_3) + e^-(NH_3)$$

In fact, the characteristic blue color of these solutions is attributed to the absorption of red photons by the solvated electrons. So, even if $Na(NH_3)$ picked up an $e^-(NH_3)$, the probability that $Na^+(NH_3)$ and $Na^-(NH_3)$ would annihilate each

other is too great to imagine the isolation of the anion. On the other hand, a complexing agent capable of surrounding and caging the cation may be able to protect it from the anion. This has been accomplished (James Dye, 1974) by trapping the alkali cation in a hole in the molecule $C_{18}H_{36}O_6N_2$, called cryptand:

$$2Na(sol) + C_{18}H_{36}O_6N_2(sol) \longrightarrow$$
$$(NaC_{18}H_{36}O_6N_2)^+(sol) + Na^-(sol)$$

Ethylenediamine, $H_2NCH_2CH_2NH_2$, a compound that is related to ammonia, is the solvent used. When the reaction mixture is cooled to $-15\,°C$, a golden colored crystalline solid consisting of $(NaC_{18}H_{36}O_6N_2)^+$ and Na^- ions is obtained (Color Plate VIIIB).

The 18 sp^3 carbon atoms and the six oxygen atoms are bonded in three zigzag chains that form a cavity, firmly holding and isolating the Na^+ cation from the Na^-, $3s^2$, anion. Each chain contains six carbon atoms and two oxygen atoms attached to the two nitrogen atoms (Fig. 21.6). Cryptand thus serves as an efficient shield in protecting the Na ions from each other so that the driving force

($\Delta G \approx -21$ kJ) now favors the formation of the ionic solid. The six O atoms serve as Lewis bases, giving the caged Na^+ a coordination number of six.

Similar compounds of potassium, rubidium, and cesium have also been prepared. Since the size of the cavity in cryptand can be altered, it should be possible to prepare compounds containing Li^-. In fact, Jean-Marie Lehn synthesized cryptand (1969) and showed that it forms very stable cage complexes with cations like Rb^+, Cu^{2+}, and Ba^{2+}; for example, $\Delta G \approx -84$ kJ for $Ba^{2+} +$

$C_{18}H_{36}O_6N_2 \longrightarrow (BaC_{18}H_{36}O_6N_2)^{2+}$. The synthesis of cryptand-like compounds containing a variety of divalent ions is also possible.

A number of similar types of compounds are involved in the transport of ions across cell membranes. The antibiotic nonactin, for example, functions by entrapping and transporting Na^+ into bacteria. The resulting increased osmotic pressure causes rupture of the bacterial cell wall.

"Der is gold in dem dere hills"—for those who search forbidden paths.

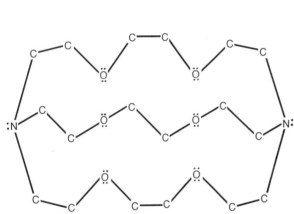

FIGURE 21.6 (a) Representation of cryptand, three zigzag chains of carbon and oxygen atoms attached to two nitrogen atoms; (b) full space-filling model of cryptand with two chains pushed aside to reveal the cavity. (Photo by Peter Harris, CUNY.)

PROBLEMS

9 Vocabulary Define and illustrate the following: (a) coordination number; (b) ligancy; (c) ligand; (d) central atom (ion); (e) splitting energy, SE; (f) isomers; (g) geometric isomers; (h) structural isomers.

10 Complex ions (a) Explain the statement: "Complex ion formation is nothing more than a Lewis acid-base reaction." (b) Illustrate this statement.

11 (a) Give the coordination number of the central metal atom in each of the following compounds: (i) $[Cu(NH_3)_4]Br_2$, (ii) $[Ag(NH_3)_2]Br$, (iii) $[Co(NH_3)_6]Br_3$, (iv) $K_2[PtBr_4]$, (v) $Na_2[ZnBr_4]$. (b) In which of these will $Ag^+(aq)$ precipitate $Br^-(aq)$ as $AgBr(c)$?

12 Give (a) the coordination number and (b) the oxidation number of the central metal atom (ion) in each of the following: (i) $[Co(NH_3)_5Cl]Br_2$, (ii) $Na_2[PtCl_4]$, (iii) $K_4[Fe(CN)_6]$, (iv) $[Ag(OH)_2]^-$,

(v) $[Ag(NH_3)_2]^+$, (vi) $[AgCl_4]^{3-}$, (vii) $[AgF_4]^{3-}$, (viii) $[Cr(NH_3)_4ClNO_2]NO_3$. (c) How many d electrons are in each of the central atoms (ions)?

13 (a) A compound, molecular formula $CuN_4H_{12}Cl_2$, (i) does not react with HCl, (ii) has an electrical conductivity corresponding to 3 ions per molecule, and (iii) gives 2 moles of AgCl per mole of compound when it reacts with $AgNO_3$. Give the formula of the complex ion. (b) Another compound, $(NH_4)_2[NiCl_4]$, (i) reacts with $NaOH(aq)$, (ii) has an electrical conductivity corresponding to 3 ions per molecule, and (iii) gives no AgCl when $AgNO_3$ is added. Write the formula of this complex ion.

14 Crystal field theory Explain the following: (a) $Cu(NH_3)_4^{2+}$ is deep blue, while $Cu(H_2O)_4^{2+}$ is light bluish-green and $CuCl_4^{2-}$ is green. (The eyes see green when the wavelength 7000 Å is absorbed.) (b) $[CoF_6]^{3-}$ and $[Cr(NH_3)_6]^{3+}$ are paramagnetic, while $[Co(CN)_6]^{3-}$ is not paramagnetic.

15 Aqueous solutions of copper salts have a characteristic bluish-green color. Addition of concentrated hydrochloric acid changes the color to green. Explain in terms of crystal field theory.

16 Give the distribution of the d electrons of the central ion according to crystal field theory (a) for $Fe(CN)_6^{4-}$, not paramagnetic; (b) for $Fe(CN)_6^{3-}$, paramagnetic; (c) for $Co(CN)_6^{3-}$ (large SE); (d) for $Cr(H_2O)_6^{2+}$ (small SE).

17 (a) The $Co(H_2O)_6^{2+}$ complex is pink (absorbs around 5000 Å). Would you expect a change in color when the H_2O ligands are replaced by CN^- ions, inducing a greater splitting energy? Explain. (b) If your answer is yes, would you expect the color to change toward blue or toward yellow? Explain in terms of crystal field theory.

18 Shape From the following complex ions, pick the one most likely to be (a) octahedral, (b) linear, (c) tetrahedral, and (d) square planar: (i) $[PdCl_4]^{2-}$, (ii) $[PtCl_6]^{2-}$, (iii) $[Zn(NH_3)_4]^{2+}$, and (iv) $[AuCl_2]^-$.

19 Isomers (a) Draw the geometric isomers of square planar $[Ni(CN)_2Cl_2]$. (b) Does square planar $[PtI_3CN]$ have any isomers? (c) Draw at least one other structural isomer of

$$
\begin{array}{ccc}
H & & H \\
| & \cdot\cdot & | \\
H-C-&S&-C-H \\
| & \cdot\cdot & | \\
H & & H
\end{array}
$$

20 Pick out the square planar arrangement(s) that has (have) two isomers: (i) $[Pd(NH_3)_2(SCN)_2]$, (ii) $[Pd(NH_3)(SCN)_3]^-$, (iii) $[PdI_2Br_2]^{2-}$, (iv) $[PdI_3Br]^{2-}$.

21 A complex absorbs photons with a wavelength of 7000 Å ($f = 4.29 \times 10^{14}$ s^{-1}). Calculate the splitting energy, SE, for the complex in (a) erg/particle, (b) kcal/mole, (c) kJ/mole. Constants: $h = 6.63 \times 10^{-27}$ erg s/particle; 1 cal $= 4.18 \times 10^7$ erg; 1 mole $= 6.02 \times 10^{23}$ particles; 1 cal $= 4.18$ J.

22 Hemoglobin 4.00 g of hemoglobin combines with 5.40 ml of oxygen, O_2, at STP. Find the number of grams of O_2 carried by one gram of hemoglobin.

23 Chromate pollution Removal of chromate salts (used for corrosion control and in chrome plating baths) from industrial waste water is necessary (chromates are carcinogenic) and may be accomplished as follows. Fe^{2+} is electrochemically produced from Fe, followed by the aqueous reactions

$$HCrO_4^- + H^+ + Fe^{2+} \longrightarrow Cr^{3+} + Fe^{3+} + H_2O$$

$$E^{\circ}_{cell} = +0.425 \text{ volt}$$

$$Cr^{3+} + OH^- \rightleftharpoons Cr(OH)_3(c) \qquad K = 1.4 \times 10^{30}$$

(a) Balance these two equations and calculate K for the oxidation-reduction reaction. (b) Calculate the number of moles and milligrams of Cr^{3+} per liter of water (solution) remaining after removal as $Cr(OH)_3(c)$ at pH $= 8.50$.

24 Library Read one of the following:
(a) "Alfred Werner's Coordination Theory," George Kauffman, *Education in Chemistry,* volume 4, 1967, page 4.
(b) "Chelation in Medicine," John Schubert, *Scientific American,* May 1966, page 40.
(c) "A Simple Approach to Crystal Field Theory," Robert Johnson, *Journal of Chemical Education,* volume 42, 1965, page 147.
(d) "Hemoglobin: Isolation and Chemical Properties," S. Russo and R. Sorstokke, *Journal of Chemical Education,* volume 50, 1973, page 347.
(e) "Cancer Chemotherapy: Renewed Interest in Platinum Compounds," *Science,* volume 192, 21 May 1976, page 774.
(f) "Effect of Carbon Monoxide on Human Physiological Processes," David Bartlett and Steven Horvath, *Proceedings of the Conference on Health Effects of Air Pollutants,* National Academy of Sciences, U.S. Government Printing Office, Washington, D.C., November 1973, pages 103–138.

ADDITIONAL PROBLEMS

25 Match one of the given colors with one of the following complex ions: $Co(NH_3)_6^{3+}$, CoF_6^{3-}, $Co(CN)_6^{3-}$; colors: green, orange, yellow. Explain your choice.

26 In the preparation of iron(II) oxide under different oxygen pressures, compounds of varying composition are obtained. One such compound, density 5.163 g/ml, has a ratio of 0.2541 g Fe to 0.08000 g O. Calculate its empirical formula, using atomic weights 55.85 and 16.00 and *retaining three significant figures* in your final answer.

27 (a) Ammonia and water form strong hydrogen bonds in two ways (page 264):

$$H_3N\text{---}HOH \qquad \text{and} \qquad H_2NH\text{---}OH_2$$

Are these isomers? Explain. (b) What is the coordination number of N in NH_5?

28 Similarities are found among transition metals in going across a period in the periodic table as well as going down a group. For the representative metals such similarities exist only in going downward in a group. Explain.

29 In the absence of oxygen, Fe(II) d orbitals in hemoglobin are not greatly separated. When Fe(II) binds oxygen, the separation energy becomes large. How many unpaired electrons are in each complex? Is the paramagnetic property of Fe(II) changed on binding with oxygen molecules?

30 The five d orbitals of a central metal ion are subjected to the *same repulsive force* (spherical electric field). Will they be repelled to higher or lower energies, or remain unaffected? If repelled, will they be split?

31 (a) The d orbitals in Fe(II) in hemoglobin contain six electrons, four of which are unpaired. Is the splitting energy, SE, induced by the porphyrin molecule (Fig. 21.1, page 665) comparatively large or small? (b) Copper(III) complexes have been prepared, many of which are not stable in aqueous solutions. One of these, comparatively stable in water, has a square planar structure that can be represented as:

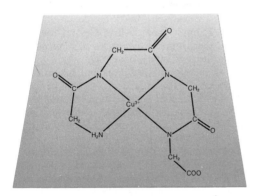

The five d orbitals are split (separated) into three distinct levels as shown:

$$\overline{\quad d_{x^2-y^2}\quad}$$

$$\overline{\quad d_{z^2}\quad}$$

$$\overline{\ d_{xy}\ }\ \overline{\ d_{yz}\ }\ \overline{\ d_{xz}\ }$$

Is this complex paramagnetic? What is the coordination number of the Cu^{3+} in this complex?

32 In the laboratories of the University of North Carolina, an insoluble ruthenium(II) complex, coordination number 6,

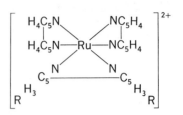

reacts with water in the presence of sunlight. Assume the following mechanism (*gs* means ground state and *es* means excited state):

$$Ru\ complex(gs) + hf \longrightarrow Ru\ complex(es^1)$$

$$Ru\ complex(es^1) + H_2O(l) \longrightarrow Ru\ complex(H_2O)(es^2)$$

electron transfer
$$Ru\ complex(H_2O)(es^2) \longrightarrow Ru\ complexO(es^3) + H_2(g)$$

electron transfer
$$Ru\ complexO(es^3) \longrightarrow Ru\ complex(gs) + \tfrac{1}{2}O_2(g)$$

(a) What is the overall reaction? Besides the intellectual and theoretical interests, does there appear to be an economic interest? (b) $\Delta H = -285\ kJ$ for the reaction $H_2(g) + \tfrac{1}{2}O_2(g) \longrightarrow H_2O(l)$. To transfer one mole of electrons to H_2O, what should be the minimum difference in kJ between the complex energy in the ground state and the energy in the excited state?

33 (a) What is the oxidation number of Ru in the complex $Ru_3(CO)_{12}$, triruthenium dodecacarbonyl, a catalyst for the important commercial reaction for the production of hydrogen in aqueous solution, $CO + H_2O \xrightarrow{100\ °C} CO_2 + H_2$? (b) Compare the temperature condition in this reaction with that given on page 629, and discuss the advantage of using this catalyst.

ANSWERS

1 (a) and (b) i, iii, v
2 (a) $Pt(NH_3)_4^{2+}$, (b) $Cu(OH)_4^{2-}$, (c) $AgCl_2^-$, (d) $Fe(CN)_6^{3-}$
3 (a) (i) square planar, (ii) tetrahedral, (iii) octahedral, (iv) planar
   (b) (i) 4, (ii) 4, (iii) 6, (iv) 4
4 $Zn(NH_3)_4^{2+}$, $2Cl^-$

5 (a) one, (b) two, (c) geometric
6 ionic
7 $[Co(NH_3)_5SO_4]^+$
8 1 and 5
11 (a) (i) 4, (ii) 2, (iii) 6, (iv) 4, (v) 4;
   (b) i, ii, and iii

12 (a) (i) 6, (ii) 4, (iii) 6, (iv) 2, (v) 2, (vi) 4, (vii) 4, (viii) 6;
(b) (i) $+3$, (ii) $+2$, (iii) $+2$, (iv) $+1$, (v) $+1$,
(vi) $+1$, (vii) $+1$, (viii) $+3$;
(c) (i) d^6, (ii) d^8, (iii) d^6, (iv) d^{10}, (v) d^{10}, (vi) d^{10},
(vii) d^{10}, (viii) d^3

13 (a) $Cu(NH_3)_4^{2+}$, $2Cl^-$
(b) $2NH_4^+$, $[NiCl_4]^{2-}$

14 (a) NH_3 largest SE, H_2O smaller SE, Cl^- smallest SE

15 H_2O larger SE, Cl^- smaller SE

16 (a) (c) 0; (b) 1; (d) 4 unpaired

17 (a) yes, (b) yellow

18 (a) octahedral: ii
(b) linear: iv
(c) tetrahedral: iii
(d) square planar: i

19 (b) no

(c)
$$H-\overset{\overset{\displaystyle H}{|}}{\underset{\underset{\displaystyle H}{|}}{C}}-\overset{\overset{\displaystyle H}{|}}{\underset{\underset{\displaystyle H}{|}}{C}}-S-H$$

20 i, iii

21 (a) 2.84×10^{-12} erg/particle
(b) 40.9 kcal/mole
(c) 171 kJ/mole

22 1.93×10^{-3} g

23 (a) $K = 3.5 \times 10^{21}$
(b) 2.3×10^{-14} mole/ℓ, 1.2×10^{-9} mg/ℓ

25 $Co(NH_3)_6^{3+}$ (orange), large SE
CoF_6^{3-} (green), small SE
$CO(CN)_6^{3-}$ (yellow), largest SE

26 $Fe_{0.910}O$

27 (a) yes, (b) 5

29 4 and 0, yes

30 higher, not split

31 (a) small, (b) no, 4

32 (a) $H_2O + hf \longrightarrow H_2 + \frac{1}{2} O_2$
(b) 143 kJ/mole electrons

33 (a) zero

GLOSSARY

central atom or ion The metal atom or ion to which anions or molecules are bonded in a coordination compound.

complex Same as coordination compound; see **coordination compound.**

coordination compound A compound containing a metal atom or ion bonded to a number of anions or molecules.

coordination number of an atom or ion The number of atoms directly bonded to the central atom or ion in a complex; the number is usually two, four or six.

crystal field theory The theory that studies the effect of ligands on the energies of the d orbitals of the central atom or ion in a complex.

geometric isomers Isomers which have different arrangements of the same atoms bonded to a given atom, such as *cis-* and *trans-*. See **isomers.**

isomers Compounds whose molecules are composed of the same number and kind of atoms but whose properties differ because the atoms are differently arranged.

ligand The anion or molecule that combines with the central metal atom or ion in forming a coordination compound.

nonstoichiometric compounds Compounds that deviate from the law of constant composition.

structural isomers Isomers which have different structural formulas; that is, the same atoms are bonded in a different sequence, such as —C—N—C— and —N—C—C—.

THE CHEMISTRY OF CARBON COMPOUNDS

22

INTRODUCTION_____22.1

"Chemical compounds that originate from living (organic) sources are fundamentally different from those compounds obtained from non-living (inorganic) matter." This view of matter was held by most chemists until the middle of the 19th century. Atoms in *organic compounds,* it was believed, were held together by a "vital force" in addition to electrical forces. This vital force, somehow associated with life processes, could only originate from living things. But unlike other recognized forces (gravitational, electrical, nuclear), no quantitative measure or description of this force had ever been made. Nevertheless, theory held that without the presence of this vital force, an organic compound could not exist. The synthesis (preparation) of organic compounds was therefore declared impossible in the absence of life or compounds extracted from living things. Practically, this meant, for example, that ethyl alcohol, CH_3CH_2OH, a substance produced by bacterial fermentation of sugars, could not be prepared from the elements carbon, hydrogen, and oxygen. However, the vital force theory was gradually abandoned after Fredrich Wöhler (1828) and, particularly, Hermann Kolbe (1845) succeeded in synthesizing organic compounds in the absence of living sources. Kolbe, for example, synthesized acetic acid, a product of bacterial fermentation, from the elements carbon, hydrogen, and oxygen. Of course, the synthesized acetic acid is *exactly* the same substance as the acetic acid obtained from natural fermentation processes. Soon after, Pierre Berthelot synthesized dozens of organic compounds, including methyl and ethyl alcohols, benzene, and acetylene. Today, a vast variety of naturally occurring compounds, including hormones, vitamins, and antibiotics, are routinely synthesized. In addition, chemists have synthesized many compounds not found naturally, such as plastics (Chap. 23), oils, antibiotics (*tetracycline*), drugs (*aspirin* and *Novocaine*), and fibers (*Dacron* and *Nylon*).

The importance of structural formula determination cannot be overemphasized. Structural formula determination nearly always precedes synthesis. For example, convincing experimental evidence supports the hypothesis that sleep is brought on by a substance produced in the brain during long periods of wakefulness. All efforts are now directed at solving the structure formula of the substance. Without this knowledge, synthesis of the substance is practically impossible.

An accurate definition of **organic chemistry** is neither available nor necessary; it is generally referred to as the study of the chemistry of carbon compounds. Practically every element in the periodic table has been combined into molecules that contain at least one carbon atom, so that classification of compounds into "organic" and "inorganic" is meaningless. A molecule is a molecule; it is not an inorganic molecule or an organic molecule. The compound

is of interest to many differently classified chemists. Since most chemical reactions involve changes in covalent bonds, many prefer to define organic chemistry as the chemistry of the covalent bond.

In addition to the synthesis of compounds, the study of organic chemistry provides basic insight into and the foundation for understanding the bonding, molecular structure, and reaction mechanisms of the complex substances involved in molecular biology (Fig. 8.9, and pages 265 and 293).

Organic chemistry is an exciting subject, but it is so vast that we shall restrict this chapter to several of the most common types of compounds and the general nature of the bonding in these compounds.

The reader is advised to use molecular models (page 571) in studying this chapter.

22.2 THE BONDING OF CARBON: ALKANE HYDROCARBONS

Carbon combines with many other elements. But the carbon atom is unusual because it forms compounds in which carbon atoms are linked together in a variety of shapes and sizes unequaled by any other element. Some molecules contain only one carbon atom, while others may contain over 1000 carbon atoms linked together in the form of chains, rings, and combinations of chains and rings. Of the known compounds (about 6.0×10^6), at least 95 % contain carbon atoms. Yet, in almost all of them the bonding of carbon is covalent,* limited largely to the use of sp^3 (tetrahedral), sp^2 (triangular planar), and sp (linear) atomic orbitals (Chap. 18).

In methane, CH_4, the carbon atom uses four sp^3 AO's, each of which interacts with the s orbital of an H atom, forming four sigma (σ) bonds (page 575). A "ball and stick" model of methane is shown in Fig. 22.1. In ethane, C_2H_6, H_3C-CH_3, the

Reminder: The self-interaction (hybridization) of atomic orbitals (page 573) is a theoretical process, not a real one.

---

*The energy required to remove four electrons is prohibitive (3405 kcal/mole); C^{4+} ionic bonding is therefore unknown. C^{4-} bonding is extremely rare; only beryllium carbide, Be_2C, and aluminum carbide, Al_4C_3, are known to contain the C^{4-} ion, and on hydrolysis they yield methane, CH_4 ($Al_4C_3(c) + 12H_2O \longrightarrow 4Al(OH)_3(c) + 3CH_4(g)$). Calcium acetylide, CaC_2, on the other hand, contains the acetylide ion, C_2^{2-}, $:C\equiv C:^{2-}$, and on hydrolysis yields acetylene ($CaC_2(c) + 2H_2O \longrightarrow Ca(OH)_2(c) + C_2H_2(g)$).

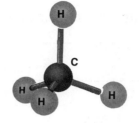 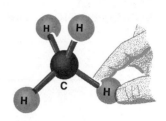

FIGURE 22.1 Ball and stick model of methane, a tetrahedral molecule.

carbon-carbon single (σ) bond is formed by the overlap (fusion) of an sp^3 AO from each C atom; each of the remaining six sp^3 AO's overlaps with an H atom, forming six σ bonds (page 576). See Fig. 22.2.

In propane, C_3H_8, H_3C—CH_2—CH_3, the carbon atoms are similarly linked together by σ bonds. The resulting carbon linkage, illustrated in Fig. 22.2, is a "zig-zag" arrangement, traditionally referred to as a "*chain*" of carbon atoms. This chain of carbon atoms, it seems, can be extended without limit.

For convenience, however, we write chains of carbon atoms in straight lines, C—C—C and C—C—C—C.

Methane, ethane, and propane are typical hydrocarbons, compounds containing only carbon and hydrogen. They are also typical **alkanes,** hydrocarbons in which the carbon atoms have only single bonds, form only chains and tetrahedral arrangements, and therefore use only sp^3 AO's for bonding.

Butane, C_4H_{10}, and pentane, C_5H_{12}, two more typical alkanes, can be represented as

$$CH_3CH_2CH_2CH_3 \quad \text{or}$$

$$H-\overset{\displaystyle H}{\underset{\displaystyle H}{C}}-\overset{\displaystyle H}{\underset{\displaystyle H}{C}}-\overset{\displaystyle H}{\underset{\displaystyle H}{C}}-\overset{\displaystyle H}{\underset{\displaystyle H}{C}}-H$$

structural (electronic) formula

$$CH_3CH_2CH_2CH_2CH_3 \quad \text{or}$$

$$H-\overset{\displaystyle H}{\underset{\displaystyle H}{C}}-\overset{\displaystyle H}{\underset{\displaystyle H}{C}}-\overset{\displaystyle H}{\underset{\displaystyle H}{C}}-\overset{\displaystyle H}{\underset{\displaystyle H}{C}}-\overset{\displaystyle H}{\underset{\displaystyle H}{C}}-H$$

Experimentally, however, two *different* butanes, two isomers (page 664) with the

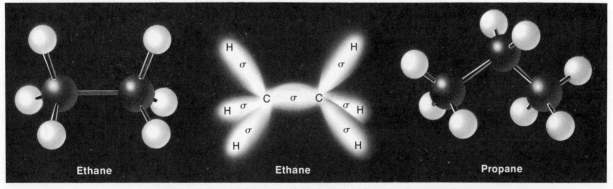

FIGURE 22.2 Ball and stick representation of ethane and propane, both tetrahedral molecules. The MO description of ethane is also shown.

TABLE 22.1
SOME PHYSICAL PROPERTIES OF THE ISOMERS
OF BUTANE, C_4H_{10}

	BUTANE (NORMAL BUTANE)	ISOBUTANE (METHYLPROPANE)
b.p.	−0.50 °C	−12 °C
m.p.	−138 °C	−159 °C
Solubility in 100 ml of ethyl alcohol, room temperature	1813 ml	1320 ml

same molecular formula C_4H_{10}, are detected. They show differences in their chemical and physical properties, listed in Table 22.1.

We can write two equally correct structural formulas for C_4H_{10}

butane   isobutane

Both are consistent with the octet rule and the common valence of carbon (four). In butane, the maximum number of carbon atoms attached to any other carbon atom is *two;* in isobutane, *three* other carbon atoms are attached to the middle carbon atom, illustrated in Fig. 22.3. It is impossible to make one model look like the other *without* breaking chemical bonds; the molecules cannot be made to fit (superimpose) on each other. The molecule labeled butane is also called *normal (n-)* butane.

PROBLEM 1   Make models (page 571) of the two isomers of butane.

A ball and stick model shows the arrangement of atoms in three dimensions, but it does not show the relative distances between atoms, the packing of the atoms in molecules. Space-filling models (Fig. 22.3 b) show that the atoms in isobutane are more crowded together, giving it a general appearance of a round (spherical) molecule, while *n*-butane appears as a zig-zag chain.

As the number of carbon atoms increases in a molecule, the possibilities for isomerism increase very rapidly. There are, for example, three isomers of pentane, C_5H_{12}; five isomers of hexane, C_6H_{14}; nine isomers of heptane, C_7H_{16}; 75 isomers of decane, $C_{10}H_{22}$; and 366,319 isomers of eicosane, $C_{20}H_{42}$.

Observe that the addition of a CH_2 group to methane, CH_4, yields ethane, C_2H_6, and that the addition of CH_2 to ethane yields propane, C_3H_8. The molecular formulas for the alkanes can therefore be generalized as C_nH_{2n+2}, where n is the number of carbon atoms. The alkanes thus make up a **homologous series,** a series of compounds in which the type of bonding is similar and whose molecular formulas can be expressed by a general formula. Some members of the alkane series are listed in Table 22.2. Typical of homologous series, the alkanes show a regular change in physical properties as the number of carbon atoms increases (Table 22.2). Also characteristic of a homologous series, the alkanes have similar chemical properties. For example, at room temperature they are kinetically stable; they do not react with oxygen or chlorine, or with acids and bases. For this reason, very reactive metals such as potassium and sodium are stored under liquid alkanes (kerosene). At higher temperatures, however, alkanes burn in excess oxygen to form carbon dioxide and

From the Greek words hepta (seven), deka (ten), and eico (twenty).

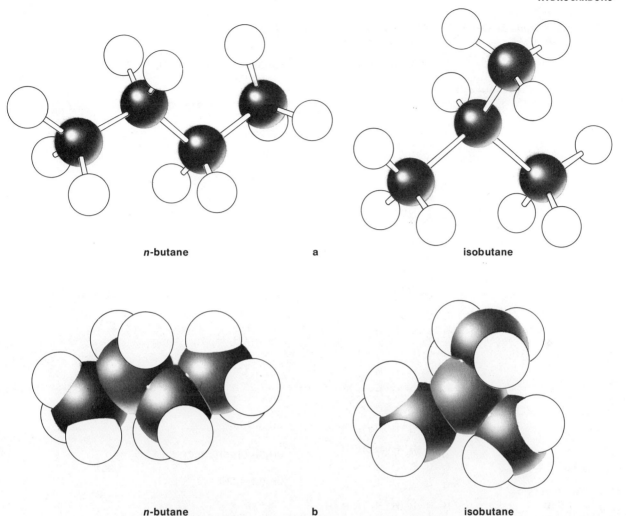

FIGURE 22.3 (a) Ball and stick models and (b) the full space (space-filling) models of the isomers of butane, C_4H_{10}. Note that the "chain" of carbon atoms is *not* straight.

water. In the presence of ultraviolet (strong sunlight) radiation, chlorine or bromine atoms displace hydrogen atoms (page 517):

$$CH_4(g) + Cl_2(g) + hf \text{ (photon)} \xrightarrow{25\,°C} CH_3Cl(g) + HCl(g)$$

methane   *chloromethane*
                                                (methyl chloride)

In similar fashion, the remaining hydrogen atoms may be displaced:

$$CH_3Cl + Cl_2 \longrightarrow CH_2Cl_2(l) + HCl$$

dichloromethane

$$CH_2Cl_2 + Cl_2 \longrightarrow CHCl_3(l) + HCl$$

trichloromethane
(chloroform)

$$CHCl_3 + Cl_2 \longrightarrow CCl_4(l) + HCl$$

tetrachloromethane
(carbon tetrachloride)

683

TABLE 22.2
BOILING POINTS OF NORMAL ALKANES, GENERAL
FORMULA C_nH_{2n+2}, A TYPICAL HOMOLOGOUS SERIES

NAME	MOLECULAR FORMULA	STRUCTURAL FORMULA	CONDENSED STRUCTURAL FORMULA*	BOILING POINT, °C
Methane	CH_4			-161.7
Ethane	C_2H_6		CH_3CH_3	-88.6
Propane	C_3H_8		$CH_3CH_2CH_3$	-42.2
n-Butane	C_4H_{10}		$CH_3CH_2CH_2CH_3$ or $CH_3(CH_2)_2CH_3$	-0.5
n-Pentane	C_5H_{12}		$CH_3CH_2CH_2CH_2CH_3$ or $CH_3(CH_2)_3CH_3$	36.1
n-Hexane	C_6H_{14}		$CH_3CH_2CH_2CH_2CH_2CH_3$ or $CH_3(CH_2)_4CH_3$	68.7
n-Heptane	C_7H_{16}		$CH_3CH_2CH_2CH_2CH_2CH_2CH_3$ or $CH_3(CH_2)_5CH_3$	98.4
n-Octane	C_8H_{18}		$CH_3(CH_2)_6CH_3$	125.7
n-Nonane	C_9H_{20}		$CH_3(CH_2)_7CH_3$	150.7
n-Decane	$C_{10}H_{22}$		$CH_3(CH_2)_8CH_3$	174.0

* Abbreviated structural formulas, called *condensed structural formulas*, are often used in place of structural (electronic) formulas. The $(CH_2)_n$ notation refers to n CH_2 units in a chain.

These reactions in which one atom is substituted for another are called **substitution reactions.**

Fortunately, because the compounds in a homologous series show similar properties, the study of the chemistry of carbon compounds may be confined to one or two members of a series instead of examining each compound individually. While the alkanes occur without a known limit to the value of n, the corresponding compounds of the other Group IVA elements form very limited series owing to the weakness of the metal-metal bond.

PROBLEM 2 **(a)** Write the molecular formula of dodecane, an alkane containing 12 carbon atoms per molecule. **(b)** Write a balanced equation for the combustion of pentane, C_5H_{12}, in excess oxygen. **(c)** Write a balanced equation for the substitution of one hydrogen atom of propane, C_3H_8, by bromine.

THE POSITION OF GROUPS OF ATOMS IN MOLECULES————————22.3

Figure 22.2 shows a ball and stick model of ethane, and reproduces the molecular orbital description of the molecule (page 681). If you were to make such a ball and stick model, you would find that you can easily and freely rotate any one end (CH_3 group) about the stick holding the two carbon atoms together. Indeed, the electronic cloud of the carbon-carbon sigma (σ) bond is evenly (symmetrically) distributed about the bond axis, the line between the two carbon atoms. This strongly suggests that the CH_3 group can be freely rotated. The arrangement of one CH_3 group relative to the other, it seems, should have no effect on the physical properties of ethane. But experimentally it is found that the arrangements do affect the properties of ethane. Freely rotating groups represent a higher degree of disorder (higher entropy) than is found experimentally for ethane. Thus, two arrangements of the two CH_3 groups are shown in Fig. 22.4. In Fig. 22.4 a, looking along the carbon-carbon bond, the three hydrogen atoms on one carbon atom eclipse (cover over, as the Earth sometimes eclipses the moon) the three hydrogen atoms on the other carbon atom. In Fig. 22.4 b, the arrangement of the hydrogen atoms is staggered; that is, one set of "rabbit-ears" (page 572) on one carbon atom points to the floor, while the set of rabbit-ears on the other carbon atom points to the ceiling. The change from the staggered to the eclipsed arrangement requires 3 kcal/mole, another way of saying that the eclipsed is less stable than the staggered arrangement because of stronger repulsion between the electron clouds of the six carbon-hydrogen bonds:

$$\textit{staggered arrangement} \rightleftharpoons \textit{eclipsed arrangement} \quad \Delta H = +3\,\text{kcal} \quad (1)$$

The energy of activation for this change is so small that the circular change staggered $\longrightarrow$ eclipsed $\longrightarrow$ staggered is extremely rapid. Hence, for most purposes, we can say that practically free rotation occurs about the carbon-carbon single bond. Then, at room temperature, a sample of ethane would contain some molecules in the eclipsed arrangement, some in the staggered arrangement, and some in all of the various arrangements between eclipsed and staggered. These different arrangements are called *conformations;* the eclipsed arrangement is called an *eclipsed conformation* while the staggered is called a *staggered conformation.*

We must stress that the possibility of separating, isolating, and studying each arrangement (conformation) separately is very remote. Thus, *conformations do not represent isomers.* They are not classified as isomers because, unlike isomers, one conformation can be made to look like the other conformation *without* breaking chemical bonds. The positions of the atoms in *n*-butane can be represented by a

number of conformations, for example, C—C—C—C and $\overset{\displaystyle C}{\underset{\displaystyle C}{|}}$ C—C, both a continuous

Hydrogen atoms are omitted for simplicity.

chain of four carbon atoms. But they represent the same substance, *n*-butane, because no chemical bonds are broken during the rotation in going from one conformation to another.

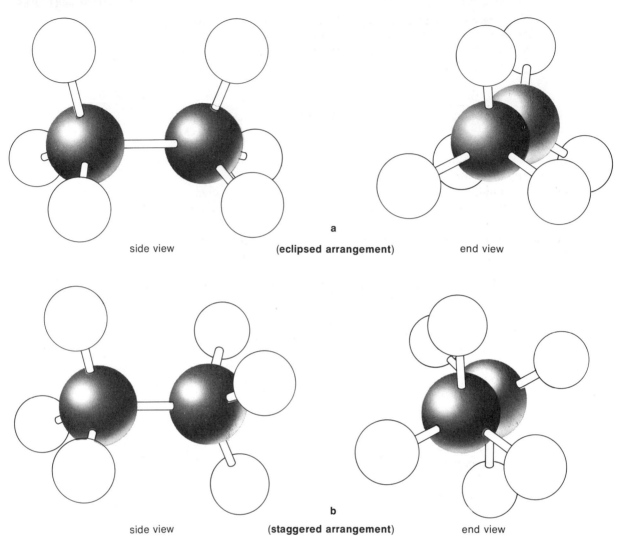

FIGURE 22.4 Two arrangements of the CH₃ groups in ethane: (a) eclipsed arrangement, and (b) staggered arrangement.

PROBLEM 3 For each given pair of molecules, pick the pair(s) (a) that represent the same substance, and (b) that represent isomers:

(i) $H_3C—CH_2$ and $H_3C—CH_2—CH_3$
      |
      CH_3

(ii) H_3C and $H_3C—CH_2—CH_2—CH_2—CH_3$
        $\diagdown$
         CH_2
            $\diagdown$
            $CH_2—CH_2$
                  |
                  CH_3

(iii) $CH_3—CH_2—\overset{\displaystyle H}{\underset{\displaystyle CH_3}{\overset{|}{\underset{|}{C}}}}—CH_3$ and $H_2C—CH_2—CH_2$
                                                              | |
                                                             CH_3 CH_3

With the use of the prefixes *n-* and iso-, we can distinguish between two isomers. It is not practical, however, to use common names for the 75 isomers of decane. In fact, the scientific naming of over a million compounds is still a problem in spite of the efforts of the International Union of Pure and Applied Chemistry (IUPAC). We shall therefore discuss only a few of the basic rules of the IUPAC system:

1. First, find the *longest continuous chain* of carbon atoms and count the atoms in it. The compound is then named as if it were obtained from the *n*-alkane (Table 22.2) with that number of carbon atoms. Thus

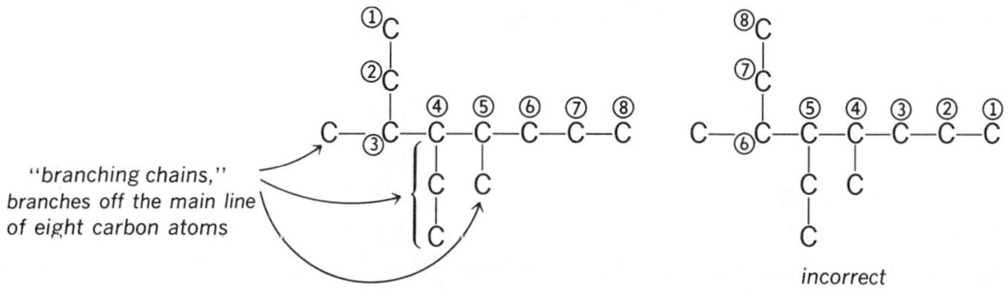

"branching chains," branches off the main line of eight carbon atoms

incorrect

is named as an octane since the longest continuous chain contains eight (circle-numbered) carbon atoms.

2. Number the longest carbon chain starting at the end which places the branching groups on the C atoms having the lowest possible numbers. A group that displaces an H atom on a carbon atom of the longest chain is called a "branch" or a "group" (see above example). In the above example, the first branch appears at the C atom numbered 3. If we had numbered from right to left, the first branch would have appeared at a C atom numbered 4.

3. Name the branches (groups). Each branch (group) is named according to the number of C atoms *it* contains by changing the *ane* ending to *yl*. Thus, CH_3— is called meth*yl*, derived from meth*ane*, and CH_3CH_2— is called eth*yl*, derived from eth*ane*.

4. Locate the groups by using the number of the C atom to which they are attached.

Our example is therefore named 4-ethyl-3-methyl-5-methyloctane, which is shortened to 4-ethyl-3,5-dimethyloctane. Notice that the group names are alphabetically arranged, ethyl before methyl. Other examples follow:

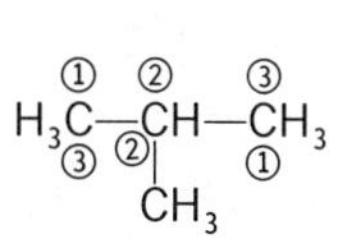

Some other group names are: —NH_2 amino, —Cl chloro, —OH hydroxy, —NO_2 nitro, —Br bromo, —F fluoro.

2-methylpropane* 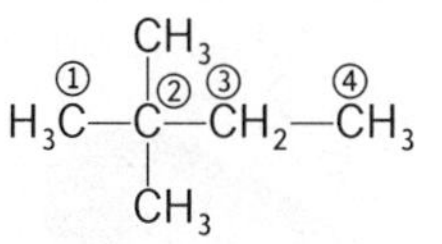   2,2-dimethylbutane   3-bromo-1,2,2-trichlorobutane
                        (*not* 3,3-dimethylbutane)

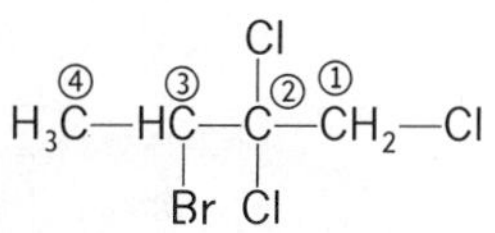

Note the repetition of numbers when the same group appears twice on the same carbon atom. The prefix *di* indicates that a group appears twice as a branch; *tri* indicates that a group appears three times; and *tetra* indicates that it appears four times.

_____

*Note that in this compound, the longest chain can be numbered from right to left *or* left to right. In both cases, the CH_3— group appears on carbon 2. Therefore, the number is frequently omitted.

PROBLEM 4   Name the following compounds by the IUPAC system:

(a) $CH_3-CH_2-\underset{\underset{Cl}{|}}{\overset{\overset{CH_3}{|}}{C}}-\underset{\underset{Br}{|}}{\overset{\overset{H}{|}}{C}}-\underset{\underset{Cl}{|}}{\overset{\overset{CH_3}{|}}{C}}-\underset{\underset{Br}{|}}{\overset{\overset{H}{|}}{C}}-CH_3$

(b) $CH_3-\underset{\underset{Br}{|}}{\overset{\overset{\overset{\overset{CH_3}{|}}{CH_2}}{|}}{C}}-CH_2-CH_3$

PROBLEM 5   Highly branched hydrocarbons are much better fuels for automobile (piston) engines than are straight-chain compounds. An arbitrary "octane number" rating, ranging from zero for *n*-heptane to 100 for 2,2,4-trimethylpentane (*isooctane*), measures the anti-knock ability of a gasoline. Write the structural formula (a) for 2,2,4-trimethylpentane, and (b) for 2,3-dimethylpentane, which has an "octane number" of 91.

22.5 HYDROCARBONS WITH DOUBLE AND TRIPLE BONDS

Carbon atoms may be linked by double and triple bonds (page 581). In ethylene, C_2H_4, $H_2C=CH_2$, the double bond consists of a σ bond formed by the overlap of an sp^2 AO from each C atom, and a pi (π) bond formed by the overlap of a p_z orbital from each C atom (page 582); see Fig. 22.5.

Hydrocarbons that possess one carbon-carbon double bond (C=C) form a homologous series known as the **alkenes**, general formula C_nH_{2n}. The rules for naming the alkenes are similar to those discussed for the alkanes: First, locate the longest continuous chain *which contains the double bond*. Number the chain, giving preference to the double bond; that is, the double-bonded carbon atoms should have the lowest possible numbers. The compound is named as an alkane except that the

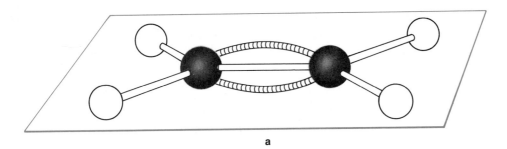

a

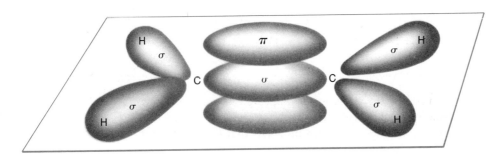

b

FIGURE 22.5   (a) Ball, stick, and spring representation of ethylene. (b) MO description of ethylene (page 582).

ending *ane* is changed to *ene*. Thus, $H_2C=CH—CH_3$, which is exactly the same as $H_3C—CH=CH_2$, is called prop*ene*.

In larger molecules, however, the presence of the double bond produces isomerism. There are three isomers of normal (straight-chain) butene, C_4H_8. Two result from the different positions of the double bond in the chain:

$$H_2C=CH—CH_2—CH_3 \qquad H_3C—CH=CH—CH_3$$

1-butene   *2-butene*

1-butene and 2-butene are isomers because they cannot be matched without breaking chemical bonds. Note that $CH_3—CH_2—CH=CH_2$ is 1-butene. Notice also that the location of the double bond is indicated by the lower numbered carbon atom involved in the double bond.

The third isomer of normal butene is due to the presence of the pi (π) bond in the double bond. Since the rotation of the CH_3 group about the σ bond in ethane relative to the other end requires only 3 kcal/mole, both staggered and eclipsed conformations exist in ethane. On the other hand, rotating one CH_2 group about the sigma (σ) bond in ethylene involves twisting the π bond; the p_z orbitals prefer overlap to separation. Destruction of the π bond requires 60 kcal/mole, the amount of energy needed to break a respectable chemical bond. Thus, two 2-butenes exist:

cis-2-butene   *trans*-2-butene

(adjacent—same side)   (diagonal—opposite side)

These two 2-butenes are isomers because they cannot be matched without breaking the chemical (π) bond. We thus have another example of *cis-trans* isomerism (page 665). On the left is the *cis*-2-butene: two groups (CH_3 and CH_3 or H and H) are on the same side of the line through the double bond. The two CH_3 groups are adjacent. On the right is *trans*-2-butene: the same two groups are now on opposite sides of the line through the double bond. The two CH_3 groups are diagonal to each other.

PROBLEM 6   **Make models of *cis*-2-butene and *trans*-2-butene. Place one model on top of the other in any position in an attempt to match them. Is it possible to match them without breaking a chemical bond?**

Theoretically, we can write an equilibrium reaction between *cis-trans* isomers, for example,

cis-1,2-dichloroethylene(*g*)   *trans*-1,2-dichloroethylene(*g*)

But the energy of activation for this change is so high, and the change is so extremely small at temperature, that for all practical purposes we can say that the change does not occur and the dichloroethylene isomers can be isolated. However, at very high temperatures, reaction rates increase, and in accordance with the Le Chatalier principle, the *trans* form is favored. The *cis* $\longrightarrow$ *trans* change also occurs when photons of the proper frequency are used.

Of course, the two groups need not be identical. Of the two isomers of $C_{23}H_{46}$,

	$C_{13}H_{27}$
cis-isomer	*trans*-isomer
(adjacent)	(diagonal)
(same side)	(opposite sides)

only the *cis*-isomer is biologically active as a housefly sex attractant.*

Molecules, of course, can have more than one double bond. Typical is butadiene, $H_2C{=}CH{-}CH{=}CH_2$, used in the manufacture of synthetic rubber (Chap. 23).

Acetylene is very rarely called by its IUPAC name, ethyne.

Acetylene, $H{-}C{\equiv}C{-}H$, is the first member of the **alkyne** homologous series, general formula C_nH_{2n-2}. The ending *yne* indicates the presence of a triple bond. The triple bond consists of a σ bond formed by the overlap of an sp AO from each C atom, and two π bonds (page 582); see Fig. 22.6. Thus, $H{-}C{\equiv}C{-}CH_3$ is propyne and $H_3C{-}C{\equiv}C{-}CH_3$ is 2-butyne.

PROBLEM 7   Write the structural formulas for (a) 1-butyne, (b) 2-pentene, (c) 1-pentene.

The presence of double and triple bonds makes alkenes and alkynes undergo similar types of chemical reactions. They combine with elements, resulting in the addition of atoms to the molecules. Typical is the addition of chlorine to ethylene and acetylene, producing 1,2-dichloroethane and 1,1,2,2-tetrachloroethane:

$$\underset{H}{\overset{H}{}}C{=}C\underset{H}{\overset{H}{}}(g) + Cl_2(g) \longrightarrow H{-}\overset{Cl}{\underset{H}{C}}{-}\overset{Cl}{\underset{H}{C}}{-}H(l) \qquad K = 4.9 \times 10^{28}$$

$$H{-}C{\equiv}C{-}H(g) + 2Cl_2(g) \longrightarrow H{-}\overset{Cl}{\underset{Cl}{C}}{-}\overset{Cl}{\underset{Cl}{C}}{-}H(l) \qquad K = 2.9 \times 10^{57}$$

Cis-9-tricosene. The name *muscalure* is proposed because it is the sex attractant for the common housefly, *Musca domestica.* Isolated from the female fly, it attracts the male fly. First isolated and identified by chromatographic (page 31) and NMR (page 753) studies and synthesized in 1971, it is typical of the insect sex attractants being investigated as substitutes for insecticides for insect control. The approved names are (Z)-9-tricosene for the *cis* and (E)-9-tricosene for the *trans* isomer, derived from the German words *zusammen* (same side) and *entgegen* (opposite side).

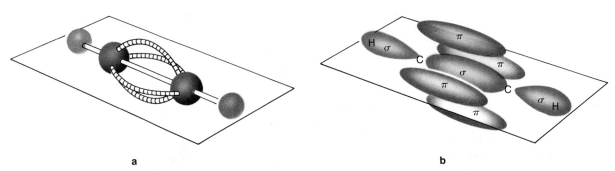

FIGURE 22.6   (a) Ball, stick, and spring representation of acetylene. (b) MO description of acetylene (page 582).

In the presence of a platinum or nickel catalyst, hydrogen adds to acetylene and ethylene, producing ethane:

$$H—C\equiv C—H(g) + 2H_2(g) \longrightarrow H—\overset{\overset{\displaystyle H}{|}}{\underset{\underset{\displaystyle H}{|}}{C}}—\overset{\overset{\displaystyle H}{|}}{\underset{\underset{\displaystyle H}{|}}{C}}—H(g) \qquad K = 1.6 \times 10^{45}$$

$$H_2C{=}CH_2(g) + H_2(g) \longrightarrow H—\overset{\overset{\displaystyle H}{|}}{\underset{\underset{\displaystyle H}{|}}{C}}—\overset{\overset{\displaystyle H}{|}}{\underset{\underset{\displaystyle H}{|}}{C}}—H(g) \qquad K = 1.2 \times 10^{19}$$

In each reaction, the double or triple bond is changed to a single (σ) bond, and the π bonds become single (σ) bonds. These **addition reactions** are typical of molecules containing double or triple bonds. Such compounds are therefore said to be **unsaturated,*** while the alkanes are said to be **saturated** because they do not undergo addition reactions.

Interestingly, ions in which carbon has a coordination number of 5, such as $CH_5{}^+$, have been prepared by George Olah.

Water is typical of a number of compounds that add to alkenes or alkynes:

$$H_2C{=}CH_2(g) + HOH(g) \xrightarrow{\text{dilute } H_2SO_4} CH_3CH_2OH(l)$$
$$\text{ethyl alcohol}$$

Page 394; dilute sulfuric acid serves as a catalyst.

PROBLEM 8   Write the balanced equation for the addition of H_2 to (a) 1-pentene, and (b) 2-pentene. Name the product of each reaction.

CYCLOALKANES _____ 22.6

Carbon atoms can be united in rings as well as in chains. When united by single bonds, the hydrocarbons are called **cycloalkanes.** The general formula of this homologous series, C_nH_{2n}, makes them isomers of the alkenes. Thus, the simplest cycloalkane, cyclopropane, is an isomer of propene:

In chemistry, none of the terms "cyclic," "cyclo," "ring," or "closed chain" means circle or circular.

cyclopropane, C_3H_6 propene, C_3H_6

Other cycloalkanes are represented in Fig. 22.7.

THE BENZENE PROBLEM _____ 22.7

Benzene, C_6H_6, a volatile liquid, is the parent compound of the so-called **aromatic hydrocarbons** used in the manufacture of many biochemicals, drugs, dyes, perfumes, explosives, wetting agents, emulsifying agents, plastics, synthetic fibers, and

---

*The addition of bromine (usually dissolved in an inert solvent such as carbon tetrachloride) provides a test to distinguish between saturated and unsaturated compounds. The characteristic red color of bromine rapidly disappears as it adds to the unsaturated compound, forming a colorless product. With saturated compounds, the red color does not disappear, since neither addition nor rapid substitution occurs.

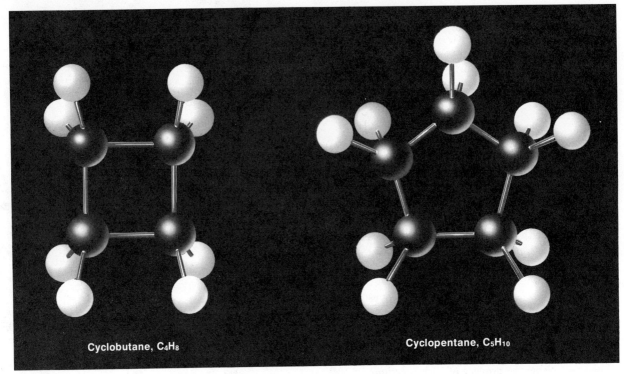

Cyclobutane, C_4H_8

Cyclopentane, C_5H_{10}

FIGURE 22.7 Ball and stick representation of some cycloalkanes.

Benzene is suspected of causing leukemia. U.S. Occupational Safety and Health Administration has imposed an allowable benzene exposure of 1 ppm. Also known as carcinogens.

Although structure of coal is unknown, 75 % (bituminous) to 95 % (anthracite) of C atoms are aromatic sp²; the others are sp³ tetrahedral.

Each corner of the hexagon represents a C atom with an H atom attached.

polymers. They are called aromatic because many of these compounds have pleasant odors; the word, in fact, is derived from *aroma,* the Latin word for a sweet smell. However, *most of them are toxic* and many are *carcinogenic agents,* chemical substances that cause cancer. *Care, therefore, should be exercised in their use.*

Benzene was first prepared (1825) by Michael Faraday by the *destructive distillation* of coal. Heated to high temperatures in the absence of air, coal is decomposed to *coke,* relatively pure carbon used for metallurgical purposes (page 634), and a gaseous complex mixture of compounds, most of which is condensed to *coal tar,* a viscous liquid which serves as a source of aromatic compounds. The rest is largely gaseous ammonia, converted to solid ammonium sulfate, used as a fertilizer, and *coal gas,* a mixture of methane and hydrogen, a useful clean fuel.

Since its discovery, the molecular structure of benzene has puzzled and fascinated the chemist in his attempts to correlate its properties with its molecular structure. The most important proposal, made in 1865 by Friedrich August Kekulé, still serves as the basis of the present hexagonal ("cyclic," "ring," "closed chain") structural formula of benzene:

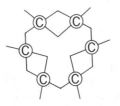

Kekule alternating
double bond formula

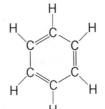

Abbreviated
structural formula

692

This formula maintains the valence of four for carbon and predicts that benzene should resemble unsaturated hydrocarbons such as ethylene. Further, it predicts that the bond lengths in the ring should differ, C=C being shorter than C—C (page 584). None of these predictions agrees with experiment. The bond stability of benzene is much greater and its reactivity much less than that indicated by three single and three double bonds. Thus, while ethylene readily adds bromine to its double bond and resists substitution, benzene resists both types of reactions but prefers substitution to addition. In summary

Bond Stability

$$C_6H_6(g) \xrightarrow{\text{experimental}} 6C(g) + 6H(g) \qquad \Delta H = +1318 \text{ kcal}$$

$$\bighexagon (g) \xrightarrow{\text{calculated}} 6C(g) + 6H(g) \qquad \Delta H = +1274 \text{ kcal} \qquad \textit{See Problem 42.}$$

Reactivity

$$C_2H_4(g) + Br_2(l) \xrightarrow[\text{readily}]{\text{addition to double bond}} C_2H_4Br_2(l)$$

$$C_2H_4(g) + Br_2(l) \xrightarrow[\text{extremely difficult}]{\text{substitution}} C_2H_3Br(g) + HBr(g)$$

$$C_6H_6(l) + 3Br_2(l) \xrightarrow[\text{extremely difficult}]{\text{addition to double bond}} C_6H_6Br_6(c)$$

$$C_6H_6(l) + Br_2(l) \xrightarrow[\text{difficult but much easier than addition}]{\text{substitution}} C_6H_5Br(l) + HBr(g)$$

Clearly, the "double bond" in benzene is not similar to the double bond in ethylene; it is more stable and less reactive.

Finally, benzene is a planar (flat) molecule with *identical* C to C bonds in a hexagonal ring at bond angles of 120°. Therefore, like CO_3^{2-} (page 585), it is *impossible to write an electronic formula for benzene consistent with its properties.*

According to the resonance method (page 585), the important contributing (fictitious) structures assigned to benzene are as follows:

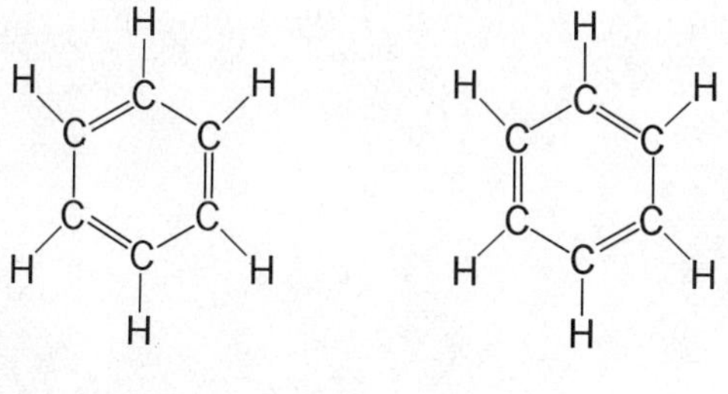

They differ only in the position of the double and single bonds.

However, the molecular orbital delocalized pi (π) bond description (page 582) gives us one very satisfactory representation of the real molecule. Each C atom is

*Use of models of six
atoms each in the
imaginary sp² state
(page 577) is
recommended.*

without an unshared pair of electrons and is bonded to three atoms. Therefore, the carbon atoms use sp^2 AO's (page 577). Two sp^2 AO's from each C atom fuse to form six σ bonds between the C atoms, forming a hexagonal ring. The remaining six sp^2 AO's fuse with hydrogen to form σ bonds:

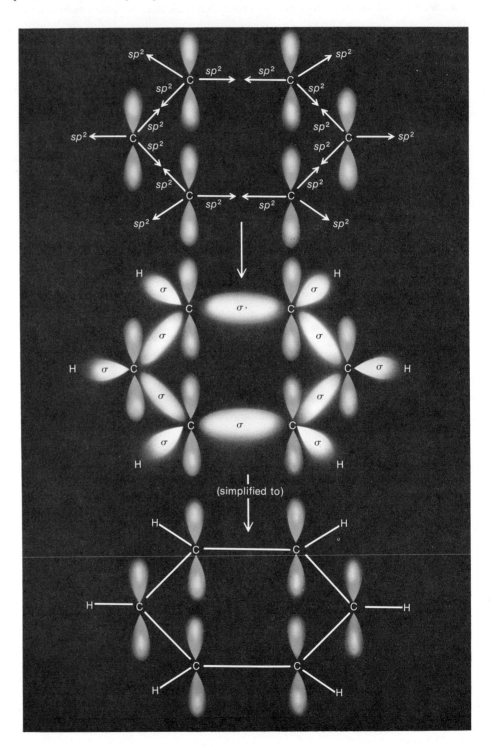

Each C atom is now left with a p_z AO. The six p_z AO's are all parallel to one another, upright and side-by-side. Each fuses with its p_z orbital neighbors to form a cyclic delocalized π bond.* The electron clouds above and below the ring embrace all six C atoms and may be crudely visualized as two hexagonal loops, one above and one below the ring of the C atoms:

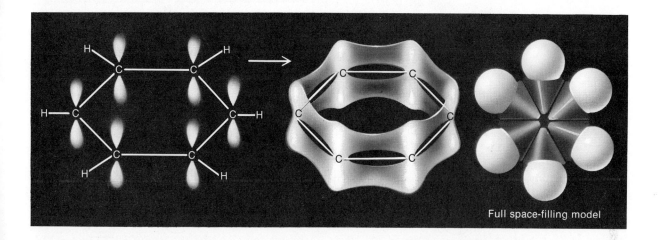

Full space-filling model

The 30 valence electrons, four from each C atom (24) and one from each H atom (6), are distributed as follows: 24 are used for the 12 sigma bonds, leaving six electrons (30 − 24) in the delocalized pi bond. These six electrons move relatively freely around the hexagonal ring.

Any compound with a cyclic delocalized π bond, characteristic of benzene, is now called an **aromatic compound.** ⬡ is an accepted abbreviation for the MO description of benzene. This description is in agreement with the known properties of benzene: its stability (page 693) is greater than that predicted from the electronic formula and this makes benzene resist addition reactions. The C—C bonds are identical and bond angles are 120°.

Benzene resists addition reactions because they involve the destruction of the highly stable cyclic delocalized π bond. This makes the required energy of activation (page 512) prohibitively high. Substitution reactions, on the other hand, do not destroy the cyclic delocalized π bond and, therefore, occur more readily. For example, in the presence of a catalyst ($FeBr_3$), bromine substitutes for hydrogen in benzene at 60 °C:

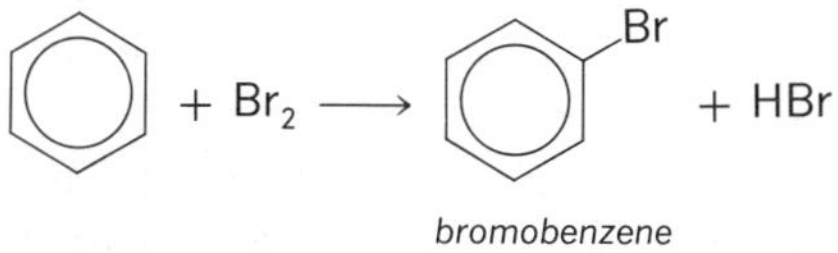

$$\bigcirc\!\!\!\!\!\hexagon + Br_2 \longrightarrow \bigcirc\!\!\!\!\!\hexagon^{Br} + HBr$$

bromobenzene

---

*Reminder: six molecular orbitals form, three bonding and three antibonding, but only one bonding orbital is shown for clarity; also, antibonding sigma (σ^*) bonds are not shown (Problem 41, page 711).

Many physiologically active compounds are aromatic; many contain at least one nitrogen atom per molecule. A few examples are given:

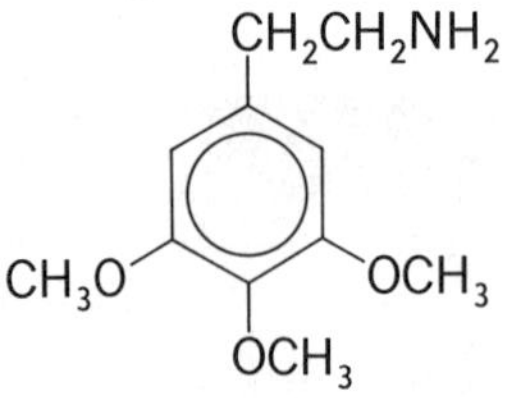

mescaline
(hallucinogen)

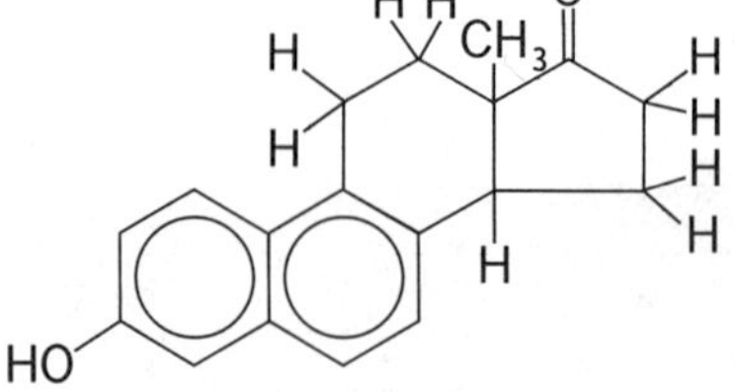

equilenin, a typical steroid
(female sex *hormone* of horse;
regulates sexual cycle)

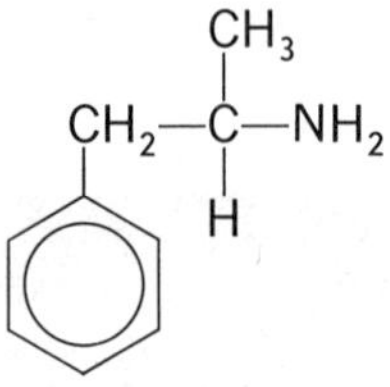

benzedrine
(stimulant)

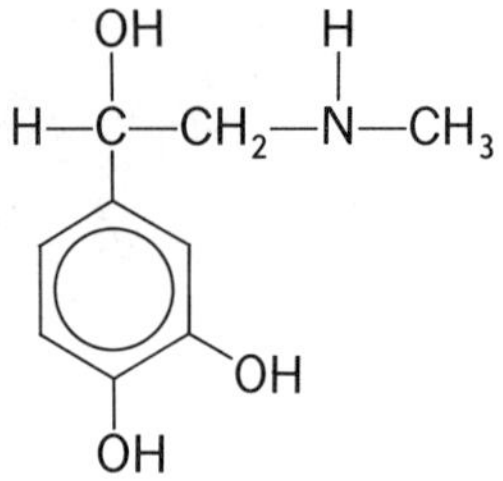

adrenalin
(stimulant)

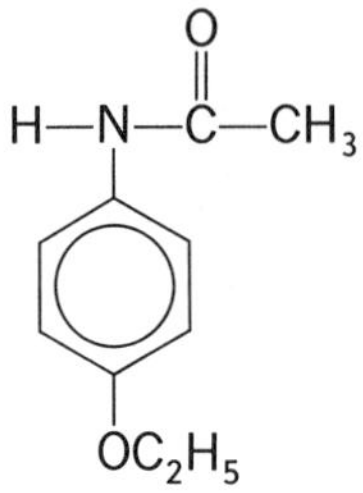

phenacetin
(pain killer)

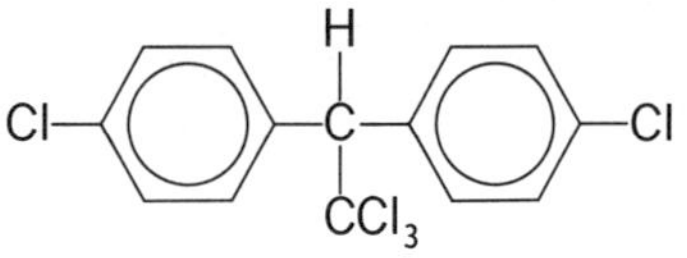

DDT
(insecticide)

Aromatic compounds with more than one benzene ring fused together are common, and many of them are physiologically active.

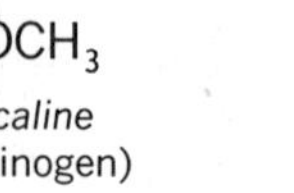

naphthalene, $C_{10}H_8$
(moth repellent)

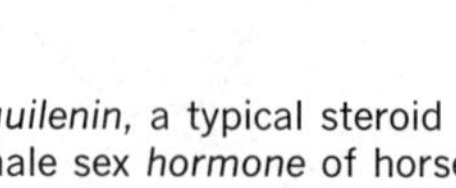

anthracene, $C_{14}H_{10}$
(industrial chemical)

The discovery that coal is converted to products soluble in pyridine, C_5H_5N,

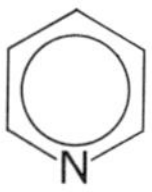

by heating for 1 min at 420 °C in liquid naphthalene tetrahydride, $C_{10}H_{12}$, may lead to new coal conversion methods.

22.8 _____ CHEMISTRY OF ORGANIC GROUPS

Replacement of one or more hydrogen atoms of a hydrocarbon with other atoms such as oxygen or chlorine, or with groups of atoms such as hydroxyl (OH), results in another compound with another chemically active site. The atom or group of atoms that replaces the hydrogen atom behaves in a characteristic manner, often practically independent of the nature of the other parts of the molecule.

This property of so-called organic compounds should remind us of the properties of so-called inorganic compounds. Writing ionic equations (page 358) merely recognizes that charged atoms, such as chloride, Cl^-, and groups, such as ammonium,

NH_4^+, and sulfate, SO_4^{2-}, behave as characteristic units during many chemical reactions, independent of their partners. This, in fact, is the basis of identification of salts (page 358). Chloride ion from *any* soluble chloride forms $AgCl(c)$ upon the addition of Ag^+ from *any* soluble silver salt. *Any* soluble ammonium salt forms ammonia upon the addition of OH^- from any soluble hydroxide: $NH_4^+(aq) + OH^-(aq) \longrightarrow NH_3(g) + H_2O$. Similarly, *any* "organic" chloride (chlorocompounds) has a characteristic set of properties due to the presence of the chloride. *Any* "organic" amine ($-NH_2$ compounds) has a characteristic set of properties due to the presence of the $-NH_2$ group. While in inorganic nomenclature, groups like SO_4^{2-} or NH_4^+ are known simply as groups, in organic nomenclature, groups like $-Cl$ or $-NH_2$ are called **functional groups,** "functional" here being used in the sense of possessing a characteristic set of properties. But classification of organic groups serves exactly the same purpose as the classification of inorganic groups: it simplifies the study of chemistry and serves as a means of identifying organic compounds. Therefore, a large part of organic chemistry includes the chemistry of functional groups. Some of the more common functional groups are given in Table 22.3. Under the heading of General Formula in the table, the functional group is attached to a carbon atom of an alkane, alkene, alkyne, or aromatic group, commonly represented as R, R', R'', and so forth. A few typical reactions of these functional groups are discussed in the following subsections.

A mass spectrometer, in which the energy of the electron beam is carefully controlled, can "shoot off" various groups and identify them by mass number (page 124).

Alcohols, R—OH   Under proper conditions, alcohols may be changed to ethers with the elimination of water:

$$2CH_3CH_2OH(l) \xrightarrow{\text{warm concentrated } H_2SO_4} CH_3CH_2-O-CH_2CH_3(l) + H_2O(l)$$

TABLE 22.3
SOME COMMON FUNCTIONAL GROUPS

GENERAL NAME	GROUP	GENERAL FORMULA	EXAMPLE	IUPAC NAME	COMMON NAME
Acid	$-\overset{\|}{\underset{O}{C}}-OH$	$R-\overset{\|}{\underset{O}{C}}-OH$	CH_3COOH	Ethanoic acid	acetic acid
Alcohol	$-OH$	$R-OH$	CH_3CH_2OH	Ethanol	ethyl alcohol*
Aldehyde	$-\overset{\|}{\underset{O}{C}}-H$	$R-\overset{\|}{\underset{O}{C}}-H$	CH_3CHO	Ethanal	acetaldehyde
Amine	$-NH_2$	$R-NH_2$	CH_3NH_2	Aminomethane	methylamine
Ester	$-\overset{\|}{\underset{O}{C}}-O-$	$R-\overset{\|}{\underset{O}{C}}-O-R'$	CH_3COOCH_3	Methyl ethanoate	methyl acetate
Ether	$-O-$	$R-O-R'$	$CH_3CH_2OCH_2CH_3$	Ethoxyethane	diethyl ether
Halide	$-X(F, Cl, Br, I)$	$R-X$	C_2H_5I	Iodoethane	ethyl iodide
Ketone	$-\overset{\|}{\underset{O}{C}}-$	$R-\overset{\|}{\underset{O}{C}}-R'$	CH_3COCH_3	Propanone	acetone (dimethyl ketone)

*Also known as grain alcohol because it is a product of the fermentation of starches and sugars found in grain products such as wheat, rye, corn, and rice. Its major use is in the manufacture of alcoholic beverages. Large quantities of alcohol in the body may cause depression, impaired perception, circulatory collapse, and death. Readers interested in the subject of alcoholism are referred to the footnote on page 133 and to "Alcohol and Alcoholism," National Institute on Alcohol Abuse and Alcoholism, U.S. Government Printing Office, 1972.

    Denatured alcohol is ethyl alcohol poisoned with such substances as methyl alcohol, benzene, or gasoline. Solutions of drugs in ethyl alcohol are called *tinctures*.

Like water, HOH, to which they are related, alcohols react with sodium:

$$HOH(l) + Na(c) \longrightarrow Na^+OH^-(aq) + \tfrac{1}{2} H_2(g)$$

$$\underset{\text{methyl alcohol}}{CH_3OH(l)} + Na(c) \longrightarrow \underset{\text{sodium methoxide}}{Na^+OCH_3^-(alcohol)} + \tfrac{1}{2} H_2(g)$$

The fact that alkyl alcohols are generally weaker acids than water, while the hypohalous acids are generally stronger acids than water, is worthy of some attention. Both types of compounds, for example, C_2H_5OH and $HOCl$, are related to water. In one case an alkyl group replaces a hydrogen atom, while a chlorine atom replaces a hydrogen atom in the other. Acidity depends on the electron density of the negative ion (the conjugate base) formed when the acid gives up a proton (page 419). The smaller the electron density, the smaller the attraction for the proton, and the greater is the acidity. How do Cl— and C_2H_5— change the electron density of the oxygen atom in HOH? Since chlorine is more electronegative (page 255) than the hydrogen it replaces, we should expect chlorine to pull negative charge away from the hydroxyl group, thereby decreasing the electron density on the oxygen atom, and so making HOCl a stronger acid than HOH. On the other hand, alkyl groups such as C_2H_5— are generally less electronegative than hydrogen. The hydroxyl group now pulls negative charge away from the ethyl group, thereby increasing the electron density on the oxygen atom, and so making C_2H_5OH a weaker acid than HOH. In summary,

Standard for comparison		
	$HOH \rightleftharpoons OH^- + H^+$	$K_w = 1.0 \times 10^{-14}$

$$Cl \longleftarrow \underset{|}{O}H \qquad \underset{\substack{\text{decreased electron}\\\text{density}}}{ClOH \rightleftharpoons ClO^- + H^+} \qquad K_{acid} = 2.8 \times 10^{-8}$$

negative charge drawn
away from oxygen

$$C_2H_5 \longrightarrow \underset{|}{O}H \qquad \underset{\substack{\text{increased electron}\\\text{density}}}{C_2H_5OH \rightleftharpoons C_2H_5O^- + H^+} \qquad K_{acid} = 7.28 \times 10^{-20}$$

negative charge released
to oxygen

Alcohols may have more than one —OH group. *Ethylene glycol,* $HO—CH_2—CH_2—OH$, commonly used as an anti-freeze (*Prestone, Xerex*), is typical. *Glycerol* (*glycerine*), $HOCH_2—CHOH—CH_2OH$, is used in the manufacture of drugs, candy, food products, and nitroglycerine, an explosive.

Compounds in which an —OH group is attached directly to an aromatic ring are called *phenols.* Phenol,* , is typical. Related to water, the acidity is influenced

by the presence of the benzene ring. The highly delocalized bond of the benzene ring pulls negative charge away from the hydroxyl group. This decreases the electron density on the oxygen atom, thereby making phenol a stronger acid ($K_{acid} = 1.3 \times 10^{-10}$) than water. Thus, like hypochlorous acid, phenol neutralizes dilute sodium hydroxide solution, while ethyl alcohol does not.

PROBLEM 9   **Difluoroacetic acid, $F_2CHCOOH$, fluoroacetic acid, FCH_2COOH, and propionic acid, CH_3CH_2COOH, are related to acetic acid, CH_3COOH. The fluorine atom pulls negative charge away from the oxygen atoms, while the methyl group releases negative charge to the oxygen atoms. Arrange the four acids in order of decreasing acid strength (strongest first). Explain.**

---

*Destruction of germs was first introduced by Joseph Lister (1865), who sprayed phenol solution in an operating room. Phenol (carbolic acid) is a very poisonous and corrosive, white crystalline substance.

Ethers   The general formula for an ether, R—O—R', shows that it can be considered as derived from water in which the two atoms of hydrogen are replaced by two groups.

Unlike alcohols, ethers do not react with sodium since they do not have an OH group. Ethers are generally less polar than alcohols and thus are generally less soluble in polar solvents like water (page 325). Also, hydrogen bonding (page 264) is much greater in alcohols and, consequently, the solubilities in water and the boiling points of alcohols' are generally higher, while ethers are generally more volatile and less soluble. For example, the boiling point of ethyl alcohol (C_2H_6O) is 78.5 °C, while its isomer, methyl ether (C_2H_6O, H_3C—O—CH_3), boils at −24 °C. However, the nonpolar character of ethers makes them suitable solvents for a variety of nonpolar compounds.

Aldehydes and Ketones   Aldehydes and ketones are characterized by the presence of the **carbonyl group,** ⌐C=O. If one or two hydrogen atoms are attached to the carbonyl group, the compound is called an aldehyde:

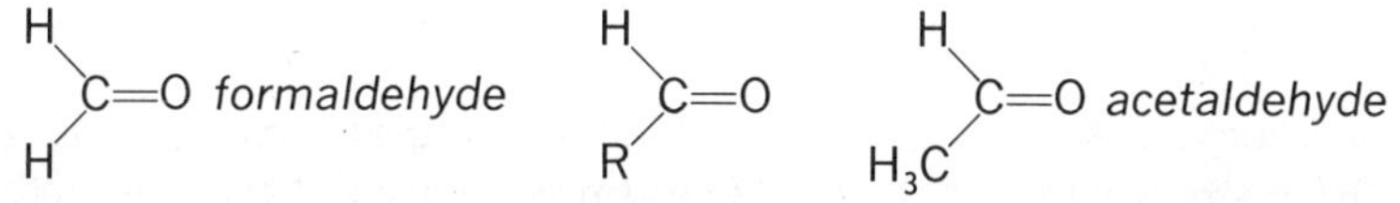

When hydrocarbon groups are attached, the compound is called a ketone:

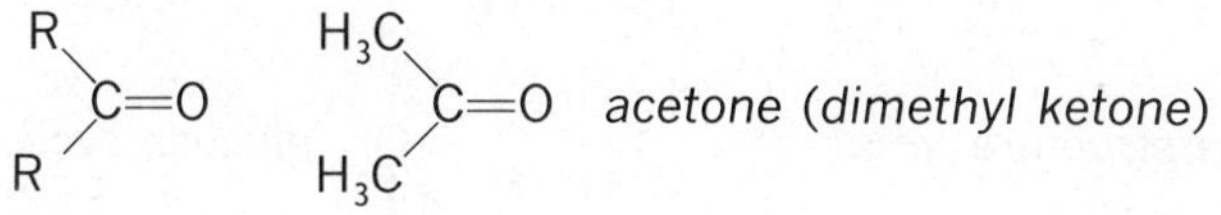

Aldehydes may be prepared by oxidation of an alcohol in which the OH group is attached to a carbon atom carrying at least two H atoms:

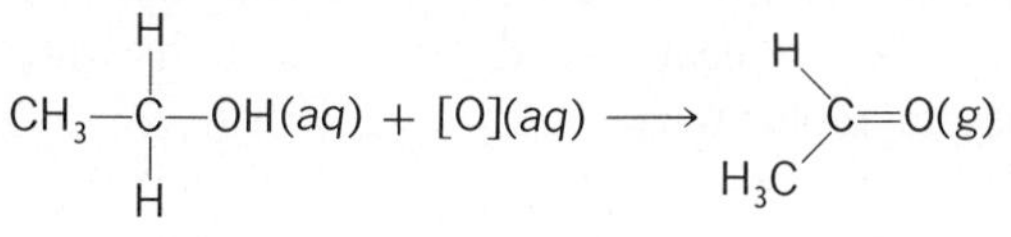

ethyl alcohol   *acetaldehyde*

[O] *is commonly used to represent an oxidizing agent, such as potassium permanganate,* $KMnO_4$.

$$CH_3OH(g) + \tfrac{1}{2}O_2(g) \xrightarrow{\text{Cu, 600 °C}} H_2C{=}O(g) + H_2O(g)$$

methyl alcohol   *formaldehyde*

On the other hand, ketones are prepared by the oxidation of an alcohol in which the OH group is attached to a carbon atom carrying only one H atom:

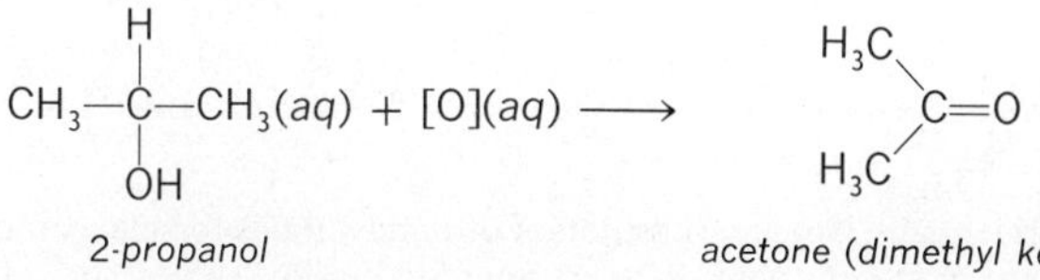

2-propanol   *acetone (dimethyl ketone)*

An alcohol with the OH group attached to a carbon atom carrying no H atoms, (CH_3)₃COH, *undergoes no reaction under the same conditions.*

Many carbonyl compounds have very distinctive odors (Table 22.4) and are therefore used as artificial flavoring agents and perfumes.

Carbohydrates are aldehydes or ketones that contain a number of OH groups; the chain structures of two sugars, called **monosaccharides,** are shown:

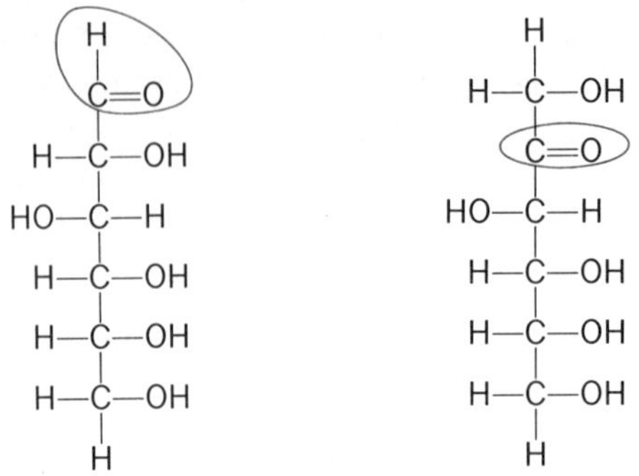

From carbo, Latin for coal, and from hydrate, a hydrate of carbon; concentrated H_2SO_4 dehydrates cane sugar, $C_{12}(H_2O)_{11}$, to a fluffy carbon.

glucose
$C_6H_{12}O_6$
(contains an aldehyde group)
Chain structure

fructose
$C_6H_{12}O_6$
(contains a ketone group)
Chain structure

A cyclic structure for these sugars is thermodynamically more stable. A small amount of the chain structure of glucose, for example, is in equilibrium with the cyclic structure:

glucose chain structure $\rightleftharpoons$ glucose cyclic structure*

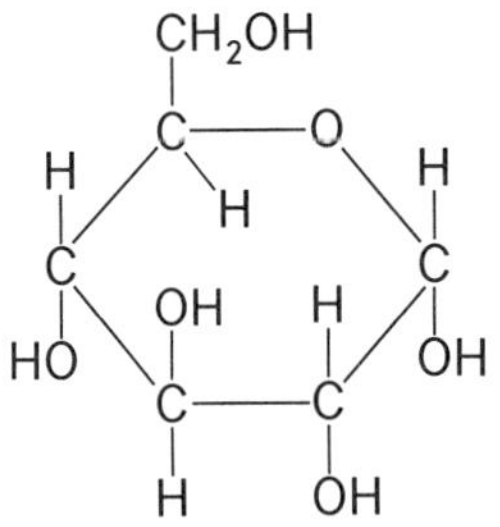

Maltose (malt sugar), $C_{12}H_{22}O_{11}$, sucrose (cane or beet sugar), $C_{12}H_{22}O_{11}$, and lactose (milk sugar), $C_{12}H_{22}O_{11}$, are typical **disaccharides,** carbohydrates made up of two monosaccharide units per molecule:

$$\text{sucrose}(aq) + H_2O \xrightarrow{\text{dilute HCl}} \text{glucose}(aq) + \text{fructose}(aq)$$

Starch, $(C_6H_{10}O_5)_n$,** and cellulose, $(C_6H_{10}O_5)_n$, are the important **polysaccharides,** carbohydrates made up of hundreds to thousands of glucose units per molecule.

---

*Two cyclic structures exist, more realistically shown with bond angles:

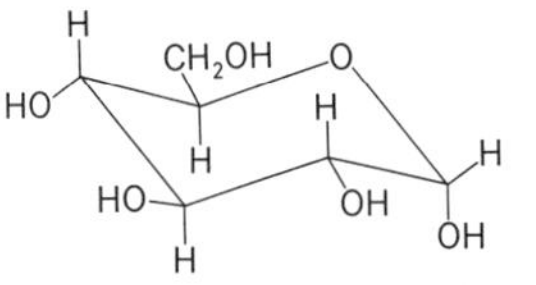

and

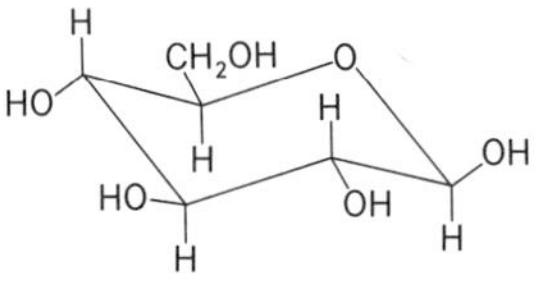

**Application of fluoride (page 396) and substitution of starchy foods for sugary foods would reduce dental caries (teeth decay) to practically zero. Readers interested in this subject are referred to "Dental Caries: Prospects for Prevention," *Science,* volume 173, 24 September 1971, page 1199.

TABLE 22.4
ODORS OF SOME CARBONYL COMPOUNDS

FORMULA	NAME	ODOR
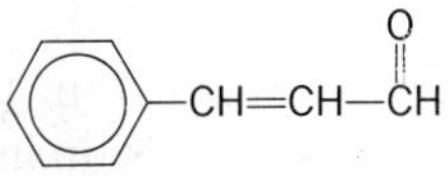	Cinnamaldehyde	Cinnamon
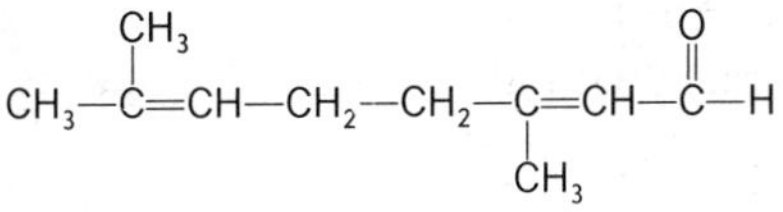	Citral	Lemon
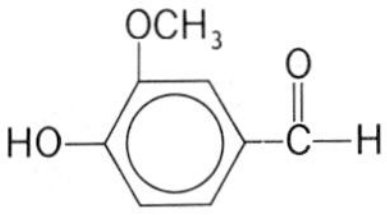	Vanillin	Vanilla
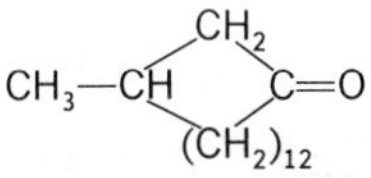	Muscone*	Musk
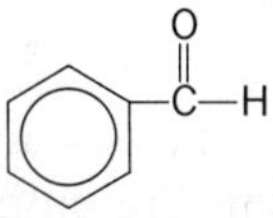	Benzaldehyde	Almond

* Used in the perfume industry.

Carbohydrates, the products of photosynthesis, constitute the primary source of our food (page 195), and cellulose, in the form of cotton, linen, and wood, constitutes an important source of clothing and shelter.

Excessive amounts of glucose in the blood with the elimination of glucose in the urine is a reliable indicator of diabetes. A chemical test for the presence of glucose involves the oxidation of the aldehyde (—CHO) group and the reduction of the oxidizing agent, Cu^{2+}. *Fehlings'* or *Benedict's* reagents are alkaline solutions of copper(II) sulfate. When reduced, copper(I) oxide, Cu_2O, appears as a red precipitate. The amount of Cu_2O produced is a measure of the amount of glucose present.

PROBLEM 10   Write the equation showing the oxidation of *n*-propyl alcohol, $CH_3CH_2CH_2OH$, to the corresponding aldehyde.

Carboxylic Acids   While ketones resist oxidation, aldehydes are easily further oxidized to carboxylic acids, compounds which possess the **carboxyl group**, Thus

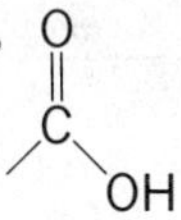

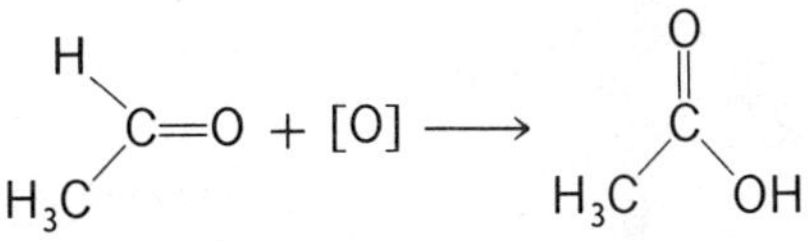

acetaldehyde → acetic acid

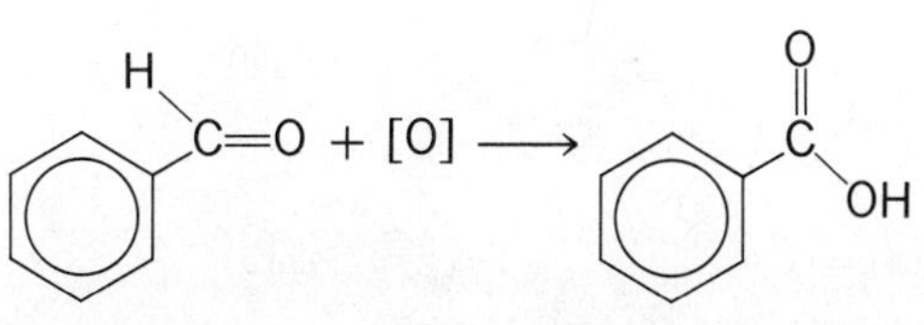

benzaldehyde → benzoic acid

Carboxylic acids are usually weak acids. Many of their salts have widespread use in the soap (page 345) and food industries. For example, sodium benzoate, C_6H_5COONa, is used as a preservative in soft drinks and many foods and as a corrosion inhibitor. Calcium propionate, $(CH_3CH_2COO)_2Ca$, is used as a mold preventive in bread.

Many of the carboxylic acids are obtained from natural sources. Lactic acid, $CH_3CHOHCOOH$, isolated from sour milk, builds up in the muscles during exercise and is, in part, responsible for fatigue.

Carboxylic acids react with alcohols by eliminating a molecule of water to form **esters:**

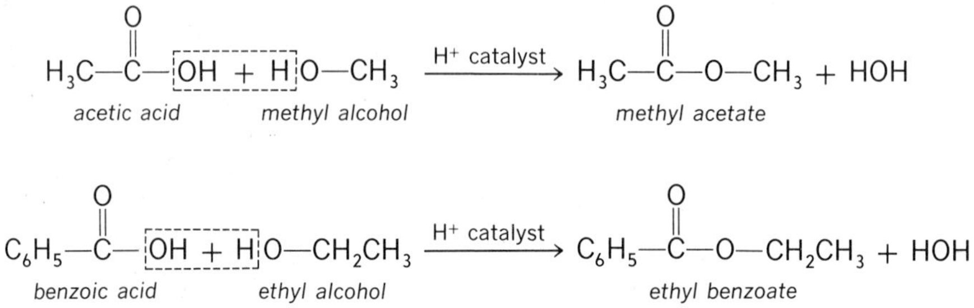

This reaction is not analogous to the reaction of a base and an acid, although water is a product of both reactions. The mechanisms are entirely different:

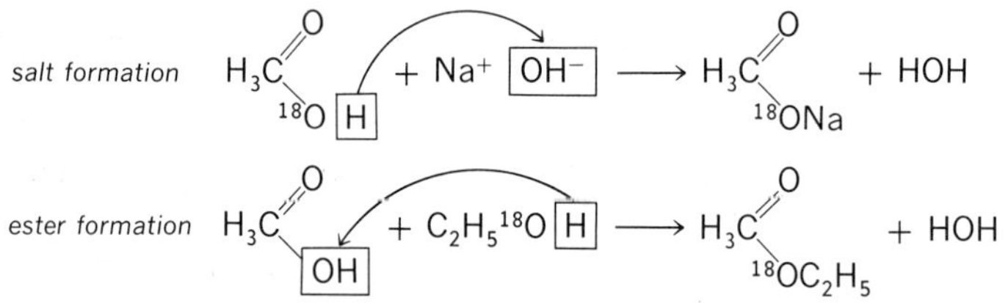

Recall page 550.

These mechanisms are established from studies using isotopically "tagged" alcohol, C_2H_5—^{18}OH, as shown. The ^{18}O *appears in the ester* and *not* in the HOH product.

Esters are widely distributed in nature. They are responsible for many of the flavors and odors of fruits and flowers, and are used as artificial flavorings in foods (Table 22.5).

TABLE 22.5
SOME TYPICAL ESTERS

NAME	STRUCTURE	FLAVOR
Ethyl formate	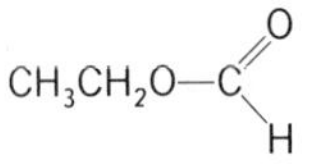 CH_3CH_2O—C with O and H	Rum
Isobutyl formate	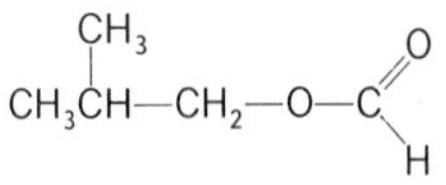 CH_3CH—CH_2—O—C with CH_3, O, H	Raspberries
n-Pentyl acetate	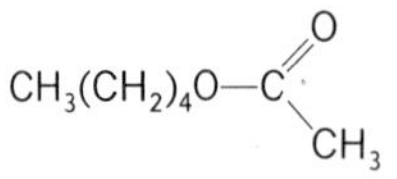 $CH_3(CH_2)_4O$—C with O and CH_3	Bananas
Isopentyl acetate	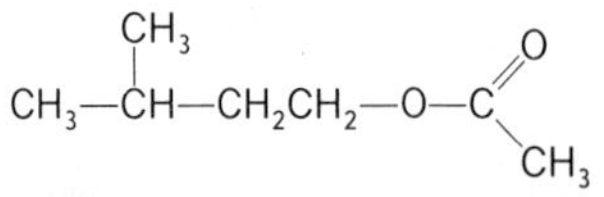 CH_3—CH—CH_2CH_2—O—C with CH_3, O, CH_3	Pears

The carboxyl group of salicylic acid can react with an alcohol to produce an ester

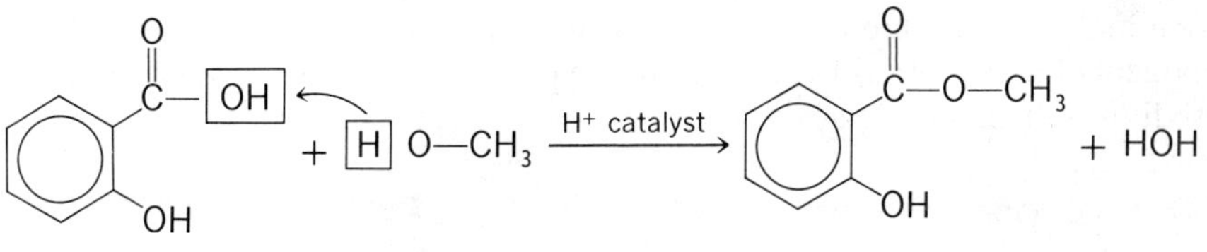

salicylic acid   methyl alcohol   methyl salicylate, oil of wintergreen

while the —OH group of salicylic acid can react with a carboxyl group, again forming an ester:

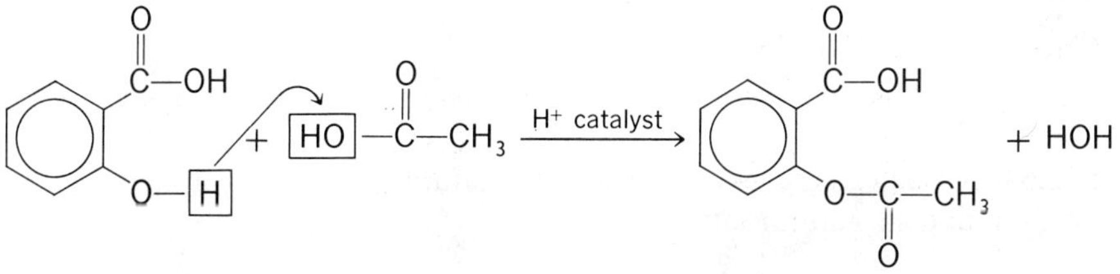

salicylic acid   acetic acid   acetylsalicylic acid, aspirin

Aspirin, used to relieve pain and fever since 1899, is probably the most widely used drug in the history of medicine.*

PROBLEM 11 **The methyl ester (strawberry odor) and ethyl ester (cinnamon odor) of cinnamic acid are used in the perfume industry. Draw the structural formulas of (a) methyl cinnamate, and (b) ethyl cinnamate. The structural formula of cinnamic acid is $C_6H_5CH=CHCOOH$.**

A clinical test is being carried out on 4524 patients to determine whether aspirin could prevent fatal heart attacks.

The reaction of an acid and an alcohol to form an ester can be reversed by hydrolysis of the ester, catalyzed by a strong base. The overall reaction is:

$$CH_3COOCH_3(aq) + NaOH(aq) \longrightarrow CH_3OH(aq) + CH_3COONa(aq)$$

methyl acetate   methyl alcohol   sodium acetate

This reaction is called saponification, from sapo and facere, Latin words meaning to make soap.

Although it appears that the methyl group, —CH_3, merely exchanges position with Na^+, evidence from experiments with ^{18}O labeled compounds shows that the OH^- attacks the ester

$$CH_3C-OCH_3 + {}^{18}OH^- \longrightarrow CH_3C-{}^{18}OH + CH_3O^- \qquad (1)$$

followed by a H transfer

$$CH_3C-{}^{18}OH + CH_3O^- \longrightarrow CH_3C-{}^{18}O^- + CH_3OH \qquad (2)$$

and combination with Na^+

$$CH_3C-{}^{18}O^- + Na^+ \longrightarrow CH_3C-{}^{18}ONa \qquad (3)$$

---

*Almost 40 tons/day of aspirin are produced in the United States. Readers interested in the action of aspirin are referred to *The Sciences,* April 1972, page 6, and *Scientific American,* January 1972, page 91.

PROBLEM 12   Show that the addition of Steps (1), (2), and (3) yields the overall reaction.

Animal and vegetable fats and oils are esters of glycerol. Stearin, the chief component of many fats, is hydrolyzed in the presence of NaOH to yield glycerol and the sodium salt of stearic acid:

From stear, the Greek word for fat.

$$CH_2-O-\overset{\overset{O}{\|}}{C}-(CH_2)_{16}CH_3$$
$$CH-O-\overset{\overset{O}{\|}}{C}-(CH_2)_{16}CH_3(aq) \xrightarrow{\text{NaOH}} CHOH(aq) + 3CH_3(CH_2)_{16}COONa(c)$$
$$CH_2-O-\overset{\overset{O}{\|}}{C}-(CH_2)_{16}CH_3$$

$$\begin{array}{c} CH_2OH \\ CHOH(aq) \\ CH_2OH \end{array}$$

stearin   glycerol   sodium stearate, a soap

Table 22.6 lists the percentages of several of the saturated and unsaturated fatty acids commonly found in natural fats and oils.

PROBLEM 13   Potassium soaps, the potassium salts of fatty acids, the main constituent of shaving creams and liquid soaps, are softer and more soluble than sodium soaps. Write the equation for the saponification of stearin with potassium hydroxide, KOH, and name the products.

Oils (liquid fats at room temperature) generally have a greater percentage of unsaturated fatty acid molecules than do solid fats (Table 22.6). Addition of hydrogen atoms to some of the double bonds converts unsaturated oils (corn, cottonseed, soybean oils) to solid fats, typical of the process used in the manufacture of margarine and vegetable shortening (*Crisco, Spry*).

Amines   Amines, $R-NH_2$, are the most important of the organic nitrogen-containing compounds. They are alkyl derivatives of ammonia and are therefore related to ammonia in structure and chemical properties. Methyl amine, CH_3NH_2, the simplest of the alkyl amines, occurs in fish, in the urine of animals fed on high-protein diets, and in some plants; it has an odor like ammonia. Nitrosodimethylamine, $(CH_3)_2\ddot{N}-\ddot{N}=\ddot{O}:$ (methyl amine in which one H atom is replaced by

TABLE 22.6
SATURATED AND UNSATURATED FATTY ACIDS*
COMMONLY FOUND IN NATURAL FATS AND OILS

NAME	FORMULA	PERCENTAGE IN		
		BUTTERFAT	COTTONSEED OIL	LARD
Myristic acid	$CH_3(CH_2)_{12}COOH$	12	1	2
Palmitic acid	$CH_3(CH_2)_{14}COOH$	25	22	29
Stearic acid	$CH_3(CH_2)_{16}COOH$	9	2	14
Oleic acid	$CH_3(CH_2)_7CH=CH(CH_2)_7COOH$	35	28	45
Linoleic acid	$CH_3(CH_2)_3(CH_2CH=CH)_2(CH_2)_7COOH$	5	44	6

*Polyunsaturated oils are esters whose *fatty acids* contain at least two double bonds. Fatty acids are long chain acids, containing mainly 4 to 18 carbon atoms per molecule, obtained from natural fats and oils.

a second methyl group and the other H atom is replaced by an —NO group), is a powerful carcinogenic agent. This compound has been identified (1971) in cigarette smoke.

Like ammonia, the amines have a nitrogen atom with an unshared pair of electrons. Thus, amines are basic compounds and, like ammonia, form ammonium salts with acids:

$$NH_3(g) \quad + HCl(g) \longrightarrow \quad NH_4^+Cl^-(c)$$

ammonia   *ammonium chloride*

$$CH_3NH_2(g) + HCl(g) \longrightarrow \quad CH_3NH_3^+Cl^-(c)$$

methyl amine   *methyl ammonium chloride*

Amino acids, acids that have an amine group, $R\!-\!\overset{\displaystyle H}{\underset{\displaystyle NH_2}{\overset{|}{\underset{|}{C}}}}\!-\!\overset{\displaystyle O}{\overset{\|}{C}}\!-\!OH,$ are essential for good health. In fact, certain amino acids are indispensable for proper growth and brain development (pages 396 and 726). Further, they are of tremendous theoretical interest because it is widely held that the original formation of proteins on earth occurred from the linkage of amino acids (page 726) and so play an important role in the origin of life. The formation of amino acids in the *absence* of water from a mixture of three gases detected in outer space (page 132), ammonia, methyl alcohol, and formic acid, under the influence of ultraviolet photons, strongly suggests that a waterless planet may support living matter.

At first appearance, amino acids do not appear to be subject to isomerism. But they are: notice that four different groups, —H, —NH₂, —R, and —COOH, are attached to the carbon atom. As in methane, the carbon atom uses four sp^3 AO's. Amino acids are therefore tetrahedral molecules. Let us construct one molecule in which —R is —CH₃ so that the —CH₃ group lies to the left, while the —NH₂ group sits on the right. Now, construct a second molecule, interchanging the —CH₃ group and the —NH₂ group so that the —NH₂ group now lies to the left and the —CH₃ group sits on the right. These two arrangements are labeled **S** (from Latin: *sinister,* left) and **R** (from Latin: *rectus,* right):

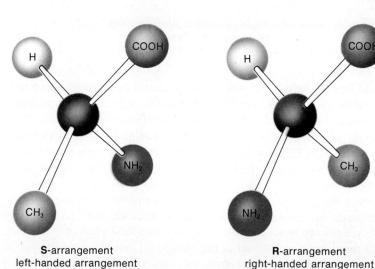

S-arrangement   **R**-arrangement

left-handed arrangement   right-handed arrangement

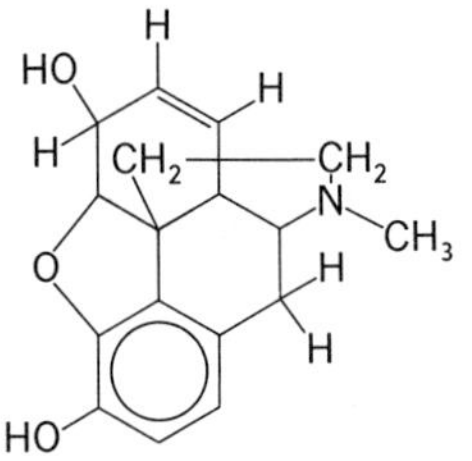

Morphine*
from opium poppy seed
(depressant, pain killer)

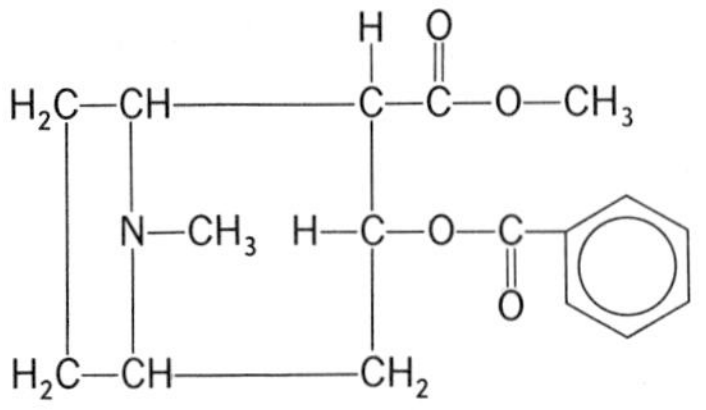

Cocaine*
from cocoa plant
(depressant, pain killer)

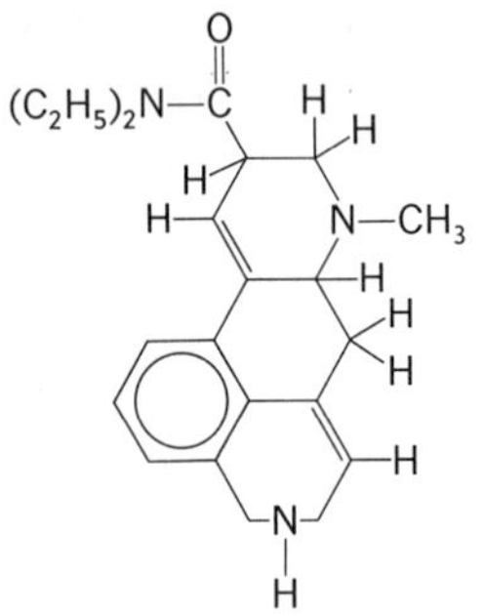

Lysergic acid diethylamide
(hallucinogenic drug, LSD)

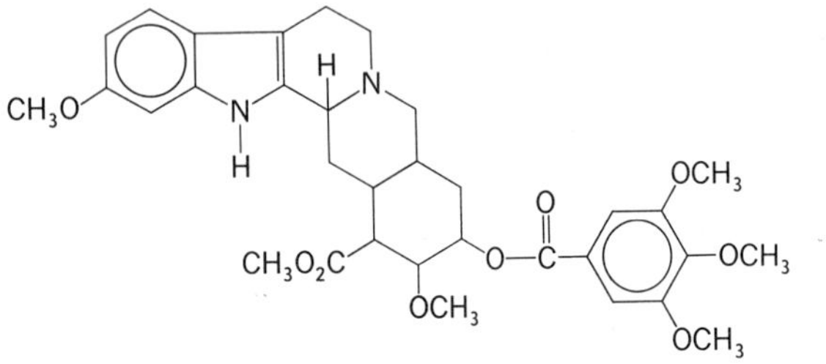

Reserpine*
(tranquilizer)
(treatment of high blood pressure)

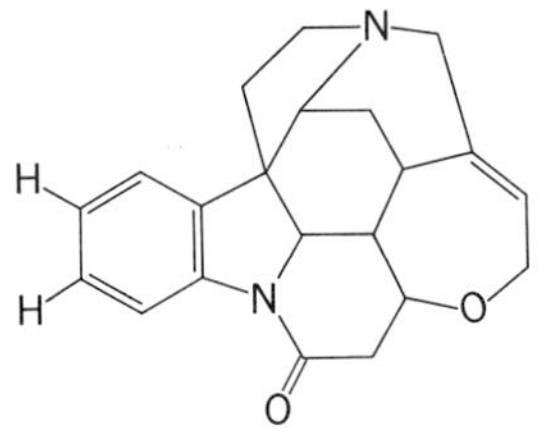

Strychnine*
deadly poison
a plant product
(stimulant)

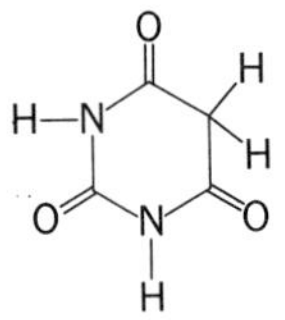

Barbituric acid
(sedative)

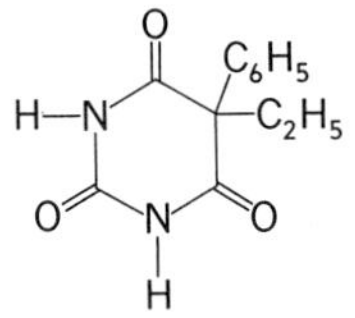

Phenobarbital
(sedative)

FIGURE 22.8 Physiologically active compounds containing nitrogen and oxygen atoms in a ring structure. *Also known as alkaloids because they are basic substances, "alkali-like," owing to the presence of an ammonia-like structure, $\equiv$N: (For clarity, all H atoms on ring structures are not shown in reserpine and strychnine).

It would be very helpful for you to construct and examine two such models. No matter how these two models are rotated or turned, they cannot be matched (superimposed) without breaking chemical bonds. Therefore, they represent two isomers. This is true for all compounds in which a carbon atom is attached to four different atoms or groups, HFCClBr, or in general, ABCDE. However, nature has a strong preference for the **S**-isomer. In fact, nearly all amino acids in living organisms have the **S**-arrangement. But after death, the amino acids in an organism slowly change to the **R**-isomer, so that this reaction may provide an important method for dating fossils millions of years old, too old to be dated by radiocarbon methods (page 537).

Many cyclic compounds contain more than one kind of atom in the ring. These compounds represent a major part of chemistry and include compounds like antibiotics and vitamins that possess significant biological importance. They play an important role in cell processes, provide the catalyst for photosynthesis, and form

For example, $t_{1/2} = 1.1 \times 10^5$ years at 20 °C for the amino acid isoleucine (Table 23.4, page 726).

the basic structure of many drugs. We shall, however, only examine briefly some examples.

Many of the **vitamins**[*] are compounds that contain rings which incorporate nitrogen atoms or oxygen atoms. The body cannot make vitamins from food. They must therefore be included in the diet for proper growth and good health. A deficiency of vitamin C, ascorbic acid,

$$HO—\overset{|}{C}\!=\!=\!\overset{|}{C}—OH$$
$$O\!=\!\overset{|}{C}\qquad \overset{|}{C}H—CHOH—CH_2OH$$
$$\underset{O}{\diagdown\;\diagup}$$

Vitamin E, believed to prevent aging by interfering with O_2 damage to cells, does not prolong the life span of human cells.

causes scurvy, an ancient disease. Citrus fruits, particularly lemons and limes, rich in vitamin C, were eaten by British sailors ("limeys") during long sea voyages. Recent studies show that the prevention of scurvy is not the only function of ascorbic acid. For example, it appears to be involved in the change of cholesterol to bile acids in the liver of animals. A vitamin C deficiency therefore results in the accumulation of cholesterol in the blood and liver. Cholesterol, $C_{27}H_{45}OH$, a steroid present in all animal tissues, is the main constituent of gallstones. It is also the substance that deposits on the walls of arteries and is so associated with heart disease.

Synthetic ascorbic acid has been available since 1937.

Niacin (nicotinic acid), ⬡—COOH, is the vitamin responsible for prevention of pellagra. Some other physiologically active ring compounds are illustrated in Fig. 22.8.

Large deficiencies lead to dermatitis, diarrhea, and dementia.

EPILOG from Margery Barnett Albertson, *The Sciences*, December 1971

"I'm no faddist,
Not gone organic,
Keep my cool and never panic.
I wash my clothes
Without an additive,
The phosphate problem
Won't drive me madditive.
I've learned to live
With BHA, MSG, EDTA;[**]
I'll probably survive sodium nitrate
Citric acid and cal. propionate.
I'm hip that hot dogs labeled 'meat'
Give us plenty of other things to eat;
But now I've had the final zap;
FDA said okay to SAP."[†]

Nevertheless, it is important to recognize that the question of the long-term effect of very low levels of toxic agents—food additives, chemical pesticides, radiation—on human health cannot be demonstrated in any laboratory experiment for practical reasons. For example, we can *assume* that a straight line expresses the relation between dosage and body cell damage, going straight down to zero dosage; no dose—no cell damage. As the dosage increases, the number of cells damaged increases. It sounds reasonable. But the number of mice needed (8 billion) to verify the small predicted effect of 0.170 rem of radiation (App. IX) with scientific confidence makes the experiment practically impossible.

---

[*] So named by Casimir Funk, who believed (1911) that the absence of a chemical substance caused the disease beriberi, induced in birds by Christiaan Eijkman (1897) when he fed them with polished rice.

[**] BHA, butyl hydroxyanisole, $C_6H_3(OH)(C_4H_9)(OCH_3)$, a food additive, serves to prevent oxidation. MSG, monosodium glutamate, $HC(NH_2)(COOH)(CH_2CH_2COONa)$, a food additive, serves as a flavor accentuator. EDTA, ethylenediaminetetraacetic acid, $(HOOCCH_2)_2NCH_2CH_2N(CH_2COOH)_2$, forms thermodynamically stable complex ions by way of the N atoms.

[†] FDA, Food and Drug Administration. SAP, sodium acid pyrophosphate ($Na_2H_2P_2O_7$, disodium dihydrogen diphosphate, page 613), gives hot dogs a rosy red color. It also reduces production time and allows processed meats to retain more fat and water. Over 2000 food additives are in use. Readers interested in this subject are referred to "Food Additives," *Scientific American,* March 1972, page 15; "Food Colors," National Research Council, National Academy of Sciences, Washington, D.C., 1971; and "How to Eat Right," Jean Mayer, *U.S. News and World Report,* 9 August 1976, page 37.

PROBLEMS

14 Vocabulary Define and/or illustrate: (a) alkane, (b) alkene, (c) alkyne, (d) aromatic compound, (e) isomerism, (f) alcohol, (g) aldehyde, (h) ketone, (i) ether, (j) carboxylic acid, (k) carbohydrate, (l) ester, (m) fat, (n) amine, (o) amino acid.

15 Nomenclature Write the IUPAC name for each compound given:

(a) $CH_3-CH_2-CH_2-\overset{\overset{\displaystyle CH_3}{|}}{\underset{\underset{\displaystyle H}{|}}{C}}-CH_3$

(b) $CH_3-CH_2-\overset{\overset{}{|}}{\underset{\underset{\displaystyle Cl}{|}}{CH}}-CH_2-\overset{\overset{\displaystyle CH_3}{|}}{\underset{\underset{\displaystyle CH_3}{|}}{C}}-\overset{}{\underset{\underset{\displaystyle Cl}{|}}{CH}}-CH_3$

(c) $CH_3-CH_2-\overset{\overset{\displaystyle CH_3}{|}}{\underset{\underset{\displaystyle CH_3}{|}}{C}}-CH_2-CH_2-CH_3$

(d) $ClHC{=}CH-CH_3$

(e) $CH_3-\overset{\overset{\displaystyle Cl}{|}}{CH}-CCl_2-CH_2-CH_3$

(f) $H-C{\equiv}C-Cl$

(g) $F_2CH-CH_2-CCl{=}CH-CH_3$

16 Each of the following names is incorrect. Draw the structure and give the correct name for each compound: (a) 3,6-difluorohexane, (b) 4,4-dichloropentane, (c) 2-ethylpentane.

17 Structural formula Draw the structural formula for each of the following compounds: (a) 1,3-dichloro-2-methylbutane, (b) dichlorodifluoromethane (*Freon-12*), (c) 2-methyl-2-butene, (d) 3-bromo-5-fluoroheptane, (e) 3-bromo-1-propene, (f) 2-heptyne, (g) 1-bromo-2-butene, (h) ethylbenzene.

18 Isomerism (a) Write the structural formulas of the three isomers of pentane, C_5H_{12}. (b) Name these compounds according to the IUPAC system.

19 Which of the following pairs of molecules, (i) through (v) given below, (a) represent the same compound; (b) represent isomers?

20 From the following pairs of molecules, pick the pair that does not exhibit *cis-trans* isomerism. For the other two pairs, label the *cis* and *trans* molecules.

(a) $\overset{\displaystyle Br}{\underset{\displaystyle CH_3}{>}}C{=}C\overset{\displaystyle H}{\underset{\displaystyle H}{<}}$ and $\overset{\displaystyle CH_3}{\underset{\displaystyle Br}{>}}C{=}C\overset{\displaystyle H}{\underset{\displaystyle H}{<}}$

(b) $\overset{\displaystyle H}{\underset{\displaystyle I}{>}}C{=}C\overset{\displaystyle CH_3}{\underset{\displaystyle I}{<}}$ and $\overset{\displaystyle H}{\underset{\displaystyle I}{>}}C{=}C\overset{\displaystyle I}{\underset{\displaystyle CH_3}{<}}$

(c) $\overset{\displaystyle H}{\underset{\displaystyle Cl}{>}}C{=}C\overset{\displaystyle H}{\underset{\displaystyle Cl}{<}}$ and $\overset{\displaystyle Cl}{\underset{\displaystyle H}{>}}C{=}C\overset{\displaystyle H}{\underset{\displaystyle Cl}{<}}$

Formulas for Problem 19

(i) $CH_3-CH_2-CH_2-CH_3$ and $CH_3-CH_2-\overset{}{\underset{\underset{\displaystyle CH_3}{|}}{CH_2}}$

(ii) $\overset{\overset{\displaystyle CH_3}{|}}{\underset{\underset{\displaystyle Cl}{|}}{CH}}-\overset{\overset{\displaystyle CH_3}{|}}{CH}-CH_3$ and $CH_3-CHCl-\overset{\overset{\displaystyle CH_3}{|}}{CH}-CH_3$

(iii) $CH_3-\overset{\overset{\displaystyle CH_3}{|}}{\underset{\underset{\displaystyle H}{|}}{C}}-O-CH_3$ and $CH_3-O-CH_2-CH_2-CH_3$

(iv) $CH_3-\overset{\overset{\displaystyle O}{\|}}{C}-O-CH_2-CH_3$ and $CH_3-CH_2-\overset{\overset{\displaystyle O}{\|}}{C}-O-CH_3$

(v) $CH_2{=}CH-CH_2-CH_3$ and $CH_3-CH_2-CH{=}CH_2$

21 (a) Write the structural formulas of the two possible products formed when HCl adds to 1-butene. (b) How many different products are possible when Cl_2 adds to 1-butene?

22 Reactions (a) Write the structural formulas of the alkene products formed when 2-pentanol,

$$CH_3-\underset{\underset{OH}{|}}{\overset{\overset{H}{|}}{C}}-CH_2CH_2CH_3,$$

eliminates a molecule of water (i) using an H atom on carbon number 1, and (ii) using an H atom on carbon number 3 when treated with warm concentrated sulfuric acid. (b) Write the structural formula of an ether that forms when methanol is treated with concentrated sulfuric acid.

23 Write balanced equations, using structural formulas, to represent the following reactions: (a) the addition of 1 mole of hydrogen to 1-butyne; (b) saponification of ethyl acetate, $CH_3COOC_2H_5$, with NaOH; (c) addition of HBr to 2-hexene; (d) ester formation with ethyl alcohol and formic acid, HCOOH; (e) combustion of benzene, C_6H_6, in excess oxygen.

24 The following series of reactions has been proposed for the synthesis of benzene for use as a major gasoline extender:

Li + C(coke, coal, charcoal, C waste)

$$\xrightarrow{950\ °C} Li_2C_2$$

$$Li_2C_2 + H_2O \xrightarrow{250\ °C} C_2H_2 + LiOH$$

$$LiOH \xrightarrow{400\ °C} Li + O_2 + H_2O$$

$$C_2H_2 \xrightarrow{350\ °C} C_6H_6$$

Balance each equation. Find the overall reaction. What is consumed and produced? What is the prime catalyst?

25 What simple chemical test would you use to distinguish between (a) propane and propene, (b) ethyl alcohol and methyl ether, (c) benzene and hexene,

(d) $CH_3-\underset{\underset{O}{||}}{C}-CH_3$ and $CH_3-CH_2-\underset{\underset{H}{|}}{\overset{\overset{}{}}{C}}=O$?

26 Oxidation number (a) Shown below is the sequence of oxidation of methyl alcohol. What is the oxidation number of carbon in each compound?

$H_3C-OH \longrightarrow H_2C=O \longrightarrow$

$$H-\underset{\underset{O}{||}}{C}-OH \longrightarrow O=C=O$$

(b) Write the corresponding sequence for the oxidation of propyl alcohol, $CH_3CH_2CH_2OH$.

27 Fats Glycerol butyrate is one of the major fat constituents of butter. The disagreeable odor of rancid butter is due largely to the acrid odor of butyric acid (four carbon atoms per molecule) formed by the hydrolysis of glycerol butyrate. Write the balanced equation for the hydrolysis of glycerol butyrate.

28 Aromaticity Diborane, B_2H_6, and ammonia react to form borazine, $B_3N_3H_6$, a liquid chemically resembling benzene. A contributing structure of borazine is

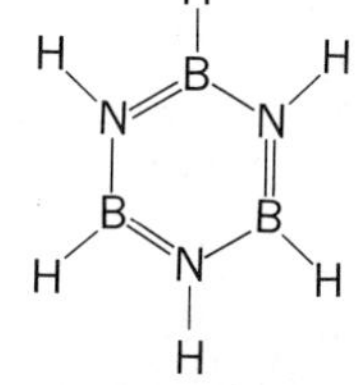

(a) Write a second contributing structure. (b) Name the AO's used by the N and B atoms, sp, sp^2, or sp^3. Sketch the MO description of borazine. (c) Is borazine an aromatic compound?

29 Acidity Phenol, C_6H_5OH, is a stronger acid than water, while ethyl alcohol, C_2H_5OH, is a weaker acid than water. Which group, $-C_6H_5$ or $-C_2H_5$, releases negative charge to the hydroxyl group? Explain.

30 When it was first discovered, benzene was called "bicarburet of hydrogen" and was assigned the formula C_2H on the atomic weight scale defined by C = 6 and H = 1. How many grams of carbon per gram of hydrogen are in benzene? Rewrite the formula using currently accepted atomic weights. Is it acceptable (a) as an empirical formula, and (b) as a molecular formula?

31 (a) When methyl chloride reacts with benzene in the presence of a catalyst, $AlCl_3$, a methyl group replaces one of the hydrogen atoms on the benzene ring. Write a balanced equation for the reaction. (b) Write the structural formulas of the products of the reaction between ethyl alcohol and formic acid:

$$CH_3CH_2OH + \underset{\underset{}{}}{\overset{\overset{O}{||}}{HC}}-OH \longrightarrow ?$$

(c) Alkenes with two double bonds are known as dienes. A typical example is 1,3-butadiene, $CH_2=CH-CH=CH_2$. Write the structural formulas of the products formed when 1 mole of 1,3-butadiene reacts with (i) 2 moles of hydrogen and (ii) 2 moles of bromine.

32 Barium ethyl sulfate is used in the treatment of stone monuments threatened by acid pollution:

$Ba(C_2H_5SO_4)_2(aq) + H_2O \longrightarrow$
$$BaSO_4(c) + C_2H_5OH(aq) + H_2SO_4(aq)$$

Balance the equation and write the electronic structures of C_2H_5OH, $(C_2H_5SO_4)^-$, and $Ba(C_2H_5SO_4)_2$. Assume covalent bonding.

33 Library Read one of the following:

(a) "A Treatise on Adulterations of Food, etc. There is Death in the Pot," Frederick C. Accum, Publisher, A. Small, Philadelphia, 1820, Preface, pages 1–30.

(b) "Conformational Analysis, 1869," Frank Brescia and Pietro Mangiaracina, *Journal of Chemical Education,* volume 53, 1976, page 32.

(c) "Occupational Carcinogenesis," *Annals of New York Academy of Sciences,* volume 271, 1976.

(d) "Using a Sex Attractant for Insect Control," Paul Hedin, *Chemical Technology,* July 1976, page 444.

(e) "Aspirin, The Uncommon Pill?" *Wall Street Journal,* 9 June 1976, page 1.

(f) "Vitamin C, Blood Cholesterol, and Atherosclerosis," Emil Ginter, *American Laboratory,* June 1976, page 21.

(g) "Origin of Atherosclerosis," Earl Benditt, *Scientific American,* February 1977, page 74.

(h) "Chemicals from Coal," Arthur Squires, *Science,* volume 191, 20 February 1976, page 689.

(i) "Gasoline from Methanol in One Step," S. L. Meisel, *Chemical Technology,* February 1976, page 86.

(j) "The Beriberi Vitamin, The Story of 26 Years of Research," *Chemical Technology,* May 1976, page 300.

(k) "Toxicological Effects of Ozone, Oxidizing Agent (Oxidant), and Hydrocarbons," Oscar Balchum and Robert Carroll, *Proceedings of the Conference on Health Effects of Air Pollutants,* National Academy of Sciences, U.S. Government Printing Office, Washington, D.C., November 1973, pages 489–499, 541–553.

(l) "Polychlorinated Biphenyls (PCB) in the Environment," Salvatore DiNardi and Anne Desmarais, *Chemistry,* volume 49, May 1976, page 14.

(m) "The Kepone Episode," *Chemistry,* volume 49, May 1976, page 20; and *Science,* volume 193, 13 August 1976, page 528.

(n) "Rerefined Oil; Saves Oil, Minimizes Pollution," *Science,* volume 193, 17 September 1976, page 1108.

ADDITIONAL PROBLEMS

34 (a) Draw six alkene isomers of pentene, C_5H_{10}. (b) Draw another isomer of C_5H_{10} that is not an alkene. (c) Write the structural formulas of the five isomers of hexane, C_6H_{14}.

35 When methylbenzene (toluene), is brominated, three isomeric monobromo products are obtained. One is . Draw the structural formulas of the other two isomers.

36 Is our vitamin requirement the same for all living animals? Explain.

37 Are HCN and HNC isomers? Are DCN and HCN isomers? (D is deuterium, ^2H.) Write electronic structures for HCN and HNC in which the octet rule is satisfied.

38 A contributing structure of pyridine, obtained from coal tar, and one of its corresponding phosphorus compound are given:

Write a second contributing structure for each compound and sketch its MO description.

39 (a) *n*-Butane has a higher boiling point than isobutane (Table 22.1, page 682). See Fig. 22.3 b, page 683, and explain in terms of London forces. (b) Explain the increase in the boiling point of normal alkanes (Table 22.2, page 684) in terms of London forces.

40 (a) Write the structural formula of the product formed when HCl adds to cyclobutene:

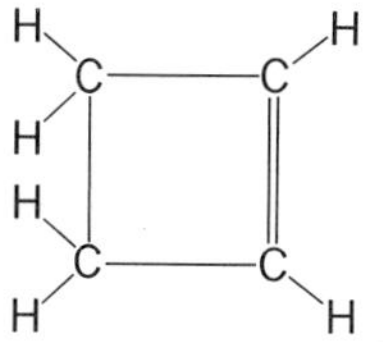

(b) Two different isomeric products are possible when HCl adds to 2-methylcyclohexene:

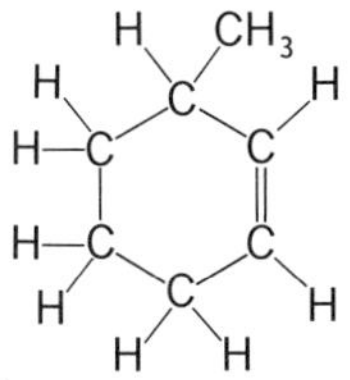

Write the structural formulas of the two possible products.

41 The fusion of six p_z orbitals in C_6H_6 generates six MO's, three bonding (b) and three antibonding (ab). These MO's take the six electrons assigned to the cyclic delocalized π bond:

Electronic excitation, the difference in energy between bonding and antibonding orbitals, ΔE, is related to the frequency of the photons absorbed by benzene. The electronic spectrum of benzene shows strong absorption in the UV range. (a) $\Delta E = 586.3$ kJ/mole. Calculate the frequency and the wavelength of the photon absorbed. (b) Benzene is colorless; explain.

42 (a) Use Table 9.1, page 295, to check the energy ($\Delta H = +1274$ kcal) required to decompose a contributing structure of benzene (page 693). (b) Delocalization of bonding electrons always increases the stability of a molecule (Problem 2, page 560). The stability due to electron delocalization is called *delocalization energy*. This means that more energy is required to break the gaseous molecule into its constituent atoms. The difference in the energy—the energy needed to decompose the delocalized (real) molecule, 1318 kcal, compared with the energy needed to decompose one of the contributing (fictitious) structures—corresponds to the delocalization energy. What is the delocalization energy of benzene?

43 The half-life for the conversion of coal to pyridine-soluble products at 425 °C is 22 s. What fraction of coal so reacts after 2.2 min?

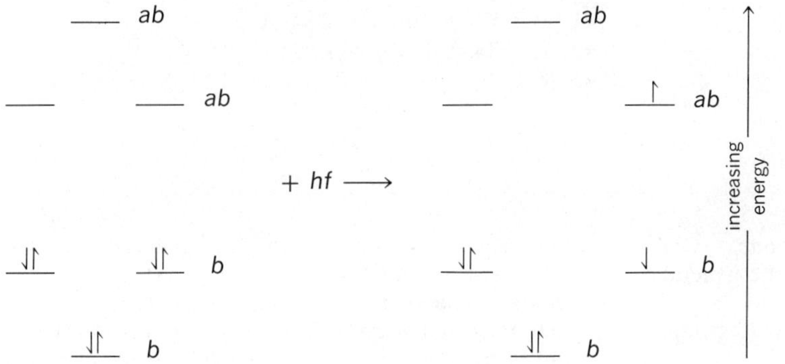

ANSWERS

2 (a) $C_{12}H_{26}$
3 (iii) isomers
4 (a) 2,4-dibromo-3,5-dichloro-3,5-dimethylheptane
  (b) 3-bromo-3-methylpentane

5 (a)

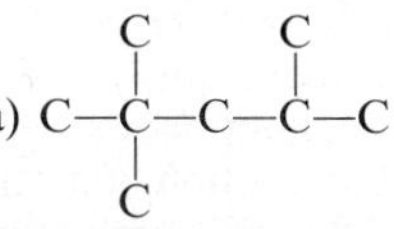

  (b)

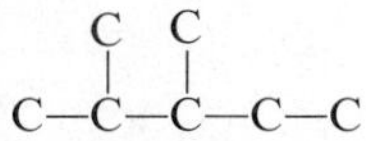

6 no

7 (a) $C{\equiv}C{-}C{-}C$

  (b) $C{-}C{=}C{-}C{-}C$

  (c) $C{=}C{-}C{-}C{-}C$

8 (a)(b) $C{-}C{-}C{-}C{-}C$, *n*-pentane

9 $F_2CHCOOH, FCH_2COOH, CH_3COOH, C_2H_5COOH$

11 (a) $C_6H_5CH{=}CH{-}\overset{\displaystyle O}{\overset{\|}{C}}{-}O{-}CH_3$

(b) $C_6H_5CH{=}CH{-}\overset{\displaystyle O}{\overset{\|}{C}}{-}O{-}CH_2{-}CH_3$

15 (a) 2-methylpentane,
(b) 2,5-dichloro-3,3-dimethylheptane,
(c) 3,3-dimethylhexane,
(d) 1-chloropropene,
(e) 2,3,3-trichloropentane,
(f) chloroethyne (chloroacetylene),
(g) 3-chloro-5,5-difluoro-2-pentene
16 (a) 1,4-difluorohexane,
(b) 2,2-dichloropentane,
(c) 3-methylhexane
18 n-pentane; 2,2-dimethylpropane; 2-methylbutane
19 iii, iv isomers
20 (a)
21 (a) $CH_3CHClCH_2CH_3$ and $CH_2ClCH_2CH_2CH_3$
(b) one
22 (a) (i) $CH_2{=}CHCH_2CH_2CH_3$
(ii) $CH_3CH{=}CHCH_2CH_3$
(b) CH_3OCH_3
23 (a) C_4H_{10}
(b) $CH_3COONa + C_2H_5OH$
(c) $CH_3C(H)Br(CH_2)_3CH_3$
(d) $HCOOC_2H_5$
(e) $12CO_2 + 6H_2O$
24 $2C + H_2O \rightarrow \frac{1}{3}\,C_6H_6 + \frac{1}{2}\,O_2$
or
$6C + 3H_2O \rightarrow C_6H_6 + \frac{3}{2}\,O_2$;

C and H_2O producing C_6H_6 and O_2;
Li_2C_2 (Li$-$C$\equiv$C$-$Li)
26 (a) -2, 0, $+2$, $+4$
28 (b) sp^2; (c) aromatic
29 $-C_2H_5$
30 CH

31 (b) $CH_3CH_2{-}O{-}\overset{\displaystyle O}{\overset{\|}{C}}{-}H$; (c)(i) n-butane
34 (a) 1-pentene; cis- and $trans$-2-pentene;
2-methyl-1-butene; 3-methyl-1-butene;
2-methyl-2-butene
(b) cyclopentane; (c) n-hexane; 2-methylpentane;
3-methylpentane; 2,2-dimethylbutane;
2,3-dimethylbutane

35

37 yes; no
40 (a)
(b)

41 (a) 1.470×10^{15} s^{-1}; 2040 Å
42 (a) 1274 kcal; (b) 44 kcal
43 98 %

GLOSSARY

alcohol A compound containing at least one $-$OH group and a hydrocarbon group, having the general formula R$-$OH.
aldehyde A compound containing an aldehyde group,

$-\overset{\displaystyle O}{\overset{\|}{C}}-$H, at the end of a hydrocarbon chain, having

the general formula R$-\overset{\displaystyle O}{\overset{\|}{C}}-$H.
alkane A hydrocarbon containing only single carbon-carbon (σ) bonds, general formula C_nH_{2n+2}.
alkene A hydrocarbon containing a carbon-carbon double bond ($\sigma + \pi$), general formula C_nH_{2n}.
alkyl group A hydrocarbon group derived from the corresponding alkane molecule by removing one hydrogen atom, such as CH_3—, C_2H_5—, symbolized by the letter R.
alkyne A hydrocarbon containing a carbon-carbon triple bond ($\sigma + 2\pi$), general formula C_nH_{2n-2}.
amine A basic substance related to ammonia in which a hydrogen atom on ammonia is replaced by an alkyl or aryl group, general formula R$-$NH$_2$.

amino acid An acid with the general formula R$-$C(H)(NH$_2$)COOH.
aromatic compound A benzene-like compound; one that has a planar cyclic arrangement of carbon atoms linked by single (σ) bonds and a delocalized pi bond.
aryl group A group derived from an aromatic molecule by removing one hydrogen atom, such as $-C_6H_5$ derived from benzene, C_6H_6.
carbohydrate An aldehyde or a ketone containing a number of hydroxyl groups; the sugars and starch are typical carbohydrates.
carbonyl group See **ketone**.
carboxylic acid A compound containing the carboxyl group, $-$COOH, general formula R$-$COOH.
conformations The different arrangements obtained by rotating one end of a molecule with respect to the other end. These different arrangements can be rotated to look alike without breaking bonds.
ester A compound formed by the reaction of a carboxylic acid with an alcohol with the elimination of water, general formula

$R{-}\overset{\displaystyle O}{\overset{\|}{C}}{-}O{-}R'$.

ether A compound in which alkyl or aryl groups are bonded to the same oxygen atom, general formula R—O—R′.

fats and oils Animal and vegetable fats and oils are esters of glycerine and carboxylic acids.

functional group A group of atoms in a molecule that gives a compound a characteristic set of properties, for example —OH in alcohols and —NH_2 in amines.

homologous series A series of compounds related by the addition of a CH_2 group and whose molecular formulas can be summarized by a general formula, such as C_nH_{2n+2} and C_nH_{2n}.

hydrocarbon A compound composed of carbon and hydrogen.

ketone A compound containing a carbonyl group,
$$\overset{\displaystyle O}{\overset{\|}{—C—}},$$
bonded to an alkyl or aryl group, general formula
$$R—\overset{\displaystyle O}{\overset{\|}{C}}—R′.$$

saponification The reaction of a strong base with an ester.

POLYMERS AND PROTEINS

23

INTRODUCTION_____23.1

Polymers, from the Greek words *poly* and *mers* meaning many parts, are large molecules (macromolecules) which have been formed by joining together many small molecules. This process of joining **monomers** (single molecules) together is called **polymerization.** When more than one kind of molecule (monomer) is joined together, the resulting macromolecule is called a **copolymer.** Daily observations reveal the important role that polymers, "plastics," play in our lives. They frequently offer a superior and economic substitute for many natural products, such as ceramics, rubber, wool, cotton, and silk.

Since polymers are usually formed by joining a large number of smaller molecules, they have high molecular weights. It is not uncommon for polymers to have molecular weights of 100,000 or greater.

Polymers are often characterized from their decomposition products. Thus, if natural rubber (from the *Hevea* tree of the Amazon Valley) is heated, the hydrocarbon *isoprene,* H ⬡ H, distills off, indicating that *natural rubber* is a polymer of

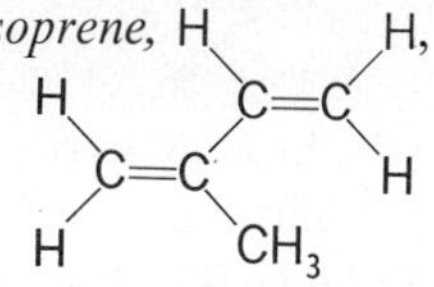

35 % of the rubber used by tire manufacturers is natural rubber; guayule, a desert plant that produces natural rubber, is therefore under study.

isoprene units. Further experimentation has shown that natural rubber has a long chain-like structure:

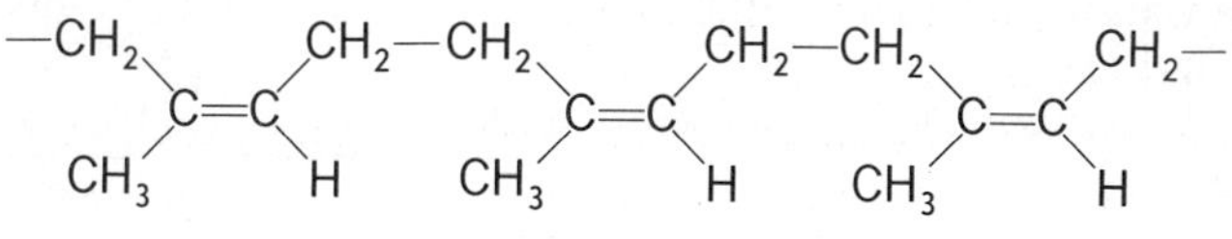

Notice that in natural rubber the —CH$_2$— linkages are all *cis*. The *trans*- isomer also exists but exhibits different properties. The *trans*-isomer, a natural nonelastic polymer, called gutta percha, has the structure

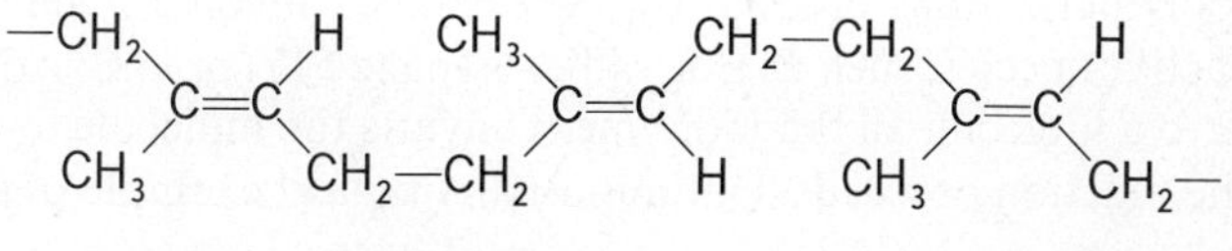

While the cis-isomer is flexible, the trans-isomer is hard and brittle. In the trans-isomer, the long molecules nicely lie alongside each other, increasing contact and thereby increasing London forces (page 259). This has the effect of stiffening the molecules.

In these cases, the repeating unit (isoprene) of the macromolecule is exactly identical to the breakdown product (isoprene). Such a polymer is called an **addition polymer,** since it seems to be formed simply by joining the monomers together:

$$\text{isoprene} \quad \frac{\textit{polymerization}}{\textit{decomposition}} \quad \text{natural rubber}$$

Many monomers, however, also form polymers with an accompanying loss of a small molecule, such as water, carbon monoxide, or hydrogen chloride. Such polymers are called **condensation polymers** and their decomposition products are not identical with the repeating units in the polymer. Thus, the polymerization of glucose to cellulose,[*] a natural polymer, is accompanied by the loss of water:

•From cellula, Latin for small cell; this is the substance that forms the walls of plant cells.

$$\text{glucose} \quad \frac{\textit{polymerization}}{\textit{decomposition}} \quad \text{cellulose} + \text{water}$$

Cellulose is a typical condensation polymer:

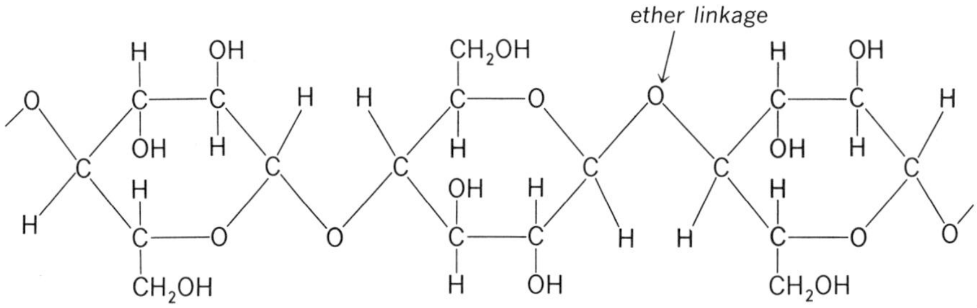

While glucose plays an important role in human metabolism, the human body cannot break down cellulose to glucose. Cattle and other grazing animals, however, break down cellulose, making it possible for them to live on a diet of plants. Bacteria in their stomachs produce an enzyme (page 728) capable of breaking the ether linkage between the glucose monomers in cellulose.

Proteins (page 726), the building blocks of animal and plant tissues, are also natural condensation polymers. Other naturally occurring polymers include silk, cotton, wool, and starch.

Since the early 1930's, chemists have made polymers, such as *Nylon, Dacron, Orlon, Plexiglas,* synthetic rubbers, and *Bakelite,* which do not occur in nature.

23.2 _____ ADDITION POLYMERIZATION

Addition polymerizations proceed by a mechanism involving the initial formation of some reactive species, such as free radicals (page 517) or ions. Addition of this reactive species to a molecule of the monomer converts the molecule to a free radical or ion. Then, the reaction proceeds continuously. A typical example of a free-radical addition polymerization is the polymerization of vinyl chloride, $H_2C{=}CHCl$, into polyvinyl chloride (PVC):

IUPAC name, chloroethene; may cause liver cancer.

$$\text{Initial formation of the free} \atop \text{radical} \cdot OH \text{ from a peroxide} \longrightarrow \cdot OH$$

Under the influence of $\cdot OH$, $H_2C{=}CHCl$ changes to a free radical by addition:

free radical I   free radical II

Then another $H_2C{=}CHCl$ molecule adds to free radical II, producing a free-radical addition product:

free radical II

addition product of two molecules, a free radical

The similar addition of many more $H_2C{=}CHCl$ molecules forms polyvinyl chloride.

An example of an addition polymerization initiated by a cation is the conversion of *styrene* into polystyrene (*Styrofoam* plastic):

Styrene is more commonly polymerized by a free radical method.

a cation, carbon atom has only six electrons in highest shell

Under the influence of the cation, in which a C atom does not have an octet, a pair of electrons, attracted from a second styrene molecule, completes the octet. However, in the addition, the cation character is not lost:

A cation containing a carbon atom with six electrons in its highest shell is called a carbonium ion.

cation   styrene   addition product, a cation

Then, similar addition of many more styrene molecules forms the polymer.

Table 23.1 gives the names and uses of some common addition polymers.

TABLE 23.1
SOME COMMON ADDITION POLYMERS

REPEATING UNIT (MONOMER)	POLYMER COMMON NAME	USES
$CH_2{=}CHCl$ vinyl chloride	PVC, "vinyl," Koroseal, Dynel	floor tile, pipe, clear plastic, film, food wrap
$CH{=}CH_2$ (phenyl ring) styrene	styrene, Styrofoam, Lustron, Styron	insulation, hot drink cups, toys, knobs
$CH_3{-}CH{=}CH_2$ propylene	polypropylene	pipes, plastic baby bottles, waterproof carpet, rope
$CH_2{=}CH_2$ ethylene	Polyethylene, Marlex	squeeze bottles, flexible cups, clear plastic food bags, surgical mesh
$CF_2{=}CF_2$ tetrafluoroethylene	Teflon	linings for frying pans, electrical insulation, gaskets, chemically resistant pipes
$CH_2{=}CH{-}CN$ acrylonitrile*	Acrilan, Orlon**	fabrics and knitted goods, carpets, blankets
$CH_2{=}\underset{\underset{methyl\ methacrylate}{}}{\overset{\overset{CH_3}{\mid}}{C}}{-}COOCH_3$	"acrylic," Lucite, Plexiglas	break-resistant windows, dental fillings, false teeth, brush handles, auto reflectors and tail lights
$CH_2{=}CCl_2$ 1,1-dichloroethene	Saran	food wrapping, auto seat covers, records
$CH_2{=}CH{-}O{-}\underset{O}{\overset{\parallel}{C}}{-}CH_3$ vinyl acetate	PVA plastic, Vinylite	luggage, pipes
$CH_2{=}\underset{\underset{chloroprene}{}}{\overset{\overset{Cl}{\mid}}{C}}{-}CH{=}CH_2$	Neoprene, "artificial rubber"	shoe soles and heels, electrical insulation, hoses

*Toxic and probably carcinogenic, acrylonitrile plastic soft-drink bottles have been banned by U.S.F.D.A.; unreacted monomer can leach out into contents.
**Combustion produces hydrogen cyanide.

Most condensation polymers are really *copolymers;* that is, they are formed from two or more kinds of monomers. Thus, a diamine reacts with a dicarboxylic acid to form nylon:

H—N—(CH$_2$)$_6$—N—H + HO—C—(CH$_2$)$_4$—C—OH ⟶

1,6-hexanediamine   adipic acid

—N—(CH$_2$)$_6$—N—C—(CH$_2$)$_4$—C— + 2H$_2$O

nylon

This is one of a series of nylons called nylon-66. The number indicates that both monomers have 6 carbon atoms. This is the nylon usually used in hosiery.

Table 23.2 gives the names and uses of some common condensation polymers.

THE ORIENTATION OF REPEATING UNITS_____23.4
IN MACROMOLECULES

Natural rubber and gutta percha are isomers (page 664). However, even in the absence of double bonds, *cis-* and *trans-*isomers occur in polymers.

If all branches (groups) are on the same side of the extended chain we have a *cis-*polymer, while if they are on opposite sides we have a *trans-*polymer. If the branches (groups) are attached without order in a random fashion, the polymer is referred to as *atactic.* Thus, propylene forms a typical *atactic* polymer with methyl groups randomly distributed.

From ataktos, the Greek word meaning without order.

However, in the early 1950's Karl Ziegler and Giulio Natta discovered that by the use of appropriate catalysts it was possible to imitate nature and control the orientation of repeating units. Thus, compounds such as "natural rubber" can now be synthesized. Further, propylene can be polymerized with regularity so that all methyl groups are either on the same side or on opposite sides of the extended chain:

The original catalyst was a mixture of aluminum triethyl and titanium tetrachloride.

atactic   cis- arrangement   trans- arrangement

The *cis-* and *trans-*arrangements are similar to the isomers resulting from the presence

TABLE 23.2
SOME COMMON CONDENSATION POLYMERS

MONOMERS	MOLECULE ELIMINATED	POLYMER NAME	USES
H_2N—$(CH_2)_6$—NH_2 hexanediamine + $HOOC$—$(CH_2)_4$—$COOH$ adipic acid	H_2O	Nylon 66	hosiery, rope, fabrics
C_2H_5OOC—⟨◯⟩—$COOC_2H_5$ diethyl terephthalate + $HOCH_2CH_2OH$ ethylene glycol	C_2H_5OH	Mylar Terylene Dacron Fortrel	fabrics
H—C=C—H O=C C=O \ / O maleic anhydride + $HOCH_2CH_2OH$ ethylene glycol	H_2O	Alkyd plastic	floor finishes, auto enamels, adhesives, cements
CH_3 | HO—Si—OH | CH_3 dimethylsilanediol	H_2O	silicones	high temperature lubricants, water- repellent, silicone rubber
$HCHO$ formaldehyde + $(NH_2)_2CO$ urea	H_2O	urea-formaldehyde resin	toys, buttons, textile coatings, adhesives
O=C=N—CH_2CH_2—N=C=O ethylene diisocyanate + $HOCH_2CH_2OH$ ethylene glycol	H_2O	polyurethane*	fibers, paints, heat insulation

*Combustion produces hydrogen cyanide.

Intermolecular attractive forces and hydrogen bonding (Chap. 8).

The cis-arrangement is called isotactic, the trans- is called syndiotactic.

of four different groups on a carbon atom. The *cis-* can be made to fit the *trans-*propylene only by breaking bonds.

In general, the greater the disorder, the lower the tendency of molecules to line up properly to form crystals, the weaker the forces between molecules, and the lower the melting point and mechanical strength of the polymer.

Thus, atactic polypropylene is a soft, mainly noncrystalline polymer with little strength and a low melting point, while the more ordered ("tactic") polypropylenes are strong, highly crystalline, and high melting polymers useful as a plastic or a fiber. Polypropylene forms the base of many chrome-plated plastics having the same appearance as metal but possessing very high corrosion resistance, and therefore they are widely used in the automobile, plumbing fixture, household appliance, and marine hardware industries.

An additional advantage of the Ziegler-Natta catalytic method is that it permits the use of much lower temperatures and pressures. For example, polyethylene is now prepared at atmospheric pressure and 35 °C instead of at about 190 °C and 1500 atmospheres required by the original free-radical method.

In some polymers, connections may also occur *between* long-chain molecules, increasing the molecular weight tremendously. These connections are called *cross-links,* and the resulting polymer is called a **cross-linked polymer.** Typical are the silicone polymers:

Silicone linear polymer
not cross-linked

Silicone cross-linked polymer

The linear silicone is a liquid, while the cross-linked polymer is a hard solid. Table 23.3 gives some typical cross-linked polymers.

TABLE 23.3
SOME TYPICAL CROSS-LINKED POLYMERS

MONOMERS	POLYMER NAME	USES
phthalic acid glycerol	glyptal	molded plastic articles, alkyd paints
phenol formaldehyde	phenol-formaldehyde resin, Formica, Bakelite	table tops, wall panels, handles, dials
urea formaldehyde	urea-formaldehyde resin	translucent light panels, adhesives, enamels
melamine formaldehyde	melamine-formaldehyde resin, Melmac	dishes, buttons

23.5 _____ INORGANIC POLYMERS

Many other elements also form polymers. We shall examine only a few of them. At temperatures below 0 °C and in the presence of an electric spark, boron trichloride, $BCl_3(g)$, polymerizes to

$$\begin{array}{ccc} Cl & & Cl \\ \diagdown & & \diagup \\ & B{-}B \\ \diagup & & \diagdown \\ Cl & & Cl \end{array}$$

, which on heating further polymerizes to form a mixture that includes $B_4Cl_4(c)$ and $B_8Cl_8(c)$:

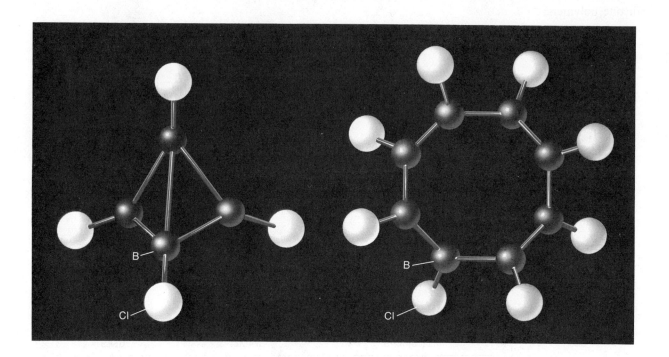

Boron and silicon are typical of many elements whose atoms are linked by oxygen atoms forming polymers. In fact, boron and silicon occur in nature only as oxy compounds. As in silicon dioxide (a polymer), the common valence of four is maintained in these silicon compounds by linking through Si—O—Si bonds (page 260). The orthosilicates contain SiO_4^{4-} ions, as independent units: typical examples include _zircon_, $ZrSiO_4$, and the _garnets_ $M_3^{II}M_2^{III}(SiO_4)_3$ in which M^{II} may be Ca^{2+}, Mg^{2+}, or Fe^{2+}, and M^{III} may be Al^{3+}, Cr^{3+}, or Fe^{3+}.

When one oxygen atom is shared between two silicon atoms

$$\left[\begin{array}{ccccc} & O & & O & \\ & | & & | & \\ O & Si & O & Si & O \\ & \diagup\ \diagdown & & \diagup\ \diagdown & \\ O & & O & & O \end{array} \right]^{6-}$$

the $Si_2O_7^{6-}$ silicates are formed, such as $Ca_2ZnSi_2O_7$.

When two oxygen atoms are shared, the long-chain polymers characteristic of

the SiO_3^{2-} (empirical composition) silicates, PO_3^- phosphates (page 613), and AsO_3^-
arsenates are formed:

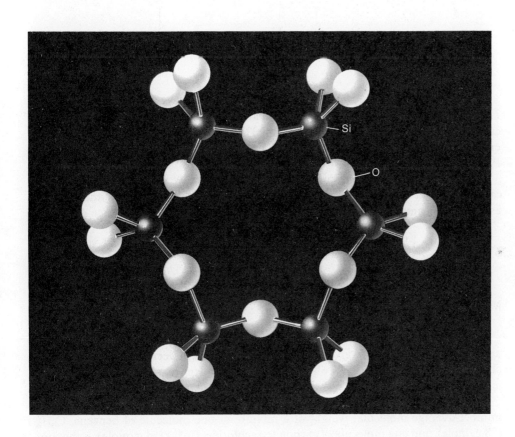

Examples are $MgSiO_3$, $NaPO_3$, $NaAsO_3$, and $CuGeO_3$.

PROBLEM 1   **Write the chain polymer structure for PO_3^- in $NaPO_3$, using at least four
repeating units.**

A silicon atom can also share its two oxygen atoms, forming a cyclic polymer.
The $Si_6O_{18}^{12-}$ ion in *beryl*, $Be_3Al_2Si_6O_{18}$ (page 639), is typical:

The $Si_6O_{18}^{12-}$ ion is balanced by 3 Be^{2+} and 2 Al^{3+} ions.

The zeolites and inorganic ion exchangers in general are polymers of SiO_4^{4-}
units in which an aluminum atom is substituted for a silicon atom in the framework.
The repeating unit is then $(Si$ or $Al)O_4$; SiO_4 is equivalent to a charge of $4-$, while
the AlO_4 group is equivalent to $5-$. The extra negative charge is balanced by positive
ions that more or less freely float in the open spaces between the combined atoms.

Technically important **glasses** are polymeric mixtures of borates (BO_3^{3-} repeating units) and silicates (SiO_4^{4-} repeating units) three-dimensionally linked in a

Oxidation numbers:
$Si^{4+} + 4\ O^{2-} =$
$+4 - 8 = -4;$
$Al^{3+} + 4\ O^{2-} =$
$+3 - 8 = -5$

disorderly fashion. In fact, a glass is defined as a liquid which has cooled to a rigid condition without crystallizing. Aluminum oxide, Al_2O_3, a very hard substance (page 259), or a metal is coated with *bioglass* in the manufacture of bone replacement parts. Bioglass, highly biologically inert and resembling ordinary glass and bone with a composition of Na_2O, 24.5 %, CaO, 24.5 %, P_2O_5, 6.0 %, and SiO_2, 45.0 %, fuses with bone as two fractured pieces of bone grow together. It is finding many uses as an implant material.

Bonding of bioglass to bone occurs through the formation of calcium phosphate between bone and bioglass.

The fibrous nature of *asbestos* results from the chain-linkage of SiO_4^{4-} units:

Tremolite, $(OH)_2Ca_2Mg_5(Si_4O_{11})_2$, is a typical asbestos, an established carcinogen; it causes lung and stomach cancer (page 203). Asbestos, beryllium, and mercury emissions have been branded hazardous air pollutants by the U.S. Environmental Protection Agency.

Readers are referred to The Sciences, page 10, March 1972, and Journal of National Cancer Institute, page 797, March 1972. Cigarette smokers are more susceptible to asbestos-induced cancer than nonsmokers.

Fluorination of graphite produces the most thermally stable polymeric fluorocarbons known, empirical formulas $CF_{1.09}$ and $C_{4.221}F$, stable at 700 °C and suitable as solid lubricants under heavy loads and as the cathode in high voltage dry cells:

$$CF_{1.1}(c) + 1.1Li(c) \longrightarrow 1.1LiF(c) + C(graphite) \qquad E°_{cell} = +4.57 \text{ volt}$$

23.6 —————————— MOLECULAR WEIGHT OF POLYMERS

Polymers are composed of high molecular-weight macromolecules. However, not all the macromolecules of a given polymer have identical molecular weights (identical chain lengths); some chains are longer than others. Hence, we generally speak of either a number-average or a weight-average molecular weight.

In a **number-average molecular weight,** each molecule is counted once. Thus, the number-average molecular weight of a mixture of one molecule of benzene, C_6H_6 (78 g/mole), and one molecule of carbon tetrachloride, CCl_4 (154 g/mole), is the sum of the two molecules divided by 2, the total number of molecules: $\frac{1}{2}(78 + 154) = 116$ g/mole.

However, number-averages may be misleading. A person weaving through traffic is hit by one of ten passing cars, while another person weaving over a basketball court is hit by one of ten thrown balls. The hit number average is the same in both situations, 1/10, but the results are devastatingly different.

In a **weight-average molecular weight,** each molecule is counted in proportion to its mass. The weight-average molecular weight is calculated by adding the *square* of the molecular weight of each molecule and then dividing by the sum of the molecular weights of all the molecules. Thus, for the one molecule of C_6H_6 + one molecule of CCl_4 mixture, the weight-average molecular weight is

$$\text{weight average molecular weight} = \frac{(78)^2 + (154)^2}{78 + 154} = 128 \text{ g/mole}$$

The weight-average is higher than the number-average, thus giving greater significance to the more massive molecules. The greater the difference between the number-average and the weight-average, the greater is the difference in the masses of the molecules of which the polymer is composed. These kinds of data yield useful information about polymers. Such data can, for example, measure the extent of chromosome (genes) breakdown (damage) due to radiation or chemicals (drugs).

Solution properties (page 336) that may be used to obtain molecular weights of polymers include freezing point depression and osmotic pressure measurements. However, osmotic pressure (page 342) methods are more sensitive and therefore more widely applied. For example, an aqueous solution containing 10 g per liter of a polymer of molecular weight 20,000 would show an osmotic pressure of 13 cm of solvent at 300 K. Molecular weights as high as 10^6 can be accurately measured. However, the method becomes ineffective at low molecular weights and is generally useless at molecular weights below 5000. In the lower molecular weight range, the freezing point depression method (page 339) may be used with thermometers sensitive to temperatures changes as small as 1×10^{-4} °C.

These methods are independent of the mass of individual molecules; they depend only on the number of molecules per kilogram of solvent or per liter of solution. In an ideal solution a molecule, 2 g/mole, has the same effect as another molecule, 20,000 g/mole. The molecular weights of polymers so obtained are therefore number-averages. The following methods, however, yield weight-average molecular weights.

Light Scattering   Particles scatter light. The larger the molecule, the greater the amount of light scattered, so that a relationship exists between the mass of the molecules and the intensity (number of photons/cm² s) of light scattered. Therefore, molecular weights calculated from light scattering are weight-average molecular weights.

Ultracentrifuge   A centrifuge is a device for whirling an object at high speed. A very high-speed centrifuge, over 10^6 revolutions per minute, is called an ultracentrifuge. The effect of this motion is the same as increasing the force of gravity a particle experiences, and so increases the rate at which the particle falls away from the center of the device (the axis of rotation). But the rate of fall (settling rate, sedimentation rate) depends on the particle size and therefore is a measure of the particle mass. Thus, the device separates particles of different mass and is successfully used to separate different protein molecules. Then, from the settling rates, molecular weights may be calculated. The molecular weight of tobacco mosaic virus (Fig. 4.9a, page 138) so calculated is 59 million.

Invented by The Svedberg in 1926.

Only in a vacuum is the rate of fall independent of particle size (mass and shape), the same for all objects (a molecule, a feather, a truck).

BIOLOGICAL MOLECULES_____23.7

The basic stuff of living matter—proteins and nucleic acids—is composed of giant polymers whose chemical composition, size, shape, and structure were almost completely unknown as recently as 25 years ago.

In this section, we shall consider these two types of polymers that are most universally characteristic of living things; in fact, the name protein is derived from *proteios,* the Greek word for holding first place.

A **protein** is a naturally occurring long-chain polymer, sometimes cross-linked, composed of from 20 to thousands of amino acids (page 705) linked in a highly organized arrangement or sequence. The empirical formula of a typical protein is $C_{1285}H_{2501}N_{343}O_{375}S_8$. All plant and animal proteins are naturally synthesized from a basic set of 20 amino acids (Table 23.4), isolated from protein breakdown. One protein is distinguished from another by the number of amino acid molecules per molecule of protein and by the order in which they are arranged. Of the 20 amino acids, nine or ten (depending on the age of the person) are **essential amino acids;** they are amino acids that cannot be synthesized by man rapidly enough to satisfy daily nutritional requirements and must therefore be included in the diet for proper health.

Amino acid malnutrition experienced early in life may cause long-term defi-

TABLE 23.4
SOME AMINO ACIDS OBTAINED FROM PROTEINS

NAME	ABBREVIATION*	FORMULA
Alanine	Ala	$CH_3CHCOOH$ with NH_2
Arginine•	Arg	$H_2NCNHCH_2CH_2CHCOOH$ with NH and NH_2
Aspartic acid	Asp	$HOOCCH_2CHCOOH$ with NH_2
Cystine	CyS—SCy	$HOOCCHCH_2SSCH_2CHCOOH$ with NH_2 and NH_2
Glutamic acid	Glu	$HOOCCH_2CH_2CHCOOH$ with NH_2
Glycine	Gly	H_2NCH_2COOH
Histidine•	His	(imidazole ring) $C—CH_2CHCOOH$ with NH_2
Isoleucine•	Ileu	$CH_3CH_2CH—CHCOOH$ with CH_3 and NH_2
Leucine•	Leu	$(CH_3)_2CHCH_2CHCOOH$ with NH_2
Lysine•	Lys	$H_2NCH_2CH_2CH_2CH_2CHCOOH$ with NH_2

•Essential amino acids for human infants and adults

*These abbreviations, part of the nomenclature of biochemistry, are commonly used in place of formulas to show amino acid sequences in proteins, as in Fig. 23.1.

ciencies (kwashiorkor*) in learning and other behavioral abilities. While proteins of animal origin contain acceptable quantities of essential amino acids, vegetable proteins do not contain balanced quantities of these amino acids. Corn diets, for example, deficient in the amino acid tryptophan, cause reduced levels of serotonin, a brain neurotransmitter (Problem 36, page 742). The necessary balance, however, can be achieved by combining vegetable proteins from several different sources, such as lentils with corn or soya with corn.

Alcoholism can be detected by measuring the ratio of two amino acids, 2-aminobutyric acid $((C_2H_5)(NH_2)C(H)COOH)$ to leucine, in the blood; the ratio increases with long-term alcohol consumption. The ratio may therefore serve as an experimental (objective) indicator for the detection of alcoholism.

---

*First described in the medical literature in 1933, the term means "deposed child," a child displaced from the mother's breast by a newborn baby, in one African language and "red boy" in another, Bantu (reddish hair is one symptom of the disease).

TABLE 23.4
SOME AMINO ACIDS OBTAINED FROM PROTEINS

NAME	ABBREVIATION*	FORMULA
Methionine•	Met	$CH_3SCH_2CH_2CHCOOH$ with NH_2 below
Phenylalanine•	Phe	C₆H₅ ring—$CH_2CHCOOH$ with NH_2 below
Proline	Pro	ring structure: H_2C—CH_2, H_2C $CHCOOH$, N—H
Serine	Ser	$HOCH_2CHCOOH$ with NH_2 below
Threonine•	Thr	CH_3CH—$CHCOOH$ with OH and NH_2 below
Tryptophan•	Trp	H_4C_6—$C(C_2H_3NH_2COOH)$, CH, NH
Tyrosine	Tyr	HO—ring—$CH_2CHCOOH$ with NH_2 below
Valine•	Val	$(CH_3)_2CHCHCOOH$ with NH_2 below

*These abbreviations, part of the nomenclature of biochemistry, are commonly used in place of formulas to show amino acid sequences in proteins, as in Fig. 23.1.

One of the most important chemical properties of amino acids is their ability to link together with the loss of a water molecule, forming a **peptide linkage,**

amino acid   amino acid

peptide linkage

Further addition of amino acids eventually leads to the formation of a protein, a condensation polymer in which amino acids are the repeating units.

The structure of a protein is generally determined in two broad steps. First, the order in which the different amino acids are linked along the chain (the *sequence* of amino acids in the molecule) is determined. The sequence of amino acids in beef insulin is given in Fig. 23.1. It is indeed interesting to record that the sequence of amino acids in gorilla insulin differs from that in man at only one site.

The arrangement of the chain in space is then determined (page 265). Like a cord, the long chain of amino acids may be shaped into a coil that looks like a spiral (helix) stairway or the thread of a screw, shown in Fig. 23.2 a. In most proteins, a number of spirals are coiled together into a cable. The cable may be looped into a circle (page 730) or wound and looped into a sphere that looks like a ball of cord (gamma globulin, hemoglobin, myoglobin), or the cables may fit side by side to look like a string or a rod (hair, wool, fibrinogen in blood plasma, tobacco mosaic virus, page 138). The long chains of amino acids may also be shaped into sheets by hydrogen bonding between chains. Such extended chains are characteristic of silks. These structures are determined by the size and shape of the R groups on the amino acids, which in turn largely determine the hydrogen bonding that holds together parts of the same chain, and that links different chains together. Fig. 23.2 shows a portion of a typical spiral (helix) of a protein molecule and other typical structures.

It is interesting to note that the helical structure of wool fibers, with hydrogen bonding *within* each helix, explains their properties. Wool is not stiff, can be stretched, and the fibers spring back. Silk, with hydrogen bonding *between* chains, is also easily bent but it resists stretching.

Proteins that are catalysts are called **enzymes.** One enzyme usually catalyzes only one particular reaction of a particular substance. A cell therefore contains hundreds of enzymes, nearly as many as there are biochemical reactions. Enzymes are very highly specific catalysts. The tightness of fit—the specificity of these reactions—is illustrated in Fig. 23.3. It is the intermolecular forces (pages 252 and 264) that provide the pliability and specificity required for biological reactions. The specificity of enzymatic reactions is further illustrated with the chemistry of histamine.

The biochemical role of histamine is still a medical mystery. Naturally existing in the body, it can nevertheless provoke allergic reactions when released. Bee stings and

A deficiency of this protein hormone, secreted by the pancreas, causes diabetes.

Heliks is the Greek word for spiral.

Hydration is also important in determining stability of protein structures.

Discovered in 1897 by Edward Buchner, it was not until 1926 that the first enzyme was isolated by James Sumner.

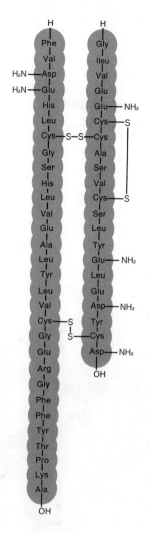

FIGURE 23.1 Amino acid sequence in beef insulin, 51 amino acids in two chains cross-linked by S atoms, worked out (1955) by Frederick Sanger. This is the first protein for which the amino acid sequence was determined.

detergents are only two of many histamine-releasing agents. It is formed by a biochemical reaction from the essential amino acid histidine:

histidine → *histamine* + CO_2

Another enzyme then binds the histamine and splits it into products that cause the allergic symptoms, crudely represented as

histamine   *enzyme* → enzyme + products

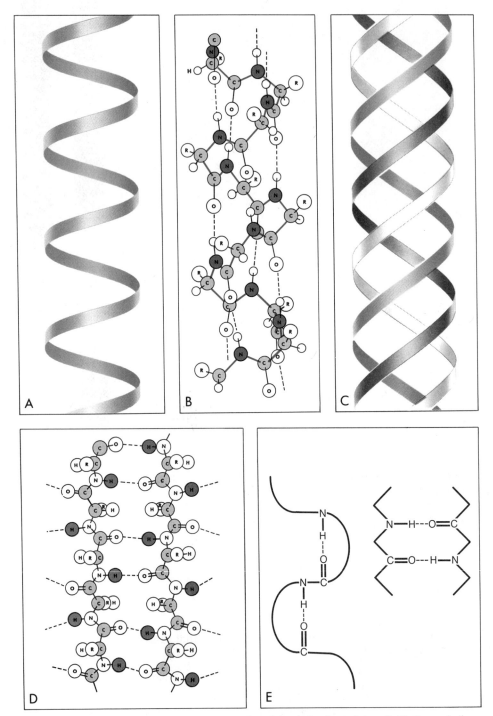

FIGURE 23.2 (a) A typical spiral (helix). (b) A portion of the chain of a protein coiled to form a helix. (c) A portion of a triple helix, three spirals coiled into a cable, characteristic of hair protein. (d) A portion of the straight-chain structure of silk protein. (e) Representation of hydrogen bonding *within* a helix and *between* chains.

730

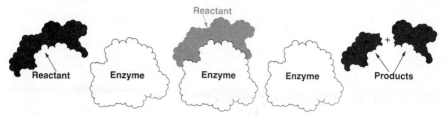

FIGURE 23.3 Representation of the catalytic action of an enzyme on a molecule. Reactant binds to the enzyme. Proper fit results in a reaction, yielding products and the original enzyme. (The action of enzymes is not as rigid as shown. Under the influence of the approaching molecule, the enzyme bends so as to grip the molecule in a perfect fit.)

The prevention of allergic symptoms is the purpose of **antihistamines.** The enzyme has a preference for diphenhydramine, $(C_6H_5)_2HC—O—CH_2CH_2—N—(CH_3)_2$, a typical antihistamine. It stops the action of the histamine by occupying the enzyme site(s) involved in the allergic reactions; no enzyme, no reaction.

A **virus,** a complex substance composed of proteins and nucleic acids, is capable of drastically changing the nature of living cells while reproducing itself.

Nucleic Acids   Nucleic acids are polymers that exist in the nuclei of cells. Every living cell contains nucleic acids. These acids are of prime importance because *they determine protein synthesis* and the *genetic code,* the hereditary characteristics of all living organisms.

These acids are also found in bacterial cells, which contain no nuclei, and in viruses, which have no cells.

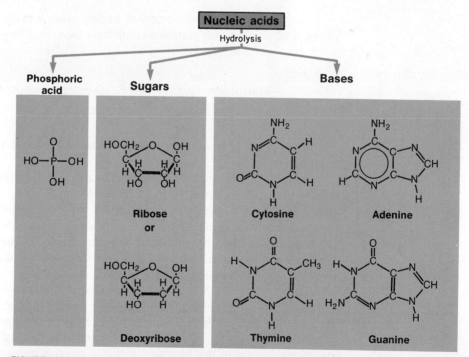

FIGURE 23.4 Hydrolysis of nucleic acids. Only four of the six major bases are shown. The difference between the two sugars is one atom of oxygen, an OH group in place of an H.

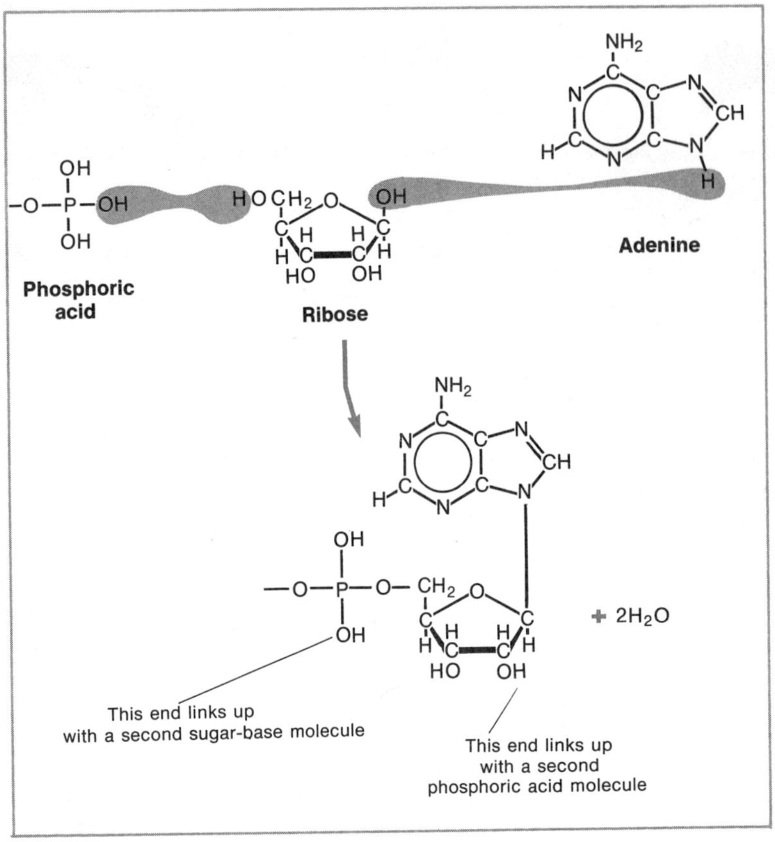

FIGURE 23.5 Formation of a repeating unit (monomer) of RNA by condensation polymerization. Different RNA and DNA molecules contain a different number of monomers. Molecular weights differ very widely; RNA molecules are generally in the range from 25,000 to 10^6 g/mole; DNA molecules range from 10^6 to 10^9 g/mole.

The repeating unit (monomer) of nucleic acids consists of three parts: a phosphoric acid portion, one nitrogen-containing base, and one sugar portion:

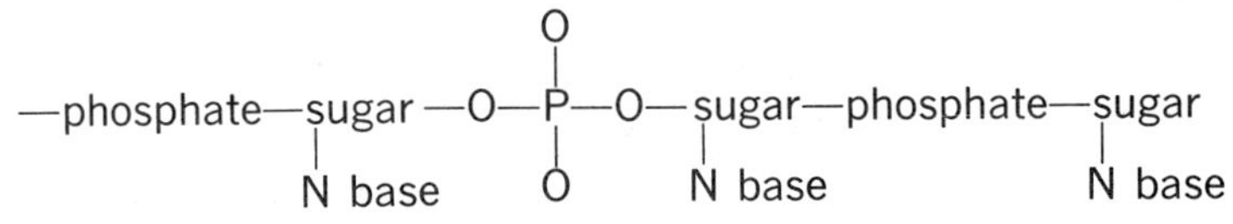

The sugar is either *ribose* or *deoxyribose,* and the base is one of six major bases, summarized in Fig. 23.4.

A nucleic acid that contains deoxyribose is called *deoxyribonucleic acid* (DNA), while one containing ribose is called *ribonucleic acid* (RNA). Fig. 23.5 shows how the three parts of the repeating unit of an RNA molecule are linked together. DNA is a long molecule with about 10^7 bases, mainly adenine, cytosine, guanine, and thymine. DNA was discovered by Freidrich Miescher in 1869. The complete biochemical synthesis of a biologically active DNA of a virus was accomplished with the use of two enzymes by Arthur Kornberg in 1967.

The structure of DNA consists of two chains wound together into a double helix, linked, in part, by hydrogen bonding between nitrogen bases. This arrangement was postulated in 1953 by James Watson and Francis Crick (illustrated in Fig. 23.6) and confirmed (1973) by an X-ray technique capable of "seeing" individual atoms. The significant feature of this structure is that it offers a molecular explanation for the synthesis of proteins and enzymes necessary for the development of living cells. DNA

Linus Pauling was the first to propose the helical structure of proteins, the basis of the conclusion by Watson and Crick.

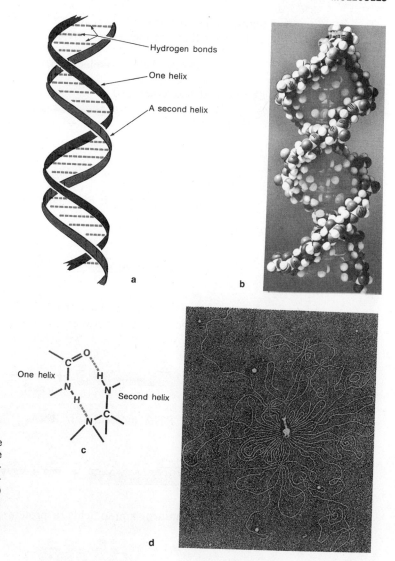

Hydrogen bonds

One helix

A second helix

One helix

Second helix

FIGURE 23.6 (a) Representation of a double helix. (b) Section of a space-filling model of the double helix DNA molecule. (Courtesy of Professor M.H.F. Wilkins, Medical Research Council, Biophysics Unit, King's College, London.) (c) Details of hydrogen bonding in DNA. (d) An electron microscope photograph of DNA from a virus. (Courtesy of Professor A. K. Kleinschmidt, New York University Medical Center.)

does not synthesize proteins. Rather, it controls the synthesis of RNA; in turn, RNA controls the synthesis of proteins.

The general steps in protein synthesis may be summarized as follows: DNA synthesizes the smaller RNA molecules, called *messenger RNA* molecules; the DNA determines the sequence of bases in the messenger RNA molecules:

DNA molecule ⟶ messenger RNA molecule

We visualize the messenger RNA molecule as

Messenger RNA

The sequence of bases of messenger RNA determines which proteins it synthesizes.

Another kind of RNA molecule, called a *transfer RNA* molecule, serves as a highly prejudiced traffic officer for amino acids; it selects only certain amino acids and carries them to messenger RNA:

$$\text{transfer RNA}_1 + \text{amino acid}_1 \longrightarrow \text{transfer RNA}_1\text{—amino acid}_1$$

abbreviated and visualized as

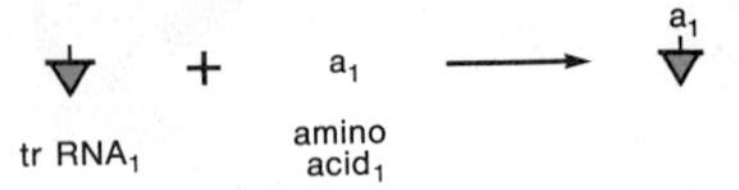

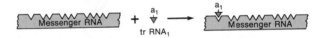

followed by

$$\text{messenger RNA} + \text{tr RNA}_1\text{—}a_1 \longrightarrow \text{messenger RNA—tr RNA}_1\text{—}a_1$$

visualized as

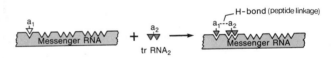

Another transfer RNA molecule, tr RNA$_2$, brings up another amino acid, a_2, and a peptide linkage is formed between the two (now adjacent) amino acids:

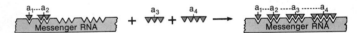

Other transfer RNA molecules, tr RNA$_{3,4...}$, in turn bring up other amino acids, a_3, a_4, . . .

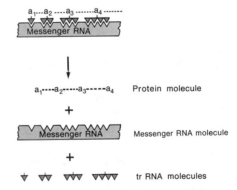

Finally, the chain of amino acids (a protein) is released:

The double helix structure can also explain how the DNA molecule duplicates itself, and so accounts for cell reproduction and heredity. *Genes* are the chemical units of heredity. They are the specific transmitters of hereditary characteristics, from the shape of the big toe to the color of the eyebrows and hair. Various specific parts of DNA constitute the genes. These genes fix the sequence of amino acids in proteins and enzymes. For these reasons, the sequence of repeating units in DNA is called the genetic code. It reproduces identical cells and produces the tools necessary to synthesize the specific proteins and enzymes required for a particular cell.

The instructions to duplicate the DNA molecule may be visualized as a long sentence containing 10^7 letters, made up mostly from four letters of the alphabet, A (abbreviation for adenine), C (cytosine), G (guanine), and T (thymine). During DNA duplication, the two chains uncoil; each chain then serves as a pattern—an impression (Fig. 23.7)—for the synthesis of a new chain. As each new chain develops, it forms the typical DNA helical configuration with the original chain. Each resulting DNA molecule then consists of one old chain and one newly synthesized chain, thus duplicating and preserving the hereditary information in the original DNA molecule (Fig. 23.7). A photograph of the unfolding of the DNA molecule of the bacterium *Escherichia coli* during the process of duplication is shown in Fig. 23.8. The bacterial DNA double helix molecule is in the form of a circle. *For simplicity,* the chains are shown parallel and not helical in the drawing. The duplication starts at the point shown by the black dot in the figure. The two chains gradually separate around the entire molecule. At the end of the process, four chains, two old and two new, are present in two DNA molecules.

Your DNA molecules are enclosed in the chromosomes located in your (biological) cells; each chromosome in your body contains one DNA molecule. Reproduction of DNA occurs when one of your cells divides into two cells.

Just as the different sequences of the twenty-six letters of the alphabet lead to an almost infinite number of words, so do the different sequences of a limited number of bases lead to an almost unlimited variety of characteristics. All forms of life on Earth, from the smallest to the largest organisms, are essentially composed of the same amino acids and DNA monomers. This makes the DNA in various plants and animals "isomer-like" in the sense of scrambled polymer chains of different molecular weights made from the same monomers. Evidence strongly supports the conclusion that the mechanisms of DNA duplication, RNA formation, and protein synthesis are essentially the same in all organisms. Scientifically beautiful; but we are not coded with the quality to love and be loved, nor are we coded to sense the dignity of man.

A small part of the DNA molecule, one complete gene of a yeast, was first synthesized by a combination of chemical and biochemical (enzymatic) methods—but largely chemical—by Har Khorana in 1972. Recently (1976), he accomplished the chemical (test tube) synthesis of an artificial gene that functions biologically just like the natural gene in a virus. The result of nine years of work with 24 postdoctoral assistants, the synthesis is regarded as a major breakthrough in molecular genetics. Changes in the gene sequence can now be made and the results observed in a test tube.

The sequence of the 5375 repeating units making up the known nine genes of a DNA molecule of a virus that infects bacteria has been determined. This significant work, the first complete sequence determination of the repeating units of a single-stranded DNA molecule, was accomplished by Frederick Sanger in 1977.

The mechanism of protein synthesis offers ample opportunity for traffic accidents. Chemicals and radiation may alter the structures so as to deny acceptance of required amino acids or the desired base sequence. According to one theory of aging, such alterations in the structure of protein-synthesizing molecules destroy the required shapes, resulting in the production of inactive proteins.

Radiation (UV, X-ray, γ-ray) hazards to living tissue start with the formation of hydrated electrons, $e^-(aq)$. The hydrated electron (page 607) is a powerful reducing agent. Its attack on the molecules of living tissue can alter their structures, resulting in the death of cells or even in the death of the organism.

Walter Sutton and Theodor Boveri (1902) showed that chromosomes carry what Gregor Mendel (1865) called "factors" and what Wilhelm Johannsen (1909) called "genes." Thomas Morgan (1911) showed that genes are arranged linearly.

F. Sanger and coworkers, Nature, volume 265, 24 February 1977, page 687.

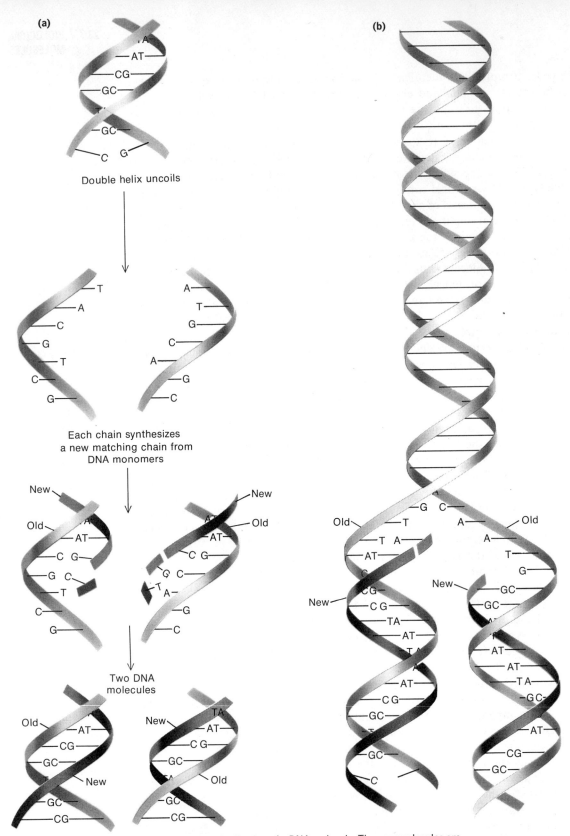

(a)

Double helix uncoils

Each chain synthesizes
a new matching chain from
DNA monomers

New

Old

New

Old

Two DNA
molecules

Old

New

New

Old

(b)

Old

Old

New

New

FIGURE 23.7 (a) Crude representation of the duplication of a DNA molecule. The new molecules are exactly the same as the old molecules. Unfolding of the double helix is gradual, as shown in (b). The letters A, T, G, and C are abbreviations for the bases adenine, thymine, guanine, and cytosine (page 731). RNA molecules and enzymes are involved in the complex process. (Adapted from ''Molecular Biology of the Gene,'' James Watson, W. A. Benjamin, 2nd edition, 1970, page 267.

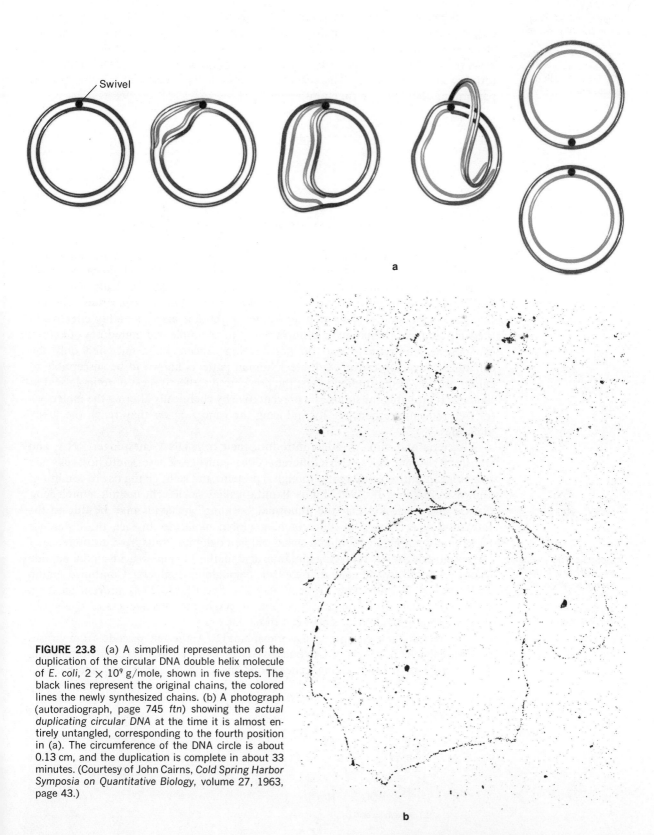

Swivel

a

b

FIGURE 23.8 (a) A simplified representation of the duplication of the circular DNA double helix molecule of *E. coli*, 2×10^9 g/mole, shown in five steps. The black lines represent the original chains, the colored lines the newly synthesized chains. (b) A photograph (autoradiograph, page 745 *ftn*) showing the *actual duplicating circular DNA* at the time it is almost entirely untangled, corresponding to the fourth position in (a). The circumference of the DNA circle is about 0.13 cm, and the duplication is complete in about 33 minutes. (Courtesy of John Cairns, *Cold Spring Harbor Symposia on Quantitative Biology*, volume 27, 1963, page 43.)

Repair of DNA damaged by UV light, mustard (toxic) gas, and amino acid starvation was first observed (1967) in E. coli (a bacterium).

It is generally known that many chemicals cause normal cells to become cancerous. A common feature of many of these carcinogens is the ease with which they change to substances that act as Lewis acids. It is, therefore, believed that these Lewis acids react with Lewis bases such as proteins and nucleic acids or DNA molecules through covalent bonding. This reaction then blocks these essential substances from performing their proper functions:

$$R{-}Cl \longrightarrow R^+ + :\overset{..}{\underset{..}{Cl}}:^-$$
carcinogen

$$R^+ \quad + \quad :N{\underset{R}{\overset{R}{-}}}R \quad \longrightarrow \quad R:N^+{\underset{R}{\overset{R}{-}}}R$$

Lewis acid   Lewis base (protein)   role of protein altered

The details of this mechanism by which chemicals produce cancer are still unknown. The objective of the use of chemicals (*chemotherapy*) in the treatment of cancer is cell destruction through interference with the functions of its nucleic acids. But, quite frequently, these drugs do not distinguish between normal and cancerous cells. On the other hand, studies show that an isomer of retinoic acid* is highly effective in preventing cancer formation in animals. Mice, for example, fed high doses of known carcinogens plus retinoic acid do not develop cancer, while mice fed only the carcinogens develop cancer. Volunteer human patients known to be susceptible to cancer are now being studied to test the preventative effectiveness of retinoic acid in humans. It probably functions as a preventative by chemically altering the molecules (or free radicals) responsible for inducing the cancer *before* they reach the DNA molecules.

Bacteria and virus invaders introduce their own DNA, messenger RNA, and transfer RNA molecules, with a different code (sequence of bases), into host cells and so synthesize entirely different ("foreign") proteins and cells, giving rise to conditions known as *diseases*. In 1949, Linus Pauling called sickle-cell anemia a molecular disease and suggested that the abnormal "sickling" behavior may be due to the formation of a chemically different hemoglobin molecule. In fact, the difference between normal hemoglobin and sickle-cell hemoglobin results from a difference of *one* amino acid, valine replacing glutamic acid, in the 146 amino acids in the peptide chains produced by the gene that controls hemoglobin synthesis. Combined amino acids such as Phe-Phe-Phe-Arg and Arg-Phe-Phe (Table 23.4) prevent sickling. However, further development is required to prove the effectiveness of these substances in the treatment of sickle-cell disease.

Glutamic acid contains an —OH group that hydrogen bonds to water, while valine does not, making the sickle-cell less soluble.

The fact that it is now possible to transplant DNA, the genetic code, from viruses and animal cells into cells of bacteria gives molecular biologists cause for concern. The transfer of nitrogen-fixing genes from one class of bacteria to another is a

---

*

13-*cis*-retinoic acid

beneficial achievement.* Of course, cells do have the ability to destroy introduced foreign DNA molecules. The danger lies in the possibility that a harmless bacterium might be transformed into an infectious one. For example, the creation of an infectious bacterium from a harmless one whose natural environment is the human intestine is a real hazard. Its consequences could rival the problems created by the uses of nuclear bombs. Strict safeguards have, therefore, been established among molecular biologists to eliminate such potential hazards to human lives.*

*Nature, volume 260, 1976, page 268.

On the other hand, planned changes in the gene stock of living things—*genetic engineering*—could be used to prevent birth defects. Our DNA molecules contain more than 50,000 genes, and the locations of about 1200 of these genes have been spotted and mapped. A gene map gives an insight into evolutionary processes. But gene mapping also is useful in prenatal diagnosis and prevention of hereditary diseases, such as hemophilia (strong tendency to bleed), muscular dystrophy (faulty muscular nutrition with loss of muscle protein), and Huntington's chorea (brain disease). A team of scientists headed by William Rutter (1977) has successfully transferred the insulin-producing gene from a rat, a mammal, to *Escherichia coli,* a bacterium. Although the bacteria are not yet producing insulin from their new gene, it is predicted that this can be accomplished in about one year. Possible practical consequences are at least twofold: the manufacture of human insulin by bacteria for use in the treatment of diabetes, and the repair of defective pancreas cells in diabetic patients. Finally, a human gene has been inserted into the same bacterium. These bacteria are happily manufacturing the human hormone somatostatin, normally produced in the hypothalamus at the base of the brain.

EPILOG

DNA and RNA indeed offer an explanation of the reproduction of the living cell in terms of molecules, with the same rules and regulations applicable to the explanation of the properties of nuts and bolts. Many scientists, particularly biologists and biochemists, therefore believe that the laws of nature apply to life itself; some scientists, particularly theoretical mathematical physicists, do not so believe, while most philosophers of science conclude that this debate among men of science is useful nonsense.

PROBLEMS

2 Vocabulary Define and illustrate the following: (a) monomer, (b) polymer, (c) copolymer, (d) addition polymer, (e) condensation polymer, (f) protein, (g) atactic polymer and tactic polymer, (h) gene, (i) genetic code.

3 Monomeric unit (a) *Saran* wrap, manufactured from vinylidene chloride, $H_2C{=}CCl_2$, has the following structure:

$$-CH_2-\underset{\underset{Cl}{|}}{\overset{\overset{Cl}{|}}{C}}-CH_2-\underset{\underset{Cl}{|}}{\overset{\overset{Cl}{|}}{C}}-CH_2-\underset{\underset{Cl}{|}}{\overset{\overset{Cl}{|}}{C}}-$$

Is it formed by addition or condensation polymerization? Explain. (b) *Dacron*, polyethylene terephthalate polymer, is prepared by the reaction of ethylene glycol, $HO-CH_2-CH_2-OH$, with terephthalic acid,

$$HO-\overset{O}{\underset{}{C}}-\bigcirc-\overset{O}{\underset{}{C}}-OH.$$

The structure of *Dacron* is

$$-O-CH_2-CH_2-O-\overset{O}{\underset{}{C}}-\bigcirc-\overset{O}{\underset{}{C}}-O-CH_2-CH_2-O-$$

*Readers interested in this subject are referred to "Recombinant DNA Research Guidelines," National Institutes of Health, Bethesda, Md. 20014, September 1976; and "The Case For and Against Genetic Engineering," *The Sciences,* September/October 1976, pages 6–12. Also see Problems 16(g)(h).

Is *Dacron* formed by addition or condensation polymerization? Explain.

4 Orientation Classify the sequence in natural rubber and gutta percha as *cis-, trans-,* or atactic. Explain.

5 Polymerization (a) Write the structural formula for the addition product of a styrene free radical and a styrene molecule:

(b) (i) Show how silicone is prepared by the condensation polymerization of dimethylsilanediol molecules:

(ii) What is the other molecule formed?

6 (a) Show how polyethylene (Table 23.1, page 718) forms from ethylene by addition polymerization under the influence of ·OH free radicals (see Section 23.2). (b) Show how urea-formaldehyde resin forms from formaldehyde and urea by condensation polymerization.

7 Structure Explain and illustrate how a liquid polymer may become rigid upon heating.

8 (a) What is meant by the sequence structure of a protein? (b) Show how the peptide linkage forms by condensation of any two amino acids (Table 23.4, page 726).

9 (a) What is the fundamental difference in the composition of the monomers of the molecules of DNA and RNA? (b) Describe and sketch the spiral nature of the structure of these polymers. (c) In words, describe the parts that make up the monomer unit of nucleic acids.

10 Cancer Studies show that in the region of Denver, Colorado, altitude 1.61 km, the incidence of skin cancer is much higher than the national average. Explain.

11 DNA Every species synthesizes specific proteins, different from the proteins of all other living species. No two kinds of animals, for example, have the same hemoglobin; the porphyrin portion is the same but

the globin (protein) portion is always different. Do all animals have the same blood cell DNA? Explain.

12 Genetic engineering Many plant proteins—corn, rice, wheat—are deficient in lysine, an essential amino acid. Would you support genetic manipulation studies directed at changing microorganisms to increase the lysine content of fermentation products (yogurt, cheese) of soybean milk? Explain.

13 Blood The normal range of hemoglobin in blood is 14.5 g to 16.0 g per 100 ml blood (men) and 13.0 g to 15.5 g per 100 ml blood (women). Express 15.0 g hemoglobin (6.45×10^4 g/mole) per 100 ml blood in terms of molarity.

14 The half-life of blood protein may be taken as 7 days. If a person contains 500 g of blood protein, what is the loss of old blood protein in 21 days?

15 (a) In general terms, how is DNA involved in the transmission of hereditary characteristics? (b) Use a zipper as an aid to explain the duplication of a DNA molecule to one of your friends.

16 Library Read one of the following:
(a) "Possible Repair of Carcinogenic Damage in Rat Kidney," Peter Swann *et al., Nature,* volume 263, 9 September 1976, page 134.
(b) "Chemical Carcinogens," Paul Rademacher and Hans-Georg Gilde, *Journal of Chemical Education,* volume 53, December 1976, page 757.
(c) "Cancer, How Can Chemists Help?" Lloyd Ferguson, *Journal of Chemical Education,* volume 52, 1975, page 688.
(d) "The Next 100 Years," Linus Pauling, *Chemical and Engineering News,* 19 April 1976, page 33.
(e) "Should the Delaney Clause Be Changed? A Debate on Food Additive Safety, Animal Tests, and Cancer," *Chemical and Engineering News,* 27 June 1977, page 24.
(f) "Metabolism of Alcohol," Charles Lieber, *Scientific American,* March 1976, page 25.
(g) "Recombinant DNA Research: A Debate on the Benefits and the Risks," *Chemical and Engineering News,* 30 May 1977, page 26.
(h) "Recombinant DNA Research," *Chemical and Engineering News,* 9 May 1977, page 3.
(i) "The Requirements of Human Nutrition," Nevin Scrimshaw and Vernon Young, *Scientific American,* September 1976, page 51.
(j) "Nitrogen Fixation," Karen Skinner, *Chemical and Engineering News,* 4 October 1976, page 22.
(k) "Menopausal Estrogens ('The Pill') and Breast Cancer," Robert Hoover, *New England Journal of Medicine,* volume 295, 19 August 1976, page 401.
(l) "Cancer," Donald Fredrickson, Henry Pilot, and Elizabeth Weinburger, *Chemistry,* February 1977, pages 9–17, 42–46.

17 What are the main forces that direct biological reactions?

18 "The genetic code is universal." What is the meaning of this statement?

19 If silicon formed double bonds, would SiO_2 be the hard substance that it is?

20 A rubber band or a plastic beverage-can holder is in a disordered state. When stretched, the polymer molecules become more ordered. (a) On stretching, does the entropy increase or decrease? (b) At room conditions (constant temperature and pressure), does a stretched rubber band spontaneously snap back? (c) Heat is absorbed during the snap back. Is the relaxed band hot or cold to the touch? What statement can you make about the relative values of ΔG, ΔH, and $T\Delta S$ for the process stretched polymer $\longrightarrow$ relaxed polymer?

21 Osmotic pressure, like freezing point depression, is a property of solutions that is dependent only on the number of solute particles per unit volume (Chap. 10). The osmotic pressure, OP, is given by $OP = MRT$, where M is the molarity of solute, mole/liter, R is the gas constant, 0.0821 liter atm/(mole K), and T is the absolute temperature. A 1.000 g sample of hemoglobin is dissolved, making 50.0 ml of aqueous solution with a measured osmotic pressure of 5.90 torr at 25 °C. What is the molecular weight of hemoglobin?

22 (a) Use your answer to Problem 21 to calculate the freezing-point depression of the hemoglobin solution. (b) Use your answer to part (a) to decide which method yields more precise molecular weights. Explain. (c) Are these number-average or weight-average molecular weights? Explain.

23 On the basis of the footnote regarding the origin of the term kwashiorkor, page 396, what statement can you make about the protein composition of mothers' milk?

24 Would you join a research team seeking to synthesize an enzyme to break down cellulose (wood, cotton, grass) to glucose for human consumption? Answer yes or no and then justify your position.

25 The antifreeze ethylene glycol is not particularly toxic, but an enzyme in the body catalyzes its conversion to very toxic oxalic acid:

$$\begin{array}{c} CH_2-OH \\ | \\ CH_2-OH \end{array} \xrightarrow{enzyme} \begin{array}{c} COOH \\ | \\ COOH \end{array}$$

(a) Find the oxidation number of carbon in the reactant and in the product. Is the enzyme effecting the oxidation or the hydrolysis of the reactant? (There are many such enzymes in the body.) In general terms, what chemical property is desirable in an antidote? (b) If one enzyme molecule converts 1.0×10^3 $(CH_2OH)_2$ molecules/second to product, find the time in minutes necessary to convert 100 g to product in the presence of 1.0×10^{-6} mole of enzyme.

26 The composition of the bases of several DNA molecules is given in Table 23.5. Calculate the ratio, A moles + G moles/C moles + T moles, and fill in the last column. What conclusions can you draw from the completed table?

27 Assume the ability to alter the genetic code in man. In general terms, what objectives would you attempt to obtain? Would fulfillment of these objectives be without adverse consequences?

TABLE 23.5
DATA FOR PROBLEM 26: DNA
BASE COMPOSITION*

	MOLES PER 100 MOLES PHOSPHORUS				RATIO
ORIGIN	Adenine (A)	Guanine (G)	Cytosine (C)	Thymine (T)	A + G/C + T
Paracentrus lividus	32.8	17.1	16.2	32.1	
Man	30.4	19.6	19.2	30.1	
Ox	29.0	21.2	19.9	28.7	
Wheat germ	28.1	21.8	16.8	27.4	
Escherichia coli (K-12)	26.0	24.9	25.2	23.9	
Avian tubercle bacillus	15.1	34.9	35.4	14.6	

* "Textbook of Biochemistry," Abraham Mazur and Benjamin Harrow, W. B. Saunders Company, Philadelphia, 10th Edition, 1971, page 167.

28 The DNA molecule of a virus is introduced into a bacterial cell. Could this lead to the production of a virus? Explain.

29 A frog egg is injected with messenger RNA molecule from the blood cell of a rabbit. The transfer RNA molecule of the egg recognizes this messenger RNA molecule. Will the frog egg synthesize rabbit hemoglobin? Explain.

30 Is a DNA molecule changed by diet or the environment? If not, how can a DNA molecule be altered?

31 (a) Genetic information is said to follow the path DNA $\longrightarrow$ a $\longrightarrow$ b $\longrightarrow$ protein. Identify a and b. (b) From the following pathway, pick out the gene: Segment of DNA molecule $\longrightarrow$ RNA molecule $\longrightarrow$ fixed amino acid sequence in a protein.

32 Explain the statement: "Proteins and nucleic acids constitute the basic stuff of life."

33 What is (a) the weight-average and (b) the number-average molecular weight of a mixture containing one mole each of benzene, carbon tetrachloride, and hexane?

34 The enzymatic hydrolysis of an amide,

$$R-\overset{\overset{H}{|}}{\underset{\underset{R'}{|}}{C}}-\overset{\overset{O}{\|}}{C}\overset{}{\underset{NH_2}{}} \ (aq) + H_2O \longrightarrow$$

$$R-\overset{\overset{H}{|}}{\underset{\underset{R'}{|}}{C}}-\overset{\overset{O}{\|}}{C}\overset{}{\underset{OH}{}} \ (aq) + NH_3(aq),$$

proceeds at a rate of about 2×10^3 amide molecules per second per molecule of enzyme. If the enzyme concentration is 1.0×10^{-8} M, find the quantity of NH_3 produced in mmol in one ml in one minute.

35 The 1975 Nobel Prize in Medicine went to researchers who showed that viruses can change normal animal cells to cancerous cells, a reaction not yet established in human cells. Explain, in general

terms, how a virus may induce a cancerous condition.

36 Brain serotonin, $HOH_3C_6-\overset{}{\underset{}{C}}-(C_2H_4NH_2)$, is syn-

thesized in the brain from the essential amino acid tryptophan, $H_4C_6-C(C_2H_3NH_2COOH)$. Write their

structural formulas. The C_6 group is aromatic.

37 A so-called "amorphous polymer" is not completely amorphous; it does contain some internal regions that are highly ordered (crystalline). Polypropylene is prepared with different degrees of crystallinity from 10 % to 90 %. Predict how the melting point, the density, and the hardness should change (increase, remain the same, or decrease) with increasing crystallinity.

38 Is the statement, "The genes are in the chromosomes," correct?

39 Plot the death rate per 100,000 from cancer of the colon (y-axis) against death rate per 100,000 from heart disease and atherosclerosis (x-axis) for each of the following countries (data from *Scientific American*, February 1977, page 84):

	Cancer	Heart disease
Japan	3.3	32.8
Finland	4.7	212
Italy	7.0	72.4
West Germany	7.8	105
Norway	7.8	147
U.S. (nonwhite)	9.8	231
Sweden	9.9	150
Belgium	10.2	100
Denmark	12	195
North Ireland	13	233
U.S. (white)	13	250

Is there a general correlation between these death rates? What does this suggest about the causes of these diseases?

ANSWERS

3 (a) addition, (b) condensation
4 natural rubber, *cis;* gutta percha, *trans*
8 (a) arrangement of amino acids in protein
9 (a) type of sugar molecule in the monomer
10 greater UV radiation due to altitude
11 no

13 2.33×10^{-3} M
14 437.5 g
19 no
20 (a) decrease; (b) yes; (c) cold, reaction occurs naturally, ΔG is negative; heat absorbed, ΔH is positive; $T\Delta S$ more positive than ΔH

21 6.30×10^4 g/mole
22 (a) -5.9×10^{-4} °C; (b) osmotic pressure; (c) number-average
23 contains essential amino acids
25 (a) -1 to $+3$, oxidation, block enzyme; (b) 27 min
26 1.03, 1.01, 1.03, 1.13, 1.04, 1.00
28 yes
29 yes

30 no; chemicals or radiation
31 (a) a—messenger RNA, b—transfer RNA; (b) segment of DNA
33 (a) 117; (b) 106.0
34 1.2×10^{-3} mmol/ml min
37 increase
38 correct
39 common cause

GLOSSARY

addition polymer A polymer formed by joining together monomer units, such as alkenes joining together by opening double bonds to form long-chain molecules. See **monomer.**

atactic arrangement A polymer in which the groups, such as —CH_3, are bonded at random to the chain.

chromosome A substance in the nucleus of an animal cell that contains one DNA molecule. See **DNA.**

condensation polymer A polymer formed when monomer units are linked by loss of small molecules like H_2O. See **monomer.**

copolymer A polymer formed by joining more than one kind of monomer. See **monomer.**

DNA Deoxyribonucleic acid, a condensation polymer whose monomer units consist of a phosphate group linked to a sugar (deoxyribose) linked to a cyclic amine. Portions of DNA constitute the genes, and DNA therefore carries the genetic information for cell reproduction and protein synthesis.

enzyme A protein molecule that serves as a specific catalyst for a particular biochemical reaction.

genes The chemical units of heredity, different portions of DNA molecules. See **DNA.**

glass An amorphous solid, a supercooled liquid in which the atoms are not arranged in a regular pattern.

isotactic arrangement A polymer in which groups, such as —CH_3 or —Cl, are all bonded on one side of a chain, a *cis*-isomer.

monomers The small molecules which react with one another to form a polymer.

peptide bond (linkage) The —C—N— linkage that joins amino acids together in proteins. *Polypeptide* is therefore another name for a protein.

polymer A long molecule formed from smaller molecules that are chemically joined together.

polymerization The reaction in which polymers are formed. See **polymer, addition polymer,** and **condensation polymer.**

protein A long-chain polymer synthesized from amino acids as the monomer units.

RNA Ribonucleic acid, a condensation polymer whose monomer units consist of a phosphate group linked to a sugar (ribose) linked to a cyclic amine. Messenger RNA, a smaller molecule than DNA, synthesized by DNA, determines which protein is synthesized. Transfer RNA molecule selects and carries a specific amino acid to messenger RNA.

syndiotactic arrangement A polymer in which groups, such as —CH_3, are bonded in alternate positions on the chain, a *trans*-isomer.

INSTRUMENTAL ANALYSIS 24

INTRODUCTION_____24.1

We have already discussed many of the ways chemists characterize matter in terms of state, order and disorder, bonding, electronic structure, geometry, and stability. The determination of melting points, freezing points, solubilities, and types of chemical reactions may serve to identify substances **(qualitative analysis).** The determination of the quantity of a substance in a sample is known as **quantitative analysis.** More generally, **analytical chemistry** deals with methods and devices that serve to identify and measure the quantities of substances. The variety of information obtainable is tremendous. What, for example, is the composition of a lunar rock? Of a Martian soil? Does it contain large carbon-hydrogen molecules characteristic of life on Earth? How much combined mercury is in one ml of lake water? What percentage of pesticide applied to crops finds its way into the human body? Is it the same in different regions of the country? How much sulfur dioxide is present per liter in our air? How do you prove that the source of lead contamination is a gasoline additive and not a natural source?

Before about 1945, answers to such questions were obtained, if at all, by complicated and time-consuming procedures requiring large amounts of samples. Since then, instruments have been developed that quickly and accurately analyze very small samples (10^{-9} ml to 10^{-3} ml). Analyses requiring the detection of one part per billion are now routinely performed. A new technique, *centrifuge chromatography,* in which a centrifuge is used to move a liquid solution through an absorption column (page 31), separates and identifies large molecules such as the waxes and lipids (fats) from tuberculosis bacteria in samples as small as 5×10^{-3} ml in several minutes. Further, some of these methods do not destroy the sample, an advantage when only small amounts of samples are available.*

These procedures, however, were precise only for concentrations of a few parts per thousand, insufficient for pollution analyses.

---

* *Nondestructive* techniques are important in the analysis of art objects, which could otherwise be damaged by sampling. For example, paintings, covered with photographic film, are placed in a nuclear reactor and a series of pictures are developed as the various isotopes generated in the painting decay. This process, called *autoradiography,* reveals details about the nature and composition of the paints.

In this chapter, we shall consider a few analytical tools, most of which depend on photon absorption.

24.2 ABSORPTION OF PHOTONS: THE ABSORPTION SPECTRUM

"White" light consists of the colors in the visible range.

Color appears only when a substance absorbs photons in the visible range (page 190). If all photons in the visible range are absorbed, the substance appears black; if a substance does not absorb photons in the visible range, it appears colorless (or white). When light from a light bulb passes through an aqueous solution of a blue dye, the solution appears blue because the molecules of the dye absorb photons in the red to yellow range. A traffic signal appears red because the glass absorbs photons in the blue-green range. Colorless substances absorb photons, but the absorption is in the ultraviolet or infrared (nonvisible) range. All atoms, molecules, and ions absorb photons in some range, but a substance is colored only if absorption is in the visible range.

The absorption of photons always corresponds to a transition between two energy states: from the ground state to an excited state, or from a lower to a higher state (Color Plate V C). Substances only absorb photons whose energies are equal to differences between two energy states:

For gaseous atoms, energy states correspond to atomic orbitals. In molecules, energy states correspond to molecular orbitals.

E(energy of photon absorbed) = difference between two energy states = hf

The greater the difference between the two states, the greater the energy and the frequency, but the smaller the wavelength of the photon (page 190).

A molecule may possess a large number of energy states, some widely spaced, others closely spaced, as illustrated in Figures 9.3 and 18.3, pages 300 and 566. The largest energy difference is between the bonding and antibonding energy states (molecular orbitals); it decreases for the difference between vibrational states; and it decreases even further for the difference between rotational energy states. Thus, while photons in the ultraviolet (UV) or visible range (Color Plate V A) are needed for transitions between bonding and antibonding energy states, photons of smaller frequency (infrared, IR, range) are needed to excite vibrational states. Photons of even smaller frequency are required to excite rotational states (microwave range).

Although all molecules have these energy states, *all energy states are quantized and characteristic of a particular molecule*. Identical molecules have exactly the same absorption characteristics; they only absorb photons of particular frequencies, different from those absorbed by other molecules. Hence, molecules, like atoms, are easily identified by the frequency of absorbed photons. The study of the absorption of photons, the **absorption spectrum** of substances, is thus a powerful tool for identifying substances. The absorption spectrum, like the emission spectrum (page 191), is a characteristic property of elements and compounds.

An *emission spectrum* gives us the frequencies of the photons *emitted* by a substance; it is obtained only when a substance is sufficiently excited to emit light. On the other hand, the *absorption spectrum* gives us the frequencies of the photons *absorbed* by a substance. An absorption spectrum is obtained by passing light (photons) of known wavelengths (frequencies) through a substance and determining which photons are absorbed. Only those photons whose frequencies (energies) correspond to the characteristic differences between energy states for the substance are absorbed. All other photons will pass through as if the substance were not in the path of the photons:

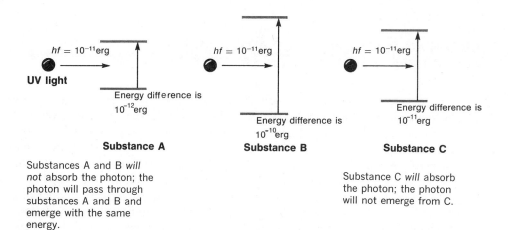

Substances A and B *will not* absorb the photon; the photon will pass through substances A and B and emerge with the same energy.

Substance C *will* absorb the photon; the photon will not emerge from C.

For example, mercury in a discharge tube emits green ($hf = 4.0 \times 10^{-12}$ erg/photon) but not yellow ($hf = 3.4 \times 10^{-12}$ erg/photon) photons, while sodium in a discharge tube emits yellow but not green photons. Therefore, mercury vapor absorbs green light ($hf = 4.0 \times 10^{-12}$ erg) and not yellow light, while sodium vapor absorbs yellow light ($hf = 3.4 \times 10^{-12}$ erg) but not green light. Hence, when a beam of green and yellow light is passed through mercury vapor and then through sodium vapor, yellow photons emerge from the mercury and no photons emerge from the sodium. The eye at the end of the train sees neither green nor yellow, only black.

Mercury emission spectrum green line, $\lambda = 4960$ Å.

Sodium emission spectrum yellow line, $\lambda = 5890$ Å.

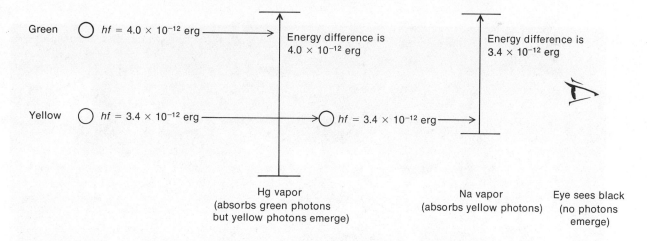

PROBLEM 1   (a) Green ($hf = 4.0 \times 10^{-12}$ erg) and yellow ($hf = 3.4 \times 10^{-12}$ erg) photons are passed first through sodium vapor and then through mercury vapor. Which photons, if any, emerge from (i) the sodium vapor and (ii) the mercury vapor? (b) Lead vapor absorbs green ($\lambda = 5524$ Å), calcium vapor absorbs violet ($\lambda = 4427$ Å), and carbon monoxide absorbs infrared ($\lambda = 46,600$ Å). A light beam composed of violet ($\lambda = 4427$ Å), green ($\lambda = 5524$ Å), and infrared ($\lambda = 46,600$ Å) photons is passed through a polluted air sample containing (i) CO, (ii) Ca and Pb vapors, (iii) CO and Pb vapors, (iv) Ca and CO vapors, (v) CO, Ca, and Pb vapors. For each case, which photons, if any, are absorbed?

By this method (photon absorption) a sample of fish, pinhead size, can be analyzed for mercury contamination in one minute with a sensitivity of 40 parts per billion (4×10^{-8} g Hg per g fish).

24.3 OBTAINING FINGERPRINTS OF ATOMS AND MOLECULES: THE ABSORPTION SPECTRUM

In principle, it is possible to design an instrument with one light source capable of emitting photons over the useful frequency range, from X-ray to radio waves, and one detector capable of detecting these photons after passage through matter. Experience, however, teaches that it is more practical to design light sources and detectors to operate within certain frequency ranges, for example, the visible, the ultraviolet, and the infrared ranges. Such instruments are generally known as **spectrophotometers,** light (photon) meters operating over a limited range of frequencies. A spectrophotometer contains a light source producing a definite number of photons of known frequencies. The photons are directed through a sample and the instrument then detects whether the photons pass through (are *transmitted*) or are absorbed by the sample, as shown in Fig. 24.1. The detector is usually coupled to a pen that moves up and down on paper moving from right to left. Thus, a graph showing absorption or transmission against wavelength is automatically obtained. The graph is the absorption spectrum of the sample. A typical absorption spectrum is shown in Fig.

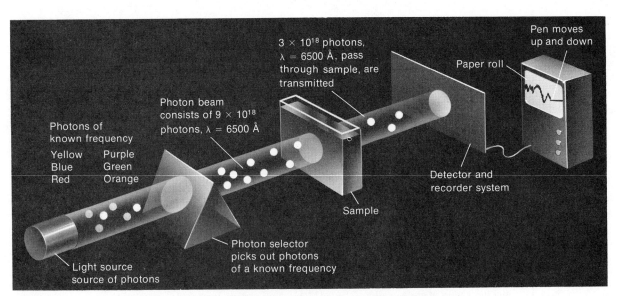

FIGURE 24.1 Outline of the essential parts of a spectrophotometer. The illustration shows that six of every nine photons are absorbed. We therefore say that the absorption at $\lambda = 6500$ Å is $\frac{6 \times 10^{18}}{9 \times 10^{18}} \times 100 = 2/3 \times 100 = 67\%$. We can also say that three of every nine photons are transmitted, or that transmission is $3/9 \times 100 = 33\%$.

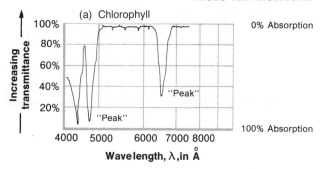

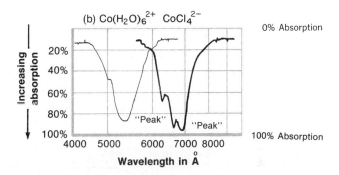

FIGURE 24.2 Typical absorption spectra (a) of chlorophyll* from green leaves, showing that high absorption occurs at 4350 Å, 4600 Å, and 6600 Å (the dips in the curve are called "peaks"), and (b) of $Co(H_2O)_6^{2+}$ and $CoCl_4^{2-}$.

*Unnecessary details are omitted. The absorption spectrum of elements is usually referred to as an *atomic absorption spectrum*.

24.2; the dips appear in the curve when absorption occurs but, by tradition, these dips are called "peaks" (or bands).

Fig. 24.3 shows typical infrared absorption spectra for (a) acetone, (b) 2-butanone, a related compound in which one hydrogen atom is replaced with a CH_3 group, and (c) ethyl alcohol. Notice that acetone absorbs very strongly at wavelength 58,500 Å. Notice that the related compound, 2-butanone, also very strongly absorbs at practically the same wavelength. In fact, one has to examine the spectra closely to detect differences. They are different, however, because no other compound has exactly the same spectrum as acetone. On the other hand, by quick examination, one sees that the absorption spectrum of ethyl alcohol differs from those of acetone and its related compound. The absorption spectra of hundreds of thousands of compounds have been recorded in systematic order to simplify identification by comparison. In this sense, spectra are like fingerprints.

5.85 μm

Reasonably priced IR spectrophotometers have been developed for the identification of organic compounds in drugs, foods, paints, and many other consumer products as well as in polluted air and water. They can be used to identify the origin of an oil spill.

The absorption at practically the same wavelength by different compounds appears strange, but it is not really surprising. Infrared absorption is associated with molecular vibrations (page 300). Hence, identical atoms more or less similarly bonded vibrate at more or less the same photon frequency. Therefore, parts of molecules can be identified because identical atoms similarly bonded absorb at characteristic wavelengths. Very typical is the carbonyl group, $>C=O$; a peak located at a wavelength of about 59,000 Å (5.9 μm) is characteristic of all compounds containing the $>C=O$ group (ketones). On the other hand, the $-C-O-$ group, as in ethyl alcohol, has a characteristic absorption at about 91,000 Å (9.1 μm), while the $-O-H$

Source: "Spectrometric Identification of Organic Compounds," R. Silverstein and G. Bassler, John Wiley and Sons, New York, 1963, page 687.

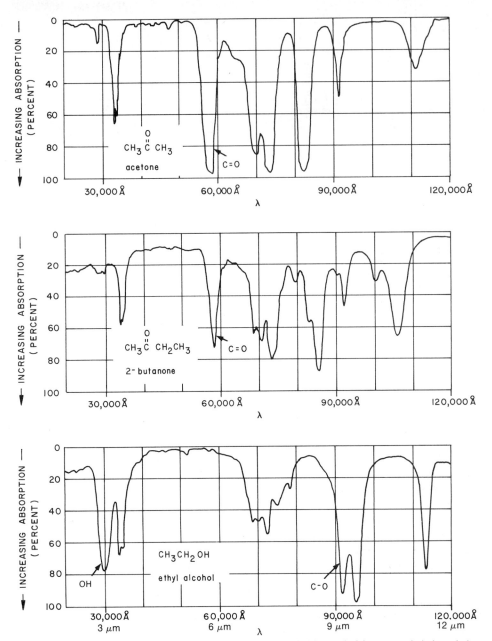

FIGURE 24.3 Infrared absorption spectra of acetone (dimethyl ketone), 2-butanone (ethyl methyl ketone), and ethyl alcohol. Wavelengths are given in angstrom units. More commonly, micrometer units (1 μm = 10^{-6} m) are used, so that 30,000 Å = 3 μm, 60,000 Å = 6 μm, and 90,000 Å = 9 μm.

group in alcohols absorbs at about 30,000 Å (3.0 μm). In this way, the structure of a compound can be determined from the identification of groups.*

PROBLEM 2 (a) An unknown compound, molecular formula C_2H_6O, absorbs strongly at 90,500 Å (9.05 μm). Which one of the two compounds shown on page 751 is the unknown?

*Identification of groups is not always a simple matter. Peaks may overlap, and changes in bonding can alter energy states so that significant shifts occur in the positions of peaks.

$$H-\overset{\overset{\displaystyle H}{|}}{\underset{\underset{\displaystyle H}{|}}{C}}-\overset{\overset{\displaystyle H}{|}}{\underset{\underset{\displaystyle H}{|}}{C}}-OH \quad \text{and} \quad H-\overset{\overset{\displaystyle H}{|}}{\underset{\underset{\displaystyle H}{|}}{C}}-O-\overset{\overset{\displaystyle H}{|}}{\underset{\underset{\displaystyle H}{|}}{C}}-H$$

Will these two compounds have the same absorption spectrum? (b) A compound strongly absorbs at wavelength 58,000 Å (5.8 μm). What group is probably present in the molecule of this compound?

Spectrophotometers operating in the visible and ultraviolet ranges are similarly used to identify compounds and specific groups.

The fraction of photons absorbed by a substance depends on the number of molecules in the path of the photons. The larger the number of molecules, the larger the number of collisions between molecules and photons, and the larger the number of photons absorbed. Hence, an absorption spectrum not only identifies a substance but may also be used to obtain the concentration of the substance.

LOCATING THE POSITION OF⎯⎯⎯⎯⎯⎯ 24.4
NUCLEI IN MOLECULES

Another powerful tool for determining the arrangement of atoms in molecules depends on locating the position of nuclei by means of their magnetic properties. A nucleus, however, identifies the atom. All the nuclei of all the atoms of an element have the same atomic number, different from the atomic number of every other element.

An unpaired electron behaves like a micromagnet, a tiny bar that can take only two positions, $\overset{N}{\underset{S}{\uparrow}}$ or $\overset{S}{\underset{N}{\downarrow}}$, in a magnetic field generated by a large powerful (external) magnet (page 203). In such strong magnetic fields, the two positions of an unpaired electron correspond to different energy states. We can visualize the interaction between the electron—the micromagnet—and the big strong external magnet as follows: in one position the electron is attracted; but in the other position it is repelled:

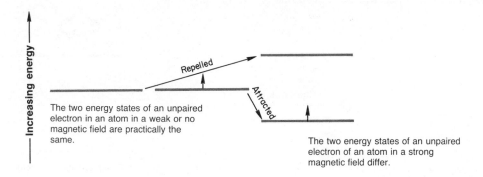

The *difference* between the two energy states depends on the *strength of the magnetic field;* the stronger the magnetic field, the larger the difference in the two energy states. This energy difference corresponds to a photon in the microwave range. A hydrogen

751

atom, a lithium atom, or a silver atom, each with one unpaired electron, in a strong magnetic field absorbs photons of the proper frequency in the microwave range:

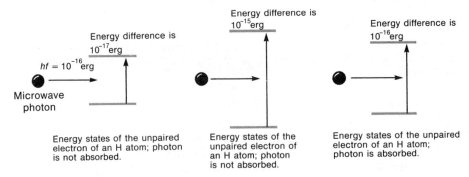

Further, although it is not necessary, we can visualize the electron transition from the lower to the upper state as shown:

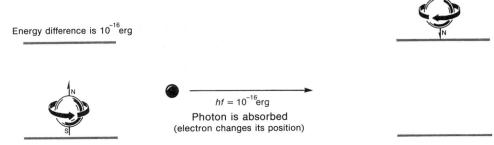

The *important feature,* however, is that a magnetic field is necessary to produce a difference in the energy states of an unpaired electron in an atom. Then a photon whose energy exactly equals the difference between the energy states can be absorbed.*

Unpaired protons and unpaired neutrons in nuclei behave in exactly the same way as unpaired electrons (page 206). An unpaired proton or an unpaired neutron behaves like a micromagnet. We shall, however, confine our discussion to the hydrogen atom whose nucleus is a proton and, therefore, unpaired.

Like the electron, the proton has two different energy states when the hydrogen atom is placed in a strong magnetic field. Like the electron, these two energy states correspond to two different positions of the proton:

For example, $^{13}_{6}C$ (6 protons all paired, 7 neutrons not all paired), $^{14}_{7}N$ (7 protons not all paired, 7 neutrons not all paired).

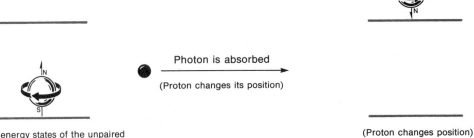

The two energy states of the unpaired proton (nucleus) of an H atom in a strong magnetic field

---

*This photon absorption, known as **electron spin resonance,** "ESR," is detectable and sufficiently sensitive to reveal clearly the presence of unpaired electrons in the lone iron atom in such large molecules as hemoglobin and myoglobin.

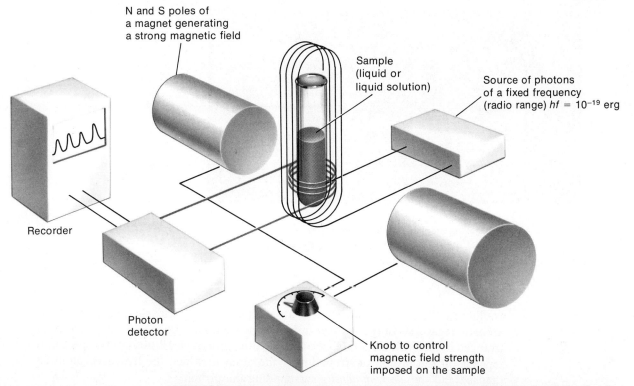

FIGURE 24.4 Representation of the essential parts of an NMR spectrophotometer. Notice that the photon energy is fixed while the magnetic field strength can be increased (increasing the difference between the proton energy states) or decreased (decreasing the difference between the proton energy states).

In principle, then, the technique of obtaining an absorption spectrum of the nucleus (proton) of the hydrogen atom is the same as that employed for IR, visible, or UV absorption spectra of atoms and molecules. The only added requirement is the presence of a strong magnetic field. We must remember also that the energy difference between the two states, ΔE, depends on the magnetic field strength. If we double the magnetic field strength, the energy difference, ΔE, becomes twice as large. The technique, known as **nuclear magnetic resonance,** NMR, is summarized in Fig. 24.4. It is called nuclear magnetic resonance because the technique involves magnetic interaction between the nucleus (the proton micromagnet) and the big external magnet, and resonance here means the energy of the photon must equal the difference in the energy states of the proton. Instead of saying, "the external magnetic field is adjusted so as to make the energy difference between the energy states of the proton (nucleus) equal to the energy of the photon," we simply say, "we have achieved nuclear magnetic resonance." This is not a new concept (Chaps. 6 and 21). No nucleus, atom, molecule, or ion at any set of conditions will absorb a photon unless it has two energy states available whose difference equals the energy of the photon.

A typical NMR absorption spectrum for water is shown in Fig. 24.5. The protons of the hydrogen atoms of water molecules absorb photons ($hf = 10^{-19}$ erg) only when the magnetic field imposed on the water has a particular value, indicated as **H** in Fig. 24.5. Now, if all hydrogen atoms (protons) in all molecules absorbed photons ($hf = 10^{-19}$ erg) at the same magnetic field strength, the proton NMR spectrum

Developed (1946) by Edward Purcell, Henry Torrey, and Robert Pound and, independently, by Felix Bloch, William Hansen, and Martin Packard (1946).

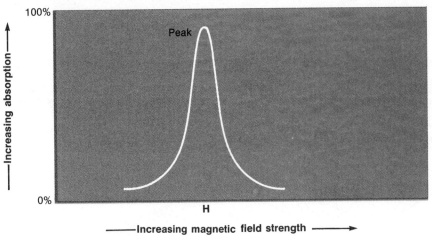

FIGURE 24.5 NMR absorption spectrum of water. Notice that in these graphs, by tradition, absorption increases from bottom to top, the opposite of Fig. 24.3.

would be useless. We would observe an identical peak at the same magnetic field strength, regardless of the number of hydrogen atoms and no matter how they were arranged in molecules. Fortunately, however, the proton NMR absorption spectrum depends on the proton's surroundings—the atom to which the hydrogen atom is attached and the *electron density* surrounding the proton.

The two protons in water, HOH, are near an oxygen atom with eight electrons. The hydrogen atoms in hydrogen sulfide, HSH, certainly appear to be similar to those in HOH, but the protons have a different environment. The protons are now near a sulfur atom with 16 electrons and so the electron density around the protons differs. The protons of the hydrogen atoms in an HSH molecule absorb the photons ($hf = 10^{-19}$ erg) not at **H** but at a higher magnetic field strength. The control knob (Fig. 24.4) has to be turned to increase the magnetic field strength before HSH absorbs the photons:

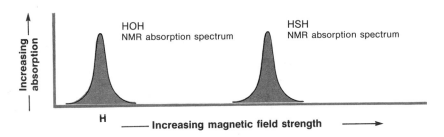

This change made in the magnetic field strength to obtain photon absorption by a proton is called a **chemical shift.**

While H:S:H absorbs the photons at a higher magnetic field strength than H:O:H, H:F absorbs at a lower strength. These changes (chemical shifts) are understandable in terms of the changes in electron density surrounding the protons.

Table 8.1, page 255 Differences in electronegativities (Fig. 8.2, page 253) are responsible for changes in the electron density. Fluorine (4.1) is the most electronegative, followed by oxygen (3.5) and sulfur (2.4). The sharing of the electron pair is thus not equal in the three molecules. Fluorine most strongly attracts the electron pair and so leaves the proton in H:F with the smallest electron density. On the other hand, sulfur least attracts the electron pairs, leaving the protons in H:S:H with the highest electron density:

We now visualize the electron cloud surrounding the proton as a shield protecting the proton from interaction with the magnetic field imposed upon it. Compared with the proton in H:S:H, the proton in H:F is naked. *The smaller the electron density, the weaker the protective shield, the greater the interaction with the imposed magnetic field, and the greater the difference between the two energy states of the proton:*

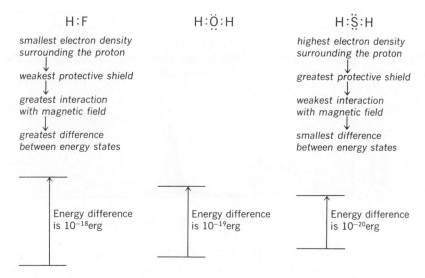

For photon ($hf = 10^{-19}$ erg) absorption to occur, the energy difference must be 10^{-19} erg. This is achieved (page 751) by decreasing the strength of the magnetic field ($<\mathbf{H}$) imposed on H:F but increasing the field strength ($>\mathbf{H}$) imposed on H:S:H.

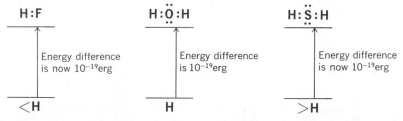

The NMR absorption spectrum of a mixture of these three substances thus appears as shown:

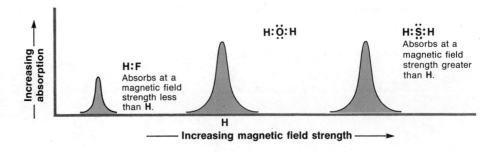

Three peaks appear because the protons in $H:F$, $H:\ddot{O}:H$, and $H:\ddot{S}:H$ are in three different environments. This graph illustrates the following information obtainable from NMR absorption spectra.

First, the *number of peaks* in the spectrum of a compound immediately gives us the number of different proton environments—the number of *differently bonded* hydrogen atoms in a molecule.

Second, notice that the areas under the curves for HOH and HSH are equal to each other but twice the area under the curve for HF. A molecule of HF has one hydrogen atom, while HOH and HSH each have two hydrogen atoms. The larger the number of protons, the larger the number of photons absorbed, and the larger the area of the absorption peak. Thus, the *area* under each curve gives us the number of hydrogen atoms of each kind in a molecule. For example, the NMR absorption spectrum of methyl alcohol, $H_3C\text{—}OH$, shows two peaks, one peak for the three H atoms in the CH_3 group and one peak for the H atom in the OH group; the area under the CH_3 peak is three times the area under the OH peak:

Actually, areas are measured relative to one another; the unit cm^2 is added for convenience.

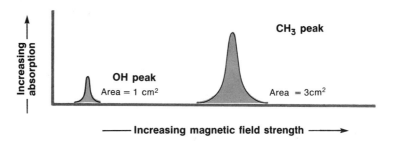

A final example, ethyl alcohol, $CH_3\text{—}CH_2\text{—}OH$, shows three peaks, one for the three H atoms in CH_3, one for the two H atoms in the CH_2 group, and a third for the H atom in OH; the area under the CH_3 peak is three times the area under the OH peak, while the area under the CH_2 peak is twice the area under the OH peak:

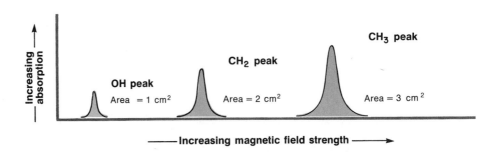

PROBLEM 3   A solution contains (a) HF, HI, and HCl; (b) HF, H_2S, and SiH_4. For each solution, sketch its NMR absorption spectrum, showing the number of peaks, indicating relative areas under the peak(s), and stating which substance absorbs at the highest magnetic field strength. (See Table 8.1, page 255.)

PROBLEM 4   A solution contains either dimethyl ketone, CH_3—$\overset{\overset{\displaystyle O}{\|}}{C}$—$CH_3$, or dichloropropane, CH_3—CH_2—$CHCl_2$, each with six H atoms per molecule. The NMR absorption spectrum shows one peak. (a) What is in the solution? (b) Explain the appearance of only one peak. (c) Predict the number of NMR peaks for chloropropyl alcohol, CH_3—CH_2—$CHCl$—OH.

Third, the *chemical shift* is fairly constant for a given group regardless of the molecule of which it is a part. For example, for R—CH_3, in which R is a saturated hydrocarbon chain (an alkyl group), the chemical shift is nearly always the same for the —CH_3 group in R—CH_3. But it is different from R—CH_2—R, which also has a chemical shift characteristic of the —CH_2— group in R—CH_2—R. The H atoms of an acid, R—COOH, an aldehyde, R—CHO, and an alcohol, R—OH, are easily identified by their characteristic chemical shifts. Tables that give characteristic proton chemical shifts in a large variety of environments make it possible for an experienced chemist not only to identify compounds but also to assign a structural formula to an unknown compound, usually in a few minutes. For example, CH_3—CH_2—Br, CH_3Br, RCH_2Br, R_2CHBr, and C_6H_5Br are readily identified from charts of chemical shifts. The proton environment in malignant tumors differs from that in normal tissue, making almost instantaneous detection of cancer by NMR possible.

Annals of New York Academy of Sciences, volume 204, 1973, page 164.

DETECTION OF SPECIFIC SUBSTANCES IN POLLUTION AND MEDICINE _____ 24.5

A variety of other instruments are available to identify many specific substances. For example, the EMF of a cell is the potential difference between two electrodes (Chap. 15). If the composition of one electrode is fixed, called a **reference electrode,** then the EMF of the cell is determined by the composition of the second electrode, called the **indicator electrode.** Indicator electrodes are available that determine the concentrations of ions such as H_3O^+ (pH), alkali metal ions, alkaline earth metal ions, Ag^+, Cd^{2+}, Pb^{2+}, halide ions, NH_3, NH_4^+, CN^-, NO_3^-, and S^{2-}. This technology is valuable for continuous detection of pollution, and for chemical analysis of biological fluids such as blood serum and urine.

Use of ion-indicator electrodes in industry and research ranks second to chromatography for analytical purposes.

As early as 1951, it was learned that oxygen diffuses through intact skin. A cell, Ag(c)-KCl(aq)-Pt(c), especially designed for attachment to the skin, makes it possible to record continuously the blood oxygen level in sick patients *without* cutting into the skin for blood collection (Fig. 24.6). The cell current is determined by the oxygen (partial pressure) concentration. Continuous recording immediately shows whether the patient is receiving proper treatment. The oxygen-carrying capacity of a patient's hemoglobin (Hb) can be measured in 20 minutes from 0.002 ml (2 μl) of blood using a spectrophotometer to record the formation of HbO_2 while an oxygen-sensitive electrode records the partial pressure of oxygen.

The sensing of air pollutants such as the oxides of nitrogen is especially worthy of our attention. Chemical techniques are unreliable at low levels. The latest technique is based on the chemiluminescent (page 196) reaction of nitrogen oxide and ozone, forming nitrogen dioxide in the excited state:

$$NO(g) + O_3(g) \longrightarrow NO_2(excited\ state) + O_2(g)$$

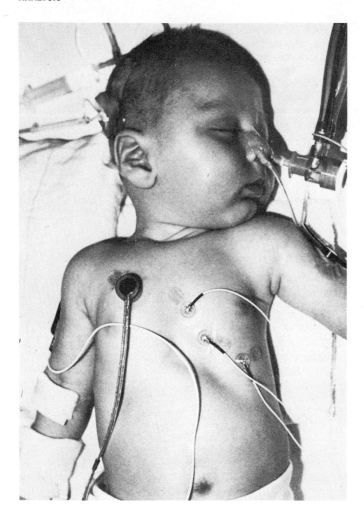

FIGURE 24.6 An oxygen-sensitive cell is attached to the right side of a sick infant in an intensive care unit. (Three electrocardiogram electrodes are attached to the chest.) (Courtesy of Renate Huch and Albert Huch, University of Marburg, *Pediatrics*, May 1976.)

The excited NO_2 then emits photons:

$$NO_2(excited\ state) \longrightarrow NO_2(ground\ state) + hf$$

The concentration of NO from 1 part per billion to 1 part per hundred by volume varies directly with the light emission, which is measured with a photoelectric cell.

Expensive instrumentation, gas chromatography (Chap. 1), mass spectrometry (Chap. 4), emission and absorption spectrometry, EMF measurements, and nuclear radiation meters are used mainly for research purposes. For example, they constitute the backbone of current research in molecular biology, and they are the workhorses of the clinical laboratory, as signaled by the recent founding of the *Society of Automated Medical Systems*. However, with changing attitudes toward control of air and water resources, the burden of proof of nonpollution is becoming the responsibility of industry and major disposal plants. These instruments are therefore being developed for inexpensive, automatic and continuous analysis of all sorts of hazardous pollutants from abietic acid and asbestos to xylene and zirconium.

Medical technology has, however, created many social problems.

"We live in critical times. The growing speed of technological change, and the growing expansion of technology over the globe, have created vast social and technical problems which must be attacked if we are to avoid major catastrophes. This attack must take the form of painstaking investigation of the effects of industrialization and thorough study of the interrelation of many factors which determine our environment. To proceed effectively will involve more basic science, not less. To quote Michael Polanyi (1958): 'The scientific method was devised precisely for the purpose of elucidating the nature of things under more care-fully controlled conditions and by more rigorous criteria than are present in situations created by practical problems. These conditions and criteria can be discovered only by taking a purely scientific interest in the matter, which again can exist only in minds educated in the appreciation of scientific value.'

The careful analysis of the problems and the necessary measures for solving them will require more, not less, of the spirit engendered in pure research. We will need more, not fewer, people trained in pure research, in the unbiased search of causes and effects."

_____ PROBLEMS

5 Vocabulary Define and/or illustrate: (a) absorption spectrum, (b) emission spectrum, (c) spectrophotometer, (d) chemical shift.

6 Spectra A method of detecting one part of pollutant NO in a billion parts of air is based on the reaction with ozone to form NO_2 in an excited state (page 186). Subsequent light emission (when NO_2 goes to the ground state) is detected. Is this method based on photon absorption (*absorption spectroscopy*) or photon emission (*emission spectroscopy*)?

7 Analysis Light emission methods detect 1.5×10^{-9} mole of lead (Pb^{2+}) in 10^{-3} ml of blood. How many (a) ions and (b) mg of Pb^{2+} are detected?

8 Clinical studies show that lithium carbonate, Li_2CO_3, is of value in treating mental disorders (manic psychoses), but above a certain dosage it is toxic. Spectroscopic methods, developed to measure accurately the Li_2CO_3 content of blood serum, can detect 5.0×10^{-8} mole/ml. This corresponds to how many (a) mg of Li_2CO_3 per ml and (b) Li^+ ions per ml?

9 The West-Gaeke method for analyzing SO_2 in air involves bubbling an air sample into a liquid that absorbs the SO_2, treating the resulting solution with a dye that reacts with the absorbed SO_2 to produce a purple color, and then measuring the intensity of the purple color with a spectrophotometer. The more SO_2 absorbed, the darker the purple color developed, and the smaller the quantity of light transmitted (more absorption). By comparing the amount of absorption in the sample solution with solutions containing known concentrations of SO_2, an estimation can be made of SO_2 concentration in the air. Given the following known SO_2 concentrations and their absorption readings:

Concentration of SO_2, ppm, ml SO_2 in 10^6 ml of air	Absorption (on an arbitrary scale from 0 to 1)
0.010	0.088
0.050	0.221
0.10	0.377
0.20	0.658
0.30	0.950

Draw a graph of absorption against known SO_2 concentration. From the graph, find the SO_2 concentration, in ppm, when a sample solution from a high-SO_2 city area has an absorption of 0.890.

10 NMR How many peaks do you predict in the proton NMR spectrum of each of the following?

(a) CH_4

(b) CH_3Cl

(c) $H_3C—CH_3$

(d) $H_2C—CH_2Cl$
   $|$
   Cl

(e) $CH_3—CH_2—CH_3$

(f) $CH_3—CHBr—CH_3$

(g) $CH_3—CHBr—CH_2Cl$

(h) $CH_3—CCl_2—CH_3$

(i) ⬡ (C_6H_6)

(j) [benzene ring with Cl, Cl]

(k) [benzene ring with Cl, Cl]

(l) $CH_3—\overset{O}{\overset{\|}{C}}—CCl_3$

(m) $CH_3—\overset{H}{\overset{|}{C}}=O$

(n) $FCH_2—\overset{H}{\overset{|}{C}}=O$

11 Refer to Problem 10. For each peak in (d), (g), and (j), how many H atoms per molecule produce each peak? Indicate the relative area under each peak.

12 From the given NMR information, decide which of the two given isomers is present in the sample: (a) $H_3C—CCl_3$ or $Cl_2HC—CH_2Cl$, NMR spectrum shows one peak; (b) $CH_3CH_2—O—CH_3$ or $CH_3CH_2CH_2OH$, NMR spectrum shows three

peaks; (c) $C(CH_3)_4$ or $CH_3CH_2—\overset{\overset{\displaystyle CH_3}{|}}{CH}—CH_3$, NMR spectrum shows one peak.

13 The NMR spectrum of the hydrate of perchloric acid shows one peak. Which is the better molecular formula, $HClO_4H_2O$ or $H_3O^+ClO_4^-$? Explain.

14 The NMR spectrum of a mixture of CH_4, H_2O, H_2S, and HF shows four peaks. (a) Identify the peaks appearing at the lowest and highest magnetic field strength. Explain. (See Table 8.1, page 255.) (b) Are the areas under the peaks equal? Explain.

15 Library Read one of the following:
(a) "Choice of Analytical Tool," *American Laboratory,* April 1971, page 8.

(b) "Magnetic Resonance," *Scientific American,* August 1958, pages 58–64.
(c) "Development of Chemical Instruments," *Chemical Technology,* June 1973, page 326.
(d) "Energy States of Molecules," *Journal of Chemical Education,* January 1970, page 2.
(e) "Analytical Methods for Trace Metals—An Overview," H. A. Laitinen, New York Academy of Sciences Conference, 5 October 1971.
(f) "Lead in the Seas—A Tough Analytical Problem," *What's Happening in Chemistry,* American Chemical Society, Washington, D.C., 1975, page 13.
(g) "NMR and Archaeological Chemistry," *Chemistry,* November 1975, page 20.
(h) "Transcutaneous P_{O_2} Monitoring in Routine Management of Infants and Children with Cardiorespiratory Problems," R. Huch, A. Huch, and coworkers, *Pediatrics,* volume 57, May 1976, page 681.
(i) "Authenticity in Art: The Scientific Detection of Forgery," S. J. Fleming, Crane Russak Co., New York, 1976.
(j) "Helping the Dying Die," *New England Journal of Medicine,* volume 295, 12 August 1976, pages 362, 364, 367.

ADDITIONAL PROBLEMS

16 The SO_2 molecules in a 1.0 ml (STP) air sample exposed to ultraviolet light are excited to an energy state from which photons of a characteristic frequency are emitted. 1.1×10^{15} photons are detected. Assume that one photon is emitted per SO_2 molecule. Calculate the concentration, in parts per million by volume, of SO_2 in the air sample.

17 The higher MO energy levels are given for a chlorophyll-like compound that absorbs photons at 310, 350, 575, and 760 nm.

Show the transitions that account for this absorption pattern.

18 Formaldehyde, CH_2O, results in irritation of the eyes, nose, and throat at levels of 0.01 to 1.0 ppm by molecule, and causes general discomfort at levels of 2.0 to 3.0 ppm; it can be tolerated for only about 20 minutes at levels of 4.0 to 5.0 ppm; and tracheal irritation and difficulty in breathing occur at levels of 10 to 20 ppm. A spectrometer indicates 1.21×10^{-7} g of CH_2O in a 20.0 ml (STP) sample

of air. Find the level of formaldehyde in ppm by molecule.

19 Tobacco smoke is a suspected source of nitrosamines, carcinogenic agents. Explain how an NMR spectrophotometer tuned to pick up nitrogen atoms in molecules may be used to distinguish the compound $(CH_3)_2N—N=O$, a nitrosamine, from $H_2N—CH_2—NH_2$, a diamide.

20 Carbon monoxide is a poison because it reacts with hemoglobin (Hb), forming HbCO in competition with oxygen. For human blood, the ratio of concentrations of HbCO and HbO$_2$ is directly related to the partial pressures of CO and O$_2$ in the lungs:

$$\frac{[HbCO]}{[HbO_2]} = 245 \times \frac{P_{CO}}{P_{O_2}}$$

Find (a) the partial pressure of CO in the lungs when the partial pressure of O_2 is 100 torr and the concentration ratio equals 1.00; and (b) the number of moles of CO in the lungs at 37 °C for a person with a lung capacity of 4.0 ℓ.

21 Predict the number of peaks and the relative area under each peak in the NMR spectrum of $CH_3—CH_2—CH_2—O—CH_3$.

1 (a) (i) green, (ii) none
  (b) (i) infrared, (ii) green, violet, (iii) infrared, green,
      (iv) infrared, violet, (v) all absorbed
2 (a) alcohol, (b) carbonyl
3 (a) 3 peaks, same area, HI
  (b) 3 peaks, 1:2:4, SiH_4
4 (a) dimethyl ketone, (c) 4 peaks
6 emission
7 (a) 9.0×10^{14} ions, (b) 3.1×10^{-4} mg
8 (a) 3.7×10^{-3} mg/ml, (b) 6.0×10^{16} Li^+/ml
9 0.28 ppm

10 (a)(b)(c)(d)(h)(i)(k)(l) 1,
   (e)(f)(j)(m)(n) 2, (g) 3
11 (d) 4, (g) 3:1:2, (j) 2:2
12 (a) H_3C—CCl_3, (b) CH_3CH_2—O—CH_3, (c) $C(CH_3)_4$
13 $H_3O^+ClO_4^-$
14 (a) HF (lowest), H_2O, CH_4, H_2S
   (b) 1:2:4:2
16 40 ppm
18 4.5 ppm
19 diamide 1 peak
20 (a) 0.408 torr, (b) 8.4×10^{-5} mole
21 4 peaks, 3:2:2:3

GLOSSARY

absorption spectrum The spectrum obtained by passing photons of known wavelengths through a substance and recording which photons are absorbed; the absorption spectrum is a characteristic property of a substance.
bioelectrode An enzyme-coated indicator electrode that measures glucose, urea, amino acids, alcohols, penicillin, cholesterol, and many other substances. See **indicator electrode.**
chemical shift In nuclear magnetic resonance spectroscopy, the change that must be made in the external magnetic field strength to cause photon absorption by a nucleus.
indicator electrode An electrode which, when used with a reference electrode, makes it possible to determine the concentration of an ion in solution. For example, a H^+ indicator electrode is used to deter-

mine [H_3O^+]; a Cl^- indicator electrode is used to determine [Cl^-]. See **reference electrode.**
nuclear magnetic resonance The absorption spectrum obtained as the strength of an external magnetic field is gradually increased so as to make the energy difference between the energy states of a nucleus of an atom in a molecule equal to the energy of a photon, whose frequency remains constant while the magnetic field strength is increased.
reference electrode An electrode of fixed and known composition whose electrode potential is fixed and known. See **indicator electrode.**
spectrophotometer An instrument which records the absorption spectrum of a substance by measuring the amount of light as a function of wavelength absorbed by a sample of the substance. See **absorption spectrum.**

Values of Fundamental Constants*

QUANTITY	SYMBOL	
Speed of light in vacuum	c	2.9979246×10^{10} cm/s
Charge of electron (proton)	e	1.60219×10^{-19} coulomb (C)
Faraday constant	F	9.6485×10^4 C/mole electrons
Planck constant	h	6.6262×10^{-27} erg s/particle
Boltzmann constant	k	1.3807×10^{-16} erg/(molecule K)
Avogadro number (constant)	L, N_A	6.02209×10^{23} particles**/mole
(Ideal) gas constant	R	8.2057×10^{-2} liter atm/(mole K)
		8.3145 Pa m^3/(mole K)
		8.3145 J/(mole K)
Molar volume (g, STP)	V_m	22.414 liters
Ice point	T_{ice}	273.1500 K ($= 0$ °C)

---

*Source: *NBS Dimensions,* January 1974, pages 4–5.

**Particles may be atoms (Na, H), molecules (H$_2$), ions (Na$^+$), electrons, other particles, or specified groups (SO$_4{}^{2-}$).

APPENDIX II

SI Symbols, Prefixes, and Abbreviations*

absolute (kinetic, thermodynamic) temperature, T

amount of substance, n

ampere (amp†), A

ångström, Å

atmosphere, atm

atomic weight (relative atomic mass of an element), A_r

calorie, cal

Celsius temperature, t

concentration of solute B (number of moles of B divided by volume of solution), c_B, [B]

coulomb, C

cubic centimeter, cm^3

cubic foot, ft^3

Curie, Ci

degree absolute, K, °K†

degree Celsius (Centigrade), °C

degree Fahrenheit, °F

degree of dissociation, α

density (mass divided by volume), ρ

disintegrations per minute, dpm

(electric) dipole moment, **p**

electromotive force, E

electronvolt,† eV

energy, E

enthalpy, H

entropy, S

equilibrium constant, in concentration, K_c

excited electronic state, He*, NO*

faraday, F

foot, ft

force, F

frequency, f, ν

Gibbs (free) energy, G

gram, g

heat, q

hertz, Hz, s^{-1}

hour, h

inch, in

ionic charge, Cl^-, Ca^{2+}, PO_4^{3-}

joule, J

kilocalorie, kcal

kilogram, kg

kinetic energy, E_k, K

length, l

liter, ℓ

magnetic field strength, **H**

mass, m

mass number, ^{14}N, $^{14}N_2$, $^{35}Cl^-$

meter, m

minute, min

molality of solute substance B, m_B

molar mass (mass divided by amount of substance), M

molar volume, V_m

molarity† of solute substance B, M_B

mole, mol, n

mole fraction of substance B, x_B

molecular weight (relative molecular mass of a substance), M_r

molecules, number of, N

ohm, Ω

osmotic pressure, π

oxidation number, $Pb_2^{II}Pb^{IV}O_4$

partial pressure of substance B, p_B

potential energy, E_p

pound, lb

pressure, p, P

quantity of electricity, Q

---

*Source: *Manual of Symbols and Terminology for Physicochemical Quantities and Units,* International Union of Pure and Applied Science, Butterworths, London, 1970.

†Use of these terms or symbols is not recommended by IUPAC.

A.2

rate constant, k
rate of increase of concentration of
    substance B, r_B
resistance, R
second, s
surface tension, σ
time, t

velocity, v, u
volt, V
volume, V
watt, W
wavelength, λ
weight, W, G
work (force $\times$ distance), w

Particles

alpha particle, α
deuteron, d
electron, e, e^-
neutron, n

photon, (hf), $(h\nu)$, γ
positron, e^+
proton, p, p^+

SI Prefixes

FRACTION	PREFIX	SYMBOL	EXAMPLE
10^{-1}	deci	d	1 decimeter, dm = 0.1 meter, m 10 decimeter = 1 meter
10^{-2}	centi	c	1 centimeter, cm = 0.01 meter 100 centimeter = 1 meter
10^{-3}	milli	m	1 millimeter, mm = 10^{-3} meter 1000 millimeter = 1 meter
10^{-6}	micro	μ	1 micrometer•, μm = 10^{-6} meter 10^6 micrometer = 1 meter
10^{-9}	nano	n	1 nanogram, ng = 10^{-9} gram, g 10^9 nanogram = 1 gram
10^{-12}	pico	p	1 picogram, pg = 10^{-12} gram 10^{12} picogram = 1 gram
10^{-15}	femto	f	1 femtogram = 10^{-15} gram 10^{15} femtogram = 1 gram
10^{-18}	atto	a	1 attogram, ag = 10^{-18} gram 10^{18} attogram = 1 gram

*The name micron, μ, is still used instead of micrometer.

MULTIPLE	PREFIX	SYMBOL	EXAMPLE
10	deca	da	1 decameter, dam = 10 meter
10^2	hecto	h	1 hectometer, hm = 100 meter
10^3	kilo	k	1 kilometer = 1000 meter
10^6	mega	M	1 megameter = 10^6 meter
10^9	giga	G	1 gigagram = 10^9 gram
10^{12}	tera	T	1 teragram = 10^{12} gram
10^{15}	peta	P	1 petameter = 10^{15} meter
10^{18}	exa	E	1 exameter = 10^{18} meter

Arithmetical Symbols

equal to, $=$
not equal to, $\neq$
approximately equal to, $\approx$
proportional to, $\propto$ or $\sim$
infinity, ∞
less than, $<$
greater than, $>$
plus, $+$

minus, $-$
multiplied by, $\times$
a divided by b, $\dfrac{a}{b}$ or a/b or ab^{-1}

a raised to the power n, a^n
square root of a, $\sqrt{a}$ or $\sqrt{}a$ or $a^{1/2}$
cube root of a, $\sqrt[3]{a}$ or $\sqrt[3]{}a$ or $a^{1/3}$
logarithm of a, base 10, log a or $\log_{10} a$

Conversion Factors

$\boxed{\text{SI Unit}}$

Length, Area, Volume

$100 \text{ cm} = \boxed{1 \text{ meter}}$

$10 \text{ mm} = 1 \text{ cm}$
$2.54 \text{ cm (exactly)} = 1 \text{ in}$
$10^8 \text{ Å (ångström)} = 1 \text{ cm}$
$5280 \text{ ft} = 1 \text{ mile}$
$1.609 \text{ km} = 1 \text{ mile}$

$10^4 \text{ cm}^2 = \boxed{1 \text{ m}^2}$

$6.45 \text{ cm}^2 = 1 \text{ in}^2$

$1000 \text{ ml} = 1 \text{ liter}$
$1000 \text{ liter} = \boxed{1 \text{ m}^3}$

$1 \text{ ml} = 1 \text{ cc}$
$1.057 \text{ qt} = 1 \text{ liter}$
$946.34 \text{ ml} = 1 \text{ qt}$
$3.7854 \text{ liter} = 1 \text{ gal}$

Pressure

$0.986923 \times 10^{-5} \text{ atm*} = \boxed{1 \text{ pascal, Pa}}$

$1.01325 \times 10^5 \text{ Pa} = 1 \text{ atm}$
$10^5 \text{ Pa} = 1 \text{ bar} = 0.986923 \text{ atm}$

$760 \text{ torr} = 1 \text{ atm}$
$1 \text{ torr} = 1 \text{ mm Hg} = 1.333 \times 10^2 \text{ Pa}$
$33.9 \text{ ft H}_2\text{O} = 1 \text{ atm}$

---

*1 atm $= 1.0336 \times 10^4 \text{ kg/m}^2$ (see Example 2, page 48). If we drop a ball of mass 1.0336×10^4 kg from a height (page 5), gravity acts on it, causing the ball to increase its speed by 9.806 m/s during each second that it remains in flight. This is written as $9.806 \text{ m/s} \times 1/\text{s} = 9.806 \text{ m/s}^2$. According to Isaac Newton (1687), if this ball is placed on a surface, it exerts a force equal to the product of its mass and 9.806 m/s², or

$$1.0336 \times 10^4 \text{ kg} \times 9.806 \text{ m/s}^2 = 1.013 \times 10^5 \text{ kg m/s}^2$$

In honor of Newton, the force defined in the SI units kg m/s² is named a newton, N, so that

$$\text{force} = 1.013 \times 10^5 \text{ kg m/s}^2 = 1.013 \times 10^5 \text{ N}$$

Then the unit of pressure, defined as force per unit area, in SI units is N/m²; thus, the force of 1.013×10^5 N acting on an area of 1 m² exerts a pressure of 1.013×10^5 N/m². We now have

$$1 \text{ atm} = 1.0336 \times 10^4 \text{ kg/m}^2 = 1.013 \times 10^5 \text{ kg m/m}^2\text{s}^2 = 1.013 \times 10^5 \text{ N/m}^2$$

But in honor of Blaise Pascal, the SI pressure unit N/m² is named the pascal, Pa, so that

$$1 \text{ atm} = 1.0336 \times 10^4 \text{ kg/m}^2 = 1.013 \times 10^5 \text{ N/m}^2$$
$$= 1.013 \times 10^5 \text{ Pa} = 101.3 \text{ kPa or roughly 100 kPa}$$

However, controversy still rages among scientists over the pascal unit. Some doubt that it will ever come into common use.

Mass

$1000 \text{ g} = \boxed{1 \text{ kg}}$

$1000 \text{ mg} = 1 \text{ g}$

$454 \text{ g} = 1 \text{ lb}$

$10^6 \text{ g} = 1 \text{ metric ton}$

Energy

$1 \text{ erg} = 1 \text{ g cm}^2/\text{s}^2$

$\boxed{1 \text{ joule, J}} = 1 \text{ volt} \times 1 \text{ coulomb} = 10^7 \text{ erg}$

$4.184 \times 10^7 \text{ erg} = 1 \text{ cal}$

$4.184 \text{ J (exactly)} = 1 \text{ cal}$

$1000 \text{ cal} = 1 \text{ kcal}$

$1 \text{ electron volt/atom} = 96.7 \text{ kJ/mole} = 23.1 \text{ kcal/mole}$

Electricity

$\boxed{1 \text{ ampere}} = 1 \text{ coulomb/second}$

$1 \text{ coulomb, C} = 1 \text{ ampere} \times 1 \text{ second}$

$96{,}500 \text{ C} = 1 \text{ faraday} = 1 \text{ mole of electrons}$

Amount of Substance

$\boxed{1 \text{ mole}}$ — mass in grams of 6.02×10^{23} particles

$22.4 \text{ liters } (g, \text{ STP}) = 1 \text{ mole}$

$6.02 \times 10^{23} \text{ particles} = 1 \text{ mole}$

Electronic Structures*

$_1$H	$1s^1$
$_2$He	$1s^2$
$_3$Li	$K\ 2s^1$
$_4$Be	$K\ 2s^2$
$_5$B	$K\ 2s^2\ 2p^1$
$_6$C	$K\ 2s^2\ 2p^2$
$_7$N	$K\ 2s^2\ 2p^3$
$_8$O	$K\ 2s^2\ 2p^4$
$_9$F	$K\ 2s^2\ 2p^5$
$_{10}$Ne	$K\ 2s^2\ 2p^6$
$_{11}$Na	$KL\ 3s^1$
$_{12}$Mg	$KL\ 3s^2$
$_{13}$Al	$KL\ 3s^2\ 3p^1$
$_{14}$Si	$KL\ 3s^2\ 3p^2$
$_{15}$P	$KL\ 3s^2\ 3p^3$
$_{16}$S	$KL\ 3s^2\ 3p^4$
$_{17}$Cl	$KL\ 3s^2\ 3p^5$
$_{18}$Ar	$KL\ 3s^2\ 3p^6$
$_{19}$K	$KL\ 3s^2\ 3p^6\ 4s^1$
$_{20}$Ca	$KL\ 3s^2\ 3p^6\ 4s^2$
$_{21}$Sc	$KL\ 3s^2\ 3p^6\ 3d^1\ 4s^2$
$_{22}$Ti	$KL\ 3s^2\ 3p^6\ 3d^2\ 4s^2$
$_{23}$V	$KL\ 3s^2\ 3p^6\ 3d^3\ 4s^2$
$_{24}$Cr	$KL\ 3s^2\ 3p^6\ 3d^5\ 4s^1$
$_{25}$Mn	$KL\ 3s^2\ 3p^6\ 3d^5\ 4s^2$
$_{26}$Fe	$KL\ 3s^2\ 3p^6\ 3d^6\ 4s^2$
$_{27}$Co	$KL\ 3s^2\ 3p^6\ 3d^7\ 4s^2$
$_{28}$Ni	$KL\ 3s^2\ 3p^6\ 3d^8\ 4s^2$
$_{29}$Cu	$KL\ 3s^2\ 3p^6\ 3d^{10}\ 4s^1$
$_{30}$Zn	$KLM\ 4s^2$
$_{31}$Ga	$KLM\ 4s^2\ 4p^1$
$_{32}$Ge	$KLM\ 4s^2\ 4p^2$
$_{33}$As	$KLM\ 4s^2\ 4p^3$
$_{34}$Se	$KLM\ 4s^2\ 4p^4$
$_{35}$Br	$KLM\ 4s^2\ 4p^5$
$_{36}$Kr	$KLM\ 4s^2\ 4p^6$
$_{37}$Rb	$KLM\ 4s^2\ 4p^6\ 5s^1$
$_{38}$Sr	$KLM\ 4s^2\ 4p^6\ 5s^2$
$_{39}$Y	$KLM\ 4s^2\ 4p^6\ 4d^1\ 5s^2$
$_{40}$Zr	$KLM\ 4s^2\ 4p^6\ 4d^2\ 5s^2$
$_{41}$Nb	$KLM\ 4s^2\ 4p^6\ 4d^4\ 5s^1$
$_{42}$Mo	$KLM\ 4s^2\ 4p^6\ 4d^5\ 5s^1$
$_{43}$Tc	$KLM\ 4s^2\ 4p^6\ 4d^6\ 5s^1$
$_{44}$Ru	$KLM\ 4s^2\ 4p^6\ 4d^7\ 5s^1$
$_{45}$Rh	$KLM\ 4s^2\ 4p^6\ 4d^8\ 5s^1$
$_{46}$Pd	$KLM\ 4s^2\ 4p^6\ 4d^{10}$
$_{47}$Ag	$KLM\ 4s^2\ 4p^6\ 4d^{10}\ 5s^1$
$_{48}$Cd	$KLM\ 4s^2\ 4p^6\ 4d^{10}\ 5s^2$
$_{49}$In	$KLM\ 4s^2\ 4p^6\ 4d^{10}\ 5s^2\ 5p^1$
$_{50}$Sn	$KLM\ 4s^2\ 4p^6\ 4d^{10}\ 5s^2\ 5p^2$
$_{51}$Sb	$KLM\ 4s^2\ 4p^6\ 4d^{10}\ 5s^2\ 5p^3$
$_{52}$Te	$KLM\ 4s^2\ 4p^6\ 4d^{10}\ 5s^2\ 5p^4$
$_{53}$I	$KLM\ 4s^2\ 4p^6\ 4d^{10}\ 5s^2\ 5p^5$
$_{54}$Xe	$KLM\ 4s^2\ 4p^6\ 4d^{10}\ 5s^2\ 5p^6$

*Experimentally determined electronic structures of the elements in their gaseous atomic ground states.

$_{55}$Cs	KLM $4s^2$ $4p^6$ $4d^{10}$ $5s^2$ $5p^6$ $6s^1$	
$_{56}$Ba	KLM $4s^2$ $4p^6$ $4d^{10}$ $5s^2$ $5p^6$ $6s^2$	
$_{57}$La	KLM $4s^2$ $4p^6$ $4d^{10}$ $5s^2$ $5p^6$ $5d^1$ $6s^2$	
$_{58}$Ce	KLM $4s^2$ $4p^6$ $4d^{10}$ $4f^2$ $5s^2$ $5p^6$ $6s^2$	Uncertain
$_{59}$Pr	KLM $4s^2$ $4p^6$ $4d^{10}$ $4f^3$ $5s^2$ $5p^6$ $6s^2$	Uncertain
$_{60}$Nd	KLM $4s^2$ $4p^6$ $4d^{10}$ $4f^4$ $5s^2$ $5p^6$ $6s^2$	
$_{61}$Pm	KLM $4s^2$ $4p^6$ $4d^{10}$ $4f^5$ $5s^2$ $5p^6$ $6s^2$	Uncertain
$_{62}$Sm	KLM $4s^2$ $4p^6$ $4d^{10}$ $4f^6$ $5s^2$ $5p^6$ $6s^2$	
$_{63}$Eu	KLM $4s^2$ $4p^6$ $4d^{10}$ $4f^7$ $5s^2$ $5p^6$ $6s^2$	
$_{64}$Gd	KLM $4s^2$ $4p^6$ $4d^{10}$ $4f^7$ $5s^2$ $5p^6$ $5d^1$ $6s^2$	
$_{65}$Tb	KLM $4s^2$ $4p^6$ $4d^{10}$ $4f^9$ $5s^2$ $5p^6$ $6s^2$	Uncertain
$_{66}$Dy	KLM $4s^2$ $4p^6$ $4d^{10}$ $4f^{10}$ $5s^2$ $5p^6$ $6s^2$	Uncertain
$_{67}$Ho	KLM $4s^2$ $4p^6$ $4d^{10}$ $4f^{11}$ $5s^2$ $5p^6$ $6s^2$	Uncertain
$_{68}$Er	KLM $4s^2$ $4p^6$ $4d^{10}$ $4f^{12}$ $5s^2$ $5p^6$ $6s^2$	
$_{69}$Tm	KLM $4s^2$ $4p^6$ $4d^{10}$ $4f^{13}$ $5s^2$ $5p^6$ $6s^2$	
$_{70}$Yb	KLM $4s^2$ $4p^6$ $4d^{10}$ $4f^{14}$ $5s^2$ $5p^6$ $6s^2$	
$_{71}$Lu	$KLMN$ $5s^2$ $5p^6$ $5d^1$ $6s^2$	
$_{72}$Hf	$KLMN$ $5s^2$ $5p^6$ $5d^2$ $6s^2$	
$_{73}$Ta	$KLMN$ $5s^2$ $5p^6$ $5d^3$ $6s^2$	
$_{74}$W	$KLMN$ $5s^2$ $5p^6$ $5d^4$ $6s^2$	
$_{75}$Re	$KLMN$ $5s^2$ $5p^6$ $5d^5$ $6s^2$	
$_{76}$Os	$KLMN$ $5s^2$ $5p^6$ $5d^6$ $6s^2$	
$_{77}$Ir	$KLMN$ $5s^2$ $5p^6$ $5d^7$ $6s^2$	
$_{78}$Pt	$KLMN$ $5s^2$ $5p^6$ $5d^9$ $6s^1$	
$_{79}$Au	$KLMN$ $5s^2$ $5p^6$ $5d^{10}$ $6s^1$	
$_{80}$Hg	$KLMN$ $5s^2$ $5p^6$ $5d^{10}$ $6s^2$	
$_{81}$Te	$KLMN$ $5s^2$ $5p^6$ $5d^{10}$ $6s^2$ $6p^1$	
$_{82}$Pb	$KLMN$ $5s^2$ $5p^6$ $5d^{10}$ $6s^2$ $6p^2$	
$_{83}$Bi	$KLMN$ $5s^2$ $5p^6$ $5d^{10}$ $6s^2$ $6p^3$	
$_{84}$Po	$KLMN$ $5s^2$ $5p^6$ $5d^{10}$ $6s^2$ $6p^4$	
$_{85}$At	$KLMN$ $5s^2$ $5p^6$ $5d^{10}$ $6s^2$ $6p^5$	
$_{86}$Rn	$KLMN$ $5s^2$ $5p^6$ $5d^{10}$ $6s^2$ $6p^6$	
$_{87}$Fr	$KLMN$ $5s^2$ $5p^6$ $5d^{10}$ $6s^2$ $6p^6$ $7s^1$	
$_{88}$Ra	$KLMN$ $5s^2$ $5p^6$ $5d^{10}$ $6s^2$ $6p^6$ $7s^2$	
$_{89}$Ac	$KLMN$ $5s^2$ $5p^6$ $5d^{10}$ $6s^2$ $6p^6$ $6d^1$ $7s^2$	
$_{90}$Th	$KLMN$ $5s^2$ $5p^6$ $5d^{10}$ $6s^2$ $6p^6$ $6d^2$ $7s^2$	
$_{91}$Pa	$KLMN$ $5s^2$ $5p^6$ $5d^{10}$ $5f^2$ $6s^2$ $6p^6$ $6d^1$ $7s^2$	
$_{92}$U	$KLMN$ $5s^2$ $5p^6$ $5d^{10}$ $5f^3$ $6s^2$ $6p^6$ $6d^1$ $7s^2$	
$_{93}$Np	$KLMN$ $5s^2$ $5p^6$ $5d^{10}$ $5f^4$ $6s^2$ $6p^6$ $6d^1$ $7s^2$	
$_{94}$Pu	$KLMN$ $5s^2$ $5p^6$ $5d^{10}$ $5f^6$ $6s^2$ $6p^6$ $7s^2$	
$_{95}$Am	$KLMN$ $5s^2$ $5p^6$ $5d^{10}$ $5f^7$ $6s^2$ $6p^6$ $7s^2$	
$_{96}$Cm	$KLMN$ $5s^2$ $5p^6$ $5d^{10}$ $5f^7$ $6s^2$ $6p^6$ $6d^1$ $7s^2$	
$_{97}$Bk	$KLMN$ $5s^2$ $5p^6$ $5d^{10}$ $5f^9$ $6s^2$ $6p^6$ $7s^2$	Uncertain
$_{98}$Cf	$KLMN$ $5s^2$ $5p^6$ $5d^{10}$ $5f^{10}$ $6s^2$ $6p^6$ $7s^2$	
$_{99}$Es	$KLMN$ $5s^2$ $5p^6$ $5d^{10}$ $5f^{11}$ $6s^2$ $6p^6$ $7s^2$	
$_{100}$Fm	$KLMN$ $5s^2$ $5p^6$ $5d^{10}$ $5f^{12}$ $6s^2$ $6p^6$ $7s^2$	
$_{101}$Md	$KLMN$ $5s^2$ $5p^6$ $5d^{10}$ $5f^{13}$ $6s^2$ $6p^6$ $7s^2$	
$_{102}$No	$KLMN$ $5s^2$ $5p^6$ $5d^{10}$ $5f^{14}$ $6s^2$ $6p^6$ $7s^2$	
$_{103}$Lr	$KLMN$ $5s^2$ $5p^6$ $5d^{10}$ $5f^{14}$ $6s^2$ $6p^6$ $6d^1$ $7s^2$	
$_{104}$	$KLMN$ $5s^2$ $5p^6$ $5d^{10}$ $5f^{14}$ $6s^2$ $6p^6$ $6d^2$ $7s^2$	Predicted
$_{112}$	$KLMN$ $5s^2$ $5p^6$ $5d^{10}$ $5f^{14}$ $6s^2$ $6p^6$ $6d^{10}$ $7s^2$	Predicted
$_{113}$	$KLMN$ $5s^2$ $5p^6$ $5d^{10}$ $5f^{14}$ $6s^2$ $6p^6$ $6d^{10}$ $7s^2$ $7p^1$	Predicted
$_{120}$	$KLMN$ $5s^2$ $5p^6$ $5d^{10}$ $5f^{14}$ $6s^2$ $6p^6$ $6d^{10}$ $7s^2$ $7p^6$ $8s^2$	Predicted
$_{121}$	$KLMN$ $5s^2$ $5p^6$ $5d^{10}$ $5f^{14}$ $6s^2$ $6p^6$ $6d^{10}$ $7s^2$ $7p^6$ $8s^2$ $8p^1$	Predicted
$_{122}$	$KLMN$ $5s^2$ $5p^6$ $5d^{10}$ $5f^{14}$ $6s^2$ $6p^6$ $6d^{10}$ $7s^2$ $7p^6$ $7d^1$ $8s^2$ $8p^1$	Predicted
$_{123}$	$KLMN$ $5s^2$ $5p^6$ $5d^{10}$ $5f^{14}$ $6s^2$ $6p^6$ $6d^{10}$ $6f^1$ $7s^2$ $7p^6$ $7d^1$ $8s^2$ $8p^1$	Predicted
$_{124}$	$KLMN$ $5s^2$ $5p^6$ $5d^{10}$ $5f^{14}$ $6s^2$ $6p^6$ $6d^{10}$ $6f^3$ $7s^2$ $7p^6$ $8s^2$ $8p^1$	Predicted
$_{125}$	$KLMN$ $5s^2$ $5p^6$ $5d^{10}$ $5f^{14}$ $5g$ $6s^2$ $6p^6$ $6d^{10}$ $6f^3$ $7s^2$ $7p^6$ $8s^2$ $8p^1$	Predicted
$_{126}$	$KLMN$ $5s^2$ $5p^6$ $5d^{10}$ $5f^{14}$ $5g^2$ $6s^2$ $6p^6$ $6d^{10}$ $6f^2$ $7s^2$ $7p^6$ $8s^2$ $8p^2$	Predicted
$_{127}$	$KLMN$ $5s^2$ $5p^6$ $5d^{10}$ $5f^{14}$ $5g^3$ $6s^2$ $6p^6$ $6d^{10}$ $6f^2$ $7s^2$ $7p^6$ $8s^2$ $8p^2$	Predicted

Characteristic Color Emitted by Atoms of Metallic Elements in a Flame

Lithium	Deep red (carmine)	Calcium	Yellowish red
Sodium	Yellow	Strontium	Bright red (scarlet)
Potassium	Violet	Barium	Yellowish green
Lead	Light Blue	Copper	Green

Standard Enthalpies (ΔH_f in kcal/mole and kJ/mole) and Gibbs (Free) Energies (ΔG_f in kcal/mole and kJ/mole) of Formation at 298.15 K

This table gives the standard enthalpy and the standard Gibbs (free) energy for the reaction in which 1 mole of the substance is formed from its elements in their stable forms at 298.15 K and at 1 atmosphere pressure.

	ΔH_f kcal/mole	ΔH_f kJ/mole	ΔG_f kcal/mole	ΔG_f kJ/mole
Ag(c)	0	0	0	0
Ag$_2$O(c)	−7.42	−31.1	−2.68	−11.2
AgCl(c)	−30.370	−127.07	−26.244	−109.80
AgBr(c)	−23.99	−100.4	−23.16	−96.90
AgI(c)	−14.78	−61.84	−15.82	−66.19
AlF$_3$(c)	−359.5	−1504	−340.6	−1425
As$_2$S$_3$(c)	−40.4	−169	−40.3	−169
BCl$_3$(l)	−102.1	−427.2	−92.6	−387

	ΔH_f kcal/mole	ΔH_f kJ/mole	ΔG_f kcal/mole	ΔG_f kJ/mole
$BaCl_2(c)$	−205.2	−858.6	−193.7	−810.4
$BaSO_4(c)$	−352.1	−1473	−325.6	−1362
$BeF_2(c)$	−245.4	−1027	−234.1	−979.5
$BiCl_3(c)$	−90.6	−379	−75.3	−315
$Br_2(l)$	0	0	0	0
$Br_2(g)$	+7.387	+30.91	+0.751	+3.14
$C(graphite)$	0	0	0	0
$C(diamond)$	+0.4533	+1.897	+0.6930	+2.900
$CO(g)$	−26.416	−110.52	−32.780	−137.15
$CO_2(g)$	−94.0428	−393.475	−94.254	−394.36
$CH_4(g)$	−17.86	−74.73	−12.12	−50.71
$CCl_4(l)$	−32.37	−135.4	−15.60	−65.27
$C_2H_2(g)$	+54.19	+226.7	+50.00	+209.20
$C_2H_4(g)$	+12.49	+52.26	+16.28	+68.12
$C_2H_6(g)$	−20.00	−83.68	−7.60	−31.8
$C_2H_5OH(l)$	−66.37	−277.7	−41.80	−174.9
$C_2Cl_4(l)$	12.5	−52.3	+1.1	+4.6
$C_3H_8(g)$	−25.07	−104.9	−5.87	−24.6
$C_6H_6(l)$	+11.72	+49.04	+29.76	+124.5
$C_6H_6(g)$	+19.82	+82.93	+30.99	+129.7
$CaH_2(c)$	−44.5	−186.2	−35.2	−147.3
$Ca(NO_3)_2(c)$	−224.28	−938.39	−117.63	−492.16
$CdS(c)$	−38.7	−162	−37.4	−156
$Cl_2(g)$	0	0	0	0
$CoCl_2(H_2O)_6(c)$	−505.6	−2115	−412.4	−1725
$CuSO_4(H_2O)_5(c)$	−544.85	−2279.7	−449.344	−1880.06
$Fe(CO)_5(l)$	−185.0	−774.0	−168.6	−705.4
$H_2(g)$	0	0	0	0
$H_2O(l)$	−68.315	−285.83	−56.687	−237.18
$H_2O(g)$	−57.796	−241.8	−54.634	−228.59
$H_2O_2(l)$	−44.88	−187.8	−28.78	−120.4
$HCl(g)$	−22.062	−92.307	−22.777	−95.299
$HBr(g)$	−8.70	−36.4	−12.77	−53.43
$H_2SO_4(l)$	−194.548	−814.0	−164.938	−690.101
$HgS(c)(black)$	−12.8	−53.6	−11.4	−47.7
$KF(c)$	−135.58	−567.27	−128.53	−537.77
$KClO_4(c)$	−103.430	−432.751	−72.46	−303.2
$MgCl_2(c)$	−153.28	−641.32	−141.45	−591.83
$NaCl(c)$	−98.268	−411.15	−91.842	−384.27
$NH_3(g)$	−11.02	−46.11	−3.94	−16.5
$NH_4NO_3(c)$	−87.37	−365.6	−43.98	−184.0
$NH_4Cl(c)$	−75.15	−314.4	−48.51	−203.0
$O_2(g)$	0	0	0	0
$O_3(g)$	+34.100	+142.67	+38.997	+163.16
$PCl_5(g)$	−89.6	−375	−72.9	−305
$PbO(c)(yellow)$	−51.94	−217.3	−44.91	−187.9
$PbCl_2(c)$	−85.90	−359.4	−75.08	−314.1
$S(c)(rhombic)$	0	0	0	0
$SO(g)$	+1.496	+6.259	−4.741	−19.84
$SO_2(g)$	−70.944	+296.83	−71.748	−300.19
$SO_3(g)$	−94.58	−395.7	−88.69	−371.1
$SiO_2(c)(quartz)$	−217.72	−910.94	−204.75	−856.67
$SiCl_4(l)$	−164.2	−687.0	−148.16	−619.90
$SnCl_4(l)$	−122.2	−511.3	−105.2	−440.16
$ZnS(c)(sphalerite)$	−49.23	−206.0	−48.11	−201.3
$ZnSO_4(c)$	−234.9	−982.8	−209.0	−874.5

Sources: "*Selected Values of Chemical Thermodynamic Properties*," NBS Technical Notes 270—1 to 7, 1968-1973; "*NBS Interim Report 76-1034*," 1976; "*Chemical Thermodynamic Properties of Hydrocarbons and Related Substances*," Bureau of Mines Bulletin 666, 1974.

General Solubility Rules

SOLUBLE IN WATER AT ROOM TEMPERATURE	**IMPORTANT EXCEPTIONS**
All Na^+ salts	
All K^+ salts	
All NH_4^+ salts	
All nitrates	
All acetates	CH_3COOAg
All chlorates	
All chloride (Cl^-), bromide (Br^-), and iodide (I^-) salts	Those of Ag^+, Pb^{2+}, Hg_2^{2+}
All sulfates	$BaSO_4$, $SrSO_4$, $CaSO_4$, $PbSO_4$, Ag_2SO_4
Na_2CO_3, K_2CO_3, $(NH_4)_2CO_3$	All other carbonates insoluble
Na_3PO_4, K_3PO_4, $(NH_4)_3PO_4$*	All other phosphates insoluble
Hydroxides of Group IA ($Li^+ \longrightarrow Cs^+$)	All other hydroxides insoluble
Sulfides of Na^+, K^+, Ca^{2+}, Ba^{2+}, Sr^{2+}, Al^{3+}	All other sulfides insoluble

---

*Soluble phosphates and sulfides react extensively with water:

$$PO_4^{3-}(aq) + H_2O \rightleftharpoons HPO_4^{2-}(aq) + OH^-(aq)$$
$$S^{2-}(aq) + H_2O \rightleftharpoons HS^-(aq) + OH^-(aq)$$

Freezing-Point Depression, K_f, and Boiling-Point Elevation, K_b, Constants

SOLVENT	FREEZING POINT, °C	K_f, $\dfrac{°C\ kg}{mole}$	BOILING POINT, °C	K_b*, $\dfrac{°C\ kg}{mole}$
Acetic acid	16.6	3.90	117.9	3.07
Benzene	5.5	5.12	79.6	2.53
Camphor	179.8	40.0	—	—
Diphenyl	71	8.00	—	—
Nitrobenzene	5.7	7.00	210.8	5.24
Phenol	41	7.27	181.8	3.56
Water	0	1.86	100	0.512

*These constants are applicable only to solutions of nonvolatile solutes. If the solute is volatile, it becomes impossible to measure the boiling point of the solvent.

Units of Radioactivity

The **rem** (**r**oentgen **e**quivalent **m**an) is the standard unit of biological effect on Man of exposure to radiation. It measures the biological effectiveness of different kinds of ionizing radiation relative to X-rays and gamma rays. It accounts for both the radiation dosage absorbed by the body and its biological damage: *rem = absorbed dose (rad) × biological effectiveness (rbe)*. The rad measures the radiation dosage in terms of energy absorbed per gram of material; 1 rad = 100 erg/g. The rbe compares the relative biological effectiveness of different kinds of radiation: rbe = 1 for X-rays, gamma rays, and electrons; 10 for neutrons, protons, and alpha particles; and 20 for high-speed heavy nuclei. Thus, the effect of exposure to 10 rads of electrons (10 rad × 1 rbe = 10 rem) is the same as that of exposure to 1 rad of alpha particles (1 rad × 10 rbe = 10 rem). Typical natural background radiation levels in the United States are about 0.125 rem per year, including radiation (about 0.025 rem) received from radioactive carbon and potassium in our bodies. Over the world, the level varies from about 0.090 to 12 rem/year. The U.S. Government radiation emission standard for nuclear power plants limits radiation to 0.005 rem/year above background for people living near a plant. The dosage limits are 0.500 rem/year for any one individual and 0.170 rem/year for the general population. A chest X-ray may deliver a dosage of 0.500 rem.

One **Curie,** Ci, is defined as the quantity of radioactive substance in which the number of disintegrations per second is 3.700×10^{10}. The mass represented by 1 Ci is thus different for each isotope, and depends on its half-life.

The **roentgen,** r, is the standard unit for measuring the intensity of X-rays or gamma rays. It is defined as the quantity of radiation that produces 1.61×10^{12} ion pairs in one gram of air, equal to the absorption of 8.4×10^{-6} J/g air.

Logarithms to the Base 10

TABLE OF LOGARITHMS

N	0	1	2	3	4	5	6	7	8	9
1.0	.0000	.0043	.0086	.0128	.0170	.0212	.0253	.0294	.0334	.0374
1.1	.0414	.0453	.0492	.0531	.0569	.0607	.0645	.0682	.0719	.0755
1.2	.0792	.0828	.0864	.0899	.0934	.0969	.1004	.1038	.1072	.1106
1.3	.1139	.1173	.1206	.1239	.1271	.1303	.1335	.1367	.1399	.1430
1.4	.1461	.1492	.1523	.1553	.1584	.1614	.1644	.1673	.1703	.1732
1.5	.1761	.1790	.1818	.1847	.1875	.1903	.1931	.1959	.1987	.2014
1.6	.2041	.2068	.2095	.2122	.2148	.2175	.2201	.2227	.2253	.2279
1.7	.2304	.2330	.2355	.2380	.2405	.2430	.2455	.2480	.2504	.2529
1.8	.2553	.2577	.2601	.2625	.2648	.2672	.2695	.2718	.2742	.2765
1.9	.2788	.2810	.2833	.2856	.2878	.2900	.2923	.2945	.2967	.2989
2.0	.3010	.3032	.3054	.3075	.3096	.3118	.3139	.3160	.3181	.3201
2.1	.3222	.3243	.3263	.3284	.3304	.3324	.3345	.3365	.3385	.3404
2.2	.3424	.3444	.3464	.3483	.3502	.3522	.3541	.3560	.3579	.3598
2.3	.3617	.3636	.3655	.3674	.3692	.3711	.3729	.3747	.3766	.3784
2.4	.3802	.3820	.3838	.3856	.3874	.3892	.3909	.3927	.3945	.3962
2.5	.3979	.3997	.4014	.4031	.4048	.4065	.4082	.4099	.4116	.4133
2.6	.4150	.4166	.4183	.4200	.4216	.4232	.4249	.4265	.4281	.4298
2.7	.4314	.4330	.4346	.4362	.4378	.4393	.4409	.4425	.4440	.4456
2.8	.4472	.4487	.4502	.4518	.4533	.4548	.4564	.4579	.4594	.4609
2.9	.4624	.4639	.4654	.4669	.4683	.4698	.4713	.4728	.4742	.4757
3.0	.4771	.4786	.4800	.4814	.4829	.4843	.4857	.4871	.4886	.4900
3.1	.4914	.4928	.4942	.4955	.4969	.4983	.4997	.5011	.5024	.5038
3.2	.5051	.5065	.5079	.5092	.5105	.5119	.5132	.5145	.5159	.5172
3.3	.5185	.5198	.5211	.5224	.5237	.5250	.5263	.5276	.5289	.5302
3.4	.5315	.5328	.5340	.5353	.5366	.5378	.5391	.5403	.5416	.5428
3.5	.5441	.5453	.5465	.5478	.5490	.5502	.5514	.5527	.5539	.5551
3.6	.5563	.5575	.5587	.5599	.5611	.5623	.5635	.5647	.5658	.5670
3.7	.5682	.5694	.5705	.5717	.5729	.5740	.5752	.5763	.5775	.5786
3.8	.5798	.5809	.5821	.5832	.5843	.5855	.5866	.5877	.5888	.5899
3.9	.5911	.5922	.5933	.5944	.5955	.5966	.5977	.5988	.5999	.6010
4.0	.6021	.6031	.6042	.6053	.6064	.6075	.6085	.6096	.6107	.6117
4.1	.6128	.6138	.6149	.6160	.6170	.6180	.6191	.6201	.6212	.6222
4.2	.6232	.6243	.6253	.6263	.6274	.6284	.6294	.6304	.6314	.6325
4.3	.6335	.6345	.6355	.6365	.6375	.6385	.6395	.6405	.6415	.6425
4.4	.6435	.6444	.6454	.6464	.6474	.6484	.6493	.6503	.6513	.6522
4.5	.6532	.6542	.6551	.6561	.6571	.6580	.6590	.6599	.6609	.6618
4.6	.6628	.6637	.6646	.6656	.6665	.6675	.6684	.6693	.6702	.6712
4.7	.6721	.6730	.6739	.6749	.6758	.6767	.6776	.6785	.6794	.6803
4.8	.6812	.6821	.6830	.6839	.6848	.6857	.6866	.6875	.6884	.6893
4.9	.6902	.6911	.6920	.6928	.6937	.6946	.6955	.6964	.6972	.6981
5.0	.6990	.6998	.7007	.7016	.7024	.7033	.7042	.7050	.7059	.7067
5.1	.7076	.7084	.7093	.7101	.7110	.7118	.7126	.7135	.7143	.7152
5.2	.7160	.7168	.7177	.7185	.7193	.7202	.7210	.7218	.7226	.7235
5.3	.7243	.7251	.7259	.7267	.7275	.7284	.7292	.7300	.7308	.7316
5.4	.7324	.7332	.7340	.7348	.7356	.7364	.7372	.7380	.7388	.7396
5.5	.7404	.7412	.7419	.7427	.7435	.7443	.7451	.7459	.7466	.7474
5.6	.7482	.7490	.7497	.7505	.7513	.7520	.7528	.7536	.7543	.7551
5.7	.7559	.7566	.7574	.7582	.7589	.7597	.7604	.7612	.7619	.7627
5.8	.7634	.7642	.7649	.7657	.7664	.7672	.7679	.7686	.7694	.7701
5.9	.7709	.7716	.7723	.7731	.7738	.7745	.7752	.7760	.7767	.7774

TABLE OF LOGARITHMS (Continued)

N	0	1	2	3	4	5	6	7	8	9
6.0	.7782	.7789	.7796	.7803	.7810	.7818	.7825	.7832	.7839	.7846
6.1	.7853	.7860	.7868	.7875	.7882	.7889	.7896	.7903	.7910	.7917
6.2	.7924	.7931	.7938	.7945	.7952	.7959	.7966	.7973	.7980	.7987
6.3	.7993	.8000	.8007	.8014	.8021	.8028	.8035	.8041	.8048	.8055
6.4	.8062	.8069	.8075	.8082	.8089	.8096	.8102	.8109	.8116	.8122
6.5	.8129	.8136	.8142	.8149	.8156	.8162	.8169	.8176	.8182	.8189
6.6	.8195	.8202	.8209	.8215	.8222	.8228	.8235	.8241	.8248	.8254
6.7	.8261	.8267	.8274	.8280	.8287	.8293	.8299	.8306	.8312	.8319
6.8	.8325	.8331	.8338	.8344	.8351	.8357	.8363	.8370	.8376	.8382
6.9	.8388	.8395	.8401	.8407	.8414	.8420	.8426	.8432	.8439	.8445
7.0	.8451	.8457	.8463	.8470	.8476	.8482	.8488	.8494	.8500	.8506
7.1	.8513	.8519	.8525	.8531	.8537	.8543	.8549	.8555	.8561	.8567
7.2	.8573	.8579	.8585	.8591	.8597	.8603	.8609	.8615	.8621	.8627
7.3	.8633	.8639	.8645	.8651	.8657	.8663	.8669	.8675	.8681	.8686
7.4	.8692	.8698	.8704	.8710	.8716	.8722	.8727	.8733	.8739	.8745
7.5	.8751	.8756	.8762	.8768	.8774	.8779	.8785	.8791	.8797	.8802
7.6	.8808	.8814	.8820	.8825	.8831	.8837	.8842	.8848	.8854	.8859
7.7	.8865	.8871	.8876	.8882	.8887	.8893	.8899	.8904	.8910	.8915
7.8	.8921	.8927	.8932	.8938	.8943	.8949	.8954	.8960	.8965	.8971
7.9	.8976	.8982	.8987	.8993	.8998	.9004	.9009	.9015	.9020	.9026
8.0	.9031	.9036	.9042	.9047	.9053	.9058	.9063	.9069	.9074	.9079
8.1	.9085	.9090	.9096	.9101	.9106	.9112	.9117	.9122	.9128	.9133
8.2	.9138	.9143	.9149	.9154	.9159	.9165	.9170	.9175	.9180	.9186
8.3	.9191	.9196	.9201	.9206	.9212	.9217	.9222	.9227	.9232	.9238
8.4	.9243	.9248	.9253	.9258	.9263	.9269	.9274	.9279	.9284	.9289
8.5	.9294	.9299	.9304	.9309	.9315	.9320	.9325	.9330	.9335	.9340
8.6	.9345	.9350	.9355	.9360	.9365	.9370	.9375	.9380	.9385	.9390
8.7	.9395	.9400	.9405	.9410	.9415	.9420	.9425	.9430	.9435	.9440
8.8	.9445	.9450	.9455	.9460	.9465	.9469	.9474	.9479	.9484	.9489
8.9	.9494	.9499	.9504	.9509	.9513	.9518	.9523	.9528	.9533	.9538
9.0	.9542	.9547	.9552	.9557	.9562	.9566	.9571	.9576	.9581	.9586
9.1	.9590	.9595	.9600	.9605	.9609	.9614	.9619	.9624	.9628	.9633
9.2	.9638	.9643	.9647	.9652	.9657	.9661	.9666	.9671	.9675	.9680
9.3	.9685	.9689	.9694	.9699	.9703	.9708	.9713	.9717	.9722	.9727
9.4	.9731	.9736	.9741	.9745	.9750	.9754	.9759	.9763	.9768	.9773
9.5	.9777	.9782	.9786	.9791	.9795	.9800	.9805	.9809	.9814	.9818
9.6	.9823	.9827	.9832	.9836	.9841	.9845	.9850	.9854	.9859	.9863
9.7	.9868	.9872	.9877	.9881	.9886	.9890	.9894	.9899	.9903	.9908
9.8	.9912	.9917	.9921	.9926	.9930	.9934	.9939	.9943	.9948	.9952
9.9	.9956	.9961	.9965	.9969	.9974	.9978	.9983	.9987	.9991	.9996

INDEX

Note: The following abbreviations are used:
App = appendix
fig = Figure
ftn = footnote, margin note
prb = problem
tbl = table

A

M